8

60L

WORLD RESOURCES AND INDUSTRIES

WORLD RESOURCES
AND INDUSTRIES

A FUNCTIONAL APPRAISAL OF THE
AVAILABILITY OF AGRICULTURAL AND INDUSTRIAL MATERIALS

REVISED EDITION

by ERICH W. ZIMMERMANN, Ph.D., LL.D.

PROFESSOR OF ECONOMICS, COLLEGE OF ARTS AND SCIENCES, AND
PROFESSOR OF RESOURCES, COLLEGE OF BUSINESS ADMINISTRATION
THE UNIVERSITY OF TEXAS

HARPER & BROTHERS, PUBLISHERS, NEW YORK

TO MY TEACHERS—

Those who taught me and those whom I have taught

Contents

PART I. INTRODUCTION TO THE STUDY OF RESOURCES

PART II. RESOURCES OF AGRICULTURE

CONTENTS

PART III. RESOURCES OF INDUSTRY

PART IV. RESOURCE PROBLEMS

Illustrations

Foreword to the First Edition

That economic life as all social life rests on a physical basis is axiomatic. Realizing this evident relationship of their science to economics, some geographers have vigorously pushed their research into the borderland which separates the two disciplines. Economists, on the other hand, perhaps preoccupied with the tantalizing and fascinating problems of value, price, distribution of income, and with similar phases of price economy in general, have shown less inclination to explore this border region and to study the physical basis on which the structure of price economy rests.

The economic geographer, approaching the study of economic life from the angle of underlying physical realities, pushes upward from the physical basis toward the cultural superstructure. The economist, in turn, whose main task is the exploration of a limited section of the cultural superstructure, probes downward toward the physical foundation. Somewhere the two efforts meet, not in competition, but in coöperation. This book is not an economic geography, as that term is generally understood. Since, however, the analysis is directed downward toward the physical basis, the starting point of the economic geographer, there are bound to be numerous contact points between this study and that of economic geography. If, in this book, I have succeeded in repaying by some modest contribution to the advancement of economic geography, the invaluable service which economic geographers have rendered the economist by promoting a fuller appreciation of physical realities, I shall consider myself amply rewarded for the effort spent in this work.

An attempt is made in this book to render more fully and more readily available, for the student of economics, material which allied social sciences, especially geography—human, social, cultural and economic—have brought to light. To a lesser degree the fields of natural science and of technology have been drawn upon. The major purpose of this book is not to enlarge the body of scientific knowledge but to render more effective the teaching of the social sciences in general and of economics in particular. In other words, this is a textbook for the use of college students. If, incidentally, some contributions not only to interpretation but also to the analysis of some specific aspects have been made, their significance is secondary.

Since the major objective of this book clearly lies in the field of education, a few remarks about educational aims are appropriate. Among the numerous objectives of a college education two main aims seem to stand out, namely, vocational training preparatory to some specific professional or business career, and general preparation for life, for citizenship, and for participation in the great struggle which is continually going on over our civilization. This book definitely serves the second purpose. It is designed to develop in the student an awareness and some appreciation of the peculiar nature of our modern machine civilization; and it is hoped that a careful study of it will help him to find his place in life more intelligently and to lead a more purposeful life. The student who, in order to qualify for some specific job, seeks to acquire some practical knowledge of a vocational nature, factual data, or technical training will find little in this book to satisfy his wants. On the other hand, the student who wants to gain a vantage point from which he may get a clearer view into wide vistas and toward distant horizons may not regret the time which he spends on this volume. In my opinion, the greatest need today is for leaders endowed with a highly developed social consciousness and a broad outlook, capable of correlating and integrating separate branches of learning. The understanding of interdependence is becoming a matter of life and death for modern civilization.

There are two distinct ways in which the topic of world resources and industries can be handled. One might be described as the encyclopedic or descriptive method; the other as the functional method. The first, being descriptive, to be thorough, must be encyclopedic in scope. In the second the emphasis is on analysis, correlation and appraisal. In its functional nature the second method appears to be in line with the trend of the times, for functional thinking, gaining importance since the Renaissance, is gradually spreading over more and more fields of learning, revolutionizing psychology, anthropology, architecture, art, and many other phases of the world of thought.

Unfortunately, the functional approach is by no means the easiest, but it seems to be the only one which furnishes dependable results without necessitating almost unlimited collection and examination of details. The use of this functional method necessarily renders the treatment, especially in the first part, somewhat abstract and speculative. I have long hesitated to present such material to my students. The experience gained during almost fifteen years of teaching this particular subject, however, has convinced me that our students are better prepared to tackle problems than we frequently assume. In my personal opinion the widespread tendency toward "teaching down" is decidedly regrettable. Perhaps there was a time when education overrated the intelligence and the tastes of American men and women; but today it would seem the danger lies in going too far in the other direction. No effort should be spared to clarify a difficult analysis, but to present complex reality in the disguise of a fictitious simplicity, merely for the sake of making the student's task easier, appears to be a procedure of very doubtful merit.

Throughout this book emphasis is placed upon functional relationships; attention is focused on the whole rather than on the parts. In this book, in other words, I have attempted to synthesize some of the findings of various sciences, to integrate data generally found in widely separated places. This synthesis necessarily forces the economist into related fields with which he can hardly be expected to be as familiar as he should be with his own specialty. I am fully aware of the danger which is involved in this trespassing on related fields. But, I am thoroughly convinced that such synthesis is one of the most crying needs of modern education, and I have therefore faced the perils of this wide roaming over many fields. The decision of bringing a book of this nature before the public must necessarily be a compromise between the desire to present a perfect compilation and the hope that a less perfect synthesis presented in 1933 may prove of as great value as one published years later. Moreover, I trust that the imperfections of detail will be pointed out by those most familiar with their respective fields.

In general, the aim of this book is comprehension or understanding through functional correlation rather than completeness of factual knowledge. Detailed information is furnished not so much for its own sake as for the purpose of illustrating principles and general functional relationships. For example, it is held more important that the student understand the peculiar nature of the forces affecting the supply and demand of the organic products of agriculture and the inorganic products of certain manufacturing industries, respectively, than that he memorize the names of leading wheat-producing regions in order of importance. To give another illustration, it seems more important that the nature of perennials as distinguished from annuals is clearly understood and that the economic implications of this nature are appreciated than that complete statistical or technological details concerning most commercial perennials are furnished. The understanding of the nature of forces possesses permanent value; the factual data themselves change constantly in response to these forces.

The purpose of stressing this is not to foist my personal views on others but merely to explain important omissions from the text of commodities and industries discussed. Tobacco, e.g., is not mentioned; the building industry, a major industry, is not treated. The statistical treatment is equally incomplete. Nowadays some admirable compilations of basic data are available, such as the *Commerce Yearbook* (two volumes), the *Agriculture Yearbook,* the Statistical Yearbooks of the League of Nations and of the International Institute of Agriculture in Rome, etc., that it appeared wiser to stress interpretation rather than to devote much space to the reproduction of data readily available elsewhere.

For the last five years, with few interruptions, the work on this book has claimed whatever time could be spared from university duties. During that period I have received the help and advice of so many that individual acknowledgment is well-nigh impossible. I trust that my generous friends will not misinterpret as ingratitude the omission of their names from this preface. Two years ago the book was completed in a rough, tentative form. This preliminary manuscript was read by Professors John E. Orchard of Columbia University and John Ise of the University of Kansas, from whose criticism I have profited much. Individual chapters were read by specialists whose advice proved most valuable. I mention, in particular, Professor A. M. White of the University of North Carolina who read chapters in which reference to chemical matters occurs, especially Chapter XXXVII; Professor P. W. Wager of the University of North Carolina who read Chapter XXII on forests; Professor Thorndike Saville of New York University who read Chapters XXVIII and XXIX on water power and electricity; Dr. O. E. Baker of the United States Department of Agriculture, Washington, who read Chapter VI on land; Dr. Albert S. Keister, Professor of Economics, Woman's College of the University of North Carolina, Greensboro, North Carolina; Dr. Claudius T. Murchison, Professor of Applied Economics, and Mr. F. Arnold, Instructor in Economic Geography, both at the University of North Carolina, who critically read a number of chapters. For their help I am deeply grateful.

During the summer of 1932 most of the manuscript was critically read by Dr. A. N. J. den Hollander, a pupil and follower of Dr. S. R. Steinmetz, well-known ethnologist and social geographer of the University of Amsterdam. Because of his thorough training in and his wide acquaintance with the European literature of social geography and allied fields and his sympathetic understanding of American problems developed during his two years' stay as a Research Fellow of the Rockefeller Foundation, Dr. den Hollander was able to make valuable suggestions for the improvement of the manuscript in general and of several chapters in particular, especially those touching on topics within the field of social geography. His assistance is greatly appreciated by the author. None of these critics in any way share the responsibility of authorship.

I also wish to express my appreciation of the financial aid granted me by the Social Science Research Council for travel in Europe. The most evident results of the European studies made feasible by this assistance are contained in Chapter XXI; their beneficial influence, however, extends, it is hoped, to many other parts of the book.

Finally, I wish to express my gratitude to all those who have aided in the preparation of the manuscript: to the University of North Carolina in general and to Dean D. D. Carroll in particular for a sympathetic attitude toward and generous active support of my work; to Dr. H. W. Odum and Dr. K. Jocher, Directors of the Institute for Research in Social Sciences at the University of North Carolina, who generously assisted in the preparation of the preliminary manuscript; to Miss Bertie McGee, Miss Nancy Herndon and especially Miss Mary Bunn for most of the actual typing; to my daughter Erika who sacrificed precious vacation time to submit herself to her father's dictation and, last but by no means least, to my wife, without whose unflinching moral support and untiring active assistance the completion of this work at this time would have been impossible.

ERICH W. ZIMMERMANN

Chapel Hill, North Carolina
June, 1933

Foreword to the Revised Edition

The reception accorded the first edition of *World Resources and Industries* by social scientists throughout the English-speaking world was a source of deep satisfaction. Such a reception could hardly have been taken for granted, for both the functional approach to resources and the insistence on a balanced consideration of geographical, economic, historical, sociological, technological, and political aspects, which I consider my chief contributions to the subject, were departures from the traditional treatment.

While these fundamental principles of resource analysis do not change with the times—they are either right or wrong, but never out of date—the statistical data and factually descriptive material used to illustrate the principles are subject to rapid obsolescence. Moreover, few if any periods in human history have seen more drastic revisions of the resource setup of the world than has the period which has elapsed since the publication of the first edition in 1933. The Great Depression, the New Deal, Hitler's rise to power, World War II, the advent of atomic energy, the cold war that refuses to stay cold—all these are events of cataclysmic force from which little on this planet can escape.

This revision was begun during the late thirties but lapsed during World War II because my time was completely occupied with other assignments and an appraisal of the world resource setup is impossible during hostilities. In this revision I have striven to accomplish three things: (1) a fuller and clearer presentation of my functional or operational approach to resources; (2) a better organization of all the materials presented, especially of individual chapters; and (3) the inclusion of thoroughly up-to-date statistics and other factual data.

The new edition is somewhat larger than the first. Those who choose to use it as a text in courses lasting one quarter or one semester may wish to omit certain portions. In that way the book can be adapted to varying needs.

In the preparation of this revised edition I was generously aided by many. Government agencies and business concerns alike complied graciously and efficiently with my numerous requests for information and aid. I profited much from critical comments on both the old and the new version. In particular my faithful disciple, Professor M. Ogden Phillips of Washington and Lee University, and my student, Mr. Marvin D. Bernstein, instructor in history at the College of the City of New York, submitted constructive criticisms of the first edition. Dr. Richard Gonzalez, economist of the Humble Oil and Refining Company, helped to make the new chapters on petroleum more authentic. Others, especially Mr. John Wildenthal, now a member of the Texas bar, and Mrs. Lydia Taylor Thomen and Mrs. Shirley Ann Pogson, all former students of mine, rendered valuable volunteer services in typing, filing, abstracting, and general legwork. Their generous help is warmly appreciated.

To Miss Dorothy Thompson, editor for Harper & Brothers, I am deeply grateful for the tireless and skilled care she has expended on the preparation of the manuscript for the publisher. Without her devoted work this volume might not have seen the light of day.

Last but by no means least, members of my

family deserve my warmest thanks not only for creating an atmosphere in which I could devote myself to sustained thought and literary effort but also for their direct aid in the preparation of the manuscript. Oftentimes when I myself despaired of deciphering my own scribbling, my wife, with uncanny skill, interpreted the hieroglyphics and patiently typed chapter after chapter, freely supplying much needed moral support into the bargain. Her work was ably and generously supplemented by that of our youngest daughter Peggy, who even through almost unbearably hot summers never flinched

and gladly contributed her mite to this family venture. Besides typing part of the bibliography, our eldest daughter Erika, prominently mentioned in the preface to the first edition, performed yeoman service in proofreading the galleys, a task for which she is eminently qualified by years of professional experience. My gratitude to my family cannot be expressed in words, nor does it need to be.

ERICH W. ZIMMERMANN

Austin, Texas
October, 1950

PART ONE

INTRODUCTION TO THE STUDY OF RESOURCES

UNIT 1. RESOURCES AND THEIR APPRAISAL

Chapter 1

MEANING AND NATURE OF RESOURCES

THE NEW RESOURCE CONSCIOUSNESS

Resources are the bases of both security and opulence; they are the foundations of power and wealth. They affect man's destiny in war and peace alike. A world that has not forgotten two World Wars and is worried over the possibility of a third is bound to be a resource-conscious world. Nor is this concern over resources confined to the "military potential" in the narrow sense of the term. For in total war "military potential" comes close to being total potential, and in cold war[1] full employment or something approaching it is a strategic objective of the first order.

Basically, concern over resources is nothing new. Peoples have always wondered where tomorrow's bread would come from. Land hunger is as old as the ages. Access to water and control over certain minerals have been crucial questions throughout human history. And yet, at least so far as the West is concerned, there is something definitely new in contemporary resource consciousness. To understand this one

[1] Reference is to the tension between the East, meaning mainly the Soviet Union, and the West, spearheaded by the United States.

must briefly review the history of economic thought of the past two centuries and bring to mind some important events of the recent past which have affected men's thought on economics in general and on resources in particular.

Economic Thought

Throughout the ages men lived under social controls, tribal taboos, tyrannies of various kinds, ranging from those of priests and medicine men to those of military dictators and Machiavellian princes. At times, certain privileged groups enjoyed considerable freedom under the law, as did Roman citizens during the Roman Empire; but the majority of the people lived under more or less rigid control, as slaves, as serfs, as subject peoples.

Then with the great discoveries and inventions there came a time of great change. The white race experienced an amazing expansion of opportunities. It was an age of empire building and colonizing, of swarming into wide-open spaces, but also an age of new industries, of new and better uses for what nature had to offer. This expansion was accompanied by a

3

growing belief in the rights and powers of the individual. Social controls were loosened both by revolution and by evolution.

In the economic realm this development manifested itself in the gradual abolition of governmental controls over business enterprise, in the belief in laissez faire, in free trade, both internal and external—in short, in what has become known as the free enterprise system. This system, which reached its highest development in the English-speaking world, achieved a tremendous release of individual energies and drives and with it an increase in economic activity and a rise in living standards never before known in the history of man.[2]

This achievement, credited to the removal of social, especially governmental, restraints and the resultant stepping-up of individual zest and performance, gave rise to peculiar ideologies such as the belief in the primacy of economics, especially its superiority over politics, and the doctrine that the best way to promote the public welfare was to let private business entrepreneurs pursue relentlessly their selfish interests. Competition was the force that would bring about the harmonizing of social and private interests.

These ideologies dominated economic thought in the English-speaking world until in the early 1890's Alfred Marshall, in his famous *Principles,* broke with the laissez-faire school when he refused "to leap the yawning gap between the individual and society," recognized that the relentless pursuit of individual interest did not assure the attainment of the common weal, and proclaimed the need of a deliberate public policy to safeguard public interests. He withdrew the theoretical prop on which economic "harmonics"[3] had rested.[4] Mar-

shall's position was supported by other leading theorists such as Pigou and later given far more militant expression by John Meynard Keynes.[5]

One of the main points on which individuals, including private business interests, and the group, represented by the government, differ is in their concern for resources, especially the basic assets such as soil, water, iron, oil, etc. Business as a rule is market-minded, commodity-conscious; its interests are largely limited to the short run. There is a natural tendency to think in terms of the present and the here and to pass off warnings about the hidden or patent impairment of basic assets with a casual "After us the deluge" or "What has posterity ever done for me?" Frequently the proper care of these assets—be they the health and education of the people, or the soil, water, and minerals—requires programs of unusual range in point of time, the results of which may not be visible for years, perhaps decades, and which in the meantime call for expenditures without corresponding immediate returns. Under such circumstances a business civilization is apt to neglect the care of its basic assets. Unless checked by deliberate interference on behalf of the public interest it is likely to sacrifice them on the altar of immediate profits.[6]

Historical Background of the New Attitude

If it is true, as many believe, that economic theory reflects the *Zeitgeist,* one must look to historical developments for the explanation of Marshall's famous declaration of independence from nineteenth-century "harmonics" and its ready acceptance by his contemporaries and successors. What, then, were the historical developments which help to explain this major shift in economic thought? Obviously an exhaustive treatment of its historical background is out of the question here. Only a few highlights can be listed, suggestive of further and deeper forces and developments but far from all-inclusive.

Undoubtedly, one of the events which stirred

---

[2] The period was also one of great technical progress. It marked the introduction of power-driven machines, of electricity, and of modern science. This technical progress, coupled with the opening of new lands throughout the world and the imperial sway held by some groups over "lesser breeds," had much to do with the unparalleled expansion of opportunities and resources and the equally unparalleled rise in living standards.

[3] The belief in the necessary harmony between individual and group interests.

[4] See Paul Homan, *Modern Economic Thought,* Harper & Brothers, New York, 1928, chapter on Alfred Marshall, especially p. 224.

[5] Most directly in his *The End of Laissez-Faire.*

[6] This statement, like all generalizations, is vulnerable to attack. It is, however, based on typical performance during the past century. There are, of course, exceptions. Moreover, fuller realization of the dangers is clearly manifest.

the American people to resource consciousness and with it to a recognition of the fact that business appeared to be neglectful of the basic social assets was the "closing of the frontier" in the sense of the completion of the settlement of the continent, the end of free land. The story of Theodore Roosevelt's eloquent appeal for a conservation policy is too well known to need recounting. It led to a period of pausing in the mad rush, taking stock, and, in a way, locking the stable after the horse was gone.[7] For the first time, people came to realize that even in God's own country the natural endowment of the continent was neither inexhaustible nor indestructible. There was a timid attempt to take inventory. Some reserves showed signs of approaching exhaustion. Even if the practical results were meager, the realization of the finiteness of the national endowment was not wholly smothered by a new "faith in bonanza," the bonanza of technics and science, of mechanical wizardry and chemical magic. With the twentieth century at the halfway mark, this early realization of the exhaustibility of the reserves of the earth's resources has matured into a clearer and more sober understanding of the facts and their meaning.

When the Great Depression led to the New Deal, Franklin Delano Roosevelt in the field of resources took up where Theodore Roosevelt had stopped. The concern over resources was a major one in the minds of the brain trusters, and it was wisely extended to human resources. The National Resources Committee, the National Resources Board, and the National Resources Planning Board, regardless of trivial changes in name, constituted a single force aimed at developing a policy to safeguard our national resources. Alfred Marshall's daring break with the past had borne fruit.

The Great Depression was the last of a series of economic slumps which more or less had come to be accepted as necessary evils. The severity of this catastrophe, however, brooked no temporizing. Since planning by private corporations had failed dismally, government planning was entitled to a try. One of its chief characteristics, perhaps its most important one, is conscious regard for basic social assets, many—

perhaps most—of which lie outside the scope of private business concern. Once the magic spell of the old "harmonics" is broken, the duty to plan for the common good is clear. Unfortunately, where to find the wisdom necessary to perform that duty is another question. Trial and error is a costly, cumbersome method but, as yet, the only one at hand.

As was pointed out before, the two World Wars contributed materially to resource consciousness in many parts of the world and through wide strata of its population. Modern total war calls for total mobilization of resources, and military potential differs from economic potential in little else but objective. This awareness of the causal nexus between resources and victory continues during so-called cold wars and is epitomized in this country in the National Security Resources Board.

Up to this point attention has been focused on spectacular events such as the closing of the frontier, the Great Depression, and the World Wars as sources of growing resource consciousness. They are by no means the only forces responsible for this new awareness. A number of quiet, slowly moving trends have contributed materially to the change in attitude. The growing size and complexity of modern nations is one of them. It points, with perhaps inevitable logic, toward a strengthening of the power of the central government. In so far as this growing complexity is due to a merging of once local or regional activities and interests into national concerns, the connection with increased need for central—in the United States, federal—controls is evident. The growth of the modern corporation is a case in point; there are many others. This trend may be regrettable and beset with grave dangers, but it cannot be conjured away by calling it names. Realities must be faced.

Another equally vital trend is marked by the decline of competition and by its corollary, the concentration of economic power. It is in part coextensive with the growth of the modern corporation and more recently of labor unions, but it draws attention to particularly ominous aspects of that growth. To appreciate this statement, one must recall that it was reliance on the all-healing power of competition which formed much of the basis of the doctrine of

---

[7] It may be more accurate to say "talking of locking the stable."

"harmonics." It was through competition and the corresponding absence of monopoly, oligopoly, and other forms of concentrated economic power that the sum total of private interests was assumed to achieve its mystic merging with the public interest, the common good. If nothing else had happened, the decline of competition by itself would insist imperatively upon a public planning policy in which regard for resources, viewed as basic social assets, would be essential.

In other parts of the world, far less fortunate than the United States, the rise of socialism and communism[8] has brought with it the virtual disappearance of private enterprise capitalism where it once existed, and precluded its emergence where it has not yet taken root. Both socialism and communism are resource-conscious. Both plan with a view to safeguarding and developing the basic social assets.

Here a fundamental point must be made clear. The fact that both socialism and communism plan does not make planning *ipso facto* socialistic or communistic. The problem is far more complex. The main point to keep in mind is the ultimate objective toward which the planning is directed. If it is directed at safeguarding and strengthening individual rights and views the dignity of the individual human being as the *summum bonum*, it is quite compatible with the highest ideals of democracy. The issue is not whether planning is right or wrong, but how to learn to plan wisely.

A rather subtle influence is what may be called a growing sense of social responsibility. This too helps to explain the increased awareness of the basic social assets. This sense of responsibility is probably best explained in terms of a keener sense of historical perspective and a fuller understanding of social processes and phenomena. It is perhaps a form of enlightened selfishness. Examples of it are Truman's Point IV program on behalf of underdeveloped areas, Nelson Rockefeller's efforts to raise the level of productivity of South American peoples, and the enlightened development policy of the United Fruit Company to improve basic assets in the areas in which it operates. All these developments are symptomatic of the growing concern with and for resources. At the same time they cannot help but bring in their train a better understanding of the nature of resources; and this, in turn, is bound to reflect favorably on policies concerning resources.

RESOURCES, AN EVOLVING CONCEPT
Early Misconceptions

The preceding analysis has shown that for centuries resources were the stepchild of economic thought. If they were recognized at all, they were absorbed into the market process, acknowledged only in so far as they were reduced to working tools of the entrepreneur—land, labor, and capital—or recognized through their effects on cost and price, supply and demand.[9]

Being neglected by the economist, the study of resources was left largely to natural scientists, especially physical geographers. It follows that the concept of resources, because it is relatively new, remains to be developed scientifically. A consensus must be achieved among scientists, social as well as natural, as to the exact meaning of the term; and popular misconceptions must be cleared up.

Some of these popular misconceptions may be briefly listed. There is a strong tendency, easily understandable but nonetheless unfortunate, to identify resources with substances or tangible things. To be sure, substances can function as resources, and indeed they play a tremendous part as resources. One has but to think of coal, iron, petroleum, copper, etc., to realize that. They are obvious, easily recognized, and considered important, whereas less patent invisible and intangible aspects—such as health, social harmony, wise policies, knowledge, freedom—are ignored, even though possibly these latter are more important than all the coal, iron, gold, and silver in the world put together. In fact, resources evolve out of the dynamic interaction of all these factors.

Similarly, the preoccupation with so-called natural resources at the expense of human and cultural resources precludes a clear comprehension of the true nature of resources and a

---

[8] In listing these two side by side no suggestion of similarity or disregard of their fundamental differences is intended or implied.

[9] Cf. the concept of resources in Arthur C. Pigou, *The Economics of Welfare* (Macmillan & Co., Ltd., London, 1920)—infinitesimal transferable units of land, labor, and capital subject to entrepreneurial control or disposition.

full grasp of their extent. Likewise unfortunate is the tendency to think of resources in terms of a single asset, e.g., coal, rather than in terms of the whole complex of substances, forces, conditions, relationships, institutions, policies, etc., which alone help to explain the way coal functions as a resource at a given time and place.

This preoccupation with single tangible phenomena in nature creates the false impression of resources as something static, fixed, whereas actually they are as dynamic as civilization itself. This static concept of resources is well illustrated by the following verse:

> The world is a bundle of hay.
> Mankind are the asses that pull.
> Each tugs it a different way,
> And the greatest of all is *John Bull*.[10]

The concept of the world, the sum total of man's resources, actual and potential, as a bundle of hay is truly fantastic. Hay is dead; it cannot grow; it is used up as it is consumed. No wonder "mankind are the asses that pull," i.e., nations that go to war over what are falsely considered static resources. As the following discussion will bring out, nothing could be further from the truth. Resources are living phenomena, expanding and contracting in response to human effort and behavior. They thrive under rational harmonious treatment. They shrivel in war and strife. To a large extent, they are man's own creation. Man's own wisdom is his premier resource—the key resource that unlocks the universe.

Finally, one more popular misconception needs to be brought out: the failure to realize that just as truly as there must be shade when there is light, so also must there be resistances where there are resources. The two words should be as inseparable as Siamese twins in all resource thinking, just as supply and demand, profit and loss, assets and liabilities are linked together by strong bonds of logic. To help dispel some of these misconceptions is one of the objectives of this analysis.

"Resources" Defined

Dictionary definitions reflect common usage and are therefore an indication of the meaning generally given to words. It is desirable that scientific usage of common words not depart too far from accepted meanings. Typical dictionary definitions of the word "resources" read as follows:

1. That upon which one relies for aid, support, or supply.
2. Means to attain given ends.
3. The capacity to take advantage of opportunities or to extricate oneself from difficulties.

Evidently resources presuppose a person.[11] They are an expression or reflection of human appraisal. The appraisal finds that something can serve as means to given ends, that one can rely on it for aid, support, or supply. The third definition reveals that resources do not necessarily exist outside the appraiser but can be lodged within him. Evidently there are subjective or internal resources as well as objective or external resources. Subjective resources, furthermore, play a dual role: a positive one of taking advantage of opportunity and a negative one of extricating the individual from difficulties or of overcoming obstacles or resistances.

Our conclusion may be clearly drawn. The word "resource" *does not refer to a thing or a substance but to a function which a thing or a substance may perform or to an operation in which it may take part*, namely, the function or operation of attaining a given end such as satisfying a want. In other words, the word "resource" is an abstraction reflecting human appraisal and relating to a function or operation. As such, it is akin to such words as food, property, or capital, but much wider in its sweep than any one of these.

Etymologically the word "resource" is related to source. The prefix *re*, meaning "again," suggests dependability through time, as indicated in the word *relies* used in the first dictionary definition. A person may have various sources of income or support, but a nation has resources. The stress on dependability points toward long-run and social implications, not, however, to the exclusion of other meanings. Here any one of the dictionary definitions listed above could serve satisfactorily.

---

[10] This verse is quoted from memory. It was seen by the author about forty years ago in London on the cover of a weekly called *John Bull*.

[11] One could also speak of the resources of plants and animals. Here the word is restricted to mean the resources at the disposal of persons or groups of persons.

Even better, though, would be a composite of all three. But the emphasis is definitely on basic long-run social assets.

THE FUNCTIONAL OR OPERATIONAL THEORY OF RESOURCES
Resources of man and MAN

This volume is dedicated to the development of a theory of resources which is in strict harmony with the functional and operational meaning of the word contained in the above definitions. This theory will now be explained.

The dictionary definitions show that resources result from an interaction between (1) man (a) searching for means to attain given ends (such as the satisfaction of individual wants and the attainment of group or social objectives) and (b) possessed of the capacity to take advantage of opportunities or to extricate himself from difficulties, and (2) something outside of man which for the time being will be called nature.

To understand resources one must understand the relationship that exists between MAN and nature. For that purpose it is necessary to conceive of the human being as existing on two levels, the animal level and the supra-animal or human (or social) level. At this point of the analysis the form *man* is used to indicate the former and *MAN* to indicate the latter. Man on the animal level constitutes part of nature. MAN on the human level represents the counterpart of nature. Nature is non-MAN. It is the cosmos in so far as it is unaffected by MAN. The sum total of changes wrought by MAN is here called culture.

Man, i.e., man on the animal level, existing without benefit of culture, by virtue of his nature, i.e., his creature wants and his native abilities, is

1. capable of drawing support from nature, e.g., oxygen from the air, water, wild food, situs, etc.;
2. exposed to harmful forces and conditions found in nature, e.g., poison, wild beasts (including "human"), hostile elements, disease, etc.

Those aspects of nature which man can utilize in the satisfaction of his creature wants (without contributions made by MAN), may be called natural resources. Those aspects of nature which harm or hinder man may be called natural resistances. The extent of want satisfaction is a function of resources *and* resistances, not of resources alone.[12]

----

[12] Erich W. Zimmermann, "Resources of Latin America, a Study in Methodology," in *Some Economic Aspects of Postwar Inter-American Relations*,

Man, i.e., man on the animal level, has only natural wants and natural capacities and therefore he commands only natural resources and is exposed to natural resistances. One can envisage him submerged in an ocean of "neutral stuff,"[13] i.e., matter, energy, conditions, relationships, etc., of which he is unaware and which affect him neither favorably nor unfavorably. Immediately surrounding him may be imagined to exist a narrow fringe of natural resources, i.e., aspects favorable to his existence, capable of satisfying his simple creature wants, and limited by the modest range of natural abilities and natural resistances, i.e., aspects unfavorable or hostile to him.

This animal man was subject to the same laws of ecology and passive adaptation which bind all other animals. His techniques, like all animal techniques, were immutable genus techniques, i.e., techniques identified with and inseparable from the structural and functional characteristics of the genus, an inheritance certain to fall to all normal members of the genus but equally certain never to be improved upon by a single member. Genus techniques are static, unalterable; they are functions of organismic attributes which the organism cannot change at will but which are changed passively under pressure from the environment.

On this animal level man found nature niggardly indeed; he barely managed to survive in the face of resistances which in the absence of cultural aids proved formidable, and on resources which were limited by the scantiness of his own capacities. The race grew slowly, for the death rate was terrific. In fact, for ages the very existence of the race hung in the balance—a situation strangely repeated in the face of the superlative cultural achievements of the atomic age.

Emancipation of MAN

Then there arrived a time, 50,000 or more years ago, when the genus Homo was singled out of all organic creatures to travel a road closed to all others—the road of active man-

----

University of Texas Institute of Latin-American Studies, 1946.

[13] This term is borrowed from the language of philosophy. The author is indebted to his colleague, Dr. David L. Miller, Professor of Philosophy, for having suggested it.

willed adaptation. Man, having learned to stand erect, to use his hand not only to grasp but to make tools, possessing a vocal apparatus of unparalleled plasticity, endowed with physical strength probably greater than that left to us after thousands of years of artificial selection, and with natural brain power probably equal to our own, began his career as the great culture-builder, the powerful earth-changer, the Prometheus who thrusts his hand into the heavens to seize divine power, who, not satisfied with what nature willingly offers, coaxes her to give more, much more, and even imitates her or improves upon her work.

Through his superior brain power, MAN has gained control over many of the other creatures found on earth. With its aid he can calculate the future effect of present and future action and can plan accordingly. His plastic vocal apparatus permits the development of articulate speech and with it the all-vital ability to communicate not merely simple impressions but also complex ideas including high-order abstractions. The spoken word is put into writing, into print; permanent records pass on knowledge from generation to generation and from place to place. Thus group relationships are formed, the development of the arts becomes a social process, and culture, the social heritage which feeds upon itself and grows cumulatively through the centuries, emerges to transform the natural landscape.

Thus MAN has emancipated himself from the limitations of passive adaptation and natural selection which hold all other creatures in bondage. He learns to make fire, to build shelter; he invents tools, tills the land, domesticates animals, harnesses the inanimate forces of nature and gains dominion over uncounted robot slaves. In short, MAN learns to exercise the supreme human prerogative of active adaptation.

His arts are no longer static genus techniques, but dynamic individually invented techniques which benefit from both the spontaneous contributions of countless individuals and the advantages these individuals derive from the all-pervasive social heritage of knowledge and experience.

Paucity of Natural Resources

This story of the rise of man from the animal to the human stage is of the utmost significance for the meaning and nature of MAN's resources as distinguished from the resources of animals. MAN's resources, to an overwhelming extent, are *not* natural resources. It is true that nature provides the opportunity for MAN to display his skill and apply his ever-expanding knowledge. But nature offers freely only an infinitesimal fraction of her treasure; she not only withholds the rest, but seems to place innumerable and, in many cases, well-nigh unsurmountable obstacles in the way of resource-seeking and resource-creating MAN.

The bulk of MAN's resources are the result of human ingenuity aided by slowly, patiently, painfully acquired knowledge and experience. To be sure, coal is found in nature. But coal readily accessible and available for human use is rare indeed. Without the aid of power-driven machinery, human inventions, and man-made contraptions, mankind long ago would have run out of coal. Coal occurs in nature, to be sure, but not coke, or sulfate of ammonia, tar, dyes, aspirin, nylon. All the elements are found in nature; but this is of no value to man, who is not even aware of their existence and even less capable of isolating and utilizing them. If there are a hundred elements, there are billions of compounds which can be built up, by commutation and permutation, out of the hundred elements. And only a fraction of them occur in nature.

The Functional Concept of Resources in the Recent Literature

Wesley C. Mitchell was absolutely correct when he wrote:

Incomparably greatest among human resources[14] is knowledge. It is greatest because it is the mother of other resources. The aboriginal inhabitants of what is now the United States lived in a poverty-stricken environment. For them no coal existed, no petroleum, no metals beyond nuggets of pure copper. Of electrical energy they had no inkling. Their agriculture was so crude that they could use only tiny patches of the soil. Their rudimentary social organization combined with their ineffective production to keep their groups small and mutually hostile. . . . Not only is knowledge the greatest of

[14] Mitchell uses this term in the sense of "man's resources" and not in the sense in which the term is used in the present book. See chap. 8.

resources, it is also the resource that we have counted upon to grow richer with every decade. The cumulative expansion of science and of its practical applications has emboldened us to expect that each generation of our descendants will discover new resources and more efficient ways of using old ones. When the future of mankind was pictured as turning upon the race between science and depletion, most men believed science would win.[15]

Knowledge is truly the mother of all other resources.[16] To be sure, not even omniscience can create matter or energy out of nothing. Nor can any science, no matter how skillful and advanced, ever restore to human use the energy once locked up in coal, oil, or gas, but spent. The difference between neolithic man, who roamed the earth in misery and fear, and man today, who lives in relative comfort and security, is knowledge—knowledge of petroleum and natural gas, of sulfur and helium, of chemistry and physics, the countless wonders of modern science—and the marvelous apparatus of cultural improvements which knowledge has devised and built for its own application. Freedom and wisdom, the fruits of knowledge, are the fountainhead of resources.

Seen in this light, the concept of resources is purely functional, inseparable from human wants and human capabilities. It is a concept which legitimately belongs to the social scientist.

The physicist claims that the quantity of matter and energy in the universe is constant; the social scientist replies that nothing is constant, that everything is in flux. In spite of the seeming paradox, both are right. The idea of the fixity of matter and energy in the universe is wholly reconcilable with the claim that resources are in constant flux. The earth is a tiny speck in the vastness of the universe, and mankind, though its numbers may be counted by the billions, is an infinitesimal fraction of that universe. The whole stays put, the fraction forever changes.

Apart from relatively minor changes wrought by man, the earth substantially remains unchanged within the time limits pertinent to mortal man. But its resources change with each change in human civilization. Since geography deals both with the earth as a planet and with the earth as man's abode, it is both a natural science and a social science. Bowman is keenly aware of the implications of this dual role of his science when he writes:

It is often said that geography deals with fixed elements because the earth remains substantially the same from generation to generation, its secular changes being slow. Nothing could be further from the truth. From the human standpoint, the earth of 1933 is not what it was in 1850 because so much of its effect upon us depends upon conscious knowing. The history of societies migrating over and settling in the diverse parts of the earth shows how constant has been the evolution of man's thought about and use of the world. The dark and forbidding mountains of one epoch become the playground and inspiration of another epoch. It has been said that before a thing *is* possible it must *be conceived as* possible. In general, man has done what he thought he could do, and lack of knowledge and the canons of his time have often held him back for long periods. Whenever a new instrument of power or a new chemical discovery or a new use for an old product is discovered the areas affected are reassessed. . . . The geographical elements of the environment are fixed only in the narrow and special sense of the word. *The moment we give them human associations they are as changeful as humanity itself!*[17]

Leon C. Marshall expresses the same idea this way: "As regards the assumption that the natural background is unchanging and unchangeable, one cannot avoid the suspicion that we have here a case where everything depends on how words and terms are used."[18]

According to Hamilton, "It is technology which gives value to the stuffs which it processes; and as the useful arts advance the gifts of nature are remade. . . . With technology on

---

[15] See Wesley C. Mitchell, "Conservation, Liberty, and Economics," in *The Foundations of Conservation Education,* National Wildlife Federation, New York, 1941, pp. 1, 2.

[16] The following discussion is based on Erich W. Zimmermann, "Resources—an Evolving Concept," *Transactions, Texas Academy of Science, 1944,* September, 1945, pp. 157-165.

[17] Isaiah Bowman, *Geography in Relation to the Social Sciences,* Charles Scribner's Sons, New York, 1934, pp. 34, 37. (The first italics the present author's.)

[18] Leon C. Marshall, "The Changing Economic Order," *Annals of the American Academy of Political and Social Science,* January, 1930.

the march, the emphasis of value shifts from the natural to the processed good."[19]

Those who still insist that the natural environment is constant and that the supply of "land"[20] is fixed face a powerful array of opposing authorities.

Nothing is more fatal to a realistic and usable understanding of resources than the failure to differentiate between the constants of natural science and the relatives of social science, between the totality of the universe or of the planet earth, legitimate domain of the natural scientist, and that small portion of these totalities which constitutes the ever-changing resources of a given group of people at a given time and place, the bailiwick of the social scientist.

And somebody had the effrontery to call the world "a bundle of hay"! It is incredible. And others insist to this very day that resources *are*, are static and fixed! One has but to recall some of the most precious resources of our age—electricity, oil, nuclear energy—to see who is right, the exponent of the static school who insists that "resources are," or the defender of the dynamic, functional, operational school who insists that "resources become."[21]

Resources and Wants

Resources are dynamic not only in response to increased knowledge, improved arts, expanding science, but also in response to changing individual wants and social objectives. Resources were defined as means of attaining given ends, i.e., individual wants and social objectives. Means take their meaning from the ends which they serve. As ends change, means must change also.[22] Thus resources must reflect every change in the purpose of the appraiser. The aims of czarist Russia in many ways differed from those of the Soviet Union. The Russian Revolution of 1917 therefore brought on a veritable upheaval of Russian resources. The resources of the United States at war are quite different from those of the United States at peace. They are bound to reflect the change in social objectives. A shift in the national mind from Hamiltonian to Jeffersonian preferences, by changing national purposes, must needs change national resources as well.

Nature and Culture

So long as the human race continues to climb upward to higher culture levels, culture is bound to become increasingly important as the dynamic force in the creation of resources. This shift of emphasis toward the cultural by no means implies a disparagement of nature's role and a disregard of physical realities.

Physical reality at all times is the basis on which human culture rests. The physical environment, appraised both quantitatively and qualitatively and viewed as changing relationships of trends and forces rather than as static conditions, therefore is at all times the foundation of human productive effort. Arts, no matter how highly developed, and wants, no matter how urgent or sophisticated, are helpless in a vacuum. Without acting on and drawing from physical nature they are unproductive. To know, however, what particular opportunities a given physical environment has to offer at a given time and place, one must first learn what man *can* and *wants* to do with it.

Nature sets the limits within which man can develop his arts to satisfy his wants. Within these limits he is free to select from the myriad possibilities offered by nature those which at a given time and place promise the best results in terms of want satisfaction in return for the human effort applied thereto.

Nature, however, does infinitely more than merely set the outer limits within which human arts and wants can operate. She makes suggestions and man is wise enough to listen. At times this suggestive power of nature is very evident, as in cases when she lures man by rich rewards or blocks his road with discouraging threats. More often nature speaks with a less audible voice. In ways hardly noticed by man she affects the development of human arts and wants. It is human willingness to respond to even these suggestions of nature that marks man as Homo sapiens. Human culture as a rule is adaptive; that is, it reflects adaptation to natural advantages or disadvantages. Less often it is independently creative, and only in rare cases

---

[19] Walton H. Hamilton, "Control of Strategic Materials," *American Economic Review,* June, 1944, p. 262.

[20] In economic parlance the word "land" is used to designate the contributions of nature.

[21] Morris Llewellyn Cooke, writing on "Resources" in Seymour E. Harris (ed.), *Saving American Capitalism* (Alfred A. Knopf, New York, 1944), suggests that modern thinking on resources points to a "doctrine of *acquired* resources."

[22] The fact that the availability of means may affect ends should not be lost sight of.

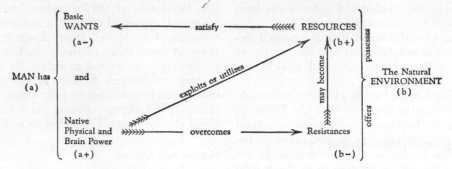

FIG. 1.1. Dynamic Interrelationship Between Primitive Man and His Natural Environment.

does it run directly counter to the dictates of nature.[23]

Dynamics of Culture

To appreciate fully the dynamic force of culture, one needs to be aware of the entire scope of its penetrating force. The effects of cultural progress on nature come readily to mind. But cultural influences are not confined to the nonman world; they do not overlook or spare man himself. Not only wants and abilities of the individual man and of groups of men are affected by culture—education, training experience, sophistication, degeneration, eugenics, etc.—but the relationships between men, social organizations, and societal institutions also come under its spell. Groups expand and become more complex; division of labor, regional and occupational, is pushed further. Improved means of communication and transportation bring always wider strata of humanity into contact; contacts grow more frequent and more intimate, and world-wide interdependence results.

Even the size of the human population is apt to be affected by cultural change. The first impact of expanding and improving culture on the numbers of people is rapid increase, even an accelerating rate of increase. But in due time, birth control or "planned parenthood" puts on the brakes. First the rate of increase declines and later the population may suffer an absolute decline.[24]

Culture thus involves a twofold process of

change. On the one hand, it comprises the sum total of the cultural modification of the nonman environments, both physical and nonphysical, artifacts as well as arts. On the other hand, it comprises cultural changes affecting human attitudes, human relations within groups as well as between groups. Government, church, trade union, trade association, standards of living, creeds, etc., are all cultural products affecting the human side of the equation.

The Resource Process

The dynamics of resources can be illustrated by diagrams. Of the two that are offered, the first (Fig. 1.1) shows the simple relationships between primitive man and nature.

It is difficult to depict in a simple diagram the more complex relationships accounting for the resources of man on more advanced levels of civilization. The idea of showing culture as a spearhead which man drives deeper into the realm of nature, converting more and more "neutral stuff" into resources—and into resistances as well—is presented readily enough, as shown in Fig. 1.2.

But to be satisfactory this diagram should be combined with the first. This, however, would complicate the picture unduly. Moreover, not all cross currents of dynamic interaction would be visible even then—especially the influence of nature on both human wants and the arts and sciences. Something evidently must be left to the reader's imagination.

Destruction of Resources

So far in the discussion of the dynamics of resources, emphasis has been placed on the resource-creating current flowing from man

---

[23] Erich W. Zimmermann, in Walter E. Spahr (ed.), *Economic Principles and Problems*, Farrar & Rinehart, New York, 3rd ed., 1936, vol. 1, pp. 165-166.

[24] See chap. 8, especially pp. 109 ff.

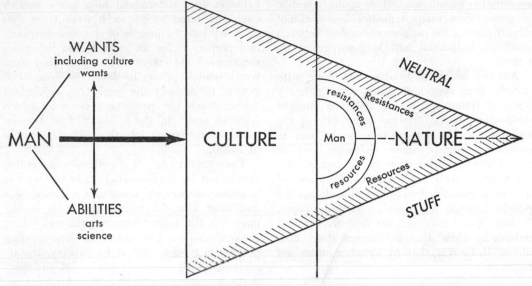

FIG. 1.2. Man, Culture, and Nature.
MAN is an abstraction. In reality, most cultural developments originate from social groups (tribes, nations, international groupings). This multiple-group origin of culture acts both as a stimulus to cultural progress and as a cause of friction. To show this multiple-group origin in the diagram would make it unduly complex. (From Erich W. Zimmermann, in *Some Economic Aspects of Postwar Inter-American Relations*, University of Texas Institute of Latin-American Studies, 1946.)

to nature and back again. But not all change is positive, leading to expansion. Man, the great culture-builder, is not only a creator of resources, he is also a destroyer. In part, this destruction is inevitable, a necessary corollary of his use of the earth. Man cannot help that coal and oil are dissipated in use. He cannot use such minerals without using them up. Less obvious is the destruction of resources by man-induced obsolescence. When Kekulé[25] dreamed up the "carbon ring" out of the smoke of his pipe and thus paved the way for the coal-tar industries, he indirectly caused the destruction of entire branches of agriculture, especially those producing vegetable indigo in India and madder root in France. A giant steelworks has no use for little pockets of iron deposits; it must rely on vast accumulations of the stuff. Thus with the advent of modern iron and steel processes, thousands of ore deposits became uneconomical, ceased to be resources, and reverted back to whence they had come—"neutral stuff." One might be tempted to speak of ex-resources.

[25] German chemist credited with vital contributions to organic, especially coal-tar, chemistry.

But far greater destruction is wrought by man not in the orderly process of rational resource use, but because of human folly and cussedness. As was mentioned before, the individual tends to take a short-sighted view of things. He "wants what he wants when he wants it" and as a rule does not reckon the consequences too carefully. What is more, he is apt to ignore, if he can, the consequences for others, especially if the others are as yet unborn. The proper use and care of complex natural processes that are governed by the laws of ecology presuppose a high degree of scientific knowledge which has been reached only very recently, after centuries of blind groping and foolish blundering. Soil erosion caused by faulty methods of farming, of overgrazing, or of unscientific cutting of timber comes readily to mind. So does the careless treatment of water supplies—stream pollution, abuse of rivers, lowering of the water table, etc. The destruction of fauna and flora which interferes with nature's creative work through natural selection and the variation of species limits or even blocks the progress of the plant and animal breeder. Of a similar nature is the wasteful exploitation of minerals. Here again, scientific progress offers many remedies but does not wholly remove the problem of conflicts between short-run individual and long-run group interests.

Another source of trouble, interfering with orderly programs and often causing heavy losses of resource values, if not their outright destruction, is the growing complexity of the social order. As nations increase in size, as economies become more elaborate, and as global interdependence grows, the task of "living together well," of good neighborliness, of The Good Society, grows more difficult and the pitfalls become more numerous and deeper. Perhaps more resources are destroyed or left unborn by class struggle, internal strife, and, above all, by war, than by all other causes put together.

Examples of Resource Creation and Destruction

Thus far, this discussion of resources has been stated in rather theoretical terms. Theoretical abstractions are hard to grasp unless examples from life are cited which bring the analysis down to earth, as it were.

It is easy to find illustrations that verify the functional or operational theory, support the claim that "resourceship" evolves out of the three-way interaction of natural, human, and cultural assets, and prove that natural resources are rare indeed.

For various reasons which need not be developed here, Latin America is a region where the processes of resource development and disappearance are unusually transparent. The examples that follow are chosen from recent Latin-American history.[26]

Rubber from the Amazon region had been known to people in the western hemisphere for centuries, but little could be done with it until Charles Goodyear discovered vulcanization in 1839. As a result of his discovery, rubber could now be used to satisfy essential human wants. Business concerns soon sprang up to manufacture and sell articles made of vulcanized rubber. The difference between the processing costs and what the purchasers of these articles were willing to pay set the price the traders could pay for rubber in its native state. This

price in turn determined how many natives could be hired to gather it from trees that grew wild in the jungles of the Amazon basin and prepare it for the market; i.e., this price determined the extent of the areas that were worth while tapping. In short, the demand of people throughout the world for vulcanized rubber goods governed the process by which "neutral stuff" in the wilds of the Amazon could be converted into the rubber resources of Brazil.

The importance of Goodyear's invention should not be overlooked. For, in this age of machine industry and science, it is the inventor and after him the technologist who usually open up the opportunity for the risk-taking businessman to set the actual resource-creating process in motion. But in its entirety, the resource-creating setup is composed of many parts—invention and technology, business enterprise, market demand, labor, capital equipment, the social and political institutions governing international trade and regulating human relationships both intranationally and internationally. Not only are all these parts essential, but there must be the proper balance between them.

Another example of resource creation is to be found in the iron deposits in Minas Gerais, in Brazil. These deposits—they are among the largest anywhere in the world—have been known about for a long, long time, and attempts have been made to work them. But it is only within the past decade or so that a truly modern industry using this iron has been developed. Among the reasons for this delay were the inaccessibility of the deposits themselves, for they were located far inland, and the lack of nearby coking coal with which to smelt the ore.

Then came the Good Neighbor Policy, and with it loans from the United States to Brazil, as well as expert advice on building a modern steel mill. As a result, the National Steel Company of Brazil put up a steelworks in the river valley back of Rio de Janeiro, and an old railroad running through a fever-ridden valley to the port of Vitoria was modernized and the valley made inhabitable. Thus the stage was set for Brazil's iron deposits—for long mere "neutral stuff"—to become Brazil's iron resources.

[26] Based on Erich W. Zimmermann, "Resources of Latin America, a Study in Methodology."

To achieve this conversion from "neutral stuff" to resources, seven things were necessary: (1) The Good Neighbor Policy, which reflected political interests and people's attitudes and the understanding between their governments. (2) Capital, in the form of both credit and machine equipment and know-how. (3) Labor, able and willing to work, which in turn is tied up with decades of labor legislation and with wage policies and social security. (4) A domestic market for Brazilian-made steel products, subsidized by a government anxious to own its steelworks and willing to pay the cost differential of Brazilian production over the world market price. (5) A foreign market for Brazilian ore, which was created by World War II. (6) Modern sanitation to make the valley livable. (7) Modern technology, which performed one miracle after another all along the line from ore to blast furnace to Siemens converter to Koppers coke oven.

This story could be told over and over again. It has many variations, but the theme is always the same. Resourceship stems from the purposeful interaction of natural, cultural, and human aspects primed and kept going by demand based on availability for use.

But there is another side to the story. The process can be reversed. Not only do modern science and technology backed by wants and needs create resources; they also destroy them and reconvert them into "neutral stuff." Again Brazilian rubber is a good example. When the possibilities of the rubber tire were first recognized, it became apparent that the supply of wild rubber would be both inadequate in amount and too costly; in short, it would constitute a bottleneck in the rubber goods industry in general and in the tire industry in particular. The rubber plantations of the Middle East—Ceylon, Malay Peninsula, Straits Settlements, Dutch East Indies, etc.—were the answer. With the aid of genetics, the European owners of these plantations succeeded in breeding new varieties of rubber trees infinitely more productive than the wild trees of the jungle. Thus cost was brought down to a mere fraction of the Brazilian figure, and the daughter industry squeezed the mother industry out of the world market until Brazilian rubber resources were little more than a memory. How

synthetic rubber production during World War II reached dimensions which dwarfed even the peak figures of Brazil's earlier output is too recent to need repeating.

All these examples prove the same basic fact: Resources *are* not, they *become;* they are not static but expand and contract in response to human wants and human actions. In these examples, two forms of human action were prominent: technics and business enterprise. But other forms of human action at times become determinant as resource makers or destroyers, overshadowing the influence of the inventor and the entrepreneur. One of the most important of these is *governmental policy*. The petroleum industry in three Latin-American countries will be used to illustrate this point.

Mexico was the first of these countries in which, soon after the turn of the present century, a large modern petroleum industry was developed. In 1921, Mexican exports amounted to over one-fifth of the world crude oil output. But after World War I the output curve went into a tailspin, for the big oil companies, whose Mexican properties had been taken over by a revolutionary government, turned from Mexico to Venezuela. In less than twenty years, Venezuela's output surpassed Mexico's peak figure. The situation in Bolivia is different. After spending years of work and investing millions of dollars, the Standard Oil interests had brought Bolivia almost to the point where she could take her place among the crude oil producers of the world. But the new rules laid down by her government made Standard Oil prefer to sacrifice the vast sums invested rather than continue under the new regulations.

This brief account of the oil industry in these three countries brings out the following facts: (1) The exploitation of oil fields, especially in the tropics, requires vast amounts of capital. (2) The markets for both crude oil and refined products are outside of Latin America. (3) It is generally the advanced industrialized countries that have the technical know-how and the general scientific background required. (4) Under these circumstances, most Latin-American oil fields can be developed on a large scale and an efficient basis only by foreign capital. (5) Therefore, foreign oil companies that are willing to risk their capital here require reasonable assurance that their investments will be safe from unpredictable and irresponsible political interference. (6) Consequently, *laws, political attitudes, and government policies,* along with basic geological and geographical facts, become the strategic factors in determining which oil fields will be converted by foreign capital from useless "neutral stuff" into the most coveted resource of modern times.

Resources—Where the Sciences Meet

Both the analysis that preceded and the examples just cited make clear that the study of resources belongs in the field of the social sciences, but that the synthesizing work of the social scientist must rest on the findings of both natural and applied scientists. The field of the social sciences is wide indeed. It embraces history, sociology, phases of anthropology, economics, government, etc. The fields of the natural and applied sciences are even wider. The study of resources thus inevitably becomes the study of synthesis. If such synthesis is not to bog down in confusion and shallowness, the field must be carefully surveyed and blocked out. This will be attempted.

Since the resources at the disposal of man evolve out of the working combination of natural, human, and cultural aspects—a combination which expands with every advance of human knowledge and wisdom and contracts with every relapse into the barbarism of war and civil strife—the study of resources logically falls into separate phases or divides into separate fields:
1. The study of the materials, energies, living organisms, conditions, etc., found in nature.
2. The study of man, on the animal as well as on the supra-animal level, viewed both individually and in society.
3. The study of human culture in all its aspects, including technology, social and political institutions, its history, nature, trends, etc.
4. The study of the interrelations between these three fields.[27]

Such a study of resources calls for the services of:

---

[27] This list is restricted to studies *directly* concerned with resources. Since all scientific effort rests on fundamentals contained in mathematics, logic, philosophy, pure science, etc., these too must be considered, though their contributions are *indirect.* Likewise, the tools of communication—alphabet, numbers, symbols, language, etc.—should not be overlooked.

1. The physical or natural sciences, including anatomy, physiology, histology, psychology, biology, zoölogy, bacteriology, botany, ecology, geology, physical geography, climatology, pedology, physics, chemistry, mechanics, etc. The function of these sciences is to reveal what is, where it is, why it is, how it is, how different segments interact, etc. Their study is purely objective, i.e., wholly detached from the human viewpoint. Their exponents are primary fact-finders of society.
2. The "applied" scientists: the engineer, the economic geologist, the human or economic geographer, the industrial chemist, the surgeon, physician, public health expert, etc. They are the technicians of society. They determine what is *technically feasible.* They apply the knowledge gathered by the fact-finders and the "pure" scientists.
3. The entrepreneurs who lend financial support to those applications of science and techniques which to them appear profitable. They narrow the field of the technically feasible by applying additional tests of feasibility. To the technician's question, "Is it technically feasible?" they add the question, "Is it financially profitable?"
4. Economists who further narrow the choice of action by asking, "What is best for society in the long run?" Their supreme task in society is that of helping to shape the grand strategy of the utilization of all resources with a view to maximizing the social benefits derived from the most effective, best, or wisest use of "scarce means applied to alternate ends." In this difficult task the economist is aided by all social scientists who throw light on the nature, structure, and function of society.

In brief, the natural scientist deals with "neutral stuff," with things *per se.* All the others evaluate and choose. The applied scientist separates the feasible from the nonfeasible or the not-yet-feasible. The businessman seeks to differentiate the profitable from the unprofitable, or the more profitable from the less profitable. The social "scientist" tries to distinguish between good and evil, between that which promotes the common good and that which harms.

One might summarize the functions of these four groups in terms of the questions which each seeks to answer:
1. What is? Where is it? How is it, and why? How does it behave and why?
2. What can we do with it?
3. How should it be used to yield the highest return to private enterprise?
4. How should it be used to yield the highest return to society?

It is evident from the foregoing that no one

group can, by itself, fully understand and appraise resources. Such an understanding and appraisal are joint responsibilities.

The appraisal of resources proceeds from:
1. The knowledge of facts of nature and culture to
2. the determination of technical feasibility to
3. the determination of profitability to
4. the formulation of the grand strategy along socio-economic lines.[28]

Stages 3 and 4 involve subjective evaluation. They lack the advantage of scientific objectivity characteristic of Stages 1 and 2.

In reality, these categories are seldom if ever as clearly distinguished as this oversimplified exposition makes it appear. Much of the work in the social sciences, such as statistics and history, is of a fact-finding, data-collecting nature, and there is no reason why the natural scientist and the applied scientist may not look beyond the physical facts and rules of technical feasibility to the ultimate social implications of their findings and work. In fact, there is good reason why they should!

Two sets of interdependent criteria may be distinguished in the appraisal of resources:
1. *The State of the Wants,* the expression of human needs, individual wants, social objectives, higher aspirations.
2. *The State of the Arts,* as the summation of human capacities along lines of both technology and social organization.

The constant flux in which these two sets of criteria exist communicates itself to the resources to the appraisal of which these criteria apply. While the physical universe may be constant, while the planet earth may undergo few changes speedy and substantial enough to affect materially the destiny of man, the resources available to the human race are in constant flux, changing reflections of changing capacities and needs.[29]

Synopsis

The presentation of the functional or operational theory of resources is inevitably complex. Roaming over wide areas of thought, one is apt to lose the thread and fail to see the forest

---

[28] During the nineteenth century in the English-speaking world the belief was widely held that the determination of profitability automatically took care of socio-economic strategy. That belief has been badly shaken and is now shared by only a small minority.

[29] Erich W. Zimmermann, "Resources—an Evolving Concept."

because of the trees. The various points discussed in this chapter, therefore, are brought to a focus in a single table. This table brings out the trinity of natural, cultural, and human aspects from which resourceship evolves; it views them as means (instrumental wealth) to ends (real wealth); it recognizes the presence of resistances, the overcoming of which absorbs a large portion of instrumental wealth, leaving only a residual ("net resources") for the promotion of real wealth. These basic concepts are elaborated by breaking down both resources and resistances into various subdivisions and by implementing the concept of real wealth with slogans and a quotation.

TRENDS IN RESOURCE DEVELOPMENT

Table 1.1 may give a false impression of a one-way flow from top to bottom, from means to ends. As was pointed out, the process is not one-way. The current flows from ends to means with equal ease. In the same way it is difficult to state when and how far man initiates the process of resource development with nature the passive factor, and when and how far nature takes the lead in coaxing, urging, perhaps even compelling man to action.

If it is difficult to determine the source of the movement, it is almost impossible to determine its direction. Studying the western world during the past few centuries, one may be inclined to view the movement as following an ascending spiral. Wants multiply, arts improve, ever higher tiers of cultural improvements are superimposed on the natural foundations.

Yet while changed or expanding wants create new resources, others are destroyed. Progress always means a net gain but seldom a pure gain. Creating the better, we must often destroy the good. Moreover, a study of all cultures past and present may lead one to a less optimistic interpretation. One gets the impression of waves rising and falling, of ebb and flow. Perhaps each successive tidal wave reaches a little higher than its predecessor and each successive ebb does not fall back as far as the preceding one. Philosophers do not agree. They do not all anticipate the Decline of the West with the fatalism of a Spengler.

TABLE 1.1. Resources, Resistances and End Values[30]

RESOURCES OR MEANS (INSTRUMENTAL WEALTH)

Natural Aspects ("Land")	Cultural Aspects ("Capital")	Human Aspects ("Labor")
I. FACTORS OF PRODUCTION		
a. *Primary or Original*		
Free gifts of nature.	....	Native abilities and drives.
b. *Secondary or Derived*		
Aspects of nature which become available for use by man as a result of improvements made by man—improvements in nature as well as in himself.	Instruments of, and aids to, production such as tools, engines, machines, factories, residences, cities, ports, canals, railroads, highways, dams, power lines, cables, telephone and telegraph lines, radio, television, irrigation, drainage, improved strains of useful plants and animals, improved soils, surplus funds, etc.	Human capacities developed through education, training, experience, improved health, etc.
II. CONDITIONING FACTORS		
a. *Primary or Original*		
Aspects of nature such as climate, topography, location, configuration, etc., in so far as their conditioning force is unaffected by man.	....	Social attitudes, favorable to "living together."
b. *Secondary or Derived*		
The same conditioning aspects of nature listed above in so far as their conditioning force is affected by man.	Facilitating agencies of commerce and finance; social institutions such as government (law and order, justice, public health, postal service, etc.), church, school, mores, state of the industrial arts, credit, accumulated knowledge, ethics, level of morals, etc.	Constructive labor attitudes, management attitudes, labor-management relations, aspirations.

RESISTANCES

Natural Aspects ("Land")	Cultural Aspects ("Capital")	Human Aspects ("Labor")
I. DIRECT OBSTACLES		
a. *Primary or Original*		
Catastrophes such as storms, floods, tidal waves, earthquakes, pestilence, drought, insect pests, disease, poisonous plants and animals, etc.	....	Human failings such as "cussedness," lack of foresight, mismanagement, failure to comprehend complexities and multiple correlations; ignorance, stupidity, greed.

b. *Secondary or Derived*

Denuded mountainsides, erosion, silted and polluted streams and harbors, depleted mineral reserves, lost strains of fauna and flora, ecological disturbances, etc.

"Bad capital" resulting from miscalculation or erroneous appraisal; obsolete equipment not yet written off, etc.

Human difficulties resulting from the complexities of modern industrial civilization; warped judgment; "false Messiahs."

II. INDIRECT HANDICAPS

a. *Primary or Original*

Distance, topographical and locational obstacles, unfavorable distribution of raw materials and energy sources, climatic handicaps, etc. . . . .

Population densities below or above the "optimum," unfortunate distribution of population relative to changing opportunities, age composition unfavorably affecting productivity.

b. *Secondary or Derived*

The handicaps listed above in so far as they are aggravated by cultural impacts.

"The dead hand of the past," vested rights, threats from stronger neighbors causing diversion of instrumental wealth into unproductive channels; business cycles, depressions; abortive policies.

Racial conflicts; class struggle; war.

OBJECTIVES OR END VALUES (REAL WEALTH)

"Life, Liberty, and the Pursuit of Happiness"

Atlantic Charter . . . "The Four Freedoms" . . . Philadelphia Manifesto

Liberty, Security, and Human Decency

"The only *final* value is human life, or rather human living, with all its richness and fullness of experience. This, I take it, is what Ruskin meant when he exclaimed, 'There is no wealth but life!' The *intrinsic* values comprise the things which constitute the positive content of living, the things we desire for their own sake—work and play, love and friendship, hearth and home, and so on, together with such general conditions as peace, security, liberty, and opportunity. The huge class of *instrumental* values includes all our material wealth of whatever kind, all our technological knowledge, all government, and all the economic processes of production and exchange. In fact *all* social institutions belong in this category of instrumental values—*means* to something nearer to the heart of man."

ALBERT B. WOLFE

Presidential address delivered at the Fifty-sixth Annual Meeting of The American Economic Association, Washington, D.C., January 21, 1944, published in *The American Economic Review*, Vol. XXIV, Number One, March, 1944, p. 2.

[30] Erich W. Zimmermann, "What We Mean by Resources," in *Texas Looks Ahead*, vol 1 of *The Resources of Texas*, University of Texas, Austin, 1944.

BIBLIOGRAPHY

Ayres, C., *The Theory of Economic Progress*, Chapel Hill, University of North Carolina Press, 1944.

Bowman, I., *Geography in Relation to the Social Sciences*, New York, Scribner, 1934.

Brownell, B., *The New Universe*, New York, Van Nostrand, 1929.

Clark, C., *The Conditions of Economic Progress*, London, Macmillan, 1940.

Davis, D. H., *The Earth and Man*, New York, Macmillan, 1943.

Dewhurst, J. F., and associates, *America's Needs and Resources*, New York, Twentieth Century Fund, 1947.

Ely, R. T., Hess, R. H., Leith, C. K., and Carver, T. N., *The Foundations of National Prosperity*, New York, Macmillan, 1923.

Escher, B. G., and den Hollander, A. N. J., "De Aarde" (The Earth), *Eerste Nederlandse Systematisch Ingerichte Encyclopaedie*, Part V, Amsterdam, E.N.S.I.E., 1948.

Fairgrieve, J., *Geography and World Power*, New York, Dutton, 2nd ed., 1921.

Fritz, W. G., "An Appraisal of Our Natural Resources," *Dun's Review*, February, 1948.

Furnas, C. C., *The Storehouse of Civilization*, New York, Bureau of Publications, Teachers College, Columbia University, 1939.

Harris, S. E. (ed.), *Saving American Capitalism*, New York, Knopf, 1948, especially "Resources," by M. L. Cooke.

Jones, C. F., and Darkenwald, G. G., *Economic Geography*, New York, Macmillan, 1941.

Kelsey, C., *The Physical Basis of Society*, New York, Appleton-Century-Crofts, 1929.

Kinsman, D. O., *Our Economic World*, New York, Crowell, 1937.

Kohn, C. F. (ed.), *Geographical Approaches to Social Education*, Washington, National Council for the Social Studies, 1949.

McCarty, H. H., *The Geographic Basis of American Economic Life*, New York, Harper, 1940.

Mather, K. F., *Enough and to Spare*, New York, Harper, 1944.

Meyerhoff, H. A., "Some Social Implications of Natural Resources," *Annals of the American Academy of Political and Social Science*, January, 1947.

Mitchell, Lucy S., and others, *My Country 'Tis of Thee: The Use and Abuse of Natural Resources*, New York, Macmillan, 1940.

Mitchell, W. C., "Economic Resources and Their Employment," *Nature*, November 2, 1940.

Mitchell, W. C., "Conservation, Liberty, and Economics," in *The Foundations of Conservation Education*, New York, National Wildlife Federation, 1941.

Moore, W. G., *The World's Wealth*, New York, Penguin Books, 1947.

Moulton, H. G., *Controlling Factors in Economic Development*, Washington, Brookings, 1949.

Patterson, E. M., *An Introduction to World Economics*, New York, Macmillan, 1947.

Smith, J. R., and Phillips, M. O., *North America, Its People and Their Resources*, New York, Harcourt, Brace, 2nd ed., 1940.

Smith, J. R., and Phillips, M. O., *Industrial and Commercial Geography*, New York, Holt, 3rd ed., 1946.

Sprout, H. and M. (eds.), *Foundations of National Power*, New York, Van Nostrand, 1946.

Stamp, L. D., *Commercial Geography*, London, Longmans, Green, 1936.

Wells, H. G., *The Work, Wealth, and Happiness of Mankind*, Garden City, Doubleday, 1931.

Whittlesey, D., *The Earth and the State: A Study of Political Geography*, New York, Holt, 1939.

Wolfe, A. B., "Neurophysiological Economics," *Journal of Political Economy*, April, 1950.

Zimmermann, E. W., "Natural Resources," *Encyclopædia of the Social Sciences*, New York, Macmillan, 1933.

Zimmermann, E. W., "Resources of the South," *Southeastern Quarterly*, summer, 1934.

Zimmermann, E. W., "Resources," in Spahr, W. E. (ed.), *Economic Principles and Problems*, New York, Farrar & Rinehart, 3rd ed., 1936, vol. 1, chap. 7.

Zimmermann, E. W., "What We Mean by Resources," in *Texas Looks Ahead*, vol. 1 of *The Resources of Texas*, University of Texas, Austin, 1944. Published in Spanish as "Lo que Debemos Entender por Recursos," *Investigación Economica* (University of Mexico), vol. 5, no. 4, 1945.

Zimmermann, E. W., "Resources—an Evolving Concept," *Transactions, Texas Academy of Science*, 1944.

Zimmermann, E. W., "Resources of Latin America, a Study in Methodology," in *Some Economic Aspects of Postwar Inter-American Relations*, University of Texas Institute of Latin American Studies, 1946.

Chapter 2

RESOURCE APPRAISAL: HUMAN WANTS AND SOCIAL OBJECTIVES

The word "resource" has been called a term of appraisal. It reflects human judgment as to want-satisfying capacity, utility. The appraisal seeks to determine whether an aspect of the environment provides or supports or serves as a source of supply of desirable goods and services. Appraisal, therefore, is at the heart of the resource process. It will be scrutinized in this chapter and the next.

Nature and Culture Wants; Standards of Living

Human wants may be divided into two groups: basic, nature, creature, or existence wants, and culture wants. Existence wants must be satisfied if the life of the individual and of the group is to go on. They vary according to age, sex, mode of life, habitat, individual constitution and, perhaps, also according to racial characteristics. Basic wants can be divided into positive and negative wants. Man needs food, air, and water to build up or maintain bones, tissues, and blood, and to support the vital processes. These are positive wants. He must ward off cold and disease and protect himself against attack. Hence shelter, clothing, armor, etc., may be said to satisfy negative

wants. These basic wants are the starting point of the economic process and consequently of resource appraisal. They found early expression in the eloquent language of tribal custom, worship, and the ceremonies of primitive peoples. Sun, light, fire, mother earth, a father spirit who sends fertilizing rain were the central ideas of ancient religious cults.

But human desires seldom, if ever, stop when basic wants are satisfied. Man tends to eat and drink more than is absolutely necessary for mere existence. He craves variety and adds touches of refinement to the form and content of basic want satisfaction. A taste for the beautiful develops. Bright colors, luster, and sheen hold a primitive appeal. Thus to the basic wants are added more refined and sophisticated desires. To the nature wants are added culture wants.

Individual wants, through established habit and social sanction, tend to crystallize into group standards of living. Once such standards have become established, any force which threatens to lower them is fiercely resisted. The peoples of the earth differ widely in living standards, and hence in their appraisal of a

21

given environment. A plot of land may yield a Japanese family a living which to them appears bounteous; it may yield a fair living to a Russian family, and no living at all to a family of native Americans. Living standards involve the idea of leisure. Under one standard man may expect nothing else but hard work from sunrise to sunset without greater reward than the bare necessities of life; under another, he may complain if six hours' labor does not yield a liberal margin over and above these necessities.

Wants and Want Doctrines

The crystallization process goes farther. Besides standards of living—that is, of wants—there develop doctrines about wants. These doctrines may be divided into negative or want discouragement doctrines—such as asceticism—and positive or want encouragement doctrines. In the past, civilizations seem to have possessed a limited driving force, and when this was spent, they have tended to stagnate, to become static. The natural tendency of wants to expand and of standards of living to push upward must then be checked. Under such conditions an attitude of resignation tends to develop. Such an attitude is prevalent among some primitive societies. Among more sophisticated peoples it may take the form of a conscious doctrine, a philosophy of want discouragement, of asceticism. The ascetic seeks happiness in self-denial, in the suppression or curtailment of wants. Whether he finds what he seeks is another question.

This negative attitude toward human wants, this ascetic doctrine, is found among some of the overpopulated countries of the East where material arts seem to have reached the limit of spontaneous improvement. Traces of this ascetic doctrine are also found during many periods of human history and in many places on the earth. In his fascinating book on Mexico, Stuart Chase tells the story of a European salesman who despairs of the "damned wantlessness" of the Indians. The enthusiasm of the Germans for oriental philosophy after their defeat in World War I is another case in point.

The opposite doctrine may be called the positive philosophy of want encouragement. It rests on the belief that material progress leads to happiness, and that progress, in turn, depends on want expansion and want multiplication. In its extreme form this modern doctrine is found in North America today. The American variant is marked by an inadequate differentiation between wants spontaneously developing in the course of social evolution and wants artificially created and imposed upon the consuming masses, not in response to organic changes in tastes and desires but in response to technical developments of factory production and corporate management, manifesting themselves in stupendous advertising campaigns. This extreme development found in North America is the culmination of a long line of changes which were set in motion by the Crusades, which reestablished the contact of temperate-zone Europe with the East, by the great discoveries, by the Renaissance, but above all, by the Industrial Revolution. So important has this conscious expansion and multiplication of wants become in modern capitalistic industry that Rathenau goes so far as to call the modern entrepreneur "the creator of new wants."

The Nature of Wants

Because of its far-reaching economic significance, a difference in the nature of existence and culture wants must here be mentioned. As has been said, existence wants must be satisfied if life is to go on. Nature demands a minimum of satisfaction up to which nature wants not only rank first in urgency, but simply must be met. Nature, however, sets not only a definite minimum, but also a maximum. A hard-working adult cannot long remain healthy and strong without a minimum daily food intake of 2000 calories, nor can he long remain fit if he regularly consumes more than 5000 calories a day. Room temperatures in the temperate zone should not fall below 65 degrees for any considerable length of time, nor should they exceed 75 degrees. More or less all elementary wants are subject to this law of absolute limitations. This is their most important characteristic.

Another feature should be mentioned. Elementary wants are generally recurring. Soon after being stilled, appetite develops anew. We ordinarily require about eight hours' rest out of every twenty-four. Thus existence wants may be said to be recurrent and hence relatively constant.

Culture wants differ in both respects, for they are neither subject to minima or maxima set by nature, nor are they constant or recurring. To be sure, the consumer habits of individuals, which, as stated above, tend to crystallize into standards of living, may develop to such a degree of intensity that physiological dispensables become psychic necessities. Conspicuous consumption plays its part, as in the case of automobiles and homes; social prestige or "caste" may establish consumption minima. Sex appeal must also be considered. Nevertheless, as a rule, culture wants are not quite as insistent in the lower ranges of consumption, nor is a saturation point reached as soon or as certainly as in the case of basic wants. This difference in the nature of wants is of vital importance in resource appraisal.

Individual Wants and Social Objectives

The wants of the individual are the foundation of all resource appraisal; but they are not all, for man seldom lives alone, a hermit, in utter isolation. Group life promotes efficiency and security. In the opinion of some observers, the social instinct is a definite part of human nature. The resource appraisal of the environment, therefore, must be enlarged or modified to take these social wants or objectives into account. Want satisfaction broadens into the attainment of social objectives. The environment must not only yield that which satisfies individual wants, but serve as the reliable basis of continued group life.

Resource appraisal—that is, the appraisal of the usefulness of the environment to man—must therefore be studied from two different angles: first, from the standpoint of individual human wants, and second, from that of social objectives. Hence the question, what forces control this division and delimit the provinces of private choice and of social control, of individual rights and liberties and of group power, respectively, assumes vital importance.

Group interests or social wants do not replace individual interests or private wants. They never can; for, after all, a group consists of individuals who must eat, drink, sleep, keep warm, and so on. Group interests supplement private wants. In a society limited by inadequate natural opportunities, social wants may encroach on private wants; but where the natural foundation of civilization is wide and firm, the satisfaction of social wants and the safeguarding of group interests are apt to result in a fuller life for the individual. Group coöperation may so stimulate and accelerate creative effort that not only group interests but also the wants of individuals are better served. In an ideal society, the attainment of social objectives is assumed to result in a fuller satisfaction of individual wants, for social aims and individual wants, in theory at least, run parallel toward the same goal. Coöperation in organized groups is essentially a device of collective want satisfaction. In reality, however, the social and private interests frequently clash in head-on collision. This is due to various reasons, some of which will be discussed.

Conflict Between Private and Social Interests

Team play is based on give-and-take. In a football game the individual player voluntarily forgoes a modicum of self-determination of action in order to improve, through better coöperation, the chances of success for his team. If team play pays, the players are rewarded for their sacrifice of self-determination with surer and greater victories. Man soon discovered that security could best be assured by group coöperation. Thus defense became a major, if not the primary, function of government. As groups grew in size, as life—both individual and group life—became more complex, the advantages of team play became less evident and the benefits of give-and-take between individual and group less manifest. Sacrifices demanded of the individual by the group in the interest of group safety were often resented.

Defense is not the only function generally delegated by individuals to the group. The guardianship over public health and internal peace are other basic tasks entrusted to the group management, if we may apply this term to government. We tend to go farther, for, on the ground that defense, health, and internal peace rests most securely on wealth and prosperity, the group becomes the champion of economic progress. As such, it may at times have to interfere with individual liberty, and consequently friction results.

This cannot surprise anyone who is at all familiar with the complexity of modern social organization. The most important social group of modern times is the state. Within it may be found innumerable social relationships, such as the family in both the narrow and broader sense, churches, lodges, trade associations, the Red Cross, D.A.R., sanitary districts, political parties, academies, the Legion, and so forth. These form a complicated pattern of organization and cross-organization, of the grouping and regrouping of individuals for specific purposes and for the pursuit of varied interests—social, political, economic, and eleemosynary.

These associations, in turn, may project their activities and affiliations beyond state boundaries as in the case of the Catholic Church, international cartels, or the Rotary Club; or they may form partisan or particularistic blocs within the state, such as the Farm bloc or the Grand Army of the Republic, and so forth. Relationships may develop among the states, such as the Triple Alliance, the Entente Cordiale, the Allies, the Central Powers, the International Postal Union, the Pan American Union, the World Court, or the United Nations. But, on the other hand, definite rivalries may also develop, for this complexity of social groupings creates friction, causes misunderstanding, and renders difficult the proper correlation between group needs and individual wants.

The diversity of attitudes and objectives threatens to turn resource appraisal into something akin to a Chinese puzzle. It is difficult to find one's way in this modern maze of loyalties—and yet good citizenship has been aptly defined as the "right ordering of all our loyalties."

Modern Man a Bundle of "Egos"

Modern man may be thought of as made up of many "egos." According to the "ego" which happens to dominate at a given moment, he will arrive at very different conclusions in the resource appraisal of his environment. An example will make this clearer. A man is appraising a parcel of real estate; he is a realtor, the father of children, the chairman of the playground committee of his community, and a member of a committee appointed by the President of the United States to study national problems of land utilization. According to the particular capacity in which he thinks, speaks, and acts at a given moment, he will hold widely different opinions and, perhaps, advocate different policies concerning the plot of ground in question.

This example is typical, and it goes to show that the average man in western civilization lives his life partly as a private individual, and partly as a member of some social group. As a private individual he seeks to satisfy his natural craving for creature comforts and to bring to realization his personal hopes and ambitions; he works for his family or for himself and in general follows his own wishes and interests. But as a citizen of his town or village, state or country, he finds that he must, to some extent, sacrifice his personal freedom and "play the game." How the individual adjusts himself to this conflict of interests—in other words, how he "orders his loyalties"—is largely a sociological problem. Here we are interested in its resource aspects. In this connection, the term "the three economies" has been used; they are described as follows:

On the basis of this relationship of the individual to the group, economic life may be divided into three phases: At one extreme are numerous activities left entirely to individual initiative and private enterprise; at the other extreme are activities such as the administration of justice and the provisions for the armed forces which are generally conceded to be matters of public or social concern. Between these two extremes there lies a "third economy" where the balance between private interest and social concern is not as readily determined, and where boundary lines are blurred. This "third economy" comprises, among other activities, extractive natural-resource industries such as mining and lumbering (the latter unless on a sustained-yield basis). The extent to which the State should interfere in private business is most debatable with regard to such activities affecting vital group assets. The power industry is another case in point. To a lesser extent even agriculture lies within the domain of this "third economy." For even soil fertility can become a wasting asset through abuse.

Nations differ widely with regard to their attitudes toward this middle zone. Some nations practically absorb it into the province of free individual enterprise, leaving to social control only a narrow fringe of public functions. Other nations take the very opposite attitude. Such differences in attitude are explained partly by historical forces which have molded national character, partly by differences in the actual situation which these nations are facing at a given time. Difference in pressure brought to bear on groups either from the outside, perhaps by hostile neighbors, or from the inside, possibly by underprivileged and restive classes, seems to account for much of the differences between national attitudes toward the control over this "third economy."[1]

Class Conflict and Social Objectives

In a utopian world all people are striving toward "the greatest good for the greatest number" and promoting the social welfare. In reality, however, social organizations, and hence social objectives, fall far short of such an ideal. At best, a modern group rests on a compromise between conflicting interests as, for instance, the interests of producers and consumers, capitalists and wage earners, country and city, agriculture and manufacturing industries, etc. Such a compromise is seldom so fair as to prove permanent or to stop the grumbling of the discontented. Thus, change is the rule rather than the exception, and internal strife is often merely stifled by force instead of being removed by equitable adjustment. In reality, the so-called group interest may not be much more than the interest of a dominant class parading in the cloak of social necessity, and national policy may aim at the social objectives of a class or a combination of classes rather than at the fullest satisfaction of the most urgent wants of the greatest number.

Groups differ materially as to the manner in which benefits and privileges are distributed among their members. In czarist Russia the beneficiaries or privileged classes constituted barely more than 10 percent of the population. In ancient Greece during certain periods, free men formed a minority. Privileges generally develop as a result of initial superior strength—physical, political, and economic. This may lead to a compromise between strong and weak, the weak assuming certain burdens in return for a guarantee of security from the strong. However, such a compromise may survive its usefulness, for the strong sometimes become the privileged class and wish to retain their privileges long after the need for protection has ceased.[2]

The intensity of the conflict between group and individual, between social and private interests, depends in the first place on the equity of group organization or, to be more specific, on the equity with which duties and rights, sacrifices and benefits are adjusted. Man functions in the resource scheme in the dual capacity of agent and beneficiary, as producer and consumer. Social order rests largely on the proper coördination of these two functions. In a nation which is so rich that, in spite of a not entirely equitable division of benefits, even the least fortunate have enough or can "make a decent living," the question of an equitable distribution of rights and duties is not apt to have as strong a claim on people's thoughts as in poorer nations. Again, the sense of social justice is not equally developed in all people. Some may vegetate in sodden poverty almost unaware of their own misery; others are quick to resent any departure from their conception of fair play. As a rule, the more highly civilized people tend to belong to the second class. It may be safe to assume also that the sense of social justice is more highly developed today than it was in antiquity.

Hence this conflict is connected with the question of national prosperity or wealth. National wealth depends, in the first place, on the natural environment itself, on the availability—or utility—of the untransformed aspects of nature. It depends, in the second place, on the arts and institutions to which that environment, in view of the racial and cultural characteristics of the human element, gives rise. Among these, the institutions surrounding population increase are of special importance, for the largess of nature may result either in an ever-growing number of people at or near a point of minimum sustenance or in a rising living standard for a restricted number. It is a popular belief that the savage is relatively free. This is not strictly true, for the rules of primitive tribal life are ironclad, and ceremonial duties can press as heavily on the savage as

[1] Erich W. Zimmermann, in Walter E. Spahr (ed.), *Economic Principles and Problems*, Farrar & Rinehart, New York, 3rd ed., 1936, vol. 1, p. 186.

[2] Cf. A. C. H. C. de Tocqueville, *De l'Ancien Régime*. Translated into English under the title *The Old Regime and the Revolution* by John Bonner, New York, 1856.

conflicting loyalties may weigh on us. Potentially, at least, every improvement in the technique of production and in the social order means the increase of individual liberty.

Prosperity and Security as Social Objectives

In addition to the social and economic aspects, the political factor must be considered. Referring to this question, Seely, the English historian, went so far as to say: "The amount of freedom that may reasonably exist in a state is in inverse proportion to the military-political pressure exerted by foreign states against its boundaries."[3] This statement may well be expanded to cover the internal dangers as well. It suggests what one may term a pressure theory of social order. According to such a theory, social control tends to vary directly, and individual freedom inversely, with the weight of the pressure to which a group is subjected from the outside, from the inside, or from both sides.

Recent history is full of examples which strikingly illustrate this principle. An extreme case is found in Russia. Here was a country defeated in war, torn asunder by internal strife, threatened from without and maligned from within, the masses of its people suffering not only from the wounds of World War I but also from the consequences of centuries of misgovernment; its economic apparatus worn out, its social structure toppling—in short, a country facing ruin. How was the final collapse averted? By practically abolishing individual freedom and delegating to the group, as represented by a handful of ambitious, energetic, and, above all, fanatic, commissars, complete authority over the direction and management of the economic, social, and even the spiritual life of Russia. Resource appraisal was almost totally socialized.

The situation in France during and following the Revolution leading to Napoleon's dictatorial control was not wholly dissimilar. More recently the case of Italy serves to illustrate the pressure theory. The march on Rome followed

the almost complete breakdown of the capitalistic system of production brought about by a stalemate between employer and employee. Although proceeding from totally different premises, fascism, like communism, is a form of government which enlarges the authority of the group at the expense of the individual. The drift toward socialism in Britain which followed the gradual and partial disintegration of the Empire and the almost catastrophic deterioration of the economic position of the ancient island workshop may be another case in point.

By indirection, the Marshall Plan and the European Recovery Program may be cited as further evidence. For is not the motivating force behind these political measures the desire to prevent the advent of communist dictatorship by bettering the economic lot of the war-weary people of western Europe and thus preventing pressure from reaching the dictator-creating point?

In contrast to these items of positive evidence of the plausibility of the pressure theory, the United States continues to shine as the great negative example. For many reasons this nation is the most prosperous, the most powerful, perhaps the happiest, certainly the luckiest country in the world. It is little wonder that the gauge registers low pressure—in general, local areas and sporadic episodes excepted—and that the individual in the United States continues to enjoy far more freedom than do people in less fortunate lands.

The Time Factor

The conflict between social and private interests develops from a fundamental difference in the nature of the group and of the individual. The group represents a succession of generations, and therefore its life must be longer than that of the individual. While history is replete with the tragic stories of the downfall of past civilizations, of glorious empires vanished from the earth, and thus furnishes proof that even groups are not permanent, yet each group, oblivious of the lessons of history, dreams of eternal life or else believes that its own civilization is built upon a firmer foundation than any that has gone before. Whether, under present conditions, this trust in permanency is justified does not concern us here.

---

[3] Quoted by G. von Schmoller, "The Origin and Nature of German Institutions," chap. 6 of *Modern Germany in Relation to the Great War*, by various German writers, translated by William Wallace Whitelock, Mitchell Kennerley, New York, 1916.

What counts is the fact that the life span of the group is longer than that of the individual. If it is not permanency that the group can hope for, it certainly is a goodly share of longevity.

What has this difference in the life span of the group and of the individual to do with resource appraisal? To the average individual, the oil resources of the year 2000 may be of little concern; their size and accessibility do not interest him, for his imagination cannot follow his children and his children's children far enough into the future. The rugged individualist is not likely to be interested in the conservation of natural funds or stocks. Moreover, to the average man the reasons which explain the downfall of Rome are matters of indifference. His reaction is apt to be, "Well, did the ruins fall on me?" More likely than not, they did, but he is not aware of it. On the other hand, the statesman, the leader, and the thoughtful citizen who is aware of his responsibilities for the continuity of group life feel very differently.

As a result of such conflicting attitudes, social and private interests cannot agree on the "tempo" of resource development. He who regards the interest of future generations, who interprets human progress in the light of broad historical developments, is not as easily drawn into the whirlpool of profit chasing or the excitement of the market place as is the man who lives from hand to mouth, knows no other happiness than immediate enjoyment, and whose motto is, "After us, the deluge." The social view stresses the long-run aspects of resource appraisal; the individual is interested in immediate results. His is the short-run view.

The "Tempo" of Exploitation

This point may be made clearer by a concrete example. A tract of timber is to be cut. The owner of the nearby paper mill is willing to pay the market price for the timber. If he can get it below the market price, so much the better. This is the extent of his interest. How cutting that timber without providing for its replacement through reforestation will affect the timber situation five or ten or twenty years hence is "none of his business." The government, on the other hand, is vitally concerned with questions of conservation, flood control, etc., and is trying to educate the wood-using public not to treat the forest as a mine but to view timber as a crop.

This example brings out the question of "tempo," to which reference was made above. The strictly private viewpoint appraises tempo purely as to its immediate effects upon the current market situation. The social viewpoint, on the other hand, weighs the effects of the rate of the exploitation of resources upon market conditions, not only of today, but also as they will probably develop in the future. Moreover, the group is concerned with aspects of the production process which lie outside the field of profit economy. Since the tempo of exploitation is a much more vital consideration in the case of the limited nonrenewable resources than in that of unlimited or of self-renewable resources, we can readily understand the keen interest which the state, as the political embodiment of the group will, takes in the conservation of the limited nonrenewable resources.[4]

---

[4] Owing to their different attitudes, the individual and the group are interested in the development of different resources. In order to make this clear, the range of resources may be subdivided as follows:
1. Resources which are exploited or utilized for individual benefit only; there is no conflict between the social and private viewpoint (chicle).
2. Resources which are used only for social ends; there is no conflict (a ferro-alloy used exclusively in armor plate for battleships).
3. Resources in the utilization of which both individuals and society at large are interested. Several cases may be given:
   a. The supply is abundant; therefore conflict may be avoided (building stone).
   b. The supply is limited; then the conflict may be:
      (1) permanent (helium).
      (2) confined to wartime (wool).

A word of explanation concerning the examples may be in place. Chicle, as the raw material of chewing gum, can hardly be said to have social significance. Battleships are used for purposes of national defense, a function universally delegated by the individual to the state. Whether or not a ferro-alloy exists which is used exclusively in the manufacture of armor plate is immaterial to us. Building stone is used in both public and private buildings, but it would be far-fetched to create a conflict between social and private interests as regards that resource. Helium is a noninflammable gas used in airships. It is rare and, until recently, was produced and used exclusively by the United States government. Some of us may remember how, during World War I, wool was withdrawn from private consumption.

The difference in the resource interests of group and individual is largely explained by the functional division of labor between them and especially by the difference in attitudes just discussed. But the division goes even deeper, for it pertains to the division of the income derived from the utilization of resources. The selfish interest of the individual naturally strives for the maximum return, "the maximization of profit." The state, on the other hand, for the sake of harmony among classes and in order to safeguard its own permanency, may be concerned with a more equitable distribution of income than the untrammeled operation of "natural economic forces" would bring about. We cannot here follow up this line of thought, for it would lead us into the larger problems of social reform—in fact, into the social problems of our times and away from the more immediate problems of resource appraisal. But to complete this analysis we must add that within the same group the divisions between private and social interest and, with it, resource appraisal, vary from time to time. In times of danger—war, civil strife—the social or long-run aspects are stressed, but in times of peace and plenty the reins with which the group holds the individual in check are slackened.

Other Conflicts

The process of appraisal which, as we have seen, is largely dominated by the conflict between group and individual interests has lost much of its original straight-line simplicity. Ever larger and more complex social structures have resulted in a maze of conflicting interests which call for a constant balancing of pros and cons, for constant compromise. Village and town economies have merged into national economies and these, in turn, have become subject to world economic influences. Thus the areal basis of resource appraisal has continuously expanded. But the straight-line simplicity of appraisal has suffered for other reasons as well. Among these, the development of economic organization and economic processes and the technique made possible by larger and better social organizations and by inventions and discoveries in every field of science rank foremost in importance. This is not the place to trace this development to its origin and follow it through in all its ramifications and refinements. Three phases, however, deserve special mention because of their revolutionary effect on resource appraisal. They are: the division of labor, especially in its regional and international aspects, the rise of capitalism, and the increasing importance of money. These three phases are closely interrelated.

Division of Labor. Prior to the division of labor, man appraised the environment as to its capacity to furnish him directly what he wanted. But after the division of labor separates a group into farmers and craftsmen, the directness of appraisal is partly lost. These functional divisions among individuals belonging to the same community develop into a division of labor among communities; this in time becomes interregional and international. States and nations specialize along agricultural, mining, or manufacturing lines; cities specialize in certain products. Thus wide areas lose their self-sufficiency and become dependent on interregional or international trade for the satisfaction of their wants and the attainment of their objectives. England, for instance, gets much of her food from abroad, exchanging manufactured goods or services for it. The appraisal of the English natural and cultural landscape, therefore, no longer proceeds along the straight line: How much food can the soil yield? It follows a devious line, and the query now is: How much surplus manufacture can be produced which can be exchanged for the food surpluses of others? The appraisal of the food-exporting country is inversely affected.

Modern transportation, communication, and trading and financing techniques render feasible interregional exchange on a world-wide scale. The people of central England, for numerous reasons, are exceptionally successful in the production of cutlery; they may exchange cutlery for Australian mutton and Argentine wheat. Therefore, to obtain food, they must make something totally different from food, something seemingly unrelated; and yet, if they cannot make cutlery and exchange it for food, they face starvation. Exchange thus has raised many goods to the level of "constructive" necessities. This applies not only to those goods which are used in the production and transportation of food and other necessities, but also to those which are exchanged for necessities. Thus, a Sheffielder may well view his forges and furnaces as his food resources. In a money economy, any commodity whose production enables men to earn the wages with which to buy the necessities of life is itself a necessity. The ship that carries food from surplus areas to deficiency areas is as necessary as the wheat field itself. Steel and coal, petroleum and water power, railroads and banks—in short, anything that keeps the wheels of modern world economy going—are necessities.

Rise of Capitalism. An essential feature of capitalistic production is the use of machines. To a large degree, it may be said, productive efficiency depends on the number and quality of machines that can be used. Hence the appraisal of the environment now stresses its capacity to yield machine and energy materials. Capitalistic production is on the whole a more efficient, but a more roundabout or indirect, way of want satisfaction. If modern man wants bread, he first digs coal and ore, makes iron and steel, builds a factory which makes agricultural implements, builds railroads that carry implements one way and farm products the other; he builds flour mills and bakeries; he establishes banks that finance, and trade that ties all these into an organic system of social economy. Even primitive man needed a stick to scratch the ground; but getting the stick was a mere incident in the task of getting the grain. Nowadays "getting the stick," which means making and operating capital equipment, assumes such importance that at times we wonder whether we are really more interested in getting bread and other consumables than in making imposing and intricate things which will help us indirectly in getting what we want. Formerly, when we wanted to eat we had to grow crops and raise animals, or hunt and fish or gather wild fruits and herbs; but now when we want food we must first dig coal, iron ore, limestone, etc., and grow sisal and many other things. Resource appraisal today must follow this roundabout way of production.

Introduction of Money. The most decided break in the straight line of primitive direct appraisal resulted from the introduction of money; for money, as the medium of exchange, greatly facilitates and stimulates the division of labor and, as the measure of value, makes the rise of capitalism not only easier but in many cases possible. Money has such a revolutionary effect on resource appraisal because in the minds of many it discredits abundance and puts scarcity on the throne instead. Money turns subsistence economy into profit economy, use economy into exchange[5] economy. The man who grows his own food, keeps sheep to supply wool, builds his own house from timber cut on his own land—in short, lives in a self-sufficient closed economy—produces not for a market but for his own use. The more he produces, the more he can consume. Hence he prays for rain and sunshine, each at its proper time. He is happy when crop yields are heavy, when herds and flocks increase rapidly. His hope lies in bounty, his happiness in abundance. His is a simple straight-line appraisal of values.

Not so under a money economy. Normally, the money value or price of a product falls as a result of abundance and rises as a result of scarcity. (Both abundance and scarcity are understood as relatives, usually of demand.) The farmer who raises a crop for the market—a money crop, in other words, as distinguished from a supply crop—prays not for plenty but for scarcity; that is, he hopes for a small supply in his market of the commodity he wishes to sell. Needless to say, he wishes his own share of that supply to be generous, and he wants to see the commodity he sells in strong demand.

Thus in an exchange economy—also known as a market or price economy—we find a strange warping of appraisal. But we find more, namely, a conflict of interest between buyer and seller. The buyer craves abundance, the seller scarcity. Moreover, a conflict of interests develops among the sellers of the same commodity (or of commodities serving like or similar purposes) in the market. Each one would like to sell much at a higher price. The price, however, cannot be high if all sell much. Therefore each seller would like to see the others crippled in their efforts by hailstorms and insect pests and similar destructive agents, if they

---

[5] Barter is exchange without the use of money; its possibilities are limited.

are farmers, or by strikes and fires, if they are manufacturers.[6]

One wonders why intelligent civilized man suffers such a condition, why he allows money thus to warp appraisal and destroy harmony. The explanation is found in the almost incredible stimulus to productive efficiency furnished by the division of labor, capitalistic production

---

[6] In his chapter in Lionel D. Edie's *The Stabilization of Business* (The Macmillan Company, New York, 1923), Wesley C. Mitchell developed this point forcefully, and used the following passage from Carlyle's *Past and Present* to prove that the situation is one of long-standing:

"England is full of wealth, of multifarious produce, supply for human want in every kind; yet England is dying of inanition. With unabated bounty the land of England blooms and grows; waving with yellow harvests; thick-studded with workshops, industrial implements, with fifteen millions of workers, understood to be the strongest, the cunningest, and the willingest our Earth ever had; these men are here, the work they have done, the fruit they have realized is here, abundant, exuberant, on every hand of us: and behold, some baleful fiat as of Enchantment has gone forth, saying, 'Touch it not ye workers, ye master-workers, ye master-idlers; none of you can touch it, no man of you shall be the better for it; this is enchanted fruit.' "

technique, and the use of money (or credit). For these man is willing to pay the price in terms of conflicting interest and warped appraisal because he finds it cheap in the light of the results achieved.

We have seen that human wants and social objectives, the forces behind all productive effort, have developed into a veritable maze in the course of history, as the result of the conflict of interests between individuals and social groups, between buyers and sellers, and producers and users. We have seen how the concept of necessities has changed. We have seen further that the division of labor and the capitalistic method of production have destroyed the simple straight-line appraisal of the environment as to its usefulness. Ten thousand years of civilization have completely changed resource appraisal. All values have become new.

Merely to realize that modern resource appraisal is different from the old, that it is complex and distorted, does not suffice. That realization alone does not solve our problems; but it is the first step to the solution, and it should prove an aid in grappling with the resource problems as they will be developed in the chapters that follow.

BIBLIOGRAPHY

Becker, C. L., *Progress and Power*, New York, Oxford, 1939.

Burgess, E. W., *Personality and the Group*, Chicago, University of Chicago Press, 1929.

Harvard Tercentenary Publication, *Authority and the Individual*, Cambridge, Harvard University Press, 1937.

Hiller, E. T., *Social Relations and Structures*, New York, Harper, 1947.

Kardiner, A., *The Individual and His Society*, New York, Columbia University Press, 1939.

Lewis, E. L., *The Individual and Society*, New York, Exposition Press, 1949.

Mund, V. A., *Government and Business*, New York, Harper, 1950.

Orton, W. A., *The Economic Role of the State*, Chicago, University of Chicago Press, 1950.

Schmidt, E. P. (ed.), *Man and Society*, New York, Prentice-Hall, 1938.

Snyder, R. C., and Wilson, H. H., *Roots of Political Behavior*, New York, American Book, 1949.

Chapter 3

RESOURCE APPRAISAL: TECHNOLOGICAL AND SOCIETAL ARTS

One of the chief distinctions between man and beast is man's ability consciously and consistently to change his environment. He alone can create cultural environments expansible and changeable almost at will. The beaver can build a dam, the bird a nest. But neither beaver nor bird can critically appraise its own work and systematically undertake the task of improving either the dam or the nest or the technique of dam construction or of nest building. Each normal beaver in the course of its life can rise to the same height of perfection as countless others before it, but not one inch higher. No animal is capable of enlarging the opportunities offered by its natural environment beyond the limits set by its own organism and by the unalterable genus technique at its disposal (see p. 8). As a result of passive adaptation to the environment, the animal organism may change. Man alone is capable of constructive criticism of his own performance and of conscious and purposeful improvement.

As was stated before, man's ability to create cultural environments is based first of all on his superior natural endowment, his native brain power, his exceptional vocal organs, his tool-making and tool-using hand, and, second, on the accumulated effects of past cultural performance. Culture is a cumulative process; it gains momentum as it proceeds.

Arts and Capital Equipment; Technological and Institutional Arts

Functionally cultural improvements may be divided into two groups: tangible changes of the natural environment such as canals, railroads, powerhouses, machines, churches, etc., which may be called capital equipment; and intangible cultural changes such as techniques, knowledge, acquired skill, etc. Since the arts are the driving force and the capital equipment the fixed result, attention in this chapter is focused on the arts rather than on the equipment. Arts generally function through equipment—mechanical skill through tools, religion through churches, government through executive, deliberative, and judiciary organization. Resource appraisal, besides being affected by changing wants and social objectives, ultimately depends on the state of the arts rather than on the supply of equipment.

Two categories of the arts may be distinguished: material or technical arts, that is, abilities to utilize substances and energies, on the one hand; and societal[1] or institutional arts, that is, abilities to regulate and improve human relations, on the other. Railroads, automobiles, telephones, telegraphs, and radios are means of conquering distance. Agricultural implements may be used to raise the productivity of the soil. The arts supporting and promoting material culture are material or technical arts. Apart from the arts which regulate the relationship of man to nonhuman nature, there are arts which regulate the relationship of man to man, the arts of societal coöperation, of team play, of good government. Since parliaments, churches, lodges, trade associations, and the laws regulating human relations are generally known as institutions, we may speak of the arts supporting and promoting these institutions as societal or institutional arts.

It is idle to speculate which arts came first—societal or material—and which are more important today. We know that civilization is based on the use of fire—one of the greatest triumphs in the field of material arts—on agriculture, on the domestication of animals, all of which are material arts. But it is doubtful whether these material arts could be developed without a parallel advance in the societal arts. The two groups of arts are branches of the same tree; they draw their strength from the same soil. Mutually dependent, they both contribute to the fuller growth of the tree of civilization.

Functional Classification of the Arts

Arts and their purposes are so numerous that it is difficult to gain a bird's-eye view. The shortest method of presenting this multiplicity seems to be a functional classification. Functionally arts may be divided into two main groups: those which render more effective man's productive efforts, and those which render the environment more amenable to these efforts.[2] In both cases the end is the same, namely, the fuller satisfaction of human wants

---

[1] All arts are social products, and therefore social arts in point of origin. To avoid misunderstanding, the word "societal" is chosen here in referring to this group of arts.

[2] In reality these two branches intertwine. Many serve both ends directly. Others serve one but have repercussions on the other.

or the more complete attainment of social objectives. The classification follows.

FUNCTIONAL CLASSIFICATION OF THE ARTS

I. *Arts designed to enlarge human capacity, raise human efficiency, and thus promote the economy of human energy.*

 A. Arts designed to improve health and to extend the duration of life, and thus to improve general efficiency.

   1. Preventive and curative medicine and surgery.
   2. Mental hygiene.
   3. Contraception and other methods which permit rationalized control of population increase. Birth control affects, generally favorably, the age composition of the population, and thus the ratio of productive to unproductive (or less productive) age groups.

 B. Arts designed to better the performance of the individual.

   1. Those which directly raise the efficiency of human activity.

     a. Education, training, etc., which improve the intellectual capacity, character, and spiritual qualities of men, and bring about a better adaptation of the worker to the work.
     b. Ways and means which improve the functioning of human organs and refine the perception of the senses, such as eyeglasses, hearing aids, skates, radio, etc.
     c. Arts of using tools and simple machines which extend the reach and in general raise the effectiveness of the human body, such as hammer, pulley, etc.
     d. Arts of using devices which permit the appropriation of "foreign" energy, such as turbines, windmills, internal-combustion engines, etc.
     e. Arts of using modern complicated and automatic machines.

   2. Those which indirectly raise the efficiency of human activity.

     a. Methods of increasing the mobility of man (this is mainly accomplished with the aid of appropriated foreign energy, e.g., riding on horseback, riding in a train, driving an automobile, flying in an airplane, etc.; this is of great importance since it expands the sphere to which man can apply his activity).

b. Ways of improving the social relations between men or groups of men by eliminating wasteful conflict.

c. The general increase of human knowledge of facts and of laws of nature.

II. *Arts designed to render nature more amenable to human use.*

A. Ways and means of enlarging the supply of usable matter and energy.

1. Arts making possible the fuller exploitation of available supplies (e.g., the application of air pressure to oil wells for the purpose of recovering supplies of petroleum which cannot be produced by ordinary methods).

2. Arts making possible the fuller utilization of products obtained (e.g., the application of the cracking process to the production of gasoline).

3. Arts permitting the recovery of waste materials, the use of by-products and the reuse of "secondary" materials (e.g., the manufacture of celotex from cane pulp, bagasse; the manufacture of artificial leather, fabrikoid, from cottonseed; the manufacture of steel from scrap).

4. Arts transforming substances from a less useful to a more useful form (e.g., the manufacture of rayon out of cotton linters).

B. Arts designed to change the form of matter or energy so as to render it usable (e.g., transforming the gravitational energy of Niagara Falls into electric energy, or transforming poisonous plants into valuable food by cooking).

C. Arts which render matter and energy mobile or increase their mobility (these are generally the same as those which make for greater mobility of man, I, B, 2, a).

This functional classification of the arts may help the reader to appreciate the diversity and multiplicity of the ways and means by which civilization is advanced. It includes both technological and institutional arts. They are the product of millenniums of patient labor, and should be viewed not as the spoils of a triumphant conqueror but as the results of a slow evolutionary process of adaptation.

Inventions as Adaptive Efforts

The rate of progress of inventions and arts varies considerably during different periods of history. Moreover, this development follows different directions in different parts of the earth.

This last-named fact is readily understood when the arts are conceived as devices or mechanisms used by various groups to adapt themselves better to their specific environment and to adapt that environment to their specific needs. The peculiar nature of a given environment and of specific needs therefore determines the general lines along which the arts develop. Besides differences in environment and needs, differences in attitudes toward material progress and the crystallization of such attitudes in patent laws and similar institutions must be taken into consideration.[3]

Comparisons of the mechanical progress made in different countries must not ignore this causality. If they do, wrong inferences may be drawn as to the relative ingenuity or progressiveness of different peoples. Inventions have a strange appeal to mass psychology; a nation tends to identify itself with its inventors and to sun itself in their glory. Emotions and sentiments therefore play an important part, and the real nature of things is sometimes misunderstood. Referring to early American inventors, Waldemar Kaempffert, the well-known writer on science and invention, says:

These men were as truly pioneers as if they had been Daniel Boone pushing into the wilderness with gun and axe. They were the unconscious builders of a new industrial empire, creators of a new civilization. Because of them "Yankee ingenuity" became proverbial, and Americans were regarded as the most inventive people on earth. The truth is that Americans all came from Europe and that there is nothing in the American air or drinking water that inspires a man with the idea of talking to another over a wire a thousand miles long. No matter where they may live, inventors are like painters and poets—responsive to their environment. A kind of social and economic pressure is exerted upon them, a pressure of which they are scarcely aware, a pressure that determines what they shall wear, sing, eat, think and invent.[4]

The theory that inventions are less the expressions of superior ingenuity but almost in-

---

[3] Cf. A. Rühl, *Vom Wirtschaftsgeist in Amerika* (1927), and *Vom Wirtschaftsgeist in Spanien* (1928), Quelle and Meyer, Leipzig.

[4] See W. Kaempffert, "A New Patent Office for a New Age," New York *Times Magazine*, April 10, 1932, p. 8.

evitable results of social conditions is supported by the fact that when a need for an invention is felt simultaneously in several places, similar inventions are the rule rather than the exception. Ogburn,[5] confining his study to major achievements, lists no less than 148 cases of simultaneous inventions, many of which were made by more than two inventors.

In every period, apparently, a people lives under a kind of social tension that must be relieved. Something must be expressed. Relief comes through an expressive artist, philosopher, military leader, or scientist, depending on the crucial social need of the moment. Hence Dante, Shakespeare, Voltaire, Bach, Newton, Watt, Morse, Bell, Edison and Marconi must be regarded as fuses that blow and that enable society to short-circuit itself by following the lines of least resistance. The leader invariably expresses the massed unconscious aspirations of the race and responds to a social tension of which he may not even be aware.[6]

American and European Inventions

Since the needs of people differ, one must expect functional variations in the general trend of inventive achievement between peoples of different nations. Different nations find themselves face to face with essentially different resource situations and problems. Their inventive efforts, therefore, must needs be directed into different channels. A comparison between this country and continental Europe brings out the importance of this diversity of inventive needs. As will be developed more fully later on, the problems which the American inventor was facing during the nineteenth century were mainly problems of labor scarcity, excess of space, and its corollary—scarcity of time. As a result, America concentrated her inventive efforts upon labor-saving devices and instru-

ments of transportation and communication. Typical American inventions are the mechanical reaper, the sewing machine, the calculating machine, the telephone, and the air brake.[7]

Europe, on the other hand, was never peculiarly handicapped by scarcity of labor or by excessive distances. Her troubles were of a very different nature. Crowded Europe suffered from an inadequacy of raw materials. Her effort, therefore, had to be concentrated upon exploiting to the fullest possible measure the resources which she did possess and upon finding substitutes for those which were lacking and which could not be readily obtained from the outside. Generally speaking, her effort had to be centered upon the invention of material-saving devices, as contrasted with the labor- and time-saving devices of the United States. European, especially German, progress in chemistry is readily explained in that way. Germany first made indigo from coal; being cut off from the nitrate of Chile during World War I, German chemical manufacturers made nitrogen from the air with the aid of coal and lignite. The blast furnace, the Bessemer converter, and the open hearth may be viewed as fuel-saving devices. The Martin brothers of France developed an open-hearth furnace which not only economizes on fuel but also makes possible the use of scrap.[8] The Koppers by-product coke oven points to material savings by the scientific recovery of by-products. Such a comparison naturally stresses essential points only, and, being based on broad generalizations, it is subject to numerous exceptions. Moreover, nowadays the intercontinental exchange of scientific ideas is so well developed that differences cannot long endure and they become increasingly blurred.

Another factor which must not be lost sight of in making comparisons of the inventive achievements of different nations is the extent to which each is supported or handicapped in its effort by nature. America has made marvelous progress along the lines of mechanical labor-saving devices not only because of the greater need caused by labor scarcity, but also

---

[5] W. Ogburn, *Social Change*, B. W. Huebsch, Inc., New York, 1922.

[6] W. Kaempffert, in a radio talk, April 22, 1921. For additional information and in part quite different ideas on this problem, see A. A. Goldenweiser, *Early Civilizations*, Alfred A. Knopf, New York, 1922; A. P. Usher, *A History of Mechanical Inventions*, McGraw-Hill Book Company, Inc., New York, 1929; O. Spengler, *Man and Technics; a Contribution to a Philosophy of Life*, Alfred A. Knopf, New York, 1932; and L. Mumford, *Technics and Civilization*, Harcourt, Brace and Company, New York, 1934.

---

[7] The air brake invented by Westinghouse, applied to railroad trains, allowed trains to operate at higher speeds and thus raised the hauling capacity of a system.

[8] See chap. 40.

because no other country in the world is blessed with the same abundance of the materials out of which these labor-saving devices can be made and with which they can be operated, as is the United States. The speed of America's progress, therefore, is partly explained by the extent and nature of her need and partly by the favorable combination of natural opportunities at her disposal. Her triumph rests on her exceptional ability to utilize her peculiar opportunities and to meet her peculiar needs.

Finally, in appraising the relationship between environment and inventiveness, the fact that environments create attitudes which in turn become cultural fixtures—established parts of the social heritage of the group—must be considered.

Historical Variations in Inventiveness

So much about the differences of place. Let us now turn to the differences of time. That in the beginning progress should be slow seems only natural. It should always be kept in mind that the first invention is infinitely more difficult than those that are based upon it. The inventions of the simple machines[9] were beyond doubt stupendous achievements of the human mind. Once in possession of this elementary knowledge, man found additional progress much easier. Moreover, for countless ages man improved his arts reluctantly, only under dire pressure. "Necessity is the mother of invention" became a commonly accepted truth. It is one of the glories of the present age that future demands are anticipated by the systematic development of the arts—which today generally means sciences—regardless of the immediate current needs. As Walter Lippmann aptly points out, the art of inventing has been invented and is consciously and voluntarily practiced. But at first it was necessity—necessity which sprang from the pitiful contrast between man's physical abilities, on the one hand, and his ambitions and aspirations, on the other —which prompted invention. It was at that stage that the idea of the niggardliness of nature developed. To primitive man nature certainly did look niggardly. The story of the ex-

pulsion from Paradise comes to mind. "In the sweat of thy face shalt thou eat bread." While there were few people, even primitive methods applied to niggardly nature made survival possible. But, as the numbers increased, the struggle became harder; and unless methods were improved, suffering, if not destruction, followed.

At first it was despair which drove man to invent, to develop his arts. Then it was necessity. One wonders whether today, at least in those regions where occidental civilization has reached its greatest "triumphs," it is the search for more pleasure or for pleasure more fully gratified which furnishes the chief stimulus for further progress.[10] In pecuniary society, that is, in money-using society, want gratification is generally predicated upon the possession of money. Hence, we may say that the profit motive, the acquisitive instinct of the "businessman"—in short, pleonexy, the desire to have more for its own sake—is one of the strongest impulses to improvements of the arts. However, this does not preclude the fact that many inventors invent for the thrill of inventing rather than for pecuniary gain.

Labor Supply and Mechanical Progress

Some writers have seen a close correlation between inventive progress and labor supply. Thinking more specifically of mechanical improvements, Van Loon has drawn attention to this significant relationship between the scarcity or abundance of labor, especially unskilled labor, and mechanical invention. Elevating this relationship to the rank of law, some writers believe that the amount of mechanical development will always be in inverse ratio to the number of slaves that happen to be at a country's disposal. And for proof, Van Loon cites the fact that a far greater number of mechanical patents were taken out in the United States in the first sixty years of the nineteenth century by citizens of the northern states than by those of the southern. Indeed, Van Loon holds that, by and large, both the Greeks and the Romans were less inventive

---

[9] The six so-called simple machines or mechanical powers are: lever, wedge, wheel and axle, pulley, screw, and inclined plane.

[10] See Simon Patten's ideas on the transition from "pain economy" to "pleasure economy" in his *The Theory of Social Forces*, Supplement to the *Annals of the American Academy of Political and Social Science*, 1896, chap. 4.

than the Egyptians because they relied more heavily on slave labor.

This relationship between the supply of cheap unskilled labor and mechanical progress has wide popular appeal but is treated very skeptically by scientists and scholars. Thus, Usher[11] is more cautious. He does not believe that the data available are adequate to permit drawing general conclusions. Referring to the interaction of population density and technological progress, he says, "These phenomena are among the most complex of any presented to the historian. They involve all the factors operating in economic history and at present we are scarcely in a position to attempt more than a preliminary analysis."

The experience of the American people during the nineteenth century can hardly be considered a sufficiently broad basis on which to build a general theory. The situation was somewhat unique in two ways. In the first place, the environment offered exceptional rewards to energetic and progressive exploitation. In the second place, the population brought with them from their former homes a considerable knowledge of arts which had been developed independently under different environmental conditions. Under such circumstances, mechanical progress was facilitated both by the peculiar nature of the environment and by the previous training and experience of man. There have been, however, other periods of history in which conditions comparable to those found during our frontier days have not produced a similar progress in mechanical development. In ancient times repeatedly, the abundance of raw materials which made some kind of existence possible has reduced the pressure of population on sustenance and in that way has retarded rather than accelerated mechanical progress. Hence the human qualities must be taken into consideration. Moreover, whatever causative force is at work is bound to produce different results in the tropics and in the temperate zone.

The Recent Technical Achievement

We now turn our attention to the remarkable spurt in the development of the arts which begins slowly with the Renaissance and gains

increasing momentum during the eighteenth, nineteenth, and especially the twentieth century.

Usher stresses the fact that invention is not essentially different from the ordinary learning process. If that is so, a widening of the opportunities to learn and a more thorough understanding of the principles of teaching should prove valuable as an indirect inducement to greater inventive activity. In the second place, the cumulative nature of the inventive process must be considered. At first inventions appear as isolated achievements, but in the course of time they grow into systems of interrelated parts and interacting forces. Lewis Mumford in his stimulating work *Technics and Civilization* brings out this fact with striking force by introducing the concept of "the machine" as distinguished from a spattering of individual machines. "The machine," as developed by Mumford, is that maze of machine equipment which is a striking feature of the modern cultural landscape in highly industrialized countries, and which has come close to holding sway over industrial peoples. This composite of machines and factories, lines of transport and communication, resembles a living organism of almost demoniac force.

Antiquity possessed great scientists, but they were too isolated in both time and space. Furthermore, human society had not yet reached those stages of stability and security which make feasible a world-wide and continued application of scientific methods and principles. In a sense, therefore, we may say that the application of science to resource utilization is a contribution of modern times. The effect of science on human productiveness is cumulative—one invention leads to another. A new discovery increases the value of an old. The inventor of today stands on the shoulders of his predecessors and they, in turn, reaped the benefits of past performances. We can push deep into the mysteries of scientific research because innumerable scientists before us have prepared the field. In the third place, the ability to accumulate larger surpluses over and above that which is necessary to sustain orderly group life and to assure normal progress deserves attention, for it is out of these surpluses that the enormous sums are taken which nowadays are spent on scientific research.[12]

---

[11] A. P. Usher, *op. cit.*, p. 3.

This surplus does not necessarily have to be viewed as consisting wholly of material things, for it also takes the form of leisure. We can afford to take a considerable number of our best minds out of the field of direct productive effort and divert them to the task of consciously and consistently expanding our knowledge of both abstract and applied science. Research in the field of social organization should yield similar results for our institutional development. This ability to accumulate surpluses is particularly important in view of the concentration of their control in the hands of a relatively small number of financiers who, for the time being at least, seem consciously or unconsciously to favor a more rapid development of the arts rather than a wider distribution of their products among the masses. Furthermore, it should be remembered that the rapid progress of science in our time is facilitated by the wide publicity which each discovery receives, and by the popularization through textbooks printed in almost every language of the civilized world and distributed throughout the world. As a result, each new thought today stands an infinitely better chance to fall on fertile ground where, like a seed, it may sprout forth and develop into products of unexpected grandeur and epoch-making importance.

Trial and Error, Rule of Thumb, and Science

All these factors help to explain the remarkable development of the arts in modern times; but they are overshadowed by the substitution of scientific methods for the earlier methods of trial and error and rule of thumb. Primitive man was an experimenter.[13] His was the wasteful "trial-and-error" method. He tried and tried again, until by chance he hit on the right procedure and attained the desired results. To accomplish his immediate object was his sole concern. Compared with such a wasteful method, the "rule of thumb" seems quite efficient. Its superiority rests upon the utilization of past experience, of experience gained by others. A rule or even a body of rules is developed which becomes the property of priests, goldsmiths, alchemists, master artisans, guilds, etc. Oftentimes these rules are carefully guarded and handed down only by word of mouth or by practical demonstration. Thus, the apprentice and the journeyman watched the master, saw how he did his work, and carefully imitated every step and every move. After years of "learning" and practicing they "mastered" their arts.

The scientific method towers sky-high above either one of these earlier methods. Perhaps no greater revolution occurred in the relationship between man and nature—the introduction of fire not excepted—than that brought on by the introduction of science.

The word "science" comes from the Latin verb *scire*, to know. Its essence is to know why one event follows another, and to understand causal relationships. Mere sequence is turned into cause and effect. As was pointed out above, the rule-of-thumb method is marked by the blind imitation of actions which experience has proved to bring about certain desired results. Neither the teacher nor the pupil knows the reason why. They know the sequence of events but not the causal relationship. The little Indian boy who fishes with bow and arrow may have learned from his father always to aim below the object, and he then knows that unless he follows this rule of thumb he cannot shoot the fish. But he does not know anything about the physical laws of the deflection of light rays which causes him to see the fish at a different place from where it actually is. He does not know that a light ray follows a different course through air and water than does an arrow propelled by the contracting force of a bowstring.[14]

This personal human aspect of the rule-of-thumb method is of far-reaching significance. The Indian boy must actually watch his father; the apprentice and journeyman must be per-

---

[12] In the early thirties Kaempffert estimated that, in the United States alone, the annual appropriations for the approximately 1500 research laboratories maintained by corporations and trade associations amounted to about $200,000,000. Since then both the number of laboratories and the amounts expended have vastly increased. The outlay varies with the swing of the business cycle.

[13] Among primitive people, the shaman, magician, or medicine man plays an important part in the promotion of arts. His power rests on the ignorance of the group and on their belief in supernatural powers.

---

[14] Cf. L. C. Marshall, *The Story of Human Progress*, The Macmillan Company, New York, 1925, pp. 111-112.

sonally around the master. In the first place, this personal element renders precarious the stock of human knowledge—if indeed we may call knowledge the mastery of a few dexterities and the learning by heart of rules of action which are mastered without being understood. Time and time again in history it has happened that valuable arts were lost through the death of a single person. Epidemics sweeping over localities which specialized in particular branches of production repeatedly resulted in a similar loss of arts. In the second place, the personal element limits the dissemination and distribution, at least of the more complicated arts, to relatively small numbers. Each master could not and would not teach more than a very limited number of apprentices. A further result of this limitation of numbers was the slow progress which the arts made throughout the major portion of human history.

Depersonalization

While the arts thus based on rule of thumb are inseparable from the personality of man, science is depersonalized or devitalized,[15] in the sense that it is detached from the frailty of a single human being. It is deposited in books; it is described in mathematical and chemical formulas. These, in turn, are disassociated from the personal carriers of the arts. The introduction of science, in other words, means above all the depersonalization of that upon which human progress rests. The highest expression of science is the mathematical formula. Especially when deposited in written or printed forms, the tenets of science, the facts and relationships discovered and expressed in mathematical formulas become the almost universal and indestructible property of mankind. The Archimedean principle, the theorem of Pythagoras survive centuries of darkness during which the valuable arts of making glass, cement, alloys, and so on, are lost, to be recovered only through reinvention. Moreover, devitalized science is fungible science. The rule of thumb is applied only to a specific task at hand—shaping a spearhead, catching a fish, etc. A scientific principle is applicable to innumerable specific problems calling for similar solutions.

[15] Cf. W. Sombart, *Der Moderne Kapitalismus,* Duncker and Humblot, München and Leipzig, 1928, vol. 3, chap. 6.

The Lopsided Development of the Arts

As we have seen, the superiority of the scientific method manifests itself in a tremendous acceleration of the rate of progress of the arts. Unfortunately, however, this acceleration pertains mainly or almost exclusively to the material or technological arts, and to a far lesser extent, if at all, to the societal or institutional arts. The scientific method requires proof by verification. Verification is not necessarily easy, but it is certainly possible in most technical problems. Not so in the field of societal arts. A chemist can prove his reaction, but nobody can prove that Christianity is better than Mohammedanism or that the democratic form of government is absolutely superior to monarchy, oligarchy, or dictatorship. The result is a relative institutional stagnation in the face of technological progress—the institutional "lag."

It would be going too far to deny all progress in the field of the societal arts. It is difficult to generalize about these manifold forms. But here, as in the field of the material arts, it holds true that wherever verification or reliable testing methods can be applied, healthy growth and real vitality are the rule. This holds true particularly in the realm of economic institutions. The corporation in its modern form and application is hardly more than one hundred years old; but in that time it has developed into one of the most progressive and virulent aspects of our social organization. The advantages of incorporation can be demonstrated, and its superiority over other forms of economic organizations as a mechanism of profit making can be verified. Even the qualifications of specific forms for specific purposes can be rendered evident.

This cannot be said of political organizations or of religious thought. Verification in the realms of politics and religion is difficult, if not impossible. Generally speaking, Republicans and Democrats are born; a Cardinal Newman who rationally selects his religion is so rare as to achieve world renown. Thus within the institutional field itself we discern striking contrasts of development. The lopsidedness of our development has become a favorite theme. Ogburn in his *Social Change* has fully developed the idea of "cultural lag." John Dewey notes that we rationalize freely about the atom, the spectrum, and other phases of the material arts, but when it comes to institutions, to the societal arts which give life to our institutions, prejudices and traditions rule all too often. The result is that, in spite of all the technical triumphs of the western world, it is doubtful whether the common man is happier now than in the past. We have as yet failed to correlate societal and material, institutional and technological, arts. As a result, we shudder at times when we think of the powers we have called forth from the depths of the earth and out of the mysteries of creation. We feel like a baby sitting on a powder barrel playing with matches. We wonder whether the proud edifice of our industrial civilization is not going to topple down on us. Some fear that the discovery of atomic energy, perhaps man's greatest triumph, may yet prove his undoing. Some clamor for birth control for machines. But John Dewey does not blame the machine. He puts the blame for present troubles on the futile effort to apply eighteenth-century principles of pecuniary society to a twentieth-century machine civilization. He says:

What stands in the way is not a machine age, but the survival of a pecuniary age. The worker is tied helplessly to the machine, and our institutions and customs are invaded and eroded by the machine, only because the machine is harnessed to the dollar. We cling to old creeds, and we profess ideas and sentiments that have no real hold on our living activities, because a regime of pecuniary profit and loss still commands our allegiance. In this fact the contradictions of Middletown, that is, of Anytown, come to an unity. The cults and rites, the folkways and folklore of a money culture form the pattern of our life, and in them alone our industrial practices and our sentimental ideals and theories harmoniously agree. Not till we have questioned the worth of a dominantly money-civilization shall we have a religion that is more than sentimental and verbal, and achieve an integrated life.[16]

Thus Dewey points not only to our strength —our technical progress—but also to our weakness—our institutional backwardness. What holds true of America applies with similar force to the entire western civilization. The removal of this dissonance from our life is the burning problem of the day. What resources the future holds in store depends largely on its solution.

---

[16] John Dewey, "The House Divided Against Itself" (review of *Middletown*), *New Republic*, April 24, 1929; reprinted by permission of the author and the *New Republic*.

BIBLIOGRAPHY

Adams, M. (ed.), *Science in the Changing World*, New York, Appleton-Century-Crofts, 1933.

Anshen, R. N. (ed.), *Science and Man*, New York, Harcourt, Brace, 1942.

Baker, J. R., and Haldane, J. B. S., *The Scientific Life*, New York, Macmillan, 1943.

Bernal, J. D., *The Social Function of Science*, Baltimore, Johns Hopkins Press, 1942 (a condensation of a larger volume published earlier in England).

Burchard, J. (ed.), *Midcentury: The Social Implications of Scientific Progress*, New York, Wiley, and Cambridge M.I.T. Press, 1950.

Carmichael, R. D., *The Logic of Discovery*, Chicago, Open Court, 1930.

Chase, S., *Men and Machines*, New York, Macmillan, 1929.

Childe, V. G., *Man Makes Himself*, London, Watts, 1948.

Cleveland, F. A., and collaborators, *Modern Scientific Knowledge*, New York, Ronald, 1929.

Compton, A. H., *The Human Meaning of Science*, Chapel Hill, University of North Carolina Press, 1940.

Conant, J. B., "Science and Society in the Postwar World," in Anshen, R. N. (ed.), *Beyond Victory*, New York, Harcourt, Brace, 1943.

Crowther, J. G., *The Social Relations of Science*, New York, Macmillan, 1941.

Farrington, B., *Science and Politics in the Ancient World*, London, G. Allen & Unwin, 1939.

Folk, G. E., *Patents and Industrial Progress*, New York, Harper, 1942.

Gibson, A. H., *Natural Sources of Energy*, New York, Macmillan, 1913.

Giedion, S., *Mechanization Takes Command*, Oxford, Oxford Press, 1948.

Gilfillan, S. C., *The Sociology of Invention*, Chicago, Follett, 1935 (a companion volume to the same author's *Inventing the Ship*).

Hamilton, W. H., "Institutions" in *Encyclopædia of the Social Sciences*, New York, Macmillan, 1932, vol. 8.

Hamilton, W. H., "Patents and Free Enterprise," *TNEC Monograph No. 31*, Washington, 1941.

Hamilton, W. H., "Control of Strategic Materials," *American Economic Review*, June, 1944.

Hausleiter, L., *The Machine Unchained*, New York, Appleton-Century-Crofts, 1933.

Huxley, J. S., *Science and Social Needs*, New York, Harper, 1935.

Kaempffert, W. B., *Invention and Society*, Chicago, American Library Association, 1930.

Kaempffert, W. B., *Science, Today and Tomorrow*, second series, New York, Viking, 1945.

Library of Congress, 79th Congress, First Session, *The Social Impact of Science: A Select Bibliography with a Section on Atomic Power*, Senate Subcommittee Monograph No. 3, Washington, August, 1945.

Lilley, S., *Men, Machines, and History*, London, Cobbett, 1948.

Linton, R. (ed.), *The Science of Man in the World Crisis*, New York, Columbia University Press, 1945.

Maclaurin, W. R., *Invention and Innovation in the Radio Industry*, New York, Macmillan, 1949.

Maclaurin, W. R., "Patents and Technical Progress —A Study in Television," *Journal of Political Economy*, April, 1950.

Mitchell, W. C., "The Public Relations of Science," *Science*, December 29, 1939.

Mumford, L., *Technics and Civilization*, New York, Harcourt, Brace, 1934.

National Resources Committee, *Technological Trends and National Policies*, Washington, 1937.

Nussbaum, F. L., *A History of the Economic Institutions of Modern Europe*, New York, Crofts, 1933.

Ogburn, W. F., "The Influence of Invention and Discovery," in *Recent Social Trends in the United States*, New York, McGraw-Hill, 1933, chap. 3.

Ogburn, W. F., "Machines and Tomorrow's World," New York, Public Affairs Committee, 1938 (pamphlet).

Ogburn, W. F., *The Social Effects of Aviation*, Boston, Houghton Mifflin, 1946.

Ogburn, W. F. (ed.), *Technology and International Relations*, Chicago, University of Chicago Press, 1949.

Peck, H. W., *Economic Thought and Its Institutional Background*, New York, Farrar & Rinehart, 1935.

Polakow, W. H., *The Power Age*, New York, Covici Friede, 1933.

Randall, J. H., *Our Changing Civilization*, New York, Stokes, 1930.

Russell, B. (Earl), *Power: A New Social Analysis*, New York, Norton, 1938.

Sarton, G., *The Study of the History of Science*, Cambridge, Harvard University Press, 1936.

Sorre, M., *Les Fondements de la Géographie Humaine*, vol. 2, *Les Fondements Techniques* (première partie), Paris, Libraire Armand Colin, 1948.

Spengler, O., *Man and Technics*, (translated from the German by C. F. Atkinson), New York, Knopf, 1932.

Staley, E., *World Economy in Transition*, New York, Council of Foreign Relations, 1939.

Stamp, J. C. S., *The Science of Social Adjustment*, London, Macmillan, 1937.

Sumner, W. G., and Keller, A. G., *The Science of Society*, New Haven, Yale University Press, 1927.

Thornton, J. E. (ed.), *Science and Social Change*, Washington, Brookings, 1939.

Usher, A. B., *A History of Mechanical Inventions*, New York, McGraw-Hill, 1929.

Veblen, T., *The Theory of Business Enterprise*, New York, Scribner, 1904.

Veblen, T., *The Instinct of Workmanship*, New York, Viking, 1913.

Veblen, T., *The Place of Science in Modern Civilization*, New York, Huebsch, 1919.

Zweig, F., *Economics and Technology*, London, P. S. King and Son, 1936.

UNIT 2. ENERGY AND RESOURCES

Chapter 4

THE NATURE AND SOURCES OF ENERGY

THE NATURE OF ENERGY

Energy and Matter

Modern science has broken down the barriers that long separated energy and matter as two distinct phases of nature. Scientists now view matter as a manifestation of energy, know the formula for the conversion of energy into matter and of matter into energy, and are engaged in stupendous efforts to convert certain fissionable elements of matter into atomic or nuclear energy.

Although aware of this scientific interpretation of the nature of energy and matter, the workaday world continues to think and speak of energy and matter as distinct and separate categories. One may realize that coal is energy but still differentiate between the substance coal which is mined, hauled, and burned and the energy which is released when coal is burned. One may be aware that water is energy but still differentiate between the substance which quenches his thirst and the electricity which Niagara Falls generates. Food provides us with both energy in the form of heat or the capacity to do work, and substance which maintains our body.

Animate and Inanimate Energy

The examples just cited illustrate a highly significant division of energy forms or manifestations into animate, i.e., those functioning in and through living organisms (plants, animals, bacteria, molds, fungi, etc.), and inanimate, i.e., those derived from nonliving matter, especially the fossil fuels, coal, oil, and gas, and from falling water. Animate energy, in turn, is divided into biotic and muscular energy. Muscular energy is the energy applied by an animal to useful work such as pulling a cart, lifting weight, etc. Biotic energy is that associated with the processes of life and growth. To be able to do work an animal must live, to live it must eat. The bulk of the food or feed intake is needed to provide biotic energy; only a fraction can be spared for muscular energy. This dependence of muscular energy on life is vital to its proper appraisal. It accounts for much of the inferiority of animate energy compared with inanimate energy.[1]

Biotic energy generated in plants is one of

---

[1] For a fuller development of this comparison, see pp. 64-73.

the main sources of useful objects obtained by man, especially by preindustrial man. Without it neither food nor feed can be produced. Timber and many other forms of vegetation serve useful purposes in providing shelter, utensils, tools, etc. Agrarian people rely almost exclusively on animate energy in both its forms—muscular and biotic. Of the two, the biotic may well be the more important.

Other Kinds of Energy

Energy, often defined as the capacity to do work, has many meanings and diverse manifestations. For one thing, work itself can mean any manifestation of energy in space and time, or it can refer to useful work, i.e., work useful to man, directed toward some human objective. When the potential energy of snow at a high altitude is released as the kinetic (motion) energy of an avalanche a colossal amount of work is being done, but it is not useful—it may be highly destructive. In this study of resources, interest naturally centers in useful work, although the importance of the destructive work of the forces of nature is fully recognized as "resistances." One speaks of mechanical energy such as that of the drop hammer, of chemical energy released when coal is burned or in the form of active acids, of electrical energy manifesting itself as heat, power, or light, and so forth. Chemical energy locked in coal is available energy; when the coal has been burned the energy may have been spent in doing work or it may have been diffused as radiation energy.

When we speak of different kinds of energy, such as potential, kinetic, animate, inanimate, available, diffused, electrical, or chemical, we should be aware of the inaccuracy of our terminology. It should be clear from the aforesaid that energy, like time and space, is a characterless concept—there can be no good or bad energy. To be exact, therefore, we should speak of different manifestations of energy. The energy of a coolie naturally reveals itself in a different manner from that contained in gasoline or in coal. Different forms of energy require different channels for their conversion into work. Thus, sunshine is converted by chlorophyll into starch or sugar or protein, whereas the energy contained in steam may call for a reciprocating engine or turbine. Energy in food or feed can be converted into work by means of organisms, but dynamite and TNT are harnessed by means of mechanisms.

Elementary and Derived Energy

The sunshine which the green leaf through photosynthesis makes available to the growing plant as carbon and carbon compounds is clearly elementary energy. Whether the vital energy possessed by living organisms and gravitational energy are likewise elementary seems less certain. The chemical energy stored up in the sugar or starch of living plants and the carbon of coal, petroleum, etc., is derived energy. All animate or muscular energy is derived energy, dependent on food intake.

Elementary energy furnishes the starting point of a long row of derivatives which modern production processes tend to lengthen. Primitive man drew energy either directly from the sun, or indirectly, through the plant or animal as food. The modern process of energy utilization is generally more roundabout. We tap the chemical energy of coal and turn it into heat; the heat, applied to water, raises steam which is valued for its expansive power, a mechanical energy, which, in a steam engine, is given the desired direction and control. The resulting mechanical energy appears as rotation and, with the aid of a dynamo, may be converted into electrical energy. This in turn may be translated into heat, light, or chemical or magnetic or mechanical energy, as the case may be.

Functional Appraisal of Kinds of Energy

The reason for this evident tendency toward an increasing complexity of energy economy lies in the functional differences of various energy forms. The ideal energy for locomotion is different from the ideal energy required for stationary work. Thus gasoline, a highly compact energy carrier which furnishes much energy per unit of weight and volume, is more suitable for driving an automobile than is wood or peat. To certain tasks either mechanical or chemical energy can be applied. Thus, wood can be turned into wood pulp by means of either chemical energy or mechanical energy, although so-called chemical and mechanical wood pulps do not always serve the same purpose.

Electrical energy owes much of its popularity to its versatility. As was mentioned before, it can be converted into heat, light, or chemical, magnetic, and mechanical energy. It is an economic factotum. However, its great defect is the cost of its storage. Chemical energy on the whole is more storable, and many carriers of chemical energy likewise excel electricity in transportability. But improvement in the technique of power transmission might enhance the popularity of electricity, especially of hydroelectricity. For electricity generated from coal and oil stands to profit most from improvements in the conversion of heat into electricity. If it takes half as much coal to generate a kilowatthour, the effect is the same as if the transportability of coal had been increased by 100 per cent. Here we can only touch on the general question of the relative desirability of different forms of energy; the technical details are discussed later.

Availability of Energy and the Laws of Thermodynamics

It has long been a fundamental tenet of physics that the total supply of matter and energy in the universe is constant. To the physicist the law of the conservation of matter and energy is basic. The economist, however, is less interested in the totality of the supply than in its availability. Unfortunately, the law of the conservation of energy, generally referred to as the first law of thermodynamics, furnishes man no guarantee of an undiminishing supply of available energy. For the second law of thermodynamics, equal in importance to the first, reveals the fact that the "quality" of energy tends to deteriorate, if we may use that expression as regards a characterless abstraction, and therefore the available supply tends to decrease. This deterioration in general manifests itself in the increase of the wave length of the energy stream. Energy can become so "diffuse" that it ceases to be available.

Human Energy

There remains to be discussed one more category of energy, human energy. Just as man plays a unique role in the overall scheme of resource development, he also occupies a unique place in the realm of energy. In fact it is the uniqueness of human energy manifestation that accounts for the uniqueness of man's role in the resource scheme.

As a source of physical energy, as a power unit used for physical work, man is hopelessly outclassed by animals and especially by the power-driven machine. In a given period of time, a ton of coal with the aid of the proper appliances can produce more mechanical work than can a thousand men in the same period of time. Moreover, the thousand men have to eat. Their food under ordinary circumstances would cost a multiple of the cost of the coal and of the overhead duly allocatable to the work performance at hand.

But not all the coal in the world can contribute as much mental and spiritual guidance, as much planning, inventing, and aspiring as one man. Man's forte is brain, not brawn. In the application of brain power man towers high above all other creatures. In the great plan of creation he seems to have been selected to be the planner of schemes and events, the director, coördinator, and manager of forces aimed at a given end, the thinker, the inventor, the discoverer, the dreamer, and, above all, the aspirer.

There is no substitute for these higher forms of human energy. The full recognition and appreciation of this uniqueness and indispensability of the higher manifestations of human energy are the key to all energy economy and resource strategy. The highest aim of that strategy must be to release man from physical toil as much as can be done without impairing his physical fitness. After all, *mens sana in corpore sano*. Only in that way can specialization be brought to its fullest fruition. Using man as a beast of burden or a work animal is a flagrant violation of the principle of specialization. Civilizations will flourish or perish according to the extent to which they follow this simple rule. Therein lies the real blessing inanimate energy holds out to man. The greatest defect of ancient civilizations which were based chiefly on animate energy, is to be seen in the fact that they thwarted man's higher abilities and aspirations; vice versa, the greatest source of strength of the modern resource pattern lies in the fact that it enables him to play the part for which his superior mental endowment has prepared him.

Past civilizations, such as the Athenian under Pericles, achieved for a small group at the expense of a submerged majority what the modern resource pattern—theoretically, at least—makes possible for all. Under the ancient resource pattern, specialization meant a functional division between a ruling minority and the mass of ruled, partly enslaved people. The modern resource pattern makes possible a division between man—the inventor, planner, director, and aspirer—and the inanimate forces of nature. Few will deny that the latter system has inherent advantages over the former. Unfortunately, however, there is a wide gap between what is possible under the modern resource pattern and what is actually being achieved. It is to be hoped that this gap will grow narrower in time.

History teaches that man is apt to apply his unique energies best in an atmosphere of freedom. Thus the problem of energy strategy merges with that of good government and the development of the societal arts. Institutions have as much to do with the ultimate efficacy of energy use as have engines, machines, and logarithm tables.

SOURCES OF ENERGY
Atomic Nature of Energy

Eugene E. Ayres, director of the Division of Chemistry of the Gulf Research and Development Company, described the atomic nature of energy in the following words:

All of the energy which the skill and ingenuity of man has contrived to convert to useful work is of atomic origin, and it seems that nearly all of the work of the future will come in various ways from this ultimate source. Our converted energy now comes from the sun, where the transmutation of hydrogen to helium is believed to provide energy in the form of light with minor supplements of thermal and ultraviolet radiation. This accounts for all of our power except for the relatively tiny additional amounts that come from radioactive transformations in the earth itself.

The present convenient and economic sources of energy are petroleum, natural gas, and coal—which are often called "stored sunlight" because they were formed from carbon dioxide and water in living organisms by the influence of solar radiation—and hydroelectric power which comes from the precipitation on our land areas of the water evaporated by sunlight from our hydrosphere. Sources of energy less convenient or uneconomic are: vegetation which can be burned to produce about as much energy as the amount of solar energy absorbed in its growth, or which can be converted to such liquid fuels as gasoline or alcohol with a considerable loss of energy; wind, which is an erratic consequence of solar radiation; and the direct conversion of sunlight into forms of energy which can be controlled, intensified, or stored. There is no doubt that some of these secondary sources of solar energy will become exceedingly important in the rather near future.

The heat of the earth itself is believed to come from the atomic degradation of a few of our elements. A little of this heat is being utilized now for power generation. And our atomic scientists are beginning to separate these radioactive elements from the inert materials with which they are associated in the earth in order that the effects of atomic degradation may be concentrated and controlled. These earthly sources of atomic energy may become important in the more distant future by virtue of nuclear and engineering research.

The only source of energy which may not be atomic in origin is that derivable from the kinetic energy of the earth's rotation. A little of this appears in the tides of our oceans, and a very little can be, and ultimately will be, harnessed.[2]

Solar Origin of Energy

Fig. 4.1[3] shows the various ways in which the earth receives solar energy, and the main manifestations of this energy on this planet. The dichotomy of current receipts (flow) and stored-up supplies (fund) of solar radiation in this figure is of particular significance. Its importance will be developed as the analysis of

[2] Eugene E. Ayres, "Major Sources of Energy," a paper read during the 28th annual meeting of the American Petroleum Institute, November 9, 1948, p. 109.

[3] This diagram is adapted from one in S. S. Wyer, *Man's Shift from Muscle to Mechanical Power*, pamphlet prepared for the Fuel-Power and Transportation Educational Foundation, Columbus, Ohio, p. 2. A similar but much simplified classification of stellar energies was presented by E. E. Slosson in an address at Northwestern University. This classification appears in B. Brownell, *The New Universe*, D. Van Nostrand Company, New York, 1929, pp. 185-186.

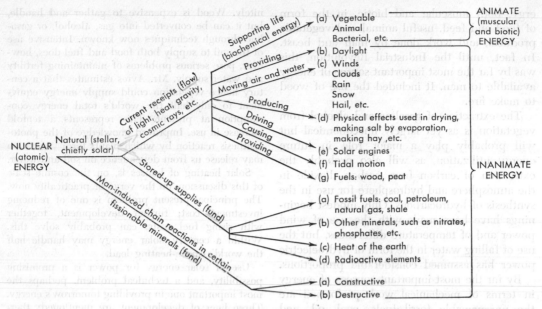

FIG. 4.1. Energies—Their Origin and Manifestations.

energy proceeds. The dichotomy of animate and inanimate energy already mentioned will also be further discussed below.

Energy Sources Classified

With special emphasis on the manner of present and future utilization, energy sources may be classified as follows:

CLASSIFICATION OF MAJOR ENERGY SOURCES[4]

I. Continuous or renewable sources of energy.
  A. Direct solar radiation utilized:
    1. Directly by means of:
      a. Optical devices such as reflectors, lenses, etc.
      b. Photochemistry, photoelectricity, and thermoelectricity.
    2. Indirectly through:
      a. Photosynthesis, upon which living organisms depend for food and feed and which in addition provides many useful materials (e.g., wood and other building materials, rubber, fibers, etc.), as well as fuels (wood, alcohol, and gasoline extracted from vegetation).[5]

[4] Based largely on Eugene E. Ayres, *op. cit.*, pp. 110-125.
[5] Carbon dioxide present in the atmosphere and hydrosphere may yield carbon which by synthesis with hydrogen may yield hydrocarbon fuels.

      b. Use of:
        (1) Water raised by the sun, moved by the winds, and caught on the descent.
        (2) Winds.
        (3) Difference in temperature between atmosphere and:
          (a) The earth ("the heat pump").
          (b) The ocean (the Claude process.)[6]
  B. The heat of the earth (traced to atomic fission) tapped through volcanic vents.
  C. Tidal power.
II. Exhaustible or unrenewable sources of energy.
  A. Fissionable elements yielding atomic or nuclear energy through acceleration of fission.
  B. Fossil fuels.
    1. Coal.
    2. Oil (including oil shale and tar sands).
    3. Natural gas.

Use of Energy Sources

Up to now only a small beginning has been made in the direct utilization of sunshine for mechanical work. In the future man will be forced to rely increasingly on this inexhaustible source of energy. Until now, the actual use of solar energy has been mainly as animate en-

[6] For a description of the Claude process, see below, p. 593.

ergy, both muscular and biotic, in the form of food and feed, useful animal and vegetable products, and work done by man and beast. In fact, until the Industrial Revolution, this was by far the most important source of energy available to man. It included the use of wood to make fire.

The extraction of gasoline and alcohol from vegetation is as yet largely uneconomical but will probably play a major role in future energy utilization, as will also probably the extraction of carbon from carbon dioxide in the atmosphere and hydrosphere for use in the synthesis of hydrocarbons. Only modest beginnings have been made with the use of wind power and of temperature differences, but the use of falling water in the form of hydroelectric power has assumed considerable proportions.

By far the most important sources of energy in terms of mechanical work performed are the unrenewable fossil fuels, coal, oil, and natural gas.[7]

Eugene E. Ayres has discussed the prospects of future energy sources and their uses. A report on his analysis follows.

The possible sources of continuous energy are reviewed and most of them discarded as insignificant in potentiality. There are only a few sites where tides are high enough to yield worthwhile power. The heat of the earth's interior is available only through a few geysers and similar geologic oddities. Wind power is neither dependable nor great in potential magnitude. Engines based on the temperature difference between the ocean's surface and depths in the tropics would require a terrific investment and would be located where power is not greatly needed. No one has yet suggested a means of using the electrical potential which exists between the earth and its atmosphere. Heat pumps, by which heat is moved from the earth to a house, just as a refrigerator moves it from a closed box to the outside, are close to practicality, but would provide only a small amount of energy. Use of water power can be expanded perhaps eightfold, but its potential is only a minor part of our future energy needs.

One of the most immediately feasible means of using the sun's energy is through extending and improving conventional agriculture and forestry. Timber from three million square miles of forest, about the area of the United States, could supply the world's present energy requirements indefi-

nitely. Wood is expensive to gather and handle, but it can be converted into gas, alcohol, or gasoline through techniques now known. Intensive use of the soil to supply both food and fuel does, however, pose serious problems of maintaining fertility and water supply. Mr. Ayres estimates that a century hence vegetation could supply energy equivalent to only half the world's total energy consumption at present. This represents a tenfold increase in use. Improved knowledge of the photosynthesis reaction by which plants form vegetation may release us from dependence on soil and water.

Solar heating of houses is, on the cosmic scale of this discussion, on the verge of practicality now. The principal present problem is one of reducing investment cost; further development, together with rising fuel costs, can probably solve this. Within a century, solar energy may handle half the world's space-heating load.

Use of solar energy for power is a promising possibility, and a technical problem, perhaps the most important one in providing tomorrow's energy. Three lines of development are mentioned: thermocouples in which an electric current flows between the light and dark ends of a circuit; photocells, as in photographic light meters; and optical concentration of sunlight to provide high temperatures for steam generation or other purposes. Given plenty of cheap electric power from solar sources, gasoline could be synthesized from water and atmospheric carbon dioxide to fuel automobiles and airplanes. Despite the development required, Mr. Ayres suggests that solar energy equivalent to present total world energy consumption will be possible within a century.

Altogether, Mr. Ayres visualizes continuous sources as supplying within a century energy equivalent to twice the world's present consumption. Of this continuing energy, solar power would provide half; vegetation, a quarter; waterfalls, a seventh, and solar space heating, a tenth.

How much energy the world will use a hundred years from now is anybody's guess. In addition to the demonstrated continuing increase in consumption, 50 per cent in 50 years, coming decades will see tremendous losses from converting one form of energy to another, notably, coal to liquid fuels, and, most important, coal to electricity.

Evaluation of our present underground reserves of fossil fuels, including uranium for atomic energy, of course requires some estimate of future demand. Mr. Ayres considers in detail the validity of the various estimates of the U.S. reserves, and narrows down the range of disagreement between them. These reserves consist almost entirely of coal, and could supply present U.S. energy needs for 193 to 1741 years. Considering future demand increases

---

[7] See chaps. 26-35.

and conversion losses, however, they are adequate for only 92 to 292 years. While these estimates are gross approximations, the important point is that continually rising demand will eventually reach a level completely beyond that which fossil fuels can supply. Either continuous energy sources, principally solar power, must be used, or demand growth must halt.[8]

CHIEF SOURCES OF ENERGY TODAY

At the present time there are two main sources of energy: food and feed, the sources of animate energy; and fuels, especially the fossil fuels but including wood and other vegetation, the sources of inanimate energy. In view of their dominant position in the present energy scheme, a brief examination of their nature and functions is called for.

The Chemical Wheel of Life

Food and feed constitute major products of that grandiose process of living nature, powered directly by the sun and based on photosynthesis. The energy of the sun is utilized by the chlorophyll of leafy green plants and in the plankton of salt and fresh water. The green plant and perhaps some bacteria[9] can make use

---

[8] See *Industrial Bulletin*, Arthur D. Little, Inc., Cambridge, Mass., February, 1949, p. 1.

[9] In its issue of April 28, 1941, *Time* contained this statement:

"To a limited degree, animals have the power, hitherto believed unique in plants, of making starch and sugar foods out of carbon dioxide and water. This startling news was announced last week in Chicago by Harvard Biochemist Albert Baird Hastings, Birgit Vennesland and co-workers at a meeting of the American Societies for Experimental Biology.

"Their discovery was made with the new biological technique: use of mildly radioactive substances as food. These can be traced through the body by detection of the rays which they give off. (In the past, scientists have lost track of food after it left the alimentary canal.) The Harvard biochemists fed radioactive baking soda to rats, found that the carbon dioxide in it was being used in the liver to build carbohydrates.

"In plants this process is achieved by a catalyst, chlorophyll, which uses energy from sunlight to make the food on which all life, plant and animal, depends. In this sense, the animal world has always been considered a great parasite upon the plant world. The catalyzing enzymes in the liver, equivalent of chlorophyll in plants, are still undiscovered, but the new discovery indicates that, although man is parasitic, he is at least not 100% so."

of solar radiation in the photosynthesis of such substances as sugars, starches, proteins, etc., acceptable as food or feed to animals and fungi. These substances are built up from elements present in air, water, and soil. Green plants, therefore, are the prime resources of all living substances. They are "energy parasites" on the sun; animals and fungi, in turn, are "food parasites" on green plants.[10] While animals can feed only on plants—herbivores—or on other animals—carnivores—or on both—omnivores— and can thus only in this indirect manner tap certain energies of the sun, they can benefit directly from other solar energies, namely, light, heat, and ultraviolet rays. These direct and indirect uses of solar energy are interchangeable to a certain extent, for a warm climate and fuller exposure to ultraviolet rays reduce the food requirements; and, vice versa, up to a certain limit, deficiency of warmth can

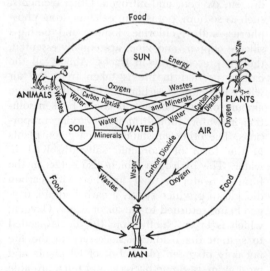

FIG. 4.2. The Food Cycle in Nature.

be made up by increased food consumption. Needless to say, body warmth can also be obtained from fire and can be conserved by means of clothing and shelter with a similar effect on food requirements.

In so far as the sun, by acting on air and water, affects climatic as well as soil conditions,

---

[10] The terminology here is that used in H. G. Wells, J. S. Huxley, and G. P. Wells, *The Science of Life*, Doubleday, Doran & Company, Inc., New York, 1931, vol. 2, book 6, chapter 5.

the contributions made to the process of photosynthesis by these other agents are in part traceable to the sun. The functional relationship of these various factors is shown in Fig. 4.2.[11]

This food cycle is referred to by Huxley as the chemical wheel of life. It is not complete without the bacterial action producing decay, for decay is not only the end but also the beginning of life. Bacterial coloring matter and chlorophyll are chemically closely related, but the functions of the two seem to be reversed.[12] Chlorophyll synthesizes sugars, starches, etc., whereas bacterial coloring matter, associated with a different mineral, seems to possess the power to break up the product of photosynthesis. The turning of the great "chemical wheel of life" is aptly described by Huxley.[13] It is given here in somewhat condensed form.

Most living substances consist of carbon, hydrogen, oxygen, and nitrogen. Other elements, such as sodium, potassium, calcium, iron, phosphorus, sulfur, chlorine, iodine, and perhaps silicon, copper, and zinc, are equally essential, though present only in traces. Almost all the carbon needed in life is taken from the air where it occurs as carbon dioxide in the average amount of 0.03 percent. It is also held in solution in water, though in very varying proportions. The other substances reach green plants in the form of inorganic salts dissolved in water. The hydrogen which also enters in the form of water is used together with carbon dioxide to produce sugar, a carbohydrate, oxygen being returned to the air or water. Oxygen, which is taken chiefly from the air, is needed to sustain the oxidation necessary to the life not only of green plants but of all plants and most animals. Some bacteria and fungi are able to extract oxygen from the substances on which they feed.

The green plant thus effects a synthesis of organic carbon and nitrogen compounds on which the rest of life subsists in parasitic fashion. To support animal life higher than that of some protozoa, the plant carbohydrates and plant proteins must not be of simpler chemical nature than sugars and amino acids. Once having entered into animal life, they continue to circulate in the animal kingdom until dissolution or decay sets in. Decay is the work of special bacteria, and thus forms an integral phase of the cycle of life. Different bacteria perform special functions. Through decay and oxidation, the carbon, nitrogen, and other elements of once living substances reappear with few exceptions in air and water. A variant of this general rule is brought about by the presence of fungi and molds which are parasitic on decay; they can utilize lower forms of food than animals. In either case, the carbon makes a complete circle, and the wheel of life turns from green plant to animal and on to bacteria and through them to decay and back again to the green plant. The sun furnishes the energy that turns the wheel; the green leaf is the prime mover, as it were; and animals and bacteria and other living substances function so as to preserve the equilibria without which the wheel does not turn smoothly.[14]

Man's Part in the Process of Life

Man is caught in this eternal process. "From dust thou art, to dust thou shalt return." But man is not caught altogether helpless; for he puts his hand to the wheel and, though he cannot stop it, he can materially modify the effect of its grinding work on him. At times he overreaches himself in his attempt to improve on nature. Inadequately aware of the importance of balances and equilibria which the ecologist is gradually revealing, he succeeds in gaining a little now at the expense of greater loss later on. As yet, human institutions and social organizations have not found the proper harmony between individual needs and wants of the day, and social and world requirements measured over longer periods. But here we are not concerned with the critical aspects of man's effort to utilize the sun and to exploit the process of nature; we merely describe these efforts.

Not satisfied with such direct benefits as he

[11] C. J. Pieper and W. L. Beauchamp, *Everyday Problems in Science*, Scott, Foresman and Company, Chicago, 1925, p. 82.

[12] New York *Times*, April 5, 1932, 18:2.

[13] H. G. Wells, J. S. Huxley, and G. P. Wells, *op. cit.*, pp. 962 ff.

[14] For a similar presentation of the chemical cycle, see *Applications of the Common Mooring*, Howard P. Emerson, Chairman, Advisory Panel on Regional Materials of Instruction for the Tennessee Valley Authority, Knoxville, rev. ed., 1943.

derives from sunshine, man has developed numerous ways of utilizing solar radiation indirectly and of appropriating energies other than his own. Two main lines along which his effort is applied may be distinguished. First of all, man forever tries to enlarge the range of his food supply. Second, he constantly seeks to appropriate energy for purposes of work. Food enables man to work. "Foreign" energy may be substituted for his own energy, or it may supplement it.

Moreover, man can appropriate the energies stored up in living plants not only through food consumption, but also by turning them into alcohol, a source of power. We may thus view plants as storage batteries of energy. Naturally they developed their capacity to store energy not to serve man, but to assure the preservation of their own kind. "The storage device is a defence mechanism made necessary by the intermittency of sunshine from day to day and from summer to summer."[15] Finally, the energy locked up in plants, especially in wood, can be released by fire.

Furthermore, man can use plants indirectly through animals which feed on them, slavery being but a variant of this form of energy utilization. Some animals are used for work or as beasts of burden; in the case of others, the energy stored up by the animal in such a form as the milk provided by nature for the preservation of the species is diverted to human use. What is more, through breeding, man can greatly enhance the capacity of animals to convert feed into energy available to him, and he can likewise speed up and otherwise aid the conversion by green plants of solar radiation into carbohydrates and other sources of energy. Thus the domestication of animals, animal husbandry, and agriculture reveal themselves as important aspects of human energy problems. Moreover, through the invention of tools and machines the control over and the direction of these energies may be greatly improved.

To summarize, we can say that man, apart from drawing certain direct benefits from current supplies of sunshine, can utilize the supplies indirectly by appropriating both food and energy from both plants and animals. More-

over, he can modify the processes of nature to his interest and thus consciously enlarge his energy supply.

Current Stellar Radiation as a Source of Inanimate Energy

We now turn to the current receipts portion of Fig. 4.1. The sun, together with gravity, causes movements of the air as well as of water, which man can utilize in many ways. Of the water which reaches the land in the form of rainfall, chiefly the "surface run-off," the rivers can be used for purposes of generating mechanical energy. The winds are utilized directly through windmills and sailing ships. The energy of moving, especially falling, water is utilized directly by objects floating downstream and indirectly with the aid of water wheels and water turbines. The relation of winds and rainfall to climate and, through it, to all organic life is fundamental. By means of mirrors and similar devices, the heat of the sun rays can be applied to solar engines which turn sunshine into mechanical energy; but as yet, this method of utilization is quite undeveloped. Finally, the current supply of solar radiation is used as heat in salt making, hay making, the drying or dehydration of fruits and vegetables, and for similar purposes.

Inanimate Energy and Stored-up Supplies of Solar Energy

We now turn to the stored-up supplies of solar energy. Stores of solar energy, such as coal deposits, oil sands, etc., are said to reflect defects of the chemical cycle of life. When the balance of the chemical process of life and decay is disturbed, the "wheel" cannot turn smoothly. Such disturbances cause leakages which paradoxically have now assumed transcendent importance for man. Our coal deposits, our petroleum reserves, our supply of natural gas, the nitrate fields of Chile, the phosphate rock of Florida, and chalk and limestone deposits found in many parts of the world owe their existence to these imperfections in the process of life and decay. Such mineral accumulations may be viewed as the results of disturbed equilibria. Coal fields are the result of "carbon spilling over," as it were, "shunted out of the cycle of life," "food capital locked out of circulation and hidden away for hun-

---

[15] H. G. Wells, J. S. Huxley, and G. P. Wells, *op. cit.*

dreds of millions of years." The explanation for such irregularities may be found in cataclysmic or evolutionary changes of the crust of the earth, as the result of which the oxygen necessary to complete the decay that keeps the wheel turning is withheld. Because of the inadequacy of oxygen, the carbon does not reappear as carbon dioxide, in which form it would be available to molds and fungi. It therefore cannot be drawn back into the food cycle. Apart from such discrepancies in the cycle of life and decay, purely inorganic processes may cause digressions from the rule, of which the mineral salt deposits are a silent witness.

It is the part of our modern civilization to take advantage of these long-hidden stores of energy, and it is to their exploitation that we owe much of our material progress and speed. The exploitation of these stored supplies of solar energy is rendered fully possible only by the exploitation of other minerals, especially metals. As conditions are today, modern large-scale coal and petroleum economy must also be iron and copper economy. The relation between the machine resources and the energy resources is very close—coal supplies the energy required to produce iron, and the iron is needed to harness the coal.

Atomic Energy

The other source of unrenewable energy, fissionable elements, is just coming into use. Its spectacular unveiling at Hiroshima has given it world-wide advertising. Remote, indeed, must be the human habitation which the echoes of that great explosion did not reach. There is still much that is insufficiently known, even to the initiated, about atomic energy. Far more is insufficiently known to laymen like the author. Because of its unparalleled military importance many facts about atomic energy known to a few insiders are military secrets.

It is known that the United States supplies the bulk of her uranium needs by imports of ores from Canada and the Belgian Congo. Little is known about the size of deposits of the fissionable elements uranium and thorium, but that they are limited and, like coal and oil, exhausted by use, is an established fact. Because of its military potentialities, research in

and production of atomic energy is everywhere a function of the government, with limited and controlled participation by private enterprise. The extent to which, and the conditions under which, atomic energy will become a source of industrial power, replacing or supplementing the fossil fuels and falling water, is as yet a matter of speculation. A good deal of research is now directed at finding the answers.[16]

One interesting and probably highly significant point regarding atomic energy was brought out recently.[17] One pound of uranium, or of plutonium into which uranium can be converted, can yield about 12 million kilowatt hours of energy. This is probably more than is ordinarily obtained in electric power stations from 12 million pounds or 6000 tons of coal. Coal, the chief fossil fuel in current use, is bulky, almost untransportable when compared with uranium or plutonium. Coal consumption, by and large, occurs near the source. Fissionable materials conceivably could be distributed throughout the world and thus lay the foundation for global industrialization. Truman's Point IV Program for the development of backward areas would receive a tremendous boost if it should prove feasible to provide undeveloped regions with concentrated doses of inanimate energy in the form of fissionable materials. Undoubtedly there would be technical difficulties but in time they could be overcome. Probably more serious would be the political problems stemming from international distrust and fear of abuse. The failure of the United Nations to solve the problem of international

---

[16] In the United States the center of research is the Atomic Energy Commission, which is also the center of production and control. However, the Commission works in close contact with both university and industrial research laboratories. The Cowles Commission for Research in Economics at the University of Chicago is engaged in an ambitious project to probe into the economic aspects of atomic energy. As early as 1945, the Social Science Research Council set up a committee to study the social aspects of atomic energy, which has sponsored a number of publications. A complete record of efforts along these lines would probably run to many pages. The basic fact is that, for the present, we are still groping for the knowledge and understanding necessary to enable us to master this powerful newcomer on our energy roster.

[17] Gerald Wendt, "A New Job for the Atom," *Harper's Magazine*, May, 1949.

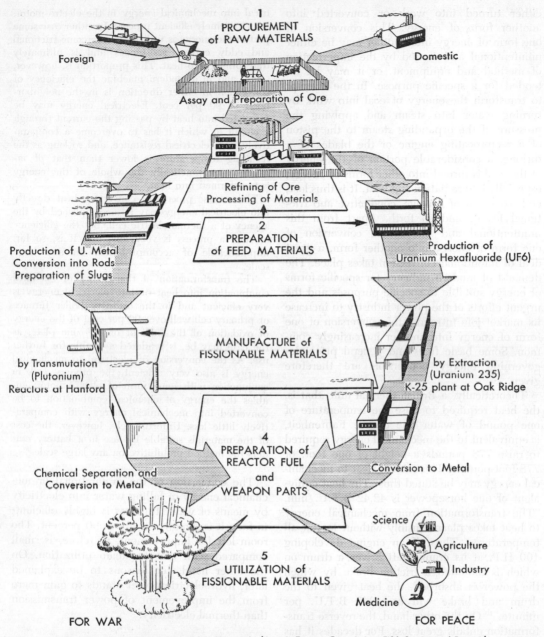

1 PROCUREMENT of RAW MATERIALS

Foreign   Domestic

Assay and Preparation of Ore

Refining of Ore
Processing of Materials

2 PREPARATION of FEED MATERIALS

Production of U. Metal
Conversion into Rods
Preparation of Slugs

Production of
Uranium Hexafluoride (UF6)

3 MANUFACTURE of FISSIONABLE MATERIALS

by Transmutation
(Plutonium)
Reactors at Hanford

by Extraction
(Uranium 235)
K-25 plant at Oak Ridge

4 PREPARATION of REACTOR FUEL and WEAPON PARTS

Chemical Separation and
Conversion to Metal

Conversion to Metal

Science
Agriculture
Industry
Medicine

5 UTILIZATION of FISSIONABLE MATERIALS

FOR WAR   FOR PEACE

FIG. 4.3. Production of Fissionable Materials. (Atomic Energy Commission, *Fifth Semiannual Report*.)

control of atomic energy is a tragic obstacle in the way of using the new miracle force for purposes of global face lifting.[18]

---

[18] See *International Control of Atomic Energy. Growth of a Policy*, and *International Control of Atomic Energy. Policy at the Crossroads*, both published by the U.S. Department of State in 1947

CONVERSION OF ENERGY

The problem of energy conversion is of such importance that it deserves special mention in the general discussion of energy. Energy is

and 1948 respectively. See also, Atomic Energy Commission, *Atomic Energy Development, 1947-1948*.

either turned into work or converted into another form of energy. This conversion of one form of energy into another may be either unintentional and caused by the imperfection of method and equipment, or it may be intended for a specific purpose. In the attempt to transform the energy of coal into work by turning water into steam and applying the pressure of the expanding steam to the piston of a reciprocating engine or the blades of a turbine, a considerable portion of the energy of the coal is turned into other forms of energy, especially into radiation and heat. It is thus lost; and we speak of leakage, conductive and frictional losses, and so forth. Apart from this unintentional and undesirable conversion of one form of energy into another form, a great deal of intentional conversion takes place. The demand of modern industry for specific forms of energy suitable to specific purposes and the urgent efforts of the power industry to increase its market join to render the conversion of one form of energy into another increasingly common. Some basic facts and general principles governing energy conversion are therefore given.

Theoretically, a British thermal unit, that is, the heat required to raise the temperature of one pound of water one degree Fahrenheit, is equivalent to the mechanical energy required to raise 778 pounds a height of one foot, or 778 foot-pounds. This ratio of heat to mechanical energy may be stated thus: The heat equivalent of one horsepower is 42.42 B.T.U./min. "The transformation from mechanical energy to heat takes place sensibly without loss at all temperatures. Thus, if an engine developing 100 H.P. at its crank shaft drives a drum on which is mounted a friction brake by which the power is absorbed, the heat given to the drum and brake will be 4242 B.T.U. per minute."[19] On the other hand, the reverse transformation entails great loss. For decades it has been the chief aim of steam engineers to make the conversion more efficient, to lessen the losses engendered.

The conversion of mechanical into electrical energy in the dynamo-electric machine, or of electrical into mechanical energy in the electro-motor, is an extremely efficient process. In either case some part of the energy is utilized to overcome frictional and eddy current resistances and is ultimately transformed into heat. This proportion is, however, small, and in a modern machine the efficiency of conversion in either direction is in the neighborhood of 90 per cent. Electrical energy may be converted into heat by passing the current through a circuit in which it has to overcome a comparatively large electrical resistance, and so long as the resulting temperature is lower than that of incandescence practically the whole of the energy is transformed into heat.

The reverse process of converting heat directly into electrical energy may be accomplished by the agency of a thermo-electric cell, but the efficiency of such a process is very low, and it is, so far, impracticable of accomplishment on any large scale.

The transformation of the energy of chemical combination into heat or into electrical energy is very efficient and in the ordinary boiler furnace or primary cell well over 90 per cent of the energy of oxidation of the fuel, or of the zinc plate, as the case may be, is rendered available for further use. As the conversion of electrical to mechanical energy is also very efficient, the primary cell, in conjunction with some form of electro-motor, enables the energy of chemical combination to be converted into mechanical energy with comparatively little loss. Unfortunately, however, the cost of the materials suitable for use in a battery renders the method prohibitive on any large scale.[20]

The conversion of the gravitational or mechanical energy of falling water into electricity by means of water turbines is highly efficient; in fact, it is somewhere above 90 percent. The room left for improvement, therefore, is small compared with that in steam utilization. On the other hand, for reasons to be explained later, hydroelectric power stands to gain more from the improvement of power transmission than thermal electricity.

MODERN ENERGY UTILIZATION

In the effort to improve the conversion factor and to adapt the energy forces to the specific requirements of modern industry, the engineer and scientist constantly develop new ways and means of energy utilization. If crude oil burned

---

[19] A. H. Gibson, *Natural Sources of Energy,* The Macmillan Company, New York, 1913, p. 22; reprinted by permission of the publishers.

[20] *Ibid.,* pp. 25-26. Some additional technical details will be found in part 3, especially chap. 29.

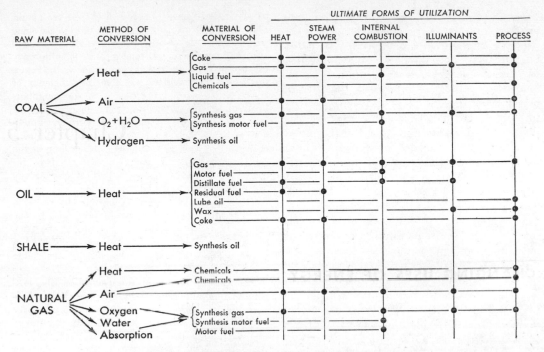

FIG. 4.4. Mineral Fuels, Their Conversion and Utilization.

under a boiler yields only a fraction of its energy in the form of usable energy, it is refined, perhaps subjected to artificial beneficiation such as cracking and hydrogenation, and thus induced to yield more energy. The same principle is applied to coal, shale, and natural gas.[21] Fig. 4.4[22] is shown here merely to illustrate the diversity of effort.

This brief outline of some of the basic facts and general principles pertaining to the physical, technical, and scientific aspects of natural energy was given not only for its own sake but especially as an introduction to the next chapter, which deals with the social and economic implications of the major changes in energy utilization, especially of the mechanical revolution which marks the shift from animate to inanimate energy.

---

[21] Eugene E. Ayres, in a letter of June 20, 1949, comments on this sentence as follows: "It is true that refining steps may lead to the production of more energy per pound and sometimes even per gallon, but perhaps it should be made clear that the refining steps do not improve the thermal efficiency of utilization of the oil in an overall sense. The BTU value of the combined salable products from a refinery is only 90 percent or less of the BTU value of the crude entering the refinery. This is, of course, because of the energy requirement for heat in the refining steps." The value of refining evidently lies not in an increase of total energy but in making refinery products which are suited to tasks that crude cannot perform. One cannot fly a plane or drive a car at high speeds on crude oil.

[22] Fig. 4.4 is based on a diagram distributed to the Round Table Conference on "The Rôle of Chemistry in the World's Future Affairs," H. E. Howe, Chairman, Williamstown Institute of Politics, Sixth Session (1926), and redrawn by Eugene E. Ayres.

BIBLIOGRAPHY

See the bibliography at the end of Chapter 6.

Chapter 5

CHANGING USES OF ENERGY

THE MECHANICAL REVOLUTION

Since the appropriation of fire and the domestication of animals probably no greater single change has occurred in the availability of energy to man than the coming of steam. The mechanical revolution marks the shift from one-sided reliance on animate energy to increasing dependence on inanimate energy. This shift in the energy supply has affected the materials used by man, it has revolutionized his methods of work and the forms of social and economic organization, and it has caused geographical adjustments as well as political realignments, to say nothing of its repercussions on the very thoughts and feelings of all those who have come under its spell, even on philosophy and religion.

Since, as we have seen, the resource appraisal of our environment depends on our own wants, aims, and methods, the mechanical revolution in a very real sense has remade the resource map of the world. One cannot, therefore, understand the resource setup of the modern world without a full appreciation of the mechanical revolution. This understanding, moreover, is aided by a comparison between the resource pattern of a region such as southern China, which has as yet been but little touched by the magic finger of steam and its companions, and the resource pattern of the industrialized Occident.

History and Energy

If we consider that nothing on this earth can happen without the expenditure of some energy and if we interpret the meaning of energy broadly enough, the suggestion of Fairgrieve that human history is the story of man's increasing control over energy may not seem unreasonable. Let us listen to his argument:

. . . it may be said that in its widest sense on its material side history is the story of man's increasing ability to control energy. By energy we mean the capacity for doing work, for causing—not controlling—movement, for making things go or making things stop, whether they be trains or watches or mills or men. In order that anything may be done, energy is required. Man's life is taken up by the one endeavor to get and to use as much energy as possible and to waste as little as possible. Any means whereby he can get more or waste less marks an advance, and is important in the history

of the world. All the discoveries which have been made of how to do things, inventions as we call them, which have marked various stages of progress, are not merely rather interesting facts that have very little to do with history. They have everything to do with it. The inventions of hieroglyphics, of writing, of numerals, of printing, of the compass, of spades, wheels, needles, of steam-engines, and of banknotes have had enormously important effects on the course of the history of the world, and are important just in so far as they enable man to use or to save energy.[1]

Fairgrieve then goes on to explain more fully how social history, military history, constitutional history—in short, all cultural history—can be interpreted as a process of improved control over energy. The machinery necessary for the use of energy consists not merely of physical equipment but includes social institutions as well. Changes of government must be interpreted as alterations and repairs of this machinery. The energy used to make, repair, and improve the machinery, though not directly used for the satisfaction of human wants, is not wasted; neither is that required to refine the lubricating oil without which the machinery does not run smoothly. Banks, organized exchanges, and newspapers furnish the lubricating oil of our economic system.

Similarly, Ostwald's claim[2] that the advance of civilization is marked by an improved energy economy can well be defended. But we must be sure to recognize the economy of energy in all its forms and disguises. We meet it in the open in the form of a central power station that makes two kilowatts grow where one grew before. It is embodied in a glass which allows the free passage of the health-giving ultraviolet rays of the sun. More often its efforts are less overt. It is hidden in the mathematical formula. It makes law and order worth while. It gives vitality to the peace pact which settles the disputes between nations, and lends value to the agreement which ends the strife between social groups, especially "labor and capital." It is the lifeblood of education. Thus the rationalized economy of energy is man's greatest

triumph and his biggest task. Incidentally, the aim of that energy economy is not *dolce far niente,* but a fuller life for the living multitude and enhanced security for the multitudes yet to be born.

A brief review of human history shows clearly the vital importance of changing energy supplies. It is often said that man was not man until he could use fire, a chemical energy with a thousand uses; he was not civilized until he had learned through domestication to appropriate the "foreign" energy of animals and, through agriculture, to harness better the "free" energy of solar radiation and the chemical energies of light, water, and soil. Slavery, an institution governing the utilization of "foreign" animate energy, was a vital factor in history, though hardly one marking as fundamental a change as those brought on by the discovery of fire, the domestication of animals, and the introduction of agriculture. The same applies to gunpowder, another source of energy which has remade the map of continents and decided the fate of nations. The wholesale supplementation of the ancient forms of energy by the modern form, inanimate energy derived from fossil fuels—in short, the mechanical revolution—means another fundamental change in man's control over energy.

One-Sided Determinism

The mechanical revolution, therefore, is here viewed as more than a mere dividing line of history. It is a Great Divide. Lest such a claim create the false impression of one-sided materialistic determinism, a word of explanation is added. It is fully realized that the importance of making available new forms or additional amounts of energy can be exaggerated; and that, correspondingly, the equal if not greater importance of the fuller utilization of old forms and of limited amounts of energy, as well as the progress made in the avoidance of waste, may be inadequately appreciated. The availability of energy depends not merely on the number of forms of energy tapped or on the amounts of energy resources which are being utilized; it depends even more on the care and efficiency with which these available supplies are being utilized. It has been said that, in a material sense, the greatest progress may be expected not from the country which possesses

---

[1] James Fairgrieve, *Geography and World Power,* E. P. Dutton & Co., Inc., New York, 2nd ed., 1921, p. 3.

[2] W. Ostwald, *Energetische Grundlagen der Kulturwissenschaft,* W. Klinkhardt, Leipzig, 1909.

the largest coal deposits, but from the country which uses its coal most efficiently and most wisely. But what is wise and efficient use? That is a difficult question which ties up with a large number of intangible and seemingly unrelated elements. It cannot be answered by a one-sided study of physical availability or an engineer's appraisal of efficiency or an economist's calculation of profitableness. An increase in the amount of energy generated or the shift to a new source of energy, taken by themselves, cannot adequately measure the progress of civilization, as will now be demonstrated.[3]

In "normal" times in the United States, incredible amounts of energy are generated, mostly from coal and oil, but also of the "elbow grease" variety. Much of it, however, may be lost in creating and maintaining a plant capacity which will never be used—misdirected investment, evil fruits of competition misunderstood and maladjusted.

Vice versa, one can well imagine a period in Roman history during which no new form of energy was made available nor increased quantities of old forms of energy were being utilized but which nevertheless was marked by remarkable progress along material lines. This seemingly paradoxical situation might be due to what Fairgrieve calls "momentum." But it may also be traceable to the establishment of law and order, to a better solution of social problems, to the extension of Roman institutions to other parts of the Empire. The mere expansion of the Empire might under certain circum-

stances mean additional progress; for larger areas permit the wider application of the principles of specialization and division of labor, principles which render the available physical resources more productive. As a matter of fact, when during the fourth century after Christ a new source of energy was being tapped and the use of water wheels in flour milling and similar operations spread, the net result in terms of social progress was probably negative. Large numbers of workers lost their employment, and the resultant social conflict rendered the gain from the expanding energy control highly problematic. But why go back so far in history? Perhaps the guns that shot down the Chartists are still to be seen in the workshops of Birmingham. As always, one must distinguish between gross income and net profit. That distinction is valid not only in balancing the books of a business enterprise, but also in appraising the energy economy of an entire civilization as well.

The effect of expanding areas tapped in correlated effort, especially of expanding markets, on increased productivity was perhaps most pronounced during the period which began around the year 1500 and which is generally called the commercial revolution. Expanding trade areas led to a regional specialization, that is, a division of labor along the lines of the natural advantages, such as climate, mineral wealth, soils, etc., possessed by different peoples and which proved highly productive. As was stressed before, probably the greatest factor making for increased productivity is the specialization which permits the fuller use of the peculiar aptitudes of man and enables the people of different regions to specialize in the tasks best suited to the peculiarities of their habitat and congenial to their tastes, attitudes, etc. Commerce goes far to promote this specialization. In short, not the gross supply of energy but the manner of utilization counts most.

Energy History

To the future historian energy history probably will appear divided into three great periods or ages: the age of predominant dependence on animate energy, the age of inanimate energy derived mainly from the exhaustible fossil fuels, and the age of inanimate energy

---

[3] If in this discussion of resources in general and of energy resources in particular more space is devoted to the analysis of physical, technical, and material aspects, this does not mean that the inestimable importance of the intangible factors which bear on the availability of energy is inadequately realized. The one-sided emphasis on the tangible must appear natural in view of the fact that its effects are more clearly discernible and more readily appraised than are the intangible. It is conceded that eras during which human progress was greatest along spiritual lines may well have resulted in greater progress both relatively and absolutely, measured in both immaterial and material ways. It is possible that the commercial revolution advanced man proportionately as much as did the mechanical revolution, and that in spite of the fact that no new source of energy was being attacked but old forms were being used more effectively. The importance of the physical and mechanical is often overestimated.

derived from continuous sources such as direct solar radiation, tidal power, carbon dioxide, etc. We are now living in the second age, the age of fossil fuels, which began sometime in the eighteenth century. That age is rushing on to its *finis* with accelerating speed and demoniac force.

It was a great event when James Watt patented his steam engine in 1776, an event comparable to that when Prometheus snatched fire from Olympus. It marked the beginning of a long series of inventions, including the steam turbine, the gasoline explosion engine, the Diesel engine, the gas combustion turbine, the different jets—turbojet, rocketjet, aeroresonator, etc.—the water turbine, and the host of other inventions which have made electricity one of the most widely used forms of energy. The steam engine was the first of a long and lengthening line of prime movers which harness the elementary forces of nature. These basic inventions in the field of energy use led to a vast number of other inventions which made possible the application of inanimate energy to industry, agriculture, transport, and communication. What is more, these inventions so raised the productivity of man that he at last found the leisure and surplus which made possible the systematic pursuit of scientific research. Mechanization and science are twin forces which have changed and are changing man's environment.

It seems strange to think of mankind as having lived on this planet for countless generations in poverty and fear without tapping the vast funds of stored-up solar radiation in the form of coal, oil, and gas or making use of the considerable power of falling water (except in mere trickles). The human race was like a poor family living in a hovel, under whose dirt floor was buried a huge treasure chest which promised the lucky owner vast wealth and power. If people knew of its existence, they did not have the key to open the lock. That key was provided by James Watt, and when the lock finally was opened, in Sombart's picturesque language "the earth became pregnant with new earths."[4]

So vast was this newly found treasure that

at first man considered it limitless. But after a couple of hundred years of accelerated and increasing drafts on "the First Natural Bank," the bottom of the chest, although not yet visible, is suspected to lie not too far below the present tapping zone.

So accustomed has man become to the use of the vast inanimate powers derived from the fossil fuels, to the joys of expanding and upward-surging enterprise, to dependence on countless robots, docile serfs that do not speak back, that even the realization of an impending Götterdämmerung cannot retard the speed with which the top spins.

So great is the confidence of modern industrial man in his own capacity to create resources, to discover ways and means of tapping new sources of energy, of finding treasure chests buried more deeply than that containing the fossil fuels, that he insists on keeping up the exhausting pace of fuel use. If, as seems possible, an increasing share of the vast energies now derived from exhaustible fuels is used to discover ways of tapping new and inexhaustible energies, that confidence may well be justified. Much will depend on the continuation of peace.

Miracle of the Fossil Fuel Age

If it were possible to give a full account of developments in the realm of energy use from the time when the first satisfactory steam engine was perfected to the middle of the twentieth century, the story would read like a fairy tale. If one realizes that at the beginning of the period only a few million tons of coal a year were produced as compared with perhaps a billion and a half tons today, that little oil was produced before the middle of the last century as compared with over three billion barrels a year today, that the first electric power station was built in the early eighties whereas electricity output today is measured by the hundreds of billions of kilowatt-hours, that the natural gas industry is virtually a newcomer and the atomic energy industry a mere infant, and if one further considers that all these energies require for their harnessing and use vast amounts of metals extracted from far vaster amounts of ore, he will get a dim notion of the miraculous performance of the past two hundred years.

---

[4] Werner Sombart, *Der Moderne Kapitalismus,* Dunker and Humblot, München and Leipzig, 1928.

Fig. 5.1[5] will give a statistical inkling of the magnitude of the change, the steepness of the curves of "progress." Fig. 5.1 shows the shift from animate energy produced by men and animals to inanimate energy derived from minerals, and its use in the United States from 1850 to 1944. Of course in no other country is the curve equally steep; nowhere else did the thrust of the mechanical revolution meet with less resistance and perform greater miracles.

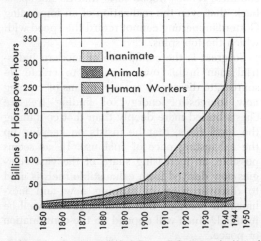

FIG. 5.1.   Estimated "Work Energy" Output in the United States, 1850–1944, by Sources.

The work output we got from mineral fuels was five hundred times greater in 1944 than in 1850. The contribution of coal, petroleum, and natural gas to our "work-energy" supply increased from less than 5 per cent of the total to more than 87 per cent. Together with water power, they do 94 per cent of our work for us today, while men and animals do a meager 6 per cent. It seems likely that by 1960 human beings will contribute a mere 2.5 per cent of our energy output.

This great dramatic shift to mineral energy is the very basis of technological progress. One could almost concentrate the whole history of economic development into this simple transition: man power to animal power to machine power.

The shift to machine power changed America from a rural agricultural nation to an industrial giant. It also made men's lives easier and richer.

In 1850, the average American worked seventy hours a week. Today he works forty-three. In 1850, our average American produced about 27 cents' worth of goods an hour. Today he produces about $1.40 worth in dollars of the same purchasing power.

In other words, on the average a man can produce about five times as much in an hour today as he did in 1850. Economists would say his output per hour or his productivity has increased over five times. It was this advance in productivity that made it possible to increase the net output of goods and services twenty-nine times from 1850 to 1944, even though working hours were much shorter and the population only six times greater. And this quintupled productivity in turn rested largely on the fact that Americans as a group had at their disposal all the marvelous advantages of mineral energy, five hundred times as much as in 1850.[6]

But, as was stated before, the fossil-fuel-based phase of the machine age is driving with irresistible force toward its end. Exhaustion of fossil fuel reserves now appears nearer than had been anticipated. What will follow? No one knows, but those most competent to predict point to the possibilities of tapping the vast and inexhaustible supplies of direct solar radiation and other continuous sources of energy.

We cannot believe that this fossil-fuel era in which we live, an era which may soon start its climactic approach to exhaustion, will be regarded by historians of the future as a period in which energy has been uniquely abundant. Instead, there is every reason to expect that succeeding eras will provide still greater abundance of energy from our constant sources. In the meantime, there is a lot of work to be done. Within a few decades a good start must have been made toward the new systems of energy production and consumption; and while this goes on, our technological rear guard will be engaged in retarding in every possible way the corrosive growth of our energy losses.[7]

---

[5] From J. Frederick Dewhurst, "Relation of Energy Output to Production in the United States," paper read before the joint session of the American Association for the Advancement of Science, the Academy of World Economics, and the American Economic Association, Chicago, December 31, 1947.

[6] Gloria Waldron and J. Frederic Dewhurst, *Power, Machines, and Plenty,* Public Affairs Pamphlet No. 142, 1948, pp. 9, 10. Largely based on J. Frederic Dewhurst and associates, *America's Needs and Resources,* Twentieth Century Fund, New York, 1947.

[7] Eugene E. Ayres, "Major Sources of Energy," a paper read during the 28th annual meeting of the American Petroleum Institute, November 9, 1948, p. 138.

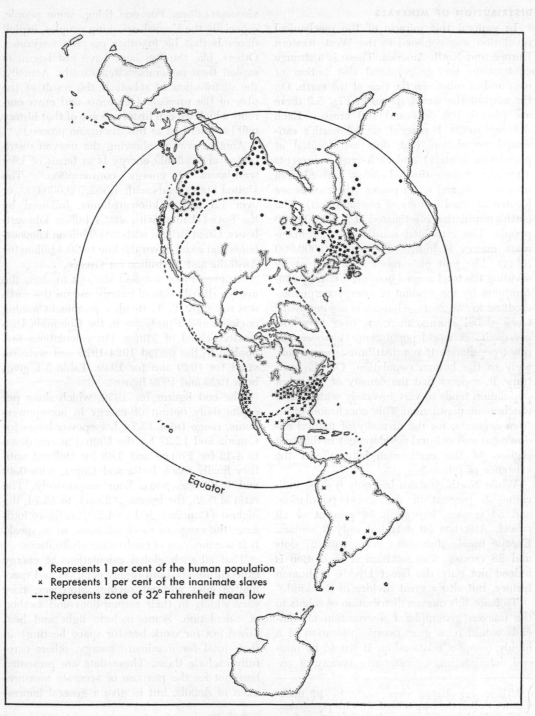

Equator

• Represents 1 per cent of the human population
× Represents 1 per cent of the inanimate slaves
--- Represents zone of 32° Fahrenheit mean low

FIG. 5.2.   Men and Robots.

DISTRIBUTION OF MINERALS

In general this miracle of the mechanical revolution was confined to the West—western Europe and North America. There is a strange contrast in the geographical distribution of men and of robots on the face of the earth. On the map of the world shown in Fig. 5.2 there are placed 100 dots and 100 crosses. Each dot represents 1 percent of the earth's estimated population (the dots are located at population centers) and each cross represents 1 percent of the estimated energy derived from mineral fuels and water power (the crosses are located at focal centers of consumption). The earth's population is estimated at 2,125,000,000 people. The estimated consumption of inanimate energy is indicated by 36,850,000,000 robots. The unit of a robot is arrived at by dividing the total annual inanimate energy consumption by the amount of energy output accredited to one average human being per year.[8] On a global average there are over 17 robots per capita of world population. However, the robot population is not distributed proportionately to the human population. On the contrary, it appears that the density of the robot population tends to vary inversely with that of the human population. This conclusion is far from accurate, for the diversity of natural endowment and cultural development in different regions of the earth materially affects the existence of robots.[9]

While North America has only 8 dots, indicating 8 percent of the world population, and 54 crosses, indicating 54 percent of all robots, Asia has 50 dots but only 9 crosses. Europe breaks just about even, with 27 dots and 28 crosses. The mechanical revolution is indeed not only the Great Divide of human history, but also a great divider of mankind.[10]

To trace this uneven distribution of robots to the uneven geographical distribution of minerals would be a gross oversimplification of a highly complex relationship. It would be mineral determinism, a most naïve variety of en-

vironmentalism. For one thing, some people, especially the English-speaking peoples, exploit minerals that lie in other people's territories. Others, like the Russians, have just begun to exploit their minerals systematically. Actually, the distribution of robots is the result of the play of the myriad of currents and cross currents which we call history. Some of that history will be described as this discussion proceeds.

Another way of showing the uneven distribution of available energy is in terms of kilowatt-hours of energy consumption.[11] The United States leads with 1,562,700,000,000, or over 1.5 trillion kilowatt-hours, followed by the Soviet Union with 460.4 billion kilowatt-hours, Great Britain with 294.9 billion kilowatt-hours and so on down the line to 30.4 billion for Australia and 2.6 billion for Greece.

An even more detailed attempt to show the uneven distribution of energy use on the earth was made by T. T. Read, a prominent mining engineer and a professor in the Columbia University School of Mines. His calculations first applied to the period 1924-1925 and were revised for 1929 and for 1939. Table 5.1 gives both 1929 and 1939 figures.

The end figures for 1939, which show per capita daily output of energy in horsepower-hours, range from 15.74 horsepower-hours for Canada and 12.27 for the United States, down to 4.32 for France and 3.48 for Holland until they finally reach India and China, with 0.49 and 0.46 horsepower-hour respectively. The ratio of 0.46, the lowest (China), to 15.74, the highest (Canada), is $1 \div 34.2$. This figure indicates the range of mechanization, so to speak. It is one measure of contrasting civilizations.

That all such global calculations of energy expenditure are both highly complex and speculative goes without saying. Moreover, they vary widely in their assumptions and method of calculation. Some include light and heat (used not for work but for space heating) in their total for inanimate energy, others carefully exclude them. These data are presented here not for the purpose of accurate measurement of details, but to give a general impres-

---

[8] These calculations were made by R. Buckminster Fuller; the map is used with his permission.

[9] See the discussion of population density as contrasted with the man-land ratio, p. 92.

[10] This point will be developed fully when the resource hierarchy of the modern world economy is discussed. See chap. 10.

[11] Such a map has been prepared by Nathaniel B. Guyol, formerly of the U.S. Department of State and now with the United Nations. See U.S. Department of State, *Energy Resources of the World*, Government Printing Office, Washington, 1949.

TABLE 5.1. Daily Output of Work[12]

	Consumption (millions of horsepower-hours)										Population (millions)		Daily Output per Capita Hp.-Hr.	
	Human		Coal		Petroleum		Water		Total					
	1929	1939	1929	1939	1929	1939	1929	1939	1929	1939	1929	1939	1929	1939
United States	40	43.8	1001a	784.4a	481	617	121	166.7	1643	1611.9	122.77	131.41	13.38	12.27
Canada	3.3	3.7	55	39.6	17.6	25.4	59	104.8	134.9	173.5	10.35	11.02	13.03	15.74
Norway	0.9	1.0	3.6	4.6	0.6	2.57	15	26.5	20.1	34.7	2.65	2.94	7.58	11.80
Belgium	3	2.8	50	43.1	1.7	3.5	...	0.03	54.7	49.4	7.99	8.39	6.85	5.89
Great Britain	15	15.4	270	302.7	28.3	45.5	4	4.4	317.3	368.0	47.71	46.21	6.65	7.96
Germany	21	37.7c	333	548.9c	9.5	27c	13	33.1c	376.5	646.7	62.34	113.15c	6.04	5.72
Sweden	2	2.1	7.5	14.4	1.9	5.3	16	20.4	27.4	42.2	6.12	6.31	4.48	6.69
Switzerland	1.3	1.4	3.9	5.4	1.0	1.3	11.5	24.4	17.7	32.5	4.02	4.21	4.41	7.72
France	14	14.2	127	101.0	12.3	25	24	43.2	177.3	183.4	40.74	42.42	4.35	4.32
Czechoslovakia	5	d	42	d	1.8	d	1.5	d	50.3	d	14.52	15.25	3.46	f
Australia	2.1	2.2	10	26.0	10	7.4	b	2	22.1	37.6	6.43	6.96	3.44	5.40
Austria	2.2	d	12	d	0.9	...	6	d	21.1	d	6.67	7.01	3.16	f
Union of So. Africa	2.3	3.4	16	25.5	1.8	3.7	b	0.09	20.1	32.7	6.93	10.16	2.90	3.22
Holland	2.5	2.9	16	21.6	3.1	5.9	b	...	21.6	30.4	7.62	8.73	2.83	3.48
Poland	10	e	48a	d	1.7	d	b	d	59.7	e	30.84	34.77	1.94	f
Chile	1.5	1.5	2.0	2.7	3.8	2.7	1.0	1.8	8.3	8.7	4.36	4.63	1.90	1.88
Japan	21	24.3	52	f	7	12.7	30	49.1	110	f	62.94	72.80	1.75	f
Argentina	3.6	4.3	4.5	f	10	14.4	0.35	0.54	18.45	f	10.90	13.01	1.69	f
Italy	14	14.7	23	20.1	4.6	10.9	27	50	63.6	95.7	41.17	44.03	1.67	2.17
Spain	7.6	8.5	13	10.5	1.8	2.85	8	11.2	30.4	33.05	22.75	25.37	1.34	1.30
Mexico	5.5	6.5	1.5	9.5	9.5	9.3	4.0	3.8	20.5	29.1	16.40	19.48	1.25	1.49
Hungary	2.8	3.7	6	17.1	0.8	1.0	b	0.04	9.6	21.8	8.60	11.14	1.12	1.96
Rumania	6	6.7	4.1	3.9	6.8	7.5	0.8	1.0	17.7	19.1	17.39	20.09	1.02	0.95
Russia	53	56.9	56	219.7	35	85.3	4	15.3	148	377.2	158.50	170.47	0.93	2.21
Bulgaria	2.0	2.2	2.4	0.6	0.3	...	0.5	0.6	5.2	3.4	5.60	6.55	0.93	0.52
Yugoslavia	4.4	5.2	4.2	9.7	0.5	...	2	2	11.1	16.9	13.29	15.63	0.84	1.08
Peru	1.8	2.3	0.4	0.2	0.9	1.3	0.5	1.4	3.6	5.2	5.50	6.92	0.66	0.75
Brazil	13	14.7	3.4	2.2	3.0	4.4	6	8.9	25.4	30.2	40.27	44.12	0.63	0.68
India	106	117.8	34	40.3	8	8.2	3	5.0	151	171.3	318.88	352.84	0.47	0.49
China	133	161.1	43	55.1	4.13	3.4			180.13	219.6	400.80	482.30	0.45	0.46

a Includes natural gas.
b Quantities omitted; too small to be important.
c Includes Austria, Czechoslovakia, and ⅔ of Poland.

d Included in Germany.
e Divided between Germany and Russia.
f Data lacking.

12 *American Economic Review*, March, 1945, p. 144.

sion of broad basic issues and elementary magnitudes.

The Mechanical Revolution as a Cultural Revolution

The substitution of mechanical energy generated from dead substances such as coal, petroleum, natural gas, or of the gravitational energy embodied in falling water, for the muscular energy generated by men and beasts in return for vegetable and animal food and feed consumed, is a change so radical—that is, going so deeply to the root—that through it the very design of civilization has been altered beyond recognition. The alteration, however, is neither complete nor perfect, for the material transformation, both technical and economic, demands a reorientation in the realm of the mind and the spirit too sudden and too drastic to be performed adequately and smoothly.

The old machinery, not only of material civilization but of the most refined cultural patterns as well, was designed to meet the great emergency of an ever-growing population pushing with increased vigor and rising impatience against the subsistence levels of the earth. Man faced a chronic condition of scarcity of food, of land, of everything. The inevitableness of scarcity has yielded to the possibility of plenty; at times even overwhelming superabundance threatens. Therefore the machinery of social and economic institutions had to be adjusted to new dangers. Philosophy, which had long served as a means of escape from the limitations of human abilities, has had to make an about-face to meet the needs of the new Prometheus who feels his powers as clearly as the old Adam realized his limitations. The positive attitude toward population increase which was demanded in the agricultural world because of the need of labor and markets had to be reversed to meet the emergence of technological unemployment and the man-replacing power of machines and engines. Agriculture, for millenniums the backbone of civilized life, lost its primacy and was forced to take its place behind mining, manufacturing, commerce, and finance. Thus the mechanical revolution necessarily involved a social revolution, a revolution in every field of human thought and action.

The Mechanical Revolution a Gradual Shift

At this point we must pause to forestall a misunderstanding. To say that the mechanical revolution is a shift from muscular to mechanical energy is to do violence to the finer meaning of words. For the word "revolution" denotes something sudden, whereas a shift is more apt to be slow and gradual. It would be more accurate, therefore, to speak of the mechanical evolution rather than the mechanical revolution, for three reasons. In the first place, the difference between ancient and modern energy usage is one of degree rather than of essence, for even the most primitive man used some inanimate energy. He did so when he ran downhill, when he floated downstream on a log, when he cooked his food over a fire. The ancients in their mining operations frequently took advantage of the expansion and shrinkage caused by changing temperatures. In building their pyramids, the Egyptians made use of gravitation in the most ingenious way. Furthermore, their priests used steam power to operate the heavy temple doors—and incidentally to awe the multitude who marveled at the miracle. The use of wind power is as old as history. But if the difference between ancient and modern energy usage is one only of degree, it is so drastic as to be in effect a difference of essence.

In the second place, the shift to the modern usage, when it did come, came gradually and not without careful preparations and forebodings. In a very real sense, James Watt stood on the shoulders of Prometheus and on those of the great but forgotten men who invented the simple machines, to say nothing of the da Vincis and Newcomens who had invented simple steam engines. His work was prompted by the evil effects of forest depletion. Without the commercial revolution, the mechanical revolution is hardly thinkable. Furthermore the Renaissance, Humanism, and even the Crusades prepared the soil.

Third, when the mechanical revolution got under way, it spread very gradually from its starting point in the Black Country of England to the rest of the Occident and still more gradually to the world at large. The application of steam power to water pumps in coal mines and of water power in textile mills was the first definite symptom. Gradually the use of steam

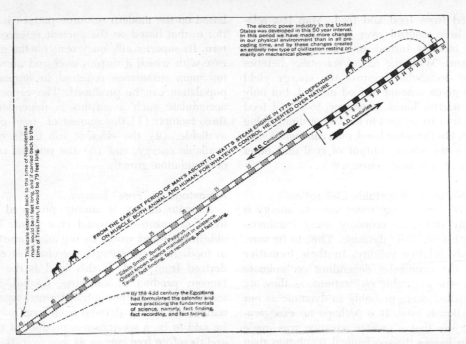

FIG. 5.3. Man's Shift from Muscle to Mechanical Power. (Prepared by S. S. Wyer for the Fuel-Power-Transportation Educational Foundation, Columbus, Ohio; reprinted by permission.)

spread to manufacturing and to transportation on land and sea. Then Fourneyron invented the modern water turbine. That secret force called electricity was next harnessed as a source of light, heat, and power—first in small plants here and there, later boldly in giant plants and in superpower zones. The gas motor followed, extending mechanical locomotion to the air and emancipating land transportation from the limits of the steel rail. The long-distance transmission of electricity was cheapened, new sources of energy were tapped, and old ones used better. Used in ever new forms, in ever wider areas, in ever better ways, mechanical energy waxes in power for good and for evil, a product of time rather than of man, a living force rather than a dead tool. As the development over which no one seems to have any control proceeds at an accelerated pace, its influence over man and his civilization grows cumulatively. Old institutions wither under its burning breath; new institutions rise.

Old and New Resource Patterns

While the mechanical revolution is evolutionary in its origin and growth, it is revolu-

tionary in effect. It has remade the resource basis of human civilization, at least of western civilization. Before James Watt started the definite shift from animate to inanimate energy, the entire civilized world had been using the same resource pattern—the ancient resource pattern. Solar radiation was used almost exclusively in its most common form, sunshine. This, in turn, was used mainly for agricultural purposes in conjunction with water—rainfall and river water—and with soil—in part, at least, a fund of stored-up solar radiation. The chief use which can be made of the products of agriculture is to feed men and beasts. Food and feed generate animate energy, the most important—in fact, almost the only—form in which energy is available wherever the ancient resource pattern is found.

The modern resource pattern which the white man is superimposing on this ancient pattern rests on a different and superior energy basis. The generation of steam power with the aid of heat produced by burning coal or other fossil fuels makes available to man a source of energy which, in the course of time, proves progressively superior to the animate energy obtained from food and feed. Man has relatively little control over the metabolism by which food is turned into energy in living organisms. With the aid of scientific dietetics he may somewhat improve the energy yield from a given amount of food or feed, but only within narrow limits. Moreover, food and feed production are subject to the law of diminishing returns. On the other hand, man can consciously improve the energy output of coal and other sources of inanimate energy.

Static Nature of Vegetable Civilization

Hence an economy using animate energy is basically static; an economy using inanimate energy is essentially dynamic. This, to be sure, has only relative validity. In their formative stages the economies depending on animate energy—the vegetable civilizations, as they are aptly called—were probably as dynamic as our civilization is now. It is perhaps no exaggeration to say that a greater advance was made by man before the mechanical revolution than since. On the other hand, it would seem within the range of possibility that, at some future stage, economies using inanimate energy—machine civilizations, in other words—may likewise reach a static equilibrium. In fact, as will be developed later on, machine civilization, as at present constituted, rests on a less permanent basis than does vegetable civilization.

Moreover, it should not be assumed that a dynamic economy or civilization is necessarily superior to a static economy or civilization. In this case, however, the assumption of superiority seems justified, for a civilization based on inanimate energy seems to offer better chances of reaching greater heights of human achievement than one based on animate energy. If man does not avail himself of these chances, the blame rests on him, not on the energy utilized. To enter into a discussion of the criteria of a "better" civilization would be the height of folly, for the determination of what is "better" involves judgment, opinion, subjective appraisal. What seems "better" to the Asiatic may be detestable to the Occidental, and vice versa.

SUPERIORITY OF INANIMATE ENERGY

Viewed in a material sense, measured in terms of economic efficiency, the civilization based on the modern resource pattern is superior to that based on the ancient resource pattern. Its superior efficiency rests on the greater ease with which a surplus over and above the minimum sustenance required to support the population can be produced. The capacity to accumulate such a surplus is dependent on three factors: (1) the amount of "free" energy available, (2) the efficient use made of the available energy, and (3) the rational control of population growth.

Advantage of "Free" Energy

Animate energy is energy produced by a living organism—an animal or a plant. To be able to live and work, an organism must take in food. Animate energy, therefore, is energy derived from food. If this food is the spontaneous product of sunshine, rainfall, virgin soil fertility, and other untransformed aspects of nature, the energy derived from food may also be said to be a spontaneous product of nature and therefore free energy. If, however, the food must first be produced by man with the aid of animals bred and raised by him and of tools made by him, animate energy is to a high degree an artificial man-made product. In that case the energy spent in producing the necessary food and feed and tools must be deducted from the total energy derived from the food before the net energy available for work can be ascertained. Since, under civilized conditions, most food and feed are not spontaneous products of untransformed nature but the result of past energy expenditure, most animate energy is not a net addition to the energy supply available to man. It is normally assumed that the energy derived from food and feed exceeds that required to produce the food and feed—in other words, that a portion at least represents a "net" product.

Whether that assumption is justified depends on animal metabolism, on the efficiency of the productive system; and this, in turn, depends largely on the quality of the natural agents utilized and the amount of surplus which can be accumulated. An intelligent, educated, healthy farmer working good land under favorable climatic conditions, using good tools and applying good techniques, is apt to produce food and feed capable of yielding an amount of energy far in excess of that used in producing the food and feed. His net product, then, is large. On the other hand, a dull and inexperienced farmer, tilling poor land under unfavorable climatic conditions and applying faulty techniques, is apt to produce food and feed capable of yielding an amount of energy hardly—if at all—in excess of that required to produce the food and feed. Virgin soil, fertility, and good climate are untransformed aspects of nature; so are native good health and ability. But education, tools, techniques, and improved hygienic conditions are cultural additions to the natural environment. They are the product of former net products of energy. Hence, an energetic, vigorous, intelligent population occupying fertile land topographically and climatically well situated, being able to produce great "net" products, will be able to use these "net" products to improve their tools and techniques and to spread education, and thus cumulatively add to their advantages. The other group will be held, if not pulled down, by the vicious circle of their initial handicap. Whatever the theoretical explanation of the superiority of inanimate over animate energy may be, the fact of its superiority is hardly disputable. The following statement furnishes strong supporting evidence:

Advantages of Mineral Energy. Whether delivered as electricity to the farm or factory, produced under the hood of an automobile, or generated in the hold of the *Queen Mary*, mineral energy provides a greater concentration of power than could the most ingenious and efficient use of untold human and animal labor. And mineral energy provides power in a more convenient, compact, mobile, and controllable form. The famous "Borax 20 Mule Team" reached a speed of six to eight miles an hour. It was probably the biggest sum of animal power ever brought under the control of a single driver—outside of the circus. But the frailest of women drives around today with three times as much lethal horsepower, and a potential ninety miles an hour under the hood. Steve Davies operates one machine with the power of 2,200 mules.

In a single day, the Consolidated Edison System in New York delivers enough electricity to do the work of three million draft horses or ten times as many hard-working men. Last year the Consolidated System turned out about as much energy as the total work output of the entire nation in 1850!

The greatest advantage of mineral energy is that it is cheap as compared with animal or human

energy. Cost is crucial. Many forms of energy have never been used because they cost too much to harness to practical uses. Wind power, for example, is both unlimited and free, but costly to use. Similarly, we have not learned a practical way of using atomic energy for peaceful purposes.

Compared to machines, men and animals are costly. The upkeep is too high. Any farmer will tell you that horses spend more time standing around eating their heads off than working. Men have to be fed, clothed, and sheltered. That is why even slave labor is not cheap. Our mechanical slaves get along on cheaper "food" and require less attention than either men or animals. Aside from the morals involved, the use of forced human labor is a sure sign of industrial backwardness.

The Value of Man Power. Electricity is delivered at a cost of one to four cents per horsepower-hour. A draft horse can be hired for 75 cents an hour. The present rate of $1 an hour for common labor would mean that human energy would cost $10 per horsepower-hour.

On the whole, animal energy probably costs thirty to a hundred times as much as mineral energy, and human energy from three hundred to a thousand times as much. No wonder we waste everything but man power! No wonder we electrify our kitchens as well as our factories! We even have "mental" labor-saving machines—for example, the electronic calculator that performs such astounding feats as multiplying 94,267,546,829,347 by 74,-392,864,576,249 in one-fiftieth of a second. No wonder Americans are accused of being demons for speed and efficiency. In purely practical terms, we want to get the most out of our costly man power, so we devise mechanical marvels to replace it, supplement it, augment it, and conserve it.

Our subway and bus systems deliver workers to their jobs in less time than it takes to harness a horse. Our DC-6's get the businessman to his next appointment before he has even finished the morning newspaper. Washing machines, electric ranges, and vacuum cleaners enable a housewife to clean and cook and work outside the home, too, if she wants to. Mimeograph machines do the work of hundreds of secretaries. The farmer has his tractors and milking machines. A mechanical cotton stripper can harvest an acre of cotton in six hours. One man with the aid of his muscles and a mule would need 140 hours.[13]

Animate Energy and Proliferation

Before the mechanical revolution few farming peoples were in the enviable position of

[13] Gloria Waldron and J. Frederic Dewhurst, *op. cit.*, pp. 11-12.

the more favorably situated. We find them in China during certain periods of her history, we find them in Egypt, in Mesopotamia; but those less favorably situated may be said to have been in the majority. Generally speaking, therefore, before the mechanical revolution agriculture was a fairly hopeless undertaking. It was carried on after a fashion under the spell of a vicious circle which prevented its rising above a certain dead level of mere vegetation and proliferation. People raised food and feed one day to generate the energy to raise more food and feed the next. If, by chance, a net product was achieved, one of two things happened. Either a powerful upper class usurped the surplus, or the human and animal population simply rose to the point where the dead level was struck again. On the whole, people raised food to generate the energy required to raise the food. In the meantime they lived. But what for?

Inanimate energy differs essentially from animate energy. It appears in many forms, of which the fossil fuels, coal, petroleum and natural gas, and, to a lesser extent, water power, are the most important. Genetically speaking, the energy lodged in a ton of coal is closely akin to the energy in a ton of corn or wheat or hay. Both came from the sun; but here the similarity ends, for coal is the product of past solar radiation; it was made ages ago—before the advent of man. At any rate, it was made without any expenditure of human energy. It is there ready to be used. Not so the corn, hay, oats, wheat, meat, and other feed and food from which animate energy is derived. To be sure, they too are products of solar radiation, but of current, not ancient, prehistoric, sunshine. Since Adam's expulsion from Paradise, sunshine has produced crops only when man helps. All solar radiation is free energy, and the sun is the only source of free energy available to man. The sun produced both the coal and the food; but while coal, petroleum, and natural gas are undiluted sunshine and therefore sources of totally free energy, food and feed, having been produced with the aid of man at the expenditure of animate energy, are not.

The fact that most coal is found some distance below the ground and must therefore be mined, whereas feed and food crops develop on the surface, is merely incidental. Food and

feed as well as coal—nowadays at least—must be moved, coal vertically and horizontally, food and feed mainly horizontally. In other words, to be available for use, both coal and feed must be transported, and transportation requires energy.[14] In this respect they are alike; but here again coal enjoys an inherent advantage, for if coal is raised and transported with the aid of coal it may be said to raise and move itself. We may use up the coal reserves more quickly, but the coal available for energy production over and above transportation is still a net product. On the other hand a ton of hay moved by an ox is not a net product, for the ox that draws it must eat, but the coal that generates the steam to pull the train does not.

Energy and the Function of Land

Since animate energy can be derived only from food and feed, any economy built on its utilization must be predominantly an agricultural economy, a vegetable civilization. This term applies even where animals play an important part, for animals live on vegetable matter. In a vegetable civilization land means wealth—land in the sense of surface, standing room, soil, the recipient of rainfall and sunshine, the natural agent for the commutation of matter. Feudalism—the system in which social status and economic as well as political power are proportionate to property holdings in the sense of landed rights—is the typical form of social control found in the agricultural economies of the Occident and of Japan. In other sections, especially in the monsoon regions of southeastern Asia, the strategic significance of water has vitally affected the control pattern. Still different patterns have evolved in other areas, but land as the source of vegetable growth is always the foundation on which economies using animate energy must build.

Since empty land is worthless, the landowner wants to see his land inhabited, he wants people to increase in numbers. His is a strong positive population policy. Birth control does not fit into his scheme. To yield a surplus to the lord or a subsistence to the peasant, land must be cultivated. The defense no less than the

---

[14] The tendency toward greater mobility inherent in modern machine civilization and the resulting increase in transportation costs will be discussed in greater detail later on.

conquest of land requires man power. Thus, in vegetable civilizations, policy is dominated by land hunger and man hunger. Under those circumstances people tend to breed to the subsistence level; if an area is filled up, migration or colonization elsewhere or war or pestilence reëstablishes the equilibrium between man and land.

Energy and Labor Efficiency

In ancient times, generally speaking, human labor was relatively ineffective. The lower classes were abused by tribute-levying conquerors, heavily taxed by their own rulers, held in bondage, or even actually enslaved. The masses of the people were ignorant and generally lacked proper training. The profit incentive and the stimulating hope of economic and political advancement were absent. Ineffectiveness is self-perpetuating. The inefficient worker, producing little or no surplus over and above the means of sustenance, cannot improve his capital equipment. At times, what little surplus could be coaxed from the toiling masses in the form of tribute or taxes was squandered by the ruling leisure class. Measured by modern standards, a worker inadequately supported by capital equipment is generally an ineffective producer. Not being able to produce and spare that which could raise his effectiveness, he is caught in a vicious circle.

In general, this condition continued until the mechanical revolution radically altered production methods. To be sure, peasant agriculture in certain sections of the world accomplished remarkable results; and in the cities craftsmanship, in some respects, reached heights never surpassed in the machine civilization. Yet, on the whole, productive effectiveness, measured by present standards, lagged far behind.

Moreover, before the mechanical revolution the life and health of workers were not guarded with the care characteristic of our modern industrial civilization. The economic value of good health is self-evident, but that of increased life expectancy is less so. Its most important economic implication is the resultant improvement of the ratio of the nonproductive to the productive period of human life. If we take fifteen years as the nonproductive period of childhood, a man who dies at the age of 30 represents the balance between the productive and nonproductive years. At 45 the ratio of productive to nonproductive labor is 2 to 1; at 60, 3 to 1, etc. The average expectancy of life in this country at present is between 50 and 60, whereas up to about 150 years ago it was probably somewhere between 30 and 40.

Because of the ineffective production methods of preindustrial days, entire families—men, women, and children—kept busy from morning till night during the working season to raise the necessities of life. There was no time for study, schooling, education. As a result, labor lacked ambition and had little chance to shake off the curse of inefficiency. However, this statement must not be misinterpreted. Within the limits set by the ancient resource pattern, a Chinese may reach the highest possible position of achievement. His knowledge of plant life, of soils and fertilizers may be as complete as our knowledge of atoms and electrons, of electricity and radioactivity—or even more so—but the effectiveness of his knowledge is reduced by the inherent defects of his system. Moreover, ignorance breeds superstition, and superstition puts innumerable obstacles in the way of progress. Being ineffective and ignorant, man had no hope. Religion therefore took on a "defeatist" character, an "otherworldliness" which acted as an opiate, not as a stimulant. Asceticism developed, which taught man to seek contentment simply by not wanting, by stifling his wants and desires.

Energy and Capital Requirements

It must be conceded that the oxcart is a simple device, compared with the train drawn by a steam locomotive over steel rails. A wheelwright can build an oxcart, but the train and rails cannot be made without blast furnaces, steel mills, and many other complex devices. Hence, the efficient utilization of inanimate energy requires large indirect and roundabout expenditures of energy. A huge array of capital equipment must be created, maintained, enlarged, and improved. But here again it must be kept in mind that this capitalistic equipment is created out of inanimate, that is, free energy; it contributes to the fuller and better use of inanimate energy; it too may be said to create itself just as the coal was said to raise itself. To be sure, if the equipment did not have to be built, either less coal, petroleum, etc., would have to be produced to yield man a given amount of ultimate consumers' goods, or more ultimate consumers' goods would have to be made available. But the ability to yield a surplus is not materially affected. In other words, an economy based on inanimate energy requires a larger overhead, but the overhead can be more easily created; in fact, to a certain extent it creates itself.

Moreover, animate energy calls for a considerable overhead, though for different reasons. In the first place, animals must not only eat but also sleep or rest. They pass through a preparatory stage during which they eat and rest, but do not work. Furthermore, they get sick and grow old. So besides feed, shelter must be provided, and care for the young, feeble, and sick. The same applies to human beings.[15] If we assume that eight out of twenty-four hours is a normal working period, continuous operation would require three shifts of animals. The overhead expense, especially the item for shelter, is therefore disproportionately large in the case of animate energy. The extra expense of taking care of the animals—and men —during the nonworking periods of life—youth, old age, and sickness—is somewhat counterbalanced by the necessity of keeping machines and engines in reserve. Keeping three shifts of animals or men simultaneously engaged in a given task is frequently out of the question. It certainly was impossible before artificial light was provided to make night work possible, and that is an accomplishment of machine civilization.

Energy and the Choice of Materials

In origin and use, animate energy is more closely related to organic matter—vegetable and animal substances—than to inorganic. As was pointed out before, the use of animate energy precludes the use of more than small and easily accessible amounts of minerals, especially metals. Only a small portion of the minerals exploited today is found on or near the surface; most of them are found at some

depth below. So long as only man and animal power is available to work the pumps, the ventilators, the hoists, etc., the limits of mining operations are closely drawn. Moreover, hand-hewn and hand-picked minerals are essentially products of human labor and therefore belong to the animate energy cycle. Only when steam power makes deep shafts and large mining operations technically possible can metals come into their own. The limitation of the metal supply hinders other operations. The limit in the usable size of a vegetable or fiber rope with its poor ratio of weight to tensile strength is reached long before that of a modern steel cable. Oil drilling now reaches depths of 10,000 feet and more. A fiber rope of this length would break under its own weight; moreover, it could not resist the heat. The same principle applies to construction above ground. High structures can be built of stone and even of brick, as is shown by the pyramids, the Tower of Babel, the Chinese Wall, the Zikkurat, and other ancient monuments. But these mineral structures of antiquity, which were built with the aid of animate energy supported only by simple machines, represented unique products of their respective civilizations, each of which was capable of producing only one or a few. Some of them almost drained the resources of their makers. Such structures, therefore, were not representative. The typical structure of ancient civilization clearly reflects the limitations of both animate energy and organic matter. A wooden beam used in construction cannot extend beyond a certain length without undue loss of strength. This places a limit on many things—on the size of tools, of machines, of vehicles, of furnaces, of factories, etc. This limitation on the size and strength of organic matter in turn reacted unfavorably on the units of energy that could be employed. The number of oxen that can be effectively used to draw a load limits the load, but the size of the vehicle that can be constructed from wood also limits the number of oxen. Suppose the Romans could have mined coal without steam to modernize metal mining; the use of coal would still have been limited, for without metal they could not have built furnaces big and strong enough to keep the fury of combustion in check. Animate energy limits the

---

[15] Cf. U. B. Phillips, "The Economic Cost of Slave-holding in the Cotton Belt," *Political Science Quarterly*, June, 1903, vol. 20, no. 2, pp. 257-275.

choice of material and thus largely precludes the use of inanimate energy.[16]

An Example of Limitations. One of the best examples by which to show the limitations of organic matter is the wooden ship.[17] By about the seventeenth century the wooden ship, after slow evolution in size, strength, speed, etc., seemed to have reached the highest level of perfection possible under the limitations of organic matter, i.e., wood. In the British "ship of the line" no noticeable improvements appeared possible so long as ships were built of wood. The limitations of the organic manifested themselves in numerous ways. The length of the ship depends largely on the size of the rudder, for its size determines the power to maneuver the ship. The size of the rudder, in turn, depends on the size of the sternpost, the strategic piece of wood in which ribs or sides are anchored and to which the rudder is attached. The sternpost was a single block of wood fashioned out of the largest and strongest oak trees available. By their size, therefore, oak trees set a limit to the size of the sternpost, through it to the size of the rudder, and, in turn, through the latter to the length of the ship. Moreover, by their number, oak trees limited the size of the fleet. The admirals would clamor for more ships; Samuel Pepys, as Secretary of the Admiralty, would scour the land for sternposts. Again and again, plans for enlargement of the fleet and for campaigns had to be given up for the simple reason that there were not enough mature oak trees. Oaks were considered mature at about 90 years of age, and there was no way of speeding up the slow process of growth.

Masts were another limiting factor in ship construction. They were made from the tallest straight trees—generally firs, pines, and other conifers—that could be found from Volhynia to New England. Their size and strength materially affected both the size and the speed of the wooden ship.

Another bottleneck was the so-called compass wood, i.e., pieces of wood taken out of the crotches where branches came out of the tree trunk. These extra-strong pieces were needed to join vital parts, such as decks and sides. Trees were bandaged to increase artificially the numbers of compass pieces which a tree would yield.

As soon as iron and, later, steel, especially alloy steel, were substituted for wood, the size of the ship increased by leaps and bounds. Metal permitted the presence of fire and thus the use of steam. To be sure, metals too have their limits, but these are set much higher and to a degree can be pushed forward by scientific and technological improvements.

Energy, Materials, Accuracy, and Scale of Production

The miracle of modern production is to a large extent explained by the scale of modern mass production. This in turn rests on the interchangeability of parts, and this interchangeability depends on the accuracy with which parts are machined. Wood cannot be worked accurately enough to make wooden parts interchangeable. Accuracy that permits interchangeability is possible only with metal. Animate energy and wood go together, and inanimate energy goes with metals. The use of metals permits increasing accuracy. Here is an intriguing account of this development.

There was the watch, an intricate mechanism made up of springs, gears and small screws. And its effectiveness or ability to tell the time depended on the accurate duplication of the parts. We know a good timekeeper must be equipped with accurate gears having the required number of teeth, equally spaced. The cost and difficulty of making gears were the chief factors that prevented everyone's having a watch. At the beginning of the 18th century a machine was built by a Frenchman to automatically divide a circular metal blank into equal parts and cut properly shaped teeth. Along about the same period another French watchmaker devised another remarkable machine—a lathe for cutting the threads on small metal screws used in watches. It was also equipped with an attachment

---

[16] It may be mentioned that in some vegetable civilizations a somewhat mystical attitude toward metals develops. For example, metal plowshares are blamed for crop failures; and the blacksmith is a semilegendary character—feared, despised, and honored alike.

[17] See R. G. Albion, *Forests and Sea Power; the Timber Problem of the Royal Navy, 1652-1862,* Harvard University Press, Cambridge, 1926; also S. Colum Gilfillan, *The Sociology of Invention,* Follet Publishing Co., Chicago, 1935.

to turn tapered parts very similar to that used on modern machine tools. As a result of these new machines watches became more numerous.

Thus it was the French who with the aid of their clock and watch-making machines opened up a new era in manufacturing. Some of these ideas crossed the English Channel and were perfected and expanded in connection with an entirely different product—the steam engine.

In the early 18th century, when the French inventors were developing machines to make accurate watches, the English were faced with a shortage of mine labor. This was very important in a country having little wood for fuel. One of the difficulties in mining coal was pumping the water from the mines. In an effort to solve this problem Thomas Newcomen developed an atmospheric steam pumping engine, which utilized atmospheric pressure to move a piston which in turn operated the mine pump.

During the next fifty years many of these engines were built to pump out mines and the design remained essentially unchanged until a small model of a Newcomen engine fell into the hands of James Watt, a Scotch instrument maker. When he saw the model, Watt was struck with the idea of using steam at greater than atmospheric pressure to move the piston of the engine instead of condensing the steam under the piston and letting the smaller atmospheric pressure do the work as in the Newcomen engine.

He made several small models, proving to himself he was on the right track. But when he tried to build a full-size engine he came face to face with a production problem. He realized that to maintain the efficiency of his new steam engine the piston would have to fit the cylinder snugly to prevent the high-pressure steam from leaking by. He gave the job to a Mr. Smeaton who was recognized as one of the best mechanics in the country. Smeaton made a cylinder a foot and a half in diameter, but it was *three-eighths of an inch out of round,* which made it useless for holding the steam pressure when a piston was fitted to it.

However, another Englishman, John Wilkinson, came to his rescue with a new idea for guiding the tool to cut a more perfect circle—the boring bar principle so well known in production today. By this method they made a new cylinder that was only one-sixteenth of an inch eccentric and was

quite satisfactory. Step by step ingenious men were discovering the rewards of accuracy and uncovering new ways of achieving it. Thus the steam engine opened up a new source of power and its applications revolutionized the century-old methods of laborious hand work, at the same time providing more things for more people.[18]

Thus the shift from animate energy to inanimate energy meant the shift from organic to inorganic work materials and brought in its turn interchangeability of parts and the modern methods of mass production.

Energy and Speed of Production

One of the greatest advantages of the modern production process utilizing inanimate energy is the speed with which work can be done. A comparison between an ancient and a modern construction job drives home the advantages of speed. If we assume that the building of an Egyptian pyramid required the work of 50,000 slaves for twenty years, while a skyscraper of comparable size can be built by 5000 laborers in six months, the number of workers at a given moment is as 10 is to 1; but if the time element is taken into account, the ratio is 400 to 1. This means that it took approximately 400 times as much food to generate the man power that built the pyramid as it took to feed the workers who built the skyscraper. For Egyptian farmers to raise that surplus food over and above their own requirements was no small tax on their agricultural skill,[19] for whereas American agriculture enjoys the benefits of considerable support by inanimate energy, Egyptian agriculture suffered from its very dependence on animate energy. Both the pyramid and the skyscraper require considerable outside work and fixed investments: quarries, roads, rafts, derricks, etc., in Egypt; mines, mills, railroads, engines, machines, etc., in the United States. While the American equipment is infinitely larger and

---

[18] C. F. Kettering and Allen Orth, *America's Battle for Abundance, a Story of Mass Production,* General Motors Corporation, Detroit, pp. 12-14.

[19] In antiquity Egyptian agriculture was decidedly more seasonal than it is now. In so far as the building of pyramids took place during the

dormant season, the problem mentioned here solved itself to some extent. This consideration, however, does not detract from the validity of the case as illustrating the relative efficiency of animate and inanimate energy. For the transformation of the Egyptian agricultural system, see S. Strakosch, *Erwachende Agrarländer; Nationallandwirtschaft in Ägypten und im Sudan unter englischem Einfluss,* P. Parey, Berlin, 1910.

more complex than the Egyptian, it is also more efficient. Moreover, most of the American equipment is relatively permanent and versatile, that is to say, it is used to build many skyscrapers and numerous other objects, whereas most of the Egyptian equipment served solely the one task of building a particular pyramid. Thus it is an open question which construction job required more overhead—the pyramid or the skyscraper.

Finally, agricultural work is drawn out because of seasonal interruptions. In most areas of the earth where agriculture flourishes, more or less all the work comes to a standstill during the winter. Moreover, during the growing period weeks may go by during which man can do no more than watch nature take its course. But man and beast must live throughout the year, the equipment must be kept in condition. Thus for numerous reasons, the fixed charges or overhead costs in vegetable civilization, while not large in absolute amounts, are very considerable when expressed in proportion to the actual work performed with its aid.

Energy and Mobility

One of the most important uses of energy is locomotion—the moving of things and people and ideas from place to place. The lack of suitable and adequate energy condemns vegetable civilizations to do without locomotion beyond a very limited range. Transportation in vegetable civilizations is hopelessly inefficient. The inefficiency applies to the road, the vehicle, and the motive power. The energy required to transport heavy and bulky goods in wooden vehicles drawn by animals over poorly built roads is so great, and the food or feed consumption necessary to yield the energy is so large, that only short distances can be negotiated.[20] Primitive water transportation requires less energy per ton-mile than land transportation. Moreover, water transportation, utilizing the river currents or wind for its motive power, may be said to be partly emancipated from the

limitations of animate energy. It may suffer because of insufficient control over the inanimate energy used and therefore it may not be comparable to modern water transportation. Furthermore, being confined to rivers and bays and coastal waters, it can affect only small portions of an area. Yet the construction of the Imperial Canal which brought tribute rice from southern China to the capital of the north, avoiding the pirate-infested coastal waters, proves the importance which may be attached to inland water transportation even in vegetable civilizations.

Efficient land transportation, however, is essentially a product of the mechanical revolution: steam power, gas explosion, electricity, turbines, Diesel engines, dynamos, duraluminum, alloy steel, cement, machine-built concrete roads, railroads, automobiles, and airplanes—all these are products of the new age; they have made transportation what it is—cheap, swift, and efficient on land, by water, and in the air. The same holds true of communication. It is a commonplace to say that modern transportation and communication have completely changed the basis of civilization.

Their aid enables the mechanized civilization to beat the vegetable civilization at its own game, for they have made possible a fuller utilization of solar radiation by agriculture. Farmers whom the mechanical revolution has endowed with mobility can move to the sunshine even if it is far from market and from water. Power, water, and fertilizers can be brought to them and their products can be shipped to distant markets. Thus farms can spread out and their broad acres can drink in volumes of sunshine, while the peasants of immobile vegetable civilizations must huddle together on small garden patches and produce their crops by adding much labor to some sunshine instead of much sunshine to some labor. Mechanized mobility, moreover, has made possible the cultivation of the great steppes, the granaries of the modern world. They are steppes because their distance from the sea or the intervening mountain barriers shut off the climatic influences of the ocean; and hence they are essentially inaccessible while transportation depends on animate energy. Without the railroad and the steamship, the great steppes could

---

[20] Cf. O. E. Baker, "Transportation in China," *Annals of the American Academy of Political and Social Science*, November, 1930, pp. 160-161; also W. H. Mallory, *China, Land of Famine*, Special Publication No. 6, American Geographical Society, New York, 1926, pp. 29-35, especially p. 33.

not have gained their present significance in world food production.

Energy and Population Increase[21]

Above all, mobility spares the agriculture of the machine civilization one of the worst curses of vegetable civilization. It cuts through the fatal connection between food supply and birth rate which was the fundamental weakness of ancient civilization. The fertility of a given piece of soil, the blessing of good climate —ample rain and sunshine, each in its time— can be utilized only by raising food. In China most food must be consumed where it is produced. Thus, immobility condemns a vegetable civilization to crowding—unless the basic natural advantages are to remain unused. But the food supply of a mechanized economy tied up with the world market by modern exchange is mobile. It does not need to be consumed on the spot; it can move thousands of miles to distant markets. Its worth to the producer through exchange can be turned into innumerable forms, none of which need to promote population increase. Mechanized agriculture, therefore, is not only efficient in terms of per-man output, but also mobile. This mobility, however, applies not only to the agriculture of industrial countries but to their manufacturing industries as well. As a result, foreign trade and the export of capital assume increasing importance and thus broaden the resource basis of mobilized economy. We see, therefore, that the energy basis is truly the foundation of a civilization. It determines the choice of materials which can be utilized, it sets a definite limit to the size of performance, it governs the degree of mobility and, in general, controls the arts, societal and technical, and through them shapes the institutions, material and nonmaterial. In short, it largely determines the type of civilization and the resource pattern on which it rests.

Drawbacks to Use of Inanimate Energy

What has been said so far has all been in favor of the modern resource pattern. Now we must turn to the reverse side of the picture.

[21] The relationship between resource patterns and population trends is more fully discussed in chap. 8. The remarks here should be interpreted in the light of the fuller discussion in that chapter.

For where there is light there must also be shadow; no advantage can be gained except at a price. The advantage of the modern system can be summarized as superior efficiency. The price paid for that advantage is security and permanency. As was pointed out above, the ancient resource pattern depends primarily on animate energy and hence on current solar radiation. The modern resource pattern is built around stored-up solar radiation—coal, petroleum, natural gas—a fund which is used up as it is used. Current solar radiation, on the other hand, is a flow, a perpetual succession of self-renewable supply units.

A civilization based on a fund of exhaustible resources cannot be permanent; it is necessarily a passing phenomenon in human history. A civilization based on a flow of renewable resources may be permanent. But fortunately inanimate energy can be derived not only from the fund of stored-up solar energy, but also from the flow of current solar energy. The ancient process which through photosynthesis produces plants which are used as food or feed to generate animate energy is not the only way in which current solar radiation can be utilized. Sunshine can also be turned into inanimate energy, either directly by the use of mirrors or indirectly by windmills, by power plants, by water turbines, etc. The ancient system depends one-sidedly on the animate energy drawn from sunshine, and the modern places undue reliance on the inanimate energy drawn from fossil fuels; the system of the future should utilize both and supplement them by turning sunshine into inanimate energy, thus reducing the strain on fossil fuels and postponing the day of their exhaustion.

The modern resource pattern lacks not only permanency but also security. On the one hand, the mechanized Occident shares with vegetable civilizations the dangers of natural disasters— floods, droughts, insect pests, etc.—although their frequency and rigor may have been reduced. On the other hand, both the complexity and the internationalization which characterize the modern economy give rise to new dangers. A modern industrial civilization may be compared to a high pyramid of cultural and institutional development, erected on a relatively narrow basis of natural resources. It is daring, lofty, impressive. As long as the system of civilization runs smoothly its splendor is dazzling; but at the first shock of an earthquake it topples over. A vegetable civilization, on the other hand, is like a giant squatting on the ground in sodden safety. Napoleon could not conquer Russia, neither could the Germans or the Allies. The decisive defeat of the Russians at the hands of the Japanese caused hardly a ripple in the huge ocean of humanity spread over the enormous area that was the Russian Empire. China still carries on after thousands of years, long after the proud structures of Greece and Rome[22] have crumbled to dust.

However, insecurity is not an inherent defect of the modern resource pattern; it is incidental rather than basic, cultural rather than natural, institutional rather than technological; most of it springs from its pecuniary aspects, which are insufficiently adapted to the resource system. Money economy and the capitalistic spirit are institutional developments which the use of inanimate energy has greatly stimulated, but they probably are not the only institutional pattern which inanimate energy can produce. In their present make-up, they represent an undigested mixture of ancient tradition and modern developments. The troubles of today, therefore, are largely brought on by machines, but they are not the necessary results of inanimate energy.

[22] Both Roman and Greek civilizations were attempts to build high commercial and political superstructures on relatively narrow resource bases which were composed largely of vegetable matter and animate energy, though reinforced by minerals.

BIBLIOGRAPHY

See the bibliography at the end of Chapter 6.

Finally, modern machine civilization may be unduly dynamic, just as the ancient pattern is unduly static. One system suffers from lack of change; the other, from too much and too rapid change. Up to a certain point, scientific progress must proceed at an accelerated rate. It must expand cumulatively, for each invention gives rise to numerous others. The capitalistic spirit which subordinates all else—or almost all else—to the maximization of profit and its twin spirit pleonexy, drives the modern production system at ever higher speed to ever greater performance—without rationally appraising the cost of speed and the worth of superefficiency. A purely pecuniary appraisal of speed is not an adequate appraisal; social and institutional implications must also be considered. Moreover, it is uncertain whether our pecuniary appraisal is faultless and whether the cost of obsolescence has been properly taken into account.

To sum up, civilizations resting on the modern resource pattern of inanimate energy-metal-science-capital are highly efficient as systems of physical production and therefore, theoretically at least, they are capable of freeing man from drudgery and of giving him leisure and wealth, the basis of higher spiritual development and the larger life. The system, as now developed, places a one-sided emphasis on the fund resources of inanimate energy, and therefore it cannot aspire to permanency unless that emphasis is shifted. The system, as at present constituted, lacks security and tends toward undue haste.

Chapter 6

ENERGY EXPENDITURE AND WELL-BEING

General vs. Close Correlation

That the people of the United States with an alleged per capita daily output of energy 34.2 times as great as that of China are better off than the Chinese people is to be expected. That there exists a general positive correlation between energy expenditure and wealth or well-being[1] few will be inclined to question. In general, it is true that to consume more one must produce more, and production involves energy expenditure. There is something almost axiomatic about this causal nexus between work and wealth. But to conclude from this simple logic that, because the per capita energy expenditure of one people is 34.2 times as great as that of another, the first people are 34.2 times as well off as the other, is something else again. In other words, it is one thing to concede a *general* correlation but quite a different thing to concede an *accurate* correlation. In fact, there are weighty reasons for holding that there cannot be an accurate correlation between energy expenditure and well-being. These reasons relate to some fundamental facts, not only of energy economy, but of resources in general, and are therefore developed here in some detail.[2]

Deficiencies of Statistical Treatment

If one takes T. T. Read's tabulation (Table 5.1) as a basis of such an analysis, it becomes clear that the coverage of energy sources is incomplete. For one thing, not all contributions of biotic energy are included, but only those manifested through muscular energy. Their omission is apt to penalize the peoples who still rely mainly on the animate energy of living organisms and are backward in the use of mechanical energy. People like the Swedish,[3]

---

[1] Terms such as wealth, welfare, well-being, etc., are very hard to define. So far as this analysis is concerned, any *reasonable* interpretation of these terms would appear satisfactory. One must be particularly careful not to "load" the definition with elements which favor one type of civilization as against another.

[2] See Erich W. Zimmermann, "Output of Work and Economic Well-being," *American Economic Review*, June, 1934, pp. 239-249.

[3] Actually in Table 5.1, Norway ranks third, right after the United States, with 11.80 horsepower-

who derive much wealth from forests, and the Norwegians, who similarly rely on fishing and whaling as important sources of income, may appear poorer than they actually are. In other words, the contribution to wealth and well-being made by solar radiation with or without the assistance of mechanical energy is insufficiently covered. It varies widely with both natural and cultural conditions prevailing in each country. Similarly, various chemical energies, especially those attributable to acids, solvents, mordents, fertilizers, explosives, etc., are not considered. They may constitute a minor factor in the total energy scheme, but in specific instances may noticeably affect well-being.

The entire measurement of energy on which Read's tabulation is based is necessarily mechanical. There just is no statistical device for qualitative appraisal. A pound of coal is treated the same whether it is burned in an open grate with a conversion coefficient of perhaps 1 percent, or in an ultramodern gas-combustion turbine with a coefficient of possibly 25 or 30. A barrel of oil is treated alike whether it is burned as fuel oil under a boiler or converted into high-octane gasoline. A gallon of gasoline is treated alike whether it is expended in a highly efficient modern engine or a ramshackle contraption of ancient vintage. No distinction is made between the work performance of a coolie pulling a ricksha and that of a "coal miner" manipulating a 1150-ton, $750,000 excavator—or of an Edison or an Einstein for that matter. Each man is given a rating of a fraction of a horsepower reflecting the average human capacity to do physical work unaided by robots or mechanical brains. The highly skilled laborer is put on a par with "the man with the hoe." Surely, the quality of human work performance and the contribution to well-being vary sufficiently among the peoples of the earth to justify questioning the possibility of there being a close correlation between mechanically measured energy and well-being. Professor Read is fully aware of these difficulties.

_____

hours per capita per day. This surprisingly high rank may be due to large amounts of hydroelectricity generated, much of it on foreign account (foreign-controlled nitrogen and electrometallurgical concerns).

Obstacles to Close Correlation

Up to this point, only the adequacy of the statistical basis for testing the correlation between energy expenditure, wealth, and well-being has been questioned. Now it will be shown that, even if the most complete and perfect measurement of energy expenditure were possible, no accurate or even close correlation between energy expenditure and wealth or well-being could be expected; fundamental realities preclude such a correlation.

Chapter 1 brought out the basic fact that a sharp distinction must be made between gross resources and net resources, net resources being defined as those available for the promotion of real wealth, or well-being, after resistance had been overcome. Well-being is not directly related to gross resources, but to net resources. Nations differ widely as to the portion of their gross resources which must be devoted to overcoming resistances. Countries differ in the _configuration_ or shape of their territory and that difference greatly affects the resistances, especially spatial resistances, to be overcome. Other things being equal, the ideal shape, i.e., the shape offering least resistance, is the circle. Again other things being equal, the more a country's configuration approaches the circle, the higher tends to be the ratio of net resources to gross resources, and the greater the contribution a given amount of energy makes to well-being. The shape of France is uniquely favorable, approaching that of the circle. Her overhead, especially the transportation overhead, is apt to be lower relative to work performance than that of countries whose shape is less favorable. The shape of Chile departs far from the ideal configuration. So does that of the effective portion of Canada—the Canadian ecumene—the narrow strip running along the international border. Chile has the advantage of a long coastline which Canada lacks.

This leads to another vital point: _the ratio of effective territory to total territory._ In most of western and central Europe and in the United States the two overlap. Virtually the entire national territory is occupied and forms a solid basis for the national economy. This is not the case in most other parts of the earth. Brazil is a vast mass of land, only localized areas of which are occupied. Any effort to tie these clusters into a single social economy meets with enormous resistance, causing large energy leaks so to speak. The same situation prevails to varying degrees in most countries of Latin America; it is perhaps even more pronounced in the Soviet Union, in most of the rest of Asia and in Africa, but probably nowhere more strikingly than in Australia.

Furthermore, countries differ greatly in *population density*. This affects the expenditures of energy required to establish "the civilizing contacts." The United States with a population density of about 50 people per square mile devotes 27.7 percent of the total energy consumed to transportation.[4] A higher population density or a different geographical distribution of the population may well affect the energy requirements for transportation.

Topography is another important element affecting energy needs. If welfare were a direct and accurate function of energy expenditure, one wonders how much better off we would be if the Rocky Mountains were twice as high. Energy expenditure depends much on speed. The correlation between speed and welfare is very complex. Much speed spells a purely useless expenditure of energy. The manner in which the bulky earth materials like coal and ores, limestone, clay, etc., are distributed over the map greatly affects what may be called instrumental energy expenditure.

One of the most vital factors affecting the relationship between energy expenditure and well-being is the *age composition of the population*. Age composition affects the number of those who contribute to the social product as well as the numbers among whom this product is divided. Well-being is apt to suffer when "the cake" made by the few must be cut into too many slices.

Nations differ in their *outlook upon security* and therefore in their views regarding the diversion of effort from wealth to safety. Well-being is apt to be greatest, relative to total energy expenditure, in countries which, because of location or for other reasons, feel most

secure and hence must divert a minimum of energy to the "unproductive" task of armaments and military preparedness. Similarly, homogeneous social groups in which there is relatively little tension and cause for civil strife are bound to enjoy a more favorable ratio of energy expenditure to well-being than less fortunate ones. Latin America is a region of high social tension. Her population is sharply divided into racial groups, economic classes, and social strata, a state of affairs which diverts much energy expenditure away from well-being toward sterile friction and obnoxious heat.

Civilizations adjust themselves to the *scarcity* no less than to the abundance *of energy*. As was brought out before (p. 64), inanimate energy mobilizes; it makes people foot-loose, gives them *wanderlust*, puts them on wheels, makes them spread out, and in general encourages them to arrange their affairs on the basis of cheap and abundant energy. In the United States much energy goes to turn the wheels of our modern motor caravans. The dancing squirrel in the revolving cage also generates much energy; but where does it go? The volume of energy used is no guarantee or dependable measure of the task accomplished. Vice versa, peoples having none or only a scanty supply of inanimate energy adjust themselves to this fact by avoiding motion as much as possible. The phrase "the sedentary masses of southeast Asia" is indeed very apt. These masses of Chinese and Hindus are sedentary because they more or less lack the mobilizing energy of coal, oil, gas, and water power. Only by careful scrutiny of the subtle ways in which sharply contrasting civilizations operate can the relationship between energy expenditure and well-being be probed intelligently and fruitfully. Without such careful scrutiny wholly wrong conclusions are likely to be drawn from energy statistics.

The very *spirit of civilization* is affected by the amount and nature of available energy, and that spirit more than any other factor determines what energy expenditure means in terms of human well-being. In North America probably no other factor more directly affects well-being than does the spirit of freedom. As Haslam aptly remarks: "It has been said that morale is to matériel in war as three to one.

---

[4] Even more—28.4 percent of all fuel energy consumed—is applied to space heating, a function of climate in which again countries differ widely. These figures were calculated by Eugene E. Ayres; see his "Major Sources of Energy," a paper read during the 28th annual meeting of the American Petroleum Institute, November 9, 1948, p. 142.

In production I think spirit is to raw materials as three to one. Human energy is the keystone of the energy arch. We cannot leave it out of our logistics."[5] Indeed, "It is the spirit that quickeneth," and measurement of the spirit is something statisticians have not yet mastered.

These diverse lines of argument, far from exhausting the fullness of reality, have, it is hoped, made clear why the relationship between energy and well-being is not and cannot be a straight and simple one, but in the nature of things is bound to be highly complex. The energy rays pass through innumerable prisms before they achieve their end result—human well-being. They pass through different prisms in different lands. The net effect is influenced by the subtle forces which we like to sum up by the simple word "history." As one ponders its effects, he comes to realize the vital importance of the intangibles and the imponderables.

Energy, Exchange, and Well-Being

There remain to be discussed several specific considerations which militate against a close direct correlation between energy expenditure and well-being. The first consideration concerns the effect of exchange—trade, especially foreign trade—on the correlation here being analyzed. The varying effects of exchange on value were mentioned earlier. In a market economy the price of goods is affected not merely by the amount of work or energy that goes into making them, but also by their relative scarcity or abundance and the relative intensity of demand. It may take twice as much energy to produce an 18-million-bale cotton crop as a 9-million-bale crop, but the smaller crop under ordinary free market conditions may well sell for more than the larger crop. The extra energy put into doubling the crop may bankrupt the producers, whereas careful adjustment of supply to demand, involving the curtailment of energy expenditure, may bring great wealth. Much of the science of economics deals with this complex interaction between supply, demand, price, gross revenues, net profits, etc. Any student of principles of economics knows that this reaction does not follow straight lines, but curves, many different curves. "The point of diminishing returns" is one of the best-known terms in all economic theory.

Energy, Capital, and Well-Being

In the modern world only a fraction of energy expenditure applies directly to the satisfaction of human wants or constitutes a direct contribution to human welfare. As was stressed before, ours is a roundabout, indirect way of producing. To satisfy hunger we do not climb a palm and cut out a coconut; we work in a hundred-million-dollar steelworks and spend our wages or salaries in stores where are sold the products of machines, hauled by railroads and motor trucks. At every point we meet capital equipment.

Capital equipment, much like culture, is the product of slow accretion. The expenditure made today may not bring a return until years later. Similarly, in a capitalistic world the well-being one enjoys today is, at least in part, the result of capital expenditures made years, perhaps decades, ago. People may coast along on the performance of their forefathers and, vice versa, they may lay the groundwork for the future well-being of generations yet unborn.

In such a world of roundabout capitalistic production where one's well-being today may result from someone else's energy expenditure ten or fifty years ago, and where one's energy expenditure today may have no effect on his own generation beyond increasing its toil and sacrifice but may contribute to the well-being of future generations,[6] statistics on energy expenditure for a single year are at least partially irrelevant to the measurement of the energy spent and the well-being enjoyed in that year. Whatever correlation exists between energy expenditure and well-being can be discovered only by the perusal of statistical records covering periods sufficiently long to encompass these slow processes of capital building and capital use.

---

[5] R. T. Haslam, vice-president of Standard Oil Company (New Jersey) in "World Energy and World Peace," address delivered at Massachusetts Institute of Technology Symposium on Logistics of Peace, June 12, 1948, pp. 13-14.

[6] The case of the Soviet Union, engaged in enlarging and improving her capital equipment at the expense of contemporary well-being in the hope of future well-being, comes to mind.

Energy, International Trade, Foreign Investments, and Well-Being

Just as a single year is an inadequate unit of time for the measurement of effects of energy expenditure on well-being, so a single nation is an inadequate unit of space. Nations exchange the products of their energy expenditure in international trade. Furthermore, some nations make foreign investments, other nations receive them. One speaks of lending and borrowing nations. International loans constitute voluntary contributions made by one nation, at the expense of its own current well-being, to the current well-being of another nation in the expectation that interest and amortization will more than compensate by a future reversal of benefits. At present, the United States is sending billions of dollars' worth of goods, chiefly capital equipment, to Europe and other parts of the world; this rep-resents a current expense to her domestic welfare but is made in the hope of future compensation, perhaps in the form of peace or of aid in war.

Moreover, in some countries much energy expenditure is made on foreign account. The oil fields of Venezuela, the Near East, and Indonesia come to mind, as do the copper, lead, zinc, and many other mines in Latin America and Africa.

The more one follows the intricacies of modern global economy and the more realistically he pictures its manifold processes and relationships, the clearer becomes the realization that there can be no direct correlation between one year's energy expenditure in one individual nation and the state of well-being in that nation in the same year. But it should be equally clear that there is no greater force promoting well-being than energy expenditure.

BIBLIOGRAPHY

Ayres, E., "Major Sources of Energy," paper read before the annual meeting of the American Petroleum Institute, Chicago, 1948.

Ayres, E., "The Fuel Problem," *Scientific American,* December, 1949.

Bush, V., *Endless Horizons,* Washington, Public Affairs Press, 1946.

Bush, V., *Modern Arms and Free Men,* New York, Simon and Schuster, 1949.

Darrow, K. K., *Atomic Energy,* New York, Wiley, 1948.

Davis, H. M., *Energy Unlimited,* New York, Rinehart, 1947.

Gamow, G., *Atomic Energy in Cosmic and Human Life,* New York, Macmillan, 1946.

Gibson, A. H., *Natural Sources of Energy,* New York, Macmillan, 1913.

Hammond, J. L., and Hammond, B., *The Rise of Modern Industry,* New York, Harcourt, Brace, 5th ed., 1937.

Hawley, G. G., and Leifson, S. W., *Atomic Energy in War and Peace,* New York, Reinhold, 1945.

Henderson, F., *The Economic Consequences of Power Production,* London, George Allen and Unwin, 1931.

Institut für Konjunkturforschung, *Die Energiewirtschaft der Welt in Zahlen,* Special Issue No. 19, Berlin, 1930.

Lilienthal, D., *This I Do Believe,* New York, Harper, 1949.

National Resources Committee, *Energy Resources and National Policy,* Washington, 1939.

Rothman, S. C. (ed.), *Constructive Uses of Atomic Energy,* New York, Harper, 1949.

Smith, E. S. C., and others, *Applied Atomic Power,* New York, Prentice-Hall, 1946.

Tutin, J. (ed.), *Atomic Energy Yearbook,* New York, Prentice-Hall, 1949.

United Nations, Committee 3, Atomic Energy Commission, *A First Report on the Scientific and Technical Aspects of the Problem of Control of Atomic Energy,* Lake Success, 1946.

U. S. Atomic Energy Commission, *Semiannual Report,* Washington, 1947.

U. S. Atomic Energy Commission, *Atomic Energy Development, 1947-1948,* Washington, 1948.

U. S. Atomic Energy Commission and U. S. Geological Survey, *Prospecting for Uranium,* Washington, 1949.

U. S. Department of State, *The International Control of Atomic Energy, Growth of a Policy,* Department of State Publication 2702, Washington, 1947.

U. S. Department of State, *The International Control of Atomic Energy, Policy at the Crossroads,* Department of State Publication 3161, Washington, 1948.

U. S. Department of State, *Energy Resources of the World* (directed by N. B. Guyol), Washington, 1949.

U. S. Department of State, Lilienthal Board, *A Report on the International Control of Atomic Energy*, Washington, 1946.

Winne, H. A., and Prentice, B. R., "Application of Atomic Energy to Industry," in A. B. Parsons (ed.), *Seventy-five Years of Progress in the Mineral Industry, 1871-1946*, American Institute of Mining and Metallurgical Engineers, New York, 1947.

Chapter 7

NATURE AND RESOURCES

SOME PARADOXES OF NATURE
Nature, Friend and Foe

So great are the blessings which nature bestows upon man that he is apt to forget, at times, the hardships she brings and the terrors she holds. The deadly cobra is no less natural than the honeybee or the nightingale, the destructive hurricane no less natural than the useful trade wind, the tidal wave no less natural than the gentle rain that wets the good earth or the waterfall that drives the turbines. Nature made the fertile soil of the prairies and the plains no less than the barren, though rich, soil of the desert. Man must take the good with the bad. He strives to lessen the hard blows and make the best of the friendly help. When one thinks of natural resources, he must not forget that there are also natural resistances.

Nature, Niggardly and Bountiful

Nature appears to man as both niggardly and bountiful. She has few free gifts to offer, though these few are priceless—air to breathe, water to drink, a place to rest, friendly climate, fertile soil, game, and so forth. But free gifts of nature support only small numbers of peo-

ple. As the earth's population increased and man spread from the most favored to less favored spots of natural endowment, the impression of niggardliness superseded that of bounteousness. But that was largely his own fault. For while nature offers few free gifts to the beggar and yields little to the brute earth-robber, she proves bountiful indeed to the strong, the clever, the persevering, and the bold. Her real treasures are deeply hidden and well guarded by obstacles—resistances. Nature rewards intelligent search and wise effort with a bounty that makes her free gifts appear miserly, valuable though they are.

Nature, Constant and Changing

If nature is thought of as the universe, it may be considered constant. As was stressed earlier, nature in that sense is the topic of natural science. The social scientist is concerned not with the totality of the physical universe, but with the meaning of nature for man, with that ever-changing portion of nature which is known to man and which affects his existence. That portion is both expanding and contracting. It expands in response to increase in knowledge and improvement of the arts. Nature reveals herself gradually to man, but no faster than he can learn.

The significance of this expansion may be driven home by means of the concept of phantom resources. Coal may be used to illustrate the meaning of that term. Let us assume that in 1900 the United States had a coal reserve of 3 trillion tons, that in that year 7 pounds of coal was necessary to generate one kilowatt-hour, and that other uses of coal were equally inefficient; that by 1950 the art of coal utilization advanced to the point where one pound of coal generates one kilowatt-hour and that other uses of coal similarly advanced in efficiency; and that during half a century the United States used up 20 billion tons of coal. Since coal is valued primarily as a source of energy and since its value as such has enhanced sevenfold, we may envisage the original 3-trillion-ton pile expanding to a phantom pile of about 20 trillion tons, an accretion which greatly overcompensates the physical loss through use and abuse. This idea is shown pictorially in Fig. 7.1.

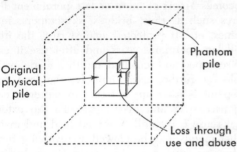

FIG. 7.1. Shrinking Weight and Volume vs. Expanding Utility of Resources.

This way of reasoning applies not only to fuels but to metals and other substances as well. If today a horsepower can be harnessed by means of one pound of metal, whereas a multiple was necessary fifty or a hundred years ago, here again the phantom pile appears.

These examples illustrate nature's expanding availability to man traceable to the improvement of the arts, advancing techniques, and science. The effect of discoveries can be similarly envisaged.

But nature's contributions are also subject to contraction. Minerals, especially fuels, are used up, dissipated in use. Others are rendered useless by obsolescence. Still others are damaged by man beyond repair, mainly because of ignorance, especially of the laws of ecology.

SIGNIFICANT ASPECTS OF NATURE
Distribution of the Natural Endowment

The natural materials and energies which man can utilize at the present stage of his development are largely confined to the earth itself and to that minute portion of solar radiation which reaches and is retained by the earth. The natural endowment is distributed very unevenly over this planet. First-class fertile soil is found in only a few spots, and so-called arable land makes up about 40 percent of the land surface exclusive of the polar regions. The major useful minerals are even more unevenly distributed. Climate varies widely. Topographical features add to the diversity of the picture, a diversity that applies to both resources and resistances.

The impact of this diversity of the natural endowment on man is clearly reflected in the uneven distribution of the people of the earth and in the wide differences in their economic development and living standards. While there is a close correlation between natural features and human achievements, the connection between the two is not one of direct causation, but a highly complex interaction involving the gamut of factors and forces which make up the history of human civilization.

Frequency of Occurrence of Resources[1]

Not only is the natural environment distributed very unevenly over the earth; its distribution embodies wide variations in both amount and frequency of occurrence of resources. On the basis of frequency of occurrence, the aspects of nature may be classified as follows: (1) ubiquities (occurring everywhere, e.g., oxygen in the air); (2) commonalties (occurring in many places, e.g., tillable soil); (3) rarities[2] (occurring in few places,

---

[1] This and the next section are based largely on Erich W. Zimmermann, "Resources," in Walter E. Spahr (ed.), *Economic Principles and Problems*, Farrar & Rinehart, New York, 3rd ed., 1936, vol. 1, pp. 167-171.

[2] "Rarity" is used in preference to "scarcity" because of the meaning the latter term has in economics. Things may be very plentiful but still be scarce in the economic sense.

e.g., tin); (4) uniquities (occurring in one place, e.g., commercial cryolite).

Frequency of occurrence is significant for several reasons. For one thing, production processes generally involve a combination of materials—for example, coal and iron. Each may occur so frequently that, by itself, it may be considered a commonalty, but usable combinations of both may be quite rare.

Furthermore, a distinction is necessary between physical presence and availability. In a competitive price economy for example, only the lowest-cost resource or resource combination may be used.

Another necessary distinction is that between absolute and relative rarity. For example, in the absolute sense the known supply of tin is extremely limited, whereas aluminum is very common. But aluminum is relatively rare at present because current practice, determined primarily by cost of recovery and market price, exploits only rich deposits of this metal.

Finally, rarity itself varies in its effects. Rarity of a vitally important substance is of much greater concern than is rarity of a dispensable luxury. Another aspect of rarity involves the relative ease with which common substances may be substituted for rare ones. For example, the rarity of aluminum is less significant for the kitchen utensil industry than for the airplane industry because the unusual lightness of this metal makes its use essential for airplane parts.

Flow and Fund Resources

The exhaustibility or permanency of resources must also be considered in connection with the frequency of their occurrence. Rarity of a resource which is self-renewable is likely to create far less serious problems than is rarity of an exhaustible resource. Thus a region may have sunshine only during relatively few periods each year, but during those periods every year the sunshine is available in undiminished amounts. A region that has small coal resources and must draw on them at the rate of 1 percent a year is in an infinitely more precarious position than a region that has water power available for its energy requirements.

Coal is a typical fund resource, water power a typical flow resource (see Fig. 4.1). The sup-

ply of coal is exhausted through use, whereas water power ordinarily is self-renewable. Other flow resources are monsoon winds, regularly recurring rainfall, and virgin forests in the absence of such unfavorable forces as natural leaching, forest fires, avalanches, etc. In general, all ecological relationships are of the flow variety, if undisturbed and subjected to no cataclysmic changes. They remain dependable resources so long as man is content with exploiting the exhaustible annual increment without interfering with the forces directing their formation. Overcutting of timber stands may affect the permanency of timber, soil, and water resources. Similarly, in many parts of the earth soil fertility under natural conditions is a self-renewable flow resource. But if depleted by continuous cultivation of plants which make heavy demands on certain of its chemicals, the soil will no longer be a self-renewable resource; it will become a wasting resource.

Not all fund resources are exhaustible; some are revolving. Most coal is burned and therefore disappears from view. Most iron, however, is used in the form of steel or cast iron and becomes a part of more or less permanent fixtures such as rails, bridges, skyscrapers, machines, etc. If protected against rust, the iron will last for many years and after use it can be scrapped and remelted and thus made available for further use. Similarly, the lead put in paint is used up; but that in batteries can be used over and over again. To the extent that reuse is possible, iron and lead and many other metals may be viewed as revolving fund resources.

"Silted" or "Choked" Flow Resources

Flow resources resemble a stream; and just as a stream can be silted up by sand, mud, and detritus, so can flow resources become "silted" or "choked." The forest when properly managed can yield an endless stream of products; when "put on a sustained-yield basis" it is a flow resource. But when abused by overcutting or otherwise mismanaged, the flow of products dwindles to a mere trickle and it becomes "silted" or "choked" up. The hydrologic cycle from ocean to cloud to rain to river to ocean is one of the most important flow resources extant. Abuse and mismanagement, such as the removal of forest cover and other vegetation essential to the proper functioning of that cycle, will cause it to slow down, turn haltingly, and finally come to a stop—another example of a "silted" flow resource. Entire civilizations have been destroyed by abuse and mismanagement that allowed their vital flow resources to become silted or choked up.

However, as was pointed out in an earlier chapter, the danger of the early exhaustion of fossil fuels is being recognized and a shift from fund to flow sources of industrial energy is definitely planned. Whether man can muster the requisite ingenuity to carry out this ambitious project remains to be seen. Informed persons are hopeful.

Animate and Inanimate Energy, Organic and Inorganic Matter

The division of energy into animate and inanimate was fully discussed in Chapter 4. Closely related to it is the division of matter, living and dead. So important is this division that one may refer to it as the *basic dualism of nature.*

The division into matter, living and dead, is related to, but not identical with, the division into organic and inorganic matter. Carbon is the element of life; there is no life without carbon. But, under special circumstances, carbon is preserved in the fossil fuels. Organic matter includes both living organisms and their derivatives, as well as the dead fuels.

Primary and Secondary Aspects of Nature

One may distinguish between primary or original aspects of nature, i.e., free gifts of nature, and secondary or derived aspects, i.e., aspects which become available for use by man as a result of improvements made by him— improvements in nature as well as in man himself. These improvements are called culture. Secondary or derived natural aspects are therefore, strictly speaking, natural-cultural resources. Nature may provide the substance or energies, but culture renders possible their use by man.

Similarly one may make a distinction between primary or original natural resistances— e.g., catastrophes such as hurricanes, earthquakes, volcanic eruptions, tidal waves, floods, etc., and disease, plant pests, poisonous plants and animals, etc.—and secondary or derived

natural resistances, i.e., those that are the result of human interference with or impact on nature. The latter may be properly referred to as natural-cultural resistances.

Direct and Indirect Factors

Natural resources and resistances can be further subdivided on the basis of the directness of their relation to the processes of production and consumption. Thus one may distinguish between the resources that function directly as factors of production—such as soil, coal, wood, animals, etc.—and climate, topography, and location or conditioning factors which affect the speed and general efficiency of the production process much as a catalyst affects a chemical reaction. The same distinction can be made in the case of resistances. One may speak of direct obstacles and indirect handicaps. Moreover, both conditioning factors and indirect handicaps, like production factors and direct obstacles, can be subdivided into primary or original and secondary or derived.

Summary

The entire first column of Table 1.1 constitutes a good summary, in outline form, of this survey of nature's role in the resource-creating process.

LAND AND "LAND"
Changing Role of Land

The earth is divided into land and water. Land in this sense consists of the continents, the islands, and the polar regions—in short, the surface of the earth, terra firma. It is used by man chiefly in the following ways:

1. As situs, standing room, room in which to move, sites on which to build shelter, factories, villages, cities, and roads.
2. As the habitat of wild fauna and flora.
3. As the source of agricultural (including pastoral and forest) products, as soil, the premier agency for the transmutation of matter, the recipient of solar radiation and of rainfall and other climatic forces, the laboratory for photosynthesis.
4. As the source of minerals, both surface and subsoil, used in manifold ways.

For countless ages, until the coming of the power-driven machine, efforts to utilize nature were largely, almost entirely, confined to the surface of the earth. Fishing was confined to rivers, lakes, or coastal waters. Land was definitely a two-dimensional concept. Its most useful manifestation was soil, crop-bearing and animal-supporting soil.

Under these circumstances, it was natural to identify natural resources in general with land. For did not the overwhelming majority of the people engage in agriculture and therefore depend on the land, in the ordinary sense of the word, for their living? Land in the commonly accepted meaning of surface, soil, etc., was the mouthpiece, as it were, through which nature spoke, the orifice of "the horn of plenty" through which she poured her gifts. If the climate was favorable, its effects on man were felt and measured in soil fertility, in the volume of crops, in the supply of feed available for herds. Likewise, the advantages of cheap water transportation, and of expanding commerce dependent thereon, were realized on the river bank and the coast—in short, on land. Thus land area, measured in acres or square miles, was an adequate indicator of man's control over natural resources in general, and it continued to be so used long after conditions had changed.

Feudalism, a system of political control and economic institutions prevailing widely during the agrarian stages of history, rested on and was built around landholding. The majority of men were mere appendages of the land, and landholding determined political power, social status, and economic well-being.

Two-Dimensional and Three-Dimensional Land

The fuller use of inanimate energy rendered necessary increasing drafts on subsoil mineral reserves for both fuels and harnessing metals. The mechanical revolution, therefore, necessarily brought into use strata of the earth which previously had been beyond the reach of man. The subsurface was made to yield its wealth both of fossil fuels, the sources of inanimate energy itself, and of the metals required for the application and control of this new energy. Moreover, man pushed the frontiers of exploitation upward as well. The air became a source of nitrogen; sunshine itself could be more fully used; radioactivity was discovered; and the energy of moving, especially of falling, water came to be exploited in different ways

and hence more fully. Generalizing, one might say that man pushed the exploitation of land vertically, both downward and upward. Land thus ceased to be identical with surface, with a thin layer of soil or surface minerals. It no longer was a two-dimensional concept; it spread out into the third dimension, to say nothing of the fourth dimension of the modern physicist. Its close identification with agriculture and animal husbandry ended. The concept came to include minerals, especially coal, petroleum, iron, copper, and similar energy and machine resources. Since minerals have gained a disproportionately great importance relative to the areas exploited, the units of surface area —acres, square miles, etc.—have lost in value as dependable measures of the natural endowment.

Economic Terminology

Unit 3 is devoted to the study of the trinity of nature, man, and culture. There is a similar trilogy of terms in economic theory—land, labor, and capital. While these terms, as used in traditional economic theory, correspond rather closely to nature, man, and culture as used in this analysis of resources, the two sets of terms are by no means identical. The difference stems mainly from the general approach followed in traditional economic theory and in the present analysis. Traditional economic theory, especially the part that deals with the agents of production—land, labor, capital—and with their proportionality is primarily a short-run analysis of private enterprises or individual firms devoted to determining the rationale of profitable production for the market. This volume, on the other hand, is devoted mainly to the broader and long-run aspects, to the basis on which private and other enterprise rests and develops through time. Land, labor, and capital, as generally thought of, are concepts from the field of capitalistic production and private enterprise. Nature, man, and culture are as broad as the mind can encompass.

Here we are concerned primarily with the concept of land as used in economic theory. The word has to do double duty, both as land in the old two-dimensional sense and as "land" embracing all the myriad manifestations of nature acting as man's partner in the process of production. As was pointed out above, there was a time when such dual use of the word did not do violence to the basic aspects of reality. Nature functioned chiefly through land, and through land in the two-dimensional sense at that. But continued use of the word, after the realities to which it applies have changed radically, is unfortunate.

Fixity of Land and the Dynamics of Nature

The use of the word land, even in the sense of "land," is unfortunate because land in the sense of surface is something fixed, whereas "land" in the sense of the totality of natural contribution is not fixed but highly dynamic. It never stands still. It changes constantly in response to the impact of changing human attitudes and actions and, above all, of ever-changing culture. That is the deeper meaning of the term trinity. The different factors or aspects are not wholly separate and independent, but interdependent; they act as an interdependent triple force. The land surface may be fixed, but nature as a factor in resource development is not fixed. The totality of land surface is as irrelevant to the study of the availability of resources as is the totality of matter and energy in the universe. What counts is the function and meaning, to man, of land and all other phases of nature.[3]

In the absolute sense, the total supply of land on the earth may be considered fixed, limited, unalterable; but functionally appraised, "land" is alterable. There have been periods in history when the supply of land (not only in the narrow but also in the expanded sense of "land") which was available to a given group using given methods of exploitation, was fixed, either because the group could not expand beyond its territorial boundaries or because control measures such as social institutions or laws artificially limited the land supply. The land available to the islander who cannot or will not move away is absolutely limited. It is not surprising to find Englishmen of the pre-steamship era worried about their limited sup-ply of land. Feudalistic regimes tie people to the land, and the supply of land at their disposal is thereby limited.

The Russian mir, the closed peasant community whose members were held to their land by feudal laws, in effect were restricted in their use of land. In fact, the mir developed in response to an excessive supply of land. The steppe offered a chance of escape from onerous tributes and exacting masters and from social restrictions in general. The coming of the mir meant the closing of that avenue of escape. Similarly, our own "frontier," especially the open spaces of the West, beckoned to settlers unsatisfied with conditions in the East. Slavery in the South was in part a defensive measure against the effects of the "frontier" on the labor market. The virtual absence of restrictions on westward migrations since the Civil War has left its indelible imprint on the very soul of this country. Thus it is apparent that the supply of land must be interpreted relatively to time and place.

CULTIVABILITY

Importance of Cultivable Land

Regardless of the rise of machine industry and the corresponding relative decline of agriculture, the problem of food supply and the question of limits of cultivable land remain crucial. As will be shown in the next chapter, the population of the earth is increasing rapidly and in some parts in an explosive fashion. The problem of providing sustenance for a greatly increased human family is serious. How much cultivable land exists is therefore a crucial question facing man.[4]

Limitations of Cultivability

As has been stated repeatedly, nature sets outer limits to man's potential resources, but within these outer limits there lies a broad and sunny land where human initiative, drive, and ingenuity are given wide play. This applies to cultivable land as to all natural phenomena.

---

[3] Howard W. Odum, in *Southern Regions of the United States* (University of North Carolina Press, Chapel Hill, 1936), discusses resources under five headings: natural, capital, technological, human, and institutional. In other words, he breaks our cultural category into three subclasses.

[4] Much light is thrown on this question in W. L. G. Joerg (ed.), *Pioneer Settlement, Coöperative Studies by Twenty-six Authors*, Special Publication No. 14, American Geographical Society, New York, 1932. See also I. Bowman, *The Pioneer Fringe*, Special Publication No. 13, American Geographical Society, New York, 1931.

The physical limitations, the outer limits, will be taken up first.

The total land area of the earth is estimated to be somewhere between 57 and 58 million square miles, or approximately 37 billion acres. Of this, almost 6 million square miles lie in the polar regions. Of the remaining 52 million square miles, about one-fourth is in grassland, about one-third in desert, and about two-fifths in forest. Agricultural experts agree that about 40 percent of the total land area outside of the arctic regions, or about 21 million square miles, may be considered arable. In any attempt to ascertain the total land area available for agriculture, a sharp distinction between two sets of limiting conditions should be made—one absolute, the other relative.[5] Obviously there is some land which, under no circumstances at present worthy of consideration,[6] can be made to produce anything. Scattered savages or nomads can eke out an existence on some land by gathering the plant or animal products that nature freely yields. But agriculture implies a settled population and can therefore be carried on only if the yield is sufficient to justify more or less permanent settlement and thereby to support a settled population. Some agricultural regions reward man's effort moderately, while others yield bountifully. Thus appraised by absolute standards of natural productivity, the land surface of the earth appears like a crazy quilt made up of many-colored patches of different materials, some rich green, some gray, others bleached white, some of rich texture, others threadbare.

At present, the question of the physical cultivability of the least productive areas is purely academic, for no need has yet been felt to attempt growing grapes in Greenland or wheat in the Antarctic.[7] In view of present popula-

tion trends, which are discussed later on, and in view of the rate of progress made in the technological arts, it seems doubtful whether the worst areas of the earth will at any calculable future date have to be put under the plow or otherwise made to yield their products to man.

In ascertaining the absolute limits of cultivability or physical productivity, four factors are generally distinguished:[8]

1. Temperature conditions, particularly growing-season temperatures and dates of occurrence of spring and fall frosts.
2. Moisture conditions; i.e., rainfall, snowfall, hail, fog, humidity, rate of evaporation.
3. Topography, or land form; i.e., the configuration of the earth's surface, degree and direction of slope, roughness or smoothness of the land.
4. Soils, including both physical structure and chemical and bacteriological characteristics.

These limiting factors are sometimes spoken of as the four physical frontiers of agriculture. The determination of these frontiers is the major task of the geographer, especially the climatologist, or the soil expert.

One example must suffice here to illustrate the governing principles. In view of its importance as the staff of life, wheat is chosen for this purpose:

Only one acre in ten of the land of the world is physically available for wheat production. Ad-

---

[5] See E. G. Nourse, *Outline of Agricultural Economics*, University of Chicago Press, Chicago, 1917, p. 127.

[6] "Circumstances at present worthy of consideration" are here understood to embrace such developments of the arts, of population trend, of standards of living, and of other pertinent factors as may reasonably be assumed to lie within the range of prophecy, the calculation being confined to a period of time clearly within the range of present economic, social, and political consideration.

[7] It is still assumed by many writers that the determination of the general cultivability of the

earth, especially as reflected in the physical limits of food production, is of vital importance, for without food human life cannot exist. Hence, the limits of food production set the limits of all production. In the light of what has been said, this question of the physical limits of world food supply is considered rather theoretical. It is safe to assume that in the calculable future the world's food supply will depend primarily on the development of the arts, especially on increased knowledge of agronomy, better techniques of plant and animal breeding, revolutionary discoveries in the field of biology, the increasing availability and efficiency of capital equipment, and, above all, on the fuller utilization of inanimate energy. But it will also depend on improved knowledge of dietetics and the prevailing attitude toward food consumption. For the calculable future, therefore, the question of the physical limits of cultivability will remain a purely academic one.

[8] O. E. Baker, "The Potential Supply of Wheat," *Economic Geography*, March, 1925, p. 21.

verse climatic conditions prevent production on nearly four-fifths of the land, and of that climatically available, about 11 million square miles, over one-third is too hilly or rough for wheat cultivation, reducing the area to 7 million square miles. Unfavorable soils still further reduce by a fifth the area climatically and topographically available, leaving only 5½ million square miles physically suitable for wheat. But this tenth of the land surface physically available exceeds present requirements, less than one acre in ten of this available land being utilized for wheat. In other words, less than one per cent of the land surface of the earth is in wheat at present. Since corn, oats, hay, vege-

error to apply the findings regarding wheat or any other selected crop to the determination of the general cultivability of the earth's surface. Crops compete with one another; they compete with pasture land and forests. Finally, the relation of minerals to agricultural production must be kept in mind. The competition between a field of fodder corn or a section of pasture and coal or petroleum is as real as that between wheat and corn in parts of the Corn Belt. The tractor competes with the horse and the mule, animate energy with inanimate, living matter with dead substance.

Cultural and Human Limitations of Cultivability

As was stated above, nature sets the outer limits. Culture and human attitudes and actions determine the range of actual use within these outer limits. Cultures differ chiefly in their command over energy. The impact of culture on cultivability of land, therefore, can best be demonstrated by comparing the cultivation of land under two civilizations which differ sharply in the extent of their command over energy. Such civilizations are those of China, a sedentary vegetable civilization, and of the United States, a highly mobilized machine civilization.

Land cultivation in China as compared with that in the United States constitutes a strange paradox. Unfortunately, accurate data are not available; indeed at this period of history the very definition of China and the delineation of her frontiers are highly problematic. It is known, however, that the area of China, if defined with due cognizance of political realities, is smaller than that of the United States, which is 3,000,000 square miles, and that the population of China is much larger than that of the United States, which is about 150,000,000 people. If one arbitrarily selects 2,500,000 square miles as the area of China and 450,000,000 as the population, the population density of China is 180 per square mile as compared with 50 for the United States. The areas presumably physically fit for cultivation have been estimated[10] at approximately 1,100,-

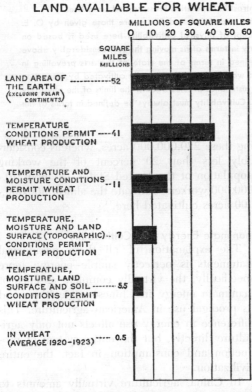

LAND AVAILABLE FOR WHEAT

MILLIONS OF SQUARE MILES
0   10   20   30   40   50   60

SQUARE MILES MILLIONS

LAND AREA OF THE EARTH (EXCLUDING POLAR CONTINENTS) ----------52

TEMPERATURE CONDITIONS PERMIT WHEAT PRODUCTION ----41

TEMPERATURE AND MOISTURE CONDITIONS PERMIT WHEAT PRODUCTION --11

TEMPERATURE, MOISTURE AND LAND SURFACE (TOPOGRAPHIC) CONDITIONS PERMIT WHEAT PRODUCTION -- 7

TEMPERATURE, MOISTURE, LAND SURFACE AND SOIL CONDITIONS PERMIT WHEAT PRODUCTION ------- 5.5

IN WHEAT (AVERAGE 1920-1923) ---- 0.5

FIG. 7.2.

tables and other crops must also be grown on land suitable for wheat, it appears unlikely that over three per cent of the world's land surface will ever be devoted to wheat production.[9]

This analysis is shown graphically in Fig. 7.2.

As Baker points out, it would be a grave

---

[9] This quotation and Fig. 7.2 are from *ibid.*, p. 31.

[10] O. E. Baker, "Agriculture and the Future of China," *Foreign Affairs*, April, 1928. J. B. Condliffe in *China Today, Economic*, World Peace Foundation, 1932, gives an even lower estimate.

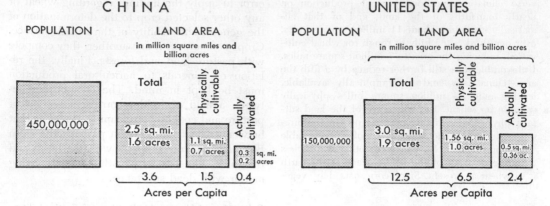

FIG. 7.3.   China and the United States—A Contrast in Population Pressure and Land Use.
The figures for physically cultivable land for both China and the United States are those given by O. E.
Baker in "Agriculture and the Future of China." The concept of physical cultivability here used is based on
the assumption of a state of the agricultural arts, particularly in terms of its moving the soil, considerably above
that prevailing in China. If physical cultivability were defined in terms of the state of the arts prevailing in
China, it is most unlikely that the physically cultivable land would exceed the actually cultivated by more than
a nominal figure. A people pressing against the means of sustenance presses against the limits of the physically
cultivable land, i.e., the land physically cultivable *by them*. Cultivability must always be defined in terms of the
arts and institutions of the country under observation.

000 square miles, or 700,000,000 acres, for
China, as compared with 1,560,000 square
miles, or one billion acres, for the United States.
About 44 percent of the total land area of
China (on the basis of our figures) is assumed
to be physically cultivable, as compared with
over 50 percent for the United States. The population density of China is over 3.5 times that
of the United States if based on the total land
area; it is almost 4.5 times that of the United
States if based on estimated areas considered
physically cultivable. Under these conditions
one would most certainly expect the Chinese
to cultivate a far greater *portion* or percentage
of their smaller total land area and a still
greater portion of their still smaller physically
cultivable land; but, paradoxically, the very
opposite is the case. The people of the United
States cultivate over half again as large an
acreage as that cultivated in China—over 360,-
000,000 acres in the United States as compared
with about 220,000,000 acres in China. These
data are shown in Fig. 7.3.

The paradox becomes even more striking
in view of the fact that about 80 percent of
the Chinese working population, or possibly
180,000,000—certainly over 150,000,000 human beings—are normally engaged in cultivat-

ing these 220,000,000 acres, whereas considerably less than 20 percent of the working
population of the United States, or about 10,-
000,000 workers, cultivate the almost 360,000,-
000 acres cultivated here.[11]

Inanimate Energy and Cultivability

The explanation of all these paradoxical
statements is perfectly simple—energy; more
specifically, the virtually complete absence of
inanimate energy in Chinese agriculture, and
its prodigal use in American agriculture. This
difference in energy use affects not only agriculture directly, but the entire system of production and consumption—in fact, the entire
civilization.

In China, agriculture virtually amounts to
food production for local consumption. The
farms must first of all support the workers that
till the field. In China, agriculture is its own
powerhouse. It provides the fuel (food) for the

---

[11] Moreover, in the United States a large acreage, although not actually cultivated, is devoted
to agricultural production.
Again the reader is reminded that these figures
are gross approximations. However, the contrasts
are so sharp that no reasonable correction of statistical data can be expected to affect appreciably
the main points brought out.

engines (labor) of production. In China, the laborer is little supported by tools, less by animals, and not at all by machine power. In China, agriculture must also support the families of the workers, those in government service, the army, etc., and finally, the landlords.

Chinese agriculture exhausts itself by trying to provide the energy needed to work the fields. So much of all human energy must go into work in the fields that little energy is left to supply locomotion, i.e., movement from place to place. In China, such movement is an unattainable luxury; hence, the sedentary character of China; hence, the division into thousands of local self-sufficient *hsiens;* hence, the incredible crowding on the cream of the land. Land that yields all the energy that is needed for its own cultivation must be wonderful land. What is more, it must be cultivated in a wonderfully intensive fashion. Fertilizer must be piled on it, water must be supplied in prodigious amounts, labor, care, and skill must be showered on every square foot, or else the equation will not balance and somebody will starve.

Human labor is incredibly slow. It takes one man fifteen days to spade an acre,[12] and correspondingly long to harvest. That cuts two good slices of precious time from the length of the campaign. It shortens the growing and ripening season and thus cuts down the choice of crops. Only crops which fit this rigorous timetable and yield fantastically will be tolerated.

While the Chinese farmer performs miracles in yield *per acre* but, in spite of truly pathetic efforts and admirable skill in which is embodied the wisdom of forty centuries, accomplishes pitifully little in terms of *per capita* yield, the American farmer, in general, lags behind in yield per acre but performs miracles in yield per capita. The chief reason is the latter's prodigal use of outside energy, chiefly inanimate energy. Inanimate energy mobilizes. It permits one farmer to cultivate hundreds, even thousands of acres. The tractor and the combine go far to explain the American agricultural marathon. Each farmer is aided by numerous robots, obedient slaves that never eat. Every

pound of rice that comes out of monsoon Asia was produced with human energy that was fueled by rice or other food. Most of the energy, other than solar radiation, that produces wheat on our prairies and plains was produced with the aid of coal and oil and electricity.

Not only is each American farmer aided by robots working beside him; numerous workers in factories, similarly aided by other robots, stand behind him, furnishing the machines and vehicles and structures that make a factory of a sort out of the modern farm. Behind the farmer stands also one of the greatest research organizations of all time, the United States Department of Agriculture, and the various state organizations and numerous county agents who incorporate in their collective knowledge the fruit of decades of systematic research, one of the brightest achievements of machine civilization. This scientific research goes far to enable the American farmer to do surprisingly well even in terms of yield per acre.

While man power is painfully slow, machine power is astonishingly fast. Artificial light turns night into day; and hence, in twenty-four hours, with the aid of tractors a farmer and a few helpers can cultivate and harvest areas of land which thousands of men could hardly cultivate and harvest in weeks. The effect in terms of lengthened growing and ripening seasons is stupendous. The choice of crops widens by leaps and bounds. Crop cultivation can be extended to colder regions.

The most dramatic effect of the use of inanimate energy in farming, beside the prodigious yield per man, is the extension of farming into regions whose counterparts in China must lie unused because of their poor quality. A vital law of cultivation reads: The fertility of cultivable land is in inverse proportion to the amount of energy supporting the cultivator.[13] Assuming reasonable prices, a farmer cultivating over a thousand acres with tractors and combines can make a profit on perhaps 12 bushels of wheat per acre, whereas a robotless peasant, cultivating a fraction of the land, may have to get 30 bushels to break even.

The machine, in other words, breaks the critical link between food and work that is the

---

[12] O. E. Baker, "Agriculture and the Future of China."

[13] Later we shall see that a similar law governs the use of mineralized land as well.

crux of Chinese agriculture. In doing so it vastly enlarges the cultivability of land. It explains why American farmers, satisfied with relatively low yields of many basic crops, nevertheless can feed themselves and their families well, can feed the rest of the nation, and can make remarkable contributions to the rest of the world.

Cultivability in an Exchange Economy

The peasant produces primarily for himself and his household. The American farmer produces to sell. Prices of the things he sells and of the things he buys thus become a vital factor in the determination of cultivability. Prices, in turn, must be related to costs, not only costs of production but also delivery costs. Accessibility to the market and to sources of supply becomes as important as fertility itself. The law governing the relationship of energy to fertility, stated above, applies to accessibility

as well. Costs, in turn, reflect not only wage rates and prices of purchased goods, interest rates, taxes, etc., but also skill, quality of management, application of service, etc. In short, in an exchange economy cultivability becomes a function of numerous factors associated with many phases of culture.

The problem of determining the cultivability of land has been developed fully, not merely for its own sake, but also to illustrate the overall problem for man, of the availability of aspects of nature. The main lesson to be learned is that availability in general, as well as cultivability in particular, is not determined once and for all and for all peoples alike. Availability no less than cultivability varies with time and place, is a reflection of the culture pattern of each age and people. A key to availability in general and to cultivability in particular is the use made of energy—more specifically, inanimate energy.

BIBLIOGRAPHY

Baker, O. E., "Agriculture and the Future of China," *Foreign Affairs*, April, 1928.

Bromfield, L., *Pleasant Valley*, New York, Harper, 1945.

Bromfield, L., *Malabar Farm*, New York, Harper, 1948.

Chase, S., *Rich Land—Poor Land, A Study of Waste in the Natural Resources of America*, New York, McGraw-Hill, 1936.

Condliffe, J. B., *China Today, Economic*, Washington, World Peace Foundation, 1932.

Ely, R. T., and Morehouse, E. W., *Elements of Land Economics*, New York, Macmillan, 1926.

Graham, E. H., *Natural Principles of Land Use*, New York, Oxford, 1944.

Hsia-Tung Fei and Chih-I Chang, *Earthbound China*, Chicago, University of Chicago Press, 1946.

Johnson, G., *The Wasted Land*, Chapel Hill, University of North Carolina Press, 1937.

League of Nations, Office of International Intellectual Cooperation, *Limits of Land Settlement*, Paris, 1937.

Lord, R., *Behold Our Land*, Boston, Houghton Mifflin, 1938.

Mallory, W. H., *China: Land of Famine*, Special

Publication No. 6, American Geographical Society of New York, 1926.

Marbut, C. F., "Soils," *Encyclopædia of the Social Sciences*, New York, Macmillan, 1933.

Renne, R. R., *Land Economics*, New York, Harper, 1947.

Salter, R. M., "World Soil and Fertilizer Resources in Relation to Food Needs," *Science*, May 23, 1947.

Sauer, C., "Destructive Exploitation in Modern Colonial Expansion," *Proceedings of the International Congress of Geographers*, Amsterdam, 1938.

Tawney, R. H., *Land and Labor in China*, New York, Harcourt, Brace, 1932.

Tennessee Valley Authority, *Soil, People, and Fertilizer Technology* (pamphlet), Washington, 1949.

Whitaker, J. R., *The Life and Death of the Land*, Nashville, Peabody Press, 1946.

Whitney, M., *The Soil and Civilization*, New York, Van Nostrand, 1925.

Wittfogel, K. A., *Wirtschaft und Gesellschaft Chinas*, Leipzig, Hirschfeld, 1931.

Wolfanger, L. A., *The Major Soil Divisions of the United States*, New York, Wiley, 1930.

Chapter 8

MAN AND RESOURCES

DUAL ROLE OF MAN

Man is both the most dynamic agent of production and the beneficiary of the entire process of resource development and utilization. As was pointed out in Chapter 1, resources are instrumental wealth which, after helping to overcome resistances, yield real wealth—the well-being of man. As an agent of production man contributes his labor, mental and physical; with the aid, "advice, and consent" of nature he builds culture to render more effective his production efforts and to lessen the impact of resistances; he discovers new ways and invents new arts; his aspirations furnish aim and purpose. As beneficiary he enjoys the advantages of advancing civilization.

One must not think of the two roles as separate in time and place. Happiness may be found in the joy of achievement and in the pride of workmanship. The greatest advances in civilization are made through the improvement of man's role as an agent of production. The greatest contribution to real wealth lies in that improvement. As was stated earlier, man is predestined to be the director, planner, and aspirer. As his role shifts from that of the toiling field hand or sweating ditch digger to that of master of robots and director of inanimate forces, he reaps the fruit of real wealth as he acts the role to which he seems predestined by his unique aptitudes. Since this is the acme of resource strategy and functional specialization, the productivity of the entire process of resource development is raised; and besides finding "real wealth" in the performance of his role as an agent of production man reaps a richer harvest of material goods and greater leisure.

It is the recognition of these fundamental truths that imbues the processes of mechanization and industrialization with meaning and significance far beyond their immediate effects on increased productivity and enlarged profits.

To be able to perform this higher role man must be physically fit and healthy, and properly educated and trained. The promotion of public health and education thus assumes an importance, in any reasonable program of resource development, that can hardly be exaggerated. Human resources are both the most dynamic and the most potent; they are also the most precious because, to repeat, they combine the task of production agent with the end object of the entire process. They constitute the *end values to be achieved* in the process.

MAN-LAND RATIO AND POPULATION DENSITY
Definition of Terms

What roles human beings are allowed to play depends largely on a highly significant ratio sometimes referred to as the man-land ratio. In all the social sciences there is no more fundamental relationship than that between man and land: "The ultimate elements offered for a scientific study of the evolution and life of human society are Man and Land; given these, there arises at once the necessity of adjustment between them. How much land there is to how many men is the fundamental consideration in the life of any society."[1]

The concept land must be interpreted in the broadest sense of natural opportunities as affected by the state of cultural development. Under no circumstances must the man-land ratio be confused with population density. The latter concept is a purely mechanical one referring to a simple *quantitative* relationship between numbers of people and numbers of units of land area—acres, hectares, square miles, etc. Population density figures are particularly meaningless when applied to large areas such as China, Canada, Brazil, the Soviet Union. The overall density figure is on the average as meaningless as would be the amount 4 inches for the average height of vegetation in Mozambique. The overall population density figure for Egypt is meaningless because Egypt is divided into the incredibly overcrowded Nile valley and the virtually empty desert spaces on both sides of that river. Brazil, as was mentioned before, is a huge area over which there are scattered clusters of human habitation, with the bulk of the people living on mere fractions of the total area. Canada's population is crowded into the strip paralleling the international boundary; the rest of her vast territory is virtually uninhabited.

The man-land ratio is a highly complex concept of a *qualitative* relationship. Statistical

data of population density per square mile are of little value to the social scientist except as a starting point. There are densely populated areas where people live in squalor and poverty; there are others whose standards of living are high. Vice versa, there are sparsely populated areas whose inhabitants barely eke out an existence; in others they live in comfort if not in wealth. The man-land ratio takes into account all the human qualities bearing on productivity and all the environmental aspects, both natural and cultural, affecting the availability of resources. A high population density figure may indicate overpopulation; but even a region with a low population density may be overpopulated. Only the qualitative and critical appraisal of human wants and abilities and of the availability of resources can furnish conclusive evidence as to the true state of affairs.

Internal and External Carrying Capacity

To determine the man-land ratio, land must not be measured simply in square miles, but evaluated as to its carrying capacity, i.e., the capacity to support human life, to satisfy human wants. In primitive closed societies whose arts and standards of living are static, this carrying capacity can be easily appraised; but advancing civilization, with its growing complexity of social organization, with its progress in arts and sciences, with the increasing importance of commerce, renders this measurement difficult. When nature largely determines productivity, as was the case in primitive times, acres or square miles indicate the carrying capacity, at least under like or similar conditions. Today the wealth of subsoil minerals invests acres with a carrying capacity which formerly did not exist. The arts and institutions become more and more important as factors determining capacity. Above all, by causing the breakdown of self-sufficiency, commerce and finance create a spatial gap between place of production and place of consumption. Carrying capacity must therefore be redefined in the light of changed conditions. To the original idea of internal carrying capacity must be added the so-called external capacity.

A self-sufficient farm or a self-sufficient manor depends physically on the land, its own internal carrying capacity. A mining camp or a village

---

[1] W. G. Sumner and A. G. Keller, *The Science of Society,* Yale University Press, New Haven, 1927, vol. 1, p. 4.

craftsman, on the other hand, depends on exchange for sustenance. They exchange the products of their own land and labor for those of other men and places. They place commercial dependence on external carrying capacity. Similarly, self-sufficient nations and commercial nations may be differentiated. England may exchange coal for wheat; we may prefer to live on the produce of our own fields and mines. England may have invested savings in foreign lands, collecting the interest in foodstuffs and raw materials. Legal claims, established by conquest or trade, on land hundreds or thousands of miles away have become important features of modern economy. Thus, the direct relationship between the number of people and the number of square miles on which they live has lost much of its meaning and with it has gone some of the meaning of population density figures.

A region nowadays must be considered overpopulated only if the internal and external capacity on which it can draw for its support is inadequate. It is estimated that the physical internal carrying capacity of Holland is sufficient to support 120 people to the square mile —the actual density in that country is around 540 per square mile. But nobody who knows economic conditions in that prosperous trading country would consider Holland overpopulated. The carrying capacity of Holland must include much of Indonesia as well as many other parts of the earth on which, because of her political, commercial, and financial position, she can draw for support. While Holland draws on Indonesia for support she also contributes to the carrying capacity of that region, whose population has grown rapidly, especially that of Java. The skills and arts of the West, Dutch capital, better organization, western sanitation and medicines go far to explain the increase in population that suggests an increase in carrying capacity.

Pent-Up and Expansive Populations

Not all peoples are in a position to draw upon external carrying capacity, either economically or politically. Moreover, nations differ widely in the extent to which they can take advantage of the opportunity of enlarging the basis of their economic support by drawing on other parts of the world. The extent to which Great Britain was able to do so for centuries is a unique experience of human history. After the defeat of her naval rivals Portugal, Spain, Denmark, Holland, and France, she had virtually the entire globe at her feet. Later on, when France, Holland, and Belgium became linked to Britain in common opposition to German expansion, they too were allowed to share in overseas colonies, to hold what they had and to acquire new ones.

One point regarding colonies which is apt to be overlooked should be made clear. There is such a thing as colonial exploitation. Slave raids and the sacking of rich cities such as the capitals of Montezuma and the Inca definitely fall in that category, as does the ruthless treatment of the rubber gatherers in both the Amazon basin and the Congo (see p. 391). But one must not lose sight of the fact that much colonial enterprise definitely comes under the heading of conversion of "neutral stuff" into resources. The colonizer creates many of the resources which he takes out and in many instances he contributes to the welfare of the native population. The hope seems justified that colonial regimes are reforming and becoming more conscious of their responsibilities toward those whom they are subjecting to control, often against their will.

The history of the United States is virtually the history of expansion, first over the continental homeland, then, later on, overseas. Similarly, the history of Russia is the history of eastward expansion to the Pacific and beyond, to which World War II added an amazing chapter of westward expansion to the Adriatic and halfway into Germany. Brazil may belong in this category, with her expansion still to come.

Fig. 8.1[2] is here reproduced not merely to focus attention on important relationships between population pressure and economic, social, and political phenomena but also to arouse critical thinking on the specific ideas suggested by the figure.

---

[2] T. N. Carver, "Some Needed Refinements of the Theory of Population," in M. Sanger, *Proceedings of the World Population Conference,* Edward Arnold & Co., London, 1927, p. 124.

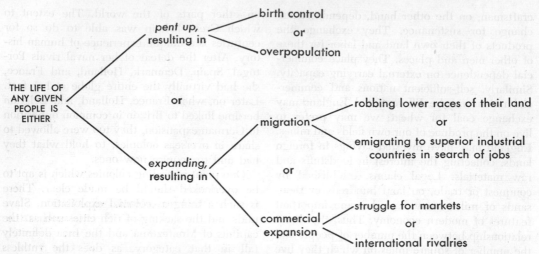

FIG. 8.1.   Pent-up and Expanding Peoples.

One point that deserves to be questioned in particular concerns the connection between the state of being pent-up and birth control. Birth control, as will be brought out more fully later on, ordinarily indicates a high level of economic productivity which can hardly be associated with the idea of being pent-up. The frontiers of science and technology are as real as geographical frontiers; and no people are truly pent-up that add billions of robots to their supporting staff and in general push back the frontiers of human knowledge and enlarge their capacity to tap the powers and riches of nature.

Sometimes people have felt pent-up when perhaps they were not. Even an illusory sense of being pent-up may affect human attitudes sufficiently to bring repercussions on group behavior.

WORLD POPULATION MAP

Major Centers

A glance at the map shown in Fig. 8.2 reveals three outstanding centers of population concentration:

1. Southeastern Asia, especially China, India, Japan, Korea, but also including Java.
2. The industrialized areas of western, northern, and central Europe, especially Belgium, Netherlands, Great Britain, and Germany, but also including other areas of Europe such as northern Italy, the Barcelona sector of Spain, parts of France, Czechoslovakia, etc.

3. The industrial areas of the United States.[3]

The three population centers listed above differ widely in historical background and economic support. Hundreds of millions of people are massed into the coastal plains and river valleys of southeastern Asia. In Europe and in the northeastern section of the United States, the great concentration centers lie over or near the coal fields; more recently, water power, petroleum, and natural gas have also proved strong drawing cards. Everywhere large numbers flock to the crossroads of commerce. Huntington[4] points out that the Asiatic centers lie in the monsoon belts, the areas of abundant food (per acre), and the centers of Europe and North America in the cyclonic storm belts, the areas of abundant energy. He refers to human energy in this connection; but, in general, these sections are also the areas of abundant mechanical energy where millions of horsepower are installed and billions of kilowatt-hours are generated from coal and other fossil fuels.

These three centers vary widely in the num-

---

[3] The clustering of the people of the earth has been effectively shown in a diagram prepared by Dr. S. Whittemore Boggs, Geographer of the United States Department of State. See S. Whittemore Boggs, "Geographical and Scientific Techniques for Political Science," American Political Science Review, April, 1948, p. 235.

[4] See E. Huntington, The Human Habitat, D. Van Nostrand Company, Inc., New York, 1927, especially chap. 2.

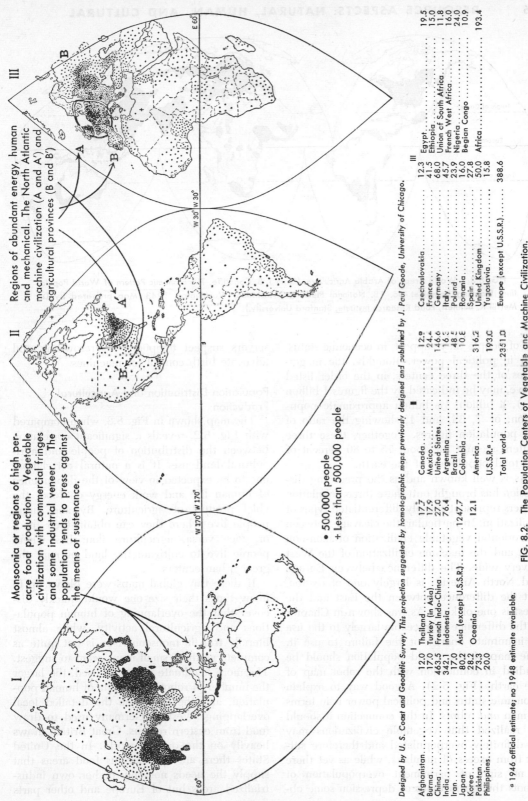

Monsoonia or regions of high per-acre food production. Vegetable civilization with commercial fringes and some industrial veneer. The population tends to press against the means of sustenance.

Regions of abundant energy, human and mechanical. The North Atlantic machine civilization (A and A') and agricultural provinces (B and B')

• 500,000 people
+ Less than 500,000 people

Designed by U. S. Coast and Geodetic Survey. This projection suggested by homolographic maps previously designed and published by J. Paul Goode, University of Chicago.

I		II		III	
Afghanistan	12.0	Canada	12.9	Czechoslovakia	12.3
Burma	17.0	Mexico	24.4	France	41.5
China	463.5	United States	146.0	Germany	68.0
India	342.1	Argentina	16.7	Italy	45.7
Iran	17.0	Brazil	48.5	Poland	23.9
Japan	80.2	Colombia	10.8	Romania	16.0
Korea	28.2			Spain	27.8
Pakistan	73.3	America	316.2	United Kingdom	50.0
Philippines	20.0	U.S.S.R.a	193.0	Yugoslavia	15.8
Thailand	17.7				
Turkey (in Asia)	17.9	Total world	2351.0	Europe (except U.S.S.R.)	388.6
French Indo-China	27.0			Egypt	19.5
Indonesia	76.4			Ethiopia	15.0
Asia (except U.S.S.R.)	1247.7			Union of South Africa	11.8
				French West Africa	16.0
Oceania	12.1			Nigeria	24.0
				Belgian Congo	10.9
				Africa	193.4

a 1946 official estimate; no 1948 estimate available.

FIG. 8.2. The Population Centers of Vegetable and Machine Civilization.
Populations of Continents and of Political Units with More Than 10,000,000 People Each, Midyear Estimate 1948, in Millions
(Source: United Nations Statistical Office, August 1, 1949.)

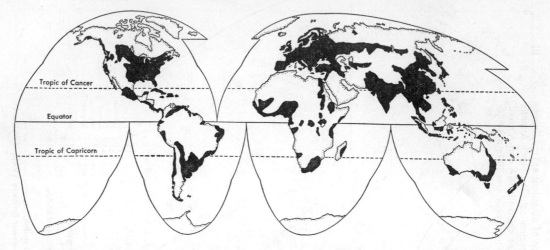

FIG. 8.3. World Areas of Arable Agriculture. (From J. B. Condliffe, *The Economic Pattern of World Population*, Planning Pamphlet No. 18, National Planning Association, Washington, 1943. Map prepared by Dr. Merrill K. Bennett, Food Research Institute, Stanford University.)

ber of people they support, in economic status, and in political power. Roughly, the magnitudes of the three centers, in the order listed above, may be indicated by the figures 1 billion (+), ¼ billion, ⅒ billion approximate population; or 7, 3½, and 1, showing the ratio of the population figures. Together, these three centers account for about 75 to 80 percent of the total population of the earth.

As is well known and as the preceding discussion has brought out, these three population centers represent sharply differentiated types of civilization. In particular, the cleavage between the oriental vegetable civilization of monsoon Asia and the machine civilization of the West is very wide. The difference between Europe and North America is largely one of degree, but the difference between the East and the West is one of kind. As was shown in Chapter 5, the difference is traceable largely to the use of inanimate energy or the failure to use it. The map of the world population should be studied in connection with the robot map of the earth (Fig. 5.2). A good way to explain economic status and political power is in terms of men *and* robots. In this connection it should be realized that vegetable civilizations may be definitely overpopulated and therefore suffer from excess of numbers, while as yet there is no sign of permanent overpopulation of robots though in times of depression some ob-

servers suspect temporary overcrowding and advocate birth control for machines.

Population Distribution and Agricultural Production

The map shown in Fig. 8.3, when compared with Fig. 8.2, reveals a significant correlation between the distribution of people and agricultural land use. It is a natural correlation, one to be expected in view of the dependence of human life and work energy on food, the chief product of agriculture. By and large, people live where they can obtain their food, or, vice versa, agriculture flourishes where people live to cultivate the land or near the great urban centers.

If these tiny global maps were blown up to many times their size one would quickly discover that the overlapping of human populations and agricultural activity, while almost literally true in monsoon Asia, is not quite as complete as these small maps seem to suggest. The more inanimate energy is used, the larger the number of robots per capita of human population, and the less close the detailed local overlapping. Western Germany used to draw food from eastern regions. Great Britain draws heavily on the outside world. In the United States there are vast surplus food areas that supply the needs not only of her own industrialized areas but of Europe and other parts

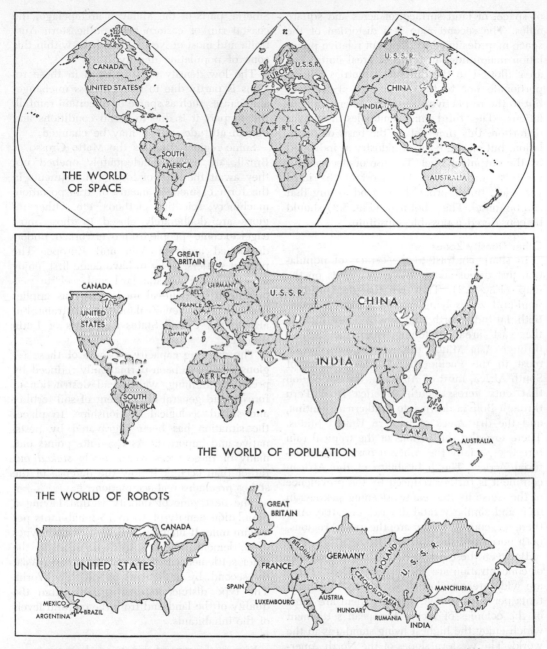

FIG. 8.4. The Three Worlds of Space, People, and Industry. (The space and robots maps used by permission of *Life*; the population map, by permission of the National Opinion Research Center.)

of the world as well. Even in countries like Argentina and Australia there is a division between local population centers and local agricultural areas. On the whole, however, the general impression conveyed by the two maps is correct.

The Three Worlds of Space, People, and Industry

The significance of the three major centers of population concentration and the difference between them is shown effectively by the three maps in Fig. 8.4. The first map is the world of space, of land surface, of acres and square miles. The second map is a distortion of the space map designed to bring out relative population magnitudes in terms of areal units. The area allotted to the different countries is proportionate *not* to the actual size of territory but to the respective size of the different populations. The third map embodies a similar distortion, this time not on the basis of population, but on the basis of industry as indicated by the output of steel. The use of steel output for this purpose may fall short of the ideal yardstick, but is probably as good as any that can be found. The robot map (Fig. 5.2) should be considered a possible substitute.

Other Density Zones

In sharp contrast to the centers of population just discussed are the empty spots on the map (Fig. 8.2). They are the great arid or semi-arid zones lying mainly along the twentieth latitude north and south. They include the vast area stretching from the Sahara through Asia Minor, through Central Asia almost to the Pacific, the Kalahari Desert of South Africa, most of Australia, the dry region that cuts across South America from Peru through Bolivia down into southern Argentina, and the dry zones of western United States. There are also the regions of the tropical rain forest, especially the Amazon basin and equatorial Africa. The habitability of the African continent is further reduced by the prevalence of the tsetse fly that causes sleeping sickness in men and similarly fatal diseases in cattle. And then, of course, there are the polar regions, both north and south.

Between these empty spaces and the centers of concentration are various gradations.[5] There are wide areas of low density, 1 to 15 inhabitants per square mile. "Among them are some of the colonies of recent European settlement which enjoy the highest living standards in the world. The western slopes of the North American continent, the Canadian prairies and the uplands of the middle-west of the United States, the inland grazing areas of South America, the drier regions of central and east Africa, coastal Arabia, the greater part of southern Siberia, parts of the Malayan archipelago, the coastal rim of eastern and southeastern Australia and most of New Zealand, lie within this zone of population density."[6]

The low density of population in these regions is partly due to more or less unchangeable causes such as sparse or uncertain rainfall. But in part it is due to social conditions and human attitudes which may be changed.

Some regions, such as the Matto Grosso of Brazil, are as yet inadequately opened up; they await the spur of foreign investments in the form of modern means of transportation, machinery, scientific methods, etc. Other regions are deliberately closed to those most eager to come—people from overworked, underdeveloped areas of Asia and Europe. The present settlers, lucky to have come first, enjoy an enviable living standard and seek to perpetuate it by political measures. This applies particularly to New Zealand and Australia, but also to the United States and parts of Latin America.

The carrying capacity of some of these regions may have been permanently reduced by predatory farming, widespread destruction of forests, and general impairment of soil fertility and sound ecological relationships. In places the situation has been aggravated by pests, native and imported.[7] As Condliffe points out, many of these areas were merely *staked out* rather than occupied; now the defense of the stakes precludes real occupation.

The next zone of density is that having a population density of 15 to 75 inhabitants per square mile. It includes two very distinct types of settlement. The first is exemplified by the older settlements in Europe, Africa, and Asia; the second, by settlements in the New World. The type distinction derives both from the quality of the land and from the cultural levels of the inhabitants.

Even in this zone of density one becomes aware of the contrast between the western European type of capitalist, mechanized farming supported by and leading naturally to urban aggregation and the Asiatic peasant type of farming, which is decen-

---

[5] See J. B. Condliffe, *The Economic Pattern of World Population*, Planning Pamphlet No. 18, National Planning Association, Washington, 1943.

[6] *Ibid.*, p. 8.
[7] A good example of the latter is the rabbit, which has been a real problem in Australia. See *ibid.*, p. 9.

tralized, more dependent upon human labor, less equipped with power and yielding much lower standards of living. This distinction must obviously be borne in mind when grouping in one zone of density the highly-developed farming regions of the middle-western American states and the poor uplands of China. The distinction is vital, perhaps the most vital of the whole problem of world population. It is a contrast between areas in which unrestrained pressure of numbers upon limited resources is kept in check only by the harsh forces of nature and those in which human control over natural conditions (especially over sources of physical energy) and not less over social organization, has enabled numbers to expand while raising living standards. On the one hand we find low levels of human livelihood, scientific ignorance, social anarchy, and natural controls over population increase—on the other, high levels of achievement, increasing scientific knowledge and conscious human control of numbers by limitation of births.[8]

This contrast may be followed all the way up to the most densely populated areas. In fact, the contrast becomes sharper as population density increases until finally it reaches its extremes in such contrasts as Pittsburgh and the Yangtze valley or London and the Nile valley.

POPULATION STATISTICS

Size of World Population

How many people live on the earth is not known. In countries whose aggregate population constitutes between two-thirds and three-fourths of the total population of the earth, periodical counts are taken more or less regularly, but even then a margin of error of probably 10 percent must be conceded.[9] This margin of error is small compared to that which affects estimates of the rest of the world's population. In particular, as was mentioned before, the size of the population of China is under dispute. The *Statistical Yearbook of the United Nations, 1949*, estimates the total world population as 2,351,000,000 inhabitants. This total is divided by continents as shown in Table 8.1.

Growth of World Population

While, as was stated above, nowadays one-fourth to one-third of the population of the

[8] *Ibid.*, pp. 10-11.
[9] See R. R. Kuczynski's article, "Population," in the *Encyclopædia of the Social Sciences*.

world is not covered by official census records, this was true of about four-fifths of the world's population in 1800. Any attempt, therefore, to reconstruct the past growth of the world's population is highly precarious, for one must rely on inference and on logic. Those well versed in the intricacies of vital statistics, actuarial science, and demography can use these delicate instruments with reasonable assurance. Fortunately, some outstanding statisticians[10] have devoted themselves to this study. The composite results of numerous studies are summarized in Fig. 8.5.[11] Notestein comments on this graph as follows:

The figure brings out three facts pertinent to this discussion.

1. The world's population has been growing at a rapid and accelerating pace during the last three centuries. Since the middle of the seventeenth century it has grown at an average annual rate of about 5 per thousand. Since 1900 the annual increase has averaged 8 per thousand. Such prolonged and rapid increase cannot have occurred frequently in the history of the race; and, obviously, increases of this magnitude have never occurred before. For example, if the average rate of increase obtaining since 1650 had been in force since the beginning of the Christian Era, an initial population of only 10 million would now amount to more than fifty times the present world population. The modern epoch of growth has been unique.

2. All sections of the world have participated in this growth, but it has been particularly marked in Europe and Europe overseas, especially prior to 1900.

3. Since 1900 the rate of growth has tended to decline in Europe, North America, and Oceania; but in Africa, Asia, and Central and South America there apparently has been some acceleration of the rate of increase.

The main facts shown by this graph may be appreciated more readily when supported by statistical evidence, such as that in Table 8.2.

[10] Among them, and best known to the present author, are Walter F. Willcox, A. M. Carr-Saunders, Robert R. Kuczynski, Warren S. Thompson, P. K. Whelpton, and Frank W. Notestein.
[11] See Frank W. Notestein, "Population—The Long View," a chapter in Theodore W. Schultz (ed.), *Food for the World*, University of Chicago Press, Chicago, 1945, pp. 36-57. Figs. 8.5 and 8.6 are reprinted by permission from *ibid.* and from Alexander Carr-Saunders, *World Population*, The Clarendon Press.

TABLE 8.1. World Population by Continents, United Nations Midyear 1948 Estimate[12]
(in millions for all units of one million or more)

Africa	193.4	Ceylon	7.1
Egypt	19.5	China	463.5
Ethiopia	15.0	India	342.1
Liberia	1.6	Iran	17.0
Union of South Africa	11.8	Iraq	5.0
Belgian Congo	10.9	Japan	80.2
Algeria	8.7	Korea	28.2
French Equatorial Africa	4.3	Lebanon	1.2
French West Africa	16.0	Mongolian People's Republic	2.0
Madagascar and Comoro Island	4.4	Nepal	6.9
Morocco	8.3	Pakistan	73.3
Tunisia	3.4	Philippines	20.0
Angola	4.6	Saudi Arabia	6.0
Mozambique	6.3	Syria	3.8
Spanish Morocco	1.1	Thailand	17.7
Gold Coast Protectorate	3.7	Turkey (Asiatic only)	17.9
Kenya	5.2	Yemen	7.0
Nigeria	24.0	French Indo-China	27.0
Northern Rhodesia	1.7	Indonesia	76.4
Nyasaland	2.2	Federation of Malaya	5.0
Sierra Leone	2.0	Hong Kong	1.8
Southern Rhodesia	2.0	Singapore	1.0
Uganda	5.0	Palestine (except Israel)	1.3
Cameroons	3.8		
Ruanda-Urundi	3.8	Europe (except U.S.S.R.)	388.6
Tanganyika	7.1	Albania	1.2
Togoland	13.3	Austria	7.0
Eritrea	1.1	Belgium	8.6
Libya	1.2	Bulgaria	7.1
Anglo-Egyptian Sudan	7.9	Czechoslovakia	12.3
		Denmark	4.2
America	316.2	Finland	4.0
Canada	12.9	France	41.5
Cuba	5.2	Germany	68.0
Dominican Republic	2.2	Greece	7.8
El Salvador	2.1	Hungary	9.2
Guatemala	3.7	Ireland	3.0
Haiti	3.7	Italy	45.7
Honduras	1.3	Netherlands	9.8
Mexico	24.4	Norway	3.2
Nicaragua	1.2	Poland	23.9
United States	146.6	Portugal (including Azores and	
Jamaica	1.4	Madeira)	8.4
Puerto Rico	2.2	Romania	16.0
Argentina	16.3	Spain (including Balearic and Canary	
Bolivia	3.9	Islands)	27.8
Brazil	48.5	Sweden	6.9
Chile	5.6	Switzerland	4.6
Colombia	10.8	Turkey (in Europe)	1.6
Ecuador	3.3	United Kingdom	50.0
Paraguay	1.3	Yugoslavia	15.8
Peru	8.1		
Uruguay	2.3	Oceania	12.1
Venezuela	4.5	Australia	7.7
		New Zealand	1.8
Asia (except U.S.S.R.)	1247.7		
Afghanistan	12.0	U.S.S.R.[a]	193.0
Burma	17.0		

[a] 1946 official estimate; no 1948 estimate available.

[12] United Nations Statistical Office, August 1, 1949.

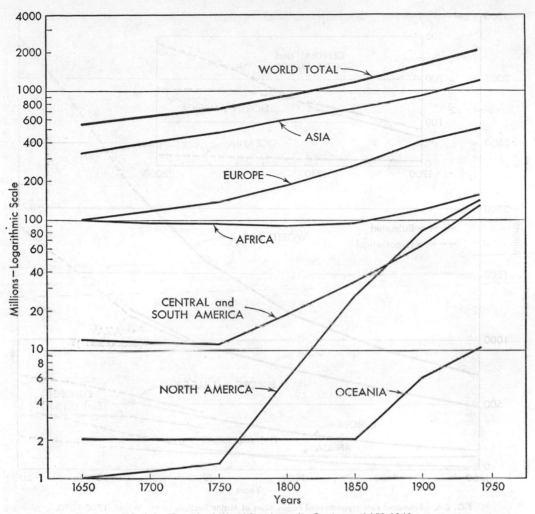

FIG. 8.5. Growth of World Population by Continents, 1650-1940.

TABLE 8.2. Estimated Population of the World, 1650-1936[13] (in millions)

Continent	1650	1750	1800	1850	1900	1936
Europe	100	140.0	187.0	266	401	533.0
North America	1	1.3	5.7	26	81	140.3
Central and South America	12	11.1	18.9	33	63	127.5
Oceania	2	2.0	2.0	2	6	10.5
Africa	100	95.0	90.0	95	120	151.2
Asia	330	479.0	602.0	749	937	1153.3
Total	545	728.4	905.6	1171	1608	2115.8

[13] 1650-1900, estimates by Willcox, revised by Carr-Saunders; 1936, *Statistical Yearbook, League of Nations, 1937-1938.*

The accelerated rate of growth of world population is indicated in the following figures showing increases for the periods indicated:

1651-1750, 33.6 percent
1751-1800, 24 percent
1801-1850, 29 percent
1851-1900, 38 percent
1901-1936, 31.7 percent (equivalent to 44 percent for 50 years)[14]

Prospects of Future Population Growth

The prediction of population growth is impossible, for no one can predict the events which will affect that growth; in particular,

[14] Note that the 33.6 percent rate for 1651 to 1750 covers an entire century, whereas the other periods run to fifty years or less.

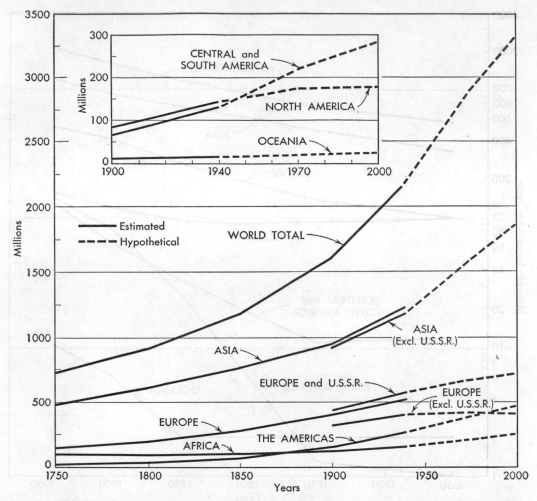

FIG. 8.6. Estimated and Hypothetical Populations of Major Sections of the World, 1750-2000.

realistic predictions of migration are impossible. Even a rough estimate of how many people will be living on this planet in the year 2000 is a wild gamble, a purely hypothetical procedure. If people behave themselves there will be more of us even fifty years hence. If world wars get bigger and better there will be far fewer. However, statisticians have worked out ingenious methods of calculating prospective growth as determined by the orderly projection of known past trends. Such prognoses are "illustrative of the underlying and orderly processes of population change."[15]

These simple truths must be understood when one studies the following attempts made by experienced demographers to give us their best hypothetical prognosis. Such a prognosis must needs be hypothetical if for no other reason than that certain basic forces and tendencies operating in the past must necessarily be assumed to be operative in the future. But no one can know whether and to what extent they will operate. The data in Table 8.3 and Fig. 8.6 were presented in the early forties by Frank W. Notestein and his associates of the Office of Population Research at Princeton University.[16]

[15] Frank W. Notestein, Irene B. Taeuber, Dudley Kirk, Ansley J. Coale, and Louise K. Kiser, *The Future Population of Europe and the Soviet Union,* League of Nations, Geneva, 1944, p. 21.

[16] One will do well to remember that these calculations were made while the Allies of World War II were still friends and before such terms as "cold war" and "iron curtain" had even been coined.

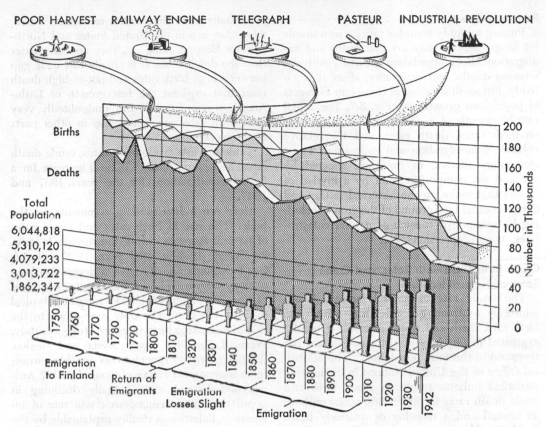

POOR HARVEST   RAILWAY ENGINE   TELEGRAPH   PASTEUR   INDUSTRIAL REVOLUTION

Births

Deaths

Total
Population
6,044,818
5,310,120
4,079,233
3,013,722
1,862,347

Number in Thousands
200
180
160
140
120
100
80
60
40
20
0

1750 1760 1770 1780 1790 1800 1810 1820 1830 1840 1850 1860 1870 1880 1890 1900 1910 1920 1930 1942

Emigration
to Finland

Return of
Emigrants

Emigration
Losses Slight

Emigration

FIG. 8.7. The Universal Cycle of Population Growth Under the Industrial Revolution, as Experienced by Sweden. (Reprinted by permission, from *Life*, September 3, 1945. Copyright Time Inc.)

This estimate of roughly 3300 million world population in the year 2000 is almost sure to prove either much too conservative or much too

TABLE 8.3.   Estimated Hypothetical Population of Major Sections of the World in 1970 and 2000 (in millions)[*]

	1970	2000
North America	176[a]	176[a]
Europe, west of the prewar border of U.S.S.R.	417	417
U.S.S.R.	251	298
Central and South America	...	283
Oceania	...	21
Africa	...	250
Asia	...	1900

[a] How precarious such prognosis is is demonstrated by the act that these estimates for North America 1970 and 2000 had already been exceeded by 1950, the populations of the United States, Canada, and Mexico totaling almost 190 million tha year. For a discussion of the unexpected upturn of the birth rate in North America in the 1940's, see Joseph S. Davis, *The Population Upsurge in the United States* (pamphlet), Food Research Institute, Stanford University, 1949; also "Fifty Million More Americans," *Foreign Affairs*, April, 1950.

liberal. Coming events will almost certainly demonstrate that it is way out of line. If these coming events spell prolonged peace and unprecedented prosperity, the figures will be far too low; if it is to be war and anarchy they will seem ridiculously high.

DEMOGRAPHY

It was pointed out in the preceding section that the prediction of future population growth is impossible but that expectation of future trends may be based on past trends. In order to be able to do this intelligently, one must know what figures mean, what forces are at work to bring about certain results; in short, he must be versed in the science of population, demography. Here only a few elementary concepts of demography are discussed briefly as an aid to the discussion of population history which follows.

Factors Involved

Putting a highly complex process into simple lay language, one may say that births and immigration affect population growth positively, whereas deaths and emigration affect it negatively. For an illustration of these four elements of population growth, see Fig. 8.7. The actual rate of growth of a given population depends on birth rates, death rates, and the relative volume of immigration and emigration. These elementary factors, in turn, are affected by age and sex composition and by a myriad of factors that make up the historical setting and environmental background of the group, including fortuitous events such as natural catastrophes, wars, depressions, etc.

Crude Birth and Death Rates, and Crude Rates of Natural Increase

The crude rate of natural increase is obtained by subtracting the death rate from the birth rate. Birth and death rates are generally expressed in numbers of births and deaths per thousand of the total population.[17] The Statistical Office of the United Nations in its monthly statistical bulletin publishes crude birth and crude death rates for about 36 nations on both an annual and a monthly or quarterly basis. Crude birth rates range from 87.1 per thousand of inhabitants for Costa Rica in October, 1947, to 12.8 for Austria in 1937. The highest annual birth rate shown in the bulletin for June, 1948, is 54.3 for Costa Rica in 1947.

Birth rates over 40 per thousand are rare and occur mainly in frontier regions of rapid economic development, possibly because of the favorable age composition resulting from the immigration of vigorous youth; these high rates also occur in tropical areas. At present, "Latin America exhibits some of the world's highest birth rates. Nobody knows exactly how high they are; according to our estimates the average rate in 1930 for the whole region was 43, which is probably too low.[18] The birth rates

are usually more than twice, sometimes thrice, what they are in the United States and Northwestern Europe. Also, . . . they are far greater than the death rates. It is chiefly this wide gap between high birth rates and not-so-high death rates that explains the fast growth of Latin-American population."[19] But, undoubtedly, very high birth rates are found also in other parts of the world.

Table 8.4 lists crude birth rates, crude death rates, and crude rates of natural increase for a few selected nations for the years 1937 and 1947.

Here are a few random comments on the table. The rise in birth rates and crude rates of natural increase during the decade is striking. While itself a good year, 1937 still suffered demographically from a depression psychology aggravated in some countries by fear of war. The figures for 1947 suggest a typical postwar reaction. The only exceptions to the rule of increasing birth rates are Hungary, Italy, Portugal, Rumania, Spain, India, and Mexico. Anyone is free to speculate on possible causes; some may appear rather obvious. In 1937 Austria and France were actually declining in population. The tremendous crude rate of increase in Palestine is readily explainable by the special circumstances prevailing in that country at present. Immigration of youth and a birth-favoring age composition have much to do with it.

Net Reproduction Rates

The meaning of crude birth rates, crude death rates, and crude rates of natural increase in "measuring long-run implications of the current vital position of a group" is obscured by the complexity of trends of growth and decline inherent in age composition and other characteristics of a group. In other words, current birth, death, and increase statistics can be very misleading. They may warrant false optimism as readily as false pessimism. High birth rates may represent the last manifestation of a dying trend or the first manifestation of a coming trend. In vital statistics, lags between cause and

[17] A more sophisticated rate is the ratio of girl babies born per 100 (or 1000) of women of child-bearing age.

[18] Estimates were made for the individual countries by various techniques, depending on the amount of data available. The actual average rate for the entire region might be anywhere between 40 and 50, but is not likely to lie outside these margins.

[19] See Kingsley Davis, "Population Trends and Policies in Latin America," in *Some Economic Aspects of Postwar Inter-American Relations,* University of Texas Institute of Latin-American Studies, 1946, pp. 25-46.

TABLE 8.4. Crude Birth Rates, Crude Death Rates, and Crude Rates of Natural Increase per 1000, for Selected Countries, 1937 and 1947[20]

	1937	1947		1937	1947
Europe			**Asia**		
Austria	12.8	18.6	India (part)	33.7	27.9 (1946)
	−13.3	−12.5		−21.9	−17.5
	− 0.5	6.1		11.8	10.4
Belgium	15.4	17.4	Japan	30.8	34.8
	−13.2	−13.1		−17.0	−14.8
	2.2	4.3		13.8	20.0
Czechoslovakia . . .	16.2	23.8	Palestine	41.5	44.4 (1946)
	−13.0	−11.9		−18.9	−12.3
	3.2	11.9		22.6	32.1
Denmark	18.0	22.1			
	−10.8	− 9.7	**English-Speaking Overseas**		
	7.2	12.4	Australia	17.4	24.0
Finland	19.9	27.3		− 9.4	− 9.1
	−13.0	−11.9		8.0	14.9
	6.9	15.4	Canada	20.0	28.6
France	15.0	21.0		−10.3	− 9.3
	−15.3	−13.0		9.7	19.3
	− 0.7	8.0	New Zealand . . .	17.3	26.4
Hungary	20.2	18.7		− 9.1	− 9.4
	−14.2	−12.3		8.2	17.0
	6.0	6.4	South Africa	24.9	27.2
Italy	22.9	21.6		−10.1	− 8.7
	−14.2	−11.2		14.8	18.5
	8.7	10.4	U.S.A.	17.1	25.9
Netherlands	19.8	27.7		−11.3	−10.1
	− 8.8	− 8.0		5.8	15.8
	11.0	19.7			
Norway	15.1	21.6	**Latin America**		
	−10.4	− 9.3	Chile	33.5	33.8
	4.7	12.3		−24.0	−16.7
Portugal	26.7	23.9		9.5	17.1
	−15.8	13.3	Costa Rica	42.2	54.3
	10.9	10.6		−18.2	−14.2
Rumania	30.8	23.8 (1946)		24.0	40.1
	−19.3	−18.0	Mexico	44.1	42.5 (1946)
	11.5	5.8		−24.4	−18.7
Spain	22.7	21.3		19.7	23.8
	−19.0	−11.8	Nicaragua	33.7	34.8
	3.7	9.5		−12.3	−10.9
Sweden	14.4	18.9		20.4	23.9
	−12.0	−10.8	Venezuela	33.7	38.5 (1946)
	2.4	8.1		−18.1	−15.0
Switzerland	14.9	19.3		15.6	23.5
	−11.3	−11.3			
	3.6	8.0			
United Kingdom . .	15.3	20.7			
	−12.6	−12.4			
	2.7	8.3			

[20] Statistical Office of the United Nations, *Monthly Bulletin of Statistics*, June, 1948.

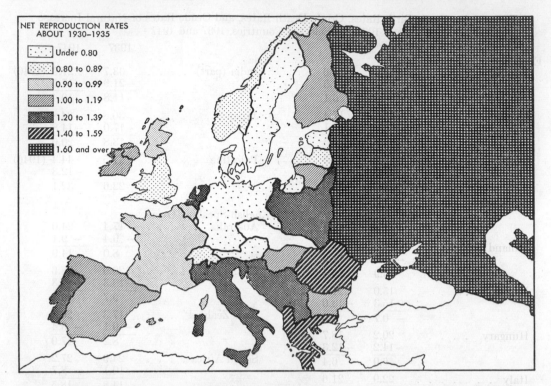

FIG. 8.8. European Net Reproduction Rates, About 1930-1935. (Figures from Office of Population Research, Princeton University; used by permission of Dr. Frank W. Notestein.)

effect, such as number of births and size of the labor force, are both common and wide. Age composition, in particular, is the resultant of numerous components that have their roots in the past, some reaching deep down, others less deep. Age composition, in turn, is one of the most important factors affecting the future vital behavior of a group. Groups may ride high on the ground swell of passing vigor, or they may hide in current stagnation a future swell the impetus for which is already working under the surface.

To measure mathematically "the long-run implications of the current vital position" of a group, statisticians use a device known as the net reproduction rate. "This rate indicates how fast the population would ultimately grow if the risks of death and the fertility of each age group remained unchanged and there were no migration. If the rate is 1.50, it means that current fertility and mortality would ultimately yield a 50 per cent increase per generation of 28 to 30 years; if it is 1.00, they would ulti-

mately yield a stationary population; if it is 0.50, the population would ultimately be cut in half every generation."[21] Needless to say, the net reproduction rate is the result of laborious calculations based on the vital behavior of each age group. It thus clearly reflects the effect of age composition on future population developments.

Fig. 8.8 shows net reproduction rates for European countries and the Soviet Union during various periods preceding World War II. Of all northern, western, and central Europe, only in the Netherlands and Ireland was the fertility[22] measured sufficient to yield continuous growth at the existing mortality rates. All the other countries were heading for actual decline unless current trends were reversed.

[21] Frank W. Notestein and others, *op. cit.*, p. 17.
[22] A distinction is made between fertility and fecundity. Fertility registers the facts of population increase; fecundity refers to the biological capacity of individual females to conceive and bear children.

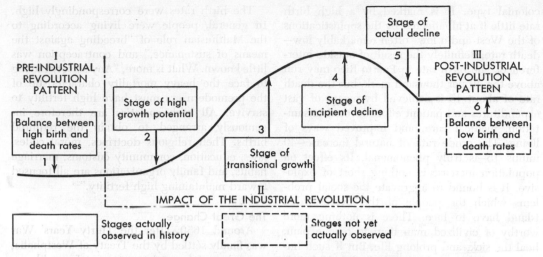

FIG. 8.9. The Impact of the Industrial Revolution on Population Trends.

Northwestern and central Europe were not the only sections of the globe where this phenomenon of net reproduction rates below 1.0 was observed during the interwar period. The meaning of the war and postwar spurt in births cannot yet be determined with assurance.[23] In the United States, the rate had been near the level required for replacement since about 1930, when the war and postwar flurry caused what is probably a temporary reversal. Australia and New Zealand manifest similar trends. All these countries are "coasting" on the momentum of past growth, but they cannot "coast" forever.

In sharp contrast to the regions heading for a decline are others manifesting positive growth rates of various sizes. Thus while the population of northwestern and central Europe is expected to decline from 234 million in 1940 to 225 million in 1970,[24] the population of southern and eastern Europe is expected to increase from 165 million to 192 million during the same period, and that of the Soviet Union from 174 million to 251 million. The population of Latin America is expected to increase from 133 million in 1940 to 203 million in 1970.[25]

Demographic Types

A distinction must be made between two distinct demographic types, both of which manifest growth. This distinction rests on the fact that some groups displaying growth are *still* growing, though tendencies toward decline are at work, whereas others are just beginning to grow, with the real upward spurt only developing. These two demographic types may be referred to as groups in the stage of "transitional growth" and of "high growth potential" respectively. The label for the types faced by prospective decline is marked "incipient decline."

Other types can be distinguished. There are two types of stationary population, one resulting from a balance between high birth and death rates, the other from a balance between low birth and death rates. Obviously a type marked by actual decline must also be recognized. As will be brought out in the next section, this type appears as the result of historical developments in which the mechanical revolution is the chief driving force. Arranged in historical sequence, these types are shown in Fig. 8.9.

Finally, a special demographic pattern or type must be recognized. It may be called the

[23] See, for instance, K.-G. Hagstroem, "Rejuvenation Tendencies in the Swedish Population," *Skandinaviska Banken Quarterly Review*, July, 1946, pp. 75-79.

[24] As calculated by Notestein and others, *op. cit.*

[25] See Kingsley Davis, *op. cit.*, p. 32. Davis

stresses the tentative nature of his calculations, which are necessarily based on inadequate data. This, in varying extent, applies to all these calculations.

colonial type. It is marked by a high birth rate little if at all affected by the sophistications of the West and a low—often remarkably low—death rate, definitely the result of outside interference. The birth rate in Puerto Rico may run above the 40 per thousand mark, but the death rate of about 15 is achieved by means of vast expenditures and patient effort devoted to sanitation, medical care, and improved ways of living. The crude rate of natural increase—40 minus 15—is truly phenomenal. Its effect on population increase is nothing short of explosive. It is bound to aggravate the social problems which the people of this overcrowded island have to face. There is nothing more worthy of civilized man than to relieve pain, heal the sick, and prolong life. But if such humane work is to yield the results at which it is aimed, a wise population policy which considers both births and deaths, and a courageous economic policy which strives to create employment opportunities for the surviving millions, are vitally needed.

THE MECHANICAL REVOLUTION AND POPULATION TRENDS

The World Before 1650

It is generally assumed that the great "vital revolution" or "demographic transition" in the midst of which we are living and the consequences of which are plaguing mankind[26] began around the middle of the seventeenth century. What happened before then is little known, but some basic facts can be conjectured. Growth, on the whole, must have been slow. It must have been slow because high death rates balanced high birth rates. Death rates were high because medicine and sanitation were virtually inoperative, because wars and internecine strife were common experiences, and because human life was worth very little.[27]

The birth rates were correspondingly high. In general, people were living according to the Malthusian rule of "breeding against the means of sustenance," and contraception was little known. What is more, "Any society having to face the heavy mortality characteristic of the premodern era must have high fertility to survive. All such societies are therefore ingeniously arranged to obtain the required births. Their religious doctrines, moral codes, laws, education, community customs, marriage habits, and family organizations are all focused toward maintaining high fertility."[28]

The Great Change

Around 1650, after the Thirty Years' War was finally settled by the Treaty of Westphalia, a number of forces began to act favorably on population growth. The growth came about through a decline of mortality, not an increase of births. "In Europe an era of peace and domestic order began to restore the ravaged continent during the seventeenth century. Then shortly afterward there followed a series of agricultural innovations that greatly increased the food supply, which was further augmented by the vast resources of the New World. Industrial innovations began to bring spectacular increases in product. Finally, sanitary and medical advances brought control over the ravaging diseases of childhood and young adult life. In short, the whole process of modernization in Europe and Europe overseas brought rising levels of living, new controls over disease, and reduced mortality."[29] While beginning with commercial and agricultural development, the movement gained momentum with the coming of the mechanical revolution, the increased use of inanimate energy which in turn fertilized all other fields of economic endeavor.

---

[26] See especially A. M. Carr-Saunders, *World Population: Past Growth and Present Trends*, Oxford University Press, Oxford, 1936; Frank W. Notestein and Regina Stix, *Controlled Fertility*, Williams and Wilkins, Baltimore, 1941; and Kingsley Davis, "The World Demographic Transition," *Annals of the American Academy of Political and Social Science*, January, 1945, and "The Shifting Balance of World Population," *Forum*, January, 1946, pp. 419-426, and February, 1946, pp. 493-498.

[27] It has been estimated that a young and vigor-

ous slave lasted only two to three years after reaching the mines operated by the Romans in Spain during the Punic Wars. In Japan under the Tokugawa shogunate the life of a peasant is supposed to have been valued at less than that of the landlord's pet dog. During the transatlantic slave trade whole cargoes of "human ebony" were scuttled to escape capture, and the death rate in transit is supposed to have been horrendous. Infanticide and exposure of the ill and weak were accepted mores in many tribal societies.

[28] Frank W. Notestein, "Population—The Long View," p. 39.

[29] *Ibid.*

Thus there began a period of rapid growth, first in northwestern Europe, and spreading from there to central and still later to southern and eastern Europe, Russia, Japan, Latin America, and India. The countries of the world, one after the other, began that strange vital revolution or demographic career mapped out in Fig. 8.9. One of the most recent episodes of this global phenomenon is the fight against the tsetse fly in Africa. Some people greet it as a great achievement, others fear its consequences.

Negative Phase of the Industrial Revolution

The first impact of the mechanical revolution and its forerunners on population was positive. It caused an almost explosive increase in numbers, especially of the white race.[30] This vast growth is shown in Table 8.5.

TABLE 8.5. The Increase of Population in Western Europe and European Settlements Overseas, 1800-1938[31]
(in millions)

Country	1800	1850	1900	1938
Belgium	3.0	4.4	6.7	8.4
Denmark	1.0	1.4[a]	2.5	3.8
Finland	1.1	1.6	2.6	3.7
France	28.2	35.8	40.7	42.0
Germany	23.0	35.1[d]	56.4	69.5
Gt. Britain	10.7(1851)	20.9	37.0	46.3
Ireland	5.3(1851)	6.6	4.5	4.2
Italy	18.1	. . .	32.5	43.4
Netherlands	2.2(1851)	3.1	5.2	8.7
Norway	0.9(1855)	1.3	2.2	2.9
Portugal	3.1	3.5[b]	5.4	7.5
Spain	12.0(1849)	14.2[c]	18.6	25.6
Sweden	2.3	3.5	5.1	6.3
Switzerland	1.8	2.4	3.3	4.2
Argentine	. . .	1.1[d](1895)	4.0[f]	13.0
Australia	. . . (1870)	1.6[e]	3.7[f]	6.9
Brazil	. . .	7.7[d]	16.6[f]	44.1
Canada	0.35[d]	2.4[g](1901)	5.4	11.3
Chile	. . .	1.3[d](1895)	2.7[f]	4.6
New Zealand	. . .	(ex Maoris) 0.8		1.6
Union of S. Africa	. . .	. . . (1904)	5.2	10.1
U.S.A.	5.3	23.2	76.1 (1940)	130.3

[a] Not including Schleswig-Holstein. Lauenburg 888,750.
[b] Not including Madeira and Azores, 343,000.
[c] Including Balearic and Canary Islands.
[d] W. F. Willcox, International Migrations, p. 77.
[e] E. O. G. Shann, Economic History of Australia.
[f] Census figures.
[g] British America.

[30] Condliffe (op. cit., pp. 14-15) comments on this explosive outburst as follows: "It is perhaps salutary to look first at the 19th century increase in the population of western Europe through the

But eventually the process of modernization which is here referred to as the mechanical revolution generated powerful negative forces which in due course brought the peoples of the West to the brink of population decline. After a long lag, the process of modernization began to affect fertility, birth rates began to fall. The negative phase of the Industrial Revolution had begun. It was bound to win. If high fertility rates were consciously sponsored and guarded by a host of social devices prompted by the specter of high mortality rates, it was only a matter of time until low mortality rates would call for a revision of the ancient codes. Institutions change slowly. Lowering the death rate meets with whole-hearted approval; lowering the birth rate meets with fierce opposition from those who view parentage as a sacred right, not as one of the highest social responsibilities.

How this reduction of fertility came about is a complicated story still partly veiled in mystery.

There is abundant evidence that the decline came about primarily through rational control, largely by means of contraceptive practices. It does not follow that contraception can be viewed as the cause of the declining birth rate in any profound sense. Relatively effective methods of contraception were widely known for centuries before they were generally used. Birth rates were reduced largely by means of contraception, but in response to drastic changes in the social and economic setting that radically altered the motives and aims of people with respect to family size.[32]

eyes of a Chinese. In the first of his famous lectures on 'The Three Principles of the People,' which have become the political bible of modern China, Dr. Sun Yat-sen laid stress on the peril—'the white peril'—which western European and American economic expansion constituted for other peoples, and particularly for China. Very similar statements may be culled from the writings of Indian and Japanese students of population."

[31] Ibid., p. 16. Principal sources: 1800 and 1900 figures from Encyclopædia of the Social Sciences, vol. 12, p. 244; 1850 figures from Guillaumin, etc., Annuaire de l'économie politique et de la statistique, Paris; 1938 figures from League of Nations, Statistical Yearbook 1939-1940.

[32] See Norman E. Himes, Medical History of Contraception (Baltimore: Williams and Wilkins Co., 1936); and Frank W. Notestein and Regina K. Stix, Controlled Fertility (Baltimore: Williams and Wilkins Co., 1940, chap. xv).

The catalogue of such changes is large and can only be suggested here. Most of them center around the growing individualism and rising levels of popular aspiration developed in urban industrial living. With the growth of huge and mobile city populations, the individual came to depend less and less on the status of his family for his place among his fellows. The station to which he was born gave place to his accomplishments and possessions as the measure of his importance. Meanwhile, the family lost many of its functions to the factory, the school, and commercial enterprises, all these developments made large families a progressively difficult and expensive undertaking; expensive and difficult for a population increasingly freed from older taboos and increasingly willing to solve its problems rather than to accept them. In short, under the impact of urban life, the social aim of perpetuating the family gave way progressively to that of promoting the health, education, and material welfare of the individual child; family limitation became widespread; and the end of the period of growth came in sight. However, during that period the population of European extraction had increased nearly sevenfold throughout the world.[33]

In a way, this negative phase of the Industrial Revolution is as vital as the positive phase. For not only does it spare industrial countries untold woe in the form of vast "technological unemployment," but it accounts for much of the superiority of the modern industrial way of life over the old vegetable coolie pattern. There are those who would deny the possibility of technological unemployment. The reasoning on which they base their argument (machines make things cheaper; the cheaper the thing, the larger the demand; the stronger the demand, the more things are made, etc.) is sound enough so far as it goes. But it does not go far enough. Unemployment[34] in the United States was not brought under control until World War II stepped demand up to abnormal size. No one knows yet what the postwar pattern will be. If the most prosperous nation of the world cannot keep its labor employed when birth control is keeping the labor force down by millions, perhaps tens of millions, what would the volume of unemployment be if the negative

phase of the mechanical revolution had never occurred?

The great question before mankind today is how fast and how soon this negative phase will spread to other parts of the earth. Our own past furnishes the answer: not until (1) the tremendous pent-up force of high growth potential has been released and spent and (2) the culture level of the masses in the countries now in the "high growth potential" and "transitional growth" stages of the demographic cycle has reached a level high enough to make "a baby grand" seem more desirable than "a grand baby." That, alas, takes time, much time. In the meantime, the pressure from the low-standard areas of rapid growth on the thinly or moderately densely populated areas of the prosperous West will be terrific. The political and military implications of this differential population growth are vast and ominous.

The Modern Demographic Pattern

Before the great discoveries and inventions and the commercial, agricultural, and industrial revolutions stirred up the ancient lethargy of vegetating and proliferating humanity, a certain balance was maintained between births and deaths. It was maintained by a high level of both, perhaps an average of 40 births and 35 deaths, or something of that order. Now the world, stirred to its very depths, shows signs of a new balance, a new equilibrium. This time it is one marked by low birth rates and lower death rates. So far as the continuity of the group is concerned, it may not make much difference whether the crude rate of increase is the result of subtracting 35 from 40 or 5 from 10. But what a difference this simple arithmetic makes in the fundamental character and performance of civilization! The difference is simply this: An ancient people with a high birth and death rate balance virtually exhausts itself in the biological process of group survival. Much female labor is absorbed in bearing and rearing children. The ratio of productive to unproductive years is pathetic. The labor force constitutes a relatively small portion of the total population. This small force, on whose shoulders rests the responsibility of feeding and otherwise caring for the whole group, is apt to be hard pressed. They turn to children for help. The whole group is overworked. Yet it

---

[33] Frank W. Notestein, *op. cit.*, pp. 40-41.
[34] See Emil Lederer, *Technical Progress and Unemployment*, League of Nations, International Labour Office, Geneva, 1938.

cannot get ahead. More or less all work is heavy work, there are no typing or telephone jobs for female labor.[35]

Under the high birth and death rate pattern vast numbers of babies are born that never live more than a few weeks or months; others linger for a few years but never reach the age at which they can repay society for the effort and sacrifice which reared them and brought them near but not up to the level of productive strength and ability. While some adults live to a very old age, many die from accidents or diseases after relatively few years of productive labor. The group may be on the brink of bankruptcy because not enough adults can pay their debts to society. The situation is aggravated by the fact that old age comes early after superhuman struggles, and is largely unproductive. Average life expectancy at birth in such a society is very low, perhaps in the twenties or low thirties.

The superiority of modern industrial civilization over ancient vegetable civilization rests largely on the different life expectancy at birth, the age composition which this implies, and the ratio of productive to unproductive members of the group which results from these conditions. A vegetable civilization cannot build up much capital because its inefficient man power exhausts itself in producing food for the wasteful structure of the group. Japan may have lost the war because her rulers had to keep a vast portion of the population in food production. The situation is worse in China. In the United States the total labor force is much larger relative to the total population, and only a small fraction is employed in agriculture; robots do the heavy work and create infinite employment opportunities at lighter tasks for the weaker members of the group; the strain of bearing and rearing children is far less on society as a whole. All this makes the whole system more productive and yields surpluses and leisure which furnish not only the capital equipment for harnessing natural energies but also the paraphernalia of good government, and funds for training, education, recreation, better health—in short, for all the

elements which lift human existence above the drudgery of the coolie and permit that most precious of all occupational specializations, specialization along the lines of man's peculiar aptitudes.

Optimum Population[36] and Population Density

Perhaps the simplest definition of the term optimum population is that it is the ideal man-land ratio. Another one is: The optimum population is that population an increase of which produces overpopulation, and a decrease of which produces underpopulation.

But this simplicity is achieved by shifting the burden of definition from optimum population to that of ideal, overpopulation, and underpopulation. Overpopulation may be defined as the man-land ratio at which, *because of excessive numbers of people,* the social economy brings lower returns in terms of the values the economy strives to achieve. Underpopulation is defined in the same way except that *excessive numbers* is replaced by *insufficient numbers.* The social economy may be considered subject to the law of diminishing returns. Returns may diminish because of an excess or deficiency of any one factor—nature, culture, or man. But the triune interrelation of the factors must never be lost sight of.

Because of this, the optimal point of each factor depends on the proportionality of all three factors. Thus, in an industrial civilization that commands many robots the optimum man-land ratio is found at a population density per square mile far below that which a robot-less vegetable civilization must maintain. This idea may be expressed in several ways.

1. The population density at which the optimum is attained depends primarily on the amount of foreign energy, particularly inanimate energy, available.

Since foreign energy can be made available only by means of capital equipment, the same principle could be expressed as follows:

---

[35] It need hardly be mentioned that this description is put in general terms and barely begins to do justice to the heterogeneity of reality.

[36] For a valuable critique of the concept of optimum population, see E. F. Penrose, *Population Theories and Their Application, with Special Reference to Japan,* Food Research Institute, Stanford University, 1934, especially chaps. 2 and 3. The reader interested in probing into this problem more deeply than can be done here will find valuable references to other literature on the subject in this book.

2. The population density at which the optimum is attained depends largely on the amount of capital equipment available.

Furthermore, since a low density is compatible with a high civilization only if the sparse population is very mobile, we can express the same idea a third way:

3. The population density at which the optimum is attained depends on the relative mobility of the population.

In view of the close relationship between the supply of inanimate energy, the availability of capital equipment, and the degree of mobility, the first formula may be said to contain the other formulas.

Such principles may appear rather abstract, but they aid the understanding and critical appraisal of national economies and the advantages and limitations of modern mechanical civilization.

One conclusion, however, may be drawn here. Fortunately we do not need to rely on population increase to bring us closer to the optimum. Every improvement in the technique —and, one might add, in the management— of transportation and communication reduces the space handicap, lowers the weight of the overhead burden, and thus brings us closer to the optimum. Too sanguine hopes should not be based on this statement, for one must not lose sight of the fact that population growth is itself a dynamic factor in the process of cultural development. Therefore, what at a given moment may appear as an ideal man-land ratio, viewed as a stage in an unfolding process, may fall short of the ideal. A declining birth rate may lead toward the optimum, but the decline, because of its momentum, may go too far. Population optimum in a machine civilization depends largely on the relationship between mechanical horsepower and human brains, not on acres of pasture land, loaves of bread, and human brawn. This relationship is so complex and dynamic that predictions of future trends seem folly.

BIBLIOGRAPHY

Carr-Saunders, A. M., "Crowded Countries and Empty Spaces," *Foreign Affairs*, April, 1950.

Carver, T. N., "Some Needed Refinements of the Theory of Population," in M. Sanger, *Proceedings of the World Population Conference*, London, Arnold, 1927.

Condliffe, J. B., *The Economic Pattern of World Population*, Planning Pamphlet No. 18, Washington, National Planning Association, 1943.

Davis, J. S., *The Population Upsurge in the United States*, War-Peace Pamphlets No. 12, Food Research Institute, Stanford University, 1950.

Davis, J. S., "Fifty Million More Americans," *Foreign Affairs*, April, 1950.

Davis, K., "The World Demographic Transition," *Annals of the American Academy of Political and Social Science*, January, 1945.

Davis, K., "Population Trends and Policies in Latin America," in *Some Economic Aspects of Postwar Inter-American Relations*, University of Texas Institute of Latin-American Studies, 1946.

Davis, K., "The Shifting Balance of World Population," *Forum*, January and February, 1946.

Dell, B. N., and Luthringer, B. F., *Population, Resources, and Trade*, New York, Little, Brown, 1938.

Dublin, L. I. (ed.), *Population Problems*, Boston, Houghton Mifflin, 1926.

Fairchild, H. P., *People: The Quantity and Quality of Population*, New York, Holt, 1939.

Ferenczi, I., *The Synthetic Optimum Population*, Paris, League of Nations, 1938.

Glass, V. D., *The Struggle for Population*, London, Oxford University Press, 1936.

Hagstroem, K.-G., "Rejuvenation Tendencies in the Swedish Population," *Skandinaviska Banken Quarterly Review*, July, 1946.

Kirk, D., "Population Changes in the Post-War World," *American Sociological Review*, February, 1944.

Kuczynski, R. R., "Population," *Encyclopædia of the Social Sciences*, New York, Macmillan, 1933; see also the bibliography there.

Kuczynski, R. R., *"Living-Space" and Population Problems*, World Affairs Pamphlets No. 8, New York, Farrar and Rinehart, 1939.

Landis, P. H., *Population Problems: A Cultural Interpretation*, New York, American Book, 1943.

Lederer, E., *Technical Progress and Unemployment*, Geneva, League of Nations, 1938.

Lorimer, F., and Osburn, F., *Dynamics of Population*, New York, Macmillan, 1934.

Lorimer, F., Winston, E., and Kiser, L. K., *Foundations of American Population Policy*, New York, Harper, 1940.

Mair, G. F. (ed.), "Studies in Population," *Proceedings of the Annual Meeting of the Population Association of America*, Princeton, Princeton University Press, 1949.

Mombert, P., *Bevölkerungslehre*, vol. 15 of *Grundriss zum Studium der Nationalökonomie*, Jena, Gustav Fischer, 1920.

Myrdal, G., *Population: A Problem for Democracy*, Cambridge, Harvard University Press, 1940.

Myrdal, G., *Nation and the Family*, New York, Harper, 1941.

National Resources Committee, *The Problems of a Changing Population*, Washington, 1938.

Notestein, F. W., "Population—The Long View," in T. W. Schultz (ed.), *Food for the World*, Chicago, University of Chicago Press, 1945.

Notestein, F. W., and Stix, R., *Controlled Fertility*, Baltimore, Williams and Wilkins, 1940.

Notestein, F. W., Taueber, I. B., Kirk, D., Coale, A. J., and Kiser, L. K., *The Future Population of Europe and the Soviet Union*, Geneva, League of Nations, 1944.

Pearl, R., *Studies in Human Biology*, Baltimore, Williams and Wilkins, 1924.

Pearl, R., *The Natural History of Population*, New York, Oxford, 1939.

Penrose, E. F., *Population Theories and Their Application*, Food Research Institute, Stanford University, 1934.

Reddaway, W. B., *Economics of a Declining Population*, London, Macmillan, 1939.

Sorokin, P., *The Reconstruction of Humanity*, Boston, Beacon Press, 1948.

Thompson, W. S., *Population Problems*, New York, McGraw-Hill, 3rd ed., 1942.

Thompson, W. S., *Plenty of People*, Lancaster, Jacques Cattell Press, 1944.

Thompson, W. S., and Whelpton, P. K., *Population Trends in the United States*, New York, 1933.

United Nations, *Demographic Yearbook, 1948*, Lake Success, 1949.

Vance, R. B., in collaboration with Banilevsky, N., *All These People*, Chapel Hill, University of North Carolina Press, 1945.

Wright, F. C., *Population and Peace*, Geneva, League of Nations, 1939. Also published as vol. 2 of *Peaceful Change*, New York, Columbia University Press, 1939.

Chapter 9

CULTURE AND RESOURCES

ORIGIN, MEANING, AND FUNCTION OF CULTURE

Man the Culture-Builder

At first there was nature. It included the earth and the sky and the stars in the sky and all that was and lived on the earth—rocks and sand, fauna and flora, earth and water, energy and matter. Then came man; and man alone of all living creatures was given the power to lift himself out of the compass of nature, the right to set his will against the will of nature and to shape nature, or parts of it, to his will to strengthen his hand in his struggle with nature. Thus there arose that lofty edifice which we call culture.

Man alone of all creatures can build culture. Culture building is a human prerogative. It stems from the human capacity to invent arts and artifacts and to elevate arts to the level of science, a capacity that derives from man's superior intellect and unique physical endowment. It is culture that permits man to inhabit every continent, to exist in the tropics and in the frigid zones of the earth. This does not mean that he wipes out the effects of climatic difference on him. His adjustment to climate is only partial. In spite of the latest devices for heating and cooling houses, people still crowd into a few areas of the more temperate zones.

Culture a Joint Product of Man and Nature

Nature and man may be called the original resource factors. Culture is the derivative. It is a joint product of man and nature. Man creates culture with the aid, "advice, and consent" of nature, out of substances found in nature, and with the aid of energies supplied by nature.

That nature aids man in culture building is obvious; it needs no further explanation. But the phrase "the advice and consent" of nature may deserve some comment. As was pointed out in the first chapter, man has a natural bent for economy. He strives to get the most for his effort. Therefore, he does not run head-on against the resistances of nature; as often as not he goes around the obstacle. If nature offers alternatives, man is apt to choose the one that offers the best results for his effort. He chooses to want what nature permits him to produce with the least effort and with the best results for his effort. Europeans eat potatoes, Asiatics eat rice, North Americans eat corn-fed meat. In Europe conditions favor the production of potatoes; in Asia rice seems to give best results; in North America, corn.[1] This statement is not meant to suggest some simple natural determinism or environmentalism.[2] The point made here is that the desire to economize effort often leads man to adapt himself consciously and willingly to nature. Nature, so to speak, advises man to choose what natural conditions render easiest to produce. Nature does not consent to men living at the North Pole or on the top of Mount Everest.

Culture and Adaptation

Much of culture may be properly viewed as a device of adaptation to nature. But it is more. It permits man to imitate nature. Rayon may be considered the outcome of a deliberate attempt to imitate the silkworm. Culture permits man to improve on nature. Novocaine is a deliberate improvement on cocaine. Culture enables man to create new substances nowhere found in nature. Nylon and a host of other chemical products fall into this category.[3] Culture gives man the power to release energies not available in nature. The energies of the accelerated fission of fissionable elements, generally called atomic or nuclear energies, are a case in point.

Culture is the sum total of all the devices produced by man, with the aid, "advice, and consent" of nature, to assist him in the attainment of his objectives. The first of these objectives is the survival of the race with the aid of limited supplies and in the face of powerful resistances. As was stressed before, mankind as yet has no collective will. The will to survive is lodged in social groups and may be pushed by one group at the expense of others. The second objective—if one may use the term to apply to an urge, not clearly and consciously planned, but springing from the depth of man's

nature—is the provision for expanding populations. Here again there is no global unity, but, on the contrary, national conflict. The third objective is apparently the provision of greater comforts and a better material existence. Finally, culture aims to quench "the thirst that from the soul doth rise," to provide the highest values, the yearning for which is the main distinction between human beings and other living creatures.

Culture and Defects of Nature

From the standpoint of man, nature not only places many obstacles in his path, but appears to possess definite defects as a partner in production. These defects manifest themselves in *insufficient* production, production in the *wrong place,* and production at the *wrong time.* The natural ancestors of our modern cereals were puny grasses bearing little seed. The natural ancestor of our modern cow had a tiny udder, barely sufficient to feed one calf. Spontaneous yields soon proved insufficient as the number of eaters increased. So man cultivated plants and turned them into veritable starch, sugar, and gluten factories; he domesticated animals to raise their output of milk and meat; he cultivated fields to make two blades grow where one grew before; he enhanced the fertility of the soil and provided more water. That is one line of cultural improvement.

Another cultural objective is to move nature's products from the "wrong place" where nature put them to the "right place" where man wants them. The cotton of the South moves to Lancashire and Japan, the mutton of Australia to the cities of England, the rubber of Malaya to the tire factories of North America and Europe. So the earth is honeycombed with rail nets, highways, steamship lanes, and skyways. Rivers are bridged, mountains pierced, and isthmuses cut through. A vast amount of effort and substance goes to provide the rolling stock, motor vehicles, ships, and planes that perform the corrective task of bringing things "from where they are to where they ought to be." A third objective of culture is aimed at correcting nature's poor timing. Man wants to eat every day. Nature produces food in rhythmic response to the seasons. So man erects warehouses, elevators, and other storage devices; he develops the art of refrigeration and

---

[1] For a fuller development of this theme, see chap. 14, especially pp. 215 ff.

[2] See Robert S. Platt, "Environmentalism versus Geography," *American Journal of Sociology,* March, 1948.

[3] E. E. Slosson develops this point in his stimulating book *Creative Chemistry* (The Century Company, New York, 1921). See also chap. 48, especially pp. 776-780.

thus corrects, at least in part, the third defect of nature.

All these corrective efforts require more than mere physical equipment. They call for vast systems of communications, for banking and insurance, and for commercial organizations, wholesale and retail.

Culture and Resistances, Human and Natural

The aspects of nature discussed in the preceding section may be treated under the broader heading of resistances. Culture has the dual function of enlarging resources and reducing resistances. It is a cushioning device that does not abolish hurricanes and earthquakes but cushions the impact of natural disasters on man. "Forewarned is forearmed." Ships advised by radio of an approaching hurricane may be able to avoid it or at least enter the danger zone at the least dangerous angle. But one need not associate natural resistances with catastrophes. Distance is such a resistance. How cultural devices help to overcome that resistance is well known. Friction is another.

As was brought out in the presentation of the functional theory of resources, resistances are by no means confined to nature. There are many human resistances also. (See Table 1.1.) Culture also functions in the form of education, sanitation, health service, training, church, government, etc. That these phases of culture are lagging behind was pointed out on page 38. That culture, moreover, generates its own resistances will be brought out more fully later on (see p. 125).

Culture an Aid to Man and Nature

Culture, a joint product of human effort and ingenuity and of nature, lends aid, in turn, to both man and nature. Just as the arts were divided into those designed to enlarge human capacities and those designed to render nature more amenable to human use (see p. 33), so culture, which includes the arts, may be similarly divided into devices designed to support and aid man and nature respectively. The labor-saving machine clearly supports man; and terracing, fertilizers, drainage, bud grafting, hybridizing help nature to produce more. Both sets of cultural devices may raise the productivity of labor; but the one achieves this goal by aiding man directly, the other by enlarging the product that man, with a given amount of labor, extracts from nature. The man-aiding devices are not all as simple as labor-saving machines. They include intangibles such as management in the widest sense of total coördination of group effort, mores promoting group coöperation, education, training, improved health, and such aids to thinking, planning, and calculating as libraries, laboratory equipment, logarithm tables, "mechanical brains," etc. They even include the division of labor and specialization, arrangements which affect productivity indirectly but nevertheless materially. Recreation, intellectual pursuit, hobbies, spiritual guidance and devotion must not be omitted. For peace of mind, clean thought, and a fresh outlook are vital aids to human performance.

Culture the Equalizing Agent

Culture varies in origin, form, and function according to the character of the natural environment and the relationship between the natural opportunities and the population. In densely populated areas lacking, deficient in, or unable to use mineral resources, especially fuels and metals, capital is usually made by man through hard work or abstention; it is applied to the land to raise its yield. Thus in Asia irrigation systems, rice terraces and similar improvements of the land are typical forms of culture. Such tangible forms of culture designed to render more effective the processes of production are generally referred to as capital.

On the other hand, where labor is scarce and natural opportunities for mechanization abound, capital, though invented and designed by man, is made with the aid of inanimate energies. In the United States these conditions were found during the nineteenth century and they in part account for the perfection and accumulation of labor-saving devices. (Time-saving devices also save labor indirectly.) Some sections of Europe resemble Asia, and others America, in this respect.

In short, in the countries relying mainly on man power for energy, where human labor is abundant relative both to the small amount of land that human labor can cultivate without inanimate energy[4] and to the paucity of natural

---

[4] See the preceding discussion in chap. 7, especially pp. 87-89.

forces that can be tapped, culture in the form of capital tends to be applied to nature in the form of land, farm land—food-yielding, human-energy-creating land. Vice versa, in countries where man has succeeded in surrounding himself with many robots—i.e., natural energy units—and where, with the aid of this potent and tireless staff of assistants furnished by nature, he can tap numerous forms and phases of nature with far greater efficiency than can the robotless coolie, nature is abundant and natural forces, guided by man, contribute to erect the structure of culture assisting him.

This equalizing function of culture may be expressed in the form of a "law": The "long" factor (i.e., the abundant factor) tends to create culture (capital) to support the "short" factor.[5]

CULTURE IN THE WORLD TODAY

Culture and the Ecumene

If one understands the ecumene to refer to the areas of the globe inhabited by man, it follows logically that the area of the ecumene is also the area of culture. Wherever man's habitat extends, there culture extends also.

But culture extends beyond the borders of the ecumene. There are desert regions in many parts of the world which once were rich agricultural areas supporting large populations. The jungle of Yucatán covers areas where civilization once flourished. There are ghost towns in the West where cities of considerable size once stood. Though no longer functioning in the service of man, the culture changes wrought by man continue to exert a certain influence. Mountains once denuded of their forest cover may be abandoned by man to nature, but the natural landscape continues to show the scars and to reveal the destructive powers of man. The fauna and flora are changed by man's eradication of entire species. The old ecological equilibrium no longer exists.

Moreover, man's cultural reach goes beyond the borders of the ecumene. The oceans are not inhabited by man, but they play an important role in cultural endeavor. The air is not inhabited, but skyways penetrate it in increasing numbers. Man's knowledge and even, in modest ways, his influence reach into interstellar space; echoes from the moon are said to have been recorded by delicate devices.

Culture and "The Machine"[6]

Until the coming of the machine the impact of culture on nature, by and large, was superficial. One may say that before the age of industrialization the cultural landscape was a mere modification of the natural landscape. The man who cultivates the field with simple tools leaves the natural landscape still visible through its transparent cultural veneer. The domesticated animal still resembles its wild ancestor; and the roads and highways, generally surfaced with materials found nearby, blend into the landscape. Houses, villages, and towns likewise seem to fit into the picture—a change, to be sure, from original nature but not a violent reversal of natural trends, not a blatant insult flung at nature's face.

The machine, on the other hand, does violence to the landscape. It pushes the culture process to extremes, bringing into existence artifacts which are no longer germane to their natural background. Before the coming of modern machines, technical development reached a limit beyond which man did not seem able to push. For thousands of years he got along with the hand loom, the hammer, the saw; he managed with a few simple machines; he dug his ditches with a spade, paved the streets, and used vehicles drawn by animals. As was pointed out before, China today uses techniques born thousands of years ago. Apart from firearms, the printing press, and the compass, European technology of the sixteenth century was but little advanced over that of Greece and Rome. The greatest advance was seen in the geographical spread of that technology, sweeping eastward as far as Siberia, and westward to America.

This premachine culture, which one may call the ancient culture pattern, resulted mainly from the direct reactions of man to his natural environment. His fields, gardens, forests, cathedrals, monasteries, and cities sprang from his hand and head, unmistakable answers to the

---

[5] The significance of this law will be brought out more fully in the next chapter.

[6] See the definition of Lewis Mumford's term on p. 36.

inevitable problems created by the natural environment, clear-cut defense mechanisms. This entire ancient culture pattern was functionally true in the sense that it developed in direct response to immediate problems. In the premachine age nature predominated over culture, for man did not dare to subjugate nature.

The coming of the machine changed all this with incredible suddenness. Within a century and a half the process of devitalizing mechanization has resulted in a new artificial environment, an environment which does not seem to blend into the natural landscape, which does not lie snugly embedded in its natural foundation and organically related thereto, but one which evolves in accordance with laws other than those of organic nature. Mathematical formulas and the laws of physics, chemistry, and mechanics govern today where once the patriarch or the guild master ruled. This new environment is not a part of the cultural landscape; it is an attachment made from foreign stuff.

To appreciate this rather abstract appraisal of the new environment which the machine has created, one will do well to compare a modern factory city with a medieval town. The latter seems to fit well into the landscape. Being built of the surface matter of the earth on which it stands, it blends imperceptibly into its natural surroundings. Not so the modern factory town. In crass contrast with the fields and woods about it, it appears as an intruder from a different world. And so it is; for does it not draw its strength from the bowels of the earth? We may admire the symmetry of modern architecture, and even more the inexorable obedience of its form to human purpose; but nothing can alter its artificiality, nothing can bridge the gap between the wonder of steel and stone, the marvel of human ingenuity which is built according to the laws of dead matter with the aid of inanimate energy and the world of nature beyond. Surely the modern machine pattern differs as much from the ancient culture pattern as the latter differs from nature itself.

Probably nowhere are purer examples of this modern machine environment found than in the United States—unless it be in the new cities of Soviet Russia where man is trying to accomplish in years what western Europe did in centuries and more than Asia did in millen-

niums. Perhaps William Allen White did not exaggerate: "The average American is a new thing in the world, a man begotten by machines. Every other kindred or tribe on earth has sprung out of the soil. Other kindreds and tribes have been enriched by some beloved environment, by mountains, by rivers, by high plateaus, or desert wastes, and to these topographical manifestations the hearts of other people lay claim. But for 300 years, the American has been on the move, trying to find his ultra-western horizon."[7] Being on the move, he could not take root. Thus the machine, the symbol of devitalized artificiality, and not the soil, the transmuting agent of organic nature, is shaping the physiognomy of this, the newest civilization.[8]

Culture and Agriculture

While the impact of the machine on the natural landscape stands out by its almost brutal violence, the cultural changes wrought in the world of living plants and animals can be easily underrated. These changes in fauna and flora date back to the earliest recorded history. Even in ancient times man transferred crops from one region to another, even from one continent to another. The greater mobility of modern man which permits travel to and communication with the remotest corners of the earth has vastly aided and accelerated the work of the plant and animal explorers. Moreover, their work is aided by plant and animal breeders as never before. The science of genetics, although relatively young, is performing miracles in adapting fauna and flora to man's needs.

South America furnishes striking illustrations of the extent to which natural fauna and flora have been changed by man. The Andes are considered the original habitat of the white potato and the cinchona tree from whose bark quinine is obtained. Today the north European plain is the center of potato culture and Indonesia has a virtual monopoly of quinine production. South America was the original habitat of cacao and hevea rubber. Today the bulk of the former is grown in Africa; of the latter, in the Middle East, Malay peninsula, Indonesia,

[7] New York *Times* Magazine Section, January 4, 1931, p. 18.
[8] This discussion of the machine environment is in part based on E. Diesel, *Das Land der Deutschen*, Bibliographisches Institut. A. G., Leipzig, 1932.

and neighboring areas. Conversely, almost all the major crops found in South America today, as well as the most important animals, were brought in from the outside. Sugar cane, coffee, wheat, rice, linseed, sheep, hogs, cattle are all of foreign origin. They have remade the landscape, at least its most productive phases.

Similarly, the South of the United States illustrates the importance of alien plants and animals. Neither horses nor sheep nor cattle nor pigs were known in North America before the landing of Columbus. The crossbreeding of cattle brought in from Europe with zebu (Brahman) cattle from India is another example of cultural modification of fauna. Cotton, the tyrant that long ruled the South, was an outlander, though possibly there was a Caribbean branch of the family tree. Tobacco, one of the few native crops, never became king. Corn, or maize, which had been brought in from Central America, until recently lingered in modest circumstances in the South while flourishing farther north, farther away from its original habitat. Now that heroic efforts are being made to rewin the South after it came close to ruin under the reign of King Cotton, what are the crops on which the soil rebuilder relies most? Soybeans from Manchuria, kudzu from Japan, alfalfa and lupin from Asia, and purple clover from Europe.[9]

Undoubtedly one of the most significant impacts of culture on the natural landscape is to be seen in the work of the railroad in converting almost uninhabitable plains and prairies into the granaries of the modern world. These granaries are the western counterpart of the rice terraces of Asia. One is the work of steam, the other the work of sweat, sweat of millions of men and women and children toiling in the steaming valleys of monsoon Asia. The replacement of short and long grasses of the plains and prairies by cereals, alfalfa, and other nitrogen-fixing forage crops is probably the most magnificent change wrought by culture-building man in the natural landscape. The countries most affected by the plains-opening miracle were the United States and Canada, Argentina, the Soviet Union and her satellites, Hungary and Rumania, and to a much lesser extent,

[9] See Louis Bromfield, "The Rebirth of the South," *Country Gentleman,* July, 1949, condensed in *Reader's Digest,* July, 1949.

Australia. That such wondrous change was not achieved without grave errors of judgment followed by grave disaster at the hands of revengeful nature is well known. But man does seem to be able to learn from his mistakes, cynical interpreters of history notwithstanding.

Culture and Human Attitudes

So far, the effects of culture on nature have been discussed. Some of the most vital effects of culture are those on man himself. Culture means education, learning, experience, religion, civilized behavior, suppression of vicious animal instincts, coöperation replacing conflict, the law of fair play and justice suppressing the law of the jungle.

Culture even affects the most intimate of human mores, those governing reproduction. When culture reaches higher levels, unrestrained breeding against the means of sustenance yields to birth control and planned parenthood.

THE ANATOMY OF CULTURE
Material and Nonmaterial (Spiritual) Culture

Culture is such a vast and complex concept that it defies orderly classification. However, some attempts along this line will be made. In the first place, the distinction between material and nonmaterial culture, indirectly touched upon in the preceding discussion, deserves closer attention.

Nonmaterial culture is more changeable. Though mind and matter are too different to admit of comparison, in a deeper sense it may be said that the modern mind differs from that of antiquity more completely than the cultural landscape of today differs from its ancient counterpart. The importance of such events as the coming of Christ, the Crusades, the great discoveries, and the Renaissance lies more in the realm of the mind than in the fields of art and architecture in which are manifested the tangible results. The difference between a modern Calvinist and a worshiper of Buddha or between a modern manufacturer and a Roman industrialist is more vital than that between an automobile and a Roman chariot. Historical sense, the ability to think functionally, the injection of scientific thought into ever-wider strata of investigation and endeavor, the capitalistic spirit with its worship of profits, and particularly the ethical concepts of social responsibility are as vital innovations as railroads, steamships, automobiles, and the other spectacular successes of the scientist and the engineer. The two changes—tangible and intangible—go hand in hand and together remake the world of nature into a world which represents an inextricable interpenetration of nature and culture.

Rarity of "Natural" Resources

At this advanced stage of human history so much culture has been added and worked into nature that it is well-nigh impossible to segregate the "natural" resource from the cultural. For example, take virgin soil fertility. Is there anything more "natural" than that? But its function as a resource depends very largely upon the particular use which man makes of it at a given place and time. Can we say that the soil fertility which is lodged in a certain area connected with a market by means of modern transportation is wholly natural? As was pointed out before, to function as a resource the soil fertility must be correlated with the man-made transportation agency. Take the case of the forests. It might be possible to find a primeval forest which is a natural resource in the pure and undiluted sense of the word, but it would be difficult. In most of the older countries, whatever forests are left are either better or worse because of human interference with natural growing conditions. Thus, a good portion of what in popular parlance goes under the name of natural resources, reveals cultural aspects upon more critical scrutiny. Moreover, if resources are merely expressions of the human appraisal of nature, how can the human element be eliminated from the resource concept? For the human appraisal depends as much upon man's objectives and upon his mental and physical abilities, his general capacity to make use of his environment, as upon the nature of the environment. Any change, therefore, which goes on in the human mind, which affects the organization of society, which influences the aims of resource utilization, injects into the resource aspects of nature a human element which is inseparable from it.

Natural and Cultural Environments

The environment must therefore be viewed as consisting of at least two distinct elements:

the natural and the cultural. Since culture is a social product, that is, an achievement of group coöperation, we may refer to cultural environments as social environments or the social heritage. Man shares the natural environment with all animals, but man alone possesses the capacity to create cultural or social environments. Through culture he has softened the rigors of nature. By superimposing the structure of social environments on nature, he has continuously expanded the habitable area of the globe until today even the arctic and antarctic regions must accustom themselves to his sight.

Through this intermingling of natural and cultural aspects the environment of modern man has grown so much in complexity that classification has become exceedingly difficult. The following, however, is one that repays careful study. It was worked out by the well-known sociologist, L. L. Bernard.[10]

I. THE NATURAL ENVIRONMENTS, or the untransformed aspects of nature:

a. *The inorganic environment*—consisting of cosmic materials and processes, physical geography, soil, climate, the inorganic resources, natural agencies and natural mechanical processes.

b. *The organic environment*—consisting of microorganisms, various parasites and insect pests, plants, animals, ecological and symbiotic relationships of plants and animals, the prenatal environment of man, and natural biological processes.

II. THE SOCIAL ENVIRONMENTS OF THE FIRST ORDER, or those physical transformations of nature which enable the organism to adjust itself more effectively and economically, although more indirectly, to the natural environments:

a. *The physico-social environment*—consisting of physical inventions, illustrated by tools, machines, houses, shelter, means of transportation and communication, cities, artificial ice, fire, clothing, instruments for scientific research, etc.

b. *The bio-social environment*—consisting of the natural organic environment as modified by training and by plant and animal breeding. Examples of this form of the social environment are domesticated plants and animals, pets, slaves, trained ser-

---

[10] L. L. Bernard, "Mind—Its Emergence as a Mechanism of Adjustment," chap. 26 of F. A. Cleveland and collaborators, *Modern Scientific Knowledge,* Ronald Press Company, New York, 1929. Also "A Classification of Environments," *American Journal of Sociology,* November, 1925.

vants, and laborers, artisans, athletes, students, soldiers, etc.

III. The Social Environments of the Second Order, or the psycho-social environments, based upon language symbols and communication:

a. *The psycho-social environment*, dependent upon *gesture language*. The content of this phase of the psycho-social environment is relatively meager. It begins in the lowest stages of savagery, but persists into the present.

b. *The psycho-social environment*, dependent upon *vocal language*. The experiences of men are symbolized verbally and communicated from one person to another until they become common possessions. These common or collective experiences are made objective through language and they take on the forms of traditions, customs, folkways, conventions, beliefs, mores, proverbs, maxims, public opinion, etc.

c. The third aspect of the *psycho-social environment* to develop appeared with the introduction of *written language*. The vocal forms of the psycho-social environment continue to function broadly along with the written forms and probably outnumber the latter. The written content is carried through books, newspapers, phonograph records, movie films, and pictures. It takes the form chiefly of poetry, drama, fiction, art, essays, history, laws, codes, philosophy, and the sciences. The sciences especially could not exist except for this written or printed medium, and they are the basis of our modern civilization. Without the sciences, both theoretical and applied, we could not have our industry, medicine, sanitation, hygiene, political institutions, and the other highly developed forms of social organization and control.

IV. The Derivative-Control and Institutional Environments. These are composite environments, made up of all forms and varying degrees of organization. But they are dominated particularly by the psycho-social environments.

Here the cultural modifications of nature are viewed as expressions of human adaptation to the environment. These adaptations are simple and direct in the early stages of social evolution, but become increasingly complex and indirect as societies grow larger and more articulate. As we study Bernard's classification, we see rising before our eyes a lofty edifice, stories piled upon stories, resting on a physical basis not of matter alone but of energies also, of processes, of relationships. Firmly linked to this natural foundation are the first stories, direct adaptation to and modification of physical nature. As the structure rises in height, the contact with physical nature becomes less direct and the purely man-made artificial cultural aspects gain in importance.

Direct and Indirect Adjustments

On the basis of their relative closeness to nature, cultural environments may be divided into direct adjustments to nature and derivative or indirect adjustments. Much culture can be readily explained as the result of the direct adaptation to situations found in the natural environment. More or less all primitive culture is of this nature. A kindled fire involves a cultural change in the natural environment. If this fire serves to keep man warm it is properly called a direct adjustment to the environmental condition of cold. Any artificial shelter belongs in this category. If man's naked hand is too weak to crush a stone and if the same hand can perform this task when armed with a hammer or an ax, the invention and production of such tool-weapons is a direct adjustment to the natural environment.

If, however, in order to get the best results from a high-speed machine tool which makes parts of machinery used in manufacturing motor trucks, alloy steel must be invented and produced which assures a sharp cutting edge at high temperatures, the adaptation to the natural environment is still there, but it has lost its directness and can only be traced step by step through the various stages of a highly complex process. The high-speed tool-steel may then be called an indirect or a derived adjustment.

Societal institutions are also adaptations to the environment, but they are generally so indirect and sophisticated that the connection is not easily realized. Man discovered early that he could defend himself against wild beasts better in groups than in individual combat, and he therefore developed institutions for social coöperation in a more or less direct adaptation to the natural environment. However, as the groups grow in size and complexity in the course of history, many institutions develop which, though still remotely related to the original idea of group coöperation, are essentially derivatives of previous institutional adjustments. Man, rationalizing and philosophizing about his original adjustment, often creates derived institutions which show little trace of a direct adjustment to environmental situations. It may not be too difficult to trace the ideas of Jeffersonian democracy to conditions which were determined by the natural environment as they existed in the time of Thomas Jefferson. It is well to remember, however, that Jefferson's mind, far from being a tabula rasa, was in reality a rich depository of previous cultural adjustments and showed innumerable imprints of adjustments which the English people, as well as others, had made in the past. But it is very difficult to trace to their natural environment the ideas of a "Democratic" politician of today who uses or abuses Jeffersonian principles merely as accepted formulas of political behavior. This example must suffice to illustrate the lack of a direct and evident connection between many institutions and environments.

Bernard's terminology provokes further comment. As was stated before, Bernard views culture as a structure rising in tiers upon a basis of nature. It is interesting to note that in his division of the natural environment into organic and inorganic, he recognizes what was here called the basic dualism of nature.

Bernard divides cultural environments into three main tiers:

1. Social environments of the first order.
2. Social environments of the second order.
3. Derivative-control and institutional environments.

The last may be viewed as a social environment of the third order. The social environment of the first order is divided into the physicosocial and the biosocial environment, thus clearly reflecting the basic dualism just mentioned. Physicosocial adjustments are those made to the inorganic (here meaning the nonliving) agents of nature, whereas the biosocial adjustments are those made to aspects of living nature. Bernard logically includes men in this category. He thus cuts right across the basic dualism and carries this fundamental dichotomy of the natural environment over to the first-order social environment which, being an environment of direct adjustment to nature, necessarily shares the dualism with nature. This dichotomy is lost in the higher tiers of cultural environment.

Bernard refers to these environments as psychosocial environments. Naturally all cultural environments are social environments because culture is a social product, the social heritage. They are called *psycho*social—as distinguished from physicosocial and biosocial on the lower level—to stress the fact that on this upper level nature no longer acts directly in a straight-line fashion, on an *ad hoc* basis so to speak; now the human mind—the psyche—enters the reaction as an independent and modifying factor. Man reacts no longer with a clean slate; the slate has been written on. The mind is grooved with impressions. These impressions were made in talking over problems with others, overhearing others, and remembering.

Thus communication becomes a vital factor in the development of the psychosocial environment. As communication advances from the halting and unsatisfactory level of gestures and sign language to the higher level of written, including printed, language, when books and libraries come into vogue, cultural adaptation comes progressively more under the influence of established crystallized human thought and seeks adjustments not to nature directly, but to a growing accumulation of previous human reactions to experiences in life. A man with a classical education will see current issues through different eyes than does a person trained in the natural sciences.

This increased indirectness, this widening of the gap between first impression and final reaction, logically leads, on the top level of derivative control and institutions, to the miraculous achievements of an Einstein on the one hand, and to the confusion of the human mind so characteristic of the modern age. Yet this confusion is not a new invention. Did not the ancient Greeks complain: "What harasses men is not so much the facts themselves as human thoughts (dogmas) on facts"?

THE DIVERSITY OF CULTURES
Human Culture and Cultures

Up to this point human culture has been treated as a sort of collective abstraction, a composite reaction of mankind to its environment. In reality, of course, there is no such abstraction as man. There are only men, women, and children. These men, women, and children live in social groups that develop their own cultures in separate culture areas. These cultures, having evolved out of reactions and adaptations to diverse environments, differ as these environments differ.

During the early stages of human existence, such cultural developments occurred in airtight compartments. As contacts increased and various group interrelations ensued—submission, conquest, merging through intermarriage, etc.—cultures lost some of this pristine simplicity, and blended or alloyed cultures developed. On a still higher level, the cultures of earlier civilizations became the object of deliberate study, as have Egyptian, Greek, Roman, and other ancient cultures, especially since the Renaissance. Likewise, a deliberate effort has been made to explore the contemporary cultures of other ethnic groups. Thus culture takes on a more complex character, and adaptation to local phenomena and solution of local problems yield some of their earlier influence to outside forces.

Problems of Cultural Impingement

These intergroup contacts tend to enrich cultures and help to accelerate their growth. But they also create serious problems. One of the best examples of this danger is Japan. For centuries the Japanese deliberately kept foreign influence to a carefully regulated minimum. Then under the guns of Commodore Perry they were forced to give up their policy of isolation and, realizing the material superiority of the West, especially in warfare, they decided to submit to a deliberate process of westernization. But values which one group of people have built up in a slow and painful process of accretion through the centuries cannot be acquired at will as one buys a gadget in a store. They can be acquired only by retracing slowly and patiently the steps that led the culture-lenders up the steep slopes of Parnassus. How the attempt to borrow certain aspects of western culture while staunchly refusing to accept others led to a sinister hybrid culture and to a tragic end is one of the great lessons of history.

Cultures possess a certain inner coherence and inner logic. They cannot be chopped to pieces without killing the soul. Hence their transfer from one part of the globe to another, from one social group to another, is not to be undertaken in a spirit of levity, but calls for deep understanding of cultural values.

An Example of Culture Transfer

How delicate is the problem of culture transfer may be illustrated by reference to the relationship between the United States and Puerto Rico. The following quotation is taken from a report prepared by the author in the capacity of Director of Research of the Interdepartmental Committee on Puerto Rico appointed by President Franklin Delano Roosevelt early in 1939. During the time that has elapsed since it was written several important changes have occurred, but the main problem of culture transfer between heterogeneous environments remains.

While it is true . . . that the problem of Puerto Rico is one of old standing and that, therefore, the entire responsibility for the present troubles cannot be charged to recent policies and administrative measures, the partial responsibility for Puerto Rican difficulties of the Government of the United States is inescapable.

That commercial opportunities largely determine the profit at which products can be sold, and that profit, in turn, affects the flow of capital investment, has been pointed out. The vital importance under these conditions of commercial opportunities in the shaping of productive power is self-evident. In the case of Puerto Rico, the extent of commercial opportunities is largely determined by United States policy. Over that policy the people of Puerto Rico have little control. To a large extent, therefore, the commercial destiny, and through it, the economic and social destiny of the Island is in the hands of the policymakers in Washington. So convinced were the lawmakers of the early nineteenth century of the all-saving grace of industrialization under tariff protection, that they viewed incorporation of Puerto Rico in the tariff system of the United States, in other words, the policy of "assimilation," as an all-embracing and dependable guarantee of Puerto Rican economic progress.

Looking back, it now appears that a policy based on this simple formula may not have been the wisest approach to the problem of Puerto Rico. In these stirring years when the United States extended its sovereign power to outlying possessions, there was neither time nor inclination to probe into the differences between the needs of a tropical island and those of a giant economy of continental expanse. In retrospect, with the lessons of forty years to draw upon, these differences can now be clearly discerned. In the briefest form, they may be shown in the following outline which suggests some of the most salient points of difference:

Island	Mainland (especially during the formative period of economic development)
1. Small size; island.	1. Large size; continent.
2. Conflict between agrarian and aristocratic survivals of Spanish origin with modern commercial and financial industrialization, largely of Anglo-Saxon origin.	2. Relative absence of such conflicts.
3. Little room for expansion.	3. Expanding elbow room.
4. High population density.	4. Generally moderate population density.
5. Paucity of resources, limiting diversity of economic activities.	5. Wealth of resources, permitting great diversity of economic activities.
6. Lack of mineral resources and resultant limitation of mechanization and mobilization.	6. Mineral resources permitting mechanization and mobilization.
7. Low living standards conducive to unrestricted propagation.	7. High living standards conducive to restricted propagation.
8. Relative isolation.	8. Numerous contacts between all parts of the Mainland.

Space does not permit the full development of each of these points of contrast. The last point, however, is so frequently overlooked that at least a few words of comment are called for.

In respect to the degree of isolation or adequacy of contacts, Puerto Rico is not comparable to non-insular (i.e., continental), domestic sugar-producing areas. Such a comparison is sometimes made to appraise the relative dependence on sugar of Puerto Rico and continental domestic sugar-producing areas respectively. Such a comparison is not valid, for the reason that continental domestic sugar-producing areas constitute mere fragments of States whose resources are infinitely more varied than those of Puerto Rico.

The Island is practically a hermetically-sealed labor market; there is neither immigration nor emigration to speak of. While thus the external mobility of Puerto Rican labor is practically zero, the mobility of the labor in continental sugar-producing areas is not inconsiderable. The same difference exists with regard to cultural contacts. In this respect, also, Puerto Rico, for reasons of distance, language, lack of educational facilities, etc., is far more isolated than continental sugar-producing areas. Puerto Rico is a sugar-producing area and little more. It cannot be compared with entire States of the Union. Neither is the comparison between Puerto Rico and other domestic sugar-producing areas valid.

The major implication of this juxtaposition of contrasting features is this: measures and policies adapted to the continental economy with its diversity of resources and multiplicity of alternate occupations, by their very nature, may prove, and in many instances have proved, ill-adapted to the Island's economy, endowed with limited resources and lacking room for expansion. This means that measures and policies devised for and adapted to the Mainland should, as a rule, not be extended to an essentially different economy without proper allowance for these essential differences. Blanket policies and laws covering both the continental economy of the Mainland and the insular economy of Puerto Rico are definitely dangerous unless, at all times, basic differences of needs and opportunities of the two economies are clearly kept in mind.

As was stated before, the basic policy adopted by the United States upon acquisition of Puerto Rico was the policy of "assimilation"; that is, the policy of assimilating the Island to the Mainland by treating it virtually as part and parcel of the continental economy. The most outstanding features of that policy are "free trade" between the Island and the Mainland, and the extension of the United States tariff to Puerto Rico. That policy should now be carefully scrutinized with due regard to essential differences of needs and opportunities in general, and to differences of density and rate of growth of population, and cultural backgrounds in particular.

The difference in population density is important. Its significance appears clear-cut against the background of historical perspective. Throughout its economic development up to the post-war period, there existed in the continental United States a chronic labor shortage. Attracted to this labor vacuum, millions of Europeans migrated to America. At the same time, labor-saving devices were developed to relieve the labor shortage still further.

Such labor-saving devices grew spontaneously out of the cultural environment of the North American continent; they could not have developed spontaneously in an over-crowded tropical island. To Puerto Rico, labor-saving devices are essentially foreign. The grafting of exogenous arts and institutions on Puerto Rico must proceed with caution.[11]

CRITIQUE OF CULTURE
Cultural Resistances

In developing the functional theory of resources the importance of resistances was stressed. It was shown that resistances are met in all three vertical columns of Table 1.1. Since cultural resistances were discussed fully in Chapter 1, there is no need for further discussion at this point.

Good and Bad Culture

The tacit assumption is that Homo sapiens does not willingly spoil his own environment and that, on the contrary, cultural changes represent improvements in the natural landscape, improvements in this sense reflecting a better adaptation of nature to human needs. As civilization becomes more complex, however, the dangers of misdirected effort and poor judgment, and at times an even complete lack of comprehension of the best interests of man, increase. Such errors of judgment may appear in the form of idle factory equipment which was never really needed, or of a barge canal never justified by social requirements, or of desolate ridges once heavily wooded but now disfigured by the scars of erosion. The error or lack of judgment may be due to an inadequate understanding of ecology, to an insufficient regard for the future, or to the inability to master the growing complexities of world economy, but above all it is due to man's refusal to reconcile properly the conflicting interests between opposing groups and between the present and the future. Hence, what may appear as culture from the standpoint of short-run private property interests may not be culture in the light of long-run social welfare.

Conflicting Cultures and Relativism

As technology reaches out for supersonic speed in flight and under the impact of modern science space shrinks and the globe appears smaller and smaller, people find themselves crowded even closer together. There was a time when the intelligentsia of the West committed the fatal error of thinking that this bringing people closer together physically would automatically bring them closer together spiritually as well. The brotherhood of man was considered a simple by-product of fast transport. *O sancta simplicitas!* Crowding people increases the areas of and opportunities for friction, and friction generates heat. Human beings are cantankerous creatures, and the stranger has always been viewed with suspicion. The least departure from local norms is a cause of ridicule and easily leads to blows. Good neighborliness is a difficult art, hard to learn. It can be learned only with endless patience and an amount of tolerance that is not easily acquired. Humanity collectively faces a tremendous task of self-education.[12]

Moreover, there is a real problem to be solved in connection with intercultural tolerance. How can a world society emerge from the welter of fanatic nationalism? Herskovits[13] advocates a creed of cultural relativism when he says: "If a world society is to emerge from a conflict of nationalism, it can only be on a basis of live and let live, a willingness to recognize the values that are to be found in the most diverse ways of life." To this anthropologist, cultural relativism is a "philosophy which, in recognizing the values set up by every society to guide its own life, lays stress on the dignity inherent in every body of custom, and on the need for tolerance."

Culture and Morals

This leads to the role of morals in the shaping of cultural values. In the view of many leaders, the present world crisis is caused by a

---

[11] Erich W. Zimmermann, *Staff Report to the Interdepartmental Committee on Puerto Rico* (multigraphed), Washington, 1940.

[12] For ideas along these lines, see June Hyer, *Trends in International Education from World War*

I Through World War II, unpublished doctoral dissertation, University of Texas, 1947; and "Implications of International Education," *Pi Lambda Theta Journal,* March, 1945, pp. 94-101.

[13] Melville J. Herskovits, *Man and His Works, The Science of Cultural Anthropology,* Alfred A. Knopf, New York, 1948.

loss of moral values. Stace[14] points out that morals formerly derived their force from an

assumed metaphysical or supernatural foundation. As this belief is disappearing morals seem to have no foundation at all. Hence, the loss of moral faith and the crisis in the human spirit. This crisis, in Stace's opinion, can be resolved when man realizes the basic truth that the laws of human nature are as objective as the laws of all nature.

---

[14] Walter T. Stace, Professor of Philosophy at Princeton University, speaking on one of the six panels of the Mid-Century Convocation of the Massachusetts Institute of Technology, April 1, 1949, as reported in the New York *Times*, April 2, 1949.

BIBLIOGRAPHY

Benedict, R., *Patterns of Culture,* Boston, Houghton Mifflin, 1934.

Bernard, L. L., "A Classification of Environments," *American Journal of Sociology,* November, 1925.

Bernard, L. L., "Mind—Its Emergence as a Mechanism of Adjustment," in F. A. Cleveland and collaborators, *Modern Scientific Knowledge,* New York, Ronald, 1929, chap. 26.

Gillin, J., *The Ways of Men,* New York, Appleton-Century-Crofts, 1948.

Herskovits, M. J., *Man and His Works,* New York, Knopf, 1948.

Kluckhorn, C., and Kelley, W. H., "The Concept of Culture," in R. Linton (ed.), *The Science of*

Man in the World Crisis, New York, Columbia University Press, 1945.

Malinowski, B., *A Scientific Theory of Culture and Other Essays,* Chapel Hill, University of North Carolina Press, 1944.

Platt, R. S., "Environmentalism versus Geography," *American Journal of Sociology,* March, 1948.

Thurnwald, R. C., "Civilization and Culture," *American Sociological Review,* June, 1936.

Wissler, C., *Man and Culture,* New York, Crowell, 1923.

Zimmermann, E. W., *Staff Report to the Interdepartmental Committee on Puerto Rico* (multigraphed), Washington, 1940.

UNIT 4. RESOURCE PATTERNS

Chapter 10

OBSERVATIONS ON RESOURCE PATTERNS

This chapter brings little new, little that in one way or another has not been touched upon in the preceding chapters. The triune interaction of nature, man, and culture has been stressed again and again, as has the bearing of energy uses on resource development in general and on factoral proportionality in particular. The contrasts between oriental vegetable and occidental machine civilizations were mentioned repeatedly. In this chapter the rather loose ends of these various interresource relationships are gathered for a brief but systematic analysis.

THE MECHANICAL REVOLUTION AND WORLD RESOURCE PATTERNS

The mechanical revolution furnishes the key to the modern global layout of resource patterns. In the world of today peoples differ in nothing more than in the use of inanimate energy, of the capital equipment which harnesses it, and of the science which renders it efficient. They differ in many other respects and in vital respects at that, but the use of inanimate energy and all it implies in terms of cultural change and impact on the availability of natural agents supplies the key to understanding these differences.

The power-driven machine raises the productivity both of labor and of nature. This increased productivity in turn permits the accumulation of surpluses over and above consumers' immediate needs. Capital equipment becomes an increasingly vital part of the production process. This equipment is made largely of metals and other inorganic matter taken from the subsoil strata of the earth. Mining for metals and for nonmetallic minerals including the fossil fuels becomes a major occupation of man, as do building machines and factories to house the machines and generating power to drive them. The power-driven machine thrives on large-scale full-time utilization—the major desideratum of "overhead economy"—and hence needs wide markets in which to sell its mass output; it draws on the four corners of the earth for the materials which go into its products. Thus transportation and communication and the building and maintaining and operating of vast rail nets, steamship lines, and air transport facilities become vital parts of the economy. Marketing the vast output of factories

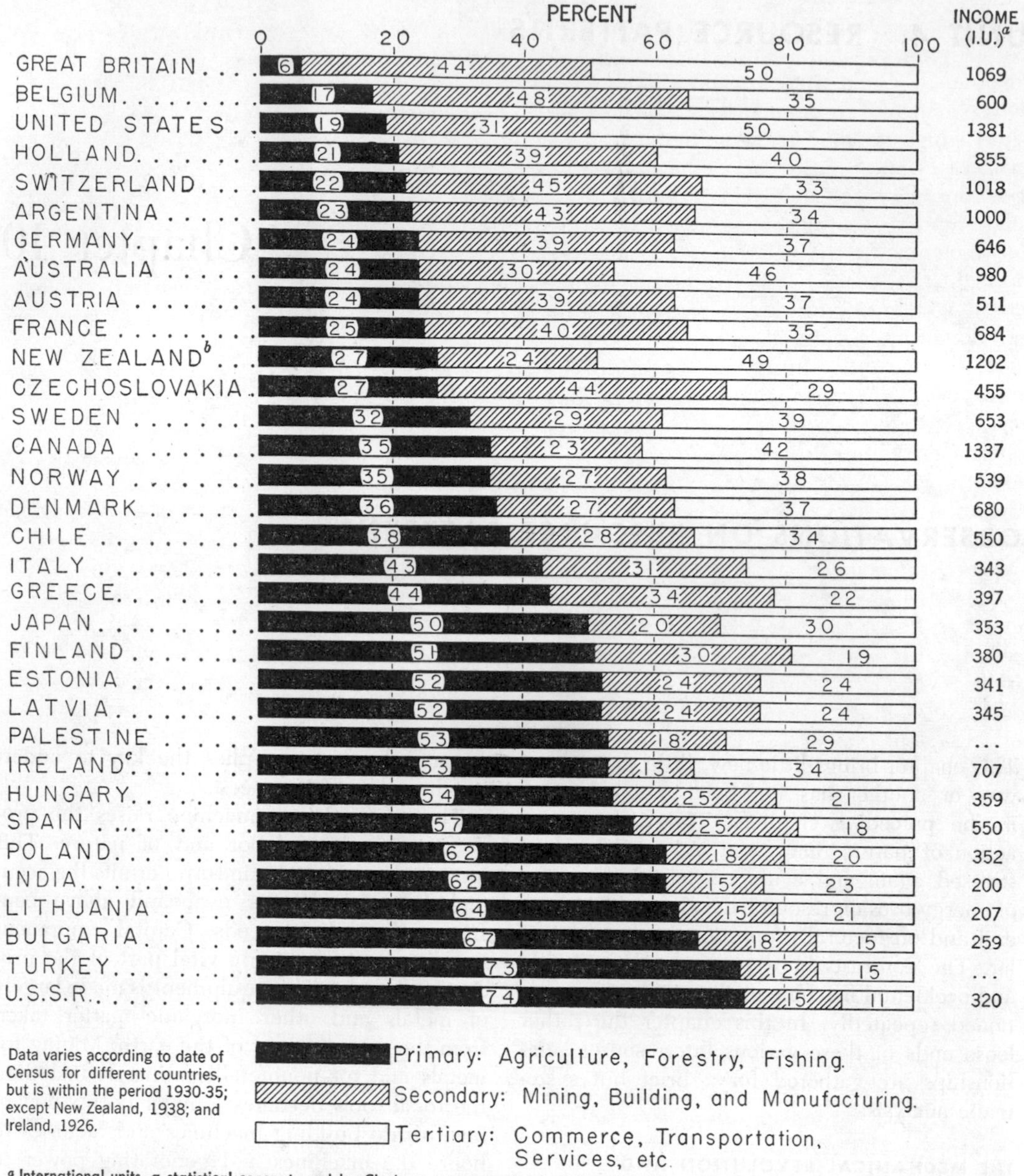

Country	PERCENT	INCOME (I.U.)[a]
GREAT BRITAIN	6 / 44 / 50	1069
BELGIUM	17 / 48 / 35	600
UNITED STATES	19 / 31 / 50	1381
HOLLAND	21 / 39 / 40	855
SWITZERLAND	22 / 45 / 33	1018
ARGENTINA	23 / 43 / 34	1000
GERMANY	24 / 39 / 37	646
AUSTRALIA	24 / 30 / 46	980
AUSTRIA	24 / 39 / 37	511
FRANCE	25 / 40 / 35	684
NEW ZEALAND[b]	27 / 24 / 49	1202
CZECHOSLOVAKIA	27 / 44 / 29	455
SWEDEN	32 / 29 / 39	653
CANADA	35 / 23 / 42	1337
NORWAY	35 / 27 / 38	539
DENMARK	36 / 27 / 37	680
CHILE	38 / 28 / 34	550
ITALY	43 / 31 / 26	343
GREECE	44 / 34 / 22	397
JAPAN	50 / 20 / 30	353
FINLAND	51 / 30 / 19	380
ESTONIA	52 / 24 / 24	341
LATVIA	52 / 24 / 24	345
PALESTINE	53 / 18 / 29	...
IRELAND[c]	53 / 13 / 34	707
HUNGARY	54 / 25 / 21	359
SPAIN	57 / 25 / 18	550
POLAND	62 / 18 / 20	352
INDIA	62 / 15 / 23	200
LITHUANIA	64 / 15 / 21	207
BULGARIA	67 / 18 / 15	259
TURKEY	73 / 12 / 15	...
U.S.S.R.	74 / 15 / 11	320

Data varies according to date of Census for different countries, but is within the period 1930-35; except New Zealand, 1938; and Ireland, 1926.

■ Primary: Agriculture, Forestry, Fishing.

▨ Secondary: Mining, Building, and Manufacturing.

□ Tertiary: Commerce, Transportation, Services, etc.

[a] International units, a statistical concept used by Clark as a common standard by which the various national monetary units are equated.
[b] Figures for 1938.
[c] Figures for 1926.

FIG. 10.1. Distribution and Per Capita Income of Working Population, by Countries, 1930-1935. (U. S. Department of State, Division of Geography; based on Colin Clark, *Conditions of Economic Progress*, published by The Macmillan Company, and used with their permission.)

and power-supported farms gives employment to millions in storing, moving, trading, insuring, financing the vast output of mine, field, and factory. Robots replace men more and more in the actual processes of production. Vice versa, the complex social economy[1] calls for ever-

---

[1] By social economy is meant an interdependent economic system marked by interregional and occupational specialization. The opposite is the "anarchic" economy, a loose agglomeration of largely independent local units like the Chinese *hsien* mentioned on p. 89.

increasing numbers of people engaged in service activities, including the professions and government. Colin Clark[2] speaks of three divisions of gainful occupations in the modern world which he calls primary, secondary, and tertiary. Primary economic activities include agriculture, forestry, and fishing; secondary economic activities cover mining, manufacturing, construction, and the generation of power—in short, the tangible aspects of industry; tertiary activities embrace services of both a business and nonbusiness nature, including transport, trade, finance, advertising, personal services, professions, government, etc. How tremendously countries differ in respect to the relative importance of these three major categories is shown in Fig. 10.1. Note the striking negative correlation between income level and prominence of primary activity.

If it is remembered that machine-powered science-aided agriculture in the industrialized countries, far from being "primary" in the original sense, is in reality secondary and tertiary activity functioning indirectly in and through agriculture, it will be realized that actually the contrasts are even sharper than the occupational statistics reveal. The fact that half the working population of leading industrial countries is occupied in tertiary service activities will come as a surprise to many. It is a clear indication of the extent of interdependence and indirectness in the modern social economy.

Recent Changes in the Industrial Map

The mechanical revolution began in England, spread to the continent of Europe, flourished there in a sharply delineated area of the northwestern and central regions, and then jumped the Atlantic to the northeastern section of the United States.

These oldest centers of industrialization remain by far the most important ones. But there are other centers, though as yet mostly minor ones. There is Japan, still highly industrialized in spite of the fearful losses and destruction suffered in World War II. There are sections of India, the Union of South Africa, Australia, eastern and southern Europe, and

some parts of Latin America, which have experienced at least the beginning of industrialization.

By far the most important newcomer among the newly industrialized countries is the Soviet Union. Emerging with new revolutionary zeal after a series of painful defeats, that country by feverish effort has managed to telescope industrial development so that today it ranks second only to the United States, but considerably after western Europe if half a dozen or more countries are lumped into a single industrial complex.

But there are degrees of industrialization, and industries differ in general character and especially in the extent to which they substitute inanimate energy for human. Much of Latin-American and Asiatic industrialization is of a low-order type represented by such manufacturing as textile and food processing which is elevated only little above agricultural activity and depends on large numbers of labor modestly supported by robots.[3]

The Economic Exclave[4]

A peculiar phenomenon associated with the spread of the mechanical revolution is the economic exclave. An economic exclave may be defined as a splinter of one economy lying inside another economy. The economy of the United States is an entity, a social-political-economic entity. Some oil fields of Venezuela, some copper mines of Chile, although lying inside foreign economies, may be viewed as splinters or exclaves of the economy of the United States. The emergence of the exclave is a logical corollary of the differential economic development of different countries. Venezuela has neither the know-how nor the capital to develop her oil deposits and process the oil, nor the market in which to sell the refined products. This is true also of Chile with regard to nitrate. So long as Chilean interests had a

---

[2] Colin Clark, *Conditions of Economic Progress*, Macmillan & Co., Ltd., London, 1940.

[3] See George Wythe, *Industry in Latin America*, The Macmillan Company, New York, 1946, and *An Outline of Latin American Development*, Barnes and Noble, New York, 1946.

[4] The term exclave is borrowed from political science where it refers to a splinter of territory which politically belongs to one sovereign state but geographically lies inside the borders of another. The Palatinate used to form part of Bavaria but geographically was separated from that kingdom.

world monopoly in the sale of that mineral, inefficient methods of production could be followed and Chileans could engage in nitrate production and sale. When that monopoly ended, only efficient, scientific, highly capitalized methods could survive the new competition with sulfate of ammonia and synthetic nitrogen. The nitrate mines were either shut down or converted into exclaves of the United States and British economies.

Economic exclaves are scattered over the earth—in the Belgian Congo, Rhodesia, The Rand in South Africa, Australia, Java and other parts of Indonesia, etc. Often they are a thorn in the side of the natives, whose nationalistic pride is injured and who do not cherish the idea of seeing foreigners exploit the stuff that nature happened to deposit in their backyard. It is safe to say that vigorous efforts will be made to nationalize exclaves. That this is not as easy as some assume is demonstrated by Mexico's experience with oil.

When one thinks of exclaves his mind is apt to turn first to minerals. However, the golden belt of plantations which runs along the equator is full of exclaves producing bananas, vegetable oil, fibers, dyewoods, tanning materials, etc.

RESOURCE PATTERNS AND WORLD WAR II
Extent and Rapidity of Change

We live in an era of rapid and penetrating change. Technology and science never rest. Their restlessness is communicated to processes and industries and reflected in an ever-changing map of world resources.

Superimposed upon the deep and rapid changes wrought by technology and science are the changes wrought by war. Today, Japan is toppled from her feet of clay. Germany, long the second-ranking industrial power of the world but now cleft wide open into eastern and western zones, is a mere shadow of her former industrial self. Britain, the world power *par excellence* of the nineteenth century, is struggling for her very existence. Having based her economic destiny on world trade and world finance, she will suffer so long as global relations are as chaotic as two world wars have left them. Western and central Europe lost, North America gained. Old historical relationships were reversed. The former helper needs help from those formerly helped. The invest-

ment streams of the nineteenth century are moving in the opposite direction. Burke's eloquent phrase, the children offering their full breasts to the aging mother, is implemented by reality.

Delaisi's World Picture

How great these changes are can be seen clearly when one reconstructs the way the world looked to informed observers as late as 1929. In that year Delaisi, a Frenchman, painted a vivid picture of the earth as it looked to him. He imagines Europe divided into two sharply differing segments which he calls Europe A and Europe B (see Fig. 10.2).[5] Europe A lies within a line drawn through Bergen, Norway; Stockholm, Sweden; Danzig, Cracow, Poland; Budapest, Hungary; Florence, Italy; Barcelona and Bilbao, Spain; Belfast, North Ireland; and Glasgow, Scotland. He describes these two Europes as follows:

Europe A is covered with a network of railways and highways; travel and trade flourish; it is the land of factories and horsepower. Clothes and lives of men are uniform. With the exception of narrow frontier strips where Polish, Czech or Italian is spoken, only three languages are used: English, French, and German, and that in spite of the fact that eleven states are covered. Europe A is an immense animal organism with functions both specialized and centralized, with cells interdependent, from family to factory or bank.

Europe B stands in sharp contrast: highways and railways are few and far between; old customs survive as well as costumes and dialects. It is like a polyp made up of millions of tiny animals living an independent life on the coral reef which they have built up through the centuries. Europe A, a great vertebrate; Europe B, a polyp.

Whence the difference? The mechanical revolution or, as Delaisi calls it, the "horsepower" revolution (the irony of the phrase is appalling!) has industrialized Europe A, in part even its agriculture, while Europe B has retained its exclusive rural character. Horsepower enables man to produce more and to consume more. According to Delaisi, "The potential wealth of nations does not depend upon the number of inhabitants, but upon the number of

[5] F. Delaisi, *Les Deux Europes; Europe Industrielle et Europe Agricole*, Payot, Paris, 1929.

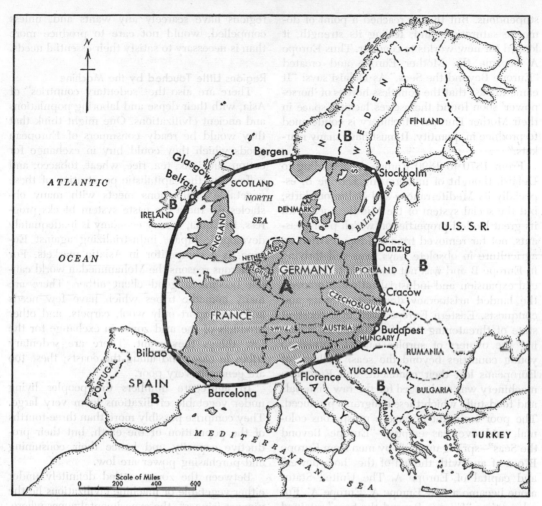

FIG. 10.2.   The Two Europes, Agricultural and Industrial (About 1920).

horse-powers at their disposal." The United States and Russia have populations of comparable size, but the United States has many times more horsepower per capita and is infinitely more wealthy. Similarly, a comparison could be drawn between Belgium, powerfully equipped with horsepower, and Greece, little touched by the mechanical revolution. Both countries have about 7,000,000 inhabitants, but the difference in wealth is striking. Delaisi concludes: "As far as sociologists are concerned, the unit to be taken into account in appraising a country's position and possibilities is man multiplied by the coefficient of horsepower." In other words, Europe A typifies machine civilization, Europe B vegetable civilization.

Why did "horsepower" develop only in Europe A? Because only there are found in usable combination iron and coal, the essentials of the mother industry—the machine industry. Likewise, only Europe A, free from the urgent need to obtain immediate returns, possessed the necessary leisure and reserves of capital to build factories and equip plants. Science inventing mechanisms, learning to direct and control machines, and schools to teach this science were found only in Europe A.

Machine Civilization in Other Continents

For some time this industrial Europe, Delaisi's Europe A, was busy with itself. The task of creating its machine equipment was stupendous. But then it reached a point of domestic saturation, and, feeling its strength, it looked for new worlds to conquer. Thus Europe A became the Mother Europe and created "Europe Beyond the Seas." As Delaisi says: "It came to pass that the countless hordes of 'horsepower' soon found themselves lacking space in their Mother Europe. Machinery is condemned to produce in quantity. It must have many markets."

From 1870 to 1890 Europe A, according to Delaisi, thought of modernizing Europe B, especially its Mediterranean and Baltic outskirts; but the social system of the Middle Ages, with its great landed properties on which poor peasants, not far removed from serfdom, carried on agriculture in obsolete ways, was still thriving in Europe B and was not favorable to commercial expansion and industrialization. Moreover, the landed aristocracy dreamed of wars and conquests. Eastern Europe lived in a constant state of threatening war. So Europe A, meaning the owners of surplus capital, turned to young countries beyond the seas. Millions of Europeans left their continent, and European machinery was exchanged for the raw materials and foodstuffs which these emigrants produced. The poor emigrant became a prosperous colonial, and overseas empires—"Europe Beyond the Seas"—sprang up, built by men from Europe B out of and with the aid of the "horsepower" and capital of Europe A. The United States alone became a new Europe A, Europe A'. For a long time "Europe Beyond the Seas" retained close relations with Mother Europe; but today the tables are turned, and Europe A is dependent on "Europe Beyond the Seas" and must compete with Europe A'. The economic axis is no longer within Europe but somewhere on the ocean.

Delaisi then deals with the intermediary zone of the tropical lands, "that golden belt of plantations," producing coffee, tea, cane sugar, spices, cacao, bananas, pineapple, rubber, palm oil, peanuts, and copra. There climate forbids manual labor for the white man, a fact which accounts for the slavery of former days, for forced labor in the form of taxation in Africa, and for the indenture of half-breeds and natives in Latin America today. (Tenant farming sometimes closely resembles these forms of compulsory labor.) The inhabitants of these regions have scarcely any wants and, unless compelled, would not care to produce more than is necessary to satisfy their essential needs.

Regions Little Touched by the Machine

There are also the "sedentary countries" of Asia, with their dense and laboring populations and ancient civilizations. One might think that they would be ready consumers of European goods which they could buy in exchange for cotton, jute, silk, tea, rice, wheat, tobacco, and coffee. But the capitalistic penetration of these vegetable civilizations meets with many obstacles. In India the caste system blocks progress. In China, money economy is inadequately developed; Japan, industrializing against Europe, is a competitor in Asiatic markets. For numerous reasons the Mohammedan world cannot become a good client either. There are many nomadic tribes which have few needs and can export only wool, carpets, and other products of the arid zones in exchange for the few things they want. There are sedentary tribes in oases and along the coasts; these too are generally very poor.

In aggregate numbers the peoples living under vegetable civilizations loom very large. They comprise possibly more than three-fourths of the population of the earth, but their productive capacity and hence their consuming and purchasing power are low.

Between the zones settled definitely under either vegetable or machine civilizations lie the pioneer fringes[6]—the experimental zones where, unless the experiments yield negative results, new culture patterns are being woven. These "marginal" zones or frontiers are found in western United States, in Canada, Australia, South Africa, Siberia, Mongolia, and Manchuria, and some sections of South America. Their boundary lines shift in response to population pressure, technological progress, the changing availability of capital, a fuller realization of the difficulties which the pioneer has to face, and so forth.

This is a brief sketch of the geographical distribution of resource patterns, culture areas and economic systems. Attention is now di-

---

[6] See I. Bowman, *The Pioneer Fringe*, Special Publication No. 13, American Geographical Society, New York, 1931.

rected to the major zones of population density (see pp. 94-95).

Changed Reality

It is hard to believe that in two short decades Delaisi's picture could have changed as much as it did. To Delaisi, Russia was a semimysterious eastern appendage of Europe B. She is that no more. She has become a Europe "A," making herculean efforts to deserve that symbol of industrial strength.

In North America petroleum, in the form of both oil and gas, has gained a position rivaling that of coal and has greatly widened the natural basis of industrialization. It has begun to alter the industrial map. North America, while laying claim to Delaisi's title of Europe A', never developed a Europe B'. The division of Europe into A and B rests on historical and political and perhaps even racial divisions which never materialized in North America, the melting pot. Only in one respect is there a semblance to Europe B which might warrant the name Europe B', and that is dependence on capital. Capital surplus in the United States is still largely generated in the older industrialized areas of the Northeast. The rest of the country, as yet, is largely dependent on northeastern capital.[7] But this too may be gradually changing. In all other respects the United States is a solid single social economy based on regional specialization, to be sure, but not split into advanced capitalistic sections and backward feudalistic sections. If Senator Grundy of Pennsylvania speaks of "the provinces that should keep quiet" and Senator Bilbo of Mississippi speaks of the satrapies of the Northeast, they use figures of speech that possess only limited relevance to reality. Above all, the United States is a single political entity in which the benefits of national progress are being shared, not yet equally, to be sure, but in a fashion clearly pointing toward increasing equality.

Perhaps the most profound changes that have happened since Delaisi wrote are in the field of ideology. Europe A, the fountainhead of capitalistic ideology, has largely deserted her old faith in laissez faire, has yielded much

ground to socialism, and, in spots, is flirting with communism, a commodity imported from the East where it has gone far to replace Christianity as the accepted religion. The battle for Europe's soul is on. The Truman Doctrine, Marshall Plan, ERP, ECA, and so forth are the weapons used by Europe A' to save Europe A from succumbing to Asiatic heterodoxy. The battlefield stretches around the globe to China, Viet Nam, Malaya, Indonesia, Burma, India, and parts of Latin America.

This ideological struggle transcends in ultimate significance even the earth-changing force of technological change and scientific progress. Perhaps it is a race between the two. For technological change and scientific progress hold out a promise of relief from the misery and hopelessness on which communism feeds. The ideological struggle is tragically vital to the future of mankind because the ideology of communism—which has a high-minded ethical, though ineffective, core—is a tool in the hands of a few powerful men who appear to be striving for world conquest through world chaos. Their motives may appear noble to them. The effect of their schemes on mankind is anything but ennobling.

MAJOR RESOURCE PATTERNS

Vegetable vs. Machine Civilization

Whenever there was need of illustrating the two extreme types of civilization extant on this globe, reference was invariably made to monsoon Asia and the United States as examples of vegetable and machine civilization respectively. The contrast is shown diagrammatically in Fig. 10.3.

The diagram is purely fictitious so far as the sizes of the cubes are concerned. Its claim to verisimilitude lies in the size relationships and in the dynamic interrelation of the three cubes representing the three aspects of resourceship —natural, cultural, and human—or the three factors of production, land, labor, and capital. As was pointed out before (see p. 94), capital is the equalizing agent between labor and land. Whichever of the two factors—labor or land— is "long" produces capital to support the "short" factor. In overpopulated areas of monsoon Asia men create rice terraces to render land more productive, to enable the land to support more men. It is a vicious circle which ends in

---

[7] See W. Prescott Webb, *Divided We Stand*, Adams Publications, Austin, Texas, 1948.

THE RESOURCE PATTERN OF MONSOON ASIA (COOLIE)

A vicious (Malthusian) cycle in which too many men try to create capital to support too little land to carry more men to try to.....ad infinitum.

THE RESOURCE PATTERN OF THE UNITED STATES (ROBOT)

An ascending spiral reaching from Nature, manifest in both (a) agriculture- and (b) industry-supporting aspects, creates capital out of the abundance of natural powers to support man, who gradually becomes the director, planner, and aspirer.

1 Natural aspects ("land")
2 Cultural aspects (capital)
  (a) agricultural, (b) industrial
3 Human aspects (man, labor)

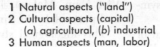
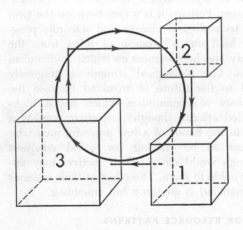
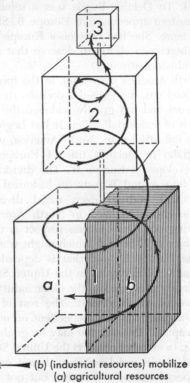

← (b) (industrial resources) mobilize
(a) agricultural resources

FIG. 10.3. Schematic Presentation of Two Extreme Resource Patterns.

frustration when the entire land area available for use at the *prevailing* state of the arts is occupied and the population has reached the limit of the carrying capacity of the land. The pattern fits perfectly the picture so carefully drawn by Robert Malthus. Population breeds against the means of sustenance. "The Four Horsemen" see to it that death rates keep up with birth rates.

The vegetable civilization of monsoon Asia is uncommonly immobile.[8] In the wet rice lands of southern China, a population density of almost 7000 to the square mile is not uncommon. The average for all China is perhaps between

---

[8] The reasons for this immobility were discussed in chap. 5, especially pp. 71-72.

1500 and 2000 inhabitants per square mile of arable land, as compared with about 100 for the United States. The lack of mobility is indicated by the fact that China in 1923 had only two miles of railroad per hundred thousand population, as compared with 11 in India (1914), 52 in the United Kingdom, 261 in the United States, and 404 in Australia.[9] At the time when China reached the height of her development, her river and canal transportation facilities proved adequate for her economic and cultural needs. She is still credited with a canal system of almost two hundred

---

[9] O. E. Baker, "Transportation in China," *Annals of the American Academy of Political and Social Science*, November, 1930, p. 166.

thousand miles, most of which, however, is used for irrigation rather than for transportation purposes. Furthermore, most of the vessels are propelled by man power.[10]

This lack of modern transportation facilities spells isolation and local self-sufficiency. E. T. Williams has aptly referred to China as a nation of village republics. "It is a civilization of small units distributed in accordance with the requirements of a human energy system of land utilization. It is a civilization of small walled cities, surrounded by clusters of little villages, united by canals and wheelbarrow paths." According to Dr. James Yen, founder of the mass-education movement, there are 1885 of these *hsien* constellations in China. In these semi-isolated communities, 85 percent of China's four hundred million inhabitants are struggling to eke out a bare existence.[11] This lack of mobility is aggravated by the lack of cultural standardization, the necessary consequence of isolation. No standard weights or measures have been adopted. Differences in language hamper trade, and differences in customs and mores hinder it. Being culturally unstandardized, human beings in China are almost as immobile as the goods themselves.

China also illustrates the permanence and the static nature of vegetable civilizations. Machine civilizations are highly dynamic. The advantages and disadvantages of these characteristics have been discussed in earlier chapters. The static nature of a vegetable civilization is institutionally reinforced, in the case of China, by special mechanisms assuring the continuity of the social organization. Among these, familism and its corollary, ancestor worship, are the most important.[12]

The contrast with the United States is striking. Here nature manifests herself in the full panoply of the basic dualism, not in a one-sided manner as a source of food sufficient to enable man to grow more food. Nature means not only rich grasslands and prairies; it means

also ores, oil, gas, and waterfalls. Inanimate energy, harnessed by metals, mobilizes everything—men, goods, and thoughts—and cuts that fatal causal nexus between food production and population size that is the curse of monsoon Asia. In the United States, food grown in California moves to New York or any other section of the country or to any part of the earth where people can afford to buy it or where it can be used to secure world peace. There is little or no connection between the size of the harvest and the number of births. Nature creates capital under man's direction. She gives birth to a billion robots that do man's bidding. Under man's direction, they build skyscrapers and dig oil wells, string power lines, generate electricity, and so forth. This capital, in turn, enables man to have higher living standards, to enjoy more leisure, to safeguard his health, to prolong his life span—in short, to yield real wealth. (See Fig. 10.3.)

While the monsoonia pattern resembles a circle—a vicious circle—the pattern of horse-power land, as one may call the United States—resembles an ascending spiral. As it reaches loftier heights, it becomes thinner. It is like a high pyramid built on a broad base but so tall that it is dangerously exposed to high winds. It is a bold structure, but the towering height is not without its risks. Vegetable civilization is like a giant squatting on the ground in sodden safety.

Resource Patterns in the United States

Exclusive of her noncontiguous territories—Alaska, Puerto Rico, Hawaii, and the Virgin Islands—the United States covers an area of almost three million square miles—about 6 percent of the land area of the earth—a massive continent which differs strikingly from Europe, that articulated peninsula of Eurasia. Within this huge territory is found an unparalleled variety of climatic, soil, topographical, and geological conditions. The number of commercially important crops which can be successfully produced is unsurpassed anywhere. Where else are such expansive cotton, corn, and wheat areas—to name only the three leading crops—assembled under such favorable producing conditions within the confines of a single political entity? Moreover, almost one-sixth of this area is underlaid with coal which

[10] W. H. Mallory, *China, Land of Famine,* Special Publication No. 6, American Geographical Society, New York, 1926, p. 29.

[11] Quoted by R. D. McKenzie in "When the East Meets West," New York *Times Magazine,* September 16, 1928, p. 1.

[12] D. H. Kulp, II, "Chinese Continuity," *Annals of the American Academy of Political and Social Science,* November, 1930, pp. 18 ff.

ranges from the poorest lignite to the finest steam coal and anthracite. The coal is ideally supplemented by petroleum, as in California, Texas, and Oklahoma, and by water power throughout the entire western third, in the extreme Northeast, and in the Southeast. No other country possesses an equal amount of energy resources; no region of comparable size can boast of an array of power resources which, in advantageous arrangement and availability, can compare with those of the United States.

Europe also has valuable energy resources; but until a Pan-Europe arises from the mess of political provincialism and petty rivalries which put innumerable obstacles in the path of progress, these resources will remain insufficiently coördinated. Political boundaries play a part of ominous importance on a continent filled with suspicion and fear, and all too often they interfere with a rational utilization of nature's wealth. Thus the United States is strong because of her excellent energy resources, but she is stronger still because of the historical development which united the separate states. America too has her squabbles—witness the fierce struggles over the Taft-Hartley Act and the Civil Rights Program—but as yet these schisms are relatively harmless compared with the events which robbed Silesia of half her value and tore the Ruhr-Lorraine unit into opposing halves.

No other continent possesses energy resources comparable in extent, variety, and availability to those of Europe and America. The same holds true of machine resources— iron, copper, lead, zinc, etc. With few exceptions, what deficiencies there are can be made good through financial control over foreign deposits.

The United States is a country of vast continental expanse, at one and the same time the most highly mineralized area and the largest producer of vegetable and animal products. But wealth arouses the envy of the less fortunate, and invites attack. Many an empire of the past has succumbed in that way. But here again nature favors the United States beyond belief. On the east and west, the wide expanse of the Atlantic and Pacific; to the north, a prosperous neighbor, a blood relation. No Verdun or Belfort marks that "international line," grim reminders of strange "neighborliness." The sit-

uation to the south does not need to arouse fears, unless it be the fear that superior strength invites abuse.

If security and abundance are prerequisites of a rich material civilization, it is not surprising to find its highest development in North America, north of the Rio Grande. While other continents were diverted by periodic warfare or fear of it, until recently the United States and her friendly neighbor to the north were able to concentrate single-mindedly on the business of wealth creation.

Unfortunately the situation is rapidly deteriorating. More and more, North America is being drawn into the whirlpool of world politics; and as the arsenal of democracy and the chief guardian of the West, the United States is being compelled to give more and more attention to military plans and is progressively being exposed to possible enemy attack. It started with the submarine and the airplane, which turned oceans into mere moats. It became worse when in World War II western Europe came close to being knocked out and the Soviet Union gained the stature of a Super Power. The conquest of China by the communists made the situation even more critical. And the knowledge of an atomic explosion somewhere in Russia went far to remove from North America the last vestige of a once superior position of security. What has been true of Europe for half a century or longer is now happening in North America. Industries are being moved to safer locations—there is talk of putting them underground—and people are being moved in response to strategic requirements. The old freedom of pursuing economic aims undisturbed by military considerations is waning rapidly. It will in time be reflected in still heavier tax burdens and in higher costs of production brought on by departures from economic rationality.

Yet, all these changes are relative. If the situation is deteriorating in North America, it is deteriorating even more rapidly elsewhere, and a certain margin of advantage may long remain. Moreover, this continent should for long feel the benefit of the momentum gained from its earlier superiority. Above all, North America's unique endowment with natural assets, as well as the blessings of the American way of life, may at least in part offset the unfavorable developments in recent global history.

From natural assets we now turn to institutions, and again an international comparison proves helpful. This time America and Europe are used for this purpose. Both regions were settled by the white man. Racially the populations of the two continents have much in common. Moreover, there has been a constant interchange of experience. But the culture patterns as revealed in the institutions and in particular in the attitude toward resources are markedly different in the two continents. This calls for an explanation.

Without wishing to imply that such complex questions can be answered by a single argument, it seems that one cause, more than any other, accounts for this difference between the two continents, namely, the fact that the white man settled most of Europe before, and most of America after, the mechanical revolution. He settled much of Europe with the broadax and sweat, much of America with railroads and steam. The European settlement spread at a snail's pace, progress was slow, the tools were primitive, and weak man was only inadequately supported by work animals and beasts of burden. After the Appalachian Mountains ceased to be the western boundary, the conquest of the North American continent was a race; with the aid of steam man could in a day settle a territory which formerly could hardly have been subdued in a decade.

This difference in manner and above all in tempo of settlement, perhaps more than any other single fact, accounts for the striking differences which exist today between Europe and America. In the first place, Europeans developed their attitudes, customs, and institutions in times of relative isolation. The result is regional particularism. Differences of languages developed; the customs of one town seemed strange to its neighbors only a few miles away. When the railroad finally came, these differences were so deeply ingrained that narrow nationalism, fanned by bitter memories of strife, replaced the former particularism. The past therefore weighs heavily upon the minds of Europeans. They are "time people"; they judge the present and the future in the light of past events. Precedent and tradition still largely govern the mind. Man thinks and acts because his medieval ancestor still survives in

him. The driver of today has to listen to the back-seat driver of the past.[13]

Contrast this situation with that existing in the United States. In general, American traditions can be traced to only a minority of those who settled the New World. Most emigrants had to unlearn their own traditions; they had to live in the present and for the future only. The present made such demands on the strength of the bold adventurer and, in return, held out such rewards for every effort made, that it became of transcending importance in shaping the new national character and weaving the new culture pattern. The immediate environment spoke louder than the soft voice of past memories. In contrast to the "time people" of Europe, the North Americans, to a high degree, are "place people," that is to say, people whose attitudes are largely determined by the physical environment through the occupation it forces upon them. The absence of strong local traditions permits widespread homogeneity in customs and the outlook on life.

But that is not all. Possibly the greatest difference between the two continents is to be found in the greater and more varied endowment in natural assets in North America and the resulting fact that a larger share of resources is available for each man, woman, and child. If a region is opened up slowly, step by step, over a long period of time, the amount of natural wealth available at any one time is not apt to be very large. If, on the other hand, a huge continent, endowed with every variety of nature's gifts, is settled with impetuous vigor, the amount of resources available for the use of each generation is infinitely greater. The historical development of Europe, therefore, has been marked by a moderate availability of natural wealth. This is in striking contrast to the almost overwhelming abundance found in this country. The creeping exploitation of European resources rendered quite difficult the production of a surplus over consumption; the process of capital accumulation was bound to be both slow and painful.

On the other hand, the whirlwind exploitation which is taking place on this continent greatly facilitates the accumulation of surplus

---

[13] Cf. Sinclair Lewis, *Dodsworth*, Harcourt, Brace and Company, New York, 1929, pp. 248 ff.

capital. It proceeds rapidly and, particularly of late, almost painlessly. Such a difference is bound to reflect upon the economic system in general and on the attitude toward natural resources in particular. It is dangerous to generalize, but one would be inclined to ascribe to this difference in the mode of settlement a certain short-sighted economy frequently found in Europe, and a certain short-sighted wastefulness characteristic of America. How this difference in opportunities and tasks has necessitated a different development of technological arts in America and Europe was pointed out above (see pp. 34-35).

America, an Experiment in Transportation

Whether this mechanization of production has brought about a state of optimum population, an ideal man-land ratio,[14] cannot be concluded with any degree of certainty. For some 150 million people to inhabit a country of continental expanse which could well support many more not only means that there are more resources available per capita than on a continent of much smaller size; it also implies a handicap of space. It is conceivable that, next to institutional maladjustments, her excessive space is the greatest weakness of the resource position of the United States.

This is a thought which to many appears rather strange. Space—abundance of space— has its glorious advantages. It develops vision, widens the horizon, allows freedom of motion, and helps in many other ways.[15] But there is no gainsaying that an excess of space is one of the greatest luxuries, one of the most expensive possessions of which a country may boast. One has only to imagine a country of continental expanse which consists of an enormous desert surrounded by a narrow margin of productive land—some people think of Australia in this way. The Australians would probably be much better off if their resources were concentrated upon a very much smaller area. The pulse of economic and social life would beat quicker, and much effort, time, and wealth could be saved if short direct connections could replace the circuitous journeys necessary at present.

North America is not as extreme a case of "elephantiasis" as Australia. And yet one wonders whether, at times, we do not show symptoms of the same trouble. When Quick[16] calls the United States an experiment in transportation, what does he mean? Paraphrasing Lincoln, he might say that it means an experiment to determine whether a nation so conceived in continental expanse can long survive. Lincoln referred to a political experiment; but the United States is also an economic experiment. Lincoln referred to the strain which experiments in political institutions place upon a democracy. Quick refers to the strain which an experiment in economic institutions places upon natural and material resources. Railroads and highways, automobiles and pipelines, telephones and power transmission lines are the means of overcoming the space handicap and of creating prosperity in spite of excessive space. In many cases at least, the automobile is not a sign of excessive prosperity but a means of overcoming America's greatest handicap, the excess of space.

Coal mines may lie a thousand miles from the iron ore. Food is grown a thousand miles and more away from the point of consumption. The magnificent transportation facilities which bring the ore to the coal or the food to the consumer are not assets in the ordinary sense of the word, but the means by which we overcome the tremendous handicaps placed in our way by the excess of space. To be sure, without our unexcelled transportation system we would be paralyzed. To understand the true function of a transportation system in our economic system, we must not compare the present situation with one in which we have no means of transportation; we must visualize ourselves living on a continent perhaps one-third the size, containing within its borders the same wealth of natural endowment which we command today, but excluding the great barren spaces which separate the productive areas today and whose conquest lays such a heavy burden upon our economic system. That is the

---

[14] Cf. chap. 8, especially pp. 111-112.

[15] Cf. Ratzel's discussion of the "Grossräumige Kolonialvölker."

[16] H. Quick, "America—An Experiment in Transportation," *Saturday Evening Post*, February 25, 1922.

meaning of the phrase: America, an experiment in transportation.[17]

The disproportionately heavy burden which transportation places upon our economic system may indicate that we are still below the optimum point. Since the construction of transportation facilities—railroads, bridges, stations, warehouses, highways, automobiles, buses, trucks, etc.—requires a great deal of iron and steel and other machine resources as well as a considerable amount of power resources, and since the operation of this transportation system requires some machine resources for upkeep and an enormous amount of energy resources for daily use—coal and Diesel oil on the railroads, gasoline in automobiles and airplanes, water power for some railroads—the per capita expenditure of machine and energy resources in this country assumes a new meaning.

One may be inclined to argue that it does not make any difference to a laborer whether he earns his living building a railroad bridge or making a Frigidaire. In other words, the production of transportation facilities implies that hundreds of thousands, if not millions, of people are earning their living in the process. But the point is this: If the same millions could earn their living making consumers' goods rather than production goods such as steel rails and railroad bridges the country as a whole would be still better off, provided we accept per capita intake of consumers' goods as an adequate criterion of national well-being. Nobody would suggest that in times of normal

business activity the American people are not well off in a material sense. It would be foolish to deny this prosperity when innumerable items of evidence stare the observer in the face. Normally, America may be considered prosperous, the per capita income of material consumers' goods probably being greater than anywhere else in the world. This, however, should not blind us to the truth.

It would be a mistake to conclude from the foregoing discussion that density of population is the only remedy for excessive space and the consequent excessive expenditure for transportation. A look at New York City will readily convince one that this cannot be so. Excessive population density necessitates heavy transportation expenditure at least as much as does excessive sparsity, though for different reasons. It is not maximum density but optimum density which can solve the problem. Since excessive space is the one great handicap under which North America labors, and since that handicap can be neutralized through improved transportation and communication, it follows that every improvement of the arts, every invention and every discovery which make transportation and communication more efficient and therefore cheaper, mean most to that country which is most dependent on efficient transportation.[18]

To repeat, the United States is an experiment in transportation, and that experiment is more apt to succeed the more efficient transportation is. Every increase in transportation efficiency means a step forward toward optimum density. In a country where friction can be abolished and an ounce of coal can move a ton of freight, where tare is reduced to a minimum, the optimum population lies at a much lower point on the population density scale than in a country where wheelbarrows and jinrikishas are the only means of transportation. The more we use radios, wireless telegraphy, and rubber-tired wheels running on ball bearings and on concrete roads, the closer we come to

---

[17] George Otis Smith, formerly Director of the United States Geological Survey, and Chairman of the Federal Power Commission, speaking before the International Railway Fuel Association on May 10, 1927, developed this idea in admirable fashion. He gave his speech the telling title "What Price Distance?" This same idea is developed in an interesting manner by M. M. Knight, "Water and the Course of Empire in North Africa," *Quarterly Journal of Economics*, November, 1928.

The huge transportation apparatus is part of John Meynard Keynes' famous "cake" in the growth of which he saw the central object of worship of the capitalistic religion of progress, and which he considered the enchanted "cake" which neither the workers that made it nor the men that owned it could ever eat. Cf. Carlyle's reference to the enchanted fruit quoted by W. C. Mitchell. (See p. 30.)

---

[18] This discussion of transportation could well be extended to include many other services which are direct or indirect corollaries of an exchange economy of continental expanse. Reference is made to marketing, advertising, banking, insurance, and all other facilitating activities.

the ideal transportation condition and the lower moves the point of optimum population on the density scale. In fact, it is not at all impossible that the rapid strides made in the realm of transportation and communication during the past two or three decades go further to explain American prosperity than almost any other single factor. The greater efficiency in electric power production and transmission which relieves the pressure on coal mining and on railroad transportation, the improvement in gasoline production, inventions in the field of wireless telegraphy, in telephony and television, all have contributed toward lowering the optimum point. The triumph of the robot and the conquest of space solve the two problems which alone stood in the way of American prosperity —labor scarcity and excess of space. As far as America's natural position is concerned, little remains to be desired except that man's wisdom be commensurate to the opportunity. It would seem rash to assume that this condition has as yet been met.

THE RESOURCE HIERARCHY OF MODERN WORLD ECONOMY

The Mechanical Revolution the Great Divide of Mankind

The mechanical revolution has shifted the center of gravity from land or soil—food-producing, man-supporting soil—to inanimate energy, to horsepower, to robots. Wealth and strength depend not primarily on the size of armies or the number of coolies, but on control over the inanimate energies of nature through the power-driven machine and through science. The two Super Powers of the world today—the United States and the Soviet Union—are leaders in the output of energy-yielding fuels and energy-harnessing steel. A united western Europe will be a powerful political unit. It will rank high in the aggregate output of coal and iron. There are no great industrial nations in the southern hemisphere. There are no Great Powers in the southern hemisphere. When Japan coveted the glory of becoming a Great Power she pushed the exploration of her limited domestic iron and coal reserves to the utmost and strove to supplement them in every conceivable way. It looks as if the feudalism of the twentieth century was the feudalism of horsepower as the ancient feudalism had been a feudalism of man power and man-power-supporting land.

Thus, political power seems to be associated in some way with industrialization, the branch of production that relies on inanimate energy. Agrarian and pastoral countries are weak countries politically. As a rule they are also poor countries. Horsepower in the modern world appears as the key not only to power but also to wealth. When agriculture was left to fight things out with industry in the open market, agriculture seemed to get the worst of the bargain. Industrial countries enjoyed stronger bargaining positions than did agrarian countries. More often than not, industries, in one way or another, to a greater or lesser extent, enjoyed the advantage of closer control over output while agriculture remained bound to the irresistible rhythm of nature. Until government intervened on the side of the weak to assure a better balance of bargaining power, agriculture seemed to grow poorer and industry richer. Cities became notorious centers of wealth, whereas the open country was neglected and backward.

Cities throve not only as centers of industry, but as centers of commerce as well. They became the great nodal points where the controls over tertiary activities such as trade, finance, insurance, professional work, education, governmental activities were centered. The great organized exchanges became symbols of these concentrations of invisible powers, as did the palatial head offices of the great corporations from which wires and wireless reach to the far corners of the earth.

From Economic Egalitarianism to Hierarchy

More and more the economic order took on the appearance of a vast hierarchy, i.e., a structure of staggered control, a structure resting on a huge basis of raw-material production with power centered in the heavy industries and the leading banks. The world economy in general, as well as individual national economies, seemed to divide more and more into active and passive elements. The right to active participation in economic control seems to spring from the capacity to earn profits and accumulate surplus; this in turn seems associated with the ability to apply science and the power-driven machine generally through cor-

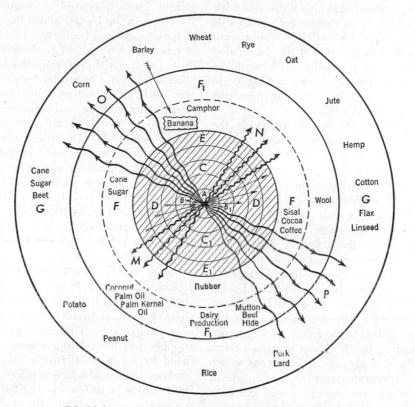

FIG. 10.4. The Resource Hierarchy of Modern World Economy.

I. The center of power (A-E_1). The power-metal-science system (including commerce, finance, transportation and communication systems). A, the focal point of fund accumulation and scientific progress. B, the basic energy resources (found in conjunction with machine resources): coal, petroleum, natural gas, falling water. B_1, the basic machine resource: iron ore. C, secondary machine resources: copper, aluminum, lead, zinc, tin, nickel. C_1, ferro-alloys. D, precious metals (basis of currency system and hence facilitating agent of commerce). E, basic capital equipment: steel industry, power industries (coal mining, petroleum, natural gas, electrical industries), construction industry, machine and machine tool industry including electrical equipment industry, transportation-communication industries (railroads, automobile industry, telephone, telegraph, radio, television, highways). E_1, secondary capital equipment: manufacturing industries associated with E but making less essential producers' goods or consumers' goods.

II. The periphery (G). The climate-soil-topography system. Agricultural annuals: foodstuffs (wheat, barley, rye, oats, corn, rice, sugar, cane and beet, bananas, potatoes, pork, linseed), fibers (cotton, flax, hemp, jute).

III. The twilight zone (F-F_1). Agricultural perennials: F leaning toward I, F_1 leaning toward II. Manufacturing industries not organically tied up with the center of power: F leaning toward I, F_1 leaning toward II.

Force field MN: Application of surplus funds and science to branches of production affiliated with the power-metal-science center (A-E_1) as seller. General results: lower cost, wider market, increased profitableness, higher or stabilized price, assured continuity of supply.

Force field OP: Application of surplus funds and science to branches of production in which the power-metal-science center is interested as buyer. General results: stimulated output by expansion of acreage or intensification of production; lower price.

porate structures. Now and then a country or region that produced agricultural raw materials would find itself in an exceptionally favorable market position and for a while it would accumulate credit. But sooner or later the market would turn against it and the credit would be dissipated in a spree of luxury buying or in desperate efforts to industrialize. At times vast credits proved uncollectible.

In the procurement of raw materials the Great Powers possessed of active control have a choice of policy. They may acquire the source of raw materials or they may prefer to have others continue as independent producers. By and large, the choice of policy between absorption of the source itself and purchase from the dependent source seems to be affected if not determined by the nature of the material involved. In general, mineral raw materials are absorbed into the corporate structure through ownership of mines, whereas agricultural products, especially the great staples such as wheat, corn, rye, potatoes, cotton, etc., are allowed to remain the product of the independent grower. An exception to this is certain perennial crops such as rubber, sugar cane, and bananas, which come under corporate control and management. To explain why the modern world economy takes on these particular hierarchical patterns is one of the chief objectives of the remainder of this volume.

This description of the hierarchical structure of modern world economy may be expressed diagrammatically, as shown in Fig. 10.4.[19] The two "fields of force," MN and OP, it will be noted, represent the alternative policies of "absorption" or "acquisition" by purchase discussed above. When industries in the power center decide on the second alternative, national policy may undertake to influence the market position in their favor.

In the modern world there are several "power centers." Moscow would undoubtedly be one, New York-Washington would be another. London and Paris are striving valiantly to hold on to their respective peaks.

Such power centers differ in vital respects.

---

[19] This diagram was first published in Erich W. Zimmermann, "The Resource Hierarchy in Modern World Economy," *Weltwirtschaftliches Archiv,* April, 1931.

Thus in Soviet Russia the power of government and of business control is combined in the Politburo. In the United States the relationship of government and business is highly complex, at times the government backing big business in its raw-material procurement efforts, and at other times acting as arbiter between big business and little business, big business and farmers, big business and consumers, etc. The difference is that between a totalitarian state and a democracy. These are two extremes; between them there are many gradations.

The hierarchical conception of the modern world economy here propounded is quite different from that presented in traditional texts on international trade theory. The traditional approach is atomistic. It thinks of the world as a single market in which two billion and more human beings meet as buyers and sellers, all on an even footing. Economic law is the great arbiter, the all-wise judge that metes out just shares to all. Each one is entitled to a certain share of the total product, the size of the share depending on the comparative aptitude of each supplier and the relative intensity of the demand for his product. In that theory all commodities possess absolute a priori comparability. It makes no difference whether one person is a goatherd and the other the chairman of the board of United States Steel; each according to his deserts.

The hierarchical concept is irreconcilable with such egalitarianism. It recognizes fundamental differences between conditions and industries. It maintains that whether one is engaged in building battleships, which can be done only with huge aggregates of materials, man power, and equipment, or growing corn on a hillside of the Central Plateau of Mexico, makes all the difference in the world. The atomistic approach is unrealistic. Economic activity takes place not in a political and social vacuum, but as part and parcel of people's struggle for existence. The struggle proceeds on all fronts simultaneously. Economic and political and social forces are all aspects of the same basic process of the human struggle for survival.

A more realistic conception of modern world economy should go far to assure better progress in the negotiations designed to lift international economic policies to a higher level.

BIBLIOGRAPHY

Delaisi, F., *Les Deux Europes; Europe Industrielle et Europe Agricole,* Paris, Payot, 1929.

Fabricant, S., *Labor Savings in American Industry, 1899-1939,* National Bureau of Economic Research, Occasional Paper No. 23, 1945.

James, P. E., *Latin America,* New York, Odyssey Press, 1942.

Nourse, E. G., and associates, *America's Capacity to Produce,* Washington, Brookings Institution, 1934.

Webb, W. P., *Divided We Stand,* Austin, Adams Publications, 1948.

Wythe, G., *Industry in Latin America,* New York, Macmillan, 1946.

Zimmermann, E. W., "The Resource Hierarchy in Modern World Economy," *Weltwirtschaftliches Archiv,* April, 1931.

PART II

RESOURCES OF AGRICULTURE

UNIT 1. NATURE AND PLACE OF AGRICULTURE

Chapter 11

THE NATURE OF AGRICULTURE

Agriculture is almost as old as recorded time, its realm almost as wide as the inhabited earth. In one bold sweep the word takes in the entire range of civilizational progress, reaching from the lowly "man with the hoe" and the still lowlier man with the stick to the sophisticated Iowa farmer harvesting hybrid corn with a tractor-pulled mechanical picker for sale to parties unknown, or to the progressive husbandman raising the efficiency of his dairy herd with the aid of thyro-protein, vitamins, and artificial insemination. It encompasses the ways of the Hindu ryot, half-buried in tradition and superstition, as well as those of the collective farmer of Soviet Russia, driven to ultramodern practice by the revolutionary zeal of his leaders; the ways of the European peasant, wise with the experience of countless peasant generations before him, as well as those of the peon, bound in ignorance and fear by the strictures of feudalism and not always free of the shackles of racial discrimination; and so on through time and space, around the world, through temperate and torrid zones, across prairies and plains, pampas and pustas, up the steep slopes of the

Andes, the Alps, and the Himalayas, through tropical jungles, across plantations of the equatorial belt and the paddy fields of Asia.

THE MEANING OF AGRICULTURE

Difficulties of Definition

To define a concept as wide and varied as agriculture is as difficult as it is to define such basic concepts as life, reality, existence. It would be easy to hide behind the technicality of the etymological derivation of the word— *ager*, field or soil; and *cultura*, the care of, the tilling of—but nothing would be gained from such pedantic erudition. For agriculture includes far more than the tilling of the field or the raising of field crops. It includes animal husbandry, tree culture, forestry, irrigation, fish hatcheries, fur farming, perhaps even hydroponics and many other varied activities. Food getting constitutes by far the most essential and largest function of agriculture; but, after all, the production of fibers, tobacco, inedible fats, wood pulp, and so on is agriculture too, and it is too important to be overlooked. Moreover, one can get food also by hunting, fishing, whaling, collecting wild berries and other free goods of nature—purely exploitative activities not usually considered agriculture.

One might be inclined to cut the Gordian knot by simply identifying agriculture with man's use of plant and animal life. But such a simple solution, by including purely exploitative activities, would seem to run counter to the accepted usage of the term agriculture which suggests, or implies, that man has a share in the genetic process that makes plants and animals grow. Moreover, the word agriculture is definitely associated with sustained settlement on the land and thus is contrasted with nomadic pastoral life in which many millions of people live over wide areas of the more arid sections of the earth. They too make use of plant and animal life.

While it is clear from the foregoing that the definition of agriculture is not an easy task, it should nevertheless be possible to line up the essential elements of the term in such a way as to circumscribe or define the concept of agriculture. The following is an attempt to do just that. *Agriculture covers those productive efforts by which man, settled on the land, seeks to make use of and, if possible, accelerate and improve upon the natural genetic or growth processes of plant and animal life, to the end that these processes will yield the vegetable and animal products needed or wanted by man.*

This statement stresses the fact that agricultural man (1) lives in relatively permanent or sustained settlement, i.e., does not move about in the fashion of the nomad, and (2) works *with* nature to make her yield more of the fruits he desires. At the same time it concedes to nature the dominant role in the agricultural process.

It is clear that this statement contains only the bare essentials of what constitutes the concept of agriculture. It does not describe in detail the ways by which man works with nature. Nor does it mention the outside aid upon which modern commercialized mechanized agriculture relies increasingly to perform its miracles of giant crops and qualitative improvements. These details hardly belong in the definition.

Dependence of Agriculture on Nature

Dependence on nature is the chief characteristic of agriculture. Reliance on, or exploitation of, the biotic energies of living plants and animals is the essence. Whereas in other activities man has managed to gain the upper hand, especially since Los Alamos and Hiroshima, in agriculture nature remains the master and man is only the helper. As the French business leader, Henry, properly states:

Although having identical aims, agriculture and industry rely upon forces and use methods that give them special and distinct characteristics. This notwithstanding that the industrialization of agriculture has been strongly urged. The two ideas are self-contradictory.

From raw materials furnished by nature industry manufactures articles, the shape, size, and composition of which it varies to meet the needs and convenience of the public. As a creator of articles of current use, the potentiality of industry is bounded only by human ingenuity. It creates the very forces it employs, harnesses them to its needs and uses them when, how and to the extent that it pleases; it increases or decreases, suspends or stops its production at will.

Far from dominating the forces that work for it, agriculture is subject to their yoke and knows them but by their effects; despite the enormous progress achieved, the mystery that enshrouds the forces is so deep that agriculture continues to be their plaything. It can but prepare conditions favourable to their action. Agricultural methods must therefore leave room for the unknown factor of the forces of nature, that industry does not have to take into account.[1]

Agricultural man is dependent on unpredictable and uncontrollable weather; on a thin sheet of soil that covers much of the earth's surface, the mysteries of which he has hardly begun to understand and the heterogeneity of which retains the fascination of a jigsaw puzzle; and above all on the biological rhythm and the caprices of plant and animal life.[2]

The implications of this threefold dependence are infinite. They spell incomplete control

---

[1] A. Henry, "General Problems of Agriculture," *World Trade,* October, 1930, pp. 323-324.

[2] Karl Brandt stresses two phases when he writes: "Being bound so crucially to extensive space and to a biological time schedule, agriculture is, by and large, unable to create the conditions that are so typically responsible for the creation of large plant units in industry." *The Reconstruction of World Agriculture,* W. W. Norton & Company, New York, 1945, p. 257.

if not lack of control all along the line. The farmer cannot say definitely how much he will produce, how good the results of his efforts will be, or when the crop will be ready for the market. His products reflect not only the vagaries of the weather but also the endless heterogeneity of nature herself. No two fleeces of wool are alike, no two bushels of wheat or tomatoes.[3] His dependence on the soil, that thin layer in which the life-giving and life-supporting elements of the earth are concentrated, spells spatial expansion which, in turn, limits the size of the agricultural enterprise and thus guarantees its competitive nature.[4] His dependence on the biological rhythm of nature, reinforcing that of the seasons, leaves the farmer little control over the time cycle or the tempo of production.

Man's Efforts to Lessen This Dependence

As was indicated above, the chief elements of the processes of nature in which man takes a hand are:

1. Climate—sunshine, rain, temperature, wind.
2. Soil (and water).
3. The life processes of plants and animals.

Man tampers with each one of these three elements with varying success. He still cannot do much with climate—he can fight frost with smudge pots and excess heat rays with cheesecloth or shade trees, he can build windbreaks and shelter belts; but by and large the Cyclopean struggle of air masses above his head, the basis of climatic change, is as yet too little understood and, what is more, almost wholly uncontrolled. Moreover, he cannot change the seasons. But he can remove excess water by

drainage and make up for deficiencies by irrigation; he can move plants and animals from regions of unfavorable climate to regions better suited to their needs. In short, while man cannot tackle climate directly on any grand scale, he can by indirect means temper its effects on him and adjust himself to it.

Soils are much more amenable to human influence than is climate. To be sure, it took man a very, very long time even to begin to understand soils, and during the stage of ignorance and inadequate understanding frightful damage was wrought. But real progress has been made of late and it is continuing. Not only is it known what crops a given soil can produce to greatest advantage, but it is now possible artificially to maintain and even enhance soil fertility. Practices have been developed which protect soil against wind and water erosion.

That brings us to the third element of the processes underlying agriculture, the living plant and animal. It is here that man has won his greatest triumphs. The domestication of both plants and animals, the progressive adaptation of their characteristics to the wishes and needs of man, are monuments to human resourcefulness and patience. Yet it is wise not to lose sight of the fact that domesticated plants and animals constitute but small minorities of their natural aggregates, that even now a cow as a rule gives only one calf a year and that pigs still have only two hams (the reckless language of the advertiser notwithstanding), and above all that it is still far from certain which will ultimately win—men or insects.

The measures man takes in his efforts to improve upon the processes of nature are both *positive and negative*, i.e., measures to promote and support the forces favorable to him and measures to fight and suppress the forces hostile to him.

These measures are by no means confined to the sphere of agriculture itself. Improvements in the realms of transportation and communication have rendered possible regional specialization and thus made feasible the fuller utilization of the peculiar features of specific soils and climates. By building cities and supporting large nonfarming populations, industry has created vast markets for both staples and specialties. Science has discovered new ways of

---

[3] There is also a vast heterogeneity of minerals, but as a rule the heterogeneity of the raw mineral product disappears in processing, whereas it remains clearly reflected in most agricultural end products.

[4] A factory or laboratory or mine may produce vast values on small areas. Single mine shafts have yielded hundreds of millions of dollars' worth of treasure. The per acre yield of agricultural production is relatively low. At $2 a bushel, a wheat farmer who grosses $100,000 a year and harvests 13 bushels an acre must draw on almost 4000 acres, or over 6 square miles. This expansive nature of agricultural production limits the economical size of the operating unit and, by forestalling concentration of ownership and control, promotes or preserves competition.

processing farm products and new uses for them.

Results of Man's Interference

Unfortunately, however, man's share in the evolution of agriculture has not been confined to *constructive* measures and beneficial influences. Man has done much harm; he has seriously impaired the agricultural productivity of nature in many parts of the earth, over wide areas of land. In fact, so great has been this *destructive* fury that some people fear a serious and permanent impairment of the original productive power of nature. Soils have been ruined by man's direct action as well as through the indirect results of his interference with delicate balances in nature. This damage extends to water supply as well as to soils. Much soil is destroyed annually by erosion. Rivers have been polluted and fish life destroyed. Gentle streams have been turned into wild raging torrents; others have dried up. Man has extinguished species of both plant and animal life that are indispensable to the full and sustained creation of new types through natural selection.

Never in history have the destructive forces of man worked with more deadly efficacy than in our machine age, and perhaps nowhere has the damage been greater than in North America. Ignorance of the delicate balance of ecological relations in nature, failure to realize the repercussions and implications of seemingly innocent actions or omissions, short-sighted emphasis on immediate market values at the expense of irreplaceable basic assets—a short-sightedness backed by institutions sprung not from the soil but from the needs and preferences of an industrial civilization—have combined to impair the productive capacity of bountiful nature. Apparently, the same tools that proved their effectiveness in producing a vast output of immediate values are equally effective in damaging the permanent assets which alone can assure the sustained flow of current production for the future.[5]

While some of the damage is irreparable, there is hope for the future. So widespread

has become the realization of the dangers involved in the thoughtless exploitation of nature that measures designed to heal the wounds inflicted by past errors and to combat malpractice in the future are finding increasing support from an enlightened public. Indeed, much has been done during the past decade that justifies hope for the future.

TYPES OF AGRICULTURE

"True" and "Spurious" Agriculture

To refer to human activities which damage the soil (*ager*) as agri*culture* seems to do violence to the very meaning of *culture* (the Latin verb from which this noun is derived is *colere*, which means to fondle, to care for).[6] Perhaps, therefore, one should distinguish between *true* agriculture and *spurious* agriculture. The former term would be confined to agriculture in which man plays a constructive role, preserving and if possible improving the soil as well as other basic assets of nature on which a permanent and preferably expanding agriculture rests. (Agriculture in locations such as the Nile and other river valleys where permanence of agriculture may be assured by nature herself depositing soil brought down from up-river areas would constitute special or borderline cases in such a division.) Soil-destroying and other asset-impairing forms of agriculture would be branded as "spurious."

In this connection it may be well to keep in mind that destructive practices, if carried on inefficiently, on a small scale, and therefore ineffectively, may prove harmless in the long run. Thus Indian agriculture, though characterized by some destructive methods, left the soil fertility of the North American continent fairly intact. But the same practices, applied far more efficiently and on a far larger scale, would prove definitely harmful.

Genetic and Extractive Agriculture

Asset-preserving agriculture is truly genetic, whereas "spurious" agriculture is extractive. It extracts substances from the soil without re-

---

[5] See Carl Sauer, "Destructive Exploitation in Modern Colonial Expansion," *Proceedings of the International Congress of Geography*, Amsterdam, 1938, vol. 2, pp. 494 ff.

[6] It is one thing to refuse to restrict the meaning of agriculture to the literal meaning of the Latin word from which the English is derived, and quite a different thing to countenance meanings that do violence to that original concept.

placing them. Perhaps our scientific understanding of the natural phenomena underlying agricultural practice is insufficient to permit us to state with assurance where the lines of demarcation lie. But to the layman, the distinction between soil conservation and land robbing seems fairly clear-cut.

In a sense, all cropping involves extraction, for all crops contain elements taken from the soil. In local subsistence farming, however, the elements so extracted are returned, or at least can be returned, to the soil as manure or other forms of waste. In some regions, however, manure serves as fuel and is not returned. But in commercial farming, the products of which are marketed not in the area of origin but in distant urban markets, perhaps abroad, there is no such assurance of the return to the soil of elements extracted therefrom. Nor is it certain that the seller's loss will be the buyer's gain. Sewage disposal in metropolitan areas in particular and in urban areas in general seldom provides for the agricultural utilization of human wastes. It is only in the case of purchased, imported *feed*stuff that the soil elements brought in have a reasonable chance of finding their way to the fields of the importing country or region. Thus most "milk sheds"—milk-producing areas such as those serving metropolitan areas—tend to build up their land out of imported feedstuffs converted into animal manure. To the extent that parts of continental Europe have depended on imported feedstuffs, their soils too have benefited at the expense of the feed-exporting areas. This is perhaps especially true of Holland and Denmark.

To what extent the application of artificial (manufactured) fertilizers can replace the elements removed from the soil by crops is still a moot question. The replacement of nitrogen, potassium, phosphorus, and lime seems to be satisfactory. Yet some experts question whether the problem of artificially replacing the ingredients lost from the original soil has been completely solved.[7] The wholesale destruction

of soil by erosion is a far more serious problem, but its solution appears a great deal nearer than it did even ten years ago.

This distinction between genetic and extractive agriculture is not confined to soil practice. It extends with perhaps even greater significance to plants and animals. For plant and animal life can be impaired by reckless exploitation as effectively and as disastrously as can the soil on which it depends. The processes of mutation and variation of species of plants and animals are tirelessly at work. Holes carelessly torn in nature's warp and woof can damage the entire texture. Once a species of plant or animal is eradicated, evolution of future plant and animal life is thereby impaired.

"Pure" and "Hybrid" Agriculture

Agriculture in vegetable civilizations, i.e., domestic agriculture serving mainly the need of the farmer's own household, is relatively free from outside influences. It is self-sufficient even in its culture pattern. It creates its own institutions. The wooden stick or plow, the human labor, the manure—all elements derive out of the creative process of agriculture itself. Such agriculture, therefore, may be called "pure" agriculture.[8]

Quite different is modern scientific mechanized commercial agriculture as it is practiced in the United States for example. It is permeated with "impurities" as it were, i.e., outside forces and influences, most of which stem from the industrial side of the economy. The chemical fertilizer, the tractor and the fuel that makes it go, the milking machine and the electricity that runs it, the family car, and the gadgets that play so great a part in modern

---

[7] The U. S. Department of Agriculture has under way, at Beltsville, Md., extensive experiments concerning the relation of the fertilization of crops to the feeding of dairy cows. These experiments, which start with heifers, will be carried on through at least two generations. It is as yet too early to draw any conclusions.

Of the many books which throw light on this progress, the following have come to the author's attention: Sir Albert Howard, *An Agricultural Testament,* Oxford University Press, London, 1940; J. A. Cocannover, *Trampling Out the Vintage,* University of Oklahoma Press, Norman, 1945; and C. E. Millar and L. M. Turk, *Fundamentals of Soil Science,* John Wiley & Sons, Inc., New York, 1943.

[8] This "purity" applies only to the agricultural practices themselves. It is inevitable that self-sufficient subsistence farming must be supplemented by the farmer and the members of his household with numerous activities such as those providing shelter, clothing, tools, transport, etc.

life, all have their origins in industry. Most of the science built into soil, crops, and livestock and even into the farming setup itself may have reached the farm via the United States Department of Agriculture, supported in part by urban or nonfarm taxpayers. Such farming is a joint venture of agriculture and industry. Along with sunshine, soil, and living energies, it makes use of the products of industry including fuels, of industry-sired science, and of industry-inspired methods. The agricultural nucleus is there, but it is heavily overlain with foreign matter. One is tempted, therefore, to refer to commercial agriculture as "hybrid" agriculture.

This modern scientific mechanized commercial agriculture, with the aid of outside help, has learned to collaborate with nature even more effectively than "pure" agriculture and has thus somewhat reduced its dependence on nature. At the same time, however, it has become correspondingly more dependent on human influences and powers. Thus modern commercial agriculture lives in dread of the business cycle and modern war's dislocations almost as much as primitive agriculture lived in dread of enemies, human and others—of feudal lords, hailstorms, floods, and famines. The very superefficiency which "hybrid" agriculture has acquired is proving a boomerang, and its victory over nature may yet prove to be a Pyrrhic victory.[9]

The "Aloofness" of Agriculture

While it is true that in our modern machine civilization agriculture comes under the spell of commerce and industry and other outside forces, it cannot be wholly absorbed into the modern pattern. It remains apart and aloof, ever conscious of its irreducible residual dependence on living nature. Living nature, which constitutes the very essence of agriculture, renders impossible the complete absorption of agriculture into the modern industrial pattern built around controlled inanimate energies and inorganic substances and, above all, around the mathematical formula. Agriculture, even commercial mechanized agriculture, has a tempo and a temperament of its own which

never fully harmonize with those of machine industry.

Moreover, agriculture remains aloof for other reasons. In many parts of the earth agriculture is a way of life—in fact, *the* way of life of countless millions and not merely a way of making a living. The Chinese peasant is part of the landscape, and Chinese culture to a large extent developed around the ways and needs of peasant life.

Agriculture, furthermore, rests on the soil and for that reason is the custodian, as it were, of a basic social asset. Civilizations differ widely in their regard for such basic assets. Some seem to live from day to day, from hand to mouth. Others, mindful of the disaster that befell earlier civilizations, view the soil as sacred, inviolate, something which must be handed down to coming generations intact, if not improved. Under such conditions building up the soil becomes a major purpose of far-seeing social policy. Where such views prevail, agriculture takes on a meaning that lifts it above the common run of business enterprise not similarly affected or afflicted with long-run social responsibility.

Finally, the farming population of the earth constitutes the vast majority of humankind. Almost everywhere they are reproducing faster than city dwellers who have succumbed to the wiles of industrialism. Whether one views the situation globally, in terms of humankind as a whole, or nationally, in terms of specific areas and peoples, it is a fundamental fact that the farming people furnish a disproportionately large share of the total human offspring. It is hardly an exaggeration to say that agriculture continues to be the cradle of man. We may regret that this is so. But so long as agriculture, far more than a business enterprise, holds a special position with regard to basic human and physical resources, this fact cannot be ignored with impunity.

THE DIVERSITY OF AGRICULTURE

In the discussion that follows, many statements will be made referring to agriculture in general: "Agriculture is the last stronghold of competition. . . . Agriculture is weak. . . . Agriculture is vital to the life of a nation," and so on. It is very tempting to make such state-

---

[9] For a fuller development of this point, see chap. 12.

ments, but they are treacherous. They suffer from the weakness innate in all generalities. And in few cases is generalizing more difficult than in the case of agriculture. For not only are there different types of agriculture, as was shown in the preceding section, but, being dependent on nature, agriculture is almost as diverse as nature herself. Moreover, to the infinite diversity of its natural basis there is added an equally infinite diversity of cultural adjustments to nature.

Agriculture comes nearer to being a truly global activity than any other human enterprise. All people must eat and most of them raise most if not all of their own food; most people prefer agricultural methods of food getting to exploitative or nomadic ways. It follows that agriculture is found among some of the most primitive tribes and among the most advanced industrial nations of the earth. So great is the diversity of agricultural practices and conditions that few general statements apply with equal or even similar force to all phases and branches of agriculture. It is necessary therefore to have a clear conception of this diversity.

Causes

It is not difficult to understand why agriculture should be more diverse than any other human activity. Modern machine industry is concentrated in relatively few areas of the earth. Similarly, modern transportation and trade, though reaching nearly all parts of the globe, are highly concentrated in a few regions in terms of both facilities and performance. And so is mining, the basis of modern industry. Agriculture, on the other hand, is well-nigh world-wide. Food is produced, mostly by agricultural methods, wherever people live. As will be shown in a later chapter, a relatively small part of the total food produced in the world moves in international trade, though interregional shipments occur more generally. Some nonfood farm products such as fibers enter international trade more freely. But no people has grown strong without some agricultural base or background and no people has ever dared to let its agriculture become wholly extinct. England came as near that point as any other country, but only after her position as *the* world power of the nineteenth century was firmly established. Today one wonders whether Englishmen regret that decision.

This global diffusion of agriculture means that it is practiced under every possible combination of climatic, vegetative, and soil conditions. It ranges from the oasis in the Sahara to the patch farm in the tropical rain forest; from the Canadian north to the steppes of Patagonia. In short, the diversity of natural conditions translates itself into a similar diversity of agricultural practices.

Even today farming is carried on under the most diverse sociopolitical and technological systems. Witness the caste system of India, the Russian state-controlled system, the primitive farm system of tropical regions, the feudal systems of eastern Europe and South America, "the factories in the field" in California, family farming in the Midwest, the tenant system of the South, and so on.

It is true that steel is made in a dozen countries, but always it is made in more or less the same way and by organizations of comparable structure and similar size. To be sure, their relations to the state may differ considerably, though even that point of difference appears to be wearing off. But wheat and cotton are produced in almost as many different ways as there are countries where they are grown. And here is the point: these crops, produced under such diverse natural, cultural, and political conditions, are fed into the common stream of world commerce and, meeting in the great trading and consuming areas of the world, crash in head-on collision, Indian cotton with American cotton and Rumanian wheat with Canadian wheat. Through their farm products the diverse sociopolitical culture patterns of the earth are brought into contact, if not into conflict.

In short, both the ancient origin of agriculture, reflected in an endless variety of culture patterns, and the global diffusions of agriculture, calling for adaptations to an equally endless variety of geographical settings, combine to render agriculture the most diverse or heterogeneous enterprise of man.

Examples

To present an exhaustive treatment of this cultural-geographical diversity would fill a large tome. It might even prove tedious. Here only a cursory and purely suggestive account must suffice.

One may begin by listing at random a few divisions:

Cropping vs. animal husbandry.
Primitive vs. scientific.
Rainfall vs. irrigation.
Extensive vs. intensive.
Labor-intensive vs. capital-intensive.
Family vs. corporate.
Tenants vs. gang labor.
Annual crops vs. perennials.
Herbacious perennials vs. tree crops.
Peasant vs. commercial cash-crop farmer.
Mixed vs. single crop.
Feudal vs. capitalistic.

This list is quite incomplete but it suffices to suggest the extent of the diversity.

A more scientific attempt at classification would be to seek out certain major criteria of distinction and use them as bases of type classification. Thus one classification would be developed on the basis of products: plants vs. animals, beef steers vs. dairy cows, hogs vs. cattle, annuals vs. perennials, staple crops vs. truck crops, single crops vs. diversified cropping. A second basis could be regions, such as monsoon Asia, humid temperature zone, subhumid, tropical, etc. A third basis might be the type of farming setup: family farm, plantation, hacienda, "factory in the field," etc. Another one could be based on the general social system, such as capitalistic, feudal, communistic, communal, primitive tribal, etc.

Implications

If, then, someone says that agriculture is weak, it is wise to remember "the factories in the field," and the plantations worth millions of dollars whose owners sit in the highest councils of the nation. If someone says that agriculture is "the last stronghold of competitive business," it is well to remember that in some parts of the earth agriculture is no business at all but a way of life, that there are instances which demonstrate that competition in agriculture can be curtailed almost as effectively as it is being curtailed in some nonagricultural activities, and that there is not too much strength left in that so-called "stronghold." Competitive enterprise that is facing monopoly does not need to be told of its own weakness.

Thus there are not many general statements that apply with equal force to all phases and branches of agriculture. But there is one that always holds true: Agriculture is dependent on nature and because of that dependence agricultural man cannot do certain things industrial man can do. "Know thyself" is the key to success. Agriculture no doubt realizes its limitations inherent in that dependence on nature. It is time that those outside of agriculture realized them too.

BIBLIOGRAPHY

Bacon, L. B., and Schloemer, F. C., *World Trade in Agricultural Products*, Rome, International Institute of Agriculture, 1940.

Baker, O. E., Borsodi, R., and Wilson, M. L., *Agriculture in Modern Life*, New York, Harper, 1939.

Barger, H., and Landsberg, H. H., *American Agriculture 1899-1939*, New York, National Bureau of Economic Research, 1942.

Black, J. D., *Agricultural Reform in the United States*, New York, McGraw-Hill, 1929.

Black, J. D., *Parity, Parity, Parity*, Cambridge, Harvard Committee on Research in the Social Sciences, 1942.

Bowman, M. J., and Bach, G. L., *Economic Analysis and Public Policy*, New York, Prentice-Hall, 1943, chap. 56.

Brandt, K., *The Reconstruction of World Agriculture*, New York, Norton, 1945, especially chap. 7.

Bromfield, L., "The Rebirth of the South," *Country Gentleman*, July, 1949, condensed in *Reader's Digest*, July, 1949.

Clark, W. H., *Farms and Farmers: The Story of American Agriculture*, Boston, L. C. Page, 1945.

Cohen, R. L., *The Economics of Agriculture*, New York, Pitman, 2nd ed., 1950.

Dummeier, E. F., and Heflebower, R. B., *Economics with Application to Agriculture*, New York, McGraw-Hill, 1934.

Engberg, R. C., *Industrial Prosperity and the Farmer*, Washington, Brookings, 1927.

Gras, N. S. B., *A History of Agriculture in Europe and America*, New York, Appleton-Century-Crofts, 2nd ed., 1940.

Grimes, W. E., and Holton, E. L., *Modern Agriculture*, Boston, Ginn, rev. ed., 1940.

Hamilton, C. H., "Social Aspects of Mechanization of Agriculture," *Rural Sociology*, March, 1939.

International Institute of Agriculture (Rome), *International Yearbook of Agricultural Statistics* (annual). Discontinued, 1946, and taken over by the FAO.

Klages, K. W. H., *Ecological Crop Geography*, New York, Macmillan, 1942.

Knight, W. R., "Agriculture," chap. 3 in W. Adams (ed.), *The Structure of American Industry*, New York, Macmillan, 1950.

Lederer, E., "Agriculture in the Orient," *Encyclopædia of the Social Sciences*, New York, Macmillan, 1930.

Malott, D., "Agriculture—The Great Dilemma," in M. P. McNair and T. Lewis, *Business and Modern Society*, Cambridge, Harvard University Press, 1938.

National Resources Committee, *Technological Trends and National Policy*, Washington, 1937, part 3, section 1, pp. 97-144.

Nicholls, W. H., *Imperfect Competition Within Agricultural Industries*, Ames, Iowa State College Press, 1941.

Nourse, E. G., "The Place of Agriculture in Modern Industrial Society," *Journal of Political Economy*, June and July, 1919.

Ostrolenk, B., *The Surplus Farmer*, New York, Harper, 1932.

"Revolution in Agriculture," *Fortune*, October, 1941 (five articles).

Rochester, A., *Why Farmers Are Poor*, New York, International Publishers, 1940.

Smith, J. R., "Agriculture: General Problems," in *Encyclopædia of the Social Sciences*, New York, Macmillan, 1930.

Taylor, H. C., and Taylor, A. D., *World Trade in Agricultural Products*, New York, Macmillan, 1943.

Temporary National Economic Committee, *Agriculture in the National Economy*, Monograph No. 23, Washington, 1940.

"32,000,000 Farmers," and "U. S. Farmer," *Fortune*, February, 1940.

Thomsen, F. L., *Agricultural Prices*, New York, McGraw-Hill, 1936.

U. S. Department of Agriculture, *Agricultural Statistics* (annual), Washington.

U. S. Department of Agriculture, "Farmers in a Changing World," *Yearbook of Agriculture*, Washington, 1940.

U. S. Department of Agriculture, *Technology on the Farm*, Special Report, Washington, 1940.

U. S. Department of Agriculture, "The Science of Farming," *Yearbook of Agriculture, 1943-1947*, Washington, 1017.

U. S. Department of Agriculture, Office of Foreign Agricultural Relations, *Graphic Survey of World Agriculture*, Washington, 1940.

U. S. Senate, 74th Congress, 1st Session, *The Relative Flexibility of the Industrial Prices*, Washington, 1936.

Warren, G. F., and Pearson, F. A., *The Agricultural Situation*, New York, Wiley, 1924.

Warriner, D., *The Economics of Peasant Farming*, New York, Oxford, 1939.

Williams, B. O., "Mechanization of Agriculture and the South," *Rural Sociology*, September, 1939.

Chapter 12

AGRICULTURE IN AN INDUSTRIAL WORLD

Between half and two-thirds of mankind live on farms, and considerably more than half of the human labor force are farmers and farm workers.[1] This large segment of the human race, comprising considerably more than one billion people, may be envisaged as divided into two uneven parts. The larger part is made up of people living in regions of the earth as yet little touched, and under conditions as yet little affected, by the mechanical revolution. Only the smaller part has been exposed to its bright and blistering rays. Among these some have felt its force more keenly than others. Whereas in Europe the impact of the mechanical revolution was cushioned by ancient customs and institutions, its full force struck the Americas and Australia almost unimpeded.[2] Thus these two extremes stand out of the global pattern: the oldest civilizations, which are as yet virtually untouched by the mechanical revolution, and the youngest, which are completely under its spell.

---

[1] This includes members of farmers' families who do farm work.

[2] See chap. 10, especially pp. 136-137.

From Fear of Famine to Fear of Glut

The contrast between these two extremes could hardly be sharper. Here are the sedentary masses of monsoon Asia, the struggling peoples of the Dark Continent and much of Latin America, tied to the soil by custom and the inadequacy of transport facilities, living in dread of famine, forever pressing against the means of sustenance. There are the farmers of the United States, Canada, Argentina, Australia, and New Zealand, backed by modern machine industry and science, living in dread of overproduction, of unsalable farm surpluses. Here fear of famine, there fear of glut. Here hungry mouths begging for food, there surplus crops begging for a market. In trying to solve the problem of scarcity man has created a new problem. How this came about will now be told. We begin with the mechanical revolution and its impact on the agriculture of the West.

THE MECHANICAL REVOLUTION AND AGRICULTURAL PROGRESS

Spread of the Mechanical Revolution

The mechanical revolution, the shift from chief reliance on animate (muscular and biotic) energy to chief reliance on inanimate energy (see p. 57), began in England, spread to the continent of Europe where it stopped at the boundaries of "Europe A,"[3] and leaped across the Atlantic to North America where it reached its fullest development, sent its outposts to other continents and, since the Revolution of 1917, has engulfed that vast sector of Eurasia which is the Soviet Union. So far as basic culture patterns are concerned, it left virtually untouched most of Africa, except the extreme northern and southern parts and some mining districts scattered through the interior, "exclaves of western industrialism"; most of Asia south of the border of the Soviet Union, except where oil and other vital materials needed by modern industry beckon the white man; and most of Latin America, except Argentina and other limited areas. There too "the exclaves of industrialism"—oil wells, sugar mills, mining camps, and factories—are found far and wide. At no time has the mechanical revolution worked with greater vigor than at the present. Never before have so many new areas felt its touch at one and the same time.

Impact of the Mechanical Revolution

The impact of a force varies with the object struck by that force. Hence the impact of the mechanical revolution on a given region is in part determined by the characteristics of that region, its natural endowment, its culture level, its population density, and the attitudes of the people.[4]

The effects of the mechanical revolution, therefore, vary from country to country. In general it may be said that it produces the most dramatic results and brings about the most drastic changes in young, newly settled lands where man is least hampered by "the dead hand of the past," and in lands which, prior to its impact, were thinly populated or settled by people living on a relatively low culture level and where much land is available to which to apply the new devices and methods. In older countries its blow is cushioned or deflected or its free ingress is impeded by firmly entrenched cultures of a higher order.

In particular, population density or, to be more precise, the stage of the demographic evolution of a country has much to do with the final results of the impact of the mechanical revolution on agriculture. Densely populated areas do not welcome agricultural mechanization as eagerly as do the vast open spaces of virgin soil. Labor-saving devices thrive most where labor is scarce. On the other hand, science may advance as rapidly in an industrialized country whose population density is 500 or 600 to the square mile as in one with a density of only 50 or 60. Then again, rapidly growing populations can absorb an increasing output of farm products more easily than can populations that have reached a point of stagnation.

One may view this differential process from another angle. The corollary of a dense population is per capita scarcity of land and, vice versa, that of a thin population is per capita abundance of land. In general it may be said that mechanization is most suitable to regions of abundant land, while the direct application of science to agriculture seems more suitable to regions where land is relatively scarce. One may be permitted to generalize, therefore, and state that the two chief mediums through which the mechanical revolution works—mechanization, or the application of machine power, and rationalization, or the application of science[5]—

---

[3] See p. 130. This shift is accompanied by progress in science, by mobilization of men, goods, and thought, and by the consequent rise of exchange.

[4] See chaps. 5 and 10.

[5] The distinction made here between mechanization, the application of inanimate energy, and rationalization, the application of science, calls for further comment. In the first place, it should be made clear that mechanization can be achieved without resort to inanimate energy. Early efforts at mechanization relied on animate energy, especially that of animals. The treadmill is an example of mechanization dependent on the muscular energy of men. In identifying mechanization with inanimate energy, emphasis is placed on typical modern practice, especially in the West. In the second place, it is readily conceded that the use of inanimate energy itself involves the application of science and could therefore be considered a phase of "rationalization" as here defined. However, it is so important a phase that it should not be placed in a subordinate position.

Perhaps rationalization should be defined as the application of science to phases of production other than those involved in mechanization. Such phases are seed selection, use of fertilizers, erosion control, etc. That these scientific procedures may call for the use of mechanical devices is understood.

affect the older, more densely populated countries of Europe in ways altogether different from the effect on the newer, more thinly populated countries of the Americas and Oceania.

Mechanical labor-saving devices replace man power and permit the cultivation of larger areas per man. They thus raise *per-man* productivity both directly by the support the machine itself gives the farmer and indirectly through the larger supply of land it places at his disposal. Science tends to raise the productivity *per acre*, per plant, per animal. It tends to intensify agriculture, whereas machines favor expansion over wider areas. In short, mechanization tends to raise *per-man* productivity while science tends to increase *per-acre* productivity.[6] Science thus helps a densely populated country to solve its food problem—at least partially. In thinly populated countries, science backed by mechanization and much land tends to create an export surplus.

This difference between *per-man* productivity and *per-acre* productivity is of vital importance. *Per-man* productivity in mechanized agriculture is traceable to the cumulative effect of two factors: abundant land and abundant capital. High *per-acre* productivity derives from one abundant factor—capital, mainly in the form of science—compensating for the scarcity of another factor—land. In countries of high *per-acre* productivity greater expenditure of labor may compensate in part for the reduced use of land.

It is very unlikely that densely populated industrialized countries will be able to raise their *per-acre* agricultural productivity to the point where, in general, more foodstuffs and other agricultural products, including feedstuffs, are available than the total population—farm and nonfarm—requires or can consume. At the same time, a country enjoying high *per-man* productivity is quite likely to produce more than its domestic needs. This is borne out by the fact that all the important industrial countries of Europe are normally net importers of farm products and the United States, Canada, Argentina, and Australia are usually net exporters.[7] It need hardly be added that as industrialization of a young country advances and the ratio of farm to nonfarm population declines, a point may be reached in the economic development when even high *per-man* productivity no longer suffices to yield exportable surpluses.

The regions where agriculture has come under the spell of the mechanical revolution may be arranged in the following categories:
1. Countries settled before the mechanical revolution (no open spaces, relatively high population density): "Europe A," including Great Britain.
2. Countries settled after the mechanical revolution (open spaces [at the time of settlement], relatively low population density): the United States, Canada, Argentina, Australia, and New Zealand.
3. Countries settled partly before, partly after the mechanical revolution: Brazil, the Soviet Union.

Commercialization of Agriculture

As has been shown,[8] the mechanical revolution brought about a more or less complete transformation of western civilization. Isolation, local self-sufficiency, and relative immobility yielded to interdependence, specialization, commercial exchange, and a high degree of mobility. The commercial revolution reaching back to the Crusades and to the great discoveries not only preceded the Industrial Revolution but helped to usher it in. In time, the two merged into that world-sweeping force we call the mechanical revolution.

Mechanization and the resulting increase in mobility cannot help but promote trade, exchange, commercialization. The machine thrives on specialization, demands it, and renders it possible. The increased output per worker of the specialized products of machine industry

---

[6] This contrast between American mechanization and European rationalization can easily be exaggerated. Europe makes—or before World War II made—considerable use of farm machinery, and perhaps nowhere is science applied to agriculture more widely than in the United States. The contrast is real, but it can be overstated.

[7] The United States has been a net importer of agricultural products but for the present is again a heavy net exporter. The position of a country in that respect naturally depends on a number of variables. Denmark is a heavy exporter of agricultural products. She is hardly to be considered an important industrial country. Moreover, she exchanges one type of agricultural product for a different type.

[8] See chap. 5.

requires an expanding market. This is opened up by trade with the aid of banking and insurance.

In particular, machine industry cannot live without commercial agriculture, i.e., agriculture which produces for the market and exchanges farm products for industrial articles. The relative self-sufficiency of manorial and peasant agriculture in the Old World and of "domestic" farming[9] in this country had to yield to the new system. Specialization had to engulf farming as it had industry. Formerly most farmers were "jacks-of-all-trades." The farm proper was a complex undertaking combining diversified farming with similarly diversified animal husbandry. The entire family worked. Besides doing numerous chores, the farmer and his family performed numerous tasks elsewhere done by industry. They made candles from tallow, soap from wood ashes and fats; they put up preserves, made butter and cheese, sheared sheep, scoured wool, spun yarn, wove cloth, tanned leather, made clothes, cut wood for stove and fireplace, built barns and houses. There was plenty for everybody to do all the year round. Farm labor proper, especially that devoted to raising crops, is highly seasonal; but when supplemented with numerous other duties there need be little idleness during any part of the year.

In such a family enterprise, a straight line leads from personal effort to reward. In the absence of "acts of God," hard work means good living, plenty to eat, warm clothes to wear, a tight roof over one's head. Much of the wisdom of "the Founding Fathers" sprang from such experience.

The mechanical revolution changed all that. It completely broke down the self-sufficiency, self-reliance, and independence of the family farm and with it the farm family; it forced farming to divest itself of its ancillary functions —candle and soap making, spinning, weaving, and whatnot—and to specialize in producing money crops. It thus forced agriculture into exchange economy and tied it hand and foot to that mysterious institution called the market.

Of course no *force* was needed to bring about the change. When a farmer discovered that he could exchange one bushel of wheat for a dozen candles which if made at home would take his wife far more time than was required to raise a bushel of wheat, he soon saw the wisdom of specializing on growing wheat and leaving candle making to a more efficient specialist. Nor did it take much coaxing to make him stop backbreaking toil by installing an electric motor or a Diesel engine. It all came about very easily and pleasantly, and few were aware of the troubles that were brewing.

The effects of the mechanical revolution on agriculture are highly complex. There are direct effects which are fairly obvious. But there are also implications and repercussions which are hidden from view when they first develop and become visible only when they have attained great force and it is too late to undo the damage. Looking back, aided by hindsight, one can uncover these hidden processes and, if he is wise, he can learn from the past. One of the most significant of the effects of the mechanical revolution on agriculture is the latter's growing dependence on the market. Its implications will be discussed later on.

AGRICULTURAL PROGRESS
Accelerated Mechanization

The essence of mechanization is the use of machines as distinguished from tools.[10] Machines can be worked by hand, or with the aid of animal or of inanimate power. (The use of the animal-drawn wagon or cart is a form of mechanization.)

The early mechanization of agriculture depended almost exclusively on animal power. (It should be remembered, however, that animals were widely used for purposes other than those involving the use of machines.) Roughly speaking, the nineteenth century witnessed increased mechanization of agriculture based on animal power. The twentieth century ushered in power-driven machinery as an integral part of the mechanization of agriculture. Table 12.1 shows the gradual decline of animal horsepower on the farms of the United States and the truly fantastic rise of mechanical horsepower. Mechanical horsepower on our farms increased from 4.3 million in 1900 to 220.1

---

[9] Meaning farming focused on the needs of the farmer's household.

[10] See chap. 4.

TABLE 12.1. Number of Agricultural Workers, Estimated Power Available on Farms in the United States, and Estimated Power per Agricultural Worker, 1850, 1900, 1930, and 1940[11]

Item	1850	1900	1930	1940
	Number	*Number*	*Number*	*Number*
Agricultural workers	3,719,951[a]	10,381,765[b]	10,482,323[b]	8,365,484[c]
Power unit	*1000 hp.*	*1000 hp.*	*1000 hp.*	*1000 hp.*
Oxen	1,701	960	....	....
Mules	446	2,194	4,146	2,916
Horses	4,347	15,545	13,025	9,282
Total animal power	6,494	18,699	17,171	12,198
Windmills		198	330	214
Steam engines		3,500	1,000	300
Engines—Gasoline, kerosene, and Diesel		600	3,036	10,635
Electricity				
Individual plants			811	537
Central station			1,383	5,583
Tractors			22,001	36,631
Trucks			22,510	41,883
Harvester-threshers			2,260	....
Automobiles[d]			62,852	124,320
Total mechanical power	....	4,298	116,183	220,103
Total animal and mechanical power	6,494	22,997	133,354	232,301
Power per agricultural worker	*Hp.*	*Hp.*	*Hp.*	*Hp.*
Animal power	1.8	1.8	1.6	1.5
Mechanical power	..	0.4	11.1	26.3
Total	1.8	2.2	12.7	27.8

[a] Data not available for 1850; figure given is for 1840.
[b] Workers 10 years old and older engaged in agriculture.
[c] Workers 14 years old and older engaged in agriculture.
[d] 40 percent charged to farm work.

million in 1940. On a per capita basis, the increase was from 0.4 hp. to 26.3 hp.[12]

---

[11] Data on number of workers and total horsepower from U.S. Department of Agriculture, Miscellaneous Publication No. 157 and unpublished material of the Bureau of Plant Industry, Soils, and Agricultural Engineering. Power per agricultural worker computed from figures given in the table. Table prepared in the Bureau of Agricultural Economics, U.S. Department of Agriculture.

[12] Several comments are in order. First, these figures show horsepower "in place," not horsepower in use. Horsepower measures capacity, not performance. To appraise the actual contribution made by mechanical prime movers such as Diesel engines and gasoline engines one should know also the "use factor," i.e., the percentage of total time, 8760 hours per year, during which the installed capacity is in use and delivering actual energy. The "use factor" of prime movers on farms is inevitably much lower than that in most industrial plants and still lower than the rates typical of central power plants.

Second, the inclusion of automobiles should be noted. Farming involves a great deal of moving about, and mechanized commercial farming is "two-thirds" motion. Hence the inclusion of mechanical devices which help to assure this essential mobility of the farmer is quite legitimate, especially since, as the reader will note, only 40 percent of the horsepower installed in automobiles is charged to the farm. Nevertheless, the rate of mechanization *exclusive of that involving the use of automobiles* is of definite interest. The totals, exclusive of automobile horsepower, are therefore shown:

	1850	1900	1930	1940
Total mechanical horsepower	....	4,298	53,331	95,783
Total animal and mechanical horsepower	6,494	22,997	70,502	107,981
Horsepower per agricultural worker:				
Animal power	1.8	1.8	1.6	1.5
Mechanical power	..	0.4	5.1	11.4
Total	1.8	2.2	6.7	12.9

One fact should not be overlooked, that is, the accelerated rate of mechanization. It took fifty years (1850-1900) to climb from 1.8 hp. per capita to 2.2. It took thirty years to move up from 2.2 to 12.7—an increase of 10.5 hp. per worker. But it took only ten years to add another 15.1 hp. per worker, shooting up to 27.8. During World War II mechanization had to slow down as a result of government restrictions on the supply of farm implements. As some experts anticipated, this was made up by record-breaking mechanization in the postwar period.

Mechanization and Farm Production

An exhaustive analysis of the effects of the mechanization of agriculture would fill volumes. Here a brief summary of effects which appear to be of importance is presented. This summary is divided into three parts: (1) direct effects on farm production proper, i.e., work done on the farm; (2) indirect effects on the distribution of farm products and procurement of farm supplies; and (3) the effects of the impact of science on agriculture.

This summary is confined to the favorable effects. If mechanization did not have favorable effects, it would hardly expand and grow by leaps and bounds as it actually does. The unfavorable implications and repercussions will be discussed later.

Effects on farm production proper.
1. The most evident effect of mechanization is an increase in *per-man* productivity. A man backed by machine power applied to scientifically designed tools and machines naturally can do far more work than one relying on his own muscular energy alone.
2. Much mechanical equipment saves labor and thus reduces cost, provided the machine works more cheaply than hand labor, which it often does, and provided its price and maintenance costs are right. (This may be considered the corollary of Point 1 above.)
3. It "mobilizes" the farmer, i.e., enables him to cover a larger acreage in a given time or a given acreage in a shorter time. The implications of this "mobilization" are numerous. A few are listed as examples:
   a. One hundred acres yielding 10 bushels per acre produce 1000 bushels; 200 acres yielding 5 bushels per acre also produce 1000 bushels. A "mobile" farmer can afford

to till poorer soils up to a point where the higher costs of mechanization and the larger land area offset the gain in higher *per-man* output.
   b. A "mobilized" farmer can do in 24 hours as much cultivating as a farmer unsupported by horsepower can do in 10 days. Similarly, harvesting is speeded up. This may add as much as 18 days to the effective growing season, and thus allow a wider choice of crops. (The actual records frequently exceed the savings in time cited in the example.)
   c. A rainy spring may delay planting until the "immobilized" farmer despairs of "making" a crop. The "mobilized" farmer manages to get his crop in on time in spite of the delay. In fact, there are cases on record showing that farmers who had two successive crops ruined by floods, excessive rain, or other causes, managed to get in a third crop in time.
4. Machines enable the farmer to build terraces, ditches, watering ponds, etc., which help to protect soil fertility and make fuller use of the water supply. (In this way the machine enables a few men to accomplish in a short time what in the Orient many men accomplish in a long time.) In addition, mechanical pumps permit large-scale irrigation and drainage operations.
5. Machines may render feasible more accurate performance of certain tasks than hand labor can achieve. Thus greater control over quality may be achieved.
6. Machines make possible quick, low-cost, and effective pest and disease control.
7. Machines render possible the recovery of by-products and the utilization of spoiled crops otherwise lost.
8. Machines relieve human beings of much back-breaking toil.
9. Machines such as tractors which replace work animals set free for other uses the acreage formerly required to feed the animals.
10. Mechanization makes possible the conversion of inanimate energy into heat and light, thus aiding in the care of both livestock and crops (brood houses, incubators, smudge pots).

Effects on distribution of farm products and procurement of farm supplies.
1. Highway, rail, water, and air transport facilities provide rapid and dependable means for reaching distant as well as nearby market areas. The implications are numerous. Some are:

Lower transport costs may widen the market and/or leave a larger share of the proceeds of the sale in the farmer's pocket. As several market areas are opened up, competition as well as demand for the farm products of a given region may increase. The distant market may be the only market capable of absorbing the particular specialty of a given farming area. Fast plane transport may create a market for a perishable specialty.

2. Refrigeration, quick freezing, and similar refinements based on mechanical processes further enhance the distribution services rendered to agriculture.

3. Similarly, the provision of transport facilities renders possible or cheaper or better the procurement of farm supplies.

Effects of the impact of science on agriculture.
1. Soil.
   a. Fertility may be restored, maintained, or enhanced by the scientific application of fertilizers.
   b. Explorers discover crops, including restorative crops, more suitable to given soils than traditional crops. These newly discovered crops may permit the extension of agriculture into newly opened regions formerly closed to the farmer because of excessive cold, aridity, etc.
   c. The scientific study of the nature of soils in general and of specific soils in particular has revolutionized farming and greatly enhanced its productivity.
2. Plants and animals.
   a. The work of the plant and animal explorer adds to the working stock of the farmer.
   b. Plant and animal breeders have contributed materially to the productivity of agriculture. Also, the hardier varieties permit the extension of crops and livestock into less favorable areas. Mendel's discovery of the laws of heredity and the progress made in the understanding of genetics and its application to agriculture may be the largest single factor accounting for the fantastic increase in agricultural output in recent times. This factor is all the more important since frequently the gains are achieved without appreciable increase in the direct cost of production. In fact, unit costs may actually drop as the output of units increases. Since most scientific discoveries affecting agriculture emanate from government agencies, their application is often free for the asking.[13]

The devious way in which science may affect agriculture is illustrated in the case of corn. Not only has hybrid corn materially raised the yield per acre but it has rendered easier the use of the mechanical corn picker. This picker works best when all ears grow at about the same level above the ground. This was accomplished by breeding this particular feature into hybrid corn.
   c. Care and feeding of animals.
3. The farm enterprise in general.
   a. Crop rotation and tillage practices, when scientifically worked out, materially contribute to the overall yield of a given farm over a period of years.
   b. Scientific methods applied to agronomy as well as to farm management in general add further to the result.

It was pointed out before (see p. 157) that mechanization and the application of science tend to differ somewhat in the manner in which they fit into existing patterns and in the overall effects they tend to produce. Moreover, science as well as mechanization affects agriculture indirectly. In fact, it is quite possible that the indirect effects are more far-reaching and more penetrating than the direct ones. Mechanization and science are the basis of modern machine industry, and modern machine industry virtually remade western civilization. It accounts for the unparalleled rise of the national income and with it the standard of living; it builds cities; it raises an ever-loftier superstructure of financial, commercial, and other cultural institutions; it turns loose economic agglomerates into social economies closely knit by a thousand lines of interdependence. It creates much of the capital surplus on which modern economic progress is largely based. It contributes the lion's share to the public funds which support education, health, and law and order. In short, not only do machine industry and mechanization and science render agriculture efficient, they create the very world in which this efficient agriculture can sell its bountiful crops.[14] But besides bestowing untold blessings

[13] Outstanding examples of the effect of science on important crops are found in the chapters that follow, e.g., wheat, sugar, fats and oils, rubber, etc.

[14] E. G. Nourse, "The Place of Agriculture in Modern Industrial Society," *Journal of Political Economy*, June and July, 1919.

on agriculture, machine industry also creates grave problems for it—problems still far from rational solution. It overstimulates production beyond the point of demand, it competes with agriculture in many lines, it robs agriculture of its former self-reliance and ties it into an institutional complex to which agriculture is ill suited by virtue of its inherent characteristics. In short, it creates the modern farm problem. This problem will now be discussed.

THE MODERN FARM PROBLEM

As one reviews this progress of the mechanization and rationalization of agriculture, he can hardly fail to feel proud of the material achievements of our age. Is it not glorious to reduce backbreaking toil and, at the same time, increase the productivity of the laborer, to make more land arable, to widen the choice of crops, to improve the genetic qualities of both plants and animals, to fight their enemies more effectively, to open new and larger markets for farm products, and, in addition to all this, to reduce the isolation and boredom of farm life, bringing farmers better educational opportunities, better health, and in general more of the blessings of our industrial civilization? To ask the question is to answer it.

And yet, despite all this progress, agriculture throughout the western world for most of the twenty years between the two World Wars was in dire distress, being kept alive by artificial respiration as it were. And what is worse, the outlook for the future is by no means rosy. At least this is the view taken by thoughtful observers who look beyond the prosperity which agriculture in many lands enjoyed during World War II and its aftermath.

Historical Setting

This agricultural distress, born of man's desire to solve the age-old problem of hunger, paradoxically brought on by the very success he attained in solving that problem, made itself felt on a large scale after World War I. For decades, in fact for a century and more, inventors had been at work trying to mechanize farming, and scientific discoveries had contributed their share to agricultural progress. And everything seemed well. Europe produced more per acre and gave her crowded millions more and more wholesome food. She bought readily from the overseas countries whose agriculture, thriving on both export trade and on increasing domestic demand, expanded by leaps and bounds. How could such success lead to failure?

One could almost say that this failure was the result of the improperly correlated effects of the commercialization of agriculture and its mechanization and rationalization. Commercialization means dependence on a market and this dependence is safe only so long as equilibrating forces are at work to keep supply and demand in balance. The secret of the farm problem may be found in the crossing of two curves suggesting vital secular trends; one curve shows the growth of agricultural production in the countries of the West, especially in those exporting overseas. That curve goes up and up. The other curve shows the rate of increase in the number of people who consume purchased agricultural products and in their purchasing power. After rising sharply during the nineteenth century, this curve began to flatten in the twentieth century, until in some countries population stood still or actually declined and purchasing power ceased to grow. This crossing of the curves occurred somewhere around the time of World War I. It signalized a major dislocation of the world market for farm products. In part, perhaps in large part, this major dislocation was caused by the simultaneous opening up of the grasslands as the major granaries, made possible mainly by mechanization, and the remarkable renascence of European agriculture based chiefly on science.

For decades the United States, Canada, Argentina, and Australia had expanded their agriculture without apparent ill effect. On the contrary, for a long time it appeared as if at last man had succeeded in achieving an economic development which favored both buyer and seller, both consumer and producer. Costs were low because land values were low, soils were fertile, and little attention was paid to depletion. Rising land values paid deferred rebates or veiled subsidies to the cropper. Exports expanded. Domestic industry and cities grew apace. The future looked rosy indeed.

The era 1895-1914 in particular is often referred to as the golden age of United States agriculture. Farm output rose 50 percent. At the same time, however, industrial output rose 150 percent (as against 50 percent during

1920-1939). Exports were holding up well; land values increased. The success story of American agriculture was told to all the world. Old Europe was derided for her conservative soil protection policies, for not selling long-run assets for quick market gains, for not commercializing her peasant agriculture with the same speed and abandon displayed in the New World, for not following the example of England where agriculture was sacrificed to other interests.

World War I came as a great shock to the agricultural interests of overseas countries. But this did not last long. Soon the war boom was on. Acreage expanded as perhaps never before. Large sections of the Great Plains felt the sharp edge of the plow for the first time. The United States and Canada especially, being nearest to the theater of war, were called upon to make up for the deficits of war-torn Europe and to still the voracious appetites of large armies in the field.

And then came the collapse, followed by violent convulsions, then by lingering sickness—pernicious surplusitis. The richest farm lands of the earth lay blighted as if under a curse. In Canada whole provinces faced bankruptcy, as did wide areas of the agricultural sections of the United States.

While it is true that World War I with its sudden insistence on expansion did much to hasten the catastrophe and to aggravate the trouble, it would be a grave error to look upon that war as the primary cause of the trouble. The evil lies more deeply embedded in the causal background of history. The roots reach much deeper—down to the very nature of agriculture itself and its incompatibility with the nature of industry. The roots can be traced to basic institutional developments. These underlying forces had been at work decades before their effects became visible on the surface. They were long hidden by compensatory or neutralizing forces—expanding exports, rapid industrialization, rising land values, and finally the war boom. "The mills of the Gods grind slowly, but they grind exceeding fine."

While the taproots of the modern farm problem are found in the surplus-producing overseas countries, other roots are spread far and wide, reaching far beyond the boundaries of the export countries. The simultaneous increase in European productivity has been mentioned. Its effects were aggravated by a rising nationalism, the fear of war and the consequent desire to be more self-sufficient than World War I had found the countries of Europe, the inability of statesmen to get world trade moving after the war, increasing interference with trade, currency disorders, and many other factors. As will be shown later, commercial agriculture can expand with impunity only if the industrial, i.e., the nonfarm, market expands at a far greater rate than does agriculture itself. And that market seemed to be suffering from a malignant disease. The rate of expansion of industry in the United States in 1920-1939 was only one-third of what it had been in 1895-1915.

In a *sense* there can be no surplus of farm products so long as millions are "in want," undernourished, or starving. But until mankind develops a great deal more compassion and foresight than it seems to possess now, that *sense* is highly theoretical. For what counts in this workaday world is hard cash on the barrel head or a cashier's check. The pieman's query to Simple Simon is still heard around the world.[15] One could say, therefore, that the modern farm problem has a religious tinge—"Am I my brother's keeper?"

Symptoms

The ancient farm problem was how to find enough to eat. The modern problem is that of finding enough eaters *able to pay* the cost of producing.[16] The problem is that agriculture, stimulated by outside forces, produces beyond the capacity of the market to absorb. It is a problem of imbalance, of disequilibrium. Surely, there is imbalance when farmers let their crops rot in the fields and on the trees while people are hungry, undernourished, or inadequately supplied with clothing and shelter. Surely there is disequilibrium when farmers are asked to pay grossly inflated prices for what they wish to buy while receiving deflated prices for what they sell.

The most telling symptom of farm distress

---

[15] Efforts now under way to improve the situation will be discussed in the next chapter.

[16] What is said here of food, the chief product of agriculture, applies with almost equal force to agricultural products in general.

in surplus-producing countries is the low return farmers earn as compared with those engaged in industry, secondary or tertiary. The difference in earnings is clearly shown in Table 12.2. The difference ranges from over 100 per-

TABLE 12.2. Net Income of Persons on Farms from Farming (Including Government Payments), Compared with Income of Persons not on Farms, United States, 1929-1945[17]

Year	Income per Person On Farms from Farming	Not on Farms[a]	Index Numbers of Income per Person[b] On Farms from Farming	Not on Farms
1929	$223	$ 871	166	179
1930	170	761	126	156
1931	114	605	85	124
1932	74	442	55	91
1933	93	419	69	86
1934	111	488	83	100
1935	159	540	118	111
1936	171	626	127	128
1937	197	671	147	138
1938	165	622	123	128
1939	173	663	129	136
1940	181	721	133	148
1941	253	850	186	174
1942	389	1046	287	215
1943	522	1250	384	257
1944	550	1320	405	271
1945	585	1294	431	266

a The income of the nonfarm population as shown here is national income minus the net income of persons on farms from farming. Income of persons on farms from nonagricultural sources has not been deducted.
b 1910-14 = 100.

cent in 1945 when wartime earning and protection policies had given farm income an unheard-of boost, to almost 500 percent in 1932 when, under the hammer blows of the Great Depression, farm prices fell faster than other income-determining factors.

The table also illustrates the instability of farm income. It will be noted that the index numbers of per capita farm income range from 55 to 431, a range of almost 1:8, while those for nonfarm income range from 86 to 271, a range of little more than 1:3. Another way of showing this instability is through the fluctuation in the "terms of trade." This is the ratio of the index number of prices of goods sold by farmers to the index number of prices of goods bought by farmers.

[17] U. S. Department of Agriculture, *Agricultural Statistics 1946*, Washington, 1946, p. 566.

The meaning of these figures comes home with a shock when it is realized that in 1937 there were about the same number of people working on the nation's 6,000,000 (plus) farms as in the nation's 200,000 (minus) manufacturing establishments—about 10,000,000 workers in each. The farmers earned 9 percent of the national income, the factory workers 23 percent!

The relationship between supply, demand, and price is typically quite different in competitive agriculture and not-so-competitive industry. In agriculture vast numbers of producers, scattered over wide areas and more or less unknown to one another, sow their crops and then wait for the results, i.e., both physical results in terms of size and quality of crop and the economic result in terms of market price. Many industries, on the other hand, produce *not* in anticipation of a future demand which may or may not materialize, but only as that demand manifests itself in increasing prices and in orders. Thus in agriculture the crop is "made" first; it determines the supply and this in turn determines the price in the light of the demand. In industry rising demand raises price and only then is a greater output stimulated.

In importing countries the main symptoms of distress caused by the general dislocation of trade and finance are excessively high food prices, due mainly to the uneconomical production of foodstuffs behind tariff walls and other restrictive barriers but also due to rising taxes and to diversion of resources from agriculture to war industries.

Nature of the Problem

The modern farm problem is just one more illustration of the fundamental difficulty facing western civilization which was previously referred to as "social lag" (see p. 38), i.e., the lagging of the societal arts behind the technological arts. To be truly successful, every new invention, every new machine, should have a counterpart invention, a counterpart device, in the realm of social institutions and social relationships. Not only must the potency of the social adjustment be comparable to the power of the impact, but also its tempo, its speed. A society that blindly promotes technological advance and one-sidedly pushes the progress of natural and applied science, relying on fate to provide the necessary corollaries in the field of societal adjustments, is bound to come to grief.

It is an old story that the introduction of every machine was accompanied by misery and resentment, and often by strife and bloodshed, on the part of workers displaced by it. There is hardly an industry which has not gone through that bitter experience. But again and again industry, benefiting from lowered costs and larger output resulting from the faster and cheaper machine processes, soon managed to employ more people than the machine displaced. So a strong faith in automatic adjustment developed and the terrors of "technological unemployment"[18] were soon forgotten or pooh-poohed as needless fears of faint-hearted souls.

It was only natural that the same reasoning should be applied to agriculture. But, as will be shown later, this was a fatal error. For not only is agriculture far less able to adjust itself smoothly to innovation, but that which proved the saving grace in the case of industry—elasticity of demand—is largely absent in the case of agriculture.[19] What made possible the expansion of output of machine-made products was the ease and, one may say, the enthusiasm with which the cheaper machine-made products were snapped up by eager buyers—in other words, elasticity of demand. Agriculture, by and large, is deprived of the safety valve without which uncontrolled mechanization and rationalization appear as dangerous as raising the temperature in a steam boiler without providing for the escape of the excess steam.

There is another aspect to be considered. It is always dangerous to transfer the arts and devices created spontaneously in one environment to another, wholly different environment. Industry and agriculture are essentially different. This difference, which rests ultimately on the basic dualism of nature, fully developed elsewhere in this volume,[20] renders the application to agriculture of machines and science sired by industry a precarious undertaking that should by no

means be stopped but that needs to be watched with the utmost care as to its effects, including its repercussions.

The problem of the economic order,[21] meaning the problem of preserving the proper balance between a diversity of producing and consuming interests, is difficult even under relatively static conditions marked by a modicum of homogeneity of factors and forces. It becomes complex and even more difficult in this age of accelerated technological and scientific progress. It is greatly aggravated by the clash of such heterogeneous elements as agriculture and industry within the same market economy.

Causes

Incompatibility of Agriculture and Industry. This incompatibility of agriculture and industry is one of the chief causes of the farm problem. The congenital weakness of agriculture which derives mainly from its dependence on nature, the living forces of the plant and animal world, and its implications have already been discussed (see p. 148). Here the question is how this congenital weakness manifests itself when agriculture, no longer left to itself as in ancient vegetable civilizations, is harnessed to the same yoke, as it were, with a far faster, stronger, and more high-strung animal—when, in other words, agriculture is tied with industry into the exchange economy. In this exchange economy, industry—secondary and tertiary industry—sets the pace, is the active force, and agriculture must follow passively.

In this new setting, the congenital weakness of agriculture, always manifest in some way or other, takes on new meanings. Left to its own devices, agriculture is inefficient, its *per-man* productivity is low, the standard of living it assures is modest at best. It leaves largely unsolved the problems of crop failure and famine. When linked up with industry through mechanization and rationalization, it becomes highly efficient, its *per-man* productivity rising to amazing heights.

Over the amount of output, the farmer has not as full control as has the manufacturer or the miner or, for that matter, most people engaged in secondary or tertiary activities.

---

[18] But see the analysis of the problem by Emil Lederer, *Technical Progress and Unemployment*, League of Nations, International Labour Office, Geneva, 1938.

[19] See p. 171 for a discussion of inelasticity of demand in agriculture.

[20] See especially chap. 7.

---

[21] See Clarence Ayres, *The Problem of the Economic Order*, Farrar and Rinehart, New York, 1938.

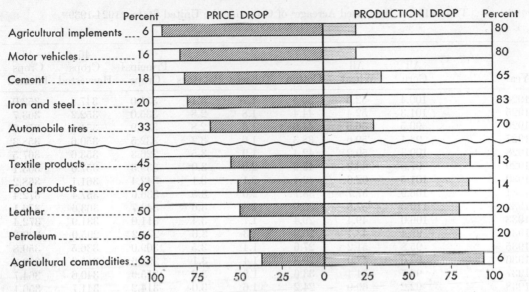

FIG. 12.1. Price and Production Trends of Agriculture and Industry During Depression (1929-1932). Note that above the wavy line the output drop is greater than the price drop. Below this line the price drop is greater than the output drop. (From Gardiner C. Means, *The Relative Inflexibility of Industrial Prices*, Senate Document No. 13, 74th Congress, p. 8.)

Weather still plays a dominant role in the determination of output, i.e., weather acting directly on growth or indirectly through insect pests, diseases, length of growing season, etc. Nor does the farmer possess full control over quality. Nor can he definitely determine the exact time of the harvest. Typically the farmer sows in the spring, takes as good care of the growing crop as he knows how and as his means permit, and lets nature take her course. To a large extent he is helpless before the uncontrolled forces of nature.

He is equally helpless before the mysterious forces of the market. The typical farm is small—a one-family enterprise. Vast numbers of farms are needed to supply the main staples such as wheat, corn, cotton, etc. Market supply has to be built up out of very small parcels varying in size, quality, time of delivery, etc.

So the middleman steps in between the farmer and the ultimate buyer to assort crops by grades, collect homogeneous parcels, and deliver them where needed. Frequently the crop goes through a processing industry—milling, baking, canning, packing, etc.—before reaching the final consumer. Vast numbers of farmers therefore do not face vast numbers of consumers, but face a far more limited number

of buyers, middlemen, and processors. The farmer's market position as a seller is generally weak.

It is equally weak as a buyer of industrial products such as tractors; service materials such as gasoline; or consumers' goods for his own use.

In general, both as a seller and as a buyer the farmer is in a weak position in the market. He may be "the last stronghold of competitive enterprise in America," but his is one of the few forms of business enterprise left that is afflicted with the old-fashioned variety of competition and not blessed with some newfangled monopolistic sort.[22]

How competitive agriculture fares in an industrial world became exceptionally clear during the Great Depression of 1929-1933. Fig. 12.1 deserves careful study. The figure contrasts agricultural implements and agricultural commodities. Such a contrast is effective but

[22] In this connection, one should bear in mind that the strong market position of industry is reinforced by such institutional developments as patents, the corporate form of enterprise entailing limited liability, holding companies, cartels, etc. Few farmers are in a position to take advantage of these devices.

TABLE 12.3.   Harvested Acreage[a] of Crops for the United States, 1924-1939[23]
(1,000,000 acres)

Year	All Corn	All Wheat	Cotton	Tobacco	Potatoes	15 Principal Crops	46 Crops Harvested	46 Crops Planted
1924	100.4	52.5	39.5	1.7	3.1	331.0	347.8	353.0
1925	101.3	52.4	44.4	1.8	2.8	335.0	352.2	363.7
1926	99.5	56.6	44.6	1.6	2.8	333.9	351.1	359.2
1927	98.4	59.6	38.3	1.6	3.2	332.5	350.6	358.3
1928	100.3	59.2	42.4	1.9	3.5	226.3	353.6	367.5
1929	97.8	63.3	43.2	2.0	3.0	339.3	357.0	363.1
1930	101.5	62.6	42.4	2.1	3.1	342.4	361.1	368.2
1931	106.9	57.7	38.7	2.0	3.5	336.6	357.4	372.4
1932	110.6	57.8	35.9	1.4	3.6	342.7	363.6	376.1
1933	106.0	49.4	29.4	1.7	3.4	311.0	331.9	372.4
1934	92.4	43.4	26.9	1.3	3.6	274.2	295.9	339.3
1935	95.8	51.2	27.6	1.4	3.5	309.0	336.5	359.8
1936	93.0	48.9	29.8	1.4	3.1	292.6	315.6	360.3
1937	93.7	64.4	33.6	1.8	3.2	315.9	340.6	364.7
1938	92.2	69.9	24.2	1.6	3.0	314.2	341.7	356.1
1939	88.8	53.7	23.9	1.9	3.0	295.6	325.4	344.1
1924-39 (Average)	98.7	56.4	35.3	1.7	3.2	321.4	342.6	361.1
Highest deviation from average, percent	12.1	23.8	26.4	25.0	12.0	6.6	6.1	4.1
Lowest deviation from average, percent	10.0	23.1	32.2	24.7	12.5	14.7	13.6	6.0

[a] Acreage is used rather than output to eliminate the effect of weather on crops. It will be noted that none of the single-crop acreage variations even approximate the industrial variations shown in Fig. 12.1. These figures might have been even more constant had the federal government after 1933 not taken steps to reduce acreages. Despite these reductions, up to World War II agricultural surpluses continued to accumulate, partly because of increased yields per acre.

not quite scientific. One should not contrast a single branch of manufacturing industry with the aggregate of agriculture. However, a sufficient number of industrial examples are cited to indicate the general character of the industrial aggregate corresponding to "agricultural commodities." In further answer to this criticism, figures for individual crops are given in Table 12.3, which shows acreage variation for both specific crops and aggregates of crops.

Further comments on Means' significant diagram seem called for. The industries listed can be divided into two groups: those whose output dropped more than price and those showing the reverse behavior. The division is clear-cut. In the first group are found mineral-using industries relying on inanimate energy and on

science more than on hand labor; in the other are agriculture and agricultural industries (textile, food, and leather products). Evidently auto tires, though containing agricultural products, follow the lead of automobiles and therefore fall into the first group. Petroleum is in the second group by a mere accident of history —the discovery of the east Texas oil field (at that time, 1929-1933, a large share of the crude oil output of the United States was still produced by independents and thus resembled agriculture structurally). The figure bears out in detail the ideas developed in the discussion of the resource hierarchy in Chapter 10.

The contrast is striking: agricultural implements, 6 and 80; agricultural commodities, 63 and 6! The price of the former holds up, come what may, while output drops to a mere 20 percent of peak production. The price of the latter drops 63 percent while output is virtually

[23] Albert L. Meyers, *Agriculture and the National Economy*, TNEC Monograph No. 23, Washington, 1940, p. 4.

constant through the biggest boom and the worst depression in history. The relative inflexibility of industrial prices, bought at a fearful cost in idle resources and paid for largely by the misery of millions of unemployed, contrasts with the relative inflexibility of agricultural output sold at a deficit, spelling prices that do not begin to cover production costs and the misery of our farmers and their wives and children.

Fig. 12.1 reveals clearly what happens when two segments of production, fundamentally different in their basic make-up, are tied to the same market process. Industry hires and fires labor as its needs vary with the ups and downs of business. It so happens that that labor, or more accurately its purchasing power, constitutes the very backbone of the market for farm products. So the institutional arrangement that relieves industry of all responsibility for labor in times of depression leaves unanswered the question of ultimate responsibility for preserving some sort of equilibrium between industry and agriculture. Except for relief given by charity agencies and for government aid to the unemployed, the bulk of the burden falls on those who constitute the weakest link in the economic chain—the farm population.

When domestic agriculture, by giving up its self-sufficiency, lost its independence and became commercialized, looking to the market for both the disposal of its products and the fulfillment of its needs, two mathematical ratios assumed fateful importance for the farmer's weal or woe. One is the ratio of the *price* which the farmer receives for his products, to the *cost* of producing them (this cost is affected by the prices he must pay for what he buys as a producer); the other is the ratio of the *price he receives* for what he sells, to the *price he pays* as a consumer. With the price he receives he is expected to cover:

1. Cost and maintenance of his farm, including interest on money borrowed for its purchase and improvement.
2. Cost and maintenance of equipment, barns, machines, etc.
3. Cost and maintenance of livestock, if any.
4. Services and supplies (seed, fertilizer, fuel, electricity, etc.).
5. Consumers' goods and personal services for himself and his family.

The proceeds of a sale depend on both the amount sold and the price. Ordinarily there is a negative correlation between these two: the more farmers sell in the aggregate, the lower the price.[24] Thus amount and price tend to offset each other to a certain extent, not necessarily in all individual transactions, but in the typical case and in the overall effect.

Unfortunately, too often and on too general a scale the prices received by farmers do not cover farm costs, if the latter are reckoned in any manner acceptable to cost accountants. The late Lord Stamp once characterized the failure of nonfarm consumers in industrial countries to pay adequately for farm products, as a blotch on the escutcheon of the West. Another Englishman once berated his countrymen for being willing to live well at the expense of the women and children of the Ukraine. (That was at a time when Britain was importing much if not most of her wheat from Russia.)

In the ideal economic world, governed by perfect competition, in which all resources are mobile enough to respond to every turn in the market, there should be no terror in these ratios. Automatic adjustments should keep them continually equilibrated. But unfortunately, the real world in which we live does not know perfect competition, and mobility is reduced to a snail's pace. The result—constant maladjustments and violent fluctuations.

By nature, agriculture is not nimble. It is sluggish, slow to respond to stimuli, especially to stimuli calling for contraction rather than expansion. Fixed charges constitute a high percentage of total farm costs. In fact, practically all costs are fixed. The direct exceptions are purchased seed, fertilizer, and hired labor (not much hired labor is employed on the "one-family farm," the mainstay of American agriculture). The biggest portion of the cost is the investment in the farm itself, including interest

---

[24] This negative correlation need not be taken for granted in the case of industry. Industry generally produces the largest volume when prices are highest, whereas in agriculture a bumper crop spells low prices. The income of industry expands under the simultaneous dual stimulus of volume and price. The farmer must multiply his large crop by a low unit price; only a short crop can be multiplied by a high unit price. Thus what is cumulative in industry is neutralized in agriculture in the offsetting action of opposing forces.

on any loans incurred in its acquisition or improvement. Another big item nowadays is equipment; a third one, taxes. Even labor (except hired labor) is a fixed cost, for there is no hiring and firing on family farms as in industrial and commercial establishments. One does not hire or fire his own family, and the family must live. If prices go down, the family is apt to work harder to make up in units of output for the low return per unit. Thus there is an element of *inverse* price elasticity in the expenditure of farm labor and the resultant supply of farm products, a tendency for output to increase rather than decrease in the face of falling prices.

The difference between farm and factory in this respect is striking. When times are bad, factory labor is dismissed and less raw and service materials are purchased. Under such conditions, it may pay to cut output to the bone. The savings in reduced variable costs outweigh the loss from fixed charges. In agriculture variable costs are of such little importance in determining total cost that their reduction in times of depression is frequently offset by fuller use of fixed capital—farm, equipment, family labor.

It was pointed out that the proper functioning of an exchange economy requires mobility of the factors of production, including labor. A word must therefore be added concerning the mobility of farm labor. One might expect that as farm prices drop and farming becomes progressively less remunerative, labor would leave the farms, i.e., that farms would go out of production, that farmers would sell out and their sons would move away, etc. Actually it does not work out that way. For one thing, farm foreclosure and bankruptcy seldom mean farm abandonment; they generally mean that one farmer tries where another has failed. One should expect that man power would leave the farms when times are bad. The exact opposite is true—additional man power streams in.

Paradoxical? Yes, but only in the eyes of the superficial observer. As soon as one probes deeper, the paradox dissolves into thin air. When times are good, industry jumps ahead by leaps and bounds while agriculture walks a little faster perhaps, but not much. Under these conditions the pull of rapidly advancing and expanding industry on labor is far stronger

than that of slowly advancing agriculture. Agricultural labor prospects may look good, but industrial opportunities look better; and that is what counts. Therefore, in good times, labor shifts from farm to factory. Vice versa, when times are bad and the industrial labor market collapses, things in factory towns look desperate. They are bad on the farm too, but at least one can eat, and sleep in the hay. So the farm appears the lesser of two evils. But the farmer who receives perhaps half of what it costs him to "make" a crop is caught between inadequate cash income and an unwelcome plethora of labor.

The problem of adjusting farm personnel to the figure set by *per-man* productivity as affected or determined by the interaction of pertinent forces of nature (weather, fertility, etc.) and of culture (implements, mechanical horsepower, science, etc.) on the one hand, and by demand as reflected in price on the other hand, is seriously aggravated by the fact that people living in rural farm areas characteristically "multiply" faster than do people in nonfarm areas. Thus in 1940 in the United States "the number of children ever born per 1000 mothers" was 3984 for rural farm classes, 3201 for rural nonfarm classes, and 2846 for urban classes.[25] This differential fertility is in sharp contrast to the reverse differential in per capita income. Thus it was found that in 1937 farm people earning 9 percent of the national income had nearly one-third of the nation's children.[26] The tempo of the transfer of people from farm to nonfarm areas, therefore, has to exceed that set by economic forces. Even if there were no mechanization or rationalization, there would still be a transfer problem. Without its solution, farm labor cannot be expected to earn wages comparable to those earned by nonfarm labor.

Under these conditions, business fluctuations, business cycles, booms and depressions affect the farmer in a way altogether different from that in which business—i.e., industry and trade —is affected. Being able to hire and fire labor

[25] *Statistical Abstract of the United States*, 1946, p. 55.
[26] A. Rochester, *Why Farmers Are Poor. The Agricultural Crisis in the United States*, International Publishers, New York, 1940, p. 13.

in accordance with his needs and the employment opportunities, the entrepreneur finds rapid adjustment possible, not to say almost painless. Depending on inanimate energy for heat, light, and power, industry is free to turn the current on or off more or less at will, whereas agriculture is tied to the biological rhythm of nature.[27]

Effects of the Mechanization and Rationalization of Agriculture. The mechanization and rationalization of agriculture meet difficulties not altogether different from those found in some other economic activities. The procedure is typically as follows. The new machine or the new scientific discovery is adopted by an individual farmer who feels or knows that he is going to profit from the innovation. If his expectations are fulfilled, his example is soon followed by others who wish, like him, to enlarge their profits. As the application of the innovation keeps spreading, there comes a time when, in response to the greater profits, the production of the crop or commodity in question increases, because of high yields or expanded acreage, or both, over and above previous production records. Unless, for some strange reason, the demand for the product happens to have increased at the same time and at a similar pace, the price must come down. To be more exact, if the innovation has reduced costs, the farmers whose costs have been reduced sufficiently to break even at the lower market price can stay in. Others still working on the old high-cost basis are forced out—or at least according to theory they are supposed to be forced out. If they are forced out, they constitute an employment problem unless they can grow something else, the demand for which is not yet fully met by existing facilities. If they are not forced out, chronic oversupply will tend to depress the market price below a remunerative level. The consumer or somebody else will gain unduly at the expense of producers in general and of high-cost producers in particular.

Frequently submarginal farmers are not forced out. Farmers whose costs are not covered by the proceeds of their sales are apt to defer maintenance of their land and equipment. Thus capital losses are incurred and the soil, the nation's number-one basic asset, suffers.

The problem, then, may be viewed as a conflict between immediate market gain (derived from the adoption of new mechanical and scientific discoveries) of individuals on the one hand, and long-run agriculture-wide interests with regard for general social assets on the other. This is one of the crucial problems of our time.

It seems hardly reasonable to expect that these difficulties are bound or even likely to resolve themselves through automatic marketwise adjustments. Such adjustments assume a minimum of self-determination and largely ignore the fundamental differences between agriculture and industry in the national economy. As has been shown, this minimum of self-determination is frequently absent in the case of farmers. It is different with a small group of giant manufacturers who constitute a modern industry and are their own inventors, research workers, machine suppliers, etc. In other words, they themselves provide the stimuli to increase production—if they want to. If obsolescence is too costly, they may decide to wait a while before adopting the new machine or process.

Demand for Farm Products. Up to this point the emphasis has been on supply factors. It is time that our attention is turned to the demand aspects of the problem. They materially add to the difficulties.

The demand for farm products suffers from several serious afflictions: (1) low price and income elasticity for farm products, (2) secular trends that unfavorably affect demand per person, (3) the instability of consumer purchasing power caused by the instability of business (cyclical disturbances), and (4) the absorption of some consumer demand by competitive products of industry. These will now be discussed.

1. The ease with which adjustment to market changes can be made depends largely on the elasticity of supply and demand. By elasticity is meant the responsiveness of one factor to changes in some other factor. Thus when economists speak of price elasticity of *supply* they mean that increases in the price received for a

---

[27] It goes without saying that industrial plants working at capacity are far more satisfactory all around than idle factories. The point made here refers merely to the difference in the degree of shock and pain suffered by agriculture and by industry.

specific product readily elicit an increase in market offerings and perhaps also in the output of the product, and that price decreases have an opposite effect. It was shown that agriculture possesses relatively little supply elasticity. While it manifests little response to price increases, it is even less responsive to price decreases. Economists also speak of price elasticity of *demand;* this refers to the readiness with which demand responds by expansion to falling prices and by contraction to rising prices.

There is also income elasticity of demand, which means the readiness with which the demand for certain goods expands or contracts as the individual's or family's income increases or decreases. Since the bulk of farm products are foodstuffs (or feedstuffs that eventually become foodstuffs when finished) and since food is a basic necessity, the demand for farm products is in general rather inelastic as to both price and income. With exceptions, lower prices for foodstuffs do not greatly stimulate demand nor do high prices readily cause contractions. However, demand for *specific* farm products does show considerable elasticity in response both to price and to income changes. Thus changes in milk prices result in considerable variation in milk consumption. By and large, however, the income elasticity of the demand for farm products is very low. The result is that as the incomes of families rise, a progressively smaller percentage of the family budget is devoted to food purchases. This progressive decline would appear even sharper if food purchases at the retail level, which cover a great many materials or services not of farm origin, could be reduced to actual farm products. Fancier foods tend to come in fancier packages and to include costlier service items.

The fundamental significance of this declining importance of food purchases is that the demand for farm products behaves quite differently from the demand for nonfarm products. Wealth does not increase the appetite for food but it creates innumerable and insatiable desires for nonfarm products. Not only are progressively fewer farmers needed to produce a given amount of farm products (because of the ever-increasing per capita productivity of commercialized agriculture) but agriculture plays an ever-smaller (relative) role in the national economy as the national income rises. To maintain the equilibrium between supply and demand, a cumulative (relative and/or absolute) contraction of agriculture is called for.

2. Nor is this all. The occupational shifts associated with industrialization and urbanization—involving change-over from physical labor outdoors to indoor labor and exacting nervous rather than physical strain—justify a considerable curtailment of average per capita food consumption. This trend is accentuated by the decline in the rate of increase of total population which is observed in all industrial countries. The effect of this decline is aggravated by changes in the age composition which further contribute to low per capita food requirements. New knowledge of nutrition as well as new popular ideas about diets brings about shifts in consumer preferences for various foods; again there is expected from agriculture an adjustive capacity which is alien to its nature. (Not all these nutritional innovations have negative effects on agriculture. In fact, entire new branches of agriculture are brought into being by newly developed consumer tastes, desires, and demands, e.g., the citrus fruit industry.)

3. The demand for farm products is adversely affected by the instability of industrial employment. However, this aspect has been discussed (see pp. 166 ff.) and nothing further will be said here.

4. Finally, the demand for agricultural products may at times be affected unfavorably by competition between them and products made by industry. History is full of such examples. The case of vegetable and animal dyes such as indigo, madder root, and cochineal being replaced by coal-tar dyes comes to mind. The substitution of mineral soda for vegetable soda is another example. Steel rope has replaced rope made from hemp; candles made from petroleum derivatives have replaced those made from tallow. Rayon and nylon compete with cotton and silk. More recently, synthetic rubber has made serious inroads into the market for "natural" rubber. Numerous other examples could be cited. There is no intention of implying that such substitutions are harmful to the common good or even to agriculture in the long run. Their effect may be favorable, unfavorable, or indifferent. All that is claimed

here is that they constitute another factor in the equation that needs watching.

Under these conditions—low supply elasticity, especially on the downbeat; the unrelenting push from the outside in the form of technological advance and scientific progress; the release of millions of acres for food products resulting from the displacement of work animals by tractors; low price and income elasticity of the demand for farm products; the declining per capita demand for food in general; shifts in demand for specific products; and the declining rate of increase of the populations of industrialized countries—the only salvation for agriculture is an expansion of nonfarm activities, secondary and tertiary, so powerful and so sustained that all the negative forces at play will be at least compensated if not overcompensated. Such powerful and sustained expansion, by the irresistible force of tempting nonfarm employment opportunities, would bring about the withdrawal of man power from agriculture at a speed sufficient to keep *per-man* productivity on the farm on an even keel with *per-man* productivity elsewhere.

Society cannot afford to let the food getter down. Its great opportunity lies in the unlimited expansibility of the demand for nonfarm products and services. The whole ingenuity of the institutional inventor should be pointed in that direction. If the farm problem is to be solved, national income must go up at a rate infinitely greater than the rate at which technological advances and scientific progress accelerate the productive achievements of farmers. If this cannot be accomplished, calling a holiday for such technological and scientific advance may make more sense than modern man is generally disposed to admit. Industrial man hates to throttle technological and scientific progress as much as the farmer hates to throttle the God-given forces of nature. Yet situations may arise when such throttling will prove the lesser of two evils.

The farm problem as it has developed since about 1920 is, then, made up really of two problems: (1) the instability of farm income which results from the impact of an erratic industrialism on a way of life and a way of producing that are constitutionally incapable of adjusting smoothly and promptly to the constant ups and downs, shifts and changes; and

(2) the relatively low average income of those engaged in agriculture, which suggests that, by and large, agriculture is overstaffed and overextended. This second problem is due partly to the relentless stimulation to which agriculture is constantly submitted both by industry-furnished machines and by government-furnished science and to which it does not respond with sufficiently prompt and effective expulsion of man power from its ranks. This second problem, in other words, is at least partly one of overemployment and resulting underproductivity.

Remedies

In considering the solution of the problem one thing seems clear enough, i.e., that agriculture cannot be expected to solve its own problems. In the first place, the roots of most of its troubles stem from outside the realm of agriculture. In the second place, agriculture retains little self-determination or autonomy. Economically the farmer is dependent on a market over which he has little or no control (which is supposed to be automatic but its automaticity has been a little one-sided of late). Financially he is dependent on banks, on corporations, on wealthy landowners, or on the government. Technologically he is dependent on the outside, mainly on industry. His research is done for him by the government, and for information he must rely mainly on the government. In industrial countries agriculture constitutes a political minority group.

That this dependent minority group of the national economy should be hailed by some as the most vital sector of our economy seems strange. Yet one can understand such "agricultural fundamentalism."[28] Is not food vital to life? Is not the soil the basis of human existence? The answer is clearly yes. But to deduce therefrom that agricultural production should be maintained at a high level, or that the farm population should be held constant, or that farm prices should be firmly riveted to a certain ratio regardless of changes in cost, would seem to draw wrong conclusions from the vital

---

[28] See Joseph S. Davis, "Agricultural Fundamentalism," in *On Agricultural Policy 1926-1938*, Stanford, Food Research Institute, 1939, pp. 24-43.

significance of the products of agriculture. As Davis well states,

In this field, as in many others, we may wisely seek to temper the cruelty of these forces; but far-sighted statesmanship will undertake, not the Canutian task of sweeping back the tides, but appropriate methods of making adaptations to them. . . . Agriculture has, and probably always will have, an important place in the life of every nation. Measures to protect agricultural resources from needless depletion, to facilitate physical and economic processes of agricultural production and marketing, to mitigate the severity of fluctuations in farm income, and to raise the plane of living among farmers are in the general interest; but they are justified on grounds independent of an allegedly peculiar importance of agriculture or farmers. Efforts to raise the level of attractiveness of farming, financially and otherwise, are desirable as part of a general policy; but most attempts to raise it in relation to the level of attractiveness of other occupations tend to be self-defeating. Efforts to make farming profitable for all who may choose to farm are foredoomed to failure.

The wealth and welfare of nations depend upon many complex conditions. Today, agriculture is not uniquely basic and the prosperity of a nation depends largely on other factors than the work of those who till the soil.[29]

Solutions are of two kinds: quick, short-run remedies designed to meet an immediate emergency; and slow, long-run permanent solutions. Subsidies, stamp plans, credit moratoriums, price support, acreage curtailment, etc., may be justified for limited emergency needs. Per-

manent solutions must go to the roots of the problem. There are congenital weaknesses of agriculture to be overcome. Science may find more and better ways of doing this. There are business cycles which are at the root of the instability of farm income. Their frequency and violence must be reduced. There are monopolistic practices in our economic make-up which interfere with the proper allocation of resources and challenge those suffering from the result to retaliate with generally unsound practices. If such monopolistic evils—for reasons of technology or politics or what have you—cannot be removed, agriculture must be protected by countervailing measures. But ultimately the solution lies in nonfarm expansion, both domestic and world-wide.

The reader may wonder why in a treatment of agricultural resources so much space is given to the discussion of history and the analysis of economic forces, to the farm problem, to industrial economics, etc., and relatively so little to actual bona-fide down-to-earth facts such as acres of this, yields of that, prices of the other. The answer is simple. If, as is maintained throughout this volume, "resources *are* not but *become,* resources evolve out of the dynamic triune interaction of natural, cultural, and human forces," it is this interaction that is the crux of the situation, the key to resource availability. Unless man learns to solve problems such as the farm problem the fruits of both nature and culture will rot on the ground, and a detailed description of both the ground and the rotting fruit would be little more than mockery.

---

[29] *Ibid.,* pp. 42, 43.

BIBLIOGRAPHY

Black, J. D., and Kiefer, M. E., *Future Food and Agriculture Policy,* New York, McGraw-Hill, 1948.

Davis, J. S., *On Agricultural Policy 1926-1938,* Stanford University, Food Research Institute, 1939.

Ezekiel, M., and Bean, L. H., *Economic Bases for the Agricultural Adjustment Act,* U. S. Department of Agriculture, Washington, 1933.

Jesness, O. B. (ed.), *Readings in Agricultural Policy,* Philadelphia, Blakiston, 1949.

Johnson, D. G., "Contribution of Price Policy to the Income and Resource Problem in Agriculture," *Journal of Farm Economics,* November, 1944.

Johnson, D. G., *Trade and Agriculture,* New York, Wiley, 1950.

Malott, D. W., *Problems in Agricultural Marketing,* New York, McGraw-Hill, 1938.

Malott, D. W., and Martin, B. F., *The Agricultural Industries,* New York, McGraw-Hill, 1939.

National Resources Committee, *Consumer Expenditure in the United States,* Washington, 1939.

Nourse, E. G., Davis, J. S., and Black, J. D., *Three Years of the Agricultural Adjustment Administration,* Washington, Brookings Institution, 1937.

Nourse, E. G., Davis, J. S., and Black, J. D., *Government in Relation to Agriculture,* Pamphlet No. 28, Washington, Brookings Institution, 1940.

Pei-Kang Chang, *Agriculture and Industrialization*, Cambridge, Harvard University Press, 1949.

Schultz, T. W., *Agriculture in an Unstable Economy*, New York, McGraw-Hill, 1945.

Schultz, T. W., "How Efficient Is American Agriculture?" *Journal of Farm Economics*, August, 1947.

Schultz, T. W., *Production and Welfare of Agriculture*, New York, Macmillan, 1950.

U. S. Department of Agriculture, Bureau of Agricultural Economics, *Achieving a Balanced Agriculture*, Washington, 1940.

UNIT 2. FOOD RESOURCES

Chapter 13

FOODS AND FOODSTUFFS

By far the most important task of agriculture is the production of food (and of feed for the animals that yield food and help to produce food). Most food is produced by agriculture. The world food problem, which is the problem of supplying something like two and a half billion human beings with adequate food, preferably 365 days a year, is primarily[1] an agricultural problem. The food problem is as far from solution as is the farm surplus problem.

What could be more natural than to link the food surplus problem of the New World with the food deficit problem of the Old? Why not a "marriage between nutrition and agriculture" and kill two birds with one stone? Surpluses are created—so one might argue—by old-fashioned price economists who refuse to recognize human need as such but recognize only "effec-

tive demand," i.e., need or want backed by purchasing power. Once the abolition of hunger is put on the agenda of man, there are no surpluses, and none is in sight for a long time to come.

This is a restless age. Men are impatient with traditional answers and timeworn catchwords. They are straining at the leash. What else can one expect after a Second World War, after Hiroshima? No one knows yet what the atomic and hydrogen bombs mean. There is just a vague but nonetheless strong realization that something drastic must be done and that old remedies may be too mild.

Nor have men forgotten the Great Depression. As they recall that nightmare, nothing seems more important than full employment, expansion, going forward. So people think with a boldness born of despair. If their thoughts seem utopian, there is a reason, there are a thousand reasons.

This "marriage of nutrition and agriculture" is one of those bold ideas. It must be examined. But before we can be prepared to do so, we must examine some elements of nutrition and the basic facts of the world food situation.

---

[1] If people raised their own food on their own land, it would be purely an agricultural problem. As it is, it is a problem of landownership, of physical distribution, of costs of distribution, of purchasing power of consumers, and of their productivity as producers of things and services to be exchanged for food. Thus the food problem constitutes a large part of, and ties up with, most economic problems.

FOODS AND THEIR FUNCTIONS

Food comprises those organic and inorganic substances—solids, colloids, liquids, and gases—which the human body must take in to live. The basic function of food, therefore, is to sustain human life. Actually food does much more. If supplied in the proper quantity and quality, it gives health. If prepared skillfully, it contributes to the pleasures of life. If served sumptuously, it adorns festive occasions.[2]

Food can be abused, e.g., eaten to excess. In that case, it ceases to function as food in the strict sense; instead, it functions as poison. Some foods such as sugar may be habit-forming and thus encourage overindulgence. As yet, however, far more people suffer from insufficiency of food—i.e., of food in general or of the right food—than from consuming too much.

Quantitative Measure of Food Requirements

"Give us this day our daily bread." Man should eat daily. In fortunate lands three square meals are taken more or less for granted. Human life may be viewed as an eternal sequence of breakfast, lunch, and dinner, of cooking meals, clearing tables, washing dishes. Life would be far simpler if we could eat once a month or once a year. But that is not the way we are built.

As it is, the ever-recurring need for food dominates human habits, institutions, and relationships. The primitive has little respite from the unending chore of stilling hunger. Even today, many millions never succeed. In the more advanced civilizations, division of labor frees a large portion of society from the physical task of food getting, though not from the economic effort necessary to provide it. Regular meal hours are the pivotal points of the working day.[3]

How much food the body needs depends on the size, age, sex (perhaps race), and metabolism of the eater, and on the amount and nature of his physical exercise and mental effort, his surroundings such as temperature, etc. Thus the food requirements of a pregnant or nursing mother are different from those of girls of like age and weight. Growing children need amounts and combinations of food different from those needed by adults. A race of six-footers must consume more food than one averaging five feet five inches in height. A lumberjack working in zero weather needs much more than a clerk working in an overheated office. A beggar shivering in rags may need more food than the passer-by in a fur coat.

A rough measurement of *amount* of food can be expressed by means of heat units, or calories. Table 13.1 shows the extent to which food requirements vary according to age, sex, activity, etc.

TABLE 13.1. Recommended Daily Allowances[4]

	Calories
Man (154 lbs.)	
Moderately active	3000
Very active	4500
Sedentary	2500
Woman (123 lbs.)	
Moderately active	2500
Very active	3000
Sedentary	2100
Pregnancy (latter half)	2500
Lactation	3000
Children up to 12 years:	
Under 1 year	90 per lb.
1-3 years	1200
4-6 years	1600
7-9 years	2000
10-12 years	2500
Children over 12 years:	
Girls, 13-15 years	2800
16-20 years	2400
Boys, 13-15 years	3200
16-20 years	3800

Functions of Food

On the basis of the functions they perform in keeping man fit and well, foods may be divided into two rations: the work, or work and heat, ration; and the maintenance ration. The former provides body warmth and energy, heat to aid digestion and to preserve the complex chemical mixtures in proper condition and relation. The latter provides the necessary substances to keep the body—its bones, tissues,

---

[2] It should be remembered that much of the money "spent on food" is actually spent on making appetizing foods available in appetizing surroundings. The physiology of eating cannot be isolated from the psychology of the eater.

[3] See Lewis Mumford, *Technics and Civilization*, Harcourt, Brace and Company, New York, 1934, p. 12.

---

[4] This table was prepared by the Committee on Foods and Nutrition of the National Research Council.

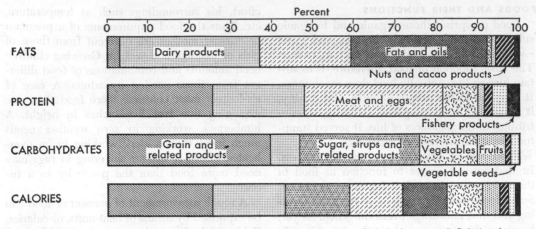

FIG. 13.1. Percentage Distribution of Consumption of Fats, Proteins, Carbohydrates, and Calories, by Commodity Groups, in Continental United States, 1942.

muscles, etc.—in repair and to provide for growth. Generally the maintenance ration constitutes a relatively small portion of the diet.

Strictly speaking, water and oxygen as found in the air are also food. To conform to popular usage of the word *food*, these essentials of life may be called auxiliary foods.

Finally there are the food accessories which constitute a very minute but very vital part of the diet: the minerals, including micronutrients such as cobalt, manganese, and copper, and the vitamins. Both vitamins and minerals have a protective function. Minerals may be used over and over again and hence may not need constant replacement. Loss of blood, however, calls for replacement of iron. Several vitamins can now be synthesized commercially.

CLASSIFICATION OF FOODS AND FOODSTUFFS

Major Food Categories

Also on the basis of the functions they perform, foods may be divided into three main classes: proteins, fats, and carbohydrates (starch, sugar, etc.). (Water and air are omitted here though their inclusion might be justified; the food accessories are likewise omitted on the ground that they are not foods proper.) Perhaps a fourth category—roughage or bulk—should be added. Since the most concentrated foods are not necessarily the best for the normal functioning of the digestive tract, substances other than proteins, fats, and carbohydrates may have to be ingested. If they lack

nutritive value, they should be classed under auxiliary foods with water and air.

Proteins form the basis of the maintenance ration. There are animal and vegetable proteins. Many nutritionists stress the need of animal proteins because of their "completeness." Others consider the question still open. Emphasis is also laid on the fact that the nutritive value of proteins depends on their "degradation products," the so-called amino acids. Different amino acids perform different nutritional functions, i.e., supply diverse needs of the body as a functioning organism. The proper way of evaluating proteins, therefore, it is argued, is not merely on the basis of origin—animal or vegetable—but in terms of specific amino acids.

The work, or work and heat, ration is made up of fats and carbohydrates. The latter are mostly starches and sugars. An important difference between fats and carbohydrates lies in the fact that fats are highly concentrated heat-energy carriers; they have a heat value of 9.3 per gram as against only 4.1 for carbohydrates. (Incidentally, the heat value of proteins is also 4.1.) This concentrated heat value is important for many reasons, of which only a few are indicated. It renders body fueling more efficient. It allows shipment of food values in smaller space.

Foods and Foodstuffs

For the sake of clarity, a distinction should perhaps be made between foods and foodstuffs. Protein is a food; meat, eggs, and milk

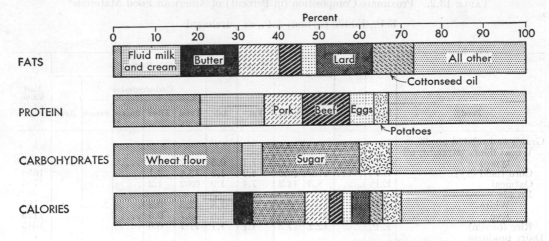

FIG. 13.2. Percentage Distribution of Consumption of Fats, Proteins, Carbohydrates, and Calories, by Specified Commodities, in Continental United States, 1942.

(all containing proteins) are foodstuffs. The relationship of foods and foodstuffs will be illustrated by the parts they played in the diet of the people of the United States in the year 1942.[5] In that year the United States produced:

16.8 billion pounds of fats.

11.6 billion pounds of proteins.

43.2 billion pounds of carbohydrates.

Exports, imports, and storage affected the totals available for consumption, imports of carbohydrates (sugar) being the major addition to domestic production. Consumption figures ran as follows:

11.1 billion pounds of proteins.

13.5 billion pounds of fats.

50.1 billion pounds of carbohydrates.

One notices how much larger the work, or work and heat, ration is than the maintenance ration: 63.6 billion pounds of fats and carbohydrates against 11.1 billion pounds of proteins, almost 6:1.

The total food production and consumption measured in calories was 173.6 and 168.7 trillion calories respectively.

From what foodstuffs were these foods obtained? Figs. 13.1 and 13.2 tell the story. It

[5] The year has no particular significance. This discussion is based on a report published by the U. S. Tariff Commission in 1944 entitled *United States Consumption of Food in Terms of Fats, Proteins, Carbohydrates, and Calories*. It contains data for the year 1942. Figs. 13.1 and 13.2 are from this report.

will be noticed that in order of importance, as measured in calories, the foodstuffs rank as follows:

Foodstuff	Percent of Total Calories
Grains and related products	25.3
Dairy products	17.6
Sugar, sirups, and related products	15.8
Meat and eggs	13.0
Fats and oils	10.9
Vegetables	8.8
Fruits	4.3
Nuts and cacao products	2.1
Vegetable seeds	1.7
Fishery products	0.5
	100.0

In terms of specific foodstuffs, the picture looks like this:

Wheat flour		19.4
Fluid milk and cream	9.1	13.5
Butter	4.4	
Sugar		13.0
Pork	6.1	
Beef	3.2	11.4
Eggs	2.1	
Lard		4.5
Cottonseed oil		3.1
Potatoes		4.6
All others		30.5
		100.0

It will also be noted that most foodstuffs and foodstuff groups except fats and oils and sugars contribute not only to one food need but to several. Thus cereals contribute 2.9 percent of the fats, 25.6 percent of the proteins, and

| Food | Basis | Refuse | Water | Protein | Fat | Ash | Carbohydrates | | | | Acid | Fuel Value per lb., Calories |
							Total	Fiber	Sugars	Starch		
Grains and related products												
Wheat flours (straight, all types)	E.P.	.....	12.0	11.2	1.1	0.5	75.2	0.4	....	.....	....	1615
Corn (field dry)	E.P.	.....	11.0	10.0	4.3	1.3	73.4	2.1	....	.....	....	1690
Oatmeal	E.P.	.....	8.3	14.2	7.4	1.9	68.2	1.2	....	.....	....	1795
Breads												
White	E.P.	.....	35.9	8.5	2.0	1.3	52.3	0.3	....	.....	....	1185
Rye	E.P.	.....	37.6	8.9	2.0	1.8	49.7	0.5	....	.....	....	1145
Rice (brown)	E.P.	.....	12.2	7.5	1.7	1.1	77.7	0.6	....	.....	....	1615
Dairy products												
Milk	E.P.	.....	87.0	3.5	3.9	0.7	4.9	....	....	.....	....	310
Cheese (Cheddar)	E.P.	.....	39.0	23.9	32.3	3.1	1.7	....	....	.....	....	1785
(For butter see Fats and oils)												
Sugar, sirups, and molasses												
Sugar	E.P.	.....	0.5	.....	.....	....	99.5	.....	97.5	.....	....	1805
Sirup (corn, table mixture)	E.P.	.....	25.0	.....	.....	0.6	74.0	....	....	.....	....	1345
Molasses (cane, light)	E.P.	.....	24.0	.....	.....	3.0	65.0	....	....	.....	....	1180
Meat and eggs												
Pork (cured, raw)	A.P.	13.0	37.0	14.7	30.0	4.7	0.3	....	....	.....	....	1510
Meat and poultry (cooked)	E.P.	.....	63.0	30.0	6.0	1.2	....	....	....	.....	....	790
Lamb (leg, trimmed)	E.P.	.....	71.0	18.4	9.1	1.0	....	....	....	.....	....	710
Liver (fresh, calf)	E.P.	.....	70.8	19.0	4.9	1.3	4.0	....	....	.....	....	620
Eggs (hen)	A.P.	11.0	65.9	11.4	10.2	0.9	0.6	....	....	.....	....	635
Fats and oils												
Butter	E.P.	.....	15.5	0.6	81.0	2.5	0.4	....	....	.....	....	3325
Oleomargarine	E.P.	.....	15.5	0.6	81.0	2.5	0.4	....	....	.....	....	3325
Lard	E.P.	.....	....	.....	100.0	....	....	....	....	.....	....	4080
Vegetables												
Beans												
Snap green	A.P.	10.0	80.0	2.2	0.2	0.7	6.9	1.3	....	.....	....	170
Dry seeds, all	E.P.	.....	10.5	22.2	1.5	3.9	62.1	3.9	3.6	35.8	....	1585
Cabbage	A.P.	27.0	67.5	1.0	0.1	0.5	3.9	0.7	....	.....	....	90
Onions	A.P.	6.0	82.2	1.3	0.2	0.5	9.8	0.8	....	.....	....	210
Peas (dry, whole)	E.P.	.....	11.6	23.8	1.4	3.0	60.2	5.4	....	45.1	....	1580
Tomatoes	E.P.	.....	94.1	1.0	0.3	0.6	4.0	0.6	3.4	.....	0.5	105
Potatoes	E.P.	.....	77.8	2.0	0.1	1.0	19.1	0.4	0.9	14.7	....	385
Fruits												
Apples	A.P.	12.0	74.0	0.3	0.4	0.3	13.0	0.9	....	.....	....	260
Bananas (fresh)	A.P.	35.0	50.1	0.8	0.1	0.6	15.4	0.4	....	.....	....	2670
Grapefruit (fresh)	A.P.	34.0	58.6	0.3	0.1	0.3	6.7	0.2	....	.....	...	150
Grapes (fresh)	E.P.	.....	81.9	1.4	1.4	0.5	14.9	0.5	11.5	.....	1.2	355
Nuts and cacao												
Brazil nuts	E.P.	.....	5.3	14.4	65.9	3.4	11.0	2.1	1.5	2.2	....	3150
Cocoa	E.P.	.....	4.3	9.0	18.8	5.2	31.0	4.8	....	.....	....	1495
Coconut (fresh)	A.P.	26.0	44.5	1.9	18.5	0.7	8.4	1.7	....	.....	....	940
Walnuts (black)	E.P.	.....	2.7	18.3	58.2	2.1	18.7	1.9	....	.....	....	3045
Vegetable seeds												
Peanuts (roasted, in shell)	E.P.	.....	2.6	26.9	44.2	2.7	23.6	2.4	....	.....	....	2720
Soybeans (dry)	E.P.	.....	7.6	34.9	18.1	4.7	12.0	5.0	8.4	2.1	....	1590
Fishery products												
Cod (raw)	A.P.	32.0	39.6	7.9	0.2	0.6	....	....	....	.....	....	150
Salmon, Pacific (canned)	E.P.	.....	67.4	20.6	9.6	2.4	....	....	....	.....	....	765
Fish, raw, class 1, medium composition	E.P.	.....	77.2	19.0	2.5	1.3	....	....	....	.....	....	445

[6] Rearranged from Circular No. 549, U. S. Department of Agriculture.

39.5 percent of the carbohydrates. Similarly, dairy products contribute 34.2 percent of the fats, 22.2 percent of the proteins, and 7.1 percent of the carbohydrates. Most foodstuffs are complex organic compounds. A kernel of corn contains a germ full of oil, as well as sugars and starches. Most pieces of ham manifestly are made up of both fat and lean meat.

Table 13.2 shows the composition of typical items that help to make up the American diet. It indicates the constituents of the edible portion of foodstuffs and the fuel value per pound in calories. It does not begin to show the almost endless variety of materials out of which the American diet is compounded. There is perhaps no other country where as large a variety of dishes prepared from as many different substances produced at home or imported are available to the consuming public. They are not all available in the same city or in the same part of the country, but the overall nation-wide variety is unusual.

It will be noted that foodstuffs contain a great deal more than the three food categories listed earlier. Water in particular is a major component. The total weight of foodstuffs produced, therefore, greatly exceeds the aggregate weight of proteins, fats, and carbohydrates.

TABLE 13.3. Total Output of Foodstuffs in the United States, 1943[7]

Food Groups	Food Output (billion pounds)[a]
Milk or its equivalent[b]	74.7
Potatoes and sweet potatoes	21.8
Dry beans and peas, and nuts	4.5
Tomatoes[c] and citrus fruit	20.1
Leafy green and yellow vegetables[c]	13.6
Other vegetables and fruit[c]	30.2
Eggs[d]	6.9
Meat,[d] poultry, and fish	23.1
Flour and cereals (baked goods equivalent)	34.1
Butter and other fats[e]	11.9
Sugar and other sweets	5.2

[a] Retail weights.
[b] Milk supplies used in butter production not included.
[c] Includes estimates for market gardens and farm production for home use.
[d] Bacon and salt side not included.
[e] Includes bacon and salt side.

[7] Willard W. Chorane, *High-Level Food Consumption in the United States*, U. S. Department of Agriculture, Bureau of Agricultural Economics, Miscellaneous Publication No. 581, Washington, 1945.

Thus the total output of foodstuffs in the United States in 1943 is shown in Table 13.3.

Primary and Secondary Foods[8]

Primary foodstuffs are foodstuffs of animal or vegetable origin which are consumed directly by man (after or without preparation, processing, etc.) in the form in which they first become edible. Primary foodstuffs include these:

1. All vegetable foodstuffs (grains, sugars, vegetable fats, pulses, tubers, fruit and vegetables, etc.).

2. Those animal foodstuffs not produced from feeds which could have served as primary foodstuffs or which were grown on land capable of producing primary foodstuffs. Thus the following are primary:

1. Beef from animals raised by grazing on range.
2. Meat or milk from goats and other animals feeding on roots and herbs in rocky terrain or on alpine meadows unavailable for agriculture.
3. Poultry and eggs obtained from chickens raised on waste and wild products not suitable for human use.
4. Pork and lard obtained from hogs fed on slop and other wastes and wild products not suitable for human use.
5. Fish and other edible products caught or gathered in the ocean, rivers, and lakes.
6. Game.

But if wheat and other edible grains are fed to animals, food derived from those animals is secondary food; or if feedstuffs for animals are grown on land which could, physically and economically, produce edible products, the food derived from such animals is secondary. Most of the animal products eaten in the United States are secondary food. The economic implications of this distinction between primary

[8] R. Pearl, *Studies in Human Biology*, Williams and Wilkins Company, Baltimore, 1924, p. 383; see also E. W. Shanahan, *Animal Foodstuffs, Their Production and Consumption, with Special Reference to the British Empire; A Study in Economic Geography and Agricultural Economics*, G. Routledge Sons, Ltd., London, 1920, especially part 2, chap. 5; and H. P. Armsby and C. R. Moulton, *The Animal as a Converter of Matter and Energy; A Study of the Role of Livestock in Food Production*, Chemical Catalogue Company, Book Department, New York, 1925, especially the introduction.

TABLE 13.4. Nutritive Value of Foods[9]

	Food	"Good" Protein	Minerals	Vitamins A	B	C	D	
	Milk	++	+++	+	+	+∅	+∅	
	Cheese	++	++	+	+	−	−	
E	Eggs	++	++	+	++	−	++	
E	Liver	++	++	+	++	−	+	
E	Fat fish (herrings, etc.)	+	....			−	++	Highly protective foods
	Green vegetables, salads	+	+++	+	+	++	−	
	Raw fruit, fruit juices	....	+++	+*	+	++	−	
E	Butter	−	−	+		−	+∅	
	Cod-liver oil	−	−	+++		−	+++	
	Yeast	+	+	−	++	−	−	Less protective foods
	Meat (muscle)	+	⊥	−	+	⊥	−	
	Root vegetables, tubers	....	....	+*	+	+	−	
	Legumes (dry peas, lentils)	....			+	−	−	
E	Cereals, bread (whole-meal)	+	⊥	⊥	+	−	−	
E	Cereals, bread (white)	....		−	+	−	−	
E	Cereals, rice (polished)	....		−	+	−	−	Non-protective foods
E	Nuts	⊥⊥	....	−	++	−	−	
E	Sugar, jam, honey	....	....	−	−	−	−	
E	Margarine, olive oil, and other vegetable oils	....	....	−	−	−	−	

E = foods of high energy or caloric value.
+++ signifies very rich.
++ signifies rich.
+ signifies present.
⊥ signifies present in small amount or traces.
− signifies absent.
∅ signifies in summer, when the cows are in pasture.
* signifies if yellow in color.

and secondary foods will be discussed later in this chapter.

THE SCIENCE OF NUTRITION AND DIETARY CHANGE

The diversity of the American diet reflects the size of the country, its wide range of climate, the variety of its agriculture, the diverse origins of its people, and above all its ability to pay for the palate-tickling fancy foods brought in from the far corners of the earth and the nourishing foods a balanced diet calls for. The poor have relatively little choice in the selection of foodstuffs. The three "M's"—meat, meal, and molasses, meaning pork, corn meal, and molasses—that for so long constituted

the basis of the diet of poor farmers in parts of the South illustrate this limitation of choice. It is in sharp contrast to the elaborate menus presented in many city restaurants and hotels.

Nutrition as a Science

For countless ages the eating habits of the average man were either rudely determined by the limitations of supply or of purchasing power or governed by rule of thumb. People ate what they could get and what their appetites called for. The accurate relationship between eating and nutrition, between ingestion of food and its effects on the capacity to do work, the building up of the body, and the maintenance of health were little understood. To be sure, trial and error had yielded many valuable lessons.[10] The

[9] *The Relation of Nutrition to Health, Agriculture and Economic Policy,* Final Report of the Mixed Committee of the League of Nations, Geneva, 1937, p. 64.

[10] Thus as early as 1804 sailors of the British navy were given lime juice (juice of a Mediterranean lemon) to prevent scurvy.

TABLE 13.5. Nutritional Requirements of the Adult Man (70 kg.)

Nutrient	Recommended Daily Allowance[a]	Supplied by	
Calories	3000	43 slices whole-wheat bread 3¾ cups sugar 9 pts. milk	
Protein	70 g.	¾ lb. broiled steak 8.6 oz. American cheese 8½ cups whole milk	11 eggs
Calcium	0.8 g.	1½ pts. whole milk 1 cup turnip greens (cooked) ¾ cup molasses	3 oz. cheese 3 cups raw dried navy beans
Iron	12 mg.	12 slices Boston brown bread 4 oz. liver ½ cup molasses	8 eggs 5 cups cooked spinach
Vitamin A	5000 I.U.	3½ oz. liver 10 squares butter 1 cup raw carrot cubes	2 oz. turnip greens 3 oz. dried apricots
Thiamin (B₁)	2.0 mg.	1 lb. dried lima beans 33 thin slices whole-wheat bread 1½ lbs. liver	2 cups peanut butter ¼ lb. ham or lean pork 30 eggs 2½ lbs. lean beef
Ascorbic acid	75 mg.	1¼ cups broccoli ½ grapefruit 1½ lemons	1 large orange ½ lb. turnip greens 3 medium tomatoes
Riboflavin	3.0 mg.	2¼ lbs. dried apricots 2 lbs. lean beef 6 lbs. beet tops	¼ lb. kidney ¼ lb. liver 3 lbs. lean pork
Nicotinic acid	20 mg.	*Good Sources* Liver, salmon, beef, lean pork, egg yolk, turnip greens, tomatoes, spinach, mustard greens, peanuts, dried peas.	
Vitamin D	Amount unknown	*Good Sources* Salmon, sardines, eggs, and butter.	

[a] Recommended by National Research Council, Committee on Foods and Nutrition.

science of nutrition is young. It rests on an advanced knowledge of physiology and food chemistry. By 1881 something akin to vitamins was being suspected, but real scientific knowledge dates from 1905. Amino acids are not yet fully explored and our knowledge of proteins still shows numerous gaps.

Once the basis was laid, progress was rapid, and by 1937 a table of the nutritive value of foods was prepared for the Mixed Committee of the League of Nations. This table, Table 13.4, is an important guide to the rationalization of diet. As it was conceived by the Mixed Committee, its importance goes far beyond that. It was meant to serve as a basis not merely for this rationalization but for agricultural and economic policy as well. For ages farmers had grown what they could grow and sell. Now that there was recognition of the vital importance of proper food and balanced diets for health, and of health for productivity, and of productivity for the entire economic development of the earth, steps were taken to direct agriculture into productive efforts deliberately brought into harmony with nutritive objectives and economic plans.

Year	Dairy Products, Excluding Butter, in Milk Equivalents[b] (quarts)	Eggs[c] (number)	Meat, Poultry, and Fish[d] (pounds)	Fats and Oils, Including Fat Cuts and Butter[e] (pounds)	Dry Beans and Peas, Nuts, and Soya Flour[f] (pounds)	Potatoes and Sweet Potatoes (pounds)	Citrus Fruit and Tomatoes (pounds)	Leafy, Green, and Yellow Vegetables and Fruit (pounds)	Other Vegetables and Fruit (pounds)	Grain Products (pounds)	Sugar and Sirups[g] (pounds)	Cocoa, Coffee, and Tea[h] (pounds)
1909	169	284	164	59	12	208	44	77	211	309	86	10
1910	160	297	157	59	12	209	44	74	205	306	89	9
1911	156	319	161	60	11	171	45	70	217	301	91	9
1912	175	302	155	58	12	192	46	75	230	300	89	11
1913	171	294	152	59	12	196	45	72	204	290	94	9
1914	164	286	148	62	12	174	52	73	225	287	93	10
1915	169	304	143	62	12	194	51	75	224	279	90	11
1916	168	290	148	62	13	158	48	73	204	289	91	12
1917	176	273	144	57	19	169	51	76	203	281	93	14
1918	188	275	150	60	18	188	48	84	202	251	92	12
1919	187	294	148	61	15	170	54	76	203	264	105	13
1920	187	290	144	57	13	166	54	88	225	249	102	13
1921	184	290	141	58	12	170	56	73	186	241	100	13
1922	183	306	146	62	12	171	53	80	227	246	118	13
1923	181	317	154	66	14	184	62	76	210	240	105	14
1924	188	314	152	66	17	166	63	84	219	236	115	14
1925	193	309	147	65	16	160	59	82	211	233	118	12
1926	195	329	146	65	16	141	59	83	240	233	120	14
1927	194	332	144	66	18	156	61	90	207	232	119	14
1928	195	328	140	67	17	166	57	85	229	239	121	13
1929	199	324	138	68	16	166	69	93	219	234	113	14
1930	199	319	137	67	16	146	60	88	216	226	124	14
1931	196	321	137	66	18	150	70	93	231	220	115	14
1932	196	302	138	66	16	155	66	92	204	210	109	14
1933	195	286	143	66	14	153	67	86	196	203	110	14
1934	193	278	152	66	17	153	68	94	194	201	109	14
1935	198	270	128	60	18	159	77	97	215	195	108	16
1936	203	278	140	64	19	144	78	92	208	202	110	16
1937	206	297	137 ·	64	18	138	81	98	230	197	108	15
1938	208	298	136	65	19	144	86	107	219	198	107	16
1939	212	302	142	68	19	132	98	104	229	195	110	17
1935-1939 average	205	289	137	64	19	143	84	100	220	197	109	16
1940	215	306	148	71	19	139	95	103	226	192	107	18
1941[i]	219	299	152	70	20	139	99	102	233	196	118	17
1942[i]	230	303	153	66	21	138	101	117	219	200	106	15
1943[i]	240	332	157	66	22	147	103	115	200	209	99	14
1944[i]	245	336	166	67	20	139	115	120	221	204	107	16
1945[i]	254	381	165	61	20	141	119	130	233	207	91	18
1946[i] (preliminary)	267	359	167	64	22	132	114	134	250	195	92	20
1947[i] (preliminary)	252	363	167	65	20	133	117	122	241	193	111	19

[a] Estimated from per capita data as usually reported by the Bureau of Agricultural Economics in The National Food Situation by means of average loss factors with the addition of unpublished estimates of supplies from town and city gardens and estimates of minor food items.
[b] Milk equivalent calculated on the basis of protein and mineral content.
[c] Allows for breakage from farm to retail.
[d] Excluding bacon and other fat pork cuts. Includes edible offal and game.
[e] Actual weight basis.
[f] Nuts on an unshelled basis.
[g] Excluding duplication in dairy products, canned fruit, etc.
[h] Roasted basis for cocoa and coffee.
[i] Civilian consumption only. Total civilian supplies divided by number of people eating out of those supplies, including allowance for members of armed forces on leave or eating in homes or civilian restaurants in this country for other reasons.

[11] *Nutritive Value of Per Capita Food Supply, 1909-1945*, U. S. Department of Agriculture Miscellaneous Publication No. 616, p. 16; supplemented by later revisions and additions.

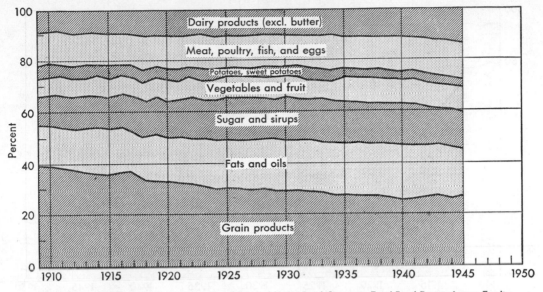

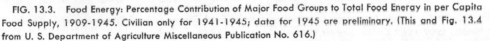

FIG. 13.3. Food Energy: Percentage Contribution of Major Food Groups to Total Food Energy in per Capita Food Supply, 1909-1945. Civilian only for 1941-1945; data for 1945 are preliminary. (This and Fig. 13.4 from U. S. Department of Agriculture Miscellaneous Publication No. 616.)

Value of Nutritional Science

When World War II brought an unexpected tightening of the food supply of the democracies in their fight for their lives, nutrition was made a cornerstone of the food policy of the Allied Nations. One result was that the masses of the people in the English-speaking world actually experienced an improvement in dietary standards during the war. This was achieved in part by means of rationing; but rationing policies rested squarely on nutritional findings.

One of the most important contributions to the task of rationalizing diets was the drawing up of a recommended daily allowance for specific nutrients, including proteins, calcium, iron, and vitamins. This table, shown as Table 13.5, was prepared by the Committee on Foods and Nutrition of the National Research Council.

Nutrition and Dietary Shifts

Whereas mainly geographical realities, habit, tradition, and economic considerations, to the virtual exclusion of all others, formerly determined people's diets, nutritional factors have gained in importance to an increasing extent. Through commercial advertising, through instruction in public schools and colleges, through dieticians being added to the staffs of hospitals, restaurants, schools, etc., the national diet has been subjected to a gradual process of rationalization in a nutritional direction.

To attribute all dietary changes to these efforts would be a great mistake. Improvements in refrigeration, the introduction of new techniques of food preparation such as quick freezing and dehydration, better transportation and storage facilities, the development and introduction of new species, and many other factors have contributed to the outcome. Table 13.6 tells the story of the dietary shifts in the United States from 1909 to 1947.

Particularly noteworthy is the decline in the consumption of potatoes and grain products by about one-third, the increase in the consumption of dairy products by about half, and the phenomenal increase in the consumption of fruit and vegetables. Figs. 13.3 and 13.4 throw further light on this development. That these dietary changes have had and are having tremendous repercussions on agricultural production goes without saying.

Limitations of Nutritional Improvements

Nutrition is an applied science; it applies the findings of numerous natural sciences. The problem of feeding mankind is an economic problem; economics is a social science. As was

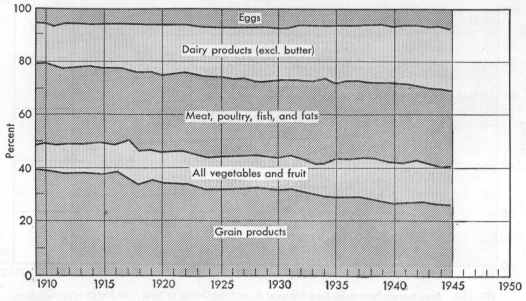

FIG. 13.4. Protein: Percentage Contribution of Major Food Groups to Total Protein in per Capita Food Supply, 1909-1945. Civilian only for 1941-1945; data for 1945 are preliminary.

pointed out before (see p. 176), there is as yet no proper linkage between these two groups of sciences. To the nutritionist, carried away with enthusiasm for newly discovered facts and keenly aware of the suffering of undernourished masses, the cautious economist may appear a cold-hearted kill-joy and, vice versa, the economist may despair of the utopian ambitions of the nutritionist. The nutritionist tends to stress the needs which seem unlimited, the economist the means which are limited.

In general, we may say that as regards short-run problems of food adequacy, the economist should have the last word, whereas the nutritionist should lead in long-run planning. One knows the limitations of the presently achievable, the other sees the goal to which his scientific knowledge points. The economist forever stresses the scarcity of means, pointing out that a dollar spent on food cannot also be spent on housing. Marginalism is a methodological tool with whose aid the economist seeks to discover the socially most desirable combination of expenditures. If he warns of letting enthusiasm go too far in raising dietary standards, this warning is no reflection on his humanity and compassion. It merely indicates his preoccupation with the hard, unpleasant facts of "scarce means," i.e., means that cannot do dou-

ble and treble duty. We must choose between an *optimal* diet and *optimal* education and *optimal* housing—at least for the present. This means that we cannot jack up our vitamin and animal protein consumption *ad infinitum* without impairing our chances of satisfying a number of other perhaps equally vital needs and wants.

Moreover, even diets may be subject to the famous law of diminishing returns.[12] If the diet of a Chinese coolie is raised from 1400 calories bare of protective items to 2800 calories entailing a minimum of protective elements, the results may be miraculous. They may clearly outweigh the cost. But as improvement follows improvement, the results may become less spectacular while the cost rises.

Finally, a word regarding fads in foods may be appropriate. Nutrition is a highly complex science, but eating is a still more complex performance involving plain hunger, fancy appetite, aesthetic considerations—and a lot of notions, sound and unsound. Sometimes skillful advertisers fish in the muddied waters of "notion." The catch in terms of profits may be tremendous. Without harking back to "the good

---

[12] See M. K. Bennett, "Essential Food Requirements in Wartime," *Journal of Farm Economics,* November, 1943.

old times" which upon scrutiny were not half so good as they appear in the nimbus of nostalgic memories, it may be worth remembering that the human race lived a long time without orange juice for breakfast and vitamin-reinforced bread, and that vast numbers still manage to do without them. This is no wholesale condemnation of nutritional progress; far from it. It is merely a suggestion that sometimes people "overdo things" just a little.

Rationalization of Diets

One of the most important facts pertaining to food consumption in the western world is the increasing rationalization which is applied to eating habits, and the enhanced flexibility of dietary customs which results therefrom. An unsophisticated person tends to show considerable obstinacy in his choice of food. He eats the foods with which he is familiar and has a decided aversion to those which are strange to him. The printed word, traveling, and other similar means of bringing people together and acquainting them with their neighbors' ways of living have done a great deal to wear down these barriers to flexibility in eating habits. Instead of suspicion, modern man shows a certain curiosity toward new foods. He has heard too often that people who eat other foods than those to which he has become accustomed have managed to survive, and so he is willing to take a chance. By rendering possible a more complete adaptation of agricultural products to market requirements, this increased rationality of dietary habits assumes considerable economic importance.

While the increased flexibility of rationalized diets is advantageous to those wishing to introduce new food products, it is correspondingly harmful to those offering for sale the older, now partially replaced products. It is good for the fruit business that the per capita consumption of canned fruits went up from 3 pounds in 1909 to 17.7 in 1948, of canned fruit juices from 0.47 to 18.1 pounds, and of frozen fruits from 0.2 to 2.92. It is bad for the wheat farmer and the flour miller that the consumption of wheat flour dropped during the same period from 207 to 135 pounds per capita.[13] More-

over, rationalization of food habits may frequently mean the reduction of aggregate food consumption. Overeating may be bad for the guilty consumer, but it is not without its advantages for the producer or dealer who furnishes the excess food.

The Obstinacy of Food Habits

The flexibility of which we are speaking has as yet affected only the most advanced portion of the western world, for there are still many regions of the world where tradition rules supreme and where food habits are preserved in the face of changing supply conditions at great cost to the consumer. A striking example of this persistence is furnished by Puerto Rico. This overpopulated island is inhabited by what is probably the largest single group of destitute people under the American flag. It is true that, within limits, the Puerto Rican food supply is determined by prices. If a certain kind of bean happens to sell a fraction of a cent lower than another kind, it is eagerly snapped up and substituted for the other. But this substitution has very decided limits. Agriculturists claim that the island could produce considerable quantities of gray beans which, from a nutritive standpoint, would answer the purpose just as well as the present pink varieties. These gray beans, it is claimed, could be produced and marketed on the island for much less than the price of the imported pink beans. But no matter how poor and hungry the Puerto Rican is, he will hesitate long before substituting a gray bean for a pink one. But why pick on Puerto Rico? Did not western Europe, in the midst of the worst food scare of World War I, proudly refuse to eat corn on the ground that it was good for chickens but not for civilized Europeans? In other words, there may be flexibility, but it is far from perfect.

INTERNATIONAL COMPARISON OF DIETS

As one surveys the eating habits of the peoples of the earth, his first impression is one of endless variety. A visit to any modern metropolis with its French, Italian, German, Hungarian, Swedish, Greek, Chinese, and other restaurants serves to give one a bird's-eye view

---

[13] *Consumption of Food in the United States, 1909-1948,* U. S. Department of Agriculture, Bureau of Agricultural Economics, Miscellaneous Publication No. 691, Washington, 1949, pp. 72-84.

TABLE 13.7.   World Population Grouped on Basis of Dietary Adequacy[14]

Group	Percent of Food Consumption Derived from Cereal-"Potatoes"	Countries in Group	Aggregate Population of Group (millions)	Percent of World Population
I	30–40	U.S.A., Canada, United Kingdom, New Zealand, Sweden, Switzerland	205	9.8
II	40–50	Denmark, Germany, Norway, Finland, Austria, Netherlands	93	4.55
III	50–60	Eire, France, Belgium, Czechoslovakia, Hungary, Estonia, Latvia, Argentina, Uruguay	93	4.55
IV	60–70	Portugal, Spain, Italy, Greece, Central and South America except Argentina and Uruguay, and Union of South Africa	204	9.7
V	70–80	Bulgaria, Poland, Japan, North Africa, Yugoslavia	156	7.4
VI	80–90	All the others	1344	64.0
			2095	100.0

of an almost endless, bewildering variety of "dishes." Yet it was shown that even in as well-fed a nation as the United States five foodstuffs —wheat flour, fluid milk and cream, butter, sugar, and pork—provided over half—to be exact, 52 percent—of the calories in 1942, and that five additional foodstuffs—beef, eggs, lard, cottonseed oil, and potatoes—supplied an additional 17.5 percent, making a total of almost 70 percent for the ten foodstuffs. The variety, therefore, is in a sense superficial. The bases of diets are relatively simple; it is the refinement that creates the impression of bewildering diversity.[15]

Bennett's Classification of Diets

That this is true of the diets of the world in general was clearly demonstrated by M. K.

Bennett of the Food Research Institute of Stanford University in a remarkable study.[16] Bennett hit on a brilliant idea of reducing diets to two major divisions, reminiscent of the two rations discussed above, though by no means identical with them. These major divisions are: (1) the cereals (wheat, rye, rice, barley, oats, corn, millets, and grain sorghums) and "potatoes" (white potatoes, sweet potatoes, and cassava), and (2) all other foods. He then classified national diets on the basis of the percentage importance of cereals and "potatoes." The result is a clear picture of the dietary situation in the world.

It appears that less than 10 percent of mankind living in the United States, Canada, the United Kingdom, Australia, New Zealand, Sweden, and Switzerland enjoy a dietary standard in which the cheaper cereals-"potatoes"

[14] M. K. Bennett, "International Contrasts in Food Consumption," *Geographical Review,* July, 1941. Courtesy of the *Geographical Review,* published by the American Geographical Society of New York.

[15] M. K. Bennett comments on this idea as follows: "Despite the great variety of food dishes consumed throughout the world, the basic foodstuffs of which the dishes are composed are relatively few, especially if regarded in more or less homogeneous groupings. Men eat the seeds of cereal grains; various starchy roots and tubers, such as white potatoes, sweet potatoes, cassava,

yams, and taro; various sugars, chiefly those of the sugar cane and the sugar beet; numerous vegetables, mostly somewhat less rich in calorie content than the starchy roots; numerous fruits; several vegetable oils, such as olive, coconut, cottonseed, soybean, and palm kernel; many varieties of nuts; flesh, mostly from cattle, pigs, sheep, and poultry; eggs, fish and whale oil; and milk in its various forms, chiefly as whole milk, butter, and cheese." *Ibid.,* p. 365.

[16] *Ibid.*

division is held to 30-40 percent of the total calories, the remaining 60-70 percent being consumed in the form of the more expensive "protective" foods. These people are the gourmands of the earth and, if proper diet is the basis of health, they should be the healthiest people on the face of the earth! And they probably are. How the rest of mankind lines up behind these plutocrats of the dinner table is shown in Table 13.7. The reader will note a rather startling correlation between this table and Fig. 10.1.

Before this comparison of national diets proceeds further, a few introductory remarks are in order. Some of them merely repeat what has been said elsewhere in a different connection and from a different angle.

In the first place, in trying to calculate the dietary standards of nations, a distinction must be made between *food disappearance, food consumption,* and *food ingestion.*[17] *Ingestion* includes only food actually eaten. *Consumption* refers to food delivered to the nation's eating places—homes, restaurants, hotels, hospitals, etc. *Disappearance* is the difference between stocks at the beginning of a period *plus* domestic production during the period *plus* imports *minus* exports and *minus* stocks at the end of the period. The calculation is complicated by the use of some products for purposes other than food. (Wheat may be burned, corn may go into inedible products such as laundry starch.) This diversion of foodstuffs to nonfood uses must be measured or estimated if disappearance is to indicate food disappearance. The difference between disappearance and ingestion is largely a matter of losses, spoilage, waste, and loss in preparation.

Another problem arises in connection with discovering the typical "adult male." To secure a uniform equivalent for populations made up of all ages it is customary in international studies to express the number of persons in terms of its equivalent in "adult males" or "consumption units." There are several methods of making the calculation. According to the method used, different equivalents are arrived at. Needless to say, adult males constitute different percentages of different populations. The percentage is high in countries like the United

States, low in countries with a high birth and death rate.

In comparing calorie intake in western countries and in China, it is important to keep in mind the difference in typical body weights. Western European adults are generally taken as weighing 155 pounds, whereas an average adult in southeastern Asia weighs only about 110 pounds. Food requirements have a close relation to body weight, activity, and climate. On the basis of these three factors, it is generally assumed that the western European requires about 50 percent more calories than the southeastern Asiatic.

International Dietary Standards

In recent years a great deal of work has been done in the field of dietary standards of the nations. Especially since the founding of the United Nations and, more particularly, the establishment of the Food and Agriculture Organization of the United Nations which is specifically entrusted with long-range responsibility for lifting dietary standards in the world, rapid progress has been made and statistical data are becoming available which only a short while ago would have seemed beyond reach. To be sure, the statistics may "look better" than they are, and no one warns more honestly and earnestly of their shortcomings than their sponsors.

One very interesting chart is Fig. 1 in *World Food Survey,* released in Washington on October 1, 1946. In this chart foodstuffs are divided into the following categories:

Cereals
Roots and tubers[18]
Sugar
Fats
Pulses
Fruit and vegetables
Meat, fish and eggs
Milk
Wine and beer

The chart gives, for seventy nations, the total calorie intake per head per day at the retail level for pre-World War II years by foodstuff groups. In addition, in a separate column, it

---

[17] See *ibid.,* pp. 367-368.

[18] This includes starchy fruit such as bananas and plantains in countries where they are a staple article of diet.

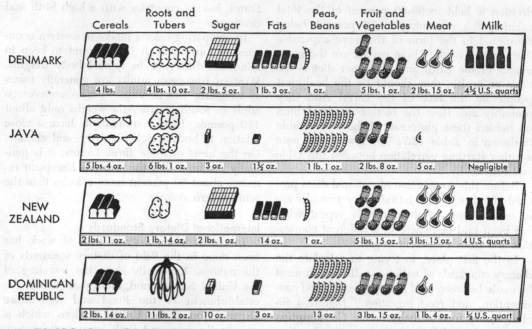

FIG. 13.5. Prewar Food Consumption in Four Countries (Quantities per Capita per Week). (This and Fig. 13.6 from FAO, *World Food Survey*.)

gives the daily *per capita* protein intake, divided into animal and vegetable protein.

In this chart, Argentina ranks first with a total daily per capita calorie intake of 3275 as against 3248 for both the United States and Denmark. Argentina also leads in protein intake, 111 grams as against 88 for the United States (and, incidentally, 101 for Iceland and Turkey and 102 for Uruguay). Korea, the former vassal of Japan, ranks lowest with 1904 calories, followed closely by Mexico and Transjordan with 1909, Colombia with 1934, and San Salvador with 1944.

The inclusion of wine and beer in the chart is somewhat of a novelty. However, they are of only moderate importance and this only in a few countries, especially France, Belgium, Italy, Spain, Portugal, Greece, Argentina, Chile, and Switzerland.

From the long list of seventy nations, the Food and Agriculture Organization (FAO) report selected four countries for the purpose of illustrating differences in national food supplies. These four include two high-standard countries in different parts of the earth—New Zealand and Denmark—and two low-standard countries—Java and the Dominican Republic.

The contrasts are shown graphically in Fig. 13.5. The report adds this comment:

In New Zealand, with a high average food consumption, the diet was well balanced. Calories from cereals amounted to a little less than 1000 and consumption of meat, milk, and fat was high. The supply of protein averaged 96 grams, of which 65 percent was of animal origin. Denmark was the highest food consumer among the Scandinavian countries. It is of interest to note that Denmark and New Zealand, though situated on opposite sides of the earth and differing in many characteristics of national life, consumed approximately similar kinds of diets. Cereal consumption was equally low and milk consumption equally high in the two countries. The main differences were that while consumption of meat, fish, and eggs in Denmark was comparatively high, the consumption of these foods in New Zealand was twice as great; but on the other hand Denmark consumed half again as much fat as New Zealand. When there is abundance and variety of food and purchasing power is high, countries tend to choose a diet fully adequate for health.

Java and the Dominican Republic, by contrast, are examples of countries with low average levels of consumption. In Java, with a total calorie supply of about 2000, the calories furnished by cereals were more than 1000 per caput daily. Carbohydrate intake was further increased by the consumption of large quantities of cassava, so that not only was the average supply of animal protein almost negligible (4 grams), but the total protein (43 grams) was the lowest recorded in all the 70 countries surveyed. The Dominican Republic was little better off; the main difference lay in the larger intake of animal protein, accounted for by the considerably greater consumption of milk, meat, fish, and eggs. Bananas have been included in the "roots and tubers" group in the case of this and other tropical countries in which they were a staple article of diet. In nutritive value they are akin to this group.[19]

CONTRASTS IN DIETARY STANDARDS
Poverty and Malnutrition

Attention was drawn to the rather close correlation between differences in dietary standards as shown by Bennett and differences in income as shown by Colin Clark (see chap. 10). Poverty is the chief cause of malnutrition. Maintenance and protective foods are expensive; they are premium-priced foods, whereas energy foods are calorie-priced. For under ten cents one can buy in the United States a pound of sugar valued at 1805 calories. In the form of lettuce, 1805 calories would "cost a fortune." Milk is probably the cheapest maintenance and protective food. Unfortunately it is scarce and often unavailable where it is most needed. And milk bought by the penny's or the nickel's worth, as the poorest of the poor often buy it, is pretty expensive milk at that.

Poverty is a reflection of low productivity. So probing further into the causes of dietary deficiency, one soon comes on conditions affecting or determining productivity—poor climate, barren soil, overcrowded land, ignorance, superstition, lack of capital, endemic diseases such as malaria, hookworm, sleeping sickness, etc. Probing still further, one finds a vicious circle from malnutrition to low productivity and around to malnutrition. Hunger and poverty feed on each other.

What holds true of international dietary comparisons is equally true of contrasts in dietary standards within countries. That point must not be neglected. Only too often are sleek well-fed landlords and merchants found among the starving masses of coolies and peasants. The extravagance of the eating habits of the rich places the malnutrition of the poor in grim perspective. The figures given in international comparisons are averages; some individuals thrive at a level way above the average, thereby pushing down the level of the rest still further.

The Place of Animal Products in Diets

One of the most significant differences in diets has to do with the consumption of animal products. It was pointed out earlier that many nutritionists consider animal proteins superior to vegetable proteins. The value of milk is universally recognized. Yet there are hundreds of millions of people who are almost total vegetarians.

To understand why this is so, it is necessary to realize that "when crops are fed to animals instead of being eaten directly by human beings, they lose 80 to 90 per cent of their calorie value before they reëmerge in the form of meat or milk."[20] One may speak of "original calories," meaning calories derived from crops, as distinguished from "derived calories," meaning calories that reëmerge as meat, milk, and other animal foodstuffs after passing through the metabolism of the food-yielding animal.

The prewar North American diet contained about 2200 calories per head daily from foods of plant origin and about 870 calories from livestock products. Roughly seven original calories are required to produce one "derived calorie." That means that besides the 2200 original calories consumed in the form of primary food, American farmers produced an additional 6090 (7 × 870) original calories to deliver the 870 derived calories in the form of secondary food. That makes a total of 8290 calories per day per head, a truly fantastic figure when compared with a total calorie intake of less than 2000. It should be kept in mind that animal foods eaten in low-diet countries are seldom secondary. Thus Puerto Rico has few cows but a fair number of goats and chickens. In densely crowded countries, animals have little chance to get near primary food. So, ordinarily, the multiplier does not apply to such

---

[19] Food and Agriculture Organization of the United Nations, *World Food Survey*, Washington, October 1, 1946, p. 10.

[20] *Ibid.*, p. 19.

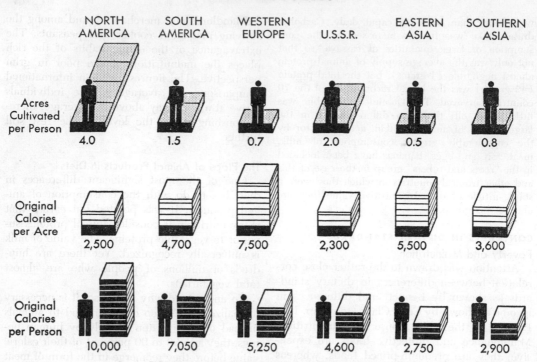

FIG. 13.6.   Food Production per Capita of Population.

countries. If it is found that the Javanese consume 100 calories of animal products a day, that hardly justifies adding 700 calories to their original production. The real figure is likely to be closer to 100.

To produce 8290 original calories per head per day requires either a prodigious supply of land[21] and machine power or a highly intensive form of agriculture, i.e., intensive both in capital (fertilizer, machine power, science) and in labor. Which method is chosen depends on the basic conditions of the country, especially the population density, more particularly the density per acre of arable land. Fig. 13.6 shows the situation at a glance.

It should be noted how differently the regions listed rank on the basis of the three criteria used:

Rank	Acres Cultivated per Person	Original Calories per Acre	Original Calories per Person
1.	North America	Western Europe	North America
2.	U.S.S.R.	Eastern Asia	South America
3.	South America	South America	Western Europe
4.	Southern Asia	Southern Asia	U.S.S.R.
5.	Western Europe	North America	Southern Asia
6.	Eastern Asia	U.S.S.R.	Eastern Asia

It may be well to keep in mind also that North and South America are food exporters, and that western Europe is a food importer and also an importer of feedstuffs which contribute to food production and to raising the productivity of the soil.

The difficulty of equalizing dietary standards in the face of such striking differences of fundamental conditions is self-evident.

Climate and Soils

That basic differences in the natural environment of people have definite and drastic effects on their diets goes without saying. The South Sea Islander eats coconuts because they thrive on the fringes of his island abode. The Hawaiian eats taro because climate and soil favor its production. Throughout the tropics starchy tubers such as manioc (from which cassava is obtained), yams, taro, yautia, etc., as well as starchy fruit such as bananas and plantains, play an important part because their cultivation

[21] In the United States, an adequate diet would require 1.72 acres to provide one person with secondary or derived foods for one year, while only 0.66 acre would suffice to provide him with all the primary foods.

fits well into the nature-culture pattern of these regions. The northlanders—people of Scandinavia, Iceland, Newfoundland, etc.—depend heavily on products of the sea to round out their diets, as anyone knows who has ever indulged in smörgåsbord. Nomads build their diets around their herds and the products they yield.

Less obvious, perhaps, is the difference between the North American diet built around corn and the European diet built around the potato. The north European plain stretching from the Low Countries into Russia is the world's ideal white potato country just as the Corn Belt of the United States is the world's largest maize-growing area.

The importance of corn in the American diet becomes evident when it is recalled that corn is the main basis of (1) dairy products, (2) pork, (3) beef, and (4) lard—four items of the American diet which make up 31.4 percent (1942 figure), or almost one-third, of the entire calorie intake. The counterpart to corn in the German diet is the potato. Those who have seen German dinner plates filled with boiled potatoes meagerly supplemented with a little meat and green vegetables have *prima facie* evidence of that importance. Furthermore, German pork comes from potato-fed hogs just as American pork comes from corn-fed hogs. Behind this striking difference in diets lie fundamental differences in climate and soil, favoring corn in the New World and the potato in the Old.[22] The important role that wine plays in the diets of countries like France, Italy, Spain, Portugal, and Chile is similarly explained by climate and soil working through old established culture patterns. If the connection is less clear in the case of the wine-producing regions of the United States—California and western New York—that is explained by the distribution of their products in forty-eight states. Large quantities of foreign wines are consumed locally.

Probably the most striking example of the effect of climate and soil on diets is rice in southeastern Asia. It will be discussed in the next chapter.

---

[22] It should hardly be necessary to repeat here what has been stressed *ad nauseam,* that in our time and world nature does not strike barehanded but acts on us through the medium and with the mediation of culture.

This adjustment of diets to basic conditions of the natural environment is one of the best illustrations of man's willingness "to stoop to conquer." Rather than force the land to satisfy his fancy by yielding at great cost to him something it is not naturally fitted for, he wisely adjusts his desires to nature's make-up. It is this sort of behavior that justifies such epithets as Homo sapiens and Home economicus.

Diets and International Trade

By and large the people of the earth depend on home-grown food—food grown in their own national soil. The chief exceptions are the industrial countries of western Europe and North America, the great urbanized areas—centers of industry, commerce, and finance—and mining camps throughout the world.

It is economic wisdom to adjust the national diet to basic conditions of the natural environment. That rule stands. But it also is economic wisdom to concentrate industry on top of coal mines and to exchange the products of industry, produced to advantage in one region of the earth, for the products of agriculture produced in other regions. By the same reasoning, it is economic wisdom for the great grasslands of the earth to be granaries, not national granaries but global granaries.

Not only is it economic wisdom, it is necessity as well. As one surveys the globe, he sees a clear-cut division into food surplus and food deficit areas. If these can be linked together by trade, all mankind will gain from the benefits of regional specialization. But trade rests on the ability to pay, to offer a *quid pro quo.* And unfortunately those parts of the earth that show the greatest dietary deficiencies show the least capacity to obtain the needed food by means of trade, i.e., by offering exports of nonfoodstuffs for imports of foodstuffs. Moreover, these unfortunate regions also lack the transportation facilities necessary for the physical distribution of foodstuffs, both those domestically produced and those that could be imported if payment through exports were possible. Therefore international trade by itself cannot begin to solve the food problem of the earth. (Proposals for its solution will be discussed later.)

International trade in foodstuffs consists mainly of grains, meat, animal and vegetable fats and oils, sugar, and such special items as

TABLE 13.8. Main Food Exports, 1935-1939, by Countries of Origin[23]

	Wheat, incl. Flour (million bu.)	Rice in Terms of Milled (billion lb.)	Sugar (thousand short tons)	Butter (million lb.)	Beef and Beef Products (million lb.)	Mutton and Lamb (million lb.)	Hog Products (million lb.)
Argentina	122.4	....	18.5		1246.4	114.7	56.3
Australia	106.1	....	437.9	220.6	309.6	194.2	31.5
Brazil			51.4		178.0	1.1	19.3
Burma	....	6.6	....				
Canada	175.3	....	....	5.5	....	....	191.8
Cuba	....	....	2878.5				....
Czechoslovakia	....	....	248.4[a]				
Denmark	....	....	....	328.6	....	....	443.6
Dominican Republic	....	....	480.1				....
Hawaii	....	....	929.9				
Hungary	22.7	....	12.9	8.0	2.3	1.0	60.5
Indochina	....	3.2					
Ireland (Eire)				50.0[a]	1.2		78.2[a]
Mauritius	....	....	311.2				
Netherlands	....	....	....	118.1		3.7	89.7
Netherlands Indies	....	....	1211.0				
New Zealand	....	....	....	305.1	171.0	412.4	62.0
Peru	....	....	327.2				11.0
Philippine Islands	....	....	888.3				....
Poland	....	....	84.3[a]			1.4[a]	112.4[a]
Puerto Rico	....	....	873.8				
Taiwan (Formosa)	....	....	50.3				
Thailand (Siam)	....	3.3					
U.S.S.R.	27.4[a]	....	134.2	37.2	....		3.6
United States	34.9		....				217.6
Uruguay	....	....	....		213.1	18.4	1.4
Yugoslavia	....	....	....			0.5	36.3

[a] Four-year average.

coffee, cocoa, bananas, fresh fruit and vegetables, wines, etc.

The grain trade falls into two clear-cut divisions: the intra-Asiatic trade in rice, and the trade in wheat exported from the thinly or moderately populated lands of the New World (including Australia) and imported by the crowded industrial countries of western Europe and the United Kingdom.

The meat trade is becoming more and more the movement of surplus products of the thinly populated lands of the southern hemisphere to

the densely populated countries of the northern, especially Europe and the United Kingdom. The natural pattern is not as clear as it might be, being heavily overlain with a film of artificial interferences with the free flow of trade.

Similarly, the trade in sugar is narrowing down to the shipment of cane sugar from tropical or semitropical islands to the industrial centers. The trade in vegetable fats and oils shows a similar trend toward tropical origins.

Table 13.8 lists the main food-exporting countries, together with the main products exported.

Up to now, with some exceptions, international movements of food have been based strictly on commercial calculations. One wonders whether in the future other considerations may gain in importance.

[23] Adapted from a table especially prepared by the Division of Statistical and Historical Research, Bureau of Agricultural Economics, U. S. Department of Agriculture.

The period 1935-1939 is chosen in preference to later years because it reflects more accurately the normal production capacities of the countries listed.

THIS BRAVE NEW WORLD

There is something smug about the bourgeois-capitalistic-democratic ideology which developed in western Europe and the English-speaking world during the nineteenth and twentieth centuries. It is parochial, provincial. It is convinced that it has found the philosophers' stone, knows the answer to the riddle of the sphinx. Its god is the only true god, its philosophy the only sound and true philosophy to which the rest of the world must accommodate itself as well as it can.

From Waterloo to the Marne stretches a century that is truly the Century of Western Civilization, the golden age of private business, private capitalism, western imperialism, the gold standard, "free trade," and all the trimmings and trappings that go with it. The unbroken success of the western powers in all realms of human endeavor—economic progress, science, technology, political control, literature, the arts—lulled the intelligentsia to sleep and conjured up a lovely dream of a globe shaped to one pattern, made to one image—the pattern and image of the West. It was only a dream, for it failed to face facts, hard bitter facts of irreversible history and unchangeable human nature. The experiences that lie between the opening of World War I and the destruction of Hiroshima have opened the eyes of the sleepers. The dream is over and at long last man, by force of circumstance, is made to face the realities of his existence.

As men awaken from a dream, their reactions vary. Some want to go back to sleep in the hope that the dream world will return. Others are sobered by the shock of awakening and strive to adjust themselves to the glaring light of a new day. Thus the leaders of today fall into two groups: those who wish and hope that the old gods still live, the old slogans still ring true; and those who are firmly convinced that nothing but bold, radically new ideas, methods, institutions, and attitudes will do if man is to survive.

The world food problem, which is the problem posited by one part of the earth cursed with an unsalable food surplus facing another part cursed with mass hunger that cannot be stilled, is but a phase of the great world dilemma in which we find ourselves. It is also a tangible practical problem, one whose solution will be clearly visible, and one which, if we fail to solve it, will be equally patently exposed to the kleig light of public opinion throughout the world.

The old approach to the food problem was that of the businessman counting costs and payment with equal care and objectivity. The world food situation was in balance when all the food produced for sale was sold at a price covering costs of production. That was all there was to it. If there were millions undernourished, if whole areas of the globe lay outside the market economy of the capitalistic world, that could not be helped; it had nothing to do with economics. And economics was supreme. All else was irrelevant; worse than irrelevant, it interfered with sound economics.

That attitude was understandable and tolerable to a degree so long as the starving masses in one part of the globe did not actively and actually impinge on the prosperous elite in the other parts—in other words, so long as the world was safely compartmentalized. But now we have One World. Techniques and science have made it one world. And it is one world even if politically it crashes wide open into two hostile camps. The eastern boundary of the United States may have been the Atlantic coast at one time, later the Rhine; now there is no boundary—not the Danube nor the Oder, not the Indus nor the Yangtze.

A first inkling of the realization by the world's leading statesmen of this fundamental fact of our time was audible in the words of the Atlantic Charter and the Four Freedoms. It spoke with clear tones in the Charter of the United Nations. It became specific and explicit in the charter of the FAO.

We now know that somehow the problem of "starvation in the midst of plenty" must be solved. But we do not yet know how it can be done. This chapter contains eloquent testimony of the fact-finding efforts made by the FAO. Finding the facts is the necessary first step.

How great are the deficits in the world food ledger? How many shelves of the world food larder are empty or poorly filled? What are the ultimate limits of the physical food-producing capacity of the earth? What would it take to bring actual productivity up to the point where adequate food is supplied for all? What is adequacy? How can this global face lifting be financed? Are the strong strong enough to lift the weak up to something approaching their level? What would be the results if success could be assured? Where would it lead? What would its repercussions be?

These and a thousand other questions arise as one tries to adapt his eyes to the new light. The questions are not only new but novel. They do not fit into the traditional patterns of thought and analysis. But they must be asked—and eventually answered. There is no choice.

Some of the questions the FAO has answered tentatively. In particular it has made a tentative calculation of world food needs in 1960 expressed in terms of percentage increase over prewar supplies. This calculation is based on the so-called "nutritive targets" set for different areas in the light of what reasonably may be achieved and on an estimated population increase of 25 percent. The estimated increases are as follows:

Foodstuff	Percent
Cereals	21
Roots and tubers	27
Sugar	12
Fats	34
Pulses	80
Fruits and vegetables	163
Meat	46
Milk	100

NOTE. Some percentages are less than the estimated 25 percent population increase, indicating an anticipated per capita decline—on the average—in these particular items: cereals and sugar. In this connection the decline in cereal consumption in the United States since around 1900 should be kept in mind. Some pulses may be considered substitutes for milk. (Pulses in this case are mature dry beans, peas, lentils, chickpeas, gram, and various leguminous seeds such as peanuts, soybeans, etc.) Included also are nuts and coconuts consumed as such, as well as cocoa and chocolate. Feed grains are not included.

According to the *World Food Survey*,[24] the fundamental requisite in achieving this increase is to raise farming efficiency in *all* countries, regardless of their nutritional level, so that the yield—per man, per acre, and per head of livestock—will be increased. But even this may not suffice alone. More potentially fertile land —the basic resource of food production—may have to be opened to cultivation, and land already under cultivation will have to be con-

[24] The following discussion is based largely on the *World Food Survey*, pp. 19-25.

served and, in far too many cases, reclaimed. This will require extensive capital and, in pest-ridden areas, extensive public health programs. "Every country has its own specific problems in increasing and safeguarding land resources, and they must be attacked in different ways. The main point is that the attack must be scientifically planned and coordinated, and adequately financed by governments."

Such a goal entails extensive economic and social changes. For example, the oppressive land-tenure systems characteristic of many regions must be abolished so that farmers will have both incentive and opportunity to improve their lot. They must also be able to obtain credit more easily and to receive a fair price for their produce; this last, of course, depends on whether consumers have adequate purchasing power. On the social side, disease control and education are requisites—the former, to open up hitherto uncultivated lands and to increase human efficiency, and the latter, in the form of more and better schools and agricultural extension services, to give farmers a knowledge of more scientific methods and the tools of modern technology.

But, surprisingly enough, increased food production also involves the removal of the submarginal element—both farmers and the land itself—from agriculture. Because the supply of land throughout the world is limited, population pressure and a nation's status as an advanced or backward country enter the picture. Advanced countries have a greater output of food per man than do backward countries, regardless of the fact that more of the latter's larger population may be engaged in farming. This leads directly to the conclusion that fewer farmers, using scientific methods and modern equipment, can produce more food than many farmers not so equipped. However, these submarginal farmers, thus deprived of their livelihood, must have other means of earning a living; and this, in turn, calls for expansion of industry and trade, both to absorb these displaced farmers and to meet the increased demand for goods and services inherent in greater agricultural productivity and the resulting higher consuming purchasing power.

Thus increased food production extends into many fields other than agriculture, and calls for extensive economic and social developments throughout the world. "With [this] development, history has shown that a change occurs in the whole attitude toward life, hope in the future replacing hopeless acceptance of hunger and poverty as man's natural lot. . . . The enormous achievements of the western nations during the war prove that technical means and intelligence and skill equal to the task of bringing about a great economic expansion are available. What is needed now is adequate international action to do the work, and the will to initiate it."

There is at least one scientist[25] who, after checking on world soils and fertilizer materials, has reached the tentative conclusion that the FAO targets can be reached—are feasible so far as natural conditions are concerned. The weak point is not nature, but culture. Can we work out the problems of machine industry, exchange, finance, education, scientific method and management, and, above all, peaceful relations among nations soon enough and well enough to permit the fullest and most effective use of our natural opportunities?[26]

Salter bases his analysis of the adequacy of soil and fertilizer resources on (1) lifelong study of the subject and (2) the estimates of future needs prepared by the FAO. His is a cool, practical approach based on and facing realities. He is skeptical of the utopian extravaganzas of demagogues. Yet his final answer to the questions, "Can the world's soil grow all the crops that will be needed to meet the FAO goals? Are fertilizer sources great enough?" is an unequivocal "yes."

An increase in the food supply can be achieved (1) by raising the yield on existing land and from existing livestock and (2) by expanding the cultivated acreage. Salter concludes that by applying United States production standards to other countries the FAO's estimated 1960 requirements for sugar, roots and tubers, and almost all cereals could be met by increasing yields, without any acreage expansion. The requirements for all other foodstuff classes call for acreage expansion.

At present, 7 to 10 percent of the total world land area is cultivated. Since about 48 percent of the total acreage is taken up by snow, ice, tundra, mountains, and deserts, only 52 percent of the land area can be considered physically arable; hence the 7 to 10 percent cultivated represents roughly 14 to 20 percent of the physically arable, leaving 30 to 36 percent of the total land area, or 80 to 86 percent of the physically arable area.

The 52 percent of the land area considered physically arable is probably the most precious possession of mankind. Its potentialities should prove of real interest to humanity. Without aspiring to become an expert in pedology (as soil science is called), the layman should know a few basic facts about this 52 percent of the earth's surface. He should know at least its breakdown into major soil categories.

Much of the food produced in the world today comes from the grasslands of the plains and prairies. Their soils are either black earth (chernozem[27]) or chestnut soils. The difference springs from the amount of rainfall, which determines the height of the original grass cover. Such soils constitute the heart of the wheatlands of North and South America, Eurasia, and Australia. They are also found in Africa but for cultural reasons are not exploited. These chernozems and chestnut soils constitute about 13 percent of the total land area and about 26 percent of the arable area.

The next important group is the lateritic soils of southeast Asia. They produce rice and many other foods and are the main support of over half of mankind. The term lateritic suggests that the parent rock base of the soil, decomposed by the action of the sun and of water, gives these soils their peculiar character. They are commonly found in tropical regions

---

[25] Robert M. Salter, "World Soil and Fertilizer Resources in Relation to Food Needs," *Science*, May 23, 1947, pp. 533-538.

[26] For a clear exposition of these difficulties, see "What a Two-World Food Problem Means," an editorial in *Business Week*, July 27, 1947, p. 100.

[27] The Russian word "chernozem" literally means black earth. Russians are recognized leaders in pedology, and several of the most widely used terms applying to soils are Russian. Another such word is "podzols," which means literally "under the ashes" and describes certain rather poor forest soils; the ashes undoubtedly refer to the widespread practice of burning woods prior to pioneer cultivation. For further details, see C. F. Marbut, "Soils" in *Encyclopædia of the Social Sciences;* and L. I. Prassolov, "Soil Types in the Agriculture of Different Countries," *Pedology*, No. 2, 1946, pp. 69-75 (in Russian with an English summary).

Table 13.9. Potential Food Production in Millions of Metric Tons from More Intensive Use of Existing Cropland Plus Development of Additional Land not Now Cultivated[28]

	Cereals	Roots and Tubers	Sugar	Fats and Oils	Pulses and Nuts	Fruits and Vegetables	Meat	Milk
Attainable production from present cropland	360.0	230.0	34.5	18.0	43.4	211.0	78.7	180.2
Attainable production from present cropland plus 1,000,000,000 new acres tropical soils[a]	717.5	469.5	177.5	69.5	55.4	470.0	89.4	188.8
Attainable production from present cropland plus 300,000,000 new acres land outside tropics[b]	395.5	296.0	35.1	19.4	44.2	211.0	86.1	314.6
Attainable production from all above sources	753.0	535.5	178.1	70.9	56.2	470.0	96.8	323.2
World food needs in 1960	363.5	194.5	33.6	20.4	65.2	411.0	95.8	300.0

[a] Obtained by applying approximate average production per crop acre in the Philippine Islands to 1,000,000,000 acres.

[b] Obtained by applying approximate average production per crop acre in Finland to 300,000,000 acres of Northern Hemisphere soils. Fats and oils and fruits and vegetables are *underestimated* because Finnish production figures on farm-made butter, meat, fruits, and vegetables were unavailable.

where heat and rainfall are especially potent as geomorphologic (earth-changing) forces. Together with similar soil types, the lateritic soils constitute 19 percent of the total land area and about 38 percent of the arable land.

A third important category is the gray and brown forest soils of northern Europe and northeastern North America. These soils are not as fertile by nature as the first two categories but can be built up to a high pitch of performance by care, skill, and general expenditures for improvements. These soils constitute approximately 7 percent of the total land area, and about 14 percent of the arable area.

This leaves the alluvial soils, marshes and swamps of tropical regions (4 and 8 percent of the total land and arable areas respectively), and the true podzols of northern Canada and the Soviet Union (about 9 and 18 percent respectively).

According to Salter:

The chernozem and chestnut soils are now largely under cultivation, and no great expansion into new areas can be foreseen. Some reclamation of alluvial soils, either by drainage or irrigation, or both, should be possible in the tropics.

The podzols of the North Temperate Zone and the red soils of the tropics and subtropics constitute

the extensive soils onto which great expansion of food production might be possible. Although these occupy an estimated 28 per cent of the world land area, probably less than 1 per cent is now under cultivation. It is recognized, of course, that a large proportion of these soils are unsuitable for agriculture because of the unfavorable topography and stoniness.

The principal areas of red soils are in Africa, South America, southeastern Asia, including India, the Pacific Islands, and southeastern North America. Most areas of red soils are now in use in southeastern Asia and India, and large areas are in use in some of the Pacific Islands and in the United States; but their resources are almost untouched in Africa and South America. If we assume that only 20 per cent of the red soils of the tropics in South America and Africa alone were to be brought into production, about 900,000,000 acres would be added for food production. To these potential cultivated new areas of red soils may be added a large area of uncultivated tropical soils found on the great islands of Sumatra, Borneo, New Guinea, and Madagascar. Assuming, then, that at least another 100,000,000 acres of red tropical and alluvial soils are available in these and other warm parts of the world, the total of 1,000,000,000 acres of tropical and subtropical soils may be used in calculating world soil potentialities.

The podzols, located almost wholly in the northern part of the Northern Hemisphere, are found mostly in Soviet Russia, Canada, and the United States. If we were to assume that only 10 per cent

[28] Robert M. Salter, *op. cit.*, p. 537.

of these soils were brought into cultivation, another 300,000,000 acres would be added to the world acreage for food production.[29]

Salter concludes that if (1) the production standards of the United States could be extended to other countries to raise their production capacity for sugar, roots and tubers, and almost all grains, and (2) 1000 million acres of tropical soils and 300 million acres of northern podzols could be added to the area now under cultivation, the world food supply could be improved, as shown in Table 13.9.

After discussing the world fertilizer situation, Salter concludes:

Here, then, is an affirmative answer to the question: Do we have the natural resources to meet world food goals by 1960? This answer is a challenge to all men, not to scientists only, for it raises immediately an even more critical question: Can we mobilize these resources to produce the needed food? This question begs many answers, because it involves the whole field of human relationships.

Science may discover and point the way, but it cannot dictate. The full measure of success in economic, social and political action comes only with the will of the majority—not from the desires of one group.

If the people of the world really have the determination to give battle to the problem of hunger, if they are willing to extend a small part of the energy and capital poured into World War II, only then can we see hope of victory.[30]

In other words, there is some hope "of making dreams come true." But there are many "if's." Above all, it is vital to keep constantly in mind that all hopes rest on peace, that war means deferment if not abandonment of hopes. Also, we must remember that raising the levels of food consumption is merely a phase of the larger problem of expanding and improving world economy.

---

[29] *Ibid.*, pp. 533-534.

[30] *Ibid.*, p. 538.

BIBLIOGRAPHY

Bennett, M. K., "International Contrasts in Food Consumption," *Geographical Review*, July, 1941.

Bennett, M. K., "Essential Food Requirements in Wartime," *Journal of Farm Economics*, November, 1943.

Bennett, M. K., "Population and Food Supply, the Current Scare," *Scientific Monthly*, January, 1949.

Black, J. D., *Food Enough*, Lancaster, Jacques Cattell Press, 1943.

Black, J. D., and Kiefer, M. E., *Future Food and Agriculture Policy*, New York, McGraw-Hill, 1948.

Black, J. D., Lewis, W., and Pickett, C. E., "America's Food and Europe's Need," *Annals of the American Academy of Political and Social Science*, 1941.

Brandt, K., "Foodstuffs and Raw Materials," in H. Speier and A. Kahler (eds.), *War in Our Time*, New York, Norton, 1939, chap. 5.

Brandt, K., "Food as a Political Investment in Europe," *Foreign Affairs*, vol. 19, 1941, pp. 516-529.

Clark, F., and others, *Nutritive Value of per Capita Food Supply, 1909-1945*, U. S. Department of Agriculture, Bureau of Agricultural Economics, Miscellaneous Publication No. 616, Washington, 1947.

Clark, F. LeG., and Titmuss, R. M., *Our Food Problem, A Study of National Security*, Hammondsworth, England, Penguin Books, Ltd., 1939.

Cochrane, W. W., *High-level Food Consumption in the United States*, U. S. Department of Agriculture, Bureau of Agricultural Economics, Miscellaneous Publication No. 581, Washington, 1945.

Cummings, R. O., *The American and His Food*, Chicago, University of Chicago Press, rev. ed., 1941.

Ladejinsky, W. I., "The Food Supply of India," *Foreign Agriculture*, July, 1942.

National Planning Association, *Must We Have Food Surpluses?* (pamphlet), Washington, 1949.

Orr, J. B., and Lubbock, D., *Feeding the People in War-Time*, New York, Macmillan, 1940.

Penrose, E. F., *Food Supply and Raw Materials in Japan*, Chicago, University of Chicago Press, 1930.

Salter, R. M., "World Soil and Fertilizer Resources in Relation to Food Needs," *Science*, May 23, 1947.

Schultz, T. W. (ed.), *Food for the World*, Chicago, University of Chicago Press, 1945.

United Nations, Food and Agricultural Organization, *World Food Survey*, Washington, 1946.

United Nations, Food and Agricultural Organization, *Yearbook of Food and Agricultural Statistics,* Washington, 1947.

United Nations, Food and Agricultural Organization, *Report on World Commodity Problems,* Washington, 1949.

U. S. Department of Agriculture, *Food and Life, Agriculture Yearbook,* Washington, 1939.

U. S. Department of State, *Point Four,* Washington, 1950.

U. S. Tariff Commission, *United States Consumption of Food in Terms of Fats, Proteins, Carbohydrates, and Calories,* Washington, 1944.

Walker, C. L., and Bolles, B., *Man and Food: The Lost Equation* (pamphlet), New York, Foreign Policy Association, 1949.

Chapter 14

MAJOR CEREAL GRAINS AND POTATOES[1]

GENERAL SURVEY

Importance of Cereal Grains and Potatoes

In the preceding chapter (pp. 187 ff.) the diets of the peoples of the earth were discussed. This discussion brought out the preponderant importance of the cereal grains and potatoes as sources of human food. It was shown that about three-fourths of all the food consumed by human beings, measured in calories, is obtained from cereals and potatoes directly consumed as primary food. This share is considerably increased when the indirect consumption of cereals and potatoes in the form of such secondary foods as meat and dairy products is taken into account.

The cultivation of the six leading grains together with white or Irish potatoes occupies more than 1200 million acres (almost 2 million square miles) of land, or roughly 4 percent of the total land area of the earth exclusive of the polar continents.

Exclusive of millets, sorghum, and tropical starch foods, recent annual crop aggregates of cereal grains and potatoes have amounted to more than 850 million net tons or 1.7 trillion pounds or approximately 750 pounds per capita for the population of the earth. In weight, the potato crop ranks ahead of all the grains; but in terms of food value, measured either roughly in calories or more accurately with due regard to all nutritive elements, the potato ranks perhaps last in the group, with wheat and rice at the head of the list. The position of the seven crops in respect to both acreage and weight is shown in Table 14.1.

Grasses and Cereal Grains

One of the largest families known in botany is the *Gramineae*, or grasses. They include such diverse genera as wheat, rice, oats, barley, rye, corn, sugar cane, the millets, the sorghums, and the bamboos. They differ so widely in appearance that the layman cannot recognize the family resemblance between "the more distant cousins."[2]

[1] Potatoes are discussed with the cereal grains because in parts of Europe their role is comparable to that of corn in the United States.

[2] The grasses constitute a bewildering array of genera, species, and varieties. Thus the genus wheat (*Triticum*) is represented by important species such as common wheat, club wheat, durum, and spelt.

TABLE 14.1. World Acreage and Production of Important Grains and Potatoes, 1935-1939 and 1946-1948[3]

Crop	Pounds per Bushel	Acreage (in millions)		Production (in billions)			
		1935-1939	1946-1948	1935-1939		1946-1948	
				bu.	lb.	bu.	lb.
Wheat	60	418.1	399.9	6.0	360	6.0	358
Rice	45	208.4	211.0	7.7	347	7.2	322
Rye	56	100.9	105.8	1.7	95	1.5	85
Corn	56	220.9	210.9	4.7	263	5.4	300
Oats	32	143.6	129.5	4.4	141	4.0	127
Barley	48	114.7	111.0	2.4	115	2.2	107
Potatoes	60	53.3	47.7	8.5	510	7.2	429
		1259.9	1215.8		1831		1728

Rice, corn, oats, and barley do not lose their hull in threshing as do wheat and rye. For this reason the figures are not wholly comparable, those for wheat and rye being deflated or those for the other grains being inflated. The hull of rice weighs as much as 37 percent of the threshed grain.

The grasses not only provide man with most of his energy food (carbohydrates, or sugars and starches), but contribute materially to the protein supply and, to a minor extent, to the supply of fat. In addition, the grasses also serve as the basis of animal husbandry either as forage (pasture) or as fodder (harvested feed). There are also incidental uses such as straw, bamboo sticks, etc.

Among the grasses the cereal grains stand out as the most important group of cultivated plants on this planet. Wheat and rice are the most important food grains, the former being consumed mainly as bread ("the staff of life") and the latter mainly in the boiled form. Others such as corn (maize), oats, barley, and rye are used chiefly, though not universally, as feeds.[4]

Most of these species are subdivided into increasingly numerous varieties such as Turkey, Thatcher, Red Fife, etc. Finally, the products obtained even from the same variety of wheat are so heterogeneous that classification and grading represent a major problem.

Similarly the sorghums, to give one more example, are divided into annual and perennial varieties (among the perennials, Johnson grass is most important in the United States). There are four groups of annual sorghums: (1) the sorgo group, made up of sweet or saccharine sorghums, (2) the grain sorghums, (3) broomcorn, and (4) the grass sorghums. Grain sorghums grown in the United States include Milo, Kaffir, Feterita, Kaoliang, and Durra, each represented by several varieties. (The names suggest African and Asiatic origins.)

[3] U.S. Department of Agriculture, *Potatoes from Foreign Crops and Markets*, Miscellaneous Publication No. 705, 1949, Table 3.

Classification of Grains

Wheat, rice, oats, rye, barley, and millet constitute the so-called *small* grains; corn and sorghum are known as *coarse* grains. The small grains except rice are sown directly in the fields. Rice is generally grown in seed beds under water and later transferred from thick growth to irrigated paddy fields. The coarse grains, corn and sorghum, are usually grown "on hills"[5] in small groups. The method of cultivation vitally affects the areas where, and the extent to which, different cereals can be grown.

Among the eight grains listed, there are only two *true* bread grains, wheat and rye. Because of the peculiar nature of their proteins, they alone yield dough which generates the gases necessary for bread making. Of these two, wheat is far superior in both bread-making qualities and the almost universal acceptability of its taste.[6] While, therefore, the human consumption of rye is limited to parts of central, northern, and eastern Europe where soil and

[4] In the United States and elsewhere barley is used largely by brewers of beer. In Germany and Russia, rye is an important bread grain. The use of oatmeal, corn flakes, hominy, corn on the cob is too well known to require comment. The grasses in general and the cereal grains in particular play different roles in different parts of the earth.

[5] That is, with earth piled around a group of plants.

[6] Exceptions are the rice-eating Asiatics who in general are said to prefer cooked rice to bread, and the Kaffirs working on South African corn plantations who are reputed to stipulate that they be fed grain sorghum.

climatic conditions favor its production, wheat is eaten almost anywhere, wherever people can afford to pay the price. For this reason wheat plays a far greater part in international trade than rye, or indeed, any other grain.

Competition Among Grains

Among the grains there has long been going on a struggle for survival and preëminence. Success in it depends partly on the plants themselves, their natural characteristics, and partly on their response to conditions of both the natural and the cultural environment. More recently, their treatment by plant breeders has played an important part in their struggle to survive or to achieve increased importance. The differential scales of population increase in different parts of the earth are also an important factor.

This struggle never ceases. At one time one cereal gains as the result of some invention, only to fall back again because of another. The advancing mechanization of agriculture has reduced the fighting power of corn. One of the great advantages of corn production is the small amount of labor required in harvesting. Therefore corn stands to gain far less from the development of harvesting machinery than do the small grains such as wheat, rye, oats, and barley, the harvesting of which by earlier methods required unusually large amounts of labor. Hence the development of mechanical harvesting machinery has favorably affected the competitive position of these small grains at the expense of corn. On the other hand, the introduction of hybrid corn, a high yielder, may more than counteract the effect of mechanized harvesting.

Jasny ranks the grains (except rice) in parallel columns as to both the prices they command and the costs which their production involves. His ranking is shown in Table 14.2.

The important fact about corn revealed by this table is its contrasting position as to cost and price in the United States, its chief producer and consumer. It ranks low in cost, but in price it immediately follows wheat, malting barley, and food rye. This suggests that over wide areas with favorable soil and climate combinations, corn is proving more profitable under ordinary conditions than the other feed grains. As a special feed for horses and hogs, corn is exceeded by oats and barley, respectively; but as a general feed, it is unexcelled and is therefore given preference in those parts of the earth where climate and soil permit its production, and by livestock producers who can afford to acquire it from abroad.

Among the food grains corn is as preëminent as wheat is among the food grains in the West and rice in the East. But while wheat owes its leading position largely to its superior acceptability in terms of taste and hence to the relatively *high price* which it can command under ordinary conditions, corn owes its favorable position mainly to its *low cost*, which, in turn, is traceable chiefly to the large yield attained where climate and soil conditions favor its cultivation.

One factor which tends to keep the leaders among the grains in check is the rotation of crops. This makes them predominant rather than exclusive occupants of certain lands. The objective of well-planned agriculture is the most profitable or otherwise most productive combination of crops, rather than maximization of a single crop. Crop rotation in turn ties up with the basic requirements of farm management, soil utilization, etc.

Wheat is closely associated with the mechanical revolution, for it stood to gain most from improved transportation and communication, mechanization, etc. The steamship connected the overseas surplus wheat-producing centers and the deficit-regions of Europe. Furthermore, the steam railroad opened up the ideal wheat-growing areas, the grasslands of the United States, Canada, Australia, Argentina,

TABLE 14.2.   Grain Rankings[7]

According to Prices	According to Costs
1.⎱ Wheat and malting barley	1. Wheat
2.⎰	2. Malting barley
3. Rye as food	3. Rye

United States		Other Countries		
4. Corn	4. ⎱ Oats for horses and		4. ⎱ Barley and oats	
5. ⎱ Oats, feed	5. ⎰ barley for hogs		5. ⎰	
6. ⎰ barley, and	6. Oats and feed barley		6. Corn	
7. ⎰ feed rye	7. for purposes other			
	8. than 4 and 5, corn,			
	9. and feed rye			

[7] N. Jasny, *Competition Among Grains*, Food Research Institute, Grain Economics Series 2, Stanford University, January, 1940, p. 420.

etc., which had been virtually uninhabitable before the advent of the railroad. Because of their flatness, these in turn were most suitable to mechanized agriculture.

Wheat is an ideal crop for such frontier regions for several reasons:

1. European capitalists who were backing frontier development were keenly interested in making available new sources of supply of the bread grain most universally wanted in Europe.
2. Most European immigrants were familiar with the plant and its needs.
3. Wheat has a more dependable market than most other staples.
4. It is easily stored and has good keeping qualities.
5. It is generally worth more per unit of volume or weight than other grains and hence can be shipped more easily.

In the international civilization built around the gold standard, foreign investments, "free trade," etc., which London long strove to establish, wheat was one of the mainstays. Moreover, it has a social prestige which is associated with its consumption.

The reason that rye and barley survive in certain parts of the world is to be found in soil and climatic conditions which permit, or more likely demand, their substitution for other grains. Thus the poorer forest soils of east central and northeastern Europe favor the production of rye; barley is found in regions extremely dry, high, and cold. Barley grown as food or feed under such difficult conditions survives only because the people producing it are more or less isolated from the commercial world. If they could, they would probably migrate to places offering greater rewards for their toil.

Other cereals tend to survive where the general level of civilization is too low to permit the proper cultivation and utilization of the more desirable grains. Buckwheat is not a grain in the strict sense, but is generally classed with the grains. The millets and sorghums give unusually good returns under most primitive conditions—conditions so primitive that wheat culture is practically out of the question.

Outside of Asia and Africa, where great masses of people continue to live almost exclusively on cereals and other vegetable foods

containing carbohydrates, the U.S.S.R. is the only important region where porridges (kasha) made chiefly from buckwheat and millet are consumed in large quantities.

Millet is grown in very hot climates where more than one crop can be produced in the same year but only a short time is available for the second one. The millets are dry-region plants; they withstand dry heat better than any other small grain. They have the ability to remain in a dormant state when moisture is unavailable and to return to active life after the supply of water in the soil has been replenished.

Millet yields are low. Its principal advantage is that a meager crop can be produced with the most primitive cultivation in the shortest time. In ancient times this insured millet its position as the predominant grain of the Old World. Although millet has lost in importance during the past thousand years or so, for these various reasons it is still very important in the areas mentioned above, where equipment and cultural practices are primitive.

Sorghums are important in Africa and monsoon Asia as food grains and in temperate areas as fodder and for the making of molasses. They require hot climates and can get along with less moisture than can corn. They can be grown on very sandy soils which are entirely unsuitable for the small grains. The growing period can be greatly shortened without materially reducing the yield.

In the southwestern part of the United States where the dry summer heat proves unsuitable to the production of corn, sorghum is widely raised for both fodder and grain. Some sorghums are grown under irrigation.

In 1944, a banner year, 181.5 million bushels of sorghum grain were harvested in the United States, over half of it in Texas. The nation's sorghum grain crop was valued at $166.7 million, and the sorghum forage crop at $132.0 million. Silage added another $6.4 million, bringing the grand total up to $305.1 million. The statistics have shown a remarkable increase during recent decades.

Behind this increase is a long record of agricultural improvements and advancements which, in turn, form the basis on which agricultural industry, i.e., manufacturing industry processing agricultural products, can build. The Corn Products Refining Company plant at

TABLE 14.3. World Production of Grains and Potatoes by Continents, Selected Periods, 1944-1948[8]

Continent	Wheat[a] Billion Bushels	Percent	Rice[a] Billion Bushels	Percent	Rye[a] Billion Bushels	Percent	Corn[a] Billion Bushels	Percent	Oats[b] Billion Bushels	Percent	Barley[b] Billion Bushels	Percent	Potatoes[b] Billion Bushels	Percent
North America (including Central America)	1.7	27.8	0.1	1.4	...	2.6	3.3	60.4	1.8	45.6	0.4	21.1	0.5	7.0
South America	0.3	4.7	0.2	2.3	...	...	0.5	9.6	0.1	0.7	0.1	2.5	0.1	1.5
Europe (excluding U.S.S.R.)	1.3	20.6	...	0.6	0.5	34.3	0.6	10.7	1.3	34.0	0.6	28.0	4.2	60.8
Asia (excluding U.S.S.R.)	1.6	26.3	6.7	93.3	...	...	0.6	11.4	0.1	2.1	0.7	33.0	...	0.7
U.S.S.R.	0.9	14.5	...	0.1	0.9	58.7	0.1	2.1	0.6	15.6	0.2	11.1	2.1	29.9
Africa	0.1	2.3	0.2	2.3	...	...	0.3	5.2	...	0.5	0.1	3.5	...	0.3
Oceania	0.2	3.2	...	...	...	...	...	0.6	...	0.5	...	0.8	...	0.5
Total	5.9	100.0	7.2	100.0	1.5	100.0[c]	5.4	100.0	4.2	100.0	2.1	100.0	6.9	100.0

[a] 1946-1948.
[b] 1944-1946.
[c] Total includes 4.4 percent, the production of the continents for which no percentages are given.

Corpus Christi, Texas, furnishes striking proof of this dynamic interaction between agricultural and industrial advance. The particular sorghum grain in that area is milo maize, a dwarf type which is valued both for its resistance to drought and disease and for the ease with which it can be harvested mechanically. The products obtained by processing milo maize include dextrose, starches, and high-protein livestock feeds.

Geographical Specialization in Grains and Potatoes

The upshot of this competition among the grains, which potatoes enter in a few places, is a rather strange geographical distribution of the productive acreage. On the one hand, it appears that grains are widely diffused in their habitat. There are few countries which do not produce some wheat. Corn is grown from the Río Negro in Argentina to the Prairie Provinces of Canada—there is hardly a country in the western hemisphere that does not produce some. And corn is by no means confined to the western hemisphere. Similarly, some rice is grown on every continent. On the other hand, all the cereals seem to have definite points of optimal performance and hence of concentration of production. This applies particularly to rice, 93.3 percent of which during the average

[8] 1944-1946 figures from *Agricultural Statistics, 1947*; figures for 1946-1948 from Foreign Agricultural circulars released in 1949.

year of the period 1946-1948 was produced in monsoon Asia. The concentration of corn in North America—60.4 percent—and of rye in the Soviet Union—58.7 percent; 93 percent if the neighboring area of Europe is added—as well as of potatoes in the same region is almost as great. Table 14.3 shows the production of major grains and potatoes by continents, in billion bushels and in percentages.

THE BREAD GRAINS: WHEAT AND RYE
WHEAT, "THE STAFF OF LIFE" OF THE WEST

While it is true that very large amounts of wheat are produced in northern China, northern India, and southern Russia, wheat is peculiarly identified with the Occident as it developed after the Industrial Revolution. The Industrial Revolution brought the steam railroad and the steamship. As has been said, the former opened up the great plains and prairies which until then had been virtually uninhabited, especially those of North America stretching from Texas to the Canadian Prairie Provinces, the humid pampas of Argentina, the pustas of Hungary and the Danubian basin, and the southeast of Australia. The steamship aided international trade; and wheat exported from the New World to industrialized Europe, especially Britain, became a major feature of the expanding world commerce. The industrialization and urbanization of parts of Europe and North America led to vast concentrations of people, most of whom depended on food

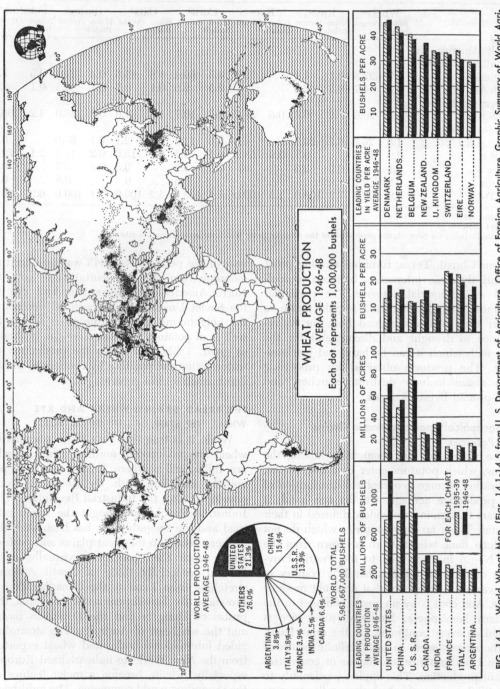

FIG. 14.1. World Wheat Map. (Figs. 14.1-14.5 from U. S. Department of Agriculture, Office of Foreign Agriculture, Graphic Summary of World Agriculture, 1949.)

brought in from the outside and could afford to eat wheat bread. Until the Russian Revolution of 1917 the Ukraine in southern European Russia was a major exporter of wheat; but the rapid industrialization and urbanization of the Soviet Union, by vastly stimulating domestic needs, reduced the flow of export wheat to an unreliable trickle, though in mid-winter of 1950 the government indicated interest in a European wheat agreement, suggesting the prospect of renewed exports. Similarly increased domestic requirements tended to level off wheat exports from the United States, but as the result of two World Wars she reversed the trend and temporarily resumed the role of major wheat purveyor to the world. Canada, Argentina, and Australia are the three countries where wheat-producing capacity normally and materially exceeds domestic needs. Their total output is exceeded by a number of countries, but their exports play a very important role in the wheat trade of the world.

TABLE 14.4. Wheat Production in Selected Areas and Countries, 1890-1948
(billion bushels)

	1890	1900	1910	1920	1930	1935–1939	1946–1948
Europe (excluding U.S.S.R.)	1.1	1.1	1.2	1.0	1.4	1.6	1.3
U.S.S.R.	0.2	0.4	0.8	0.3	1.0	1.2	0.9
United States	0.4	0.6	0.6	0.8	0.9	0.8	1.3
Canada	–	0.1	0.1	0.3	0.4	0.3	0.4
Argentina	–	0.1	0.1	0.2	0.2	0.2	0.2
Australia	–	0.1	0.1	0.1	0.2	0.2	0.2
India	0.2	0.3	0.4	0.4	0.4	0.4	0.3
China[a]	–		–		–	0.8	0.9

[a] No production figures are available for the period 1890-1930, but estimates for the period range from 0.7 to 1.0 billion bushels.

Table 14.4 shows the wheat output of leading selected areas and countries in billion bushels. Europe (excluding the U.S.S.R.), the United States, Canada, Argentina, and Australia are the leading wheat growers of the West. They normally produce between two-thirds and three-fourths of the world output.

Wheat Geography, Natural and Cultural

As one looks at the wheat map of the world (Fig. 14.1), he is struck by the concentration of wheat production within two latitudinal ribbons of land, a major one in the northern hemisphere, stretching clear across the map between latitudes 30° and 55° north and a minor one between 20° and 40° south. This geographical concentration within these two bands is primarily a result of climatic and, to a lesser degree, soil conditions. Wheat, like all plants, has a certain tolerance for drought, humidity, heat, and cold. Where the limits of tolerance are exceeded, wheat growing is too risky and too disappointing to warrant the expense and effort. Not only must the wheat grower shun regions of excessive cold, heat, aridity, and humidity, he must seek the areas where adequate heat and moisture are so distributed during the year that the seasonal requirements of the plant are properly met. The ideal climate for wheat is the so-called Mediterranean climate, with its dry warm summers and cool moist winters.

The limit-setting power of nature is indicated in the map of Europe (see Fig 14.2) showing how the lines indicating minimum rainfall set the southern limits, and the lines indicating minimum summer temperatures set the northern limits, of European and Near Eastern wheat production. In other words, nature sets certain outer limits to man's endeavor to push crop production. What happens within these limits, although likewise influenced by nature, is to a large degree the result of human choices made in the light of culturally conditioned circumstances.

To begin with, the wheat plant itself as we know it today is largely a product of culture, the result of centuries of plant breeding aimed at raising the vigor and productivity of the plant. Even the best natural wheats probably never approached a bushel an acre. Today 50 bushels and more can be harvested. The original strains from which uncounted generations of men have developed the almost innumerable varieties of wheat grown today in different parts of the earth occurred in highly restricted habitats. If today wheat is grown successfully on over 400 million acres, this is largely because man, by persistence, patient and ingenious effort, has artificially widened the habitat of wheats. He has bred drought- and frost-resistant varieties, varieties which resist disease and pests, which in general make far more out

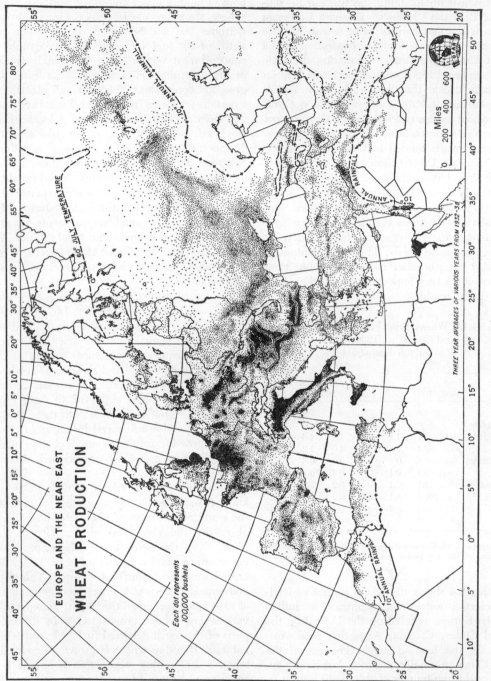

EUROPE AND THE NEAR EAST

WHEAT PRODUCTION

Each dot represents
100,000 bushels

THREE YEAR AVERAGES OF VARIOUS YEARS FROM 1932-38

FIG. 14.2.

of the natural conditions on which they depend than did the original strains.[9]

The division of the wheat crop into winter wheat and spring wheat is part of this story of man's effort to expand the area where wheat can be grown. Winter wheat is sown in the fall and harvested in the spring or early summer. It thrives in a mild winter climate, especially

---

[9] There are three main methods of improving the wheat strains grown in a particular region: (1) the introduction of new varieties from foreign countries—the work of the plant explorer; (2) selection, from natural hybrids, of the most promising varieties; (3) hybridization, or the selection of the best strains from the progeny of artificial crosses. While the first two methods are almost as old as history, the third dates from about 1870 and is based mainly on the work of Mendel.

Some of the most important varieties grown in the United States were developed by introduction from abroad. For example, the variety that founded the hard spring wheat industry came originally from Galicia, Poland, and reached the United States by way of Germany, Scotland, and Canada. From it descended the wheat that became known as Red Fife, which in turn became one of the parents of the Marquis and Ceres wheats. Hard red winter wheat was introduced by a group of Mennonites who brought seed grain from southern Russia. Durum wheat was also introduced from Russia. Baart and Federation white wheats were introduced by the United States Department of Agriculture from Australia in the early part of the twentieth century.

Important varieties developed by hybridization are Fulcaster, Ceres, and Thatcher.

Durum wheat is practically immune to rust. Marquillo, developed from Marquis × Iumillo (durum), was the first hard red spring wheat grown commercially in which the rust resistance of the durum parent was transferred to a common hard red spring wheat. The more recent production, Thatcher, distributed in 1934 and developed from the double cross, Marquis-Iumillo × Kanred-Marquis, is one of the most promising new varieties. It is resistant to stem rust and is a widely adapted, high-quality wheat.

Working in South Dakota, E. S. McFadden, of the U.S. Department of Agriculture, produced the Hope and H-44 wheats by crossing Marquis wheat with Yaroslav emmer. These wheats, nearly immune to black stem rust and resistant to leaf rust, bunt, and loose smut, have been extensively used for further breeding for disease control. Rust is probably the most devastating of all diseases that attack wheat. In 1935, 1937, and 1938 stem-rust epidemics caused losses of more than 100 million bushels each year.

For a full account, see the *Yearbook of Agriculture, 1941*, p. 501.

---

the so-called Mediterranean climate. Where winters are severe, wheat is sown in the spring and harvested late in the fall. Such a rational adaptation is a cultural achievement which goes far to modify the impact of raw nature. It is found in the United States, where spring wheat is grown in the North and winter wheat in the areas around Kansas and farther south. It has its counterpart in the Soviet Union, in China, and in all areas where wheat culture has been pushed beyond the limits of a mild winter climate.

Successful wheat growing requires far more than the mere knowledge that wheat will thrive in a given area. People to grow the wheat must be able to live in the area. The classical case of the great grass plains of the earth was mentioned—it took climate and soil *and* the railroad to turn these vast unsettled areas into the granaries of the earth. Moreover, there must be a market for wheat that is grown over and above the needs of the grower. Markets must be reachable by ship and cable and opened up by the trader and the banker.

It is true that wheat does well in many parts of Europe where soils are rich. Many of these soils were not naturally rich; they were made rich by a century or more of careful husbandry and scientific agronomy. The transatlantic wheat trade impoverished the soils of the exporter and enriched those of the importer. The invention of synthetic nitrogen and the discovery of potash and phosphate deposits have had much to do with the richness of European soils.

How much wheat a country grows is a complex function of natural and cultural conditions. Among the latter, national policy is a vital factor. The Soviet Union's five-year plans for the collectivization and mechanization of wheat farms, the tariff policies of nations seeking self-sufficiency in essential foods, the "triple A," soil conservation, the Marshall Plan—all these are just samples of an almost endless array of artificial measures by which governments can exercise considerable influence over wheat production in their own countries no less than in others.

What has been said of the wheat map applies more or less to all the world maps showing the geographical distribution of major crops. Wheat, however, being the most "western" of all the crops, has probably felt the interfering hand of culture more keenly and more generally than any other crop.

Wheat Yields

Wheat is produced under such widely differing natural and cultural conditions, and by such highly diverse methods, that results in terms of yields per acre show similarly great variations. Table 14.5 illustrates this point.

TABLE 14.5. Wheat Yields in Bushels per Acre in Selected Countries, Selected Periods 1925-1948[10]

Ranking of Countries[a]	1925–1929	1930–1934	1935–1939	1946–1948
1. Denmark	42.0	43.0	45.4	45.8
2. United Kingdom	33.4	33.6	33.8	33.0
3. Germany	29.4	32.1	34.6	....
4. New Zealand	33.9	30.2	32.3	37.0
5. Egypt	25.8	27.6	31.3	25.5
6. Japan	26.5	27.1	28.8	....
7. France	22.0	23.0	22.8	22.6
8. Italy	18.8	20.8	22.1	19.7
9. Argentina	12.8	13.8	14.0	16.7
10. Canada	18.6	13.6	12.2	15.8
11. United States	14.1	13.5	13.2	17.8
12. Manchuria	16.6	13.0	12.4	....
13. Australia	10.6	12.2	12.9	13.4
14. Soviet Union	11.2	10.8	11.9	10.8
15. Eritrea	3.9	5.6	....	....

[a] Ranking based on 1930-1934 yields.

The wide difference in yields shown in this table reflects the diversity of both natural and cultural conditions under which wheat is grown in different parts of the world. In general, yields are low where natural conditions are unfavorable and where the level of cultural development is low; they are lowest where both nature and culture are inefficient. Vice versa, favorable conditions of nature and a high level of cultural development result in high yields.

Besides this rough general rule further factors must be taken into consideration. Crowded countries like China and Egypt, that suffer from land scarcity and must dispose of a large labor force, tend to seek the most from their limited land and by much labor, much capital, and intensive cultivation manage to extract high yields. Countries like Canada and the United States, having large areas of land on which wheat may be grown and leading in the technique of mechanized farming, do not need to

[10] *Agricultural Statistics, 1941 and 1949.*

strive toward maximizing the yield per unit of land but instead seek the highest profit for the farming venture and incidentally achieve very high yields per worker engaged in farming. As was pointed out before (pp. 89-90), agriculturists unaided by robots must concentrate on limited areas of highly productive land, whereas strong horsepower support emancipates the farmer from such limitations and enables him to wrest good returns from much poorer (which includes less accessible) acres. A high per-acre yield is no more an unerring proof of superior agronomic skill than is a high per-worker yield. Agricultural practice reflects adjustments to varying circumstances, and efficiency is a relative term depending largely on factoral proportions such as man-land ratios, etc.

In appraising the variations in yields another factor must be kept in mind: the size of the cultivated area. In comparing such yields as the Danish (45.4 in 1935-1939), the German (34.6 for the same period), and the United States (13.2 for the same period), it is important to consider the acreages involved—Denmark, 319,000 acres; Germany, 4,250,000 acres; the United States, 57,293,000 acres. It is one thing to maintain a high yield on a garden plot, such as Denmark, and a totally different thing to achieve it on an area almost 200 times as large.

Wheats vs. Wheat

Far from representing a homogeneous commodity like sugar, wheat is a generic term covering a large variety of widely different types. There are so many different kinds of wheat that the generic concept has little practical significance. Not all wheats are used in the manufacture of bread. There are varieties, such as durum, which are used chiefly or almost exclusively in the manufacture of alimentary pastes, such as macaroni, spaghetti, vermicelli, ravioli, etc. Others are used almost exclusively for cake, biscuits, etc. Some wheat, because of its inferior quality, may be disqualified as human food. Apart from these basic differentiations, there are minor distinctions which may seem unimportant but which, especially in modern times, have assumed extraordinary economic significance.

This diversity is particularly pronounced in a large country like the United States where

TABLE 14.6. Major Classes of Wheat Grown in the United States[11]

Classes	Producing Areas	Uses	Percent Distribution by Regions, 1940-1944
Hard red spring	North central states: North Dakota, South Dakota, Minnesota, Montana	Bread flour	29
Durum	North central states	Macaroni, spaghetti, other alimentary pastes	29
Hard red winter	South central states: Kansas, Nebraska, Colorado, Texas, Oklahoma	Bread flour	37
Soft red winter	Corn states: Missouri, Illinois, Indiana, Ohio	Flour for biscuits, pastries, etc.	17
White wheats	Far-western states: Washington, Idaho, Oregon, California	Cracker and pastry flours	17

wheat is grown over a wide range of latitude and under diverse climatic and edaphic conditions.[12] The United States can be divided into definite zones, each of which produces its own peculiar type of wheat. The five major classes of wheat grown here, together with their chief sources and uses, are listed in Table 14.6.

The relative importance of these different classes varies from year to year with shifts in markets and changes in the weather. It is reflected in price differentials which likewise vary. The average cash prices of wheats on June 4, 1949, in cents per bushel, were as follows:[13]

No. 2 Hard amber durum in Minneapolis   229
No. 2 Hard (winter) in Kansas City   199
No. 1 Dark Northern (spring) in Minneapolis   227
No. 2 Red (winter) in St. Louis   214
Soft white in Portland (Oregon)   215

Each of these five major classes is represented by numerous varieties resulting from tireless efforts of plant breeders and plant explorers to reach always greater perfection in the adaptation of plant to environment and to combat with ever-increasing success the fight against pest and disease.

All classes and varieties are graded on the

[11] C. P. Heisig, E. R. Ahrendes, and D. E. Merrick, *Wheat Production in Peace and War*, U.S. Department of Agriculture, Bureau of Agricultural Economics, 1945, p. 21.
[12] Edaphic conditions pertain to soil and topography.
[13] U.S. Department of Agriculture, *The Wheat Situation*, May-June, 1949.

basis of weight per bushel, moisture, presence of damaged kernels, foreign matter, other wheats, etc. Thus the class, hard red spring wheat, may be subdivided into three subclasses: dark northern, northern, and red. Each of these in turn falls into one of five grades.

The following tabulation suggests foreign wheats which roughly correspond to those in the United States:

United States Wheats	Foreign Wheats
Hard red spring	Manitoba northern
Durum	Durum produced in Canada, Italy, North Africa
Hard red winter	Argentina hard types such as Tipo Duro
Soft red winter	Argentina soft types such as Tipo Blando
White	Australia White

The hard wheats are also known as strong wheats. They rank high in protein (gluten) content, a characteristic important in the manufacture of bread with the aid of yeast that expands the cell structure. The flours obtained from strong wheats produce large loaves of bread per unit of flour.

Hard wheats came into their own as the result of an important change in milling practice introduced from Hungary during the 1870's. This process is known as the *steel-roller* or *gradual reduction* process. In this process rapidly revolving steel rollers are substituted for the old-fashioned buhrstones. When hit by one of the sharp edges of the revolving steel roller, wheat which has been steeped until it is close to the bursting point cracks and yields some of its flour content. This process is repeated perhaps fifteen or twenty times on successive floors, the unfinished product falling from one roller to the one next below until the maximum of flour has been extracted. Hence the name, gradual reduction process. The flour at each stage of extraction is blown by a power blower through reels of bolting cloth—another epochal improvement over the old-fashioned milling process which relied on gravity and simple sieves.

This process is particularly suited to milling hard wheats. For when such wheats are crushed between buhrstones, instead of the chaff being neatly separated from the flour as is the case with soft wheats it is crushed with and discolors the flour. The buhrstone process yielded whiter flour from soft wheats than from hard wheats. The introduction of the steel-roller process reversed this and resulted in premium prices for hard wheat. It added superior color and unity to the "strong" character of such wheat. This, in turn, brought on a revolutionary change in the wheat map of the United States and of other countries which produce both soft and hard varieties.

This is a classical example of the impact of culture on wheat geography that was mentioned above. Many other examples could be added, such as the effect of the motor truck on the bread-baking industry and its repercussions via the milling industry on wheat growing.

International Trade in Wheat

As we have seen, industrialization and urbanization and the opening of the frontier made wheat one of the most important commodities of international trade. During the last half of the nineteenth century the United States produced far more of this grain than her population could consume. Wheat exports provided an excellent way of paying interest on and eventually amortizing the debt owed to European, especially British, lenders. These exports also provided the means by which settlers supported themselves while their land increased in value to the point where its sale furnished "the deferred rebates" for wheat sold below the true cost of production. As the population of the United States increased and the balance shifted in favor of industrial and other nonagricultural

activities, exports began to dwindle and to be confined to culls not wanted by the domestic milling and baking industries. But the two World Wars put this country back among the major wheat exporters. Although in some years during the thirties the United States was actually on a wheat import basis and in the period 1935-1939 averaged only 39 million bushels of exported wheat and flour (as wheat), by 1945 exports had risen to 389 million bushels and were maintained at a high level for several years. This figure is well above average wheat production in Canada, almost double that of Argentina, and more than double that of Australia.

Wheat exports of late have become a political weapon. They play a major part in the "cold war," the East-West struggle between communist tyranny and capitalistic or socialistic democracy. To some extent the taxpayer is expected to support them with the same grim determination with which he supports the construction and support of the navy, the army, or the air force. A far cry indeed from the a-political economics of the eighteenth and nineteenth centuries!

In the nineteenth century Russia was a leading exporter of wheat. If our nation's wheat exports in that century cannot be understood without considering our economic history—settlement of the continent, rising land values, immigration, industrialization, foreign loans and their servicing and repayment—Russian wheat exports cannot be understood without some knowledge of that nation's social history. The keys to Russia's wheat exports in that century are serfdom, feudalism, the landlord's power to ship out wheat for his own financial benefit even if the people around him were underfed, perhaps actually starving.

What was said of nineteenth-century Russia applies on a smaller scale and with some modification to Rumania and Hungary. The social revolutions following 1917 have gone far to remove the feudalistic basis of wheat exports. In Rumania and Hungary latifundia have been cut up and parceled out to the peasants and the workers. In the U.S.S.R. agriculture has been placed in the service of industrialization. Little wheat is produced in the Soviet Union which is not sorely needed for the new urban proletariat spawned by the Revolution.

TABLE 14.7. Wheat Yield, Production, and Exports in the Major Exporting Countries, Selected Periods, 1929-1948[14]

	1935-1939[a]	1940	1941	1942	1943	1944	1945	1946	1947	1948	1944-1948[a]
Yield (bushels per acre)											
Canada	12.1[b]	18.8	14.4	25.6	16.8	17.8	13.6	17.2	13.9	16.6	15.7
Argentina	12.1[b]	17.1	13.2	13.8	14.9	9.7	9.6	14.9	21.0	14.2	13.9
Australia	11.8[b]	6.5	13.9	16.8	13.9	6.2	12.5	8.9	15.9	15.4	11.8
Production (million bushels)											
Canada	312	540	315	557	284	417	318	421	337	393	377
Argentina	222	300	238	235	250	150	144	221	245	170	182
Australia	170	82	167	156	110	53	142	115	220	200	146
Exports[c] (million bushels)											
Canada	173	231	226	215	344	343	340	260	246	194	282
Argentina	122	96	83	69	89	104	69	90	85	80	84
Australia	107	76	41	38	65	55	41	40	12	60	40[d]

[a] Average.
[b] 1929-1939 averages.
[c] Includes wheat, and wheat flour as wheat. The conversion of flour into wheat equivalent was made by the author and is partly estimated
[d] 1945-1949 averages.

Even India with her starving millions used to export wheat to the West. There, as in most wheat-exporting countries, railroad construction opened up new wheat land at a rate faster than the domestic demand could absorb the wheat. Punjab wheat could not be hauled overland to the main deficit areas of India because of the lack of transport facilities. The railroad that was built roughly parallels the Indus River and connects the Punjab with the port of Karachi. Once the wheat reached tidewater at Karachi, the West could outbid competitive buyers. But this, too, has stopped and India, like Russia and Rumania, has dropped out of the ranks of wheat exporters.

That leaves Argentina, Australia, and Canada to be considered. All three are New World countries, with a relatively low population density and with agricultural land in excess of their domestic needs. They are the countries which the railroad and the steamship turned into wheat-exporting specialists. Their yields are relatively low and rather unreliable, but in parts of these countries wheat growing appears to be the most remunerative use of the land,

[14] Food and Agricultural Organization, *Wheat,* Commodity Series Bulletin, 1949; export figures, 1947, 1948, and 1944-1948, from U.S. Department of Commerce.

and output exceeds domestic needs. Hence the exports.

The International Wheat Agreement of 1949

As we have seen, wheat is a vital food in many countries and plays a major role in the export trade of some of them. Hence wheat production and trade, no less than the wheat supply, are a vital concern of governments. Under laissez faire the free play of economic forces was relied on to accomplish the proper adjustment between the two great needs—an adequate supply at a reasonable price for the consumer, and an adequate reward for the grower and the trader. This reliance rested on the assumption that competition controlled all phases of business enterprise. However, in a warring world government interference becomes a common experience and it is now encouraged by the rising concern for social justice. Thus the foundation has been knocked from under the theoretical structure of a smoothly functioning world economy.

For years economists and statesmen have been concerned over the unsatisfactory way the world wheat economy has been functioning. The idea of bringing around a conference table the deficit and surplus countries—the international buyers and sellers of wheat—took form and finally, after many failures, bore fruit

TABLE 14.8. Supply and Distribution of Wheat in the United States
for Selected Years[15]
(in million bushels)

	1927	1932	1937	1943	1947
Carryover stock	109.5	375.3	83.2	618.9	83.8
New crops	875.1	756.3	873.9	843.8	1367.2
Imports	0.2	–	0.1	136.4	0.1
Total supply	984.7	1131.6	957.7	1599.1	1451.1
Continental U.S. disappearance					
Processed for food	502.7	492.4	474.6	491.6	486.3
Seed	89.9	83.8	93.1	77.4	90.7
Industrial	–	–	–	107.5	0.1
Feed	85.4	142.8	133.5	497.8	185.7
Total domestic	678.0	718.9	701.2	1174.3	763.5
Military procurement	.....	.....	.....	62.8	146.5
Exports	191.2	31.9	100.1	42.3	341.0
Shipments[a]	2.7	3.0	3.3	3.1	4.2
Total disappearance	871.9	753.8	804.6	1282.5	1255.2

[a] Shipments to Alaska, Puerto Rico, Virgin Islands, and Hawaii.

in the International Wheat Agreement, signed in the spring of 1949. The purpose of the agreement was to give wheat-exporting countries an idea of the demand for the next four years, and the approximate price they would receive, and to assure the importing countries of an adequate supply at a reasonable price. The terms of the agreement have been kept loose enough to take the uncontrollability of the weather into account, but this should not prove a formidable obstacle because four-year averages and widely separated producing areas are involved. Two nations are not signatories— Argentina, who held out for excessive prices, and the U.S.S.R., who held out for excessive quotas. The agreement is a bold experiment in economic rationalization, and its success or failure will be watched eagerly by advocates of laissez faire and social planning alike.

Disposition of the Wheat Crop

Few people not familiar with the facts are likely to realize what a small proportion of the domestic wheat crop is eaten as bread in the United States. Table 14.8 throws light on the

[15] U.S. Department of Agriculture, *The Wheat Situation*, May-June, 1949, p. 18.
The year begins on July 1.

disposal of our wheat supply during selected years.

In the crop year 1927-1928 the United States had new crops of 875.1 million bushels, of which 502.7 million bushels were processed for food. In processing in this country, i.e., mainly milling or converting wheat into flour, about one-fourth of the volume is lost as "clears" which go into feeds. This leaves a little over 400 million bushels, or about 46 percent of the crop, for flour. The rest is set aside as seed, used for industrial purposes and feed, exported, or shipped to noncontiguous territories.

The effect of World War II, with its heavy imports of wheat in 1943, its huge diversion of wheat to industrial purposes, chiefly alcohol for synthetic rubber, and cattle feed, and military procurement is clearly shown in the table, as is the increased size of the crop and the heavy exports in the postwar period.

RYE, A REGIONAL SUBSTITUTE FOR WHEAT

As was mentioned before, wheat and rye are the only true bread grains. Neither is used exclusively for bread. Rye may be grown for feed, and wheat may be fed to animals or burned as fuel if an excess supply threatens to

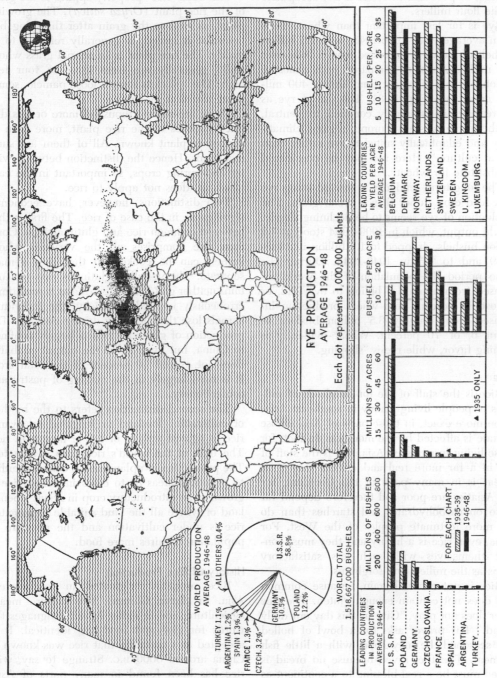

RYE PRODUCTION
AVERAGE 1946-48

Each dot represents 1,000,000 bushels

WORLD PRODUCTION
AVERAGE 1946-48

TURKEY 1.1%
ARGENTINA 1.2%
SPAIN 1.3%
FRANCE 1.3%
CZECH. 3.2%

POLAND
12.2%

GERMANY
10.5%

U.S.S.R.
58.8%

ALL OTHERS 10.4%

WORLD TOTAL
1,518,667,000 BUSHELS

LEADING COUNTRIES
IN PRODUCTION
AVERAGE 1946-48

MILLIONS OF BUSHELS
200 400 600 800

U. S. S. R.
POLAND.
GERMANY.
CZECHOSLOVAKIA.
FRANCE.
SPAIN.
ARGENTINA.
TURKEY.

FOR EACH CHART
1935-39
1946-48

MILLIONS OF ACRES
15 30 45 60

▲ 1935 ONLY

BUSHELS PER ACRE
10   20   30

LEADING COUNTRIES
IN YIELD PER ACRE
AVERAGE 1946-48

BELGIUM.
DENMARK.
NORWAY.
NETHERLANDS.
SWITZERLAND.
SWEDEN.
U. KINGDOM.
LUXEMBURG.

BUSHELS PER ACRE
5 10 15 20 25 30 35

FIG. 14.3.

depress the price, or if the grain is damaged by frost or pest and therefore is not acceptable to the flour millers.

Rye is far less important than wheat. Thus in an average year, 1946-1948, only 1.5 billion bushels of rye were harvested from a little over 100 million acres, as compared with almost 6 billion bushels of wheat from almost 400 million acres (see Fig. 14.3). The use of rye as a bread grain is largely confined to central, northern, and eastern Europe, regions climatically and edaphically suited to rye rather than wheat culture.[16] Here rye may be considered a substitute for wheat.

The long-term tendency is toward using rye as a feed crop rather than a bread grain. The production of rye seems to be declining slowly. World output, which in 1900-1904 stood at 1.8 billion bushels, dropped to 1.7 billion in 1935-1939 and to 1.5 in 1946-1948. During the same period the population of the world increased from about 1.6 billion to over 2.2, or almost 38 percent, and wheat production increased from roughly 3.5 billion bushels to about 6, or 70 percent. Wheat evidently is gaining favor, while rye is "slipping."

RICE

Rice is the staff of life for hundreds of millions of people living mainly in southeast Asia; to be more exact, in those parts of Asia whose climate is affected by the monsoon. In fact, for those living in monsoon Asia, rice is the staff of life in a far more real and critical way than wheat is in many parts of the Occident, for the Asiatics are poor and therefore depend far more on carbohydrates and starches than do the more fortunate peoples of the West. For some, even rice is a luxury and they must content themselves with such less satisfactory crops as the millets and sorghums.

Rice is not a bread grain, because common rice does not contain enough gluten. The rice eater does not pray, "Give us this day our daily bread." His prayer asks for a bowl of boiled rice seasoned, he may hope, with a little fish or meat. The fuel saved because no bread is baked must be a real blessing to a continent as poor in fuel supplies of all sorts as Asia is.

---

[16] K. H. Klages, *Ecological Crop Geography,* The Macmillan Company, New York, 1942, p. 341.

Types of Rice

The word "rice" properly applies to the grain of the rice plant (*Oryza sativa*). The growing plant, as well as the grain after threshing but before it is hulled, is generally referred to as paddy. The rice plant is an annual grass whose stalks generally are from three to four feet high. The spikelets form a loose panicle, somewhat like that of oats.

There are several thousand more or less distinct varieties of the rice plant, more than of any other plant known. All of them are summer crops. Hence the distinction between winter and spring crops, so important in the case of wheat, does not apply to rice.

Two distinctions, however, have economic significance in the case of rice. The first is that between common rice and glutinous rice. Common rice comprises all the varieties whose kernels can be cooked so that they remain separate. The so-called glutinous rice (it contains neither gluten nor dextrine as is sometimes erroneously implied) is sticky; the individual kernels lose their identity during cooking. The production of glutinous rice is largely confined to China, but even there the output probably does not exceed 10 percent of the total crop. It is used largely in the making of pastry and confectionery.

The second distinction refers to the method of cultivation—lowland or irrigated or swamp rice as against upland or hill or mountain rice. The bulk of the world's rice crop is irrigated. The production of upland rice is confined either to primitive areas or to cases in which rice is grown as an introductory crop in newly opened land or where all the land suitable to irrigated rice is under cultivation and the pressure of population requires more food.

History of Rice Production

Rice probably originated in southeastern Asia. In classic Chinese, rice culture means agriculture, and in many Asiatic languages the words for rice and food are identical. It is accepted as a certainty that rice was known in China around 3000 B.C. Strange to say, wild rice has been found in many parts of Asia, Australia, Africa, and even South America, but not in China. Rice culture probably started in swamps and flood areas where no tools were required, and where a farmer and his family, by splashing around in the water, could destroy the weeds and prepare the soil adequately.

The cultivation of rice eventually spread to all five continents, but nowhere is rice as important as it is in monsoon Asia. This region of the earth produces from 90 to 95 percent of the total output, the remainder being scattered among a large number of small producing areas. The most important rice-producing regions outside of monsoon Asia are Brazil and the United States, followed by Egypt, Italy, and Madagascar. Table 14.9 shows the distribution of the world rice acreage by continents.

TABLE 14.9. World Rice Acreage, by Continents[17] (in millions of acres)

	1935-1936 to 1939-1940 (average)	1940-1941 to 1945-1946	1946-1947 (estimated)
Asia	179.0	186.5	191.0
The Americas	4.1	7.8	7.5[a]
Europe	1.0	0.7	0.5
Africa	4.0	5.0	5.0
Total	188.0	200.0	204.0

[a] About 1.5 million acres in the United States.

Compared with the meteoric rise of wheat production during the nineteenth century, the increase in rice production has been rather slow. This is to be expected of a crop of such antiquity, one that has reached the limit of production in most areas to which it is best suited. While wheat acreage could expand to a multiple of its present size, a corresponding expansion in rice acreage would meet with great resistance. Unfortunately, as was stated before, the rice-eating people of monsoon Asia increase in number more rapidly and their need for food is far more pressing than is true of a considerable portion of the wheat eaters. Table 14.10 shows rice production in bushels (45 pounds) and as a percentage of the estimated world total.[18]

[17] FAO, Cereal Review, Part 3 Rice, June 25, 1947, p. 4.
[18] For production figures in tons, from 1910 to 1940, see V. D. Wickizer and M. K. Bennett, The Rice Economy of Monsoon Asia, Food Research Institute, Stanford University, 1941, pp. 23, 316-317.

Geography of Rice Production

Monsoon Asia includes a number of countries in which climatic conditions associated with monsoons profoundly influence both agricultural and economic life. The monsoon climate is marked by a summer maximum and a winter minimum of rainfall, with a seasonal reversal of the wind direction from the ocean toward

TABLE 14.10. Rice Production in Million Bushels (Rough Basis) and as Percentage of Estimated World Total[19]

	1935-1939 Million Bushels	Percent	1946-1948 Million Bushels	Percent
China	2452.7	33.6	2297.0	31.9
India	1394.5	19.2	1499.0	20.5
Japan	595.8	8.2	553.3	7.6
Pakistan	542.3	7.4	578.2	8.0
Burma	348.5	4.8	244.6	3.4
French Indo-China	319.9	4.4	252.0	3.5
Java and Madeira	313.1	4.3	260.0	3.7
Thailand	213.1	3.0	217.0	3.0
Korea	195.8	2.7	133.0	1.8
Philippine Islands	104.9	1.4	112.0	1.5
Brazil	64.4	0.9	117.0	1.6
		89.9		86.5

the Asiatic highlands in the summer (summer monsoon) and from the highlands toward the ocean in the winter. It is the moisture supplied by the summer monsoon which makes possible the vast irrigation system on which rice culture depends. The countries whose agriculture and economic life are most affected by this monsoon climate include Japan, Korea and Formosa, China south of the Yangtze, French Indo-China, Thailand, Burma, British Malaya, India, Pakistan, and the adjacent islands, mainly Ceylon, the Philippines, and Indonesia (see Fig. 14.4). It is the area which was described in Chapter 8 (p. 95) as that of "abundant food," abundant in this case referring to aggregate supply rather than to per capita availability. This area constitutes the most densely populated portion of the globe.

Rice culture is peculiarly adapted to regions of dense population, for rice is probably the most highly intensive-labor crop extant. Al-

[19] Agricultural Statistics, 1948.

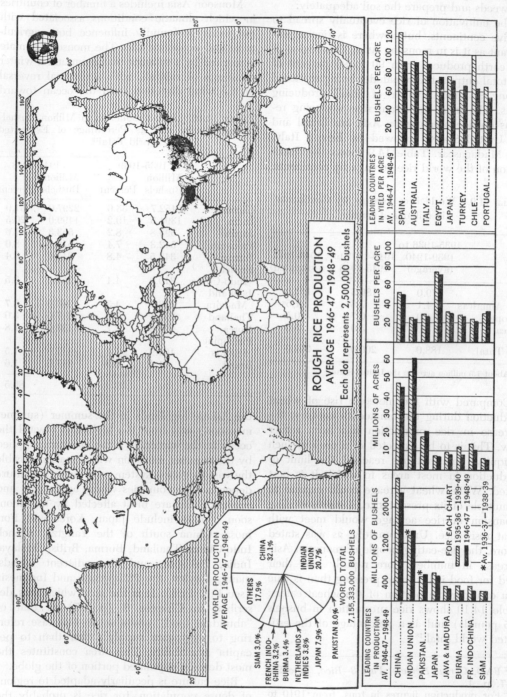

ROUGH RICE PRODUCTION
AVERAGE 1946-47—1948-49
Each dot represents 2,500,000 bushels

WORLD PRODUCTION
AVERAGE 1946-47—1948-49

CHINA 32.1%

INDIAN UNION 20.7%

OTHERS 17.9%

SIAM 3.0%
FRENCH INDO-CHINA 3.2%
BURMA 3.4%
NETHERLANDS INDIES 3.8%
JAPAN 7.9%
PAKISTAN 8.0%

WORLD TOTAL
7,155,333,000 BUSHELS

LEADING COUNTRIES
IN PRODUCTION
AV. 1946-47—1948-49

MILLIONS OF BUSHELS
400   1200   2000

CHINA
INDIAN UNION
PAKISTAN
JAPAN
JAVA & MADURA
BURMA
FR. INDOCHINA
SIAM

FOR EACH CHART
1935-36 — 1939-40
1946-47 — 1948-49
* Av. 1936-37—1938-39

MILLIONS OF ACRES
10 20 30 40 50 60

BUSHELS PER ACRE
20 40 60 80 100

1930-1940

LEADING COUNTRIES
IN YIELD PER ACRE
AV. 1946-47 1948-49

BUSHELS PER ACRE
20   40   60   80 100 120

SPAIN
AUSTRALIA
ITALY
EGYPT
JAPAN
TURKEY
CHILE
PORTUGAL

FIG. 14.4.

though the edible portion of the wheat crop may exceed that of the rice crop, rice farmers far exceed wheat farmers in number. Rice is produced typically on tiny plots by subsistence farmers, whereas a considerable portion of the world wheat crop is produced commercially on large tracts with the aid of machinery. Modern mechanized wheat production is almost the exact counterpart of typical rice production. In order to make the best use of scarce soil resources, rice is sown in seed beds and transplanted by hand into the paddy fields. This alone entails a great deal of hand labor. The paddy fields constitute one of the greatest cultural achievements of man. Providing the proper amount of fresh water entails careful terracing and the building of ditches and dikes, all of which must be maintained with minute care if disastrous floods are to be avoided. The water must be lifted to the highest terraces and the amount must be kept constant. So to the tedious labor involved in cropping is added the stupendous labor entailed by a marvelous but laborious water economy.

Rice culture requires level land, heavy fertile soil and an impervious subsoil, plenty of water, and a temperature of over 70° Fahrenheit. These conditions limit rice culture to specific areas and cause the intensity of it to vary considerably from one region to another. In general, rice culture is confined to the flat bottomlands of river valleys and to coastal plains. Rice must have no less than 40 inches of annual rainfall and cannot be successfully cultivated above 3000 feet. In general the climate is tropical or subtropical. Where the climate in China is too cold or too dry for successful rice cultivation, millets, sorghums, and wheat are generally cultivated. Because rice is an irrigated crop and therefore requires overhead expenditures in the form of terraces, leveling, pumping or water lifting, etc., only rich soils which permit continuous cultivation through considerable periods of time can be considered adequate. Ideal rice land is ill suited to most other crops, although in some areas—especially in Japan and central China—wheat is grown during the months when rice cannot be grown.

Rice cultivation requires practically no capital except that needed for the land. The crop can be stored successfully in climates where the storing of other grains proves difficult if not impossible. Above all, irrigated rice is by far the most dependable of all crops and hence is most suitable where there is extreme pressure of population against a meager subsistence. Where the water supply is adequate, two crops and sometimes even three can be produced on the same land in the same year.

Such crops as sugar cane, cassava, and yautia (related to taro) require longer growing seasons and are far more difficult to store. Moreover, they are more subject to disease and pests and consequently are less suitable to the conditions found in monsoon Asia, in spite of the fact that larger yields per acre can be achieved under favorable circumstances.

Structure of the Rice Industry

The rice industry differs essentially from the wheat industry in the prevalence of subsistence farming. A large percentage of the rice crop is probably consumed by those who produce it. In this case, the rice is threshed on the farm but hulled and cleaned in a local mill on a custom basis. Large mills, usually financed by foreign capital, are found in the large cities, especially in those parts of monsoon Asia where surplus rice crops are produced and where there is a flourishing export trade in rice. This is true particularly of Rangoon in Burma, Bangkok in Thailand, and Saigon in French Indo-China.

International Trade in Rice

A considerably smaller portion of the world rice crop enters international trade than is true of the wheat crop. There used to be a heavy movement of rice from Korea and Formosa (Taiwan) to Japan, but since Taiwan was a Japanese possession this was not international trade in the strict sense of the term. Much of the international trade is intra-Asiatic, involving movement from the surplus areas mentioned above to the deficit areas of India and China primarily. Considerable intranational and interregional trade in rice goes on within the larger countries of monsoon Asia, especially in China and India. In China rice moves primarily from the surplus areas of the south to the deficit areas of the north, while in India the general direction of the trade is from east to west.

World War II played havoc with the international trade in rice. Before the war, Burma used to export an annual average of about 150 million bushels of rice, and Siam (Thailand) and Indo-China contributed about 65 million bushels each, making a total of 280 million bushels. Political disturbances in the exporting countries had unfavorable effects on the production of rice, and as a result the surplus available for export dropped to little more than one-fourth. This is all the more serious in view of the increase in population and the curtailment of domestic production in the deficit countries.

Minor relief is furnished by increasing exports from Egypt and Brazil. In Egypt rice production was pushed at the expense of the cotton crop, about 10 million bushels of rice being available for export during the calendar year 1947; but this is not expected to continue. However, Brazil may be expected to produce a surplus of rice and thus contribute to the world supply during the period of acute shortage.[20]

Outlook for Rice Production

Rice may be said to occupy today a position which wheat held in the eyes of Sir William Crookes[21] toward the turn of the century. The future is uncertain and the outlook grave. Probably the best appraisal of the situation is the following by Wickizer and Bennett:

Whatever the future may hold, it is difficult to visualize any type of world order in which the problems of the Far East will cease to be of growing significance to the Western world. A genuine understanding of these problems involves recognizing rice as something more than just food for millions of people. Rice not only reflects the social and economic pattern of life for the agricultural masses of Monsoon Asia, but it is also a symbol of their hopes. Rice is the peasant farmer's means of subsistence, his first need and principal possession, his medium of exchange and standard of value. It is natural that this powerful identification of rice with his economic well-being should carry over into his family, social, and religious life. Eventu-

ally, if imperfectly, the expression of man's hopes is translated into the political sphere. When rice is scarce or dear and families must go hungry, man will work harder and longer, but when his position seems to be without hope, he will also fight and kill to survive. Political maneuvering often obscures the underlying stresses and strains upon static, or even advancing economies. So long as it remains the lifeblood of Monsoon Asia, there will be a crying need for more rice, both to satisfy the primitive wants of millions and to enhance the importance and dignity of human life for other millions.[22]

A COMPARISON OF WHEAT AND RICE

The question is sometimes raised: Which is the leading cereal crop, wheat or rice? While the question itself is not important, an attempt to answer it brings out some interesting facts.

Recent figures show these crude facts: In the average year during the period 1935-1939 the output of wheat and rice amounted to 360 and 347 billion pounds respectively and in the average year during 1946-1948 to 354 and 324 billion pounds respectively. This suggests a slight lead of wheat over rice; but, because of incomplete statistical coverage, especially of rice-growing countries, this may be ignored. Roughly 330 billion pounds, or 150 million metric tons, may be taken as a reasonable working estimate for both wheat and rice crops.

However, this apparent equality in the size of the two crops is misleading. For, as was pointed out earlier, wheat loses its hull in threshing whereas rice is hulled not in harvesting but during milling. Since the hull does not serve as human food, it must be deducted from the rice figures if they are to be comparable to the wheat figures. It is assumed to weigh about 37 percent of the paddy or rough rice, as the threshed rice is called. Removing the hull converts rough rice into brown rice. Removing the brown skin or bran converts brown rice into cleaned or white rice. This entails a further loss of 10 percent. (In the Occident white rice is sometimes polished with glucose and talc.) Wheat, as was mentioned above, loses about one-fourth of its weight in conversion into flour.

Wheat and rice differ not only in the mechanics of conversion but also in the uses to which the two crops are put. Because of the

[20] See FAO, *Cereal Review, Part 3—Rice*, June 25, 1947, p. 2.

[21] A British scientist who in the early nineties predicted a world wheat famine within half a century.

[22] V. D. Wickizer and M. K. Bennett, *op. cit.*, p. 312.

TABLE 14.11. A Comparison Between Wheat and Rice[23]

	Wheat	Rice
1. Acreage	400,000,000 acres (irrigation negligible)	200,000,000 acres (mostly irrigated)
2. Crop		
Weight	150,000,000 tons (metric) or 330 billion lb.	150,000,000 tons (metric)[a] or 330 billion lb.
Volume	5,500,000,000 bushels (60 lb.)	7,333,000,000 bushels (45 lb.)
3. Yield	825 lb. or 13.75 bu. per acre	1040 lb. or 23.1 bu. per acre
4. Disposition of crop		
Total crop	150,000,000 tons	150,000,000 tons
Diversion to non-food uses		
Seed	18,000,000 tons (12%)	6,000,000 tons (4%)
Feed	12,000,000 tons (8%)	6,000,000 tons (4%)
Industrial uses	.....	6,000,000 tons (4%)
Total diversion	30,000,000 tons (20%) −30,000,000 tons	18,000,000 tons (12%) −18,000,000 tons
Balance	120,000,000 tons	132,000,000 tons
Loss in conversion to food		
Hulling	.....	48,840,000 tons (37%)
Other	30,000,000 tons (25%)	8,316,000 tons (6.3%)
	−30,000,000 tons	57,156,000 tns. (43.3%) 57,156,000 tons
Balance available for human consumption[b]	90,000,000 tons (wheat flour)	78,844,000 tons (clean rice)
5. Consumption		
Number of consumers	880,000,000 (estimated)	880,000,000 (estimated)
Per capita consumption	225 lb.	187 lb.

[a] Paddy or rough (unhulled) rice as harvested.

[b] About 60 percent of the wheat crop emerges as wheat flour. Some of the wheat fed to animals (including millwaste) reappears as human food (chicken, eggs, meat, milk, etc.).

About 50 percent of the paddy crop emerges as clean rice. Some of the paddy fed to animals and some of the mill waste (bran) may reappear as human food. The calculation here used for the conversion of rice is based on standard milling practice. Since much rice is processed by primitive methods, which may remove less bran than standard equipment, the recovery rate may be slightly higher than 50 percent.

differences in production methods, wheat and rice differ widely in seed requirements. While only 4 percent of a rice crop must be set aside for seed purposes, the corresponding figure for wheat is probably nearer 12 percent. While probably 8 percent of the wheat crop is normally diverted to feed animals (exclusive of mill wastes), the figure for rice is probably about half of that. More rice than wheat is probably diverted to industrial purposes such as paper manufacture, beer and wine making, etc.

When all these deductions for losses in conversion and diversion to other uses are made, it appears that about 60 percent of the total wheat crop usually reaches human consumers; the figure for rice is slightly under 50 percent. However, the local and rather primitive processing of large portions of the rice crop may

[23] These figures are pre-World War II approximations.

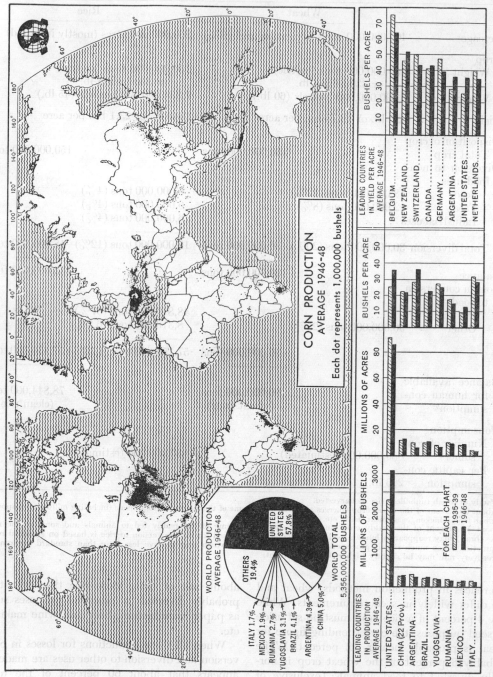

CORN PRODUCTION
AVERAGE 1946-48
Each dot represents 1,000,000 bushels

WORLD PRODUCTION
AVERAGE 1946-48

UNITED STATES
57.8%

OTHERS
19.4%

WORLD TOTAL
5,356,000,000 BUSHELS

ITALY 1.7%
MEXICO 1.9%
RUMANIA 2.7%
YUGOSLAVIA 3.1%
BRAZIL 4.1%
ARGENTINA 4.3%
CHINA 5.0%

LEADING COUNTRIES
IN PRODUCTION
AVERAGE 1946-48

MILLIONS OF BUSHELS
1000   2000   3000

UNITED STATES
CHINA (22 Prov.)
ARGENTINA
BRAZIL
YUGOSLAVIA
RUMANIA
MEXICO
ITALY

FOR EACH CHART
1935-39
1946-48

MILLIONS OF ACRES
20   40   60   80

BUSHELS PER ACRE
10 20 30 40 50

LEADING COUNTRIES
IN YIELD PER ACRE
AVERAGE 1946-48

BUSHELS PER ACRE
10 20 30 40 50 60 70

BELGIUM
NEW ZEALAND
SWITZERLAND
CANADA
GERMANY
ARGENTINA
UNITED STATES
NETHERLANDS

FIG. 14.5.

result in a considerably higher percentage being recovered for food than is true when modern milling practices are used. This should be kept in mind in studying Table 14.11.

By far the most difficult problem is appraising the nutritive value of wheat and rice. There are many varieties of wheat and many varieties of rice. Wheat contains more protein than rice. The protein content of wheat ranges between 9 and 20 percent for ordinary varieties, whereas rice seldom contains more than 7 percent. The fat content of wheat is 1.5 percent as against 0.90 for rice. On the other hand, rice makes up for these relative deficiencies by a high percentage of starch. If we calculate the caloric value of the various food elements according to the Rubner formula (1 gram of protein and 1 gram of carbohydrate each equal 4.1 calories; 1 gram of fat equals 9.3 calories), we find that one pound of polished rice is rated at 1640 calories, as against 1563 for wheat flour; unpolished rice is rated at 1620 calories per pound.

But calories alone do not tell the whole story. The almost complete absence of cellulose in rice accounts for its extremely high digestibility. Thus 80 percent of the protein, 93 percent of the fat, and 99 percent of the carbohydrates (including starch)—or 96 percent of the entire dry contents of rice—are digestible. This figure compares with 95 percent in the case of wheat flour. In other words, rice excels wheat not only in caloric value but also in digestibility.

THE MAJOR FEED CROPS: CORN, BARLEY, AND OATS

Whereas wheat, rye, and rice are the primary food grains, corn, barley, and oats are largely feed grains. As such, they perform a dual role, for they are the basis of the work done by work and draft animals and the raw material for the production of meat, milk, butter, and other secondary foods. In parts of the earth where tractors are replacing work animals, the first role is losing its importance. However, it may be partly counterbalanced by an increased per capita consumption of meat and other animal foods.

Corn[24] or Maize

Corn is by far the most important grain crop used for feed, the average 1935-1939 crop figures being 4.8 billion bushels (shelled, 56 pounds) for corn, 2.2 billion bushels (48 pounds) for barley, and 4.3 billion bushels (32 pounds) for oats. On a weight basis the three crops ranked as follows: corn 268.8 billion pounds, barley 105.6, and oats 137.6. Postwar figures favor corn even more, mainly because of the large crops the United States has been harvesting.

Like the potato, peanut, tomato, lima bean, tobacco, cacao, and many other important agricultural products, corn is a native of America and hence was unknown to the rest of the world until the discovery of the New World. Today it is more widely distributed over the earth than any other crop grown by man[25]—another proof of the extent to which our landscape is a cultural rather than a natural landscape. It is true that wheat is grown on a larger acreage, but corn culture is more widely diffused geographically (see Fig. 14.5). While, as was pointed out above, wheat production is largely confined to two fairly narrow ribbons, corn is cultivated in virtually every country from Canada to Argentina, from Hungary to South Africa, and from the Soviet Union and northern China to Australia and New Zealand. This wide geographical distribution is the result of remarkable plant breeding and cultural adaptation. "From a wild plant not even known today, the American Indians gradually developed types of corn that were adapted to climatic conditions in whatever parts of the continent the red men made their homes." As a result of this achievement which Schaben calls the greatest plant breeding job in all history,[26] maize spread from its original habitat in Central America or Peru throughout the agricultural regions of the earth. In the region farthest from the equator corn is grown not for the ear but for green fodder which is used in the form of ensilage, a chopped-up feed prepared in silos.

---

[24] "Corn" means kernel; hence the word is often used to designate any leading cereal or kernel crop. Thus, when the British repealed the Corn Laws, corn meant wheat. When the East German speaks of corn (Korn), he refers to rye; the West German means wheat. In the United States maize is the leading cereal crop, hence it is known as the corn crop.

[25] L. J. Schaben, "Corn's Role in Feeding the Hungry," Foreign Agriculture, July, 1948, p. 139.

[26] Ibid., p. 141.

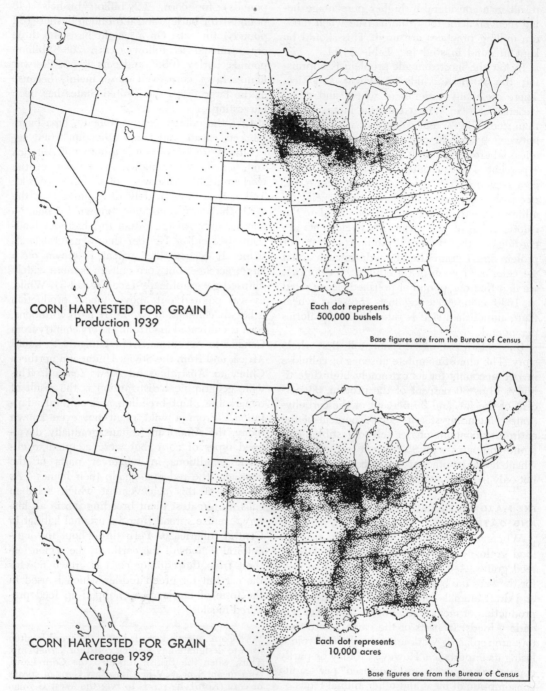

FIG. 14.6. Corn Harvested for Grain, Production and Acreage, 1939. (Figs. 14.6 and 14.7 from U. S. Department of Agriculture, Bureau of Agricultural Economics.)

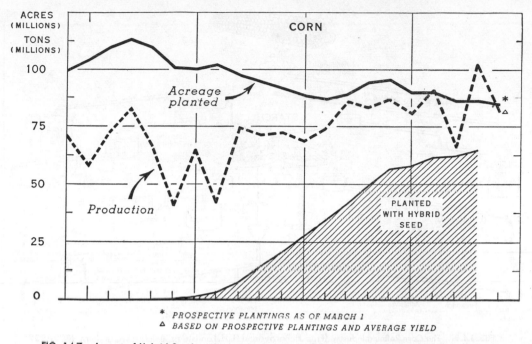

FIG. 14.7. Impact of Hybrid Seed on Corn Acreage and Production in the United States, 1929-1949.

"A significant peculiarity of corn is the wide difference between strains developed to meet the needs of diverse conditions of temperature, moisture, length of growing season, and other environmental factors. Each climate has its characteristic varieties. Some grains are less than two feet tall and require no more than

TABLE 14.12. World Corn Production, 1935-1939 and 1946-1948[27]

| | 1935-1939 | | 1946-1948 | |
	Million Bushels	Percent	Million Bushels	Percent
United States	2315.6	48.7	3095.0	57.3
Argentina	302.0	6.4	229.0	4.2
China	262.0	5.5	266.7[a]	5.0
Brazil	215.2	4.8	216.0	4.0
Yugoslavia	176.0	3.8	...	...
Rumania	172.0	3.8	...	...
U.S.S.R.	170.0	3.7	113.0	2.4
Italy	112.8	2.4	93.0	1.9
India[b]	107.8	2.3	105.0	2.2
Mexico	67.5	1.4	101.3	2.1
All others	849.1	17.2	1143.0	20.9
World total	4750.0	100.0	5362.0	100.0

[a] 1946-1947 only.
[b] Including Pakistan.

60 to 70 days to mature. Others grow more than 20 feet tall and require over 300 to 340 days to mature."[28] Corn is also adapted to a wide variety of soil conditions.

Just as wheat production is widely diffused but at the same time is concentrated in a few places with optimal conditions, corn too has its regions of optimal returns. A glance at Fig. 14.5 shows this concentration of corn production in a few places—the Corn Belt of the United States, around Rosario in Argentina, parts of southeastern Europe, Java, and parts of China. While it is true that corn is grown from Canada to Argentina, it is also true that over half the crop in 1946-1948 was raised in the United States. Table 14.12 shows world production of corn for 1935-1939 and 1946-1948.

Corn production varies widely as regards yields. During the period 1935-1939 yields ranged from 9 bushels per acre in Mexico to almost 41 in Canada, 45.4 in New Zealand, and 47.1 in Germany. How widely they vary even within a single country is shown by Table 14.13 and Fig. 14.6.

Yields in the United States are increasing,

[27] Foreign Agriculture circular, April 18, 1949.

[28] L. J. Schaben, *op. cit.*, p. 140.

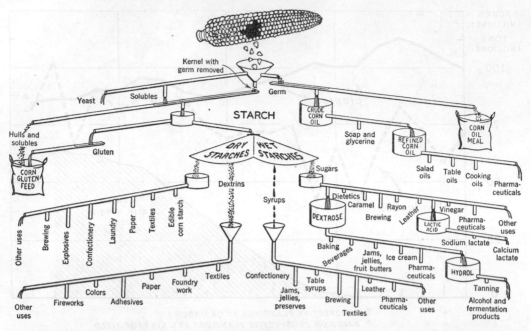

FIG. 14.8.   The Corn Refining Industry. (From H. Barger and H. H. Landsberg, *American Agriculture, 1899-1939.*
National Bureau of Economic Research, New York, 1942; based on data from Corn Industries Research
Foundations.)

chiefly because of the introduction of high-yielding hybrid corns. This is shown in Fig. 14.7. The rapid expansion of acreage planted with hybrid corn is indeed spectacular. As a result of the use of hybrid corn, total production

TABLE 14.13.   Corn Yields by States, 1946[29]

State	Bushels per Acre
Iowa	57
Illinois	57
Washington	52
Indiana	51
New Jersey	45
Mississippi	16.5
Alabama	15.5
Louisiana	15.0
Montana	14.0
Georgia	13.5
Arizona	11.0

has increased while acreage has declined. In 1931-1935 the average acreage harvested was 102.3 million; the amount harvested was 2330.4 million bushels; the yield per acre was 22.8 bushels. In 1944-1948 the acreage harvested was 90.6 million, or 11.4 percent *less* than dur-

ing the earlier period; production averaged 3.1 billion bushels, or about a third *more;* and the yield averaged 38 bushels, or almost 70 percent *higher.*[30]

Another great innovation which adds greatly to the value of the corn crop is the feeding of ground corncobs to cattle. Formerly the disposal of these mountains of cobs was a real problem. Then the Ohio Experiment Station of the U. S. Department of Agriculture discovered that ground corncobs, mixed with some high-protein meal and some vitamin-bearing hay, make excellent feed.[31]

Corn seeds differ widely in content. The typical Corn Belt corn holds more water than the flint corn of Argentina; hence the latter is more transportable. This accounts in part for the fact that Argentina was for long the world's premier exporter of corn, although her crop is but a fraction of that of the United States.

---

[29] *Statistical Abstract of the United States, 1948,* p. 655.

[30] For a discussion of even greater potential yields, see Jay Richter, "Our Lazy Acres Can Yield Far More Food," magazine section of the New York *Times,* October 9, 1949, p. 24.

[31] See John Dos Passos, "Revolution on the Farm," *Life,* August 23, 1948.

Most of our crop is converted into meat and commercial products, generally on the farm where it is grown. But corn also yields industrial products, as Fig. 14.8 shows.

Formerly corn consumed as primary food played a fairly important part in the diet of the people of the United States, especially in the South. It is still widely consumed in Latin America as tortillas, tamales, fritos, etc. Nor should corn flakes, cornstarch pudding, and salad oil made from corn oil be forgotten. Considerable amounts of corn are consumed directly in Europe, especially in Rumania where it is a major part of the diet. In Italy polenta prepared from corn meal is a staple dietary item.

Barley

Russia is the leading producer of barley, but since 1939 no reliable data seem to be available. The importance of this grain for Russia lies in its hardiness. While the northern limits of wheat growing are around Leningrad, barley production extends up to the Arctic Circle. Next to the Soviet Union, China is the leading producer, followed by the United States, Germany, and India.

TABLE 14.14.   World Barley Production, Leading Countries,[a] Selected Years[32]

| | 1935-1939 | | 1944-1946 | |
	Million Bushels	Percent	Million Bushels	Percent
China	341.0	14.2	307	14.6
United States	238.6	10.0	269	12.9
Germany	168.9	7.0	105	5.0
India	118.4	4.9	115	5.5
All others	1490.1	63.9	1289	62.0
Total	2357.0	100.0	2085	100.0

[a] Excluding U.S.S.R.

Barley is fed to animals, is eaten by man, and is converted into malt from which beer is brewed. A considerable part of our own and of Germany's crop is used for the latter purpose.

Oats

Table 14.15 shows the leading producers of oats, again with the Soviet Union omitted. Although the U.S.S.R. is a leading producer, since 1944 no reliable data have been available.

[32] U.S. Department of Agriculture.

One reason why oats is very important in the United States is the way it fits into the crop pattern of the Corn Belt. Oats needs attention either before or after corn does. It

TABLE 14.15.   World Production of Oats by Leading Countries,[a] Selected Years[33]

| | 1935-1936 | | 1944-1946 | |
	Million Bushels	Percent	Million Bushels	Percent
United States	1045.3	23.0	1401.0	33.3
Germany	404.9	10.6	...	...
Canada	338.1	7.7	427.1	10.2
France	328.7	7.5	207.8	4.9
Poland	180.7	4.1	...	...
United Kingdom	138.6	3.2	224.3	5.3
All others	1889.7	46.9	1598.6	46.3
Total	4326.0	100.0	4165.0	100.0

[a] Excluding U.S.S.R.

is also hardier than corn, which accounts for its widespread growth in north central Europe. Since World War II, Europe, including the European section of the Soviet Union, has grown less, while the United States and Canada have grown more. In 1935-1939 the output of the two latter countries amounted to little more than a third of the world total, but in 1944-1946 it was considerably over half of the total crop. This is surprising in view of the rather close identification of oats as feed for horses. Evidently other animals thrive on it too.

The lightness of oats—only 32 pounds to the bushel, as against 60 pounds for wheat—militates against any important role for oats in international trade. Furthermore, oats are sold in the most competitive market, the feed market.

POTATOES

As was stated at the beginning of this chapter, the inclusion of potatoes with the cereal grains is supported by Bennett's table comparing the diets of nations. It will be recalled that he groups "potatoes" with cereal grains. His use of the term "potatoes" includes, along with the white potato, a number of other starch-yielding plants such as the sweet potato, yam, banana, plantain, yautia, taro, cassava, sago palm, etc. Most of these foods are of importance in tropical or subtropical countries. There are virtually no statistical data on these foods, ex-

[33] U.S. Department of Agriculture.

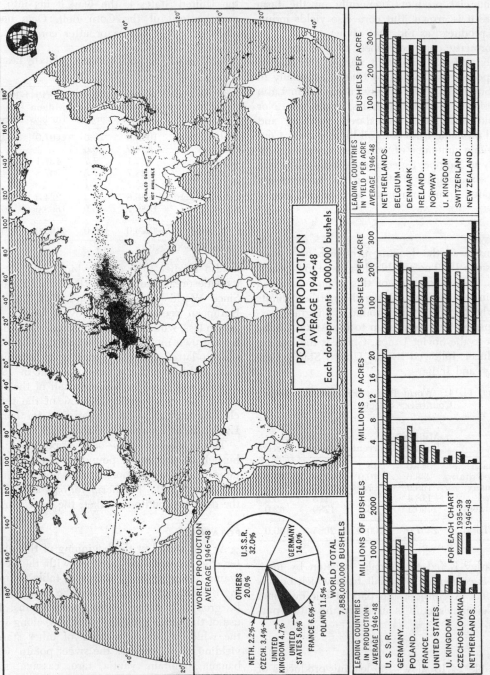

FIG. 14.9. World Potato Map. (U. S. Department of Agriculture, Office of Foreign Agriculture, Graphic Summary of World Agriculture, 1949.)

cept for the banana in so far as it enters international trade. Here the discussion will be confined to the white potato, *Solanum tuberosum*, a member of the nightshade family.

Like corn, the potato is a native of America. But while corn is today the western hemisphere's largest crop, the potato reached its highest development in the cool climate and on the sandy acid soils of the North European plain. Potato culture reaches as far inland as the Urals and is almost as highly concentrated as is rice culture in monsoon Asia—even more so than corn is in North America. Corn and potatoes constitute the respective bases of the hog-raising industries of North America and Europe. But whereas in richer and less densely populated North America almost all the corn is fed to animals which furnish the luxury of secondary food, in less prosperous and more densely populated Europe a large portion of the potato crop serves directly as human food, with many industrial materials such as alcohol and starch as by-products.

TABLE 14.16. World Potato Production[34]

	1935-1939 Million Bushels	Percent	1944-1946 Million Bushels	Percent
U.S.S.R.	2134.3	25.1	...	...
Germany	1835.9	21.6	...	...
Poland	1300.4	15.3	...	...
France	575.2	6.8	408.9	6.0
Czechoslovakia	372.7	4.4	270.2	3.9
United States	355.5	4.2	426.1	6.2
United Kingdom	182.7	2.2	360.9	5.2
Spain	171.0	2.0	109.8	1.6
Belgium	116.9	1.4	58.9	0.9
Austria	106.0	1.2	57.6	0.8
Italy	100.9	1.2	75.5	1.0
Netherlands	100.7	1.2	131.3	1.9
All others	1171.5	13.4	5018.2	72.5
Total	8523.7	100.0	6917.4	100.0

The concentration of potato culture in Europe is shown in Fig. 14.9 and in Table 14.16, showing world potato production in 1935-1939 and 1944-1946.

As was mentioned earlier, in volume (bushels) and weight (pounds) the world potato crop exceeds any other crop. However, the potato as purchased contains 20.8 percent refuse and 62.6 percent water, leaving food values of only 16.6 percent, of which 14.7 per-

cent are carbohydrates. The composition of wheat flour is 12 percent water and 88 percent food values. But, as we have seen, only about 50 percent of our wheat crop is converted into flour. A pound of wheat flour has over 1600 calories, while a pound of potatoes (as purchased) has less than 300.

In yield per acre the potato stands up well. In Germany the average annual yield during the period 1935-1939 was 256.4 bushels, while in the United States during the same period the per-acre yield was 13.2 bushels for wheat and 25 bushels for corn. At 295 calories per pound of potatoes, 1615 for wheat, and 1690 for field-dry corn, calories per acre for the above yields are as follows:

Potatoes (Germany)	4,538,280
Wheat (United States)	1,279,080
Corn (United States)	2,366,000

In appraising these yields, the general nature of agriculture in the two countries must be kept in mind, agriculture in densely populated Germany being far more labor-intensive than that in our country. In the United States potato production is concentrated in rather sharply circumscribed areas such as Aroostook County in Maine, Monmouth County in New Jersey, Long Island, parts of Delaware, Idaho, Colorado, California, North Dakota, Florida, etc. There is a certain degree of regional specialization, both in type of potato produced and in the time of the year when the crops reach the market.

More than seventy diseases and insect pests attack the growing potato crop.[35] But sprays and spray equipment have been greatly improved and new varieties resistant—or even immune—to diseases have been developed. The struggle for a better and more dependable potato crop is proceeding on a truly international basis and holds out promises of much further improvement.

This is true, in varying degrees, of all the crops discussed in this chapter. Progress during recent decades has been almost spectacular, a fact which must not be lost sight of when the grave problem of food for future billions of human beings is considered.

---

[34] *Agricultural Statistics, 1948.*

[35] F. J. Stevenson, "The Potato—A Leading World Food Crop," *Foreign Agriculture,* October, 1948, p. 215.

BIBLIOGRAPHY

Azzi, O., *Le Climat du Blé dans le Monde*, International Institute of Agriculture, Rome, 1930.

Bennett, M. K., and associates, *International Commodity Stockpiling as an Economic Stabilizer*, Stanford, Stanford University Press, 1949.

Britnell, G. E., *The Wheat Economy*, Toronto, University of Toronto Press, 1939.

Clark, J. A., "Improvement in Wheat," *Agricultural Yearbook, 1936*, U. S. Department of Agriculture, Washington, 1936.

Davis, J. S., *Wheat and the A.A.A.*, Washington, Brookings Institution, 1935.

de Hevesy, P., *World Wheat Planning and Economic Planning in General*, London, Oxford University Press, 1940.

Elwood, R. B., and associates, *Changes in Technology and Labor Requirements of Crop Production: Wheat and Oats*, WPA National Research Project, Report No. A-10, Philadelphia, 1939.

Food Research Institute, *Wheat Studies* (monthly), Stanford University.

Heisig, C. P., Ahrendes, E. R., and Merrick, D. E., *Wheat Production in Peace and War*, U. S. Department of Agriculture, Bureau of Agricultural Economics, Washington, 1945.

International Institute of Agriculture, *Le Maïs dans le Commerce Mondial*, Rome, 1932.

Jasny, N., *Competition Among Grains*, Stanford University, Food Research Institute, 1940.

Percival, J., *The Wheat Plant*, London, Duckworth, 1921.

Schaben, L. J., "Corn's Role in Feeding the Hungry," *Foreign Agriculture*, July, 1948.

Stevenson, F. J., "The Potato—A Leading World Food Crop," *Foreign Agriculture*, October, 1948.

Timoshenko, V. P., *Agricultural Russia and the Wheat Problem*, Stanford University, Food Research Institute, 1932.

United Nations, Food and Agriculture Organization, *Cereals Review, Part 3—Rice*, Washington, 1947.

United Nations, Food and Agriculture Organization, *Commodity Series: Wheat*, Washington, 1947.

United Nations, Food and Agriculture Organization, *Report on World Commodity Problems*, Washington, 1949.

U. S. Department of Agriculture, "Grass," *Yearbook of Agriculture, 1948*.

U. S. Department of Agriculture, Bureau of Agricultural Economics, *The Wheat Situation*, Washington (issued periodically).

U. S. Department of Agriculture, Office of Foreign Agricultural Relations, *A Graphic Summary of World Agriculture*, Washington, 1949.

U. S. Department of Agriculture, Office of Foreign Agricultural Relations, *Foreign Agriculture* (monthly).

Wickizer, V. D., and Bennett, M. K., *The Rice Economy of Monsoon Asia*, Stanford University, Food Research Institute, 1941.

Chapter 15

CANE AND BEET SUGAR

Among the "big four" of the American diet, sugar is a newcomer, for only comparatively lately has it been recognized as a staple food, not only in the United States but among white people in general.

There are many kinds of sugars. The present discussion is limited to sucrose,[1] a sugar extracted from sugar cane, a product of the tropics and subtropics, and from sugar beets, produced in temperate-zone countries. Cane sugar is much the older, for beet sugar is the product of nineteenth-century science and machine industry and of modern economic nationalism. Hence the early history of sugar is concerned solely with cane sugar.

SUGAR HISTORY TO WORLD WAR I
Early Beginnings

Sugar obtained from cane has been known in the tropics since the remotest times on record.[2] But not until about 1000 A.D. did Europe become acquainted with it through the Arabs,

[1] The scientific name for the sugar contained in beets and cane.

[2] The word "sugar" (su-gur) is of Hindu origin; today cane juice is called gur in India.

who in turn owed their knowledge to the Persians and Hindus. Sugar culture spread from Asia to the Mediterranean, and later to the New World.

During the seventeenth and eighteenth centuries, the West Indies and Brazil were Europe's chief sources of supply, only negligible quantities being shipped from Asia. The economic and military struggle between France and England that culminated early in the nineteenth century so reduced the trade in sugar that this commodity became even scarcer and more valuable.

Rise of Beet Sugar

In a sense, Napoleon may be said to be responsible for founding a new industry—the extraction of sugar from sugar beets. The Milan and Berlin Decrees which were promulgated to strike England through her trade forbade commercial intercourse between the European continent and England, and thus deprived Europeans of sugar, which was derived largely from British-controlled sources or moved over British-controlled trade routes.

It had long been known that innumerable

other plants besides cane contained sugar; in fact, the Prussian chemist Marggraf had succeeded, as early as 1747, in extracting sugar in quantity from a forage beet, but the process was not commercially successful. Realizing the danger of depriving numbers of people of a commodity to whose use they had become accustomed, Napoleon offered a reward to anyone who could devise a commercially successful process of extracting sugar from beets—or any other source. This stimulus was so successful that by 1850 beet sugar represented 14 percent of the world sugar production.

Cane sugar had long enjoyed certain initial advantages of climate, cheap labor, and colonial preference; but it suffered a serious setback when in 1834 slavery was abolished in all British colonies and possessions. The movement soon spread to other parts of the world and culminated in our Civil War. This setback was all the more serious because it came at a time when governments and science were seeking to outdo each other in promoting the beet sugar industry.

Governments in the beet-growing belts have always been extremely solicitous of the beet sugar industry. There are both physical and economic reasons for this. Sugar beet cultivation renders possible almost complete conservation of soil fertility, and the industry yields valuable by-products which greatly assist other agricultural activities such as dairying and cattle and sheep raising. Furthermore, the amazing root system of the sugar beet materially raises the productivity of the soil. Finally, sugar offers an excellent basis for taxation; even a moderate tax yields considerable amounts of revenue. Sugar is also important to countries striving for national self-sufficiency in food.

Perhaps the most powerful force behind the growth of the beet sugar industry was just plain politics, for even during the second half of the nineteenth century agrarian interests still constituted very powerful pressure groups in many European countries. Germany, long the leading producer of beet sugar, illustrates this point. Her landed aristocrats were suffering from the growing competition of overseas staple grains, especially those of North America. Sugar was an ideal estate crop, except for a shortage of labor. So great was the pressure which the landed aristocracy could exert on the government that not only was migrant foreign labor provided and the industry protected against the competition of imported sugar, especially cane sugar, but it was even granted subsidies. The subsidy idea was adopted by several other European countries, with the result that European beet sugar manufacturers were enabled to dump their surpluses on foreign markets, especially the British.

The rise of the beet sugar industry in the United States stemmed from somewhat different causes, chiefly the problem of finding remunerative use for the vast tracts of land which the onward sweep west had opened for settlement. Soon after large areas, especially in Michigan, Utah, Colorado, Nebraska, Wyoming, Montana, and California, were found climatically and soil-wise suited to sugar beet culture, pressure groups sought and obtained protection for this new crop. By the nineties the industry was well established.

The next step, technical advance in beet culture, was in part the result of European taxes on sugar. Because taxes were levied on the amount of beets used rather than on the sugar produced, an efficient producer who extracted a large amount of sucrose from a given beet tonnage felt the tax far less than his inefficient competitor. Partly in response to this stimulus, but also driven by their natural desire for improvement, scientists succeeded, by means of selection and scientific crossbreeding, in raising the sugar content of beets from roughly 5 percent early in the nineteenth century to almost 20 percent a hundred years later.

As a result of the technical and governmental measures just described, Europe's beet sugar output exceeded the total world output of cane sugar during the last decade of the nineteenth century and the first decade of the twentieth. In 1900-1901, the world output of beet sugar amounted to 6 million tons (62 percent), as against 3.4 million tons (38 percent) for cane sugar.

Comeback of Cane Sugar

But the victory of beet over cane sugar was exceedingly short-lived, for since 1920-1921 the output of beet sugar has averaged roughly only one-third of the total world production.

The renascence of the cane sugar industry began with the Brussels Sugar Convention, called in 1902 largely on the initiative of the British Colonial Secretary. As we have seen, England, the ardent advocate of Empire preference, had become the dumping ground of the sugar surpluses—both cane and beet—from all over the world. While the resulting low prices were welcomed by industrial and private consumers, Britain's cane-growing colonies clamored for relief from this depressed market situation, which they ascribed to unfair competition. Since artificial factors, such as open or concealed bounties or subsidies, had a great deal to do with the depression of the sugar market, Great Britain threatened to close the British market to bounty-fed sugar exporters by levying countervailing duties to the exact amount of the bounties and premiums granted by the exporting countries.

In the Brussels Sugar Convention, Germany, Austria-Hungary, Belgium, Spain, France, Great Britain, Italy, the Netherlands, and Sweden engaged themselves and their colonies not to allow any open or secret premiums on the production or exportation of sugar, to limit the duty on foreign sugar on the basis of the charges imposed on the home product, and to levy an additional compensating duty on bounty-fed sugar or to prohibit its importation altogether.

Two wars—the Sino-Japanese War of 1895 and the Spanish-American War of 1898—were major contributing factors to the renascence of cane sugar. Japan's acquisition of Formosa enabled her to become independent of outside sources and to build up a strong cane sugar industry under her political control. Similarly, when Puerto Rico and the Philippines came under American rule, their sugar industry was modernized and generally encouraged. As a result of this, and of a reciprocity agreement with Cuba, the aggregate production of Puerto Rico, the Philippines, and Cuba rose from its all-time high of 1.3 million tons in 1894, under Spanish rule, to over 3 million tons in 1914. In addition, many cane-growing countries stimulated production by means of high import duties and, in some cases, embargoes on foreign sugar.

The above factors are all more or less artificial. Even more important, perhaps, were certain natural factors favoring the growth of the cane sugar industry. For more than a century prior to 1880, nothing—apart from the introduction of steam for power and heat—had been done to improve cane sugar production methods; but around that year scientific work along these lines was begun almost simultaneously in Louisiana, Java, and the West Indies. The results of this work could not bear fruit until the turn of the century, when conditions were favorable to large investments. Huge amounts of capital flowed from the United States into Puerto Rico, Hawaii, and Cuba, and to a lesser extent into the Philippines; European capital flowed into such cane sugar islands as Java, Mauritius, Jamaica, and Barbados. The badly organized and somewhat haphazard industry yielded to the new spirit in both technique and management. Large manufacturing companies revolutionized the agricultural side of cane growing; modern *centrales* and refineries sprang up, and cane sugar was soon being produced as efficiently as beet sugar.

To speak of the ascendancy of cane over beet sugar, however, does not mean that beet sugar production decreased. It kept on growing, at least for a while, but cane sugar production grew faster and soon outstripped the beet sugar output.

WORLD WAR I AND THE SUGAR INDUSTRY

The expansion of both beet and cane sugar production during the years preceding World War I had resulted in mountainous stocks and falling prices, and had brought the industry to the verge of disaster. However, the war necessitated a drastic curtailment of beet sugar production and stimulated cane sugar production to a vigorous expansion which, being pushed too far and too long, led to disaster as soon as beet sugar production returned to normalcy. This in a nutshell is the story of the war's effect on sugar.

Some of the details, however, are both valuable and interesting. The curtailment of beet sugar production was due to various causes: actual fighting in sugar beet areas; dislocation of international trade; lack of labor, coal, and lime; and the need to expand the areas producing basic foodstuffs which could no longer be obtained from foreign sources. When the war was over, a tragic underrating of the resilience of Europe's beet industry led to overexpansion of cane sugar production, especially in Cuba. This fatal miscalculation was further aggravated by the inauguration of rising tariffs throughout almost the entire civilized world, and the successful propagation of a new variety of cane, P.O.J. 2878.[3] "In Java especially but also in other parts of the world this alone caused an increase of 20 to 25 per cent in the yield of sugar per acre."[4]

In the face of such technological improvements and of expanding investments, the efforts of almost all the countries toward increased self-sufficiency could lead to but one end—disastrous overproduction. The Brussels Sugar Convention had been allowed to lapse and was finally revoked, first by Java in 1919 and then by the other countries in quick succession. The European nations promptly imposed even higher duties than those in effect before the signing of the Convention in 1902, and this drove other countries to take similar steps. Great Britain stimulated domestic beet production by means of direct subsidies, with the result that her output rose from zero to 450,-000 tons in 1930-1931. At the same time, the preferential policy adopted with growing enthusiasm by the British Commonwealth of Nations led to the expansion of cane sugar production in affiliated countries. In 1913 Great Britain imported all the sugar she consumed, but almost none was Empire-produced; by 1929 more than one-half her imports came from Empire sources.

The effect of American investment and tariff policies on the sugar output of Cuba, Puerto Rico, Hawaii, and the Philippines is likewise unmistakable—both beet and cane sugar production was pushed with unprecedented vigor. Geerligs cites three reasons for this policy.[5] (1) The various nations, determined not to be "caught short" again in the event that their sugar supply was interfered with in the future by war or any other cause, were bent on building up a sugar industry within their own borders, regardless of cost. (2) Sugar constitutes a valuable export item; hence countries that produced enough sugar to satisfy their domestic needs wanted to expand production so that they would have a surplus with which to pay for vitally needed imports. (3) Beets are a valuable crop from the point of view of the farmer, for they increase soil fertility and thus, in crop rotation, increase the production of subsequent crops. Furthermore, other crops brought very low prices, which would be still further depressed if land was withdrawn from beet cultivation, for such land would necessarily be sown to these other crops.

Of particular importance is the spectacular about-face of India as a member of the world sugar economy. This vast country with its population of hundreds of millions "entered the twentieth century as a major importer of sugar initially from the beet-sugar producers of Europe, but increasingly after 1902 from Java. Subject only to a low revenue tariff, India's imports rose until 1928-29. Beginning in 1930 and 1931, a protectionist policy reduced India's imports sharply; by 1936-37 they were almost entirely eliminated. By 1940 India was prepared to assume the role of an exporter."[6]

So long as the nations which had for years suffered from a sugar shortage consumed more sugar, in their regained freedom, than ever before, the balance between supply and demand was not seriously disturbed. But this could not go on forever. By 1925, sugar stocks had begun to accumulate, and Cuba embarked on her policy of restriction. When the financial collapse in 1929 led to a drastic curtailment of sugar consumption, there followed a series of international agreements aimed at the solution of the sugar surplus problem. This phase of the story is discussed later in the chapter (see p. 256), for it can be treated more effectively after some basic factors relating to sugar production and consumption have been discussed.

IMPORTANT SUGAR STATISTICS

Fig. 15.1 shows the world production of cane and beet sugar in million long tons. It is an amazing story depicting a rise from over 17 million long tons in 1910 to almost 36 million in 1948. The figure shows that wars involving

---

[3] The letters P.O.J. stand for *Proefstation Oost Java* (Dutch for East Java Experiment Station).

[4] H. C. P. Geerligs, "The World's Staples. IV. Sugar," *Index* (Svenska Handelsbanken, Stockholm, Sweden), June, 1931, p. 137. This study was of great value in the preparation of this chapter.

[5] *Ibid.*, pp. 132-133.

[6] B. C. Swerling, *International Control of Sugar, 1918-1941*, Food Research Institute, Commodity Policy Studies No. 7, 1949, pp. 21-22.

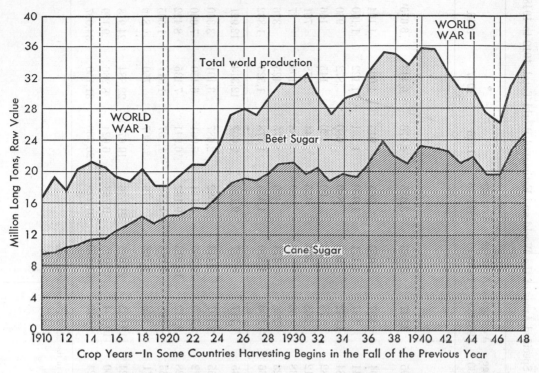

FIG. 15.1.   World Production of Cane and Beet Sugar, 1910-1948. (U. S. Department of Agriculture, World Sugar Situation, 1948.)

heavy fighting in Europe are hard on beet culture.

Both World Wars brought a definite slump in beet sugar production, measured both in tons and in percentage of total sugar output. In each case, however, recovery was fairly rapid. Thus, by 1924 beet sugar production was almost back to the pre-World War I level, and in 1948 it was only slightly below the level reached during the late thirties—11.4 million long tons in 1948 as compared with 12 million in the period 1935-1939.

Particularly striking is the long steady climb of cane sugar production from 3.4 million long tons in 1902 to almost 22 million in 1929. The depression called a halt to the climb, but by 1937 the earlier record was broken with an output of 24 million long tons, and even this was surpassed in 1947 with 25 million long tons and in 1948 with 26 million long tons. The 1937 peak is explained in part by higher yields. The 1947 and 1948 bumper crops reflect the momentum gained during World War II by countries called upon to better their own record

and at the same time pinch hit for those *hors de combat*.

Table 15.1 breaks down the recent story of cane and beet sugar into details by showing the leading producing regions.

SUGAR AND WORLD POLITICS

The sugar-producing countries of the world differ widely as to the ratio of their sugar output to their domestic needs. Some have a huge surplus, some a small one, some are self-sufficient, others have a deficit.

1. The largest sugar market, amounting now to over 7 million tons of sugar a year, is the continental United States, which depends largely on its own production and that of its noncontiguous territories, Puerto Rico, Virgin Islands (negligible quantities), and Hawaii. To them must be added the Philippines, which under the Philippine Trade Act of 1946 were granted a United States market quota of close to a million tons. This is far more than that commonwealth will be able to produce for some time to come. In this group also belongs Cuba,

TABLE 15.1. Production of Sugar, Thousand Short Tons, Raw Value, in Specified Areas of the World and Estimated World Total, 1910 to 1948[7]

Area	Average 1911-15	Average 1916-20	Average 1921-25	Average 1926-30	Average 1931-35	Average 1936-40	Average 1941-45	1946	1947	1948
North America, Hawaii, West Indies, and Central America:										
Cuba (cane)	2,295	3,928	4,684	5,295	2,847	3,183	3,685	4,476	6,448	6,675[b]
Puerto Rico and Virgin Islands (cane)	373	476	481	694	897	980	965	915	1,091	1,104
Other West Indies (cane)	326	436	504	741	887	1,121	1,070	1,131	1,122	1,100
Hawaii (cane)	567	594	623	884	1,042	986	880	680	872	950
Central America (cane)	30	62	75	82	78	83	90	120	145	166
Mexico (cane)	163	69	158	212	268	364	455	444	578	701
Canada (beet)	11	17	32	38	66	76	99	88	109	87
United States (cane)	311	221	210	123	236	474	429	475	425	376
United States (beet)	610	789	994	1,066	1,396	1,520	1,453	1,278	1,523	1,832
Total	4,686	6,592	7,761	9,135	7,717	8,787	9,126	9,607	12,313	12,991
South America (cane)[a]	563	1,080	1,361	2,155	2,197	2,414	2,682	2,687	3,191	3,300
Europe (beet) (includes U.S.S.R.)	7,836	3,920	5,143	8,372	8,759	10,295	8,114	5,061	6,450	7,060
Asia (cane)[a]	4,567	5,830	5,869	8,328	9,412	10,813	9,192	6,941	7,135	8,422
Africa (cane)	459	573	599	763	998	1,295	1,289	1,197	1,311	1,505
Australia and Fiji (cane)[a]	301	332	404	671	836	1,106	876	807	750	819
Total cane	9,971	13,606	14,968	19,924	19,635	22,685	21,526	19,676	22,884	24,918
Total beet	8,441	4,721	6,169	9,500	10,284	12,025	9,753	6,624	8,266	9,179
Total cane and beet	18,412	18,327	21,137	29,424	29,919	34,710	31,279	26,300	31,150	34,097

Figures are for crop years. In various countries of the northern hemisphere harvesting begins in the fall of the previous year.
[a] Includes very small amounts of beet sugar in certain years.
[b] Cuban Sugar Stabilization Institute figure.
[7] U.S. Department of Agriculture, *World Sugar Situation*.

since 1901 closely tied to the economy of the United States. Cuba in the late forties was assured a United States quota of almost 40 percent of the total sugar sales in that country; with consumption at 7,250,000 tons, this amounts to about 3 million tons. This leaves Cuba with about 3 million tons to be sold elsewhere, which means mostly in so-called free markets, and for domestic consumption. Her sugar consumption is small relative to her tremendous output.

2. The next market is the British Empire, which constitutes a market roughly half as large as that of the United States. India is not included because she is autonomous in her sugar policy; besides, Pakistan and Burma are now independent. The British Empire can meet roughly half of the sugar needs of the United Kingdom. The other half is one of the two big prizes of the "free market."

3. France and Portugal rely mainly on their own colonies for their sugar imports.

4. The Soviet Union, together with her satellites, likewise is self-sufficient.[8] This eastern bloc may in time become an exporter of sugar. Both Poland and Czechoslovakia fell heir to former German beet areas which may yield exportable surpluses in the future as they did before World War II. Whether the Kremlin will favor such exports remains to be seen.

Besides these largely self-sufficient areas there are great surplus-producing areas—Cuba, which in some years produced over 6 million tons above her own needs; Java, which at present is out of the running, largely because of internal disturbances but also because of the loss of her former markets, mainly Asiatic; and the Philippines, which for years to come will sell its exportable surplus to the United States.

The areas participating in transoceanic or international trade in sugar fall fairly easily into the following categories: (1) those areas in which it is an important if not the principal export crop— Cuba, Java, Peru, Dominican Republic, Mauritius, Fiji Islands, British West Indies and British Guiana, Puerto Rico, Hawaii, the Philippines, French West Indies (Guadeloupe and Martinique), and Formosa (formerly Japanese Taiwan); (2) those which sell abroad their surplus above domestic needs—

Australia, South Africa, Poland, Czechoslovakia, and to a lesser extent Brazil, Hungary, Belgium, and Germany; (3) normally self-sufficient areas— the French, Portuguese, and Japanese empires; Italy; British India (since 1937); the USSR; and Argentina; (4) those which supplement by imports an inadequate domestic production—United States, United Kingdom, Canada, Switzerland, China, and to a lesser extent Turkey, Egypt, Sweden, and Eire; and (5) a declining list of smaller countries dependent entirely on imports—Chile, Greece, Finland, New Zealand and Uruguay, among others.[9]

GEOGRAPHY OF WORLD SUGAR PRODUCTION

The World Sugar Map

The map of the world in Fig. 15.2 shows areas which grow beets and cane respectively. It reveals the obvious: Cane is a product of the tropics and subtropics and beet is a product of the temperate zone. In general, the beet- and cane-growing areas are very distinct.

The line of cleavage naturally shows little regard for political boundaries. Hence a number of countries produce both cane and beet sugar, among these being the United States (see Fig. 15.3), Argentina, Spain, Italy, Japan, and Australia. Until recently no beet sugar was produced in the southern hemisphere. Now several areas—Australia, Argentina, and Uruguay—produce limited amounts. Nor was Asia credited with any beet sugar production. Now Japan, Manchuria, Iran (Persia), Turkey, and probably the U.S.S.R. (in Asia) contribute to the growing total of Asiatic beet sugar production.

This expansion of beet culture in recent decades reflects both the powerful trend toward national self-sufficiency—autarky—and the achievement of the plant breeders who succeeded in adapting plants to new habitats.

CANE AND CANE SUGAR

Climatic and Soil Requirements

Sugar cane yields satisfactory results only in a belt straddling the equator, whose northern and southern boundaries are practically identical with the isotherms of 20° centigrade (68° Fahrenheit). This means that cane growing is largely confined to regions in which the mean annual temperatures do not range below 20° centigrade (68° Fahrenheit). Where this

---

[8] Self-sufficiency does not indicate a degree of satiation, but merely implies that a country imports very little sugar, or none at all.

[9] B. C. Swerling, *op. cit.*

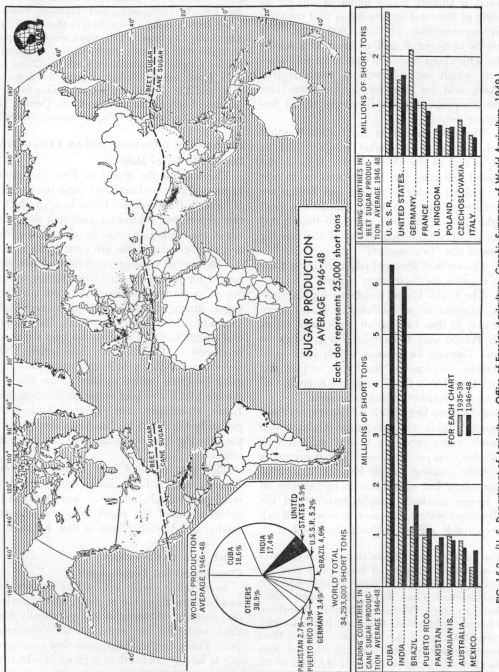

FIG. 15.2. (U. S. Department of Agriculture, Office of Foreign Agriculture, Graphic Summary of World Agriculture, 1949.)

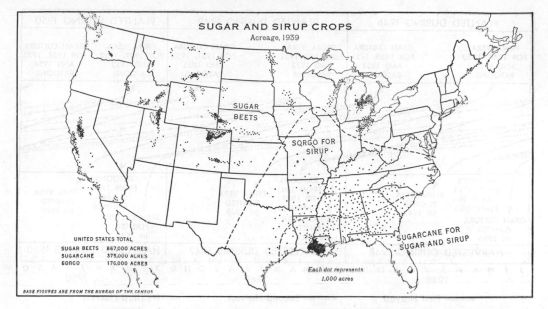

SUGAR AND SIRUP CROPS
Acreage, 1939

SUGAR BEETS

SORGO FOR SIRUP

SUGARCANE FOR SUGAR AND SIRUP

UNITED STATES TOTAL
SUGAR BEETS   867,000 ACRES
SUGARCANE   375,000 ACRES
SORGO   176,000 ACRES

Each dot represents 1,000 acres

BASE FIGURES ARE FROM THE BUREAU OF THE CENSUS

FIG. 15.3.   (U. S. Department of Agriculture, Bureau of Agricultural Economics.)

is violated, as in northern India, Louisiana, and Argentina, frost damage can be severe. Cane requires an annual precipitation of about 60 inches, or compensating facilities for irrigation. The most favorable meteorological conditions for cane growing are an even, high temperature with a heavy rainy season and a dry season sharply defined, or else little rain and ample irrigation facilities.

Sugar cane culture requires soil with high natural fertility, topsoil with a high water-retaining capacity, and a subsoil that permits rapid drainage. The moisture-retaining topsoil is necessary to provide the large quantities of water demanded by the cane during its period of rapid growth. The subsoil must be porous, since an impermeable clay subsoil, particularly if near the surface, holds the water so that the plants suffer from lack of aeration. The rich alluvial soils of the Mississippi delta, soils of volcanic origin in many parts of the world, notably in Java and Hawaii, and the drained muck soil of Florida are used for growing cane.

Sugar Cane Cultivation

Sugar cane is a herbacious perennial, i.e., its rootstock lives for several years[10] and continues to send up new crops year after year. These spontaneous unplanted crops are known as stubble or ratoon crops. Gradually ratoon crops become weaker and new planting is resorted to. Planting consists of placing in furrows small pieces of sugar cane with at least one joint. The sprout emerges from the joint. The first crop harvested after planting is known as a planted crop as distinguished from ratoon crops. Cane may be harvested 12 months after planting or be allowed to mature as long as 20 months and over. By spacing plantings over several periods of the year, by harvesting 12, 15, and 20 months' cane, and by harvesting ratoon crops of various ages, it is possible to draw out the harvesting season and thus maintain a flow of cane to the mill over perhaps as much as 6 months in the year (see Fig. 15.4). It is far more economical to operate a mill with a 6 months' cane grinding capacity of 1,300,000 than one of double this capacity which squeezes the entire operation into 3 months and stands idle the remaining 9 months. Overhead costs are virtually cut in half by carefully planning planting and harvesting with a view to the longest possible grinding period.

One thing is certain. Cane must be ground fresh. As soon as it ripens it must be cut, lest it lose sucrose by inversion;[11] and it must be

---

[10] Records of 20 to 25 years are not unknown.

[11] See the section on sugar chemistry, p. 245.

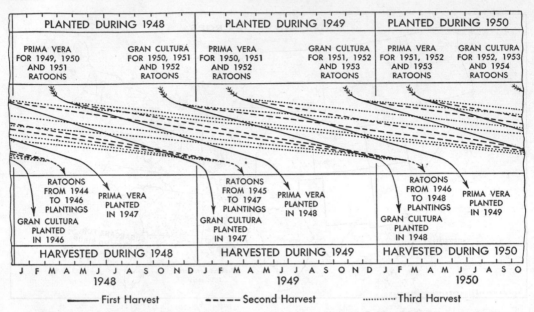

FIG. 15.4. Long-Range Aspects of Planning Sugar Production. (Prepared and drawn by the Puerto Rico Sugar Producers' Association for Erich W. Zimmermann's *Staff Report to the Interdepartmental Committee on Puerto Rico*, Washington, 1940.)

Prima vera (spring) cane is planted about April and harvested in June of the following year. Gran cultura cane is planted in the fall and allowed to mature in about 18 months.

ground right after cutting. This calls for close coördination of field and mill operations. This goes far to explain the fact that nowadays a large part of the cane is grown by the sugar mill companies themselves. The so-called company cane has made heavy inroads into *colono* cane, i.e., cane grown by independent growers who may be large estate owners or small farmers little better off than sharecroppers. A modern sugar mill may grind as much as one to two million tons of cane in one season. This requires large investments in machinery, laboratory equipment, transportation and handling devices, etc. Before these heavy investments are made the owners seek assurance of a continued supply of cane. This is done in two ways: (1) by acquiring land near the mill and growing their own cane and (2) by tying independent growers to the mills by so-called *colono* contracts.

One may wonder why sugar mills do not produce all the cane needed to keep their grinding capacity occupied. The answer cannot be given in general terms; it must rest on consideration of the specific circumstances in each case. However, the fact that in many parts

of the tropics sugar cane is a crop which by a wide margin yields the largest return per acre goes far to explain the general desire, on the part of landowners in the region where a *central* is located, to produce cane in preference to any other crop. If the *colono* contract is fair, the mill can reasonably count on a continued supply of cane from *colonos*. Company cane, however, furnishes a welcome backlog of raw-material supply for the mill.

Formerly the *ingenio*, the grinding machine, was a primitive wooden contraption, a dozen of which could be found on one plantation. In those days the plantation was the center around which the world turned. When Martinique developed the *central* system, under which scores if not hundreds of machines were replaced by a single modern large mill, centrally located (hence *central*), the mill became the hub of the sugar universe and plantations by the hundreds had to adjust their operations to the needs of the mill to assure it as long and as continuous a grinding season as possible.

It was the big sugar companies which, along with government experiment stations, carried on scientific research and were responsible for

A 2000-year-old salt mine in China is worked by coolies with handmade wooden equipment. (From Ewing Galloway.)

▲ Toting and lifting, old and new. (Top picture, from Standard Oil Co. (N.J.), photo by Corsini; lower, Kennecott Copper Corporation.)
▼

◄ Power-driven equipment of American oil wells permits a few men to drill far deeper than do primitive Chinese methods. The pressure of natural gas or water lifts the oil. (By Ewing Galloway, N.Y.)

▲

"A 10-ton, 500-coolie-powered, rice-burning roller" building an airfield in China. The rice consumed by 500 men is far costlier than its equivalent in Diesel oil. (Official U.S. Army photo, from Ewing Galloway.)

Modern road construction equipment gives a few men machine power greater than a thousand coolies have. (By Le Mont. From Ewing Galloway, N.Y.)

◄

▲

Land transport. The pay load carried by this human caravan exploring for minerals in Africa is small compared to the load necessary to feed the carriers. (By Ewing Galloway, N.Y.)

Prospecting from the air. A photographic survey made from a plane may in a few hours yield better results than six months "on safari." (From Ewing Galloway, N.Y.)

◄

▲ Water transport. "Trackers" pulling a junk upstream through a gorge in the Yangtze River in China. Such stupendous effort is tolerated only when human labor is "dirt cheap." (By Ewing Galloway, N.Y.)

Water transport. With an electric locomotive one man can move a vessel through this lock. Human power alone could not budge it. (By Ewing Galloway, N.Y.) ▶

◄ Flagstone paths in western China. Some 500-mile stretches have no roads fit for wheeled vehicles. What cannot be floated on rivers or canals must be toted. (By Ewing Galloway, N.Y.)

Effortless modern luxury travel contrasts sharply with primitive toilsome travel in China. (By Ewing Galloway, N.Y.)
▼

Generators at Bonneville Dam. Here nature, the "long" factor, supports man, the "short" factor. (By Louis Tager, from Ewing Galloway, N.Y.)

Power-driven machines deliver carded wool for worsted goods in Worcester, Mass. (By Ewing Galloway, N.Y.)

Rice terraces of Luzon. In overcrowded areas man, the "long" factor, supports land, the "short" factor. (From Ewing Galloway, N.Y.)

Sticks are used by Chinese wool carders in Peiping. (By Deane Dickason, from Ewing Galloway.)

Agriculture and industry meet. This plant in Texas converts maize into syrups, feeds, and other products. (Corn Products Refining Company.)

Self-propelled combines harvest wheat in Texas. (Standard Oil Co. (N.J.), photo by Russell Lee.)

Threshing rice in the Philippines. Labor is cheap and time is plentiful. (By Burton Holmes, from Ewing Galloway.)

Paddy fields are one of the most impressive examples of capital. (Standard Oil Co. (N.J.), photo by Corsini.)

A Diesel tractor-drawn loader that loads a ton of beets a minute. (From Ewing Galloway, N.Y.)

Vacuum pans for melting down and crystallizing sugar. (American Sugar Refining Company.)

Harvesting cane in Cuba. The machete and oxcart are still widely used. (American Sugar Refining Company.)

Shredding and rolling sugar cane. (American Sugar Refining Company.)

Wild coconut stand in the Philippines. Fish, fruit, and nuts are abundant, so the natives need not work hard for a living. (By Ewing Galloway, N.Y.)

Floating coconut rafts downstream. (From Ewing Galloway.)

Philippine coconut plantations generally yield larger crops per acre than do wild stands. (By Ewing Galloway, N.Y.)

In husking coconuts, the workers stand in the stream in which the nuts are floating. (By Ewing Galloway, N.Y.)

A giant variety of soybean. (From Ewing Galloway, N.Y.)

Raising beef cattle in Idaho requires a lot of land. (Standard Oil Co. (N.J.), photo by Collier.)

Culling soybeans in Idaho. (From Ewing Galloway.)

Sheep and lambs grazing on the range in Montana. (U.S.D.A. photograph by Lee.)

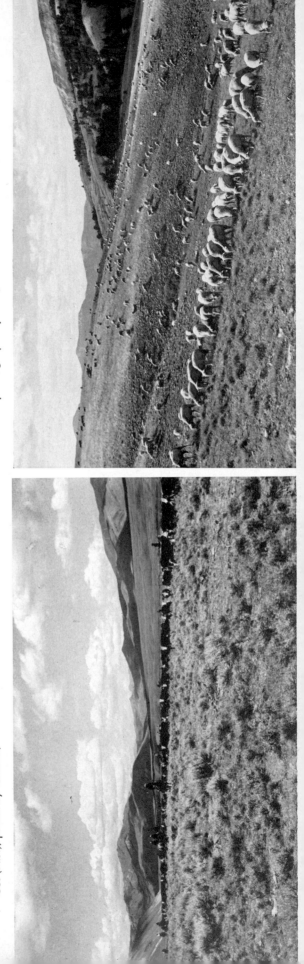

the rapid application of scientific discoveries to actual performance.

The relation of the mill to cane culture varies widely from country to country. Some of these variations will be brought out in the discussion of the leading cane sugar-growing regions (see pp. 250-254).

Cane periodically sloughs down the older series of leaves as new ones form. The older leaves develop a mottled entanglement around the stalks which, if allowed to remain, impedes the work of the harvesters and, if permitted to reach the mill, seriously reduces efficiency. To remove it, cane fields in Hawaii are invariably burned over before they are cut. Burning is also practiced in Cuba and other areas. After being burned over, the cane stalks are left almost clean and undamaged. Since mature cane is composed of approximately 87 percent liquid and only 13 percent solids, a quick fire has almost no effect on it. However, cane that has been burned over must be harvested immediately because the heat tends to make the sugar sap deteriorate quickly.

Raw Sugar Manufacture

The extraction of sugar from the cane "is an industriochemical process"[12] that involves the simultaneous production of an important list of by-products, as well as complications in the way of joint costs and large-scale operations. Briefly, the following steps are required: (1) The juice is first extracted from the cane by passing the cane through rollers at low speed under high pressure. The fiber residue, or "bagasse," which is practically dry after milling, serves as fuel for the boilers. (2) The juice must be purified. Milk of lime is added to neutralize the acidity, which would otherwise "sour" the liquid by converting its sucrose (sugar) to noncrystallizable form. The solution is then heated in closed tanks; nonsoluble impurities are precipitated and other foreign matter is removed as the liquid is passed through frame filter presses. (3) The juice is boiled in multiple-effect evaporators in order to drive off excess water. (4) A further boiling process in vacuum pans induces the sucrose to crystallize. The final product at this stage is poured out of the vacuum pans as "massecuite," a

dense mush of crystals and liquid. A mixer with revolving shaft and paddles keeps the massecuite in motion and prevents it from solidifying into "concrete." (5) Separation of the sugar from the molasses is effected by centrifugal action. The crystals are trapped in a wire basket; the liquid flows free and is returned to the evaporators for the removal of further sucrose. Ultimately "exhausted" or "final" molasses is obtained, containing about 35 percent sucrose which defies further extraction.

The operation of modern machinery requires both highly trained personnel and costly instruments. This accounts for the movement toward larger mills.

Beside sugar, cane yields two important by-products: the dry pulp called bagasse, and molasses. Most of the bagasse is used by the mill for fuel, but some of it is converted into fiberboard.[13] With each ton of sugar about 50 gallons of "blackstrap" molasses are produced which goes into industrial alcohol and cattle-feed. During World War II the synthetic rubber industry consumed considerable amounts of high-test, or "invert," molasses.

Sugar Refining

The sugar mill ordinarily turns out "raw" sugar, i.e., sugar containing up to perhaps 8 percent of molasses and other impurities. Standard raw sugar is 96 degrees centrifugal.[14] This raw sugar, in the case of Cuba and other Caribbean islands, customarily was shipped to mainland refineries where virtually all the impurities were removed by means of intricate machines and processes. Sugar refineries on the

---

[12] B. C. Swerling, *op. cit.*, p. 8.

[13] The Celotex Company of New Orleans, Louisiana, was the first to utilize bagasse for this purpose. When in the twenties they succeeded in turning out a satisfactory fiberboard for bagasse, the cane output of Louisiana had been cut way down (1926-1927, 42,112 long tons; 1927-1928, 63,207 long tons) by the mosaic disease. A building boom was on and the demand for celotex far exceeded the amount which the available bagasse could furnish. So the Celotex Company took a hand in the cane situation by helping to introduce the P.O.J. 2878 variety. The situation improved rapidly—in 1929-1930, the crop amounted to 178,223 long tons.

[14] The 96 degrees is taken from the polariscope, an instrument which measures the sucrose content; centrifugal is derived from the centrifugal machine which separates the sugar crystals from the molasses.

mainland antedate the *central* system. When only primitive *ingenios* were used in the tropics to produce a low-grade brown sugar, shipping the intermediate product to an industrially advanced country for final processing seemed natural. But when the sugar mill in the tropics reached its present size and stage of perfection the old arguments against refining did not ring quite so true. However, there may still be some justification for the old-time division of the process. The sugar mill handles cane. Its optimum size is determined by the volume of a bulky raw material that holds about 87 percent moisture. Raw sugar is only about one-ninth or one-tenth, if not less, the weight of cane. The optimum size of the refinery is determined by the volume of raw sugar. One such refinery can handle the output of perhaps a score or more of *centrales*. So refineries continue to do a large business. However, their continued progress is probably contingent on tariff protection. Since 1934 the sugar laws of the United States have put strict quotas on "direct-consumption" sugars[15] which the sugar-growing islands can ship to the mainland.

The refining process still used in most United States refineries requires bone char or bone-black. From 70 to 100 tons of char are needed for each 100 tons of raw sugar treated. This process may in the near future be replaced by a revolutionary new process involving magnetic filtration based on an ion exchange process.

In many cane-growing countries other ways of producing direct-consumption sugar have been in vogue for decades. Moreover, bona fide refineries have also been built in the tropics. The first of them was built in 1926 by the Hershey Chocolate Company, which owned several *centrales* in Cuba and added a refinery to its raw sugar mill system. A flaw in our tariff of 1930 (Smoot-Hawley tariff)[16] gave sugar refiners in Cuba and noncontiguous territories of the United States an artificial stimulus that was sharply resented by mainland refiners. This

---

[15] This term includes all sugars ready for consumption, whether they have been subjected to refining in the strict sense of the word or not.

[16] The duty on refined sugar was set below that on 99.9 percent raw sugar; i.e., the rate of raw sugar duties was not correlated with the refined rates. The result was that offshore refineries were given a slight advantage over mainland refineries.

flaw became apparent when, beginning in 1934, quota laws superseded the tariff law as the main regulator of sugar imports. Java, Mauritius, and other cane sugar-growing regions have long exported direct-consumption sugar. Refining companies have protected their position in part by integration with sugar properties. An example is the American Sugar Refining Company, which owns two large *centrales* in Cuba, the Canagua and Jaronu. This company owns about one-third of the entire sugar refining capacity of the United States. Another example of integration is the California and Hawaii Sugar Refining Corporation, Ltd., whose plant is located in Crockett, California. Most of it is owned by twenty-four Hawaiian sugar companies.

BEETS AND BEET SUGAR

The modern sugar beet was evolved in Silesia from a white beet (*Beta vulgaris*) formerly grown as a forage crop. Originally, when grown in southern latitudes, the sugar beet was an annual; but when taken north it adapted itself to the climatic conditions of the northerly latitudes by becoming a biennial, developing roots and foliage and storing up sugar in the taproot the first year and flowering and producing seed the second year. By systematic seed selection the sucrose content has gradually been increased from about 5 percent in the original Silesian root to 20 percent or even more. At the same time the purity of the sap has been increased by a reduction in the saline impurities.

Fig. 15.5 shows some botanical features of the sugar beet. Of special interest is the diagram of the root system. The numerous roots, which penetrate the soil to a depth of several feet, are broken off and left to decay when the beets are harvested. They are said to add an average of one ton of humus per acre. As the roots decay, the air penetrates the network of minute channels, aerating and making fertile the lower strata of the soil; the root channels fill with winter moisture and form an underground reservoir which supplies the roots of succeeding crops with summer moisture.

The sugar beet grows best on fertile sandy loam or clay loam soils and in a temperate climate favored with abundant sunshine, cool dry air, and moisture timed to certain periods of its growth. Moisture is needed when the seed is

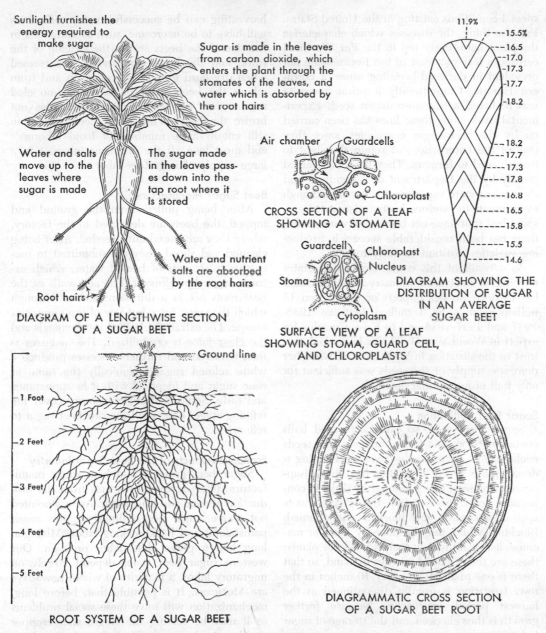

Sunlight furnishes the energy required to make sugar

Sugar is made in the leaves from carbon dioxide, which enters the plant through the stomates of the leaves, and water which is absorbed by the root hairs

Water and salts move up to the leaves where sugar is made

The sugar made in the leaves passes down into the tap root where it is stored

Water and nutrient salts are absorbed by the root hairs

Root hairs

DIAGRAM OF A LENGTHWISE SECTION OF A SUGAR BEET

Air chamber   Guardcells

Chloroplast

CROSS SECTION OF A LEAF SHOWING A STOMATE

Guardcell   Chloroplast

Nucleus

Stoma

Cytoplasm

SURFACE VIEW OF A LEAF SHOWING STOMA, GUARD CELL, AND CHLOROPLASTS

11.9%   15.5%
15.5
16.5
17.0
17.3
17.7
18.2

18.2
17.7
17.3
17.8
16.8
16.5
15.8
15.5
14.6

DIAGRAM SHOWING THE DISTRIBUTION OF SUGAR IN AN AVERAGE SUGAR BEET

Ground line

1 Foot

2 Feet

3 Feet

4 Feet

5 Feet

ROOT SYSTEM OF A SUGAR BEET

DIAGRAMMATIC CROSS SECTION OF A SUGAR BEET ROOT

FIG. 15.5. The Story of Beet Sugar. (Farmers and Manufacturers Beet Sugar Association, *The Story of Beet Sugar from the Seed to the Sack*, 1933.)

germinating and the beets are forming. Later, when sugar is being elaborated, too much moisture tends to produce large size and small sugar content; but if several weeks elapse between rains and harvesting the beets recover their high sugar content.[17]

Until World War II cut the United States off from European seed sources, practically all the beet seeds used in this country were imported from Europe, chiefly from Germany. But the seeds were not too well adapted to the

[17] P. G. Wright, *Sugar in Relation to the Tariff*, McGraw-Hill Book Company, Inc., New York, 1924.

special conditions existing in the United States. For one thing, the diseases which characterize the plant here—curly top in the Far West and cerospora leaf spot east of the Rockies—are not prevalent in the seed-breeding areas of northern Europe. Consequently a prime requisite was to breed a disease-resistant seed. Experimental work along these lines has been carried on by the beet sugar companies, since they control the enterprise and retain the right to furnish seed to farmers. They have been aided greatly by the Department of Agriculture and the various state experiment stations. Although experiments to produce beets resistant to cerospora leaf spot have not been wholly successful, there has been considerable success in producing varieties resistant to curly top.

As a result of this work, the United States now has a beet seed industry which enabled her to decrease her imports of seeds from 15 million pounds to 3 million between 1936-1937 and 1937-1938 and to have a surplus for export in World War II. This is in marked contrast to the situation in World War I, when her domestic supply of the seeds was sufficient for only half of her annual demand.

Sugar Beet Cultivation

Sugar beet seeds, so called, are seed balls containing from one to five or more true seeds enclosed in a hard woody covering. Planting is done in the spring after the frost has disappeared, the seed being planted by drills in continuous rows. Soon after the green shoots appear, the rows are blocked and thinned. Blocking, which may be done by hand or machine, leaves uniformly spaced blocks of plants; these are then thinned, always by hand, so that there is one plant about every 10 inches in the row. Irrigation is usually discontinued as the harvest period approaches because further growth is thus checked and the storage of sugar is facilitated.

Sugar beets are harvested by means of a plowlike lifter which gets under the beet and raises it. The beet is then pulled from the ground and topped; i.e., the top is cut off below the crown, since any part that grows above the ground is practically sugarless. Both pulling and topping are done by hand. Although mechanical harvesters have been invented, they have not been widely adopted. Before machine

harvesting can be successful, many difficulties will have to be overcome, such as variations in the size of the beets and in the spacing of the rows, and the large clods which are formed when dry hard ground is broken up and from which the beets must be separated—no clod crusher has yet been devised that does not bruise the beets. Thus sugar beet cultivation still entails large numbers of hand laborers[18] and must face all the problems inherent in a large supply of migratory labor.

Beet Sugar Manufacture

After being pulled from the ground and topped, the beets are delivered to the factory, where they are stored until needed. After being cleaned and sliced, they are submitted to successive treatments of heated water, which extracts sugar by diffusion. The cell walls of the beet roots act as a diffusion medium through which the sugar juice but few of the impurities escape. The extract is clarified by chemicals and the clear juice is crystallized. The molasses is then removed and further processes produce a white refined sugar, chemically the same as cane sugar and identical with it in appearance and taste. Some beet sugar factories cover the refining stage; others sell the raw beet sugar to refineries.

Economic Aspects of the Beet Sugar Industry

Sugar beet growing and beet sugar manufacture differ in several respects from the production of cane and cane sugar. As was pointed out above, sugar beet culture requires much painstaking and backbreaking labor. Michigan long had a grave child labor problem. Our western sugar beet states depend largely on migratory labor, a majority of whom nowadays are Mexicans. It is possible that, before long, mechanization will solve these social problems as it may be solving the Negro sharecropper problem in the South. Until then, beet culture will bear the stigma of being something not quite "100 percent American."

Although in the tropics sugar cane is usually

---

[18] Works Progress Administration, *Changes in Technology and Labor Requirements in Crop Production: Sugar Beets*, National Research Project, Philadelphia, 1937. Considerable progress in solving the mechanical problems has been made since this study was completed.

the best crop in terms of money income per acre, this is not true of sugar beets. Sugar beets are largely grown by independent farmers who, once their contract with a sugar mill has expired, may prefer to switch to another crop. The fact that the beet crop is an annual crop in contrast to the cane crop which may ratoon for years materially aids this crop-choosing autonomy of the beet grower. This increases the risk of investing in beet sugar mills, which the mill owner seeks to reduce by crop lien contracts with beet-growing farmers. In Europe many beet sugar mills belong to coöperative beet growers, thus establishing a harmony of interest between field and mill ownership and operation.

Unlike sugar cane which as a rule[19] is a one-crop proposition, or monoculture, sugar beet growing is an integral part of a complicated crop rotation system and through by-product utilization ties up with other branches of farming. This organic interrelation with the entire agricultural structure of a region counteracts to some extent the other factors making for elasticity of supply.

NOTES ON SUGAR CHEMISTRY

Sugar is a carbohydrate, which means that it is made up of carbon (C), hydrogen (H), and oxygen (O). The familiar sugar of the household is sucrose, $C_{12}H_{22}O_{11}$. This may be either beet, cane, or maple sugar. The first two are refined to the point where any original differences in taste are lost, but maple sugar is sold in the less refined state and therefore retains some of its peculiar taste.

Besides sucrose, another sugar, known as glucose and not as sweet as sucrose, is widely used especially by the baking industry. Glucose is obtained from starch by chemically combining with two molecules of water. Until recently, glucose was also called dextrose because, like sucrose, it deflects a beam of light to the right.[20] Since chemists are now able to synthesize levulo-glucose, the term "dextrose" for all glucose no longer appears appropriate.

Glucose differs from sucrose not only in the size of the molecule ($C_6H_{12}O_6$ as against $C_{12}H_{22}O_{11}$) but also in the relationship of H_2O

(water) to carbon. Two glucose molecules ($2 \times C_6H_{12}O_6$) make a total of $C_{12}H_{24}O_{12}$ atoms, which is one molecule of water (H_2O) more than sucrose: $C_{12}H_{22}O_{11}$. If given a chance, nature is prone to add the additional molecule of water after the sucrose has formed. If sugar cane stands after the maximum of sucrose has formed, a chemical reaction sets in through which sucrose is "inverted" into a combination of glucose and fructose called "invert sugar." What happens in the inversion is this:

$$C_{12}H_{22}O_{11} + H_2O \rightarrow \qquad C_{12}H_{24}O_{12}$$

$$\qquad\qquad\qquad\qquad C_6H_{12}O_6 \quad C_6H_{12}O_6$$

$$\text{sucrose} + \text{water} \rightarrow \underbrace{\text{glucose} \quad \text{fructose}}_{\text{invert sugar}}$$

Glucose, as was stated before, deflects a light beam to the right, but fructose deflects it so much more strongly to the left than glucose does to the right that the net effect of invert sugar is a deflection to the left. The glucose-fructose combination therefore deflects the beam *inversely* to the direction in which sucrose deflects it. Hence the name "invert sugar." It is practically useless, and is therefore avoided.

Invert sugar results not only in the grower's sugar cane plant, but also during the process of extracting the sugar from the cane and, to a lesser degree, from beets. Invert sugar constitutes a large part of molasses.

Economic Implications

The economist may well ask why he should be taken on these excursions into chemistry. The answer lies in the economic implications of these chemical reactions. What are these implications?

In the first place, as is well known, the carbon, hydrogen, and oxygen which constitute sugar are extracted by nature from air and water through photosynthesis. They therefore constitute a net addition to man's food supply which does not draw on the existing supply of chemicals in the soil, provided the rest of the cane or beets is returned to the soil. This is a fact worth remembering and understanding!

In the second place, nature's tendency to let sucrose turn into invert sugar is also of great economic significance. To get the maximum return from the cane harvest, it is vitally necessary that cane be cut at the "right" time, i.e.,

---

[19] Java excepted; see p. 254.
[20] Dextrose and levulose are derived from Latin words meaning right and left respectively.

TABLE 15.2. United States Sugar Supply by Sources, 1936-1948[21]

| | Continental United States | | | | Noncontiguous Territories | | | | | |
| | Beet | | Cane | | Puerto Rico | | Hawaii | | Cuba | | Philippines | |
	Million Long Tons	Percent	Million Long Tons	Percent	Million Long Tons	Percent	Million Long Tons	Percent	Million Long Tons	Percent	Million Long Tons	Percent
1936	1.2	22.1	0.4	6.8	0.7	13.2	0.8	14.0	1.6	29.7	0.8	14.0
1937	1.0	18.2	0.4	7.3	0.8	13.4	0.8	14.3	1.8	31.7	0.8	14.3
1938	1.2	21.0	0.5	8.2	0.7	12.8	0.7	13.2	1.7	29.9	0.8	14.4
1939	1.4	24.6	0.5	9.2	0.8	14.0	0.7	13.2	1.4	24.8	0.8	14.2
1940	1.4	25.0	0.3	6.1	0.7	12.7	0.8	14.1	1.6	27.9	0.8	14.2
1941	1.6	23.8	0.3	4.9	0.8	11.9	0.7	11.3	2.4	36.1	0.7	10.6
1942	1.5	31.3	0.4	8.0	0.7	14.7	0.6	13.3	1.5	32.3	...	...
1943	1.3	24.6	0.4	7.5	0.5	9.7	0.7	12.4	2.4	46.0	...	...
1944	1.0	16.2	0.4	7.4	0.6	10.5	0.6	10.2	3.1	54.8	...	...
1945	.9	17.1	0.4	7.6	0.7	14.4	0.5	10.8	2.5	49.5	...	...
1946	1.2	24.5	0.4	9.0	0.7	15.0	0.5	11.2	1.9	40.2	...	...
1947	1.3	21.5	0.3	5.0	0.8	12.5	0.6	10.2	3.2	50.8	...	...
1948	1.4	23.3	0.4	6.6	0.8	13.8	0.6	10.0	2.5	42.9	0.2	3.3

when the maximum of sucrose has formed and before inversion occurs. This necessity in turn, as will be shown below, affects the entire structure of the cane sugar industry—size of holdings, size of mill, cane planting program, length of grinding season, etc. Since no like emergency exists in the case of beets, a sharp difference in structure between the beet and cane sugar industries results.

Finally, the fact that chemists can synthesize glucose from starch is of great significance in appraising the sugar supply situation, the competitive forces at work, and the balance between supply and demand.

THE SUGAR ECONOMY OF THE UNITED STATES

General Structure

By the American sugar economy is meant the system of facilities and arrangements through

which the American people obtain their sugar supply. It embraces not only such physical features as beet sugar fields, cane sugar fields, transportation facilities of every description, raw sugar factories, sugar refineries, warehouses, retail stores, laboratories, and offices, but also those invisible arrangements of property rights, contractual relationships, and controls exercised by holding companies, banks, and government agencies. Since 1934 this system has included an increasing element of governmental controls and aids.

In terms of geography the areas of our sugar supply can be divided as follows:

Nearby
1. Continental supply—beet and cane.
2. Caribbean supply—Cuba, Puerto Rico, Virgin Islands.[22]

Distant
1. Hawaii (Honolulu to San Francisco, about 2400 statute miles).
2. Philippine Islands (Manila to San Francisco, about 7400 statute miles).

---

[21] *Farr's Manual of Sugar Companies*, 1948, p. 55. Besides the sources listed in the table some full-duty countries make occasional shipments. However, in no year during the period 1936-1948 covered by the table did such full-duty shipments exceed 1 percent.

[22] The Virgin Islands produce a negligible amount.

On the basis of political status the different sources may be grouped as follows:

1. The continental United States—beet and cane.
2. The noncontiguous territories—Puerto Rico, Virgin Islands, Hawaii.
3. Countries tied to the United States by special political arrangements—Cuba and the Philippines.

The relative importance of these sources of supply is shown in Table 15.2.

Apart from the temporary eclipse of the Philippines as a source of supply, the increased dependence on Cuba is the most striking feature of this table. In this connection the fact that during the Great Depression important Cuban sugar properties came into the possession of mainland interests may have some significance. During World War II Cuba was able to expand output rapidly—as she had during World War I—whereas mainland sugar cane and beet growers had a hard time to get the labor and supplies necessary for sustained production. Moreover, some other crops gained in relative profitableness and hence diverted interest from cane and beet production.

Sugar Legislation

Sugar has been subjected either to tariff duty, to quota laws, or to wartime control ever since 1789, with the exception of the period from October 2, 1890, to August 28, 1894, when it was on the free list and domestic beet sugar was subsidized.

The duty levied on sugar was 1 cent a pound in 1789; it was raised by successive steps until it reached 3 cents in 1816, was reduced to 2.5 cents a pound in 1832, and was shifted to 30 percent ad valorem in 1846. During 1861 it dropped temporarily to 0.75 cent a pound, then was raised by successive steps to 4 cents a pound; this level was reached in 1864 and remained in force until 1870. From then until the free trade period of the early nineties the duty was gradually lowered. In 1894 it was put at 40 percent ad valorem, in 1897 restored to a specific basis at 1.685 cents a pound, lowered in 1914 to 1.256 cents, raised in 1921 to 2 cents, in 1922 to 2.206 cents, and in 1930 to 2.5 cents. Under the Reciprocity Treaty of 1901 Cuba was entitled to a rebate of 20 percent after 1902, and therefore her sugar was subject to a rate of 1.348 cents a pound from 1903-1914, 1.0048 cents a pound from 1914-1921, 1.6 cents a pound from 1921-1922, 1.7648 cents from 1922-1930, and 2 cents from 1930-1934.

In 1934 the United States did not abolish tariff protection of sugar but put into operation quota laws which superseded the tariff as the main determinant of the amount and sources of her sugar imports. Under the quota system, which was in force until 1942 (with an interruption in 1939), the tariff rate was changed as follows:

	On Cuban Sugar	On "Full-Duty" Sugar
June—Sept., 1934	1.5	1.875
Sept., 1934 Sept., 1939	0.9	1.875
Sept., 1939—Dec., 1939	1.5	1.875
Dec., 1939—Jan., 1942	0.9	1.875
Jan., 1942—July 1, 1942	0.75	1.875
July, 1942—1947	0.75	0.9375
1948	0.50	0.6875

While before 1934 the tariff rate determined the price at which outside sources could supply the American market and, through price, indirectly affected the volume of imports from specific sources, after 1934 the volume was determined by quotas and, during 1942-1947, by direct government purchases. The tariff rate merely affects the price which outside suppliers may receive.

In 1934 the Jones-Costigan Sugar Act was passed; in 1937 it was superseded by the Sugar Law of 1937. This remained on the statute books until December 31, 1947, though suspended on April 13, 1942. The Sugar Act of 1937 as amended expired on December 31, 1947, and was superseded on the following day by the Sugar Act of 1948.

The political interest of the United States in Hawaii goes back to the 1870's, when it was feared that these islands might be snapped up by "a great naval power." In order to draw them closer and remove the danger of foreign control, the United States let Hawaiian sugar enter duty-free. This meant that the Hawaiian sugar price could rise by the amount of the duty collected under the prevailing revenue tariff. When in the nineties the tariff was removed and subsidies to mainland sugar producers—cane as well as beet—were substituted, the Hawaiian sugar industry was in a panic and annexation followed. This made duty-free Hawaiian sugar a permanent fixture in the United States market.

Puerto Rico and the Philippines were annexed after the victorious outcome of the Spanish-American War. All these islands—Hawaii, the Philippines, and Puerto Rico—have gained progressive significance as naval and military strongholds. To safeguard a military outpost it is not enough to build ramparts and dry-docks, airfields and barracks. The economic stability of the population must also be assured; the people must have at least one steady and adequate source of income. The sugar industry became that in all three cases. It developed later in the Philippines than in Hawaii and Puerto Rico. Moreover, the sugar industry never reached the dominant position there that it did in the others.

The political position of the Philippines is different from that of Puerto Rico or Hawaii. After the passage of the Independence Act of 1933 and after the Philippines became a commonwealth in 1935, the difference became increasingly pronounced. However, the Philippines continue to enjoy a large sugar quota under the Philippine Trade Act of 1946 and the Sugar Act of 1948.

Cuba retained her independence, but her proximity to the United States gives her a unique status in relation to our economy. For one thing, Cuba ceded to us the powerful naval base at Guantánamo Bay. Then, under the Pratt Amendment (1901) she submitted to a degree of financial surveillance and political control. The 20 percent rebate under the Reciprocity Treaty has already been mentioned.

The Great Depression threw the sugar industry of the United States and her supply areas into a state of hopeless chaos. To resume order, the Congress decided to abandon competition, modified by the tariff, as the regulator of the sugar trade. Our entire sugar demand was farmed out, so to speak. In the struggle over quotas the continental beet and cane growers proved politically strongest—sugar is produced in about fifteen states, which means thirty Senators in support of continental claims —and they received quotas equaling if not exceeding their productive capacity. The rest was allocated among the other sources, i.e., the noncontiguous territories, Cuba and the Philip-

pines. As if bound to solve or alleviate the sugar problem, our demand for sugar increased from 5.1 million long tons in 1934 to over 7 million in 1948.[23] The several sugar laws passed since 1934 provide for compensatory payments to those who comply with the quota restrictions on output as well as with certain other regulations aimed at social betterment.

CONSTITUENT PARTS OF THE AMERICAN SUGAR ECONOMY

Apart from the seashore refineries which handle primarily offshore raws, the domestic sugar industry of the United States is divided into the cane and the beet sections. Cane is produced in only two states; sugar beets, however, are grown, and beet sugar manufactured, in no less than half the states of the Union, although production and manufacture are concentrated in nine states (see Table 15.3). Only two of the beet-producing states—Ohio and Michigan—have adequate natural rainfall; all the others depend on irrigation.[24]

The Beet Sugar Industry

The beet sugar industry of the United States is divided into two interdependent economic sections: the farmers who grow the beets, and the manufacturers. There are from 75,000 to 100,000 sugar beet growers who cultivate from 750,000 to 1,000,000 acres and sell their beets to 80 or 90 factories operated by some 25 companies.

Since more than 95 percent of the sugar beet crop is grown by independent farmers who may switch to other crops, the sugar manufacturers must do everything possible to assure themselves of adequate supplies of beets. Among the devices used for this purpose are (1) contracts with farmers specifying the acreage to be planted and the conditions under which cultivation is to be carried on; (2) aid in providing farmers with sufficient labor; and (3) financial assistance in the form of credit.

---

[23] To be sure, during World War II sugar was rationed, but this was necessitated mainly by shipping shortages.

[24] Crops grown under irrigation tend to show greater regularity of aggregate output than crops depending on rainfall, partly because of the regularity of the water supply and partly because the heavy investment in irrigation works necessitates more constant output to meet fixed charges.

Table 15.3. Sugar Beets—Acreage, Production,[a] Prices Received by Farmers and Farm Value, 1901 to 1947, and by States, 1944 to 1947[25]

Yearly Average or Year and State	Acres Harvested (thousands)	Tons per Acre	Production (1000 tons)	Price per Ton (dollars)[b]	Farm Value (1000 dollars)
United States					
1901-1905	228	9.22	2,079c	4.89	10,166
1906-1910	386	10.13	3,910c	5.18d	20,254d
1911-1915	541	10.66	5,738c	5.63	32,318
1916-1920	700	9.49	6,623	9.56	63,314
1921-1925	693	10.06	6,972	7.46	52,040
1926-1930	701	11.01	7,718	7.32	56,480
1931-1935	799	10.88	8,686	5.42	47,119
1936-1940	859	12.23	10,500	5.14	53,938
1941-1945	705	12.10	8,780	8.31	72,972
1934	770	9.8	7,519	5.16	38,776
1935	763	10.4	7,908	5.76	45,565
1936	776	11.6	9,028	6.05	54,636
1937	755	11.6	8,784	5.27	46,249
1938	930	12.5	11,615	4.65	54,052
1939	917	11.8	10,781	4.76	51,342
1940	916	13.4	12,292	5.16	63,409
1941	754	13.7	10,311	6.47	66,705
1942	954	12.2	11,674	6.87	80,156
1943	548	11.9	6,532	8.86	57,898
1944	558	12.1	6,755	10.70	72,026
1945	713	12.1	8,626	10.20	88,074
1946	802	13.2	10,562	11.20	118,638
1947	887	13.8	12,248	12.00	146,572
California					
1944	71	16.9	1,199	11.00	13,189
1945	93	16.9	1,568	10.70	16,778
1946	122	17.0	2,079	11.30	23,493
1947	156	17.9	2,792	....	....
Colorado					
1944	117	12.2	1,427	10.70	15,269
1945	152	12.1	1,835	10.20	18,717
1946	153	12.5	1,920	10.20	19,584
1947	169	14.5	2,450	....	....
Idaho					
1944	43	14.4	618	10.30	6,365
1945	53	15.3	809	9.90	8,009
1946	76	16.8	1,274	11.50	14,651
1947	103	17.3	1,782	....	....
Michigan					
1944	59	8.8	519	12.10	6,280
1945	78	8.0	627	11.20	7,022
1946	95	8.6	814	14.10	11,477
1947	67	7.0	469	....	....
Montana					
1944	64	10.7	682	10.60	7,229
1945	81	10.7	865	10.30	8,910
1946	73	12.2	891	10.90	9,712
1947	77	11.6	893	....	....
Nebraska					
1944	46	10.7	490	10.20	4,998
1945	59	10.8	635	9.20	5,842
1946	60	13.8	825	10.40	8,580
1947	72	11.2	806	....	....
Ohio					
1944	13	8.7	113	12.00	1,356
1945	21	9.9	208	11.60	2,413
1946	26	9.0	234	14.00	3,276
1947	22	7.2	158	....	....
Utah					
1944	31	12.8	396	10.10	4,000
1945	32	13.7	437	9.70	4,239
1946	41	13.9	568	10.60	6,021
1947	45	15.9	716	....	....
Wyoming					
1944	28	11.0	307	10.30	3,162
1945	35	9.9	346	10.00	3,460
1946	36	11.7	421	10.80	4,547
1947	36	12.6	454	....	....

a Prior to 1924 acreage and production include a small quantity produced in Canada for U.S. factories. U.S. totals include data for a few states not shown separately.

b Season average price.

c Beets used by factories 1901-1912.

d Four-year average.

25 *Statistical Abstract of the United States*, 1948, p. 672.

The Cane Sugar Industry

Louisiana and Florida. The history of the Louisiana industry has been marked by several severe crises. As early as 1853, output reached 260,000 tons, only to drop to 40,000 in 1856 because of the cane rot. There was a sharp recovery in 1861, but production was greatly curtailed during the Civil War and was down to 5000 tons in 1864. That war was followed by thirty years of recovery in the industry, culminating in a crop of 355,000 tons in 1894.[26] Thereafter, output was marked by alternating ups and downs. Red-rot mosaic brought production down to a new low of 50,000 tons in 1926, but the introduction of new varieties (notably P.O.J. 2878) restored the level of production to between 200,000 and 250,000 tons prior to the Sugar Act of 1934. The quotas for Louisiana and Florida for 1948 were 500,000 tons.

The agricultural unit of Louisiana is intermediate in size between the small farm typical of the beet sugar area of the continent and the large plantation typical of the insular cane areas. About 20 per cent of the production of the state is on farms under 150 tons of sugar in output, equivalent to some 100 acres in cane. Another 20 per cent lies between this limit and farms of around 1,000 tons output. The next 20 per cent includes the range between 1,000 and 3,000 tons. The remaining 40 per cent is produced on plantations ranging in size from 3,000 to 15,000 tons of sugar. Apparently, the typical enterprise is a moderate-size plantation, although large plantations are very important. Only about one-third of the land under cultivation is in sugar cane.[27]

While the Louisiana industry is one of the oldest in the history of the United States, cane growing in Florida is a relatively recent venture. It was started for the purpose of providing a more adequate supply of bagasse, needed at that time in the manufacture of celotex. The sugar industry is centered around a modern mill at Clewiston in the Everglades region near Lake Okeechobee. The raw sugar is sent to Savannah, Georgia, for refining.

Hawaii. The preferential position in the United States market accorded Hawaiian sugar by the treaty of 1875 (see above, p. 247) encouraged mainland, especially New England, capital to flow into Hawaii on a large and increasing scale. The land on which sugar cane can be grown there without heavy expenditure for irrigation, fertilizer, and other improvements is limited to stretches of fertile volcanic soils along the coast, mainly on the windward —i.e., east and north—sides of the mountains. Expansion beyond these modest limits requires heavy capital outlay. In 1876 the famous Hamakua "ditch" on the Island of Maui, the first large-scale irrigation project in Hawaii, was started. It delivered 40 million gallons of water a day and was followed by the construction of another Maui ditch that delivered 50 million gallons a day.[28] This went on until "the great mountain systems above the sugar lands today are ridged with ditches, filled with colossal pipes and honeycombed with tunnels." Approximately 40 million dollars have been sunk in Hawaiian irrigation projects.

Not only is the land on which sugar cane can be grown under natural conditions strictly limited, but the labor supply is also limited. The islands are by no means overcrowded, even after strenuous efforts to import foreign labor—Chinese, Japanese, Portuguese, Filipinos, and others. In 1914 the population was only 219,650, and in 1940 it was 426,007.[29] Therefore, not only must capital come to the aid of inadequate natural resources; it must also come to the support of inadequate human resources. Hence vast sums are spent for mechanical devices used in the field, for transport, and in the mills. Finally, capital also goes into research and laboratories to improve the cane varieties best adapted to Hawaiian conditions and in other ways to raise the efficiency of cane culture and sugar manufacture.

Under these circumstances—the necessity for large capital outlay to bolster up limited nat-

---

[26] Direct subsidies were paid to beet and cane sugar producers from 1892 to 1894.

[27] M. Lynsky, *Sugar Economics, Statistics, and Documents*, United States Cane Sugar Refiners' Association, New York, 1938, p. 42.

[28] J. W. Vandercook, *King Cane, an Epic of Sugar*, Harper & Brothers, New York, 1939, pp. 66 ff.

[29] Compare this with Puerto Rico—1914, 1,196,-816; 1940, 1,877,662. The area of the Hawaiian Islands is 6419 square miles as against 3435 for Puerto Rico, giving a density per square mile of 66.3 in 1940 for Hawaii, as compared with 546 for Puerto Rico.

ural and human resources—it is natural to find strong corporate organizations dominating the Hawaiian sugar industry, both the cane-growing and the sugar-making phases. Cane growing in Hawaii is definitely "big business," only about one-eighth of the sugar cane being grown by tenants and independent farmers. These "adherent planters" are known as *pali*. Under the quota laws, contracts were signed with about 4000, not directly by the government but through the agency of the corporations.

Not only is the corporation the dominant factor in the Hawaiian sugar industry, but the 39 sugar companies are held together by an exceptionally strong internal organization. These companies are grouped under so-called "factors" who act as supervisors and relieve the plantation sugar companies of many details, thus permitting them to concentrate on problems of cane growing and sugar manufacture. Thirty-six of the 39 companies are organized under five such factors.

Another unique feature of the Hawaiian industry is its high degree of integration, which, through ownership by 31 of the Hawaiian sugar companies of the capital stock of the California and Hawaiian Sugar Refining Corporation, Ltd., extends from the beginning in the cane field to the finished sugar in the sack. This corporation, together with another refinery in the San Francisco area, handles almost the entire Hawaiian crop not consumed on the island. In comparing the efficiency of Hawaiian cane-growing practices with those elsewhere, it is necessary to keep in mind the fact that in Hawaii cane generally is allowed to remain standing in the field 18 months and more, whereas in Cuba annual harvests are general. In other words, in Hawaii figures showing tons of cane *per acre-year* are considerably less than the figures showing tons of cane *per acre*.

Puerto Rico. Both Hawaii and Puerto Rico are noncontiguous territories of the United States and as such are entitled to ship their sugar to the mainland market free of duty. Since 1934, together with the other areas contributing to the United States sugar supply, both these areas have been subject to quota restrictions.

While the Hawaiian industry felt the stimulus of its access to the United States market and the influx of American capital as early as 1875, Puerto Rico did not receive this encouragement until after the Spanish-American War. Thus her modern sugar industry is virtually a creation of the twentieth century.

Around the turn of the century Hawaii produced about 300,000 tons of sugar as compared with about 100,000 for Puerto Rico.[30] Now both areas are producing at a rate approaching one million tons, suggesting that in Hawaii sugar production almost trebled in forty years while in Puerto Rico it grew tenfold.

Much of the growth is the result not of expanding acreage but of increased cane yields. In 1908-1909 Hawaii harvested a little over 100,000 acres of cane land, obtaining a yield of 32.8 tons of cane per acre; in 1933, before restriction, the acreage still fell considerably below 150,000, but yields were running in the high fifties and low sixties. In Puerto Rico the acreage expanded rather rapidly up to about 1920, but after that it increased no more than 20 percent in twenty years. Cane yields, on the other hand, jumped about 50 percent during the same period. This was accomplished in both areas largely by the introduction of Javanese "noble" canes, especially P.O.J. 2878, and their hybridization with locally adapted varieties.

Puerto Rico resembles Hawaii in her limited supply of natural resources. But unlike Hawaii, Puerto Rico is very densely populated. The presence of more than two million people on the island, however, does not affect industry, as a casual observer might expect.[31] In Puerto Rico the main effect of a dense population seems to be one of making everybody conscious of the social problem, of responsibility for the vast numbers of human beings who are trying to make their living on the island. More recently stern legal measures to enforce various social reforms have been taken—minimum wages, minimum payments for cane delivered by independent farmers, the breaking up of sugar estates, quasi-socialization of sugar mills

---

[30] See p. 252 for the still more rapid growth of production in the Philippine Islands.

[31] Population is by no means a dependable measure of the labor supply. Directly or through political pressure, or both, a labor union may succeed in creating scarcity of a particular type of labor, e.g., cane labor, and thus encourage ratooning in the face of population pressure.

and *centrales*, etc. In an effort to survive under these hammer blows, the Puerto Rican industry does what it can in terms of rationalized scientific management, mechanization, etc. Thus, in the midst of tens of thousands of unemployed, one sees the latest mechanized devices, notes a progressive shift to ratooning, observes increased expenditures for scientific research.

The Philippines. The real upswing of Philippine sugar production did not start until after World War I. At that time the bulk of Philippine production consisted of inferior grades (muscovado), only 219,370 tons of centrifugal sugar being produced in 1920. Ten years later the inferior product had almost disappeared, and centrifugal sugar had passed the million-ton mark. In 1933 almost 1,600,000 tons of centrifugal sugar were produced and sugar had become by far the most important export of the Philippine Islands. This was sharply cut after 1934, when quota laws were enacted, and after 1935, when the Philippines were declared an independent commonwealth.

The Philippine Island group is the largest of the so-called "offshore" producing regions, its area of 115,600 square miles comparing with 6419 for Hawaii, 3435 for Puerto Rico, and 44,100 for Cuba. Sugar cargoes to the United States require one or two months' travel, according to their destination. Philippine stock afloat is normally an important market factor. While Puerto Rico lies in the path of West Indian hurricanes, the Philippines are occasionally visited by typhoons.

The organization of the Philippine sugar industry is altogether different from that of Hawaii, Puerto Rico, or Cuba. In these three areas the cane-growing, sugar-manufacturing corporation is the focus of initiative and control. In the Philippine Islands this lodges in thousands of landowners and tenants who produce large crops of cane extensively and who have their cane ground on a custom basis in factories, the building of which was encouraged and assisted by the government. These mills, unlike those located in Hawaii, Puerto Rico, and Cuba, generally do not buy the cane; they merely perform the necessary service for the growers. The latter may engage the mill as the selling agent, but in most cases they sell through a corporate sales agency. Contracts running as long as thirty years cover the relationship between grower and mill.[32] One reason for this is the Philippine land law, which forbids large holdings.[33] Under these circumstances capital did not venture into manufacturing on a large scale until specially prompted by government action.

Cuba. The population of Cuba is little more than twice as large as that of Puerto Rico, while the land area is almost thirteen times as large. The ratio of cultivable land is even more heavily in her favor. In per capita natural resources Cuba towers high above her sister sugar islands. But wealth and land are by no means synonymous, and few people know that better than the Cubans.

Before World War I Cuban sugar income[34] ran in the neighborhood of $120 million. Then it jumped to 800 million immediately after the war. In 1921 it fell abruptly to 250 million, spreading bankruptcy and social unrest. After a moderate respite the income fell further to an annual average of 78 million during the period 1931-1933. That meant revolution. Under the quota law and the low tariff rate of 0.9 cent a pound effective under the Reciprocal Trade Agreement of 1934, which was later reduced to 0.75 cent, Cuban sugar income went back to $150 million, little more than the pre-World War I average but meaning more in view of lower costs. Eighty-three percent of her sugar income in 1937 came from the sale of raw sugar, 14 percent from the sale of molasses, syrups, alcohol, and rum, and 3 percent from the sale of refined sugar. Cuban sugar income during the forties was very high. During 1941-1946 the United States ceiling price for refined sugar ranged between 5.25 and 5.60 cents per pound, while refined beet sugar prices were 10 cents per hundred pounds lower. From January, 1946, to August, 1947, however, ceiling prices for sugar increased over 50 percent.

Under the stimulus of World War I, Cuba's output of sugar rose from 2,758,000 tons in 1913-1914 to 4,554,000 tons in 1919-1920; it reached a peak of 5,857,000 tons in 1929-1930. By that time enormous stocks had accumulated, amounting to 1,897,000 tons at the beginning

[32] See U.S. Tariff Commission, *United States-Philippine Trade,* Report No. 118, 1937, p. 48.
[33] *Ibid.,* pp. 8-9.
[34] Gross income from all sources.

of the 1932 grinding season. Hence the output had to be controlled. It fell to 2,266,000 tons in 1933-1934, staged a moderate recovery in 1937-1938, reached a high of 3,380,000 tons but dropped back to less than 3 million tons in 1941-1942, rose to 4.7 million in 1943 and reached a high of 6.5 million tons in 1946.

A characteristic feature of the Cuban sugar industry is its division into an old, western section of moderate-sized sugar mills and plantations dominated by old local interests, and the newer, eastern section of which foreign-controlled—especially United States—mills constitute an important part. The largest mills are in the three eastern provinces, Oriente, Camaguey, and Santa Clara.

As in Puerto Rico and Hawaii, so in Cuba the mill is the dominant factor. About one-fourth of the cane grown in Cuba is company cane, about three-fourths *colonos* cane. But, for many reasons, during the past decade more and more *colonos* have lost their independent status, until today as many as 90 percent are not independent growers but for all practical purposes may be considered part of the company setup. The company determines the amount and kind of cane to be grown, the time of planting, the manner of cultivation; it finances the *colono* and in general has the controlling hand. So great has been the dependence on the mills of many of the planters, especially the small, family-size farm units, that, under the United States Sugar Acts of 1934 and 1937, special legal safeguards have been devised for the protection of these farmers. The contracts between mills and *colonos,* of which several types are in use, have been more or less standardized and under them the minimum rights of the planters have been assured.[35]

A recent development of the Cuban sugar industry is the opening up of refineries on the island. Until the early twenties practically the only sugar refining done in Cuba was for local consumption. By 1925 the shipments of Cuban direct-consumption sugar to United States ports amounted to over 25,000 tons. A steady climb brought this to 492,037 tons in 1933, after which year the Cuban sugar refining industry was stabilized at about half a million tons' output. The reason for this development, which had a modest counterpart in other sections of the world, will be discussed later.

As a result of the quota system, the price of sugar in the United States not infrequently exceeds the world price by more than the duty which Cuban raw sugar has to pay. In this sense, the quota law may be said to furnish a veiled subsidy to Cuban sugar interests. This subsidy aids the maker of both raw and refined sugar.

Until the passage of the quota laws—the Sugar Acts of 1934, 1937, and 1948—the United States tariff was probably the most important single factor determining for better or worse the economic destiny of the Cuban sugar industry and of Cuba in general. The Reciprocity Treaty of 1901 gave Cuba a 20 percent preference below the full duty rate; it gave Cuba an edge on other foreign producers. As late as 1897-1901 over half of the sugar consumed in the United States was imported from foreign countries other than Cuba. The foreign sources soon dried up, supplying in a typical year less than 1 percent, while Cuba's share of the United States market expanded as follows:[36]

1897-1901	16.7%	1917-1921	48.6%
1902-1907	38.0%	1922-1926	56.2%
1908-1911	41.7%	1927-1930	49.4%
1912-1913	50.4%	1931-1933	30.3%
1914-1916	49.2%	1934-1939	29.2%
			(quota)

Of the 150 to 160 sugar mills located in Cuba, less than half, or about 70, are really Cuban-owned; approximately another 70 are definitely American-owned; and the remainder are either Canadian-owned or of mixed Cuban-American ownership. As a result of the fantastic gyrations of sugar prices, the equally fantastic gyrations of Cuban production, and the varying reception given Cuban sugar in the American market, the financial experience of the Cuban sugar companies has been irregular, to say the least. Receiverships have become common, and in their train have gone reorgan-

---

[35] See Foreign Policy Association, Commission on Cuba, *Problems of the New Cuba,* 1934. See also J. W. F. Rowe, *Studies in the Artificial Control of Raw Material Supplies, No. 1 Sugar,* Royal Economic Society, Memorandum No. 23, October, 1930, p. 59.

[36] Figures up to 1930 from U. S. Tariff Commission, *Sugar,* Report No. 73, p. 38; figures from 1931-1939 from U. S. Tariff Commission, *Statistics—Sugar,* 1940, p. 27.

izations involving the auction of mill properties which generally played into the hands of a few powerful financial interests. Since the foreign-owned mills are usually more modern, faster grinding, and larger, their share of the business for the most part considerably exceeds that indicated by the number of the mills.

Several of the Cuban properties are integrated with concerns in the continental United States. Among these, the American Sugar Refining Company, the United Fruit Company, and the Hershey Chocolate Company deserve special mention.

TWO FOREIGN PRODUCERS: DOMINICAN REPUBLIC AND JAVA

In addition to these chief contributors to the United States sugar supply, American capital is heavily involved in the Dominican Republic, which occupies the eastern portion of Hispaniola, the second largest island in the West Indies. Labor is cheap even for that part of the world. Two large corporations produce about four-fifths of the sugar, most of which goes—or at least does in "normal" times—to Great Britain. Very little can enter the United States over the hurdle of the full-duty rate. For a number of years a not inconsiderable portion of the cane grown in the Dominican Republic was shipped to Puerto Rico for grinding, from where it could enter the United States duty-free.

Java is second only to Cuba as a natural producer of sugar for export. The Java sugar industry thrived as long as there was a world market willing to buy sugar from the cheapest source. Java may not have been able to boast of having the lowest-cost sugar property, but she could produce three million tons of sugar more cheaply than any other region on earth. This was due to favorable climate, good soil, cheap labor, and, above all, to the scientific achievements of the Dutch technicians and managers.

A peculiar feature of the Java industry before World War II was the law forbidding corporations to own land. They had to lease, and leases did not generally exceed three years. There was no native *colono* class which could be trusted with the task of growing cane for the mills. Hence all cane was "administration" cane, i.e., cane grown by and for the mills on leased land; this fact may account in part for the high scientific standards and low cost of Javanese cane production. How stable a social order had been developed through centuries of maturing colonial administration of the Netherlands government became evident when Java had to cut her output from 3 million tons to half a million. This proved a terrific blow to the industry itself, but so safeguarded were the native interests from the gyrations of industrial performances that a social upheaval was avoided. That later events contributed to the stringent curtailment of Dutch colonial rule in Indonesia does not necessarily refute this statement.

WORLD SUGAR CONSUMPTION

If the 36 million tons of sugar produced in 1948 had been distributed evenly among an estimated world population of 2250 million people, each man, woman, and child would have received a yearly allotment of about thirty pounds. At 1820 calories to the pound, this would equal about 54,600 calories per head per year, or about 150 calories per head per day. Actually, as Table 15.4 shows, sugar consumption varies widely among the peoples of the earth, ranging from 11 calories a day in Madagascar to 603 in Denmark.

The heavy consumption of sugar characteristic of the richer countries of the West is a rather modern phenomenon. Sugar consumption in the United States in 1821 is estimated at less than 8 pounds per head. By 1850 it had risen to about 30 pounds; in 1902 it stood at 66.4 and in 1928 reached a peak of 103 pounds. Since then it has fluctuated between 70 and 100 pounds with the ups and downs of the business cycle and the vicissitudes of war. In France sugar consumption increased from about 3 pounds at the end of the Napoleonic Wars to about 24 pounds around 1900 and approximately 50 pounds before World War II. In Denmark it jumped from a little over 50 pounds in 1900 to 100 pounds in 1913-1914 and to 123.4 pounds in 1928.

For several decades before World War I world sugar consumption increased about 3 percent a year, doubling about every twenty-five years. After World War I the increase amounted to 4.5 percent, a rate 50 percent faster than the prewar rate. The Great Depres-

TABLE 15.4. Per Capita Daily Sugar Consumption, Pre-World War II, in Calories and as Percentage of Total Food Consumed[37]

Country	Calories	Percent
Denmark	603	18.5
Australia	582	18.6
Canada	518	16.6
United States	515	15.8
New Zealand	507	15.1
Sweden	506	16.6
Iceland	504	17.0
United Kingdom	465	15.5
Costa Rica	447	22.3
Cuba	438	15.0
Switzerland	418	13.7
Eire	416	13.6
Norway	391	12.5
Puerto Rico	377	17.0
Netherlands	373	12.6
Argentina	347	10.6
Uruguay	319	10.9
Finland	300	10.1
Belgium	285	9.9
Chile	283	11.4
Czechoslovakia	275	9.9
Germany	264	8.9
Austria	264	9.0
Brazil	263	10.3
French Morocco	253	10.4
France	247	8.0
Honduras	240	11.5
Union of South Africa	220	9.6
Palestine (Israel)	200	7.8
Mexico	197	10.3
Tunisia	186	8.2
El Salvador	180	9.3
Dominican Republic	168	7.8
Algeria	168	7.5
Syria and Lebanon	164	7.1
India	163	8.2
Peru	152	7.0
Spain	143	5.1
Ceylon	140	6.5
Poland	132	4.9
Philippines	124	6.1
U.S.S.R.	121	4.3
Hungary	117	4.2
Greece	113	4.5
Burma	103	4.4
Malaya	100	4.3
Colombia	98	5.1
Portugal	88	3.2
Italy	80	3.1
Yugoslavia	55	2.1
Rumania	55	2.1
Bulgaria	44	1.5
China	14	0.6
Madagascar	11	0.5

[37] Food and Agriculture Organization, *World Food Survey*, Washington, July 5, 1946, pp. 36-38.

sion slowed the rate down to about 1.5 per-cent during the thirties. World War II played havoc with normal consumption trends.

Considering the fact that sugar is the cheap-est energy- or calorie-priced food (1820 calories for less than 10 cents in the United States), one may be tempted to assume that sugar is a poor man's food and that the poorest nations are the heaviest consumers of it. Table 15.4 disproves such theorizing. Not only are the richest nations the heaviest consumers in terms of calories per head, but their diet seems to lean more heavily on sugar than that of poorer nations. Thus in the well-to-do nations sugar provides almost one-fifth of the total calorie supply, whereas in the poorer countries it sup-plies less than 1 percent.

The reasons for this seemingly anomalous behavior are varied. A poor country unable to produce sugar at home is likely to lack the foreign exchange necessary to pay for sugar imports. Poor countries are apt to have poor transport facilities and this adds materially to the cost of food brought in from the outside.

Sugar is not a basic food like bread or cas-sava or rice. Its major function is to sweeten such drinks as tea, coffee, cacao, fruit juices, etc., and such luxury foods as cakes, preserves, candies, etc. The demand for sugar, therefore, is joined to the demand for liquid and solid foods which are definitely beyond the reach of poor people. This joint demand also accounts for the fact that even in a country as wealthy as the United States sugar consumption varies considerably with the business cycle.

Sugar consumption is also affected by taxa-tion. In countries where sugar is considered a luxury, heavy excise taxes may be levied which may materially curtail consumption further. Import duties may have a similar effect.

Finally the fact that wines and fruit contain sugar must be kept in mind in considering the low sucrose consumption in such countries as Italy, Greece, and Portugal.

THE WORLD SUGAR SURPLUS PROBLEM
Nature of the Problem

When the people of some countries consume just a few pounds of low-grade sugar a year while others eat about 100 pounds per capita, there obviously can be no real sugar surplus in the world. Assuming a world population of

2,250,000,000 people and a per capita consumption of 100 pounds, a real surplus would occur if the world output of sugar were to exceed something like 112 million short tons. As a matter of fact, actual production has never exceeded 36 million short tons.

If, nevertheless, one speaks of a world sugar problem, he evidently has in mind something different from a general flooding of the world market. The surplus problem which engaged the minds of statesmen during the twenties and thirties, which led to revolution in Cuba and to numerous international conferences and several international agreements, involves excessive cane or beet growing and sugar production resulting in unremunerative prices.

This surplus problem developed after World War I as a result of the following factors:

1. Europe's unexpectedly rapid recovery of her beet sugar-producing capacity during the twenties.
2. The failure of Cuban sugar interests to read the handwriting on the wall.
3. The introduction of P.O.J. 2878, which raised yields in almost all cane-growing areas of the world.
4. The vigor of economic nationalistic and of imperial preference policies which cut the so-called "free market," i.e., the market in which outsiders may sell, to a mere fraction of its former size.
5. The Smoot-Hawley Tariff Act of 1930. Among these nationalistic-imperialistic measures this Act deserves special mention because of the vital role of the American market for Cuba, the center of the surplus trouble. This Act not only fostered the expansion of cane and beet production in the United States proper, but encouraged its rapid expansion in Hawaii, Puerto Rico, and the Philippines.
6. The Great Depression, which drastically reduced the effective demand for sugar.

The International Sugar Agreement of 1931[38]

During the twenties Cuba, the country hardest hit by the progressive restrictions on the free market, tried single-handedly to tackle the problem of surpluses and disastrous price drops,

but without real success. In 1930 when the Smoot-Hawley Act was passed and the depression set in, American—especially New York—interests with a stake in Cuban property in general and in Cuba's sugar industry in particular, began, under the leadership of Thomas L. Chadbourne, a lawyer with property interests in several Cuban mills, to play with the idea of marketing quotas for all areas supplying the United States market. Some form of "gentlemen's agreement" was reached which served as the basis for wider international action. Conferences were held in Amsterdam between Cuban and Javanese interests; in Brussels between American, Polish, Czechoslovakian, Hungarian, and Belgian representatives; in Berlin with Germany. An International Agreement was signed in May, 1931. It was to remain in effect until September 1, 1935. At the time of its signing, the above countries claimed almost 50 percent of world sugar production, but by 1933-1934 their share had dropped to less than 25 percent. While these countries cut down their own output by 6.4 million tons, or almost one-half, total world production declined only by 1.7 million tons, indicating that outsiders raised their production by 4.7 million tons. Thus the Philippine output rose 80 percent, that of Formosa (then Taiwan) leaped forward, and India went on an expansion spree. Under those conditions, the International Agreement proved a dead letter by 1933. Revolution broke out in Cuba. In the United States the "triple A" program was taking shape. The Chadbourne agreement was a victim of unrestrained economic nationalism, which seems happiest when it deprives people of cheap supplies of vital staples.

The International Sugar Agreement of 1937

When the Chadbourne agreement lapsed in 1935 an International Sugar Committee was set up. After a series of preliminary discussions, a second attempt at international control was made in 1937. This time it was not a matter of a private lawyer negotiating with trade association officials, but a regular governmental conference on the top level. Twenty-two countries were represented.

The participation included (a) countries that produced almost exclusively for export—Cuba, Java,

---

[38] This discussion is based largely on B. C. Swerling, *op. cit.*

Peru, Dominican Republic, Haiti; (b) exporters that also enjoyed a sizable internal market—South Africa, Australia, Belgium, Brazil, Czechoslovakia, Hungary, Japan, Poland, Portugal, the U.S.S.R., and Yugoslavia; (c) countries largely self-sufficient in sugar—France, Germany (which had ceased to export in the thirties), and India; and (d) countries requiring large imports—Canada, China, the United States, and the United Kingdom, each of whom had an important producer interest in the commodity.[39]

As a result of the conference, the International Sugar Agreement was signed in 1937 by twenty-two nations including the Philippines, but ratification was distressingly slow. The agreement was realistic in its recognition of a sharply delineated "free market." The whole scheme rests on the recognition of this vital entity and on the fact that its determination is a matter of sovereign nations taking care of their own interests, political as well as economic. In other words, while the Chadbourne agreement approached the problem of quota allocation from the supply side, the procedure was now reversed and the expectable demand for "free market" sugar was made the starting point.

Various flexible provisions were inserted to take care of departures from the anticipated. Stocks were subjected to control.

The members of the conference were aware of the danger of letting prices rise to a point where consumption would be discouraged. The price arrived at was one which would leave a *reasonable* profit for the efficient producer.

The agreement never got a fair test. During the first year it was under a shadow because of the failure of speedy ratification. This contributed to a weakness of the market price. The second year brought the impact of the approaching war. During the third year, the signatories divided themselves into combatants, on both sides of the struggle, and neutrals. The agreement, however, was kept under a wrap, so to speak, to be in readiness if postwar developments should once more call for a concerted effort at orderly world marketing.

Swerling stresses the fact that while other international agreements may attempt to protect inefficient producers at the expense of the efficient, the International Sugar Agreement was an effort to assure the survival of the most efficient producers—such as Cuba, Java, and the Philippines—in the face of economic nationalism run rampant.

Sugar in World War II[40]

The war started with larger than usual stocks of sugar on hand in most of the important producing and consuming countries. The war also found governmental controls over sugar production and marketing in virtually every country where this crop was of economic significance. The International Sugar Agreement had been signed in 1937, and the Sugar Act of 1937 was in force in the United States.

Sugar was in shorter supply than most other foods in the United States throughout nearly all of World War II. It was the first food to be rationed after the outbreak of war and the only one not removed from ration control before 1946. The shortage of sugar existed in varying degrees in most of the United Nations and was generally more serious for our European allies than for the United States. This shortage of sugar was in marked contrast to the situation in prewar years when sugar was abundant and prices were extremely low from the producers' standpoint.

The wartime shortage in the United States had a combination of causes. It was largely the result of the loss of supplies normally produced in the Philippine Islands and Java, the reduced production in Europe, particularly Russia, three years of small crops of beet sugar in the United States beginning in 1943, and a very short Cuban crop of sugar cane in 1945. In addition, the use of sugar to make industrial alcohol which was needed in previously unheard of quantities largely because of the program for making synthetic rubber further reduced the amount of sugar produced for use as food.[41]

The most important events affecting sugar supplies in the main consuming countries were the following:

1. The overrunning of Java and the Philippines by the Japanese.

---

[39] *Ibid.*, p. 53.

[40] This discussion is based largely on Roy A. Ballinger, *Sugar During World War II*, War Records Monograph No. 3, U. S. Department of Agriculture, Bureau of Agricultural Economics, 1946.

[41] *Ibid.*, p. 1.

2. The sharp decline of sugar production, especially beet sugar, in the continental United States.
3. The war damage to sugar production in Europe, especially in the Ukraine.
4. The shipping shortage, which played havoc with normal overseas delivery.

The sharp decline of sugar production in the United States, which was most pronounced in the beet-growing states, was caused mainly by the diversion of labor to more lucrative industrial employment and the diversion of land to crops which yield larger total receipts from sales and subsidies.

Our government's policy was aimed at supplying reasonable amounts at reasonable prices and at the same time assuring growers and manufacturers a sufficiently high return to warrant continued production. The Commodity Credit Corporation administered by the Secretary of Agriculture spent over $380 million on its various sugar programs during the years 1942-1946. In general, the high-income tax classes subsidized the low-income tax consumers of sugar.

After May 14, 1944, the Commodity Credit Corporation was the sole buyer of Cuban sugar. It absorbed the duty on this sugar in its sales price and used the funds to defray its expenses.

Shortly after Pearl Harbor, the United States and Great Britain established a Combined Food Board which Canada joined in 1944. Sugar, one of the commodities controlled by the Board, was allocated to the various allied nations. However, the War Shipping Board exercised direct control over actual deliveries.[42]

One peculiar feature of the war sugar situation was the strong demand for invert molasses. While blackstrap molasses is the normal by-product of cane sugar production, invert molasses is made out of the entire cane. Instead of cane being converted into sugar and blackstrap molasses, only a high grade of molasses, invert molasses, is produced. The main demand for invert molasses stemmed from the synthetic rubber industry. This molasses normally is a cheaper source of industrial alcohol than grains. Its production also provides a means of disposing of surplus cane which cannot be converted into sugar under control laws.

Sugar was rationed in the United States from 1942 until 1946. This rationing, together with other control measures, kept retail prices for consumers within reasonable bounds, but they mounted sharply after rationing was ended. The following figures, showing the average annual retail price in the United States, tell the story:

1937	5.6	1943	6.83
1938	5.31	1944	6.76
1939	5.43	1945	6.68
1940	5.20	1946	7.68
1941	5.71	1947	9.73
1942	6.82	1948	9.37

This story of sugar reveals the extent to which the international production of agricultural staples is beset with many problems for which the rules of market economics offer much help but not a complete solution.

---

[42] Especially in 1942, shipping shortages interfered with sugar deliveries. In that year large parts of the Cuban sugar cane crop were not harvested but allowed to stand two years. The Cuban sugar crop in 1942 was only 3.2 million tons as against 3.8 million in 1941 and 4.7 million in 1943.

BIBLIOGRAPHY

Babst, E. D., Occasions in Sugar (speeches, articles, etc., 1909-1937), New York, published by self, 1940.

Ballinger, R. A., Sugar During World War II, U. S. Department of Agriculture, Bureau of Agricultural Economics, War Records Monograph No. 3, Washington, 1946.

Brandes, E. W., and Sartoris, G. B., "Sugar Cane: Its Origin and Improvement," Agriculture Yearbook, 1936.

Clark, V. S., and associates, Porto Rico and Its Problems, Washington, Brookings Institution, 1930.

Coons, G. H., "Improvement of the Sugar Beet," Agriculture Yearbook, 1936.

Dalton, J. E., Sugar: A Case Study of Government Control, New York, Macmillan, 1937.

Davis, J. S., International Commodity Agreements: Hope, Illusion, or Menace? Committee on International Economic Policy in coöperation with

Carnegie Endowment for International Peace, 1947.

Farr's Manual of Sugar Companies (annual), New York, Farr and Co.

Gayer, A. D., Homan, P. T., and James E. K., *The Sugar Economy of Puerto Rico*, New York, Columbia University Press, 1938.

Gilmore, A. B., *Hawaii Sugar Manual* (annual), New Orleans, La.

Lynsky, M., *Sugar Economics, Statistics, and Documents*, New York, U. S. Cane Sugar Refiners' Association, 1938; supplement, 1939.

Rowe, J. W. F., *Studies in the Artificial Control of Raw Material Supplies, No. 1, Sugar*, London, Royal Economic Society, Memorandum No. 23, 1930.

Smith, D., *Sugar Beet Mechanization and Implications for Puerto Rico* (pamphlet), Washington, Association of Sugar Producers of Puerto Rico, 1948.

Smith, D., and Requa, W. M., *The Facts About the Sugar Industry of Puerto Rico*, Washington, Association of Sugar Producers of Puerto Rico, n.d.

Swerling, B. C., *International Control of Sugar, 1918-1941*, Stanford University, Food Research Institute, Commodity Policy Studies No. 7, 1949.

U. S. Department of Agriculture, *World Sugar Situation* (annual).

U. S. Tariff Commission, Report No. 73, second series, Washington, 1937.

U. S. Tariff Commission, *United States-Philippine Trade*, Report No. 118, Washington, 1937.

Vandercook, J. W., *King Cane, an Epic of Sugar*, New York, Harper, 1939.

Wright, P. G., *Sugar in Relation to the Tariff*, New York, McGraw-Hill, 1924.

Chapter 16

ANIMAL AND VEGETABLE FATS AND OILS[1]

Vegetable and Animal Sources of Fats and Oils

Fats and oils play an important part in nature's scheme to support and sustain life. They are found in plants and animals alike. No less than 1800 different vegetable oils have been studied, in addition to scores of animal fats and oils. Many of them have as yet no commercial significance; others are of purely local importance.

World production of fats and oils in 1948 is estimated to have amounted to 21.7 million metric tons, of which animals contributed 8.4 million tons, or 38.7 percent. This is exclusive of butterfat consumed in the form of milk and of other animal fats consumed in the form of meat. The largest items of animal fats were slaughter fats and butter, including ghee, a liquid butter obtained from cow and buffalo milk. These were followed by whale oil and fish oil. Thirteen vegetable oils are believed to make up over nine-tenths of the remaining 61.3 percent of the world fat supply. In terms of available supply these vegetable oils probably rank as follows:

1. Peanut (groundnut)
2. Coconut
3. Soybean
4. Cottonseed
5. Rape and mustard seed
6. Olive
7. Palm and palm kernel
8. Linseed (flaxseed)
9. Sesame
10. Sunflower seed
11. Tung nut
12. Oiticica
13. Babassu

Table 16.1 shows world production and exports of animal and vegetable fats and oils both for the period before World War II and for 1948.

These vegetable oils and fats are obtained from trees, especially palm trees, and from ani-

[1] The distinction between fats and oils is one not of substances but of aggregate states of matter. A fat is thought of as solid, and an oil as liquid. The same substance, however, may at one temperature be a solid, and therefore considered a fat, and at another temperature be a liquid and therefore considered an oil. Lard is called a fat because, at normal temperatures prevailing in this country, it is a solid. Similarly, linseed oil is called an oil because, at normal temperatures, it is a liquid. But lard can be easily liquefied in frying, and linseed oil can be easily solidified in cold storage.

Chemically, the reaction to temperature is related to the degree of saturation with hydrogen. By raising the degree of saturation, the temperature at which a substance solidifies can be lowered.

TABLE 16.1. World Production and Exports, Main Classes of Fats, Pre-World War II and 1948[2]

(million metric tons, oil equivalent)

Class of Fat	Prewar Average Production	Prewar Average Exports	1948 Production	1948 Exports
Edible—soap group				
Peanuts (groundnuts)	2.2	0.8	2.5	0.5
Soybeans	1.3	0.4	1.5	0.1
Cottonseed	1.5	0.2	1.3	0.1
Rape and mustard seed oil	1.0	...	1.2	...
Copra (coconut)	1.9	1.1	1.8	0.9
Palm kernels and palm oil	1.0	0.8	0.9	0.7
Olive oil	1.0	0.1	1.1	0.1
Whale oil	0.5	0.5[a]	0.3	0.3[a]
Fish oil	0.4	0.1	0.2	0.1
Butter and ghee	4.2	0.5	3.1	0.3
Slaughter fats	5.3	0.4	4.8	0.3
All other (including sunflower seed)	1.5	0.1	1.8	0.1
Total	21.8	5.1[b]	20.5	3.5
Special technical group				
Linseed (flaxseed)	1.1	0.6	0.9	0.2
All others (including tung nuts, castor, perilla, oiticica)	0.3	0.2	0.3	0.2
Total	1.4	0.9	1.2	0.4
Total, all fats and oils	23.2	6.0	21.7	3.9

[a] All whale oil production is considered exports.

[b] Includes rapeseed and oil exports of 43,000 metric tons oil equivalent, and margarine, shortening, and soap exports of 27,000 metric tons oil equivalent, which are too small to show separately.

Production is estimated availability as oil during the period covered, not oil equivalent of reported crop. That is, adjustments have been made for use as feed, seed, waste, or for food as such, as well as for unreported production and, wherever possible, for variations in farm stocks, olive oil carry-over, etc.

Exports include oil equivalent of exports of oil-bearing materials as well as exports of oil as such. However, they include only exports of indigenous products, not reëxport trade.

mal crop plants. Most of them are produced in tropical or semitropical regions. Soybean, linseed or flaxseed, rapeseed, mustard seed, and sunflower seed are the main oil-bearing plants produced in the temperate-zone region.

The distinction between trees or perennials and annual crops has several important implications.[3] Tree crops are either wild or cultivated. If wild, their output is largely a function of available capital and labor to open up

wild forest areas and of trade and transport facilities, all governed by the all-important price-cost ratio. If cultivated, either in small groves by natives or in large plantations by foreign capital, because of the heavy overhead investments and the long "gestation" period (trees may take from five to ten years to reach the bearing stage) they are affected by short-run price fluctuations in a manner altogether different than are annual crops. Adjustment to sudden and sharp fluctuations of demand is impossible in the case of cultivated tree crops.

Data for world production of animal fats are difficult to obtain. This is due mainly to the fact that a large portion of the output is "invisible," i.e., not registered as such in production statistics. Thus the butterfat in milk, when consumed in liquid form as fresh milk, is not counted as fat consumption. Similarly, fatty portions of meat are ignored. Bacon, which comes close to being a fat, is generally included under meats. The statistics for animal fats resemble those for vegetable fats and oils in that much local consumption is not covered.

TABLE 16.2. Average Yields of Oil and Oil Meal per Hundred Pounds of Oil-Bearing Material, Ratio of Oil Meal to Oil, and Value of Oil Meal per Dollar of Oil, in the United States[4]

Oil-Bearing Material	Yield per Hundred Pounds Oil (pounds)	Yield per Hundred Pounds Oil Meal (pounds)	Oil Meal per Pound of Oil (pounds)	Value of Oil Meal per Dollar of Oil[a] (dollars)
Cottonseed	15.5	45.0	2.90	$0.58
Flaxseed	34.0	64.0	1.88	0.38
Peanuts	29.0	43.6	1.50	0.30
Soybeans	15.0	80.0	5.33	1.07
Sesame seed	47.0	48.0	1.02	0.20
Copra	63.0	35.0	0.56	0.11
Palm kernels	45.0	53.0	1.18	0.24
Babassu kernels	63.0	35.0	0.56	0.11
Sunflower seed	25.0	73.0	2.92	0.58

[a] Based on an assumed value of oil per pound five times that of oil meal.

So far as world trade in fats and oils is concerned, before World War II the total volume of vegetable fats and oils exported was about 4.5 million metric tons *in terms of oil,* as against less than a million for butter and slaughter fats, and about 650,000 metric tons of marine-animal fats, mainly whale oil.

[2] Food and Agriculture Organization, *Report on World Commodity Problems,* Washington, September, 1949, p. 39.

[3] For a systematic development of this, see chap. 22.

[4] Peter L. Hansen and Ronald L. Mighell, *Oil Crops in American Farming,* U. S. Department of Agriculture, Technical Bulletin No. 940, 1947, p. 8.

Most oil-bearing materials yield both oil and meal. The latter is valued chiefly as a high-protein feed concentrate, and secondarily as fertilizer. The yields of both oil and oil meal vary widely, as Table 16.2 shows.

The statistical treatment of some vegetable oil crops is further complicated by the fact that crops may either be harvested as hay fed to animals or be plowed under as green manure, or be grown as the source of a seed or bean crop. This applies particularly to the soybean. In the United States this crop was for many years used chiefly as hay or green manure; only gradually, as genetic and marketing problems were solved, did its use for the oil and meal extracted from the seed develop.

The origin of selected fats and oils, both vegetable and animal, may be briefly summarized as follows:

1. Plants
   a. Trees, especially palms
      Babassu palm
      Coconut palm
      Elaeis palm
      Oiticica palm
      Olive tree
      Tung tree
   b. Annual crops
      Castor (bean)
      Corn (germ of seed)
      Cotton (seed)
      Flax (seed)
      Hemp (seed)
      Mustard (seed)
      Peanut (nut)
      Poppy (seed)
      Rape (seed)
      Sesame (seed)
      Soy(a) (bean)
      Sunflower (seed)
2. Animals
   a. Land animals
      Beef—oleo fat
      Cow—butter
      Hog—lard
      Sheep—tallow
   b. Marine animals
      Cod—liver oil
      Menhaden—entire fish
      Whale—oil from blubber

Modern Science and Fats and Oils

Nature offers a bewildering array of fats and oils. Each oil seems different from every other.

There are differences of taste and smell, different reactions to temperature and temperature change, different chemical reactions and actions on other substances, and so forth. Heterogeneous reality appeared to the early explorer as a veritable jungle without law and order, without rhyme or reason.

Gradually, as science advanced, man discovered that, far from lawless and disorderly, nature's scheme was wondrously arranged. What was needed to discover the order in the midst of the jungle was to penetrate the most minute detail of matter, the atom, and find the secret behind molecular structure—in short, chemistry. About 1840 a French chemist, Chevreul, demonstrated that fats and oils are glycerides of fatty acids. The most important of these acids are lauric, myristic, palmitic, stearic, oleic, linoleic, ricinoleic, erucic, elaeostearic, and licanic. The characteristics of fats and oils depend on the amount of specific fatty acids in their composition.

The most common acids are linoleic, oleic, and stearic acid. Like all fatty acids they consist of carbon and hydrogen with very little oxygen. All three have 18 carbon atoms and 2 oxygen atoms, but whereas linoleic acid has only 32 hydrogen atoms, oleic has 34 and stearic 36. Their formulas are as follows:

Linoleic acid	$C_{18}H_{32}O_2$
Oleic acid	$C_{18}H_{34}O_2$
Stearic acid	$C_{18}H_{36}O_2$

The seemingly slight difference in hydrogen is very important, for it is this difference that accounts for the different melting points of the various fatty acids and thus determines whether a substance is a fat or an oil at a given temperature. In other words, the melting point goes up with the hydrogen content.

The presence or absence of various acids in a given fat or oil not only determines whether it is a solid or a liquid but also affects its general properties. Stearic acid is called "saturated" because it contains as much hydrogen as it can hold. On the other hand, oleic acid and, to a greater degree, linoleic acid are "nonsaturated"; i.e., they are eager for more and more hydrogen if they can get it, or for more of something else—e.g., oxygen—if they cannot. This eagerness to absorb oxygen accounts for the hardening on exposure to the air which gives linoleic acid oils, such as linseed oil, their valuable property as drying oils. Oils containing oleic acid are known as semidrying.

Modern users of fats and oils are not satisfied with their natural composition; hence the molecular structure is deliberately altered through chemical manipulation—especially hydrogenation—so as to change oils into fats, inedible products into edible ones, etc. This artificial interference is of course held within reasonable bounds by the costs of the materials needed and the services required. One should keep in mind, moreover, that the fat and oil economy of the world is far removed from the ideal of free competition. Tariff and quota regulations dominate as much in this sphere as in almost any other. Cost relationships, therefore, are by no means the only factors determining the opportunities open to the chemist and engineer.

Hydrogenation, i.e., the injection of hydrogen atoms into the molecule, was one of the greatest achievements of industrial chemistry. It laid the foundation of the margarine industry and continues to add to the raw materials which that industry can utilize. Thus more and more fats and oils are brought into competition with butter and once this competition is freed from present legal restraints it should bring rich blessings to consumers.[5]

Actually, the impact of hydrogenation goes even further. Most of the oil- and fat-bearing raw materials such as soybeans, palm kernels, coconuts, babassu nuts, etc., yield not only oils but also oil cake. Oil cake is a valuable high-protein feed concentrate which materially aids in the dairying and meat-raising industries and thus stimulates and encourages their expansion. Moreover, the rich manure obtained from such feeding materially increases the fertility of the land and constitutes a net importation of soil fertility. Export of agricultural products entails a loss of fertility; imports of feed are likely to constitute a gain.

The effect of modern science on fats and oils technology is well brought out in the following:

Along with hydrogenation there were other substantial advances in the technology of refining and processing fats and oils and in preparing them for use in the food industries. Similarly in the nonfood and industrial fields a continued stream of new technology has greatly modified the production of soaps, paints, and other industrial products. In Germany, synthetic fats have been developed from coal and considerable quantities were manufactured during the war because of a shortage of natural fats.

Recent research in this country has resulted in several processes for producing high-quality drying oils and for improving food fats and oils by preventing the development of undesirable flavors. A dehydrating process applied to castor oil made it possible to use this oil in the drying industries during wartime. The development of suitable antioxidants for lard now makes possible the production of bland shortenings from animal fats. Initial commercial success with this process indicates that it may be a notable further step affecting the interchangeability of fats.

Enormous expansion in soybean production in the United States has directed much attention to the processing methods for soybean oil. Soybean oil may be said to be rather intermediate between food oils and drying oils in its characteristics. Hence research efforts have been devoted to improving its qualities in either direction. Lack of stability in flavor has been one of the chief difficulties in using soybean oil in food preparations. Considerable progress has been made in overcoming this problem. The wartime findings of German chemists, recently made available, are especially significant as they indicate a more effective and efficient method of eliminating and preventing the development of objectionable flavors. . . .

Perhaps the most promising new process is that of "fractionation." By this is meant the physical separation of an oil into two or more fractions or segments, each differing in chemical structure. In the case of soybean oil one fraction would be a superior food oil and the other a better drying oil. . . .

Several other processes for separating soybean and other oils have been studied and have been tried with some success. These include fractional distillation, crystallization, selective absorption, and molecular distillation. Distillation procedures are at present the most important of the fractionation processes and are used commercially by several companies. With improvements likely to follow,

---

[5] In Europe, where margarine is used more freely than in the United States, it went far to replace the lard once imported in large amounts from the United States. Thus, by making possible the production of margarine from very cheap raw materials, hydrogenation let loose a double attack on the Corn Belt—one directly aimed at the butter which domestic margarine consumption replaces, and the other indirectly aimed at the lard replaced by margarine made from whale oil, etc., and consumed in the European market.

fractionation may become as striking a landmark in the history of fats and oils technology as hydrogenation. Like hydrogenation, fractionation operates to increase the range of substitution possible between different fats and oils.

Development of fatty derivatives for industrial use is another field of current chemical research that holds promise. The fatty acids that are found in the vegetable oils are an important source of raw materials for manufacturing detergents, emulsifiers, resins, plasticizers, synthetic drying oils, and many other products.[6]

USES OF FATS AND OILS

Classification of Uses

As technology advances, the uses to which different oils and fats can be put are being enlarged through chemical manipulation. Nevertheless, certain oils are definitely preferred for certain uses. Thus linseed oil, tung oil, and oiticica oil are primarily drying oils. Coconut and babassu oils, because of the dominance of lauric acid (which accounts for the lathering effect in soaps) in their chemical composition, are apt to move to soap factories unless the coconut oil is needed for vegetable shortening or margarine. The following classification[7] lists the diverse uses under each oil or fat.

USES OF ANIMAL AND VEGETABLE OILS AND FATS

VEGETABLE OILS

Castor: medicine; alizarin assistant; soap (fine toilet, especially transparent soaps); lubricant for heavy machinery and airplanes; leather preservative; flypaper; illuminant.

Coconut: soap (the Cochin oil is suitable for cold-process soap making. All coconut oil makes soaps of good lathering quality. Marine soaps that will lather in hard water may be made from it); "nut" margarine; lard substitutes; used by bakers and in the confectionery trade; emulsions; cosmetics; perfumes; ointments; salves.

Corn: salad oil; margarine; lard substitutes; alizarin assistant; soap; linoleum; leather dressing; vulcanized rubber; waterproof fabric; paint.

Cottonseed: lard substitutes; salad oil; margarine; sardine packing; cooking; medicinal emulsions; soap; washing powder; glycerin; waterproofing preparations; illuminant.

---

[6] Peter L. Hansen and Ronald L. Mighell, *op. cit.*, pp. 27-28.

[7] P. G. Wright, *The Tariff on Animal and Vegetable Oils*, The Macmillan Company, New York, 1928, Appendix.

Hempseed: paint and varnish (inferior to linseed); soft soap.

Linseed: paint; varnish; linoleum; printers' ink and lithographic ink; patent leather; imitation leather; foundry cores; soap; glycerin; putty; vulcanizing; when cold pressed and refined it is edible.

Olive: salad oil; alizarin assistant; soap (Castile); wool spinning; sardine packing; lubricant; illuminant.

Palm: soap; candles; tinplate ("palm oil grease," palm oil, mixed with cottonseed oil and mineral oil, preserves the surface of the heated plate till dipped in tin); in textile mills for softening and finishing cotton goods.

Palm kernel: (very similar to coconut oil) soap (especially cold-process soap); margarine.

Peanut: salad oil; margarine; sardine packing; cooking; medical emulsions; cosmetics; illuminant (for miners' lamps); kid gloves, wool, and silk manufacture; artificial leather; soap; putty.

Perilla: paint; linoleum.

Poppyseed: paints (especially artists' colors); soap (potash soaps and when added to olive oil stock makes the product less brittle); used as an edible oil in some countries.

Rapeseed: lubricant; illuminant; soap; quenching steel plates.

Sesame: margarine; cooking; enfleurage (extraction of perfume from flowers); soap (Marseilles mottled soap); lubricant; illuminant; rubber substitutes.

Soybean: soap; glycerin; paint; varnish; linoleum; printers' ink; foundry cores; salad oil; lard substitutes; margarine.

Tung: paint (inferior to linseed because of opacity and inelasticity of film, but desirable for enamel paint); varnish, especially spar varnish, as it does not turn white.

ANIMAL OILS

Butter: used chiefly as butter but also used in the manufacture of margarine.

Greases: soap; lubricant.

Lard: used as lard and also in the manufacture of margarine and lard substitutes; ointments; salves; inedible grades used in making soap, lard oil, and lard stearin. Lard oil is an illuminant, a lubricant, and is used in oiling wool and dressing leather. Lard stearin is used for stiffening lard of lower titer.

Menhaden and other fish oils: soap; paint (especially for painting smokestacks or other surfaces exposed to heat); linoleum; currying leather; tempering steel.

Oleo oil and oleo stearin: the former used primarily for margarine and to a minor extent for lard substitutes. The latter is used for the same pur-

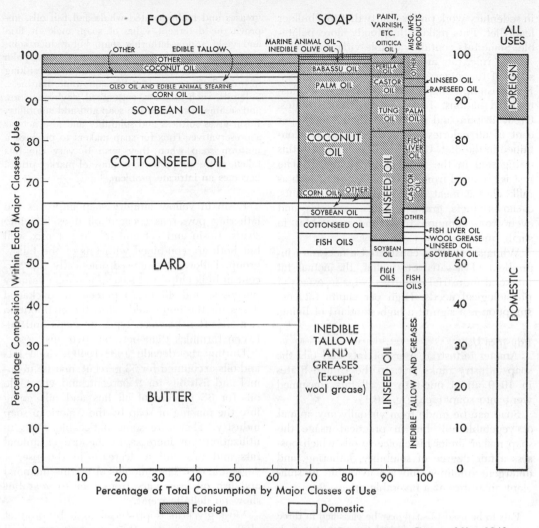

FIG. 16.1. Apparent Consumption of Fats and Oils in the United States by Major Classes of Use, 1940. (This and Fig. 16.3 are from U. S. Tariff Commission, *Fats, Oils, and Oil-Bearing Materials in the United States*, Washington, 1941.)

poses but with the primary and secondary use reversed.

Tallow: lard substitutes; margarine; soap; ointments; salves; tallow oil; tallow stearin. Tallow oil is used as a lubricant and an illuminant; tallow stearin is used by tanners for dressing leather, and by candle makers.

Whale: soap; leather dressing; tempering steel; illuminant; margarine.

Fats and Oils in the Human Diet

In industrialized countries by far the most important use made of fats and oils is in the form of food. In the United States in 1940,

69 percent of all fats and oils consumed were consumed as food. See Fig. 16.1. Fats are the most concentrated energy foods. Although both proteins and carbohydrates are rated at 4.1 calories per gram, a gram of fat is valued at 9.3 calories. Fats are widely interchangeable in the human diet with carbohydrates such as cereals, starchy root crops, and sugar.

Because of their high energy concentration per unit of weight, fats do not burden the alimentary tract as much as do other energy foods. They satisfy hunger longer. They are easily digested. In particular, people engaged in sedentary work prefer a fatty diet to a bulkier lean diet. Fats make other foods more palatable. Some fats contain valuable vitamins.

As a rule, fats are expensive compared with some of the sugars and starches they replace.[8] Fat consumption is highest in well-to-do industrialized nations. Thus, "in the United States, Great Britain and Germany about 30-35 per cent of all calories are derived from fat contained in the diet. Usually up to one half of this is ingested in the form of visible fats."[9] The rest is obtained from "invisible" sources such as milk, cheese, meat, eggs, fishery products, nuts, cacao products, grain products, avocados, and even from common fruits and vegetables in small quantities.

While some fat is considered a necessary ingredient of a satisfactory diet, the actual fat intake in industrial countries is far in excess of physiological needs. High per capita fat consumption is a sign of a high standard of living.

Industrial Uses

Among industrial users of fats and oils the soap industry ranks first. In the United States in 1940 about one-fifth of all fats consumed went into soap (see Fig. 16.1).

Soap can be made from virtually any animal or vegetable oil, but in practical usage the soap maker limits his choice to oils which possess a fair degree of solubility, lathering, and detergent qualities and are available in sufficient quantities at a favorable price.

Fats to be used in soap may be classified in three groups having certain technical characteristics such that, whereas substitutions may in general be made within groups fairly readily, extensive substitution between groups results in changes in types of soaps produced.

Fats of the tallow class, that is tallow, palm oil, greases and hydrogenated-whale and fish oils, improve the detergent value of soap, make it firm and yield a slow-lathering soap, but reduce solubility. The nut oil class, including coconut, palm kernel, and babassu oils, give solubility, resulting in quick lathering and, at the same time, hardness. Soft oils, such as foots, cottonseed, soybean, corn, and sesame oils, soften the soap and add solubility. Rosin gives softness and solubility and also acts as a preservative. Thus for soap makers to produce a uniform soap when they wish to vary the fats taken, or the proportions, because of market prices, becomes an intricate problem.[10]

Rosin in yellow laundry soap improves the lathering power as coconut oil does in white soaps. Rosin and coconut oil do not mix well but both are combined with fats of the tallow group. Tallow fats are used practically 100 percent in bulk chips and flakes for public laundry purposes, and 40 to 75 percent in packaged flakes for the household. Thus the competition is more often between types of soaps and between formulas than between two oils.

During the decade 1931-1940 animal fats and oils accounted for 53 percent, marine mammal and fish oils for 9 percent, and vegetable oils for 38 percent of all fats and oils going into the making of soap by the American soap industry. There are some noticeable shifts in utilization: an increase in the use of animal fats and oils and a decrease in the use of vegetable oils. The amounts of marine mammal and fish oil used vary from year to year but show no definite trend.

Most glycerin is produced as a by-product of the soap industry. It is a constituent of all animal and vegetable fats and oils, occurring in chemical combination with fatty acids. During the soap-making process this combination is broken and the glycerin is set free. Large soap makers usually recover most of the glycerin produced, but smaller factories do not unless glycerin prices are high.

A small part of the glycerin produced in the United States is manufactured by "fat splitters," who separate a fat or oil into its two components, glycerin and fatty acids, without producing soap in the process. The two separate products are then sold to industrial users. During

---

[8] However, Karl Brandt reports that "in 1928 at the peak of prosperity the German laborer could buy for one Reichmark 10 percent more calories in the form of margarine than in the form of bread. In 1932 at the depth of the depression, a Reichmark bought more than twice as many calories in margarine as it would in bread." In interpreting these statements one must remember that German wheat prices were maintained at artificial levels way above the world price. *Fats and Oils in the War,* Food Research Institute, War-Peace Pamphlet No. 2, 1943, p. 11.

[9] *Ibid.,* p. 3.

[10] U. S. Department of Agriculture, Bureau of Agricultural Economics, *The Fats and Oils Situation,* August 16, 1937, p. 9.

part of World War II the use of coconut oil and other quick-lathering oils was restricted largely to processes that recovered a high percentage of the glycerin. These oils yield about 25 percent more glycerin per pound of oil used than other fats and oils.

In the early thirties a process for the manufacture of glycerin by the fermentation of sugar or molasses was put into large-scale use. Sugars suitable for this process are grape sugar, glucose, fructose, inverted saccharose, and treated starch.[11]

The drying industry consists principally of the paint and varnish, linoleum and oilcloth, and printing-ink manufacturing industries. During the decade 1931-1940 the drying industry used an average of 683 million pounds of fats and oils. Of this amount, land and marine animal oils and fats accounted for only 4 to 6 percent, the rest being vegetable oils. The two most important oils in this field are linseed oil and tung oil. During this entire period linseed oil accounted for between two-thirds and three-fourths of the total annual consumption, as compared with a range from 13 to 20 percent for tung oil in every year except 1940, when it accounted for only 8.5 percent.[12]

Paints and varnishes accounted for 83.5 percent, linoleum and oilcloth for 14 percent, and printing ink for 2.5 percent of the fats and oils used by the drying industry in 1940.

Consumption of perilla oil accounted for 1.8 percent of the total in 1931; the percentage increased to 13.6 in 1936 but fell to 2.4 in 1940. China is the main producer of tung oil and China and Japan are the main producers of perilla oil. During World War II the United States was cut off almost entirely from these sources of supply. The consumption of soybean, castor, oiticica, and fish oils increased during World War II. Imported oils accounted for 80 percent of the total used in 1937 but for only 44 percent of that consumed in 1940.

THE WORLD SITUATION
Geographical Survey

Table 16.3 enables us to arrive at a world survey of the oil-growing-processing industry

and the international movements of both raw materials and oils. The table lists the chief countries which produce oil-bearing raw materials, export and import these raw materials, produce oil from them, and export and import the oil.

From the table we learn that the United States, the leading producer of cottonseed, does not export cottonseed but processes it before exporting. Both India and Egypt, the two runners-up, export cottonseed, but only Egypt exports cottonseed oil as well. Most of the cottonseed exported from these countries goes to the United Kingdom, a leading processor of oil seeds. Various reasons may account for this practice. Commercial treaties may call for delivery of part of the seed crops from India and Egypt to Britain. The local industries may serve mainly local needs. The greater value of cottonseed meal in Britain because of its wider use as cattle feed may account for the ability of British oil mills to outbid Indian and Egyptian mills for it.

China does not export peanuts as do India and Africa, but exports peanut oil. Africa in particular possesses little control over her industries and is generally underdeveloped in that respect.

Palm kernels are evidently exported to industrial countries for extraction of palm-kernel oil, whereas palm oil is extracted locally, the difference being explained in part by the greater technological difficulties encountered in processing palm kernels.

Japan evidently functioned as a middleman processor for Chinese oil-bearing materials such as soybeans (Manchuria) and perilla.

Conditions Before World War II

The most striking development in the world fats and oils situation was the rapid increase, during the thirty years preceding World War II, of the vegetable oil industry, especially in the tropics. From 1909-1913 to 1934-1938 the average annual world production of vegetable oil crops increased from 10.4 to 15.0 million metric tons, and exports of these products increased even faster, from 2.3 to 4.2 million metric tons. As was mentioned before, the situation regarding animal fats is partly obscured by the important part played by "invisible" supplies. The breakdown of this thirty-year

---

[11] E. R. Riegel, *Industrial Chemistry*, Chemical Catalog Company, Inc., New York, 1933, p. 525.

[12] For a fuller discussion of the tung oil situation, see pp. 284-285.

TABLE 16.3. Leading Sources of Vegetable Oils and Whale Oil, and Chief Countries Importing and Exporting Such Oils and Oil-Bearing Materials[13]

Oil	Chief Countries					
	Producing Raw Material	Exporting Raw Material	Importing Raw Material	Producing Oil	Exporting Oil	Importing Oil
Cottonseed	United States, India, Egypt.	India, Egypt.	United Kingdom.	United States, United Kingdom, Egypt.	United States, United Kingdom, Egypt.	Canada, Germany, Netherlands.
Peanut	India, Africa, China.	India, Africa.	France, Germany.	France, Germany, China.	France, Germany, China.	United Kingdom, Netherlands.
Olive	Spain, Italy, Greece, Portugal, North Africa.			Spain, Italy, Greece, Portugal, North Africa.	Spain, Italy.	United States, France, United Kingdom.
Coconut	Philippine Islands, Netherland East Indies, Ceylon, British Malaya, India, South Pacific Islands.	Philippine Islands, Netherland East Indies, Ceylon, British Malaya, India, South Pacific Islands.	United States, Netherlands, Germany, France.	Philippine Islands, Netherland East Indies, Ceylon, India, United States, Netherlands, Germany, France.	Philippine Islands, Ceylon, Netherlands.	United States, United Kingdom.
Linseed	Argentina, United States, India, U.S.S.R., Canada.	Argentina, India, Canada.	United States, United Kingdom, Netherlands, Germany.	United States, United Kingdom, Germany, Netherlands, U.S.S.R.	Netherlands, United Kingdom.	United Kingdom.
Soybean	China.	China.	Japan, United Kingdom, Germany.	China, Japan, United Kingdom, Germany.	China, Japan, United Kingdom, Germany.	United Kingdom, Netherlands.
Sunflower	U.S.S.R., China.	U.S.S.R., China.	Germany, United Kingdom.	U.S.S.R., China, United Kingdom, Germany.		
Rapeseed	India-China.	India-China.	Japan, United Kingdom, Germany, Netherlands.	Germany, India - China, Japan, United Kingdom, Netherlands.	Japan, United Kingdom.	United States.
Sesame	India-China.	China.	Netherlands, Germany, United Kingdom, France, United States.	India-China, Netherlands, Germany, United Kingdom, France, United States.	Netherlands	United States.
Palm-kernel	Africa, Netherland East Indies.	Africa, Netherland East Indies.	Germany, United Kingdom.	Germany, United Kingdom.	Germany, United Kingdom.	United States.
Palm	Africa, Netherland East Indies.	Africa, Netherland East Indies.		Africa, Netherland East Indies.	Africa, Netherland East Indies.	United States, United Kingdom.
Hempseed	U.S.S.R.			U.S.S.R.		
Tung	China.			China.	China	United States.
Perilla	China.	China.	Japan	China, Japan	China, Japan	United States.
Whale	Antarctic waters.			Norway,[a] United Kingdom.[a]	Norway, United Kingdom.	United States, Germany.
Corn	United States.			United States		

a That is, vessels registered under flags of these countries.

NOTE. In general, the conditions in this table are those of about 1930. The ordinary flux of world affairs and the violent impact of war have wrought some changes, among the most important of which are probably: (1) the emergence of the United States as the leading producer of soybeans; (2) the rapid growth of sunflower culture in Argentina; (3) the increasing production of tung oil in the United States.

[13] U. S. Tariff Commission, Report to the Congress on Certain Vegetable Oils, Whale Oil and Copra, Report No. 41, 2nd Series, 1932, p. 66.

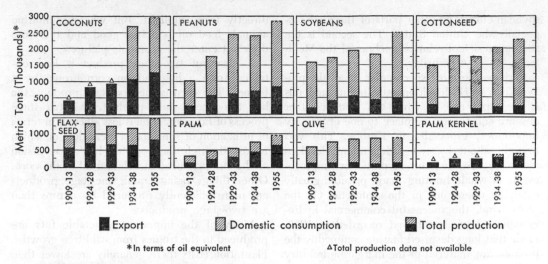

FIG. 16.2. Production and Export of Major Oil Crops, 1909-1938, with Estimate for 1955. (From P. L. Hanson and R. L. Mighell, *Oil Crops in American Farming*, U. S. Department of Agriculture, Technical Bulletin No. 940, 1947.)

growth by specific vegetable oils is shown in Fig. 16.2, which also gives estimates for 1955.[14]

This rapid increase is to a large degree a corollary of general economic progress and population increase, but is also due to special developments such as exceptional progress in oils and fats technology, the improvement of international trade and transportation, and the growth of the plantation system.

The introduction of the plantation system of production in the Netherlands Indies together with the use of an improved variety of the oil palm more than anything else were responsible for the large increase in production of tropical oils. After the system had proved successful in producing palm oil in Sumatra it was used in Malaya, and later coconut plantations were established in the Philippines. Only a small part of the world's production of coconuts originates in the plantations but the plantation system has proved itself, so far as production is concerned, for the yields are reported to be about twice as high as those obtained in small groves.

In the production of palm oil and palm kernels in Sumatra a high degree of efficiency has been reached. Before the war plantations averaged about 3000 acres and each had its own oil-pressing plant and small-gage railroad for transportation within the plantation.

An idea of the production possibilities of palm oil may be had from the data on yields reported from Sumatra by agricultural authorities in the Netherlands Indies. The average yields of palm oil per hectare[15] from 1931 to 1936 were as follows:

Year	Kilograms per Hectare
1931	1780
1932	2060
1933	2232
1934	2393
1935	2369
1936	2581

A later report shows that the production in 1940 had increased to 3233 kilograms per hectare, or 2880 pounds per acre. This compares with less than 200 pounds of soybean oil per acre in the United States. If most modern methods and increased quantities of fertilizer are used, even higher yields may possibly be obtained in the future.[16]

Along with this rapid increase in the production of vegetable oils, especially in the tropics, two other developments should be mentioned. The first is the growth, particularly under Japanese leadership following political penetration of Manchuria, of soybean production there, and of the subsequent spread of

---

[14] Peter L. Hansen and Ronald L. Mighell, *op. cit.*, p. 6.

[15] 1 hectare=2.471 acres. 1 kilogram=2.2046 pounds.

[16] Peter L. Hansen and Ronald L. Mighell, *op. cit.*, p. 7.

soybean culture to other parts of the earth, especially the United States. The second is the stagnation, if not relative decline, of the Mediterranean olive industry.

Perhaps the most spectacular of all the pre-World War II developments in fats and oils is the rapid rise of whale oil from a rather obscure and secondary place to one of primary importance, especially in Europe. This was brought about by two independent developments. On the one hand, revolutionary improvements in whale hunting made possible greatly extended operations in the Antarctic. On the other hand, the successful commercial hydrogenation of whale oil, first recorded in 1930, made that long-despised marine commodity the premier raw material of the margarine industry in Europe.

Whale oil has a unique appeal to those countries sufficiently advanced industrially to be able to build and operate complex factory ships and in which, for some reason, foreign exchange is scarce. Whale oil is the domestic product of the owner of the whaling ship. It is not *bought* in the Antarctic; it is *collected* or *produced* there. The whales are a free good for anyone who can get close enough to harpoon them and who has the facilities necessary to convert a dead whale into salable products—whale oil, sperm oil, whale meat, fertilizer, etc.[17]

Economic Impact of Overseas Oil Supplies on Temperate-Zone Farming

One of the most important repercussions of the rise of oil production in the tropics is its impact on the cattle, dairying, and hog industries of temperate-zone countries.

Fats obtained from domesticated land animals may be called "two-stage" products, as contrasted with all vegetable fats and with the animal fats obtained from marine and from wild land animals. Vegetable oils and fats as well as those obtained from marine animals are "one-stage" products. Of course, biologically speaking, all marine animal fats are two-stage products in the sense that the animals live on something like plankton or other first-stage products and, unlike plants, do not create starches, fats, sugar, etc., by photosynthesis directly from sunlight. But whatever marine animals feed on is a free good and therefore does not enter the economic picture.

A clear-cut two-stage product is lard obtained from a hog fed on corn grown by a farmer. The corn is the first-stage product, the hog the second-stage product. This two-stage process of fat production is less efficient in terms of utilization of sunshine, a great deal of which is lost through the corn-fed hog's conversion of the sun-produced starch and oil in the corn. Other things being equal, one-stage products are more efficiently produced by nature than are two-stage products.

Many of the important vegetable fats are produced in the tropics from wild tree growths. Plantation costs there generally are lower than the costs of temperate-zone diversified farming. The supply of wild vegetation is strictly limited in most temperate-zone countries, whereas wild tropical vegetation is frequently exploited with the aid of cheap labor. Whatever cost advantages such tropical settings may involve are, however, often offset by long hauls and other transportation handicaps.[18]

This interzonal conflict comes to a head in the competition between the fats and oils produced in the tropics and those produced in the Corn Belt of the United States.[19] The world as a whole is turning to greater reliance on vegetable fats and oils, and thus the United States among all modern nations is left as the champion of animal fats, especially hog fats. This country has long been a heavy exporter of animal fats, but our foreign sales are meeting with increasing resistance. As yet, the willingness of the European market to absorb a large portion of our lard output has prevented the situation from becoming desperate. However, if Europe follows in our footsteps and turns to lard substitutes, the problem of our hog surplus, which is essentially a hog fat surplus, will become critical.

The whole question of the substitutability of

---

[17] For further details, see pp. 282-284.

[18] For much useful information on the cost of producing tropical oils, especially in Africa, see the fascinating series of articles on Unilever, the great British-Dutch soap and margarine combine, in *Fortune*, December, 1947, and January and February, 1948.

[19] This looming conflict is treated fully in A. E. Taylor, *Corn and Hog Surplus of the Corn Belt*, Food Research Institute, Stanford University, 1932.

vegetable and animal fats and oils is brought into bold relief by this danger threatening what has long been considered the soundest and most prosperous section of American agriculture, the Corn Belt. The belief that "corn is the most efficient plant in the Temperate Zone in fixing the energy of the sun's rays and that the hog is the most efficient animal for converting the sun-energy of corn into fat"[20] is a fundamental part of our agricultural tradition. This statement probably still holds true; but the growing importance of the tropics—and, incidentally, of the ocean also—as sources of oils and fats robs this tenet of much of its practical meaning.

The role which the ocean plays in this interzonal conflict deserves further comment. By far the most important marine animal source of fat is the whale. While whale oil is merely an incidental factor in the frontal attack on the Corn Belt, it is decidedly the major factor in a dangerous flanking maneuver that threatens the Corn Belt by way of Europe.

During the first decades of this century Europe was the great market for lard exports from the Corn Belt. Then chemists learned how to convert whale oil into margarine and whalers perfected the art of killing the speedy and ferocious whales of the Antarctic. Europe, especially Britain and Germany, preferred margarine to lard. Soon lard imports from the United States declined and gradually disappeared.

A corn-fed hog is a lard hog. The profitable sale of the lard is an integral part of a successful corn-hog economy. The loss of the European market was a severe blow felt the more keenly because it was synchronized with the frontal attack executed by the tropical fats.

World War II interrupted whaling and in general played havoc with the fat economy of Europe. So that continent once more was only too willing to eat lard, especially when it was offered freely under UNRRA and the Marshall Plan, or provided through CARE by friends and relatives. But now whaling is fast coming back and the old struggle between whale-based margarine and corn-hog lard will be resumed, if it has not been resumed already. The nexus between Antarctic whales and Iowa hogs may be loose, but the impact of this competition is both real and sharply felt.

Effects of World War II

Most of the effects of World War II on the oils and fats situation were temporary. The occupation of much of Asia by the Japanese and of Europe by the Nazis thoroughly dislocated regular trade movements. Thus the United States was cut off from her regular sources of supply (see Fig. 16.3) of several oils and fats: from the Philippines, which had been her chief source of coconut oil and of copra (dried coconut meat); from the Netherlands East Indies, which had ranked first as a source of palm kernels and palm oil; from China, virtually her sole source of tung oil; from Japan and Kwantung, sole sources of perilla oil, etc. However, she immediately turned to substitutes, especially to domestically produced soybeans, and to babassu and oiticica oil imported from Brazil.

Many of the war measures designed to solve emergency problems were short-lived. But several will have lasting effects, for the genetic and technological and marketing adjustments made under pressure of war needs will continue to bring permanent benefits long after the emergency has passed. First of all, certain technical innovations stimulated or accelerated by the war are part of the heritage of the age. Soybeans will continue to be cultivated in the United States as a major source of oil. Similarly, the spectacular expansion of sunflower acreage in Argentina which has put that country in first place in the world output of sunflower seeds will not be swiftly wiped out. For one thing, people's tastes are said to have adjusted themselves to the new blend of olive and sunflower oils.[21] Having developed an oil extraction industry sufficient to take care of her entire oil-bearing crops, Argentina is not likely to return to her prewar practice of selling unprocessed oil seeds, especially linseed.

One of the permanent effects of the war is the increased degree and spread of autonomy among many native peoples which will manifest itself in a clamor for, if not an insistence

---

[20] *Ibid.*, pp. 6, 7.

[21] It was the uncertainty of Mediterranean olive oil supplies that was largely responsible for the expansion of sunflower production in Argentina.

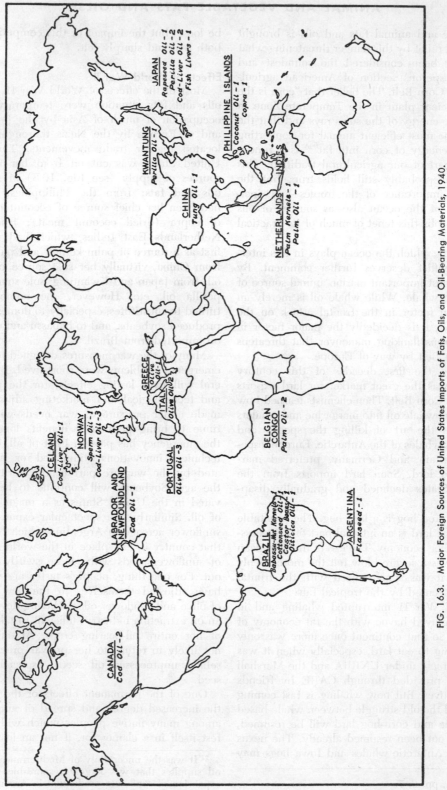

FIG. 16.3. Major Foreign Sources of United States Imports of Fats, Oils, and Oil-Bearing Materials, 1940.
The order of importance of each country as a source of supply is indicated by the number following the name of the import.

CANADA
Cod Oil - 2

LABRADOR AND NEWFOUNDLAND
Cod Oil - 1

ICELAND
Cod-Liver Oil - 1

NORWAY
Sperm Oil - 1
Cod-Liver Oil - 3

PORTUGAL
Olive Oil - 3

ITALY
Olive Oil - 3

GREECE
Olive Oil - 1

ARGENTINA
Flaxseed - 1

BRAZIL
Babassu-Nut Kernels - 1
Cottonseed Oil - 1
Castorseed - 1
Oiticica Oil - 1

BELGIAN CONGO
Palm Oil - 2

KWANTUNG
Perilla Oil - 1

CHINA
Tung Oil - 1

JAPAN
Rapeseed Oil - 1
Perilla Oil - 2
Cod-Liver Oil - 2
Fish Livers - 1

PHILIPPINE ISLANDS
Coconut Oil - 1
Copra - 1

NETHERLANDS INDIES
Palm Kernels - 1
Palm Oil - 1

TABLE 16.4. Total Measurable World Supplies of Butter and Other Visible Fats
(1000 metric tons, fat equivalent)

Area	Prewar (Old National Boundaries)	1947 Estimate (New National Boundaries)
1. Total production—Europe (excluding U.S.S.R.), North America, Australia, and New Zealand	7,806	7,534
United States[a]	3,072	4,460
Canada	226	266
United Kingdom[a]	159	42
Australia	244	197
New Zealand	166	165
Continental Europe (excluding U.S.S.R.)—Total	3,039	2,507
Northern and Western—Subtotal	1,040	728
Ireland	63	35
France	351	258
Belgium	94	48
Switzerland	33	25
Netherlands[a]	134	66
Denmark	184	144
Norway[a]	42	25
Sweden	91	105
Finland	48	22
Central and Eastern—Subtotal	1,363	590
Germany[a]	889	400[b]
Czechoslovakia	146	79
Austria	63	31
Poland	265	80
Danubian Countries—Subtotal	422	264
Southern Europe—Subtotal	1,114	925
Italy	451	276
Spain	450	470
Portugal	86	80
Greece	127	99
2. Export supplies from other areas—total	5,096	2,385–3,000
South and Central America	755	676–726
Africa and Middle East	1,002	705–745
India and Ceylon	613	198–218
Whale Fisheries and Iceland	555	339
East Indies, Malaya, and South Pacific	981	260–280
Philippines	356	550–600
China and Manchuria	658	85–105
Japan[a]	78	...
U.S.S.R. and Baltic	69	...
Other countries	29	...
Grand Total	13,030	10,420–10,585

[a] Exclusive of whale oil.
[b] All occupied zones.
[c] Net exports, excluding transit trade (e.g., through Singapore).

upon, greater domestic consumption of domestically produced fats and oils. India is eager to raise the dietary levels of her people and higher fat consumption is a major factor in such reform.

This puts increased pressure on the industrial nations to assure this fat supply. Industrial nations like Britain and France who still hold large colonial possessions are engaged in ambitious schemes to raise the fats and oils output of the colonies that offer greatest opportunities for expansion; this means mainly equatorial Africa. The British "groundnut scheme"[22] in charge of the Ministry of Foods is particularly significant (see p. 277).

As Table 16.4[23] shows, the world's commercial supplies of fats and oils are still 20 to 25 percent below the prewar peak, which, in view of a 12 percent increase in the population, suggests an even greater lag in per capita supplies.

INTERCHANGEABILITY OF FATS AND OILS
Multi-Angular Competition

As was stressed in the first part of this chapter, fats and oils represent a bewildering heterogeneity in terms of genetic, geographical, and economic origins. On the other hand, science and technology have developed ways of breaking through the jungle of diversity and reducing most of the fats and oils to a competitive level through substitution. Fats and oils probably represent the prime example of commodity competition. This competition is multi-angular in the sense that it has not one but several fronts. The following outline suggests its complexity.

I. Biological or Genetic Front
  A. Vegetable vs. animal
    1. Vegetable oil shortening made from cottonseed, corn, coconut, palm, vs. butter and lard.
    2. Margarine made 90 percent from vegetable oils, vs. butter and lard.
    3. Vegetable oils in margarine, vs. animal fats in margarine, as interchangeable raw materials of oleomargarine.

    4. Vegetable vs. animal oils in soap.
    5. Vegetable vs. animal oils in paints and varnishes.
  B. Vegetable fats and oils[24]
    1. Shortening and margarine—almost all compete.
    2. Soap—coconut, palm, cottonseed, soybean, babassu, and corn compete.
    3. Paint and varnish—all the vegetable drying oils, such as linseed, tung, perilla, oiticica, soybean, compete.
  C. Animal fats and oils
    1. Whale oil vs. oleo fat or tallow as raw material of margarine.
    2. Whale oil in margarine vs. butter and lard.
    3. Fish and whale oils vs. tallow and grease in soap.
II. Geographical Front
  A. Interzonal conflicts
    1. Tropics vs. temperate zones.
    2. Arctic and Antarctic vs. tropics and temperate zones.
  B. Interregional conflicts
    1. United States—south (cotton, peanuts) vs. north (lard, oleo, butter).
    2. Europe—south (olives) vs. north (butter, sunflower seeds, etc.).
    3. China—north (soybeans) vs. south (peanuts).
III. Economic Front
  A. Overall conflicts
    1. Products of land-labor (e.g., some tropical nuts)
                  vs.
    2. Products of capital-labor (whale oil)
                  vs.
    3. Products of land-capital (products of the Corn Belt).
  B. Other conflicts
    1. Main products—Tung oil, linseed oil (in western hemisphere), butter (in butter-manufacturing sections)
                  vs.
    2. By-products—Cottonseed (of lint cotton), buttermilk (of butter), oil cake (of many nut and seed oils), oleo fat (of beef), tallow (of mutton or wool or of mutton and wool), corn oil (of starch and glucose)
                  vs.
    3. Joint products—Lard (with bacon and ham and other pork products), butter

---

[22] In Britain peanuts are known as groundnuts.
[23] This table was prepared by the staff of the United Nations Food and Agriculture Organization for the International Conference held in Geneva in August, 1947.

[24] In this competition, *annual herbaceous field* crops are pitted against *perennial* tree crops; *cultivated* crops against *wild* crops; *domestic* crops against *foreign* crops.

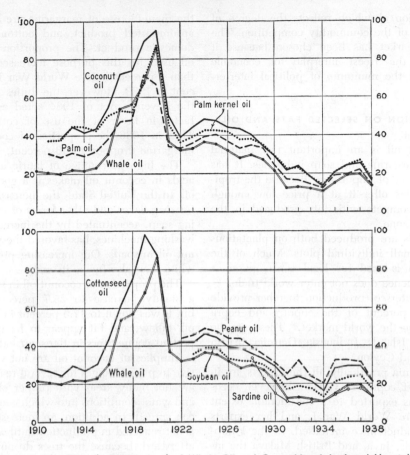

FIG. 16.4. London Prices (Index Numbers) of Whale Oil and Competitive Animal and Vegetable Oils, 1910-1938. (From Karl Brandt, *Whale Oil, an Economic Analysis*, Food Research Institute, 1941.)

(with calves and carcasses of milk cows), palm oil and palm kernels, soybeans and fodder and soil-improving crops.

Artificial Interference

Just as competition anywhere is likely to be tempered by interference by governments, tariffs, and otherwise on behalf of powerful pressure groups, so the commodity competition between fats and oils is held in check. The best-known example is the protests of the dairy interests against the onslaught of margarine, the spokesman for a score of raw materials which science has enabled to become effective substitutes for butter. As is usually the case, the interests of the unorganized consuming public are ignored, or at least inadequately safeguarded in this struggle of the Titans. The

issues involved are too complex to be developed in this volume.

Intercommodity Competition and Price Behavior

This intercommodity competition naturally is reflected in the price behavior of the different fats and oils. Their prices may be visualized as being built around a center—possibly the price of whale oil—with the spread (premiums or discounts) reflecting the different additional costs which must be incurred before one fat or oil is on an absolute equality, in terms of "utility at a price," with the others. Such costs may be the cost of importation or of manipulation; they may cover sales and advertising costs, etc.

Fig. 16.4 shows how the prices of different fats and oils move in harmony—imperfect, to be sure, but nevertheless harmony—the degree of perfection of which reflects the degree of perfection of the commodity competition. The London market has been chosen because it embodies the freest interplay of economic forces and the minimum of political interference.

INFORMATION ON SELECTED FATS AND OILS
Coconut Oil

Coconut oil is an important raw material for the margarine and soap industries. It has held its place of importance because the tropical countries offer it at a price low enough for it to compete with fats produced in the temperate zone.

Coconuts are produced both on plantations and on small individual plots. Much of the production is used for local consumption as food and hence does not enter world trade.

Five centers of production together provide about 94 percent of the copra[25] and copra products on the world market.[26] These are the Philippine Islands, Indonesia, Oceania, British Malaya, and Ceylon.

In Oceania practically all the exports are in the form of copra. In Ceylon, however, coconut oil was exported to a considerable extent even before World War I, and her exports of this product have increased. In the Philippine Islands, Java, and British Malaya the industry preparing coconut oil for export was established during World War I. Production and export were stimulated by a scarcity of fats in the belligerent countries.

In 1936 net exports of copra and of coconut oil, calculated in copra, were 1,633,000 metric tons, about two-thirds coming from the Philippine Islands and the Netherlands Indies.

As has been said, the margarine and soap industries are the main users of coconut oil. Many qualities of the oil make it exceptionally suitable for the manufacture of margarine. The most important is probably the melting point, which approaches that of butter.

In the United States the chief oils used in

the manufacture of margarine are coconut oil, an imported product, and cottonseed oil, a domestic product. The proportion of coconut oil used for this purpose increased from less than 1 percent before World War I to 75 percent in 1933. However, the duties imposed by the Revenue Act of 1934 acted as a limiting factor in favor of the use of cottonseed oil. Thus in 1936 the proportion of coconut oil in margarine dropped to 46 percent.

The high percentage of lauric and myristic acids in coconut oil makes it a good lathering oil. In the United States the increasing demand for soap flakes and other forms of easily lathering soap, accentuated by the increasing use of washing machines, has favored the use of coconut oil in soaps. Our increasing preference for white soap also favors its use.

The proportion of coconut oil in soap showed a steady increase to 25.7 percent in 1932, but it was down to 17.5 percent in 1935. Palm oil, tallow, and fat appear to be its most important competitors in the soap industry.

Supplies of coconut oil are not very responsive to price changes for several reasons. There are not many areas with proper climate, soil, and water conditions into which coconut groves can spread. In addition, an increased planting is not reflected in production until several years afterward, because the trees do not bear until they are from seven to eight years old and do not reach full bearing capacity before the fifteenth year.

An interesting point here is the fact that during a period of low prices a soap industry developed in the Philippines to make use of the copra which could not be exported.

Palm and Palm-Kernel Oil

The center of the palm and palm-kernel oil industry is equatorial Africa. Here the United Africa Company, a subsidiary of Lever Brothers, the English soap and margarine maker, is "the world's largest trading company."

Africa is a great exporter of (1) palm oil extracted from seeds by natives on plantations and (2) palm kernels from which oil is expressed in the industrial importing countries. This is done for two reasons. First, the extraction of oil from the kernels calls for greater technical skills and better equipment than are generally found in tropical countries. Second,

---

[25] The dried meat of the coconut.

[26] Formerly, exports of copra and coconut oil from the Netherlands Indies went mainly to the mother country; from the Philippine Islands, to the United States; from British Malaya, to Great Britain, Germany, and the Netherlands; from Oceania, to Great Britain; from Ceylon, to India.

palm kernels give a larger yield in oil meal than the seeds themselves. This oil meal has a good market in industrial countries with their flourishing dairying and cattle industries, but not in Africa.

Besides equatorial Africa, Indonesia is also an important source of these oils and oil products. The fantastic success of the plantations in Sumatra, which was mentioned above (see p. 269), will encourage expansion elsewhere.

Peanuts

In an average year in the period 1934-1938 the production of unshelled peanuts was distributed as follows:[27]

	Million Metric Tons
United States	0.5
China	2.5
India	2.7
Africa	0.4
South America	0.1
	6.2

From this crop, 2.4 million tons of peanut oil were extracted, of which 0.7 million tons entered international trade. It is evident from the foregoing that if the European nations wish to increase their imports of peanuts and peanut products they will have to count progressively more on Africa as a source.

As was mentioned earlier, Britain is engaged in an ambitious "groundnut scheme," which supposedly was recommended in 1946 by Frank Samuel, a director of Lever Brothers' United Africa Company (UAC).[28] While the British Ministry of Foods is in charge of the scheme, the UAC is responsible for its actual execution.

The scheme embraces 2 million acres of selected land in Tanganyika, from which it is hoped to produce eventually as much as 600,-000 tons of peanuts. This would be a great help to fat-hungry Britain, who can spare no dollars for anything she can secure without them. In this respect fats produced in your own colonial back yard are like whale oil taken out of the Antarctic. For like the Antarctic, which has no currency at all, colonies have no currency except that of the mother land.

Actual operation of the project began in 1947 but met with many difficulties which had to do mainly with capital equipment. Railroads proved inadequate to handle the increased traffic, and the brush-clearing equipment, most of which was discarded army surplus from various theaters of war, was not heavy enough to handle the African brush.[29]

In the United States, peanut production has increased rapidly, as the following figures show:

Year	Acreage	Harvested Product (million pounds)	Farm Value (million dollars)
1916–1920	1,694,000	796.9	$ 51.1
1947	3,378,000	2251.6	229.8

In 1948, Georgia led, with a production of almost 1.1 billion pounds out of a total of almost 2.9 billion, or 37.6 percent. The bulk of the remainder was produced in Alabama, North Carolina, Texas, Florida, Virginia, and Oklahoma.

Flaxseed

Flax is grown either for fiber (from which linen is made) or for seed, called linseed or flaxseed. In the average year during the five-year period 1934-1938, about 3 million metric tons of flaxseed were produced in the world, of which over half was credited to Argentina. Neighboring Uruguay also produces flaxseed. Because of the difficulty of marketing caused in part by the shipping shortage, Argentina was unable to export and had to resort to government measures to curtail acreage. However, her new policy of crushing the seed at home is bound to affect future trade developments.

Other important producing countries are the Soviet Union, India, and the United States. In the period 1910-1945 our domestic linseed production averaged about 17.9 million bushels

---

[27] FAO, *Yearbook of Food and Agricultural Statistics*, Washington, 1947.

[28] See *Fortune*, January, 1948, p. 139.

[29] See Howard Akers, "Britain's African Peanut Project," *Foreign Agriculture*, May, 1949, pp. 111-114.

Discussions in Parliament late in 1949 suggested that things have not been going at all well. While the total appropriation of about £25,000,000 is reported to have been spent, a mere dribble of peanuts is all that the government has to show for it.

and net imports averaged 15 million. During World War II our output jumped to about 51 million bushels. This was in part a reciprocal development of the curtailment of Argentina's output, for before World War II the United States was a chief buyer of Argentine flaxseed. After the war our output declined. Production is concentrated in Minnesota and North Dakota. Until the war flaxseed yields had been declining somewhat, whereas wheat yields in the same region were increasing rather remarkably.

Most of the linseed oil produced in the United States is consumed by the drying industry, as Table 16.5 shows.

TABLE 16.5. Utilization of Linseed Oil by Classes of Products in the United States, 1931-1945[30]

Class of Product	Quantity (*1000 pounds*)	Percentage of Total
Drying industries:		
Total	547,107	95.3
Paint and varnish[a]	466,113	81.2
Linoleum and oilcloth	63,188	11.0
Printing inks	17,806	3.1
Soap	1,626	0.3
Miscellaneous[b]	24,361	4.2
Compounds and vegetable cooking fats	911	0.2
Loss, including that in foots	102	c

[a] Total of reported and unreported linseed oil used in paints and varnishes.
[b] Includes uses of linseed oil in leather, lubricants, pharmaceuticals, rubber, core oils, textiles, cleaning and polishing, sulphonation, brake lining, etc.
[c] Less than one-tenth of one percent.

Linseed oil meal, a byproduct in the manufacture of linseed oil, is a valuable protein supplement for cattle and sheep feeding. During the last 10 years the average production has been more than 600 million pounds.

One of the most recent commercial developments in the United States is the manufacture of cigarette, condenser, carbonizing, Bible paper, and fine flax papers from seed flax straw. In addition, considerable tonnages of the shive (segment left after fiber is removed) are used in wallboard and container-board manufacture.[31]

[30] Weber H. Peterson, *Flaxseed in American Farming*, U. S. Department of Agriculture, Technical Bulletin No. 938, 1947. Compiled from records of the Bureau of the Census.
[31] *Ibid.*, p. 4.

Soybeans

During the period 1934-1939 the average annual output of soybeans amounted to about 11.9 million metric tons, which were produced in the following countries:[32]

	(million metric tons)
China	5.6
Manchuria	3.9
United States	1.2
Korea	0.5
Japan	0.3
Java	0.2
All others	0.1
Total	11.9

By 1946, however, the situation had shifted, mainly because of the rapid rise of soybean production in the United States. In that year, the output figures were as follows:

	(million metric tons)
United States	5.4
China	4.5
Manchuria	3.5
Japan	0.4
Korea	0.1
All others	0.4
Total	14.3

The story of soybean production in this country is told in Table 16.6. The 1948 crop was even larger than the 1946 crop. The tremendous increase in production since 1942 is the cumulative result of years of preparatory research designed to adapt varieties to conditions here and to develop mechanical devices suitable for the new crop.

Of particular importance in the use of soybeans is the shift from hay to beans. Soybeans for beans are an important crop in three general regions—the north central region, the Mississippi delta, and the Atlantic coast. The north central region has over 90 percent of the acreage, and greatly overshadows the other two. Whereas in 1925-1929 only 24 percent of the total acreage planted was harvested for beans, the corresponding figure for 1947 was 81 percent. In the Corn Belt the figure ran as high as 93 percent.

More and more the soybean is being transferred from its role as an industrial raw mate-

[32] FAO, *Yearbook of Food and Agricultural Statistics*.

TABLE 16.6. Acreage, Yield, and Production of Soybeans in the United States, 1924-1947[33]

| Year | Acres Planted | | | Acres Harvested | | | Yield per Acre Harvested | | Production | |
	Grown Alone (1000 acres)	Interplanted[a] (1000 acres)	Equivalent Solid[b] (1000 acres)	For Beans[b] (1000 acres)	For Hay (1000 acres)	Grazed or Plowed Under (1000 acres)	For Beans (bushels)	For Hay (tons)	Beans (1000 bushels)	Hay (1000 tons)
1924	1,567	417	1,782	448	1,147	187	11.0	1.13	4,947	1,299
1925	1,539	476	1,785	415	1,175	195	11.7	1.01	4,875	1,185
1926	1,871	502	2,127	466	1,431	230	11.2	1.18	5,239	1,687
1927	2,057	571	2,350	568	1,556	226	12.2	1.18	6,938	1,837
1928	2,154	556	2,439	579	1,609	251	13.6	1.23	7,880	1,974
1929	2,429	743	2,807	708	1,774	325	13.3	1.16	9,438	2,051
1930	3,072	786	3,473	1,074	2,062	337	13.0	.94	13,929	1,938
1931	3,835	909	4,304	1,141	2,772	391	15.1	1.26	17,260	3,479
1932	3,704	893	4,165	1,001	2,738	426	15.1	1.25	15,158	3,433
1933	3,537	813	3,957	1,044	2,506	407	12.9	1.16	13,509	2,917
1934	5,764	858	6,207	1,556	4,227	424	14.9	1.08	23,157	4,545
1935	6,966	1,028	7,503	2,915	4,044	544	16.8	1.34	48,901	5,422
1936	6,127	2,115	7,183	2,359	3,116	1,708	14.3	.96	33,721	3,002
1937	6,332	2,261	7,464	2,586	3,469	1,409	17.9	1.36	46,164	4,731
1938	7,318	2,541	8,587	3,035	3,724	1,828	20.4	1.43	61,906	5,335
1939	9,565	2,710	10,920	4,315	4,590	2,015	20.9	1.48	90,141	6,772
1940	10,487	2,589	11,782	4,807	4,819	2,156	16.2	1.34	78,045	6,450
1941	10,068	2,555	11,345	5,889	3,546	1,910	18.2	1.30	107,197	4,616
1942	13,696	2,426	14,912	9,894	2,621	2,397	19.0	1.36	187,524	3,555
1943	14,191	2,475	15,428	10,397	3,177	1,854	18.3	1.21	190,133	3,837
1944	13,118	1,861	14,050	10,232	2,563	1,235	18.8	1.18	191,958	3,041
1945	13,007	1,537	13,777	10,661	1,939	1,177	18.0	1.28	192,076	2,476
1946	11,662	1,530	12,427	9,806	1,533	1,088	20.5	1.29	201,275	1,984
1947[c]	12,894	1,518	13,654	11,125	1,372	1,157	16.3	1.21	181,362	1,666

[a] Grown with other crops.
[b] Acreage grown alone, with an allowance for acreage grown with other crops.
[c] Preliminary.

[33] Edwin G. Strand, Soybeans in American Farming, U. S. Department of Agriculture, Bureau of Agricultural Economics, Technical Bulletin No. 966, Washington, November, 1948.

rial to an important food. Instead of soap and paint and varnish as before World War II, now margarine, shortening, and salad oil are the main uses for it.

In oriental countries the soybean is grown primarily for the seed, which is used largely in the preparation of numerous fresh, fermented, and dried food products. For centuries the protein part of the diet of millions of oriental people has been supplied or supplemented, to a great extent, from soybean products. Fermented, the soybean yields all the different sauces, which furnish the basic flavoring of their food; pressed, it gives oil for cooking; sprouted, it furnishes a fresh vegetable rich in vitamins; picked when green, it makes an excellent green vegetable; ground dry, it makes flour; soaked, ground, and mixed with water, it provides bean milk, and the curdled milk furnishes bean curd—the boneless meat of the Orient—used in the form of various cheeses and as a meat substitute. The roasted beans are often salted; they are also used in cakes and candies; fermented bean pastes are used in soups and in preserving vegetables; and boiled beans are mixed with millet, rice, or kaoliang. The soybean has meant bread, meat, milk, cheese, and vegetables to these peoples and furnished what is said to be a well balanced diet at a relatively low cost.[34]

Cottonseed and Cottonseed Oil

"Cotton thirds itself," says an old "rule of thumb." Very roughly speaking, three pounds of seed cotton as it is picked from the plant yield one pound of lint and two pounds of seed.[35] A given amount of seed cotton yields a third of its weight in lint cotton; the expression "thirding," in other words, pertains to weight. In value the relation between lint and seed is quite different.

During 1938-1940 farmers in the United States received for their lint cotton about 9 cents a pound, or $180 a short ton. A short ton of cottonseed at that time sold for approximately 1.075 cents a pound, or $21.50. One-third of the weight—lint—sold for four-fifths of the combined value. A pound of lint brings about eight to nine times as much as a pound of seed. The cotton ginner who removes the seed usually retains part of it as payment for his services.

In an average year during the same period, 1938-1940, the United States produced 12.1 million bales of cotton and 5.4 million tons of cottonseed. The farm value of the lint crop on the average was $547.1 million a year and that of the cottonseed $116.2 million. This value, in turn, reflects the price of the commodities which are obtained from the seed.

The figures quoted above are those which obtained when the United States was still at peace. In wartime the market values are quite different. In March, 1942, shortly after Pearl Harbor, lint cotton was selling at around 18 cents a pound and cottonseed brought $44.18 a short ton. At that rate a short ton of lint cotton was worth $360—again about eight or nine times as much as the seed. The ratio remained about the same while the absolute values doubled.

It is not so very long ago that cottonseed was a waste product, a nuisance to be got rid of. In 1874 only about 5 percent of the cottonseed crop was crushed, but by 1909-1913 it had increased to 75 percent. Up to 1909 the market for cottonseed and cottonseed products, not the size of the cotton crop, determined how much seed was crushed. After that time roughly all the seed, except what was necessary for farm purposes such as seeding, was crushed. In other words, from then on, the size of the cotton crop determined the amount of cottonseed sent to the crushing mills. The early mills crushed the seed without removing the fuzz called linters, with the result that these linters absorbed considerable quantities of oil. However, since the invention of machines to remove linters and the rise of the cellulose industries it pays to remove the linters.

Cottonseed yields four products: cottonseed oil, cake or meal, hulls, and linters.[36] The average value of the four products during the decade preceding World War II is shown in Fig. 16.5.

It will be noted that the products vary widely in value. Thus cottonseed oil,[37] which accounts for only 15.6 percent of the weight, brings in

---

[34] W. J. Morse, "Soybeans Yesterday and Today," *Foreign Agriculture*, May, 1948, p. 93.

[35] More accurate calculation gives about 65 pounds of seed for every 35 pounds of lint.

[36] Not all seed has linters; seed without linters is called "naked seed."

[37] Cottonseed oil makes up from 14 to 18 percent of the vegetable oil produced in the world and about three-fourths of that oil produced in the United States.

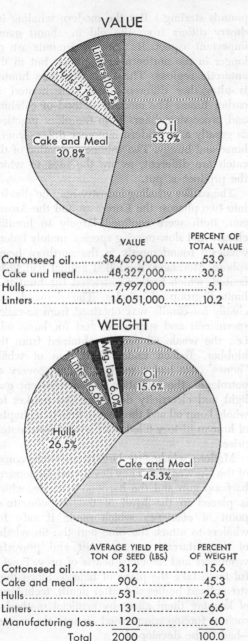

VALUE

	VALUE	PERCENT OF TOTAL VALUE
Cottonseed oil	$84,699,000	53.9
Cake and meal	48,327,000	30.8
Hulls	7,997,000	5.1
Linters	16,051,000	10.2

WEIGHT

	AVERAGE YIELD PER TON OF SEED (LBS.)	PERCENT OF WEIGHT
Cottonseed oil	312	15.6
Cake and meal	906	45.3
Hulls	531	26.5
Linters	131	6.6
Manufacturing loss	120	6.0
Total	2000	100.0

FIG. 16.5. Yield in Value and Weight of Cottonseed Products, Ten-Year Average, 1930-1939. (From "The Cottonseed Oil Industry," unpublished paper by H. E. Klontz; based on National Cottonseed Products Association, *Cottonseed and Its Products*, 1941.)

53.9 percent of the market value, or 3.5 times its pro rata share. Linters comprising 6.6 percent of the total weight contribute 10.2 percent of the total income, or better than 1.5 times

their share. Thus the two pay more than their share. The other two products are definitely of the by-product type; they may help defray overhead but they do not pay their way. Hulls in particular, which account for about one-fourth of the weight and contribute about 5 percent of the value, are relatively useless compared with cottonseed oil and linters.

In the United States cotton is grown on about 2 million separate farms. After being picked, the seed cotton is hauled to gins, where the lint is removed from the seed. The seed then goes to crushing mills where the hulls and linters are removed and the oil is pressed out of the kernels. The oil cake that remains is used as stock feed or fertilizer; the linters are a raw material for the cellulose industries. The hulls are used for food and industrial purposes, and the oil after being refined is used largely in the food industries.

From the crushing mill the crude cottonseed oil goes to refineries, where it is made edible. About 90 percent of the oil produced in the United States goes into food products, mainly shortening. The cottonseed oil-refining industry is highly concentrated in the hands of a few large concerns which use the oil in food manufacture. The five largest companies together produced 86.8 percent of all the shortening (lard not included) shipped in 1933. The Big Four meat packers—Swift, Armour, Wilson, and Cudahy—produced 65 percent of all the vegetable shortening as compared with 48 percent of the total output of federally inspected lard.[38]

The principal market for cottonseed oil is shortening, which must be sold in competition with lard. The price of lard is therefore an important factor in determining the price of cottonseed oil.

Lard, however, is not the only competitor of cottonseed oil. Soybean, peanut, and corn oil from the United States; coconut oil from the Philippines; palm and palm-kernel oils from Africa; and babassu oil from Brazil can all be used in making the same products in which cottonseed oil is used. In some products these various oils can replace cottonseed oil entirely; in others, they can replace it partially.

For example, soybean oil is a serious com-

[38] Walton H. Hamilton and associates, *Price and Price Policies*, McGraw-Hill Book Company, New York, 1938, p. 277.

petitor of cottonseed oil in the shortening industry. However, because of its tendency to revert from the solid to the liquid state soybean oil is not yet satisfactory when used as the sole ingredient of shortening and similar products. But it can be blended to the extent of 50 percent, and this has enabled it to alter appreciably the competitive position of cottonseed oil. In 1931 soybean oil accounted for less than 1 percent of the raw materials used in shortening; in 1940 it supplied 18 percent of that market. Its rapidly increasing use after 1942 was described above.

International Trade. Only about 5 percent of the total production of cottonseed enters world trade. Great Britain is the largest importer, deriving the seed principally from Egypt and from her African colonies.

Interesting to note are the changes in the position of various countries in the cottonseed oil trade. Before World War I the United States was the principal exporter. In 1935 for the first time she had a net import of cottonseed oil and since that year has been the largest single importer of it. In 1938 she imported more than 61 percent of all the cottonseed oil imported. Among cottonseed-producing countries that have greatly increased their exports of the oil are Brazil, China, and Egypt. As the result of the Japanese invasion and the subsequent wars, however, China's exports of it have been reduced greatly since 1938. Brazil's exports increased from the 1925-1929 average of 352,000 pounds to more than 51 million pounds in 1939; that year she was the premier exporter of cottonseed oil.

Whale Oil

One of the most important recent contributions to the fat and oil supply of the world is whale oil, obtained in the Antarctic regions by novel methods and processes devised by modern science.

Whaling is an old industry. Brandt[39] quotes whale oil prices for the period 1675-1939. (Incidentally, they range from a low of 7 pounds sterling a long ton in 1700 to 86 pounds sterling a long ton in 1920. In 1939 the London price for No. 1 whale oil ranged from 14 to 40

pounds sterling.) But the modern whaling industry differs from the old in almost every important aspect. Its hunting grounds are no longer in the northern hemisphere, but in the antarctic regions. The type of whale hunted is altogether different from that hunted in earlier times. The modern method of catching and processing differs from the older practices as greatly as a modern motorcar differs from a horse and buggy. The volume and value of the catch are different, as are the uses to which the product is put.

The earlier whaling industry may be divided into two phases: the European and the American. Both were confined largely to hunting clumsy and slow-moving species, mainly baleen whales,[40] found mostly in the northern hemisphere. Moreover, the killed animal had to be floated, which further restricted the hunt to a limited group of whales. The demand was chiefly for candle wax obtained from so-called spermaceti and sperm oil, and for lamp oil— i.e., the whale oil proper, obtained from the blubber. Baleen under the name of whale "bones" also had a market. The discovery of petroleum, the invention of incandescent gaslight and electricity destroyed the market for whale lamp oil and thus wrote finis to a chapter of human history filled with adventurous enterprise.

Modern whaling is largely an achievement of the Norwegians. They developed the modern harpoon gun and the harpoon grenade, which is placed in the head of the harpoon, to a point of efficiency which made it safe for whalers to attack the blue and the fin whales of the antarctic regions—swift and powerful swimmers and ferocious beasts of prey. Powerful teeth take the place of baleen. Since their streamlined bodies sink after death, techniques of keeping them afloat by artificial methods— such as forcing compressed air into the carcass —had to be developed.

The length of the voyage necessitated revolutionary changes in the size of the vessel used. The modern factory ship for trying oil at sea was the result. The first one was built in 1903 but was soon followed by even larger

[39] Karl Brandt, *Whale Oil. An Economic Analysis,* Food Research Institute, 1941, p. 238.

[40] Baleen is the horny protrusions from the whale's jaws which serve as a sieve to keep out all but very small marine animals. The baleen whale has a very small throat.

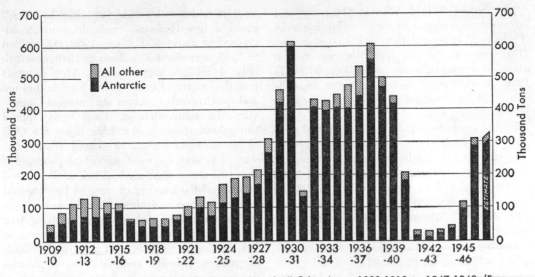

FIG. 16.6.   Whale Oil Production from Antarctic and All Other Areas, 1909-1910 to 1947-1948. (From Karl Brandt, *Whaling and Whale Oil During and After World War II*, Food Research Institute, War-Peace Pamphlet No. 11, 1948.)

and more efficient units. Slipways for pulling the whales up, and giant claws for hoisting them, were developed. The equipment for cutting up and rendering the carcass became increasingly effective and bulk storage for oil was introduced.

The killer boats which do the actual hunting have become so efficient that a single crew can bring in around 200 whales a season. The largest factory ship can treat up to 30 large blue whales or 45 fin whales every 24 hours. From this gross weight of around 3000 tons of raw material per day, 500 tons of whale oil can be produced daily by a personnel of 60 to 70 men. The largest factory ship afloat is the *Unitas*, having a gross registered tonnage of 21,845 tons[41] and a carrying capacity of 30,000 cargo tons. Each factory ship is accompanied by a small fleet of killer boats which themselves run as large as 380 tons. Factory ships are equipped with every conceivable device—radio, radar, noise-reducing propeller gear, searchlights, etc.

As long as whale oil could be used only for soapmaking, its market was limited. But after World War I, when a technique was developed whereby the oil could be rendered edible and thus used as a raw material for margarine, its market expanded greatly. This technique seems to have been perfected about 1931. In 1935 whale oil constituted 60 to 70 percent of the raw materials used in Germany in the manufacture of margarine.[42] The corresponding figure for the United Kingdom is 39 percent. The result of this favorable development on both supply and demand was a rapid increase in whale oil production, as is shown in Fig. 16.6.

This spectacular advance is a striking illustration of what might be termed the "conjuncture of technical progress." For behind the inventions which directly rendered feasible the rapid expansion of antarctic whaling there stood numerous others, such as Sabatier's discovery of hydrogenation, progress in meteorological science, progress in mineral oil techniques which has resulted in more compact fuels for ship engines, the development of the Diesel engine which permits longer round trips without refueling, radio, radar, and others equally important.

[41] Karl Brandt, *Whaling and Whale Oil During and After World War II*, Food Research Institute, Stanford University, 1948, pp. 67, 83.

[42] Whale oil is particularly attractive to people who (1) cannot readily obtain foreign exchange with which to buy imported material and (2) possess the capital and technical experience necessary to build and operate modern whaling ships.

Just before World War II Germany and Britain were engaged in a race to lay in stocks of whale oil in preparation for the coming war. This accounts for the rapid increase in the whale oil output between 1931-1932 and 1937-1938. At that point Germany began to withdraw and the total output dropped almost to zero in 1942-1943.

Efforts are being made by international convention to limit the whale catch to prevent depletion of the herds. At present the catch during each "pelagic" season of about four months is limited to the equivalent of 16,000 blue-whale units. One blue-whale unit equals 2 fin whales, 2.5 humpback whales, and 6 sei whales.

During the war the whaling fleet of the world, which at its peak had consisted of 36 active and one laid-up factory ships and 416 killer boats, was virtually destroyed or dismantled. However, so great is the value of whale oil that in 1946-1947 a new and highly efficient fleet was put into operation. A modern factory ship costs about $6 million; a killer boat, about $500,000.

The number of nations interested in whaling is rapidly increasing, and it promises to become one of the most competitive industries in the world. How conservation measures will stand up under the strong competitive pressure remains to be seen.

Tung Oil

Because of its quick-drying qualities tung oil is important in the paint and varnish industries. As its other name, "Chinese wood oil," suggests, it is produced chiefly in China, which consumes about 40 percent of the annual output and exports the remainder. Before Pearl Harbor the United States took annually from 60 to 75 percent of China's exports.

Dissatisfaction with the price and quality of the Chinese product led to efforts to build up a tung oil industry in the United States. These early efforts proved especially valuable when, as a result of the war in China, supplies of the oil became increasingly difficult to obtain. After the "China Incident," tung tree planting in the United States proceeded at a rapid pace.

The tung oil industry in this country began in Florida, where the first trees were planted in 1906 and the first seed harvested in 1913.[43] From a few thousand trees the number increased to about 350,000 in 1930, 3.6 million in 1935, and about 13 million in 1940, of which only 4 million were bearing. This suggests that the output of tung oil will soon be trebled and quadrupled. From an area around Gainesville the cultivation of tung trees spread throughout the belt stretching along the Gulf of Mexico from Florida to eastern Texas; Mississippi is now the most important producer.[44] Fig. 16.7 shows the tung tree belt of the United States and the number of trees of bearing and nonbearing age in each state in the belt.

There are four distinct types of tung tree growers: individual entrepreneurs, tung promoters, lumber companies, and paint and varnish companies. Lumber companies have planted the trees on cut-over land. At present this is a side line for these companies, but it may become more important as actual lumbering activities diminish. As yet, the activities of the paint and varnish companies have been confined to demonstration projects to encourage individual farmers to grow the trees.

There are economic factors tending toward larger orchards. When a farmer has only a few trees as part of a diversified farm program, he can easily care for them himself; but a planting of over 100 acres requires additional labor and equipment. The capital equipment necessary to cultivate a 200-acre orchard is sufficient to cultivate a 2000-acre orchard. Thus middle-sized orchards are more or less eliminated.

Since the oil amounts to approximately 12 to 18 percent of the weight of the dry, unhulled nuts, at present it does not pay to transport tung nuts to a mill more than fifty miles away. However, if a machine were perfected which would enable the hull to be removed on the farm, the oil yield would be raised and the structure of the industry would be changed radically. The hulled nuts could then be shipped

[43] M. Ogden Phillips, "Tung Oil: Florida's Infant Industry," *Economic Geography*, October, 1929, p. 351.

[44] L. Swearingen, "The American Tung Oil Industry Comes of Age," *Domestic Commerce*, U. S. Department of Commerce, June 11, 1942, pp. 3-7, 11. See also M. Ashby, *The Tung Oil Industry of the United States*, The Imperial Institute, London, 1940; and G. F. Deasy, "Tung Oil Production and Trade," *Economic Geography*, July, 1940.

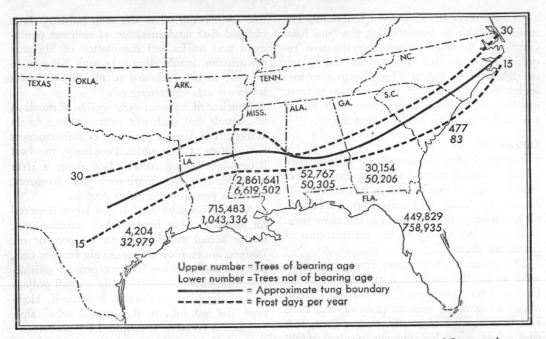

FIG. 16.7. Tung Tree Belt of the United States Before World War II. (U. S. Department of Commerce.)

longer distances to large terminal oil-extraction mills.

Owing to the importance of tung oil in the paint and varnish industries, the industrial countries have tried to circumvent the necessity of obtaining this oil from China. Consequently experiments in growing the trees have been undertaken in many areas besides the United States, particularly in British and French territories, the Netherlands Indies, the U.S.S.R., and South America. In the British territories, production has become of importance in Burma, India, Australia, and New Zealand. In South America commercial plantations have been planted in Argentina, Brazil, and Paraguay. In Argentina, according to the Department of Rural Economy and Statistics, 87 metric tons of wood oil were produced in 1935 with a yield in oil of 26 percent.[45]

It is too early to draw definite conclusions from these experiments because the commercial production of tung oil in these countries is still a young industry. Our own industry, which was started in 1906, furnishes little more than 12 percent of our domestic needs. Imports

of tung oil ranged from 27 million pounds in 1921 to a high of 120 million in 1929, dropped to 76 million in 1932, and reached an all-time high of 175 million in 1937. After that they dropped rather sharply and practically ceased after Pearl Harbor. By 1948 they were back to 108 million pounds, only to be cut in half again in 1949. During World War II our domestic needs had to be met elsewhere. The most effective pinch hitter was oiticica oil, which is discussed next. In the meantime our domestic tung oil industry is making good progress. Production of tung nuts, in tons, is reported as follows:[46]

1937-1941 (average)	19,553
1942-1946 (average)	33,958
1947	53,200
1948 (preliminary)	67,200

Upon being transplanted from China to the United States the tung tree was greatly improved. The gestation period was sharply reduced, the yield per tree and per acre greatly enhanced, and the bearing period considerably lengthened. Indeed, the quality of the oil was so improved by uniform and scientifically controlled practices that our domestic oil sells at

[45] Oils and Fats, International Institute of Agriculture, Rome, p. 241.

[46] U. S. Department of Agriculture, op. cit., p. 8.

a premium over the imported Chinese oil. The main difficulty in transplanting the tree from China has involved climate, for the tree requires a climate that is warm but has a long enough cold period to allow the tree to lose its leaves and bud again. It is sensitive to frost, however, and several crops have been almost completely lost as a result of frost injury.

Oiticica Oil

Extracted from the nut of the oiticica tree, which is found only along rich alluvial river banks in the states of Ceará, Rio Grande de Norte, Maranhão, and Paraibá in Brazil, oiticica oil is similar to tung oil and has the same uses. It is used principally in the manufacture of paints for ships.

The entire output comes from nuts from wild trees, the orchard-planting system not having been introduced as yet. Hesitation about introducing orchard planting has been laid to a number of causes, among them fear that a less expensive synthetic product might be discovered.

There seems to be a two-year cycle in the production of oiticica nuts, a full crop being followed by a small one.

Babassu Oil

With the United States cut off from the coconut oil and copra formerly supplied by the Philippines, increased interest has been shown in babassu oil produced in the Amazon region of Brazil. Babassu oil contains a high degree of lauric acid, making it an admirable substitute for coconut oil in the soap industry. It is claimed that modernization of railroad equipment and tracks and completion of highway construction would permit enough babassu to be sent to the seaboard to fill all our needs for lauric acid-containing oils.[47]

Bunches of babassu nuts weigh as much as 88 pounds and each nut averages four to six kernels. The largest producer of babassu nuts is the state of Maranhão. Peculiarly, the best babassu-producing section lies along a river navigable only one month each year. However, railroads penetrate the other regions.

Another consideration is the labor required for cracking the hard-shelled babassu nut, whose kernel analyzes about 67 percent oil. Women are employed extensively for this task, for machine cracking has not proved satisfactory. Since labor is scarce, only a small proportion of the total production is utilized. However, the nut falls to the ground when ripe, and hence no labor is required for picking.

Until these problems of machinery, labor, and transportation are solved, and capital is invested in the industry, little increase in exports can be expected. The fact that one can travel for hours by airplane and see nothing but babassu trees is interesting, but it does not indicate availability for economic use. What better example of the difference between "neutral stuff" and "resources" could be found!

---

[47] D. R. Crone, "Oil-nut Odyssey," *Foreign Commerce Weekly,* June 13, 1942.

BIBLIOGRAPHY

Akers, H., "Britain's African Peanut Project," *Foreign Agriculture,* May, 1949.

Brandt, K., *Whale Oil, an Economic Analysis,* Stanford University, Food Research Institute, 1941.

Brandt, K., *Fats and Oils in the War,* Stanford University, Food Research Institute, War-Peace Pamphlet No. 2, 1943.

Brandt, K., *Whaling and Whale Oil During and After World War II,* Stanford University, Food Research Institute, 1948.

Crone, D. R., "Oil-nut Odyssey," *Foreign Commerce Weekly,* June 13, 1942.

Deasy, G. F., "Tung Oil Production and Trade," *Economic Geography,* July, 1940.

Deasy, G. F., "Location Factors in the Commercial Coconut Industry," *Economic Geography,* April, 1941.

Dewees, A., *Fats, Oils, and Oleaginous Raw Materials,* U. S. Department of Agriculture, Statistical Bulletin No. 59, Washington, 1937.

Dies, E. J., *Soybeans, Gold from the Soil,* New York, Macmillan, rev. ed., 1943.

"Fats and Oils. There's Time to Do a Job," *Fortune,* April, 1942.

Hamilton, W. H., and associates, *Price and Price Policies,* New York, McGraw-Hill, 1938.

Hanson, P. L., and Mighell, R. L., *Oil Crops in American Farming,* U. S. Department of Agriculture, Technical Bulletin No. 940, Washington, 1947.

International Institute of Agriculture, *The Tung Oil Tree and the Tung Oil Industry Throughout the World*, Rome, 1938.

International Institute of Agriculture, *Studies of Principal Agriculture Products on the World Market*, Nos. 4 and 5, *Oils and Fats Production and International Trade*, Rome, 1939; No. 6, *Olives*, Rome, 1940.

Morse, W. J., "Soybeans Yesterday and Today," *Foreign Agriculture*, May, 1948.

Pabst, W. R., *Butter and Oleomargarine*, New York, Columbia University Press, 1937.

Peterson, W. H., *Flaxseed in American Farming*, U. S. Department of Agriculture, Technical Bulletin No. 938, Washington, 1947.

Phillips, M. O., "Tung Oil: Florida's Infant Industry," *Economic Geography*, October, 1929.

Russell, J. A., "Synthetic Products and the Use of Soy Beans," *Economic Geography*, January, 1942.

Strand, E. G., *Soybeans in American Farming*, U. S. Department of Agriculture, Technical Bulletin No. 966, Washington, 1948.

Swearingen, L., "The American Tung Oil Industry Comes of Age," *Domestic Commerce*, June 11, 1942.

Tomasevich, J., *International Agreements on Conservation of Marine Resources*, Stanford University, Food Research Institute, 1943.

"Tung Oil," *Fortune*, October, 1949.

"Unilever I: The Heritage," *Fortune*, December, 1947; "Unilever's Africa," *ibid.*, January, 1948; "Unilever III: The Conversion," *ibid.*, February, 1948.

U. S. Department of Agriculture, *The Fats and Oils Situation* (periodical).

U. S. Department of Agriculture, "The Production of Oiticica Oil in Brazil," *Foreign Agriculture*, October, 1940.

U. S. Tariff Commission, *Report to the Congress on Certain Vegetable Oils, Whale Oil and Copra*, Report No. 41, second series, Washington, 1932.

U. S. Tariff Commission, *Fats, Oils, and Oil-Bearing Materials*, Washington, 1941.

Wright, P. G., *The Tariff on Animal and Vegetable Oils*, New York, Macmillan, 1928.

Zapoleon, L. B., *Inedible Animal Fats in the United States*, Stanford University, Food Research Institute, 1929.

Chapter 17

ANIMALS AND ANIMAL PRODUCTS

THE ANIMAL IN MODERN CIVILIZATION

Animals enter into human life in so many ways that animal resources and animal products are mentioned and discussed in different chapters throughout this part. In this chapter a general appraisal of the role animals play in modern civilization is attempted.

Animals and Ecology

Animals play an important role in the ecology of man's environment. Bees carry pollen and fertilize plants. Birds and many other animals kill insects, among them many harmful ones. Insects, in turn, play a vital part in the chemical cycle of life. Worms loosen the soil and thus raise its productivity. Beasts of prey keep the number of ruminants under control and thus check overgrazing. Scavenger birds hasten the return of carrion to the chemical cycle of life and reduce the danger from disease germs.

These are a few illustrations chosen at random from a well-nigh unlimited number. In the aggregate the contributions made by animals through their part in the ecology of nature are of inestimable value to man. Their net effect, however, is sharply reduced by the harm done by animals, especially insects. It is to be remembered, however, that this harm is greatly enhanced by human interference with natural ecological relationships. A wheat belt that stretches with relatively minor interruption from the Prairie Provinces of Canada to Texas is an invitation extended by man, not by nature, to insects to sweep through hundreds of miles which they could not do had not man removed the natural barriers to their spread.

Human Attitudes Toward Animals

To primitive man, most animals must have appeared as dangerous enemies, perhaps also as competitors. Widespread animal cults, prevalent among most early races, bespeak the dread with which man viewed especially the larger animals. The bull and the ram in particular so impressed him that he worshiped in them the mysteries of nature. The Egyptian god Apis, the sacred bull, represented divine power in its highest form. The ram of Jupiter Ammon was a symbol of animal fertility, and Ammon was the all-ruling and all-creating god of nature. In Egyptian sculpture man is pictured as a tiny figure standing between the front legs and underneath the head of a gigantic ram.

As man's powers unfold, his dominion over the animal kingdom becomes as complete as that over the vegetable kingdom. The most unruly of the animals are extinguished; many others are exploited; a small minority, exceptionally amenable to human influence, are domesticated. Strange to say, the smallest members of the animal world are holding out the longest. Experts warn that the battle between man and the insect pests, to say nothing of microbes, still hangs in the balance.

The domestication of animals was as revolutionary a change in the arts as that wrought by the mechanical revolution. It was the conquest of animate energy, as the latter was the conquest of inanimate energy. One operates through biological improvements, the other through mechanical inventions. The domestication of wild animals took not only colossal courage but also patience and, above all, ingenuity.[1] Our strange predilection for inorganic substances and inanimate energies is explained by the fact that they respond more readily to the human manipulation possible at an advanced stage of civilization and that, in an age of science, they yield better results more quickly. In primitive times, inventing was harder. Without the microscope and other precision instruments, without the knowledge of Euclid and Newton, genius found the animal kingdom a more fruitful field.

---

[1] As Clarence Day humorously remarked: "The great age of invention was in the pre-historic times, long ago. The era we live in is also an age of invention—our stupendous achievements have dwarfed all the past, in our own eyes; but, of course the inventions of old were more basic than ours. The invention of writing, and wheels, the invention of zero, of needles, and wheat . . . were made by great men, and aside from these there were some highly ingenious devices which were made in a field which we are wholly neglecting today. Consider, for instance, the man who invented the cow. There was plenty of milk in the world, yes; but what was it doing? It was galloping around in the forest in hostile containers. No thief could rob one of these animals without getting hurt. Their udders were the private and intimate stay of their families. Then a genius was born, a genius who experimented with animals as we do with chemicals." *Harper's Magazine*, July, 1931, p. 127.

The Narrow Limit of Domestication

For thousands of years no new animals have been domesticated. According to Huntington,[2] of about 3500 species of mammals, only 19 have been domesticated; of 13,000 species of birds, only 9 have been domesticated; of 3500 species of reptiles, 1400 species of amphibians, and 13,000 species of fish, none have been domesticated. Of 470,000 species of insects, only two, the silkworm and the bee, have been domesticated.[3]

Needless to say, domestication is not the only way in which man can exploit the animal kingdom. Hunters and fisherman may depend on animals as their main sources of supply without even attempting to domesticate the animals on which they prey. Eternal wandering is the price which the hunter pays for his one-sided exploitative attitude. The nomad cares for his flocks and herds but exploits the grasslands on which they feed. More complete domestication involves the systematic care of both the animals and their feed supply. Man is served by a number of animals whose domestication has never been attempted and is not even thought of. Thus, insects are used to fight other insects. Moreover, many animals perform functions in the processes of nature whose usefulness to man, being indirect and roundabout, is not always fully realized.

Domestication at first involved merely taming, accustoming the animal to the sight of man and subjecting it to human will. Animals were domesticated for the sake either of food, such as milk and meat, or of work, especially draft and burden bearing. Later on, man resorted to breeding with a view to developing more useful types than those produced by natural selection.

Importance of Animals

In order to appraise the importance of animals in modern civilization, one must survey the uses to which they are put.[4] The usefulness

---

[2] E. Huntington and F. E. Williams, *Business Geography*, John Wiley & Sons, Inc., New York, 1926, chap. 13.

[3] Huntington considers only "really important" animals. Fox and muskrat farming must also be mentioned.

[4] Cf. O. Antonius, *Stammesgeschichte der Haustiere*, G. Fischer, Jena, 1922.

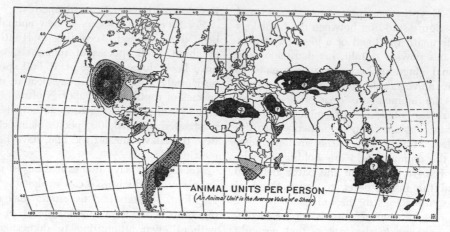

FIG. 17.1.

The per capita distribution of domestic animals, according to the same unit as in Fig. 17.2, follows the equally definite law that regions with few inhabitants per square mile tend to have many animals per capita. Comparing this map with the one below, one finds that the regions of high density per capita distribution are generally regions of low density per unit-area.

of animals to man depends on the height of civilization he has reached and the kind of civilization he has made for himself. These, in turn, depend on, and therefore vary with, both time and place. In primitive times hunger outclassed all other basic needs in urgency. Animals were hunted for their meat, and some became a source of milk supply. Their exploitation as a source of other goods besides food—fur, leather, tools, weapons, etc.—was at first incidental.

When animals were pressed into service as sources of energy, again the first thought was of food. The ox pulled the plow and thus helped man to increase the yield or widen the expanse of his field. Moreover, the domesticated animal became man's ally in his pursuit of and battle with other animals. The cormorant, the falcon, the ferret, the dog, the elephant, and, above all, the horse, proved and still prove useful in that way. Some animals are valued as pets, as companions, as protectors; others function in the sports of nations, as in horse races, dog races, cock fighting, bull fighting, etc. Again, others such as carrier pigeons, dogs carrying first-aid kits and otherwise aiding their masters, cavalry horses, etc., serve in war. Finally, the use of animals made by the medical profession must not be overlooked. Without vivisection, and without guinea pigs, white rats, and numerous other animals on which the

effect of serums, vaccines, drugs, etc., is tested, man could hardly have reached his present stage of medical knowledge.

The appraisal of the part which animals play in human life would be incomplete without a reference to those which are hostile to man. In this country alone, estimates of the damage done by insect pests, in the form of loss of crops and other property, run into staggering totals. If the indirect damage done through increased risk, excessive price fluctuation, and impaired health, which is traceable to insects and other animals, is taken into account, these figures are swelled to alarming proportions. The expenditures for screening windows and doors and for modern insecticides such as DDT are very large.

This damage is partly offset by the indirect benefits which man derives from animals. Such benefits, though not subject to measurement, are undoubtedly important. Animals such as Hannibal's elephants, the horses of the Hyksos and of Cortez, have had considerable effect on the course of history. Fishing has aided the development of shipbuilding and seafaring. Some people believe that meat consumption assures both physical and mental vigor and that therefore the meat-eating races often conquered the vegetable eaters; but Carlyle said that "not the beef of England but the oats of Scotland built the British Empire." To complete this ap-

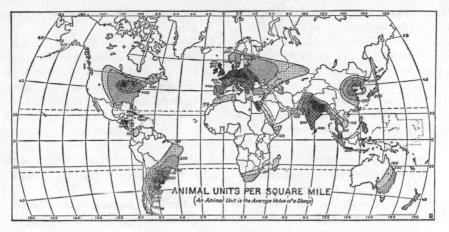

FIG. 17.2.

The areal distribution of domestic animals, when all types of animals are added together on the basis of their relative value, follows the very definite law that regions with many inhabitants per square mile tend to have many animals per square mile. A comparison of this map with that in Fig. 17.1 reveals the striking and significant fact that high animal density per unit-area corresponds with low density per capita.

praisal, the relationship of available work animals to slavery and other social institutions would also have to be analyzed.

The use made of animals varies widely among nations. In the industrial sections of the Occident, animal foods make up a considerable part of the national diet, furnishing between one-fifth and one-third of all the calories consumed. On the other hand, probably at least two-thirds of the population of the earth abstain from meat and eat but sparingly of other animal foods. The same industrial nations are heavy consumers of animal fibers, especially wool and, until recently, silk. The dense sedentary populations of Asia depend more generally on vegetable fibers, especially cotton. Throughout the tropics, cotton and, to a lesser degree, linen are generally preferred to wool. The industrial nations owe much of their advance to the possession of coal and other sources of inanimate energy. Broadly speaking, they can therefore dispense with animals as beasts of burden and as draft animals, and vice versa, the agricultural regions lacking railroad facilities continue to depend on animals.

It has been estimated that about four-fifths of the population of the earth still rely almost exclusively on animals for the supply of their "foreign energy."[5]

GEOGRAPHICAL DISTRIBUTION OF DOMESTIC ANIMALS

Huntington has prepared two maps (Figs. 17.1 and 17.2)[6] which throw light on the numerical relationship between animal and human population and on the geographical distribution of animals throughout the world. In these maps the animal unit is based on the following table of approximate relative values:[7]

Poultry	0.1	Llamas	1.5
Goats	0.5	Asses	1.5
Reindeer	1.0	Cattle	5.0
Dogs (for work)	1.0	Horses	12.5
Sheep	1.0	Mules	17.5
Swine	1.5	Camels	20.0

In his text accompanying the maps Huntington speaks of definite "laws" governing the areal distribution of animals. One may question the need of reference to "laws," for, after all, the explanation of the phenomena shown in these two maps seems rather simple.

Areal Distribution and Types of Animal Husbandry

In the first place, one must keep in mind the versatility and adaptability of animals. Besides furnishing numerous by-products, practically all animals serve several purposes. Thus cattle

[5] E. Huntington and F. E. Williams, *op. cit.*, chap. 13.

[6] *Ibid.*
[7] *Ibid.*

furnish meat, milk, fat (especially oleo fat),
and hides; hogs supply meat and lard; sheep,
meat, wool, and tallow; chicken, meat and
eggs; etc. The ratio of the yields varies with
the category and the breed. Thus there are
cattle bred for milk like the Holstein (quantity) and the Jersey (cream), and cattle bred
for beef like the Hereford, Aberdeen Angus,
shorthorn, etc. There are wool sheep such as
merino and Rambouillet, and mutton types
such as Shropshires, Hampshires, and Lincolns.
Besides the single-purpose types, there are dual-
purpose breeds which seek to combine the best
qualities of both. These are best exemplified by
the dual-purpose sheep which may be surpassed in mutton qualities by the best mutton
breeds and in wool qualities by the best
merinos but is unsurpassed in yielding a superb
combination value of mutton and wool. Breeds
are selected to meet the production and marketing conditions of various regions.[8]

In analyzing the maps of the geographical
distribution of domestic animals, the manner
in which man makes use of animals must be
considered. In particular, four chief uses may
be distinguished:

1. Nomadic herding. This is practiced mainly
   in the arid and semi-arid regions of the
   earth, especially in the Arab world.
2. Livestock ranching. This is practiced in
   thinly populated semi-arid or subhumid regions beyond the margins of agriculture,
   such as the western third of the United
   States (except the Pacific coast), the drier
   regions of Argentina, the relatively inaccessible pasture lands of the *sertão* (back-
   lands) of Brazil, the Orinoco plains (llanos)
   of Venezuela, and parts of Australia.
3. Commercial livestock and crop farming.
   This is a highly advanced and rather intensive form of agriculture, requiring both capital and skilled labor, and generally found in
   economically advanced countries in areas
   adjoining densely populated, highly urbanized and industrialized regions. This form
   of animal husbandry is found in the Corn
   Belt of the United States, the humid pampas of Argentina, in many parts of the
   United Kingdom, and in the western, north-

ern, and central regions of continental
Europe.
4. Commercial dairy farming. This is the most
   intensive use of land involving animal husbandry. It also tends to orient itself toward
   the great urban market but includes New
   Zealand and parts of Australia.[9]

As one examines these four types of animal
husbandry, it becomes rather evident what the
general magnitude of the animal population
density must be, both per capita and per square
mile. Each class will now be examined in this
connection.

1. In desert regions, in the absence of modern means of transportation, men can survive
only by relying on animals for two vital purposes—transportation and food supply. In the
Sahara the camel and horse serve the first,
sheep the second. Here, as in the days of Abra-
ham, animals constitute the bulk of man's
wealth, which here means movable wealth. At
best, the desert can support only small numbers
of animals and men per square mile, and even
when supported by a considerable number of
animals the human population per square mile
of desert land is infinitesimal. It follows that
(a) there are many animals per person, and
(b) there are few animals (and still fewer
men!) per square mile.

2. Turning to the second class one finds a
similar situation. When it requires ten acres
to support a steer and a man wants to support
himself and his family by cattle ranching, he
must have (a) large herds of cattle and (b)
about ten times as many acres of land—owned
ranch land or open range—as he has head of
cattle. The results again are quite obvious:
many animals per person and few animals (and
still fewer men) per square mile.

3. The situation changes radically as one
moves from these submarginal outposts of agri-

---

[8] See "Science in Farming," *Yearbook of Agriculture, 1943-1947.*

[9] Possibly a fifth class of agricultural activity involving animal husbandry should be added, i.e.,
subsistence crop and livestock farming. This is
found in economically backward regions among
less-developed social or racial groups. Such farming is found in the mountainous regions of South
America, on a diminutive scale in the Appalachian
Mountains of the United States, in the Balkans, in
parts of Africa, etc. In Mediterranean agriculture
animals play a not negligible role, but one considerably subordinated to their role in the four
categories listed here.

culture to the very heart of intensive farming. If an area of fertile land—fertile either because of natural advantages such as those present in the humid pampas of Argentina, or because men have slowly built it up to a high pitch of productivity, as in many parts of Europe—lies near large urbanized centers such as Buenos Aires or the Ruhr or London or has easy access to large overseas markets in industrialized countries, it pays to cultivate it rather intensively and stock it heavily with high-grade livestock that gives good returns for a combination of succulent pasture of alfalfa and concentrated forage in the form of hay, corn, cottonseed meal, etc. The animal population is necessarily dense per square mile and if the urban centers are included in the area covered by the animal census, the human population density is naturally high also. If, in the case of the humid pampas of Argentina, the adjoining urban market areas were omitted from the animal census area, the animal population would naturally be out of all proportion to the human population.

4. The same reasoning applies to the commercial dairy regions of the earth, but with even greater force. Naturally regions with intensive dairy farming must have a population density considerably greater than, for instance, the ranch lands of western Texas or the range lands of the intermountain districts. Just how great this density is depends on (a) the degree of mechanization of both agriculture and animal husbandry and (b) the extent to which the dairy zone depends on shipped-in feed concentrates. Again, if the metropolitan district served by a milk shed is included in the dairy belt, naturally the population density is very high.

It appears, in other words, that much depends on the size of the area selected for measuring the density of the animal and human populations. As was suggested before, whether such rather obvious numerical relationships should be traced to "laws" seems questionable. If, as is done in the texts accompanying the maps (Figs. 17.1 and 17.2), a "law" is to be invoked, perhaps it should be the old von Thünen "law,"[10] according to which concentric circles of lessening intensity of land use tend to arrange themselves around the metropolitan centers. In this connection, it is well to remember that Denmark, economically speaking, adjoins London and that the humid pampas of Argentina make heavy shipments to Great Britain.[11]

The animal situation of southeastern Asia deserves special mention. India and Pakistan are said to possess one-third of all the cattle in existence. Yet, the contribution of these large numbers of cattle to the economic life of the people of India is quite modest, especially so far as food is concerned. Their chief service is as draft and work animals. Here economic "law" yields to religious considerations. China may possess one-fourth of all the hogs in existence. They are scavengers, living on garbage and slop, and hence demonstrate the intensive economy of every scrap of food or could-be-food. Water buffaloes and some cattle are kept in the rice regions. Farther north, horses appear. But, by and large, apart from hogs and perhaps ducks and chickens, animals are considered competitors for human food and hence their number is inconsiderable when compared with the size of the human population.

It is clear that the purchasing power of the people has something to do with the relative density of animal and human populations. Apart from India, which is a case by itself, the greatest concentrations of animals are found in the agricultural zones physically or economically tributary to the wealthy industrial urbanized centers of "the West." It is in these centers that the chief markets for meats and dairy products are found. The milk sheds and meat-producing centers are as near to them as joint considerations of production and transportation costs will permit.

The high density of the animal population of western and northern Europe is in part explained by the heavy imports in normal times of feed concentrates such as cottonseed meal, poonac (derived from copra after the coconut oil has been extracted), palm-kernel cake, soybean cake, peanut cake, linseed cake, etc., brought in from the four corners of the earth. Finally, tariff protection has had much to do

---

[10] Formulated in the celebrated book, Johann Heinrich von Thünen, *Der Isolierte Staat.* See the *Encyclopædia of the Social Sciences,* vol. 14, p. 627.

[11] See S. G. Hanson, *Argentine Meat and the British Market,* Stanford University Press, 1938.

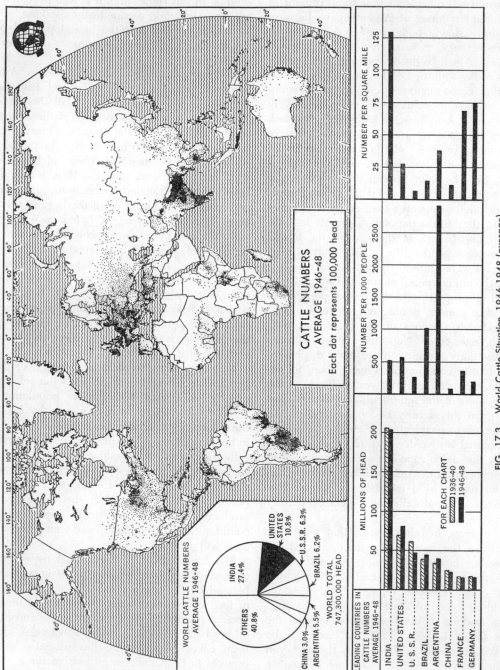

FIG. 17.3. World Cattle Situation, 1946-1948 (average).

(Figs. 17.3, 17.4, 17.5 from U. S. Department of Agriculture, Office of Foreign Agricultural Relations, *Graphic Summary of World Agriculture*, 1949.)

TABLE 17.1. Prewar Number of Livestock and Production of Meat and Milk, by Continents[12]

| Area | Number[a] | | | Production | | | |
| | Cattle | Sheep | Hogs | Meat[b] | Milk | Meat | Milk |
	(million head)			(million metric tons)		(pounds per capita)	
North America	96.6	59.6	61.3	8.4	54.8	99.6	649.1
South America	105.6	101.0	31.3	3.7	6.3	87.1	149.5
Europe	110.2	130.8	81.9	12.2	105.1	69.2	596.6
U.S.S.R.	48.5	79.7	23.9	3.3	23.3	42.9	301.8
Asia (excluding U.S.S.R.)	283.4	141.7	82.7	...	...	...	...
Oceania	18.1	144.0	2.1	1.4	9.8	319.6	2226.8
Africa	61.4	99.5	3.3	...	0.9	...	...

[a] Approximate figures adapted from reports of Office of Foreign Agricultural Relations, U. S. Department of Agriculture· "Prewar" pertains to the years immediately preceding World War II; the years used for averages vary slightly from country to country.
[b] Carcass meat, excluding offal.

with the more recent developments, especially since World War I.

The inordinately larger concentration of domesticated animals in the temperate zones of the southern hemisphere is explained in part by the distance of these regions—especially Argentina, Uruguay, Australia, New Zealand, and South Africa—from the markets. Meat and dairy products constitute concentrated values derived from vegetable matter, natural or cultivated pasture, or harvested forage. A pound of meat or butter or cheese ordinarily is worth considerably more than a pound of wheat. Hence, in distant supply areas, there is a natural trend toward raising the lower vegetable value to the higher animal value before shipping.

The distribution of domestic animals cannot be explained satisfactorily by reference to a few "laws" or principles. A realistic approach calls for consideration of various other factors, such as fortuitous events—droughts, pests, diseases, wars, etc.—secular trends such as the shift from main reliance on animate to inanimate energy observed in countries touched by the mechanical revolution, and major historical phenomena such as the closing of the frontier in North America. These are mainly cultural rather than geographical forces affecting the areal distribution of domestic animals. A striking example of cultural influence on the animal population is furnished by current developments in the United States, where the coming of the tractor and the automobile rendered useless millions of draft and work animals. The horse and mule population in the United States

is therefore rapidly declining—horses, from 19.8 million in 1910 to 6.6 million in 1948; mules, from 4.2 million in 1910 to 2.5 in 1948. Tractors on farms of the United States increased from 0.8 million in 1929 to 3.2 million in 1947 (January 1).

Recent Developments in Animal Distribution

Meats. The world distribution of herds and of output of meat and milk, by continents, is shown in Table 17.1.

The high rank of Europe (excluding the U.S.S.R.) as a producer of both meat and milk, especially the latter, may surprise some readers. If the output of European Russia is added, Europe's meat output constitutes half the total world production and the output of milk is almost three-fifths of the world total. However, the per capita picture is somewhat different.

The situation becomes more realistic as one turns from continents to countries. It would be difficult to find a sharper contrast in meat and milk production than that between Argentina and Bolivia, between the United States and Mexico, or between Denmark and Greece. Continental averages, in other words, are of little significance. In fact, one could go further and contrast Wisconsin with Mississippi or Nevada with New Hampshire. How the countries ranked before World War II is shown in Table 17.2. Their ranking after World War II is shown in Figs. 17.3 (cattle), 17.4 (hogs), and 17.5 (sheep).

[12] Food and Agriculture Organization, *Livestock Products Review, Part 1—Meat Products,* June, 1947, p. 3.

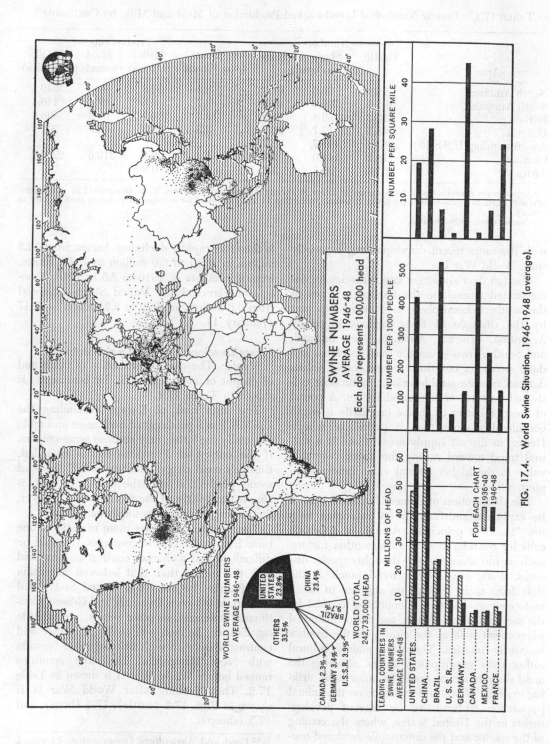

FIG. 17.4. World Swine Situation, 1946-1948 (average).

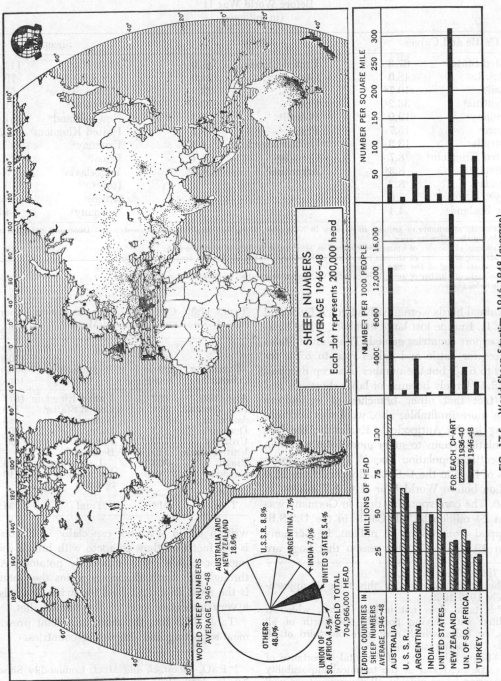

FIG. 17.5. World Sheep Situation, 1946-1948 (average).

TABLE 17.2. Production of Cattle, Hogs, and Sheep, per Leading Producing Country,
Before World War II[13]
(in millions)

Cattle and Calves		Hogs		Sheep	
United States[a]	67.3	United States[a]	48.0	Australia[e]	111.3
U.S.S.R.[a]	48.0	Germany[a]	24.0	U.S.S.R.[a]	79.7
Brazil[b]	40.7[d]	U.S.S.R.[a]	23.9	United States[a]	53.1
Argentina[b]	33.2[d]	Brazil[b]	23.6[e]	Argentina[b]	41.8
Germany[a]	19.9	Poland[b]	7.3	New Zealand[c]	31.0
France[a]	15.7	France[a]	7.1	United Kingdom[b]	26.2
Australia[c]	13.3	United Kingdom[b]	4.5	Uruguay[b]	17.9
United Kingdom[d]	8.7	Canada[a]	4.1	Brazil[b]	12.3
Uruguay[b]	8.3[d]	Argentina[b]	4.0	Yugoslavia[a]	9.5
Canada[a]	8.2			Italy[a]	9.5
Italy[a]	7.6			Greece[a]	8.2
New Zealand[a]	4.4			Germany[a]	4.3[f]

[a] Estimate of number of animals in country in November, December, or January. November and December estimates are included in the following year.
[b] Estimate of number of animals in country in May, June, or July of specified year.
[c] Estimate of number of animals in country in February, March, or April of specified year.
[d] Estimate based on less than five years.
[e] Estimate of number of animals in country in August, September, or October of specified year.
[f] Includes goats.

Animal herds were greatly affected by World War II. Europe lost large numbers, while overseas export countries gained. The United States figures for cattle and calves rose to 82.4, for hogs to 61.3, but the number of sheep dropped to 42.4 (largely because of labor shortages and the fact that other branches of agriculture were more profitable; also, wool was accumulating in the Antipodes). Evidently, the hog population seems to suffer more from war than the cattle population does.[14] Thus, the numbers of hogs in the U.S.S.R. declined from 23.9 million before World War II to 8.7 million in 1946. The corresponding drop in Germany was from 24 million to 7.1. Cattle in the U.S.S.R. dropped from 48 to 42 million, in Germany from 19.9 to 13.7. One reason that hogs are

---

[13] *Ibid.*, Table 2.
The period covered by this table is approximately 1935-1939.
This table does not include China, which is credited with having possibly one-fourth of all hogs, or India, which may have one-third of all cattle (including carabao).
[14] "Being fully aware of the vital importance of the cattle herd and of the technical impossibility of restoring losses quickly, all governments as well as the farmers have exhausted all other reserves first to keep the cattle herd (essentially cows) intact so far and so long as possible." Karl Brandt, *The Reconstruction of World Agriculture*, W. W. Norton & Company, New York, 1945, pp. 139-140.

TABLE 17.3. Countries Leading in Prewar Exports and Imports of Meats[15]

Exporting Country	Exports (1000 metric tons)	Importing Country	Imports (1000 metric tons)
Argentina	692	United Kingdom	1617
New Zealand	301	United States	119
Australia	259	Germany	83
Denmark	215	Italy	61
Uruguay	150	France	27
United States	110	Belgium-	
Brazil	103	Luxemburg	16
Canada	88	Netherlands	10
		Spain	1
Total	1918	Total	1934

written off in wartime, especially in Europe, is the fact that they compete with human beings for edible crops, especially potatoes. All through the north European plains the potato is the most important feed for swine. It is also a very important part of the human diet.

Table 17.3 lists the more important prewar meat-exporting and -importing countries.

---

[15] FAO, *Livestock and Meat*, Commodity Series No. 12, May, 1949, pp. 27, 30.
The period covered is 1935-1939 for Canada and the United States, 1935-1938 for continental Europe, and 1934-1938 for others. Trade figures from International Institute of Agriculture converted to carcass weight equivalents.

As a result of World War II which, as was pointed out, sharply reduced European herds and created an abnormally large meat deficit in the European market, the United States, which had been a net importer of meat before the war, returned to her older position as a leading meat exporter. In 1946 she exported half a million metric tons of meat. These shipments dropped sharply in 1947 after UNRRA funds had been exhausted.

TABLE 17.4. Net Exports of Meat[16]
(thousand metric tons)

Country	1946	1947
Argentina	690	694
United States	500	270[a]
New Zealand	371	366[b]
Canada	294	191
Australia	269	234
Uruguay	131	126[c]
Denmark	128	134
Brazil	101	78
Paraguay	28	26
Ireland	20	...

[a] Total 1947 exports assumed to be twice the January-to-June program.
[b] Production for export in year beginning October, 1946. Unofficial estimates of actual shipments during the calendar year 1947 are considerably lower than this.
[c] Excluding jerked beef.

South America exports largely chilled meats; Australia and New Zealand export frozen meats. Australia specializes in mutton from dual-purpose sheep, while New Zealand's exports come from prize herds of mutton-type sheep. South America, especially Argentina and Uruguay, is a heavy exporter of beef. Pork exports from the southern-hemisphere countries have not yet reached large proportions.

Hog products differ materially according to breed and feeding. Hogs are fed waste in China; potatoes supplemented with root crops and barley or other grains in northern Europe; forest products such as beechnuts, acorns, and other nuts fallen from forest trees in Yugoslavia, sections of the U.S.S.R., and the southern United States; corn (maize) in the United States, Canada, Argentina, and Brazil, etc. Hogs are the chief finished products of our corn crop, close to half the crop being devoted to this purpose. The corn-fed hog is a lard hog. Such a hog weighs about 229 pounds (1930-1939 average) and yields approximately 125 pounds of finished pork and 30 pounds of rendered lard, the lard constituting slightly less than 20 percent of the weight of the finished products (other than by-products and edible parts removed in dressing the carcass). Hogs fed on peanuts develop a special flavor. Potato-fed hogs are considerably leaner than corn-fed hogs.

Dairy Products. Next to meats, dairy products are the most valuable products obtained from animals. Table 17.5, which pictures the dairy situation, is rather incomplete because such important countries as the U.S.S.R. and Germany are not listed. The figures in general represent estimates. The apparent prominence of the United States in all fields—milk, butter, cheese, canned and dried milk—is in part due to this incomplete coverage.

Before World War II the exporting countries ranked as shown in Table 17.6 in volume of exports of milk products.

As a result of World War II, the United States, which had been a net importer of all dairy products except evaporated and condensed milk, became a heavy net exporter of milk products. Her net exports, in thousand metric tons, were as follows:[17]

	1946	1947
Butter	0.5	4.5
Cheese	85.7	67.1
Evaporated and condensed milk	518.5	229.0
Powdered milk	153.3	132.0

UNRRA and lend-lease shipments to liberated countries were largely responsible for this increase in the movement of dairy products.

On the whole, the import situation is relatively simple. Ordinarily the United Kingdom takes the lion's share and the other industrial countries such as Germany share the rest.

Poultry and Eggs. Poultry and eggs are another important group of animal products. The position of leading poultry-producing countries for selected years is shown in Table 17.7. The 1945-1947 figures indicate the rapid step-up in the United States and Canada which offset in part the virtual collapse of poultry production in parts of Europe.

[16] *Ibid.*, Table 4.

[17] FAO, *Livestock Products Review, Part 2, Dairy Products,* June, 1947, Table 2.

Table 17.5. Production of Milk and Major Manufactured Dairy Products[18]

(thousand metric tons)

Country	Milk				Butter				Cheese				Canned Milk				Dried Milk			
	Prewar	1946	1947	1947 as % of 1934-1938	Prewar	1946	1947	1947 as % of 1934-1938	Prewar	1946	1947	1947 as % of 1934-1938	Prewar	1946	1947	1947 as % of 1934-1938	Prewar	1946	1947	1947 as % of 1934-1938
United Kingdom	8,231	8,387	8,100	98	43.7	23.7a	24.0a	55	49.4	25.0	22.3	45	171.7	86.3	60.9	35	15.2	28.8	33.3	219
France	10,849	6,900	7,300	67	201.8	152.0	158.0	78	164.7	125.0	138.0a	84	...	17.5	19.0	...	...	...	1.0	...
Belgium	2,688	...	1,860	69	64.3	53.6a	57.7a	90	5.0	7.0	...	...	...	0.6	0.7	...	2.5	1.4	1.4	56
Netherlands	4,845	3,521	3,685	76	91.2	52.7	57.0	63	120.9	65.3	67.0	55	138.3	...	33.0	24	25.6	13.6	...	...
Switzerland	2,165	1,700	1,756	81	26.2	18.0	18.5	71	50.7	38.4	43.4	86	6.4	6.8	11.0	172	1.1	2.8	...	...
Norway	1,288	...	1,127	87	11.3	6.4	10.0	88	17.7	9.3	8.0	45	...	...	...	...	...	...	...	...
Sweden	4,215	3,525	4,345	103	84.1	99.6	92.0	109	32.3	44.5	45.0	139	...	...	...	...	...	...	...	...
Finland	2,361	...	1,410	60	27.8	25.2	25.6	92	8.9	3.4	5.8	65	...	...	...	...	...	...	...	...
Denmark	5,075	4,575	4,425	87	181.7	140.9	144.0	79	31.1	57.4	47.0	151	18.5	11.8	18.5	100	...	...	...	...
United States	46,574	54,115	54,239	116	988.2	673.7	805.0	81	291.8	495.3	500.0	171	894.5	1,449.0	1,500.0	168	115.4	370.5	410.4	356
Canada	6,811	7,683	7,810	115	155.8	144.7a	150.0	96	52.5	64.1	83.0	158	41.9	104.2	105.0	251	10.7	25.1	27.6	258
Argentina	2,984	3,115	3,200	107	30.0	50.9	51.0	170	30.8	94.3	94.0	305	...	4.3	4.5	...	...	...	...	...
Australia	5,352	4,960	4,968	93	197.9	144.3	155.0	78	19.8	43.8	42.5	215	17.6	51.3	...	...	7.7	16.0	6.0	...
New Zealand	4,706	3,712	4,363	93	168.8	154.2a	151.0	89	91.3	77.0	84.6	93	5.1	9.0	9.2	180	7.9	...	13.8	175

a Estimate based on factory production using 1945 percentage of total.

[18] Ibid., Table 1.

Milk production figures exclude quantities fed to livestock. Estimates for 1947 are mostly calendar year, but sometimes 1946-1947. Because of varying sources and inadequate data for recent years all figures are preliminary and subject to revision. Figures for 1947 are forecasts based on the best available data. Prewar refers to the years immediately preceding World War II, usually 1934-1938.

TABLE 17.6. Prewar Exports of Butter, Cheese, and Preserved Milk, per Principal Exporting Country[19] (in thousand metric tons)

Butter		Cheese		Evaporated and Condensed Milk		Powdered Milk	
Denmark	149.1	New Zealand	87.7	Netherlands	161.5	Netherlands	16.8
New Zealand	140.1	Netherlands	59.6	United States	26.2		
Australia	99.8	Canada	32.9	Denmark	18.3		
Netherlands	49.5	Italy	19.8	Canada	10.4		
Sweden	22.8	Switzerland	17.1	New Zealand	10.1[b]		
Ireland	13.3	Denmark	8.2	Australia	7.0		
Finland	13.3	Australia	8.1	Switzerland	5.9		
Poland[a]	8.5			Ireland	5.8		
Argentina	8.3						

[a] Prewar Poland and Danzig.
[b] Condensed and powdered combined.

TABLE 17.7. Poultry Production[20]
(in millions)[a]

	1935–1939	1945	1946–1947
United States	409.9	530.2	475.4
China	344.9[b]		
U.S.S.R.	208.0[c]	....	....
Germany	89.7		
United Kingdom	71.7	56.7	62.0
France	69.3[c]	....	....
Canada	55.0	84.7	85.5[e]
Poland	50.0[d]	....	....
Argentina	43.2[c]	....	....
Belgium	33.8[c]	2.4[f]	5.5
Netherlands	32.8	4.5[f]	9.5
Denmark	29.1[c]	16.4	18.5
Spain	29.0[c]	....	....
Ireland	15.6	15.2	18.3
Australia	15.6[c]	....	....

[a] Prewar and 1945 figures based on calendar year; 1946-1947 figures based on production year, July, 1946, to June, 1947.
[b] Prewar figure for China, 1934 to 1937 average.
[c] Less than five-year average.
[d] Laying hens, 1931.
[e] 1946 figure.
[f] 1945-1946 figures.

TABLE 17.8. Egg Production, 1934-1938[31]
(thousand metric tons)[a]

United States	2218.6
China	734.0[b]
U.S.S.R.	625.0[c]
Germany	400.0[c]
France	393.8
Italy	314.0[b]
United Kingdom	241.1
Poland	170.0[b]
Canada	164.9
Denmark	124.2
Netherlands	123.6
Belgium	111.9
Spain	104.5
Argentina	104.0[b]
Australia	90.9

[a] Conversion: Official estimates given in number of eggs were converted to metric tons by using 16,000 eggs = 1 metric ton.
[b] Prewar figures, generally 1935-1938 averages; for Argentina, 1935-1939; for China, 1934-1937 averages.
[c] Less than five-year average.

Egg production for 1934-1938 is shown in Table 17.8. These figures should be compared with those for poultry in Table 17.7. For example, note the ratio of the poultry-eggs figures for the United States and China.

The world sheep situation will be discussed in Chapter 20. Here only a table showing mutton and lamb production is provided.

[19] *Ibid.*, Table 2.
All figures preliminary and subject to revision.
[20] FAO, *Livestock Products Review, Part 3—Poultry and Eggs*, June 24, 1947, Table 1.

ANIMAL INDUSTRIES OF THE UNITED STATES
Animals and Agriculture

In Chapter 13 the fact was stressed that in well-to-do countries animal products constitute a more important part of the diet than they do in poorer countries. This predilection for animal products is particularly pronounced in countries which combine a high standard of living with abundant land. The outstanding country in this class is the United States. It is not surprising, therefore, to find that in this country animal products contribute over half of the farm income. The items of which the farm in-

[21] *Ibid.*, Table 1.

come was made up in 1945 are shown in Table 17.10.

In 1945, income from livestock constituted 57.4 percent of the total farm income other than government payments. This percentage is increasing, as Table 17.11 shows. Here the farm output of the United States during the period 1897-1901 is compared with that during 1935-1939. It should be noted that in 1897-1901 animal products made up 58.8 percent of the total income; in 1935-1939 they amounted to 62.8 percent. Note also the shift from meat to dairy products and to poultry and eggs.

TABLE 17.9.　Estimated Production of Mutton and Lamb in Specified Countries[22]
(thousand metric tons)[a]

	1934-1938	1945	1946
Southern hemisphere			
Australia	322[b]	328	346
New Zealand	261	303	321
Argentina	171	324	313
Uruguay	78	37	37
Brazil	7	15	14
	839	1007	1031
Northern hemisphere			
U.S.S.R.	444	...	...
United States	395	478	445
United Kingdom	206	136	150
France	99	57[bc]	56[bc]
Greece	62[c]	43[c]	48[c]
Yugoslavia	50	...	...
Italy	49[c]	31[cd]	36[cd]
Germany	40	...	...
Others	81	...	...
	1426		

[a] Carcass or dressed weight of animals; excludes offal.
[b] Year beginning July 1.
[c] Includes goat meat.
[d] FAO estimates.

It is not surprising that the total value of animal products should exceed that of crops sold for cash and consumed on farms. For animal products in general constitute an advanced stage of processed crops. A hog is corn and other feeds, including slop, condensed, refined, and converted into a more desirable product. Milk is edible (or drinkable) hay; eggs may be inedible waste converted into a highly nutri-

[22] FAO, *Livestock Products Review, Part 1—Meat Products*, Table 3.
Data relate to prewar boundaries.

tious human food. The care of animals requires a great deal of labor and capital. Especially in its more advanced forms it is a more intensive type of agriculture than cropping.

The feed crops which make the livestock products possible constitute the major part of the crop production of the United States. The

TABLE 17.10.　Sources of Farm Income, 1945[23]
(millions of dollars)

	1 Cash Receipts from Farming	2 Value of Home Consumption	3 Total Value (1 plus 2)
Cattle and calves	$3,218.8	$ 36.6	$3,255.4
Hogs	2,289.1	386.3	2,674.5
Sheep and lambs	319.2	3.4	322.6
Broilers	279.1	...	279.1
Chickens (other)	581.2	190.5	771.7
Eggs (chicken)	1,463.8	250.3	1,714.1
Turkey	242.6	7.2	249.8
Other poultry	30.0	4.4	34.3
Butter, farm	24.1⎱		
Cream	488.9⎰		
Milk, retail	345.3⎱	561.8	3,632.1
Milk, wholesale	2,212.0⎰		
Wool	134.6	...	134.6
Other	97.5	6.5	104.0
Total livestock	$11,725.4	$1,447.0	$13,172.3
Total crops	9,055.5	696.1	9,751.7
Government payments	770.6	...	770.6
Grand total	$21,551.5	$2,143.1	$23,694.6

corn crop is our largest crop. All but a fraction of it is a supply crop used to produce animal products. Even most of the portion sold as such by farmers goes to other farmers or to stock-feeders who feed it to animals. With the exception of the minor portions which go into starch, glucose, and other commercial products, which are consumed directly as human food, and which are exported, our entire corn crop of 3 billion bushels, more or less, is fed to domestic livestock.[24] In recent years the corn crop has been valued on the farm at around $3.5 billion. Of this, close to $3 billion goes into

[23] *Agricultural Statistics, 1946*, pp. 570-572.
[24] Some recent crops have run considerably over 3 billion bushels. Corn crop figures (in billion bushels) for the period 1939-1948 have been running as follows: 2.6, 2.5, 2.7, 3.1, 3.0, 3.1, 2.9, 3.2, 2.3, 3.7.

livestock. Much of the oat crop, worth over a billion dollars in 1945, is fed to animals. All the hay crop, worth $1.6 billion that same year, goes to market in the form of livestock. Add grain sorghum and parts of the peanut, soybean, and diverse grain crops, and we reach a staggering total value constituting a large share

TABLE 17.11. Percentage Composition of the Agricultural Output of the United States, 1897-1901 and 1935-1939[25]

	1897-1901	1935-1939[b]
Vegetable crops[a]		
Grains	17.7	12.6
Cotton (lint only)	9.8	8.8
Tobacco	2.5	3.0
Sugar crops	0.4	1.1
Potatoes	3.2	3.5
Dry edible beans	0.2	0.6
Hay	2.1	0.3
Citrus fruits	0.2	1.9
Noncitrous fruits	3.2	3.1
Oil crops	1.8	2.2
Hops	0.1	0.1
Total vegetable crops	41.1	37.2
Animal products		
Poultry and eggs	9.2	12.4
Meat animals	32.5	27.2
Milk and milk products	15.9	22.1
Wool	1.2	1.1
Total animal products	58.8	62.8

[a] Exclusive of crops fed to animals.
[b] Exclusive of new crops not represented in the statistical records of 1897-1901. Their value during the 1935-1939 period was approximately 6 percent of the total. Almost all the new crops are vegetable crops.

of the total market value of animal products. The acreage required to raise the feed crops far exceeds that needed for food crops.

In new countries beef cattle production generally begins as a range industry; that is to say, animals, branded to indicate ownership, are allowed to range freely on land not yet divided among private owners. This range method yields to ranching, which is also a large-scale

[25] Adapted from H. Landsberg and H. H. Barger, *American Agriculture, 1899-1939. A Study of Output, Employment and Productivity*, National Bureau of Economic Research, New York, 1942, p. 27.
The figures are based on average quantities produced (excluding seed and feed) in either period, weighted by average farm prices for the ten years 1897-1901 and 1935-1939.

enterprise but which is carried on on the private property of the rancher instead of on the public domain. Both the range and the ranch industries flourish in the pioneer fringe; they are frontier industries. As the tide of homesteaders rises, the range yields to the ranch, which in turn is itself broken up into fields, provided that natural and geographical conditions favor agricultural development. The growing domestic demand for beef is met by farmers who keep relatively small numbers of cattle. These may be dual-purpose herds, that is, animals kept primarily for beef production but also with a view to milk supply and, incidentally, for the sake of calves or dairy herds. The dairy industry in particular becomes the chief source of veal and contributes materially to the beef supply. In this country the contribution is estimated as high as one-fourth. Needless to say, the quality of meat obtained from dairy cows which may average from five to ten years of age is generally inferior to the quality obtained from young steers.

In industrialized countries, therefore, the shift is from the extensive animal industries of the pastural variety to more intensive types which fit into a general system of intensive farming, rather than from primary to secondary food. Grazing, especially when overstocking of pastures is tolerated, is a form of mining rather than of cropping, and cannot be permanent. Consequently, the shift from the range to the feed lot is often necessary for no other reason than to assure continuity of supply.

Another factor to be considered is the change in tastes. City people generally prefer the tender corn-fed "native beef" produced in the Corn Belt to the tough grass-fed western beef. Thus beef production does not cease, but is organically built into the economic structure of the national economy, which calls for the intensified use of both land and labor accomplished with the aid of a liberal application of capital. What does cease, however, is the beef production for export, for only where cheap land is available is this feasible. Beef production in the Corn Belt and the dairy sections is so definitely a part of the American economic system, with its relatively high wages, high prices, etc., that protection of the domestic market through import duties becomes necessary and the possibility of competing in the world markets tends to disappear. The calving grounds shrink more and more before an expanding agriculture, and the ranger and rancher are forced to look across the borders into Canada and Mexico for new "open spaces." In the meantime, the large packers, like Armour and Swift, no longer able to supply the European market with United States beef, transfer their beef-exporting interests to newer lands such as Argentina, Paraguay, Venezuela, South Africa, Australia, New Zealand, etc. Only oleo fat, a beef product and an important raw material of the oleomargarine industry, continues to be exported from the United States to the less fortunate countries of Europe.

Geographical Shifts

There was a time when most beef was raised out west and was brought to the Corn Belt for fattening and general finishing. Today, over two-thirds of the cattle normally slaughtered in the Corn Belt or shipped to central markets from farms of the Corn Belt are bred within that region.

Within the Corn Belt, a decided westward movement of the center of the cattle-feeding industry can be observed during the past century. In the thirties Ohio occupied the premier position; this had shifted to Illinois in the seventies and to Iowa in the nineties. Today, eastern Nebraska has advantages, as regards both cost and quality. The following summary of the present regional distribution of the beef cattle industry contains, besides the two broad divisions of the western ranges and the Corn Belt, a number of other sources of cattle.[26]

A. Grazing regions
  1. Western ranges
  2. Flint Hills, Kansas
  3. Osage pastures, Oklahoma
  4. Mineral Point region, Wisconsin
  5. Appalachian region
B. Feeding regions
  1. Corn-belt
  2. Tarkio, Missouri
  3. Wood County, Ohio
  4. Lancaster District, Pennsylvania
  5. Cake feeding area, Texas
  6. Pulp feeding area, Colorado-Nebraska

  7. Idaho-Utah region
  8. Big Hole Country, Montana
  9. Southern California and Salt River Valley, Arizona
C. Non-specialized region
  1. Cotton-belt

The connection between Texas cake feeding and the cotton industry of that state and between the pulp feeding of Colorado-Nebraska and the beet sugar industry of those states is self-evident. Peculiarities of the cattle industry in the cotton belt are the poor quality of the so-called "piney woods" cattle, and the establishment of Brahman cattle production over wide areas of the cotton belt as a defense against the scourge of the Texas fever tick and as a means of utilizing pastures too poor to carry more improved breeds.

Animal Husbandry in a Mechanized World

During recent decades the animal industries in the United States have made remarkable progress in efficiency. This is clearly evident in Fig. 17.6, showing the production of livestock products—meats, including poultry, lard, eggs, and dry weight equivalent of milk—and number of animal units of livestock on farms, 1910-1944. It will be noticed that while the number of animal units of livestock increased about 45 percent, the production of livestock products increased approximately 80 percent. This is explained by more efficient animal husbandry. Thus in 1942 milk production per cow was 14 percent higher than it was in 1924. Eggs produced per hen increased 46 percent during the same period.

The increase in the number of animal units of livestock producing meat and other edible products was made possible in large part by the decrease, after 1918, of the number of work animals—horses and mules—which amounted to more than 50 percent by 1944. This made available 50 to 55 million acres of crop land for the production of meat, lard, milk, and eggs. The saving in feed for horses and mules in grain alone amounted to about 13 million tons in 1944 compared with 1920—enough to feed 26 million hogs to market weight.[27]

---

[26] Armour's Livestock Bureau, *Monthly Letter to Animal Husbandmen*, September, 1931, p. 5.

[27] C. W. Crickman, *Feed Grains and Meat Animals in War and Peace*, U. S. Department of Agriculture, Bureau of Agricultural Economics, Washington, November, 1945, p. 25.

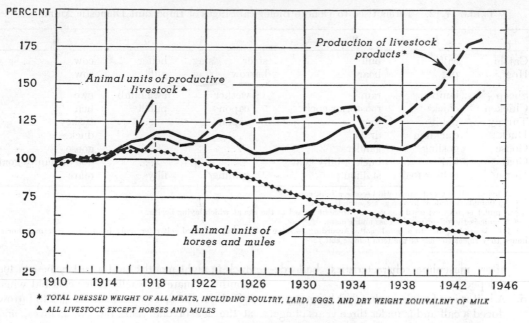

PERCENT

* TOTAL DRESSED WEIGHT OF ALL MEATS, INCLUDING POULTRY, LARD, EGGS, AND DRY WEIGHT EQUIVALENT OF MILK
▲ ALL LIVESTOCK EXCEPT HORSES AND MULES

FIG. 17.6. Production of Livestock Products and Number of Animal Units of Livestock on Farms, United States, January 1, 1910-1944. (Index numbers 1910-1914 = 100) (C. W. Crickman, Feed Grains and Meat Animals in War and Peace, U. S. Department of Agriculture, Bureau of Agricultural Economics, Washington, 1946.)

The developments just cited—displacement of horses and mules by mechanical devices and the increased productivity of the average unit of livestock—inevitably affect the ratio of the animal population to the human population in the United States, and this in spite of the fact that per capita consumption of most animal foods has been on the increase. While our population increased from about 38 million in 1867 to about 147 million in 1949, or almost fourfold, the number of cattle during the same period increased from about 30 million to about 80 million—less than threefold—of hogs, from about 35 million to about 57 million, about 63 percent; the number of sheep dropped from 45 to 29 million.

ANIMAL "FACTS OF LIFE"[28]

The majority of people living in industrial countries have little opportunity to observe

[28] In the preparation of this section the author had the benefit of valuable aid from Thomas H. Bartilson, Senior Animal Husbandman, Acting in Charge, Animal Husbandry Division, U. S. Department of Agriculture, and R. J. Eggert, Associate Director of the American Meat Institute, Chicago, Ill.

farm animals and are therefore unfamiliar not only with the basic facts of animal husbandry, but also with the elementary terms used.

Among animals as among humans the sexes tend to be divided about equally in numbers. However, in animal husbandry only a selected minority of males are used for breeding purposes.[29] The others are castrated (desexed), usually quite early in life, but sometimes after masculine characteristics have developed. Among females also, distinctions are made on the basis of sexual maturity. These biological differentiations give rise to a number of terms describing them.

Thus a herd of cattle may be made up of calves, bulls, steers, stags, heifers, and cows. These terms designate the following biological types:

1. A calf is a bovine less than 12 months old.
2. A bull is a male bovine with sexual organs and capable of reproduction.
3. A steer is a castrated male bovine that has not been used for reproduction.
4. A stag is a male bovine that was castrated

[29] One mature ram is kept for each 40 to 50 ewes in the breeding flock.

TABLE 17.12. Terms Used to Denote Biological Stages of Important Domestic Animals

	1	2	3	4	5	6
Cattle	calf[a]	bull	steer	stag	heifer	cow
Hog	pig	boar	barrow	stag	gilt	sow
Sheep	lamb	ram	wether		ewe lamb	ewe
Chicken	chick[b]	rooster or cock	capon		pullet[c]	hen
Turkey	poult	tom	capon		...	turkey
Duck	duckling	drake	...		...	duck
Goose	gosling	gander	...		...	goose
Goat	kid	buck or billy goat	...		...	doe or nanny goat
Horse[d]	colt or foal	stallion	gelding		filly[e]	mare

[a] A heifer calf is a calf which will become a milk cow.
[b] An immature male is known as a cockerel.
[c] A pullet is so called until one year old without regard to the age at which laying begins.
[d] A mule is the offspring of an ass and a mare.
[e] Filly is applied also to a female colt. (According to some authorities, the word colt refers only to an immature male horse; hence they reject the use of the term female colt.)

after masculine characteristics had developed.

5. A heifer is a female bovine that has not produced a calf and is under three years of age.
6. A cow is a female bovine that has produced a calf and usually is over three years of age.

Other domesticated animals are similarly classified on the basis of sex and biological status. Table 17.12 gives a summary of the most important of these terms for the most important domesticated animals. In this table the numbers 1-6 refer to the following biological stages:

1. Sexually immature and before castration.
2. Mature male, uncastrated.
3. Male castrated before maturity.
4. Male castrated after maturity.
5. Female before bearing offspring.
6. Female after bearing offspring.

Giving birth is expressed by different terms for different animals. Thus birds like the hen, the turkey, the duck, and the goose lay, a cow calves, a sow farrows, a ewe lambs, a mare foals, etc.

The cycle of animal reproduction is affected by several factors such as the length of the gestation period, i.e., the period elapsing between conception and birth, the age at which females reach maturity, the frequency of conception, and the size of the litter. These factors materially affect the flexibility of husbandry operations in response to changing market conditions. A hen begins to lay when six months old, a

duck in eight months, and a turkey hen in ten months. A mare is usually four years old when it foals for the first time. A sow begins to farrow at the age of one year, but cows, ewes, and does are usually two years old before they have young. Gestation periods[30] differ similarly. They are as follows:

Hen	21 days
Turkey hen	28 days
Duck	28 days
Goose	30-34 days
Sow	112-114 days
Ewe	146-150 days
Cow	283 days
Mare	340 days

That all these facts have an important bearing on the rate of reproduction goes without saying. A sow farrows in the spring when one year old, has an average surviving litter of 7, of which 3 or 4 may be female; it may have another litter of equal size in the fall. The 6-8 female pigs born in one year are potential sows, each of which in the next year may add 3-4 surviving females per litter. Under these conditions the hog population grows rapidly and can be adjusted fairly rapidly to changing demand and price conditions.

On the other hand, the reproduction rate of horses is much slower and the cycle much longer. As was mentioned before, most mares do not foal before they are at least four years old. The gestation period is about eleven

[30] In the case of poultry one speaks of the incubation rather than the gestation period.

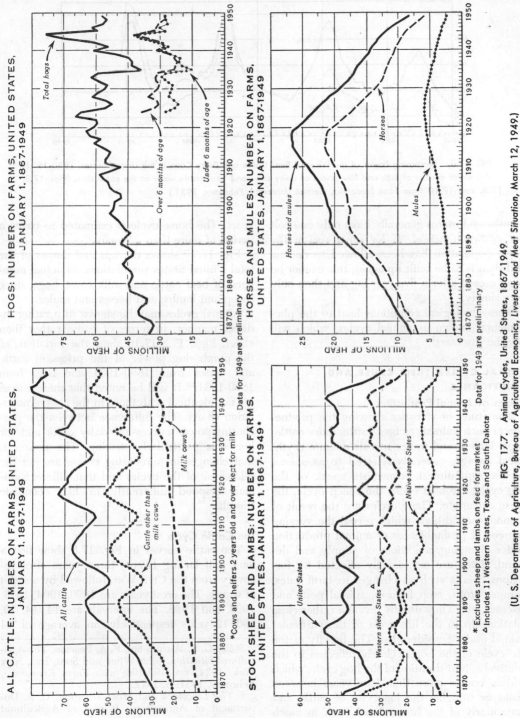

HOGS: NUMBER ON FARMS, UNITED STATES,
JANUARY 1, 1867-1949

Data for 1949 are preliminary

ALL CATTLE: NUMBER ON FARMS, UNITED STATES,
JANUARY 1, 1867-1949

*Cows and heifers 2 years old and over kept for milk   Data for 1949 are preliminary

HORSES AND MULES: NUMBER ON FARMS,
UNITED STATES, JANUARY 1, 1867-1949

Data for 1949 are preliminary

STOCK SHEEP AND LAMBS: NUMBER ON FARMS,
UNITED STATES, JANUARY 1, 1867-1949*

* Excludes sheep and lambs on feed for market
△ Includes 11 Western States, Texas and South Dakota

FIG. 17.7. Animal Cycles, United States, 1867-1949.
(U. S. Department of Agriculture, Bureau of Agricultural Economics, Livestock and Meat Situation, March 12, 1949.)

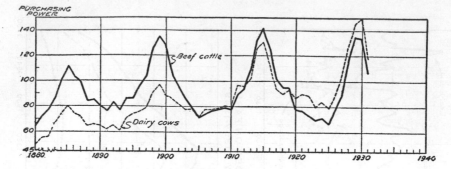

FIG. 17.8. Purchasing Power of the Prices of Beef Cattle and Dairy Cows in the United States, 1880-1931. The major centers of high and low prices of dairy cows and beef cattle occur at the same time. (Figs. 17.8, 17.9, and 17.10 from *Farm Economics*, Cornell University, February, 1931.)

months and mares generally have only one colt per gestation period. If for some reason the horse population has been allowed to decline and then is to be built up again, this cannot be done except after a five-year lag and then only very slowly.

These biological conditions lead to the phenomenon known as animal cycles, which will now be discussed.

ANIMAL CYCLES, THEIR CAUSE AND SIGNIFICANCE

Cycles of Animal Production

The study of statistics showing the production of such animals as beef cattle, dairy cattle, hogs, horses, and mules reveals definite rhythmical swings, generally referred to as animal cycles. Agricultural economists speak of the hog cycle, the beef cycle, the sheep cycle, the horse cycle, etc. These cycles are the result of economic conditions which reveal the varying degrees of profitableness of animal production under changing conditions of supply and demand. They are occasionally affected by fortuitous events such as changes in tariff rates, bumper crops, crop failures, animal pests and diseases, etc. They usually reveal a rather close relationship to the life cycle of the particular animal under consideration. The brevity of the life cycle of the hog is clearly reflected in the relatively short duration of the hog cycle, which seldom covers more than four years between peaks or troughs; the longevity of cattle and particularly of the horse shows itself in much longer swings. The curve of cattle production moves in cycles of an average length of 14

years. The horse cycle is estimated to cover a period of more than 25 years.[31]

Fig. 17.7[32] shows the ups and downs of the total United States populations, in actual numbers, of beef cattle and milk cows, hogs, stock sheep and lambs, and horses and mules.

Animal cycles may be shown in a rather indirect manner, in terms of cause rather than effect. Figs. 17.8-17.10 show the variations of the purchasing power of the prices of cattle and horses from 1880-1931 and hogs from 1860-1931.[33] It will be noted that these curves are not identical with those in the animal population charts. The difference between the purchasing-power curves for dairy cows and for horses is particularly striking. The reason is that changes in purchasing power are not the sole cause of the cycles and that different animals respond differently to like economic stimuli.

The Cattle Cycle

The cattle curves in Fig. 17.8 show first a long pull lasting twenty-three years after recovery from the Civil War, followed by a series of waves. The crest years are 1890, 1904, 1918, 1934, and 1946. The intervals are 14, 14, 16, and 12 years respectively, an average of 14

---

[31] See G. F. Warren and F. A. Pearson, *The Agricultural Situation*, John Wiley and Sons, Inc., New York, 1924, pp. 190-196; also *Farm Economics*, February, 1931, p. 1472.

[32] *The Livestock and Meat Situation*, U. S. Department of Agriculture, Bureau of Agricultural Economics, February, 1949, p. 2.

[33] *Farm Economics*, February, 1931, pp. 1473, 1474, 1477.

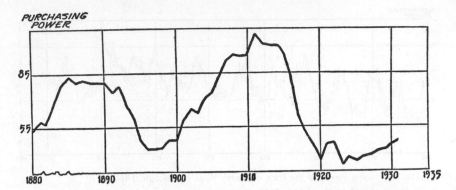

PURCHASING
POWER

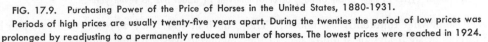

FIG. 17.9. Purchasing Power of the Price of Horses in the United States, 1880-1931.
Periods of high prices are usually twenty-five years apart. During the twenties the period of low prices was
prolonged by readjusting to a permanently reduced number of horses. The lowest prices were reached in 1924.

years. It will be noted that the milk cow population shows no cyclical characteristics, but is marked by an uninterrupted and almost even increase. Only the severe drought of the thirties left a clearly visible dent in the curve. The difference in the curve for beef cattle and for milk cows is accounted for by the slaughter age. Beef cattle are slaughtered when they are an average of 22 months old, but the average age is considerably higher for dairy herds. Moreover, the total number of milk cows is growing considerably faster than the total number of cattle raised mainly for meat. Dual-purpose cattle further complicate the situation. Cyclical changes are accounted for principally by changes in the number of beef cattle, especially where downward adjustments are made.

The Hog Cycle

In the United States corn provides the main feed for hogs. To bring a hog to marketable weight may require the feeding of from 6 to 12 bushels of corn, according to the breed and the diet. The average is about 8 bushels.[34]

Under these circumstances it is natural that the price of corn exercises a strong influence on hog-raising operations. In particular, the hog-corn price ratio, expressed by the number of

bushels of corn which the price of 100 pounds of live hog will buy in the market during the months of September to December, has a strong bearing on the farrowings the following spring. The variations in the hog-corn price ratio derive primarily from changes in the size of the corn crop, but may also be affected by other factors such as the ratio of the corn price to other feed prices.

During the period 1896-1914 the hog-corn price ratio averaged 11.4, meaning that during that period 100 pounds of live hogs sold at an average price which would buy 11.4 bushels of corn. During the period 1924-1947 the ratio ranged from a low of 6.8 in 1934 (drought) to a high of 17.2 in 1938 and 1942. The number of sows farrowed in the spring of 1934 was 5.5 million, as compared with 12.2 and 8.7 million in 1942 and 1938 respectively.

In the final analysis the hog cycle reflects problems of demand anticipation and of general projection of business calculations into the future. As Haas and Ezekiel have bluntly put it: "The basic reason for the continuation of the hog production cycle has been a failure of producers to look ahead. Because corn is high and hogs are cheap *right now* is no reason to conclude that the same situation will hold *next year.*"[35] The same general thought is ex-

---

[34] The ratio of the amount of corn fed to bring a pig to marketable weight is known as the conversion ratio. It refers to actual feeding operations and indicates the number of bushels of corn required to produce a marketable hog of standard weight. See A. E. Taylor, *The Corn and Hog Surplus in the Corn Belt*, Food Research Institute, Stanford University, p. 104.

[35] G. C. Haas and Mordecai Ezekiel, *Factors Affecting the Price of Hogs*, Bulletin No. 1440, U. S. Department of Agriculture, Bureau of Agricultural Economics, 1926, p. 23. See also Geoffrey Shepard, *Controlling Corn and Hog Supplies*, U. S. Department of Agriculture, Technical Bulletin No. 826, 1942.

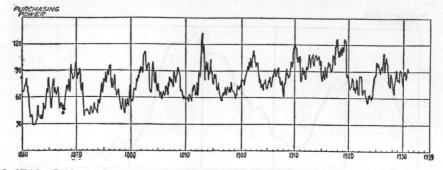

FIG. 17.10. Purchasing Power of the Price of Heavy Hogs at Chicago, 1860-1930.
The major cycles of high prices of hogs occur at intervals of about five to seven years.

pressed somewhat differently as follows: "The bad effects of such lack of stability are, in the last analysis, due to no one person or institution, but to all the producers of hogs collectively. The reason for the existence of these cycles is that it is customary for the majority of producers to react in the same way to business conditions, as they exist at a particular moment. For example, a temporary depression brings about liquidation on a scale too rapid for the subsequent and inevitable period of scarcity and high prices. The result is that scarcity becomes so emphasized in the minds of producers that their actions in stimulating production soon destroy the previously existing favorable price conditions."[36]

The Sheep Cycle

While cattle cycles are moving on the incline, each crest higher than the preceding, while hogs were more numerous at the peak of World War II than they had ever been in the United States, our sheep population reached its zenith in the eighties of the past century—1884 to be exact. At that time there were 51.1 million sheep in this country, a peak almost reached in 1942, when the figure was 49.8 million. Our sheep population is divided into two distinct regional groups, the so-called native and the western flocks. In 1867 there were 37.6 million sheep in the "native sheep states" east of the Mississippi, as against 7.4 million in the western states. In 1886 the two regions stood even, the native flocks having dropped to 22 million and the western flocks having increased to that number. From then on, native flocks declined

[36] *Monthly Letter to Animal Husbandmen*, January, 1928, p. 1.

until in 1947 they were below 10 million head, whereas western sheep numbered 35.2 million. In the east dairying has been the main competitor of sheep raising.

Our sheep industry like the cattle industry needs tariff protection against foreign products, especially wool from the southern hemisphere and beef from Argentina. Changes in tariff rates have a strong influence on the size of sheep flocks. Since wool is a war material of high priority, wars tend to stimulate sheep production. However, in World War II, sheep-raising costs rose so high that, after a short increase, the number of sheep were sharply curtailed.

While a sheep cycle is definitely discernible, the influences acting on the sheep industry are too numerous and diverse for it to show a clear-cut pattern.

The Horse Cycle

The horse cycle is definitely blurred by the secular trend marking the replacement of animate energy by inanimate energy, manifested in the use of tractors instead of horses and mules.

SUMMARY OF FEEDS AND ANIMAL FOODS

The world production of feedstuffs and animal foodstuffs furnishes a good illustration of regional specialization. Four major groups can be distinguished:

1. Countries of the temperate zone producing a surplus of animal foodstuffs.
2. Tropical countries producing a small surplus of animal foodstuffs, but especially oil seeds from which valuable concentrated feedstuffs are obtained.

3. Countries specializing in commercial elaboration, i.e., in the production of highly finished animal foodstuffs for international trade.

4. Deficiency areas, i.e., highly industrialized areas.[37]

The first group comprises Canada, Argentina, Uruguay, Paraguay, the Union of South Africa, southern Chile, southern Australia and New Zealand, and eastern Europe, especially Hungary and the neighboring Danubian countries. These regions differ widely in the contributions which they make. The younger colonial countries export mainly chilled or frozen beef, and mutton and lamb, as well as hides and wool. In addition, New Zealand and parts of Australia and of Canada export dairy products. Some of these regions also export animal feedstuffs. Thus, Argentina and the United States export corn; the United States intermittently exports some cottonseed meal and oil cake; and Argentina exports linseed oil cake. More or less all these countries make occasional shipments of mill feed, inferior grain, and so forth. Hungary and the Danubian countries export primarily feedstuffs, corn, mill feeds, etc. Manchuria normally exports soybeans and soybean cake.

The tropics must be sharply divided on the basis of altitude into highlands and lowlands. More or less all tropical highlands are potential surplus producers of animal foodstuffs; but as yet only Brazil, Venezuela, and Rhodesia have reached a stage in their development which permits them to take advantage of this possibility. The lowland regions function almost exclusively as exporters of vegetable oils and fats which yield concentrated feed as by-products.

In the third group—the elaborating countries —Denmark, Holland, Switzerland, and Ireland rank first; but a coastal section of Finland, southern Sweden (Scania), and northwestern France (Normandy and Brittany) also deserve mention. Their exports take the form of bacon (especially Denmark), condensed milk and chocolate (Switzerland), and dairy products

and higher-grade meats in general. It must be understood that within the industrial countries also there are usually some localities which specialize in such elaboration. Needless to say, the industrial countries are the markets which absorb the surplus products of the various groups.

FUR RESOURCES AND THEIR UTILIZATION

One of the latest developments in the field of animal industries is the farming of fur-bearing animals. For countless ages man depended on the wild life of the forest and the plain for his supply of furs. Two momentous changes have brought about the inadequacy of this natural supply. In the first place, as civilization pushes on, wild animals are deprived of their home and sustenance. Regions once abundant with wild life are now centers of human population. Their appearance has been changed beyond recognition; they have been robbed of their forest cover; cultivated crops have replaced the natural vegetation; streams are polluted, and the shrill noises of civilization disturb the peace. That these changes have drastically affected the supply of fur-bearing animals goes without saying. However, it does not follow that the total available supply has necessarily been reduced, for improved means of transportation and communication have opened up new regions or made possible the more intensive exploitation of sections of the earth formerly exploited only extensively or sporadically.

The second great change has come about on the demand side. Among many savages and primitive peoples, skins are common necessities. In sparsely populated regions the supply of skin- or fur-bearing animals is generally adequate; but in the densely populated countries of advanced civilization good furs are usually rare and, therefore, the highly valued possession of a small minority. Moreover, they generally were recognized as symbols of social distinction, and their use has at times often been regulated by custom if not by law. When, with the rise of democracy, feudal privileges, class distinctions, and social prerogatives were abolished, the right to wear fur became merely a question of purchasing power. With rising standards of living, ever larger sections of the population wore furs, and their use became almost universal. Styles decreed the use of fur

[37] Cf. E. W. Shanahan, *Animal Foodstuffs, Their Production and Consumption; with Special Reference to the British Empire*, E. P. Dutton & Co., Inc., New York, 1921, especially p. 27.

trimming, with the result that the consumption of textile raw materials, especially wool, decreased. The increase in the demand for fur was most pronounced in the United States, the country which witnessed both the widest spread of democracy and the most rapid increase in the purchasing power of the masses.

This development resulted in an unheard-of pressure on the available supply of furs, and brought about a number of changes in fur resources and their utilization. In the first place, the quest for fur-bearing animals was pushed with relentless vigor into the remotest and least accessible corners of the earth. This expansion, however, failed to bridge the widening gap between supply and demand. It was materially narrowed by two rather ingenious improvements by which the fur trade and the fur manufacturing industries succeeded in diluting the supply. One was the inclusion in the list of commercial furs of new species of fur-bearing animals, such as the kangaroo, "wombat," the South American chinchilla, and many others. The other was the progress made in the art of dyeing and otherwise manipulating furs. The trade learned to make remarkably clever imitations of rare, and therefore costly, furs. Even cats and dogs have been enlisted to furnish raw materials for an industry which cannot afford to miss a single trick if the well-nigh insatiable demand in times of prosperity is to be met. Fortunately for the rich connoisseur, a few rare furs are left which cannot be imitated.

Another measure, although designed to protect rather than to enlarge the existing fur supply, is the proper care of herds through legal control. The best-known example of this is the Fur Seal Convention of 1911. This international agreement, which was signed by the United States, Great Britain, Japan, and Russia, furnishes protection to the fur industry on the Pribilof Islands, about 300 miles off the coast of Alaska in the Bering Sea. These small islands are the breeding grounds of the North American or Alaska fur seal herd.[38] This agreement resulted in an increase of the herd from a little over 200,000 seals in 1912 to almost a million in 1929.[39]

Measured in its effect on numbers, fur farming is probably the most fruitful effort which has been made toward enlarging the supply of furs. As the craze for furs spread, it was soon realized that many of the more valuable fur animals had almost disappeared from our forests and streams. Only the skunk, muskrat, opossum, and raccoon were left in considerable numbers in this country, particularly in the Mississippi Valley states. Fortunately, the possibilities of raising fur animals in captivity have been demonstrated to be considerable and the fur farming industry in this country is now on a fairly substantial basis, representing an investment of many million dollars in the United States alone. The industry owes much of its success to the early practices of the Indian and pioneer trappers who controlled propagation for the sake of improving the furs. Science came to the rescue with the discovery that the silver color in foxes is a Mendelian recessive trait, and that therefore a silver fox, being of a recessive color, always breeds true. As a result, fox farming spread, to be followed soon by muskrat farming. In fox farming the animals are penned and fed and handled in every respect like ordinary domestic stock, but muskrats remain in their natural marshland habitat, merely being protected against animal and human enemies. It has been clearly demonstrated that the beaver, the raccoon, the skunk, the chinchilla, the karakul sheep, and other fur-bearing animals can also be grown profitably in captivity; and the industry is spreading not only in North America but also in Europe.

In summary it can be said that the part the animal plays in human life varies with each change of civilization. At first the primary source of food and valued for its skin or fur, the animal was later used as a source of energy, i.e., as a draft and work animal. Industrial countries tend to rely increasingly on inanimate energy; their growing wealth invests animals with new values as providers of luxuries and delicacies. Animal resources are thus another valuable illustration of the functional nature of resources.

---

[38] Fur seals should not be confused with common hair seals which are widely distributed throughout the world.

[39] For further details, see *Fur Resources of the United States*, a special report to supplement the exhibit of the United States government at the International Fur Trade Exhibition, Leipzig, Germany, 1930, pp. 33–43.

BIBLIOGRAPHY

Bennett, M. K., *Animal Products in National Diets* (reprint of paper), Stanford University, Food Research Institute, 1950.

Black, J. D., *The Dairy Industry and the A.A.A.*, Washington, Brookings Institution, 1935.

Cassels, J. M., *A Study of Fluid Milk Prices*, Cambridge, Harvard University Press, 1937.

Crickman, C. W., *Feed Grains and Meat Animals in War and Peace*, U. S. Department of Agriculture, Bureau of Agricultural Economics, Washington, 1945.

Dirlam, J. B., *The Fluid Milk Industry*, in Adams, W. (ed.), *The Structure of American Industry*, New York, Macmillan, 1950, chap. 9.

Fitzgerald, D. A., *Livestock and the A.A.A.*, Washington, Brookings Institution, 1935.

International Institute of Agriculture, *Studies of the Principal Agricultural Products on the World Market*, No. 2 *Meat*, No. 3 *International Trade in Meat*, Rome, 1936.

Malott, D., and Martin, B. F., *The Agricultural Industries*, New York, McGraw-Hill, 1939, chaps. 2, 3.

Mann, L. B., *Western Cattle and Sheep Areas*, Farm Credit Administration, Circular No. C-103, Washington, 1936.

Moulton, C. R., *The Animal as a Converter of Matter and Energy*, New York, Chemical Catalogue Co., 1925.

Shanahan, E. W., *Animal Foodstuffs, Their Production and Consumption, with Special Reference to the British Empire*, New York, Dutton, 1921.

Shepard, G., *Controlling Corn and Hog Supplies*, U. S. Department of Agriculture, Technical Bulletin No. 826, Washington, 1942.

Taylor, A. E., *Corn and the Hog Surplus of the Corn Belt*, Stanford University, Food Research Institute, 1932.

United Nations, Food and Agriculture Organization, *Livestock Products Review*, 1947.

U. S. Senate, 74th Congress, 2nd session, *The Western Range*, Document No. 199, Washington, 1936.

UNIT 3. FIBERS

Chapter 18

FIBERS—WHERE "THE KINGDOMS" MEET

FIBERS AND FOODS: A STUDY IN CONTRASTS

Compared with the production of foodstuffs and feedstuffs, all other branches of agriculture appear dwarfed. This is true whether the comparison takes into account acreage, volume, and value of output, or the number of people engaged in production. Against the gigantic task of providing one meal—preferably several meals—a day for between 2 and 2.5 billion people, other things seem almost picayune. No human need approaches the need for food in imperative urgency and unrelenting recurrence.

Among the items constituting nonfood agriculture, the production of fibers looms largest and most important. Food, clothing, and shelter are customarily listed as primary needs in that order. Fibers furnish the raw material for most clothing and help furnish the home. Besides, they serve numerous purposes in industry, transport, and even agriculture itself.

A multiple link ties fibers to food production. In the first place, fibers play a vital part in the food economy. They furnish binder twine used in harvesting grain, nets to catch fish, bags to transport wheat, coffee, sugar, and other food crops, ropes with which to haul, and material

for many other services. In the second place, genetically speaking, foodstuffs and fibers have many points of contact. The cotton plant furnishes both the premier fiber and an important edible fat, sheep furnish both wool and meat, the coconut palm furnishes both coir fiber and valuable food, and so forth. Finally there is a definite interrelation between the need for food and the need for clothing. It is in the nature of an inverse correlation. The more warmth the body retains through adequate clothing, the less heat needs to be supplied by food, and vice versa.

Textiles made from fibers generally rank second after food among consumers' expenditures. As is true in the case of food, so also in the case of fibers the agricultural raw material is heavily overlain, as it were, with form, place, and time utilities that accrue on the way from the crop on the farm or ranch to the meal on the table, both in the home and outside, and to the finished suit in the clothing store or the drapery in the living room. This pyramiding of both services and materials on top of the original farm product reaches its greatest height in the case of luxury goods.

As was previously pointed out, not all food is produced by agricultural methods. Whale oil, an important ingredient of margarine, alongside of cottonseed oil, coconut oil, soybean oil, etc., is not a product of agriculture. Neither is fish in most cases, nor game and wild fruit. While agricultural food production is thus supplemented by collecting products of nature from land and sea, the agricultural producer of fibers faces his most formidable rival in modern machine industry that turns out rayon, nylon, aralac, or any one of the lengthening list of man-made fibers. Here again a certain tie-in may be observed. Thus, some rayon is made from cotton linters; aralac, from casein derived from milk.

Structurally the demand for food differs considerably from the consumer demand for textile fibers. Food disappears in consumption. Each meal calls for a renewal of the supply, as it were. Compared with food, clothing is definitely durable and household goods are perhaps even more so. Hunger permits but little postponement in want satisfaction. The decision to buy a new suit or a new dress or to redecorate the home can be postponed, if need be, for years.

Moreover, all of us must eat; the physiological need for food is universal. But not all people need to wear clothes, and countless millions live in "homes" containing not one ounce of fiber or fiber derivatives. Climate exercises a far more decisive influence on fiber consumption than it does on food consumption. The spread between the best-dressed Beau Brummel and the poorest-clad beggar—or the naked savage for that matter—is far greater than that between the best-fed gourmand and the starving urchin. Per capita food consumption of nations, as was previously shown, ranges from a little under 2000 calories to somewhat over 3000, the best-fed nation consuming on the average less than twice as much as the poorest-fed nation.[1] On the other hand, even if the naked savage is entirely left out of the picture, differences in fiber consumption between the richest and poorest countries run as high as 9 to 1 or even 10 to 1.

Fiber consumption shows a remarkably close correlation with income or purchasing power or standard of living. This correlation is evident whether the same group is observed at different periods of varying income levels or whether different social groups—nations, income groups, etc.—are compared at the same time.

In the United States the average amount spent for clothing increases more rapidly with increasing income than do the amounts spent for food, housing, and household operation. In the late thirties, clothing expenditures made up about 7.5 percent of the total expenditures of people in the income class under $5000. The percentage was double (and the absolute amount eight times as great) for the income class of $20,000 and over.[2]

The sensitivity of clothing expenditures to changes in total income reflects the postponability and the partial dispensability of clothing purchases as well as the price range within which diverse-quality materials and finished products may be purchased. This sensitivity is by no means uniform. Both rigid traditions, such as wearing a black suit at a funeral or a white dress at a wedding, and customs and social attitudes may modify it considerably. Such considerations played a great part in feudal societies and remain important wherever caste survives. Democratic ideas and the rising importance of fashions affect this sensitivity in various ways. For example, the wish to be fashionable is a potent factor in the determination of clothing expenditures.

To a considerable extent, people adjust their food habits to the productive capacities of their country or the region in which they live.[3] Monsoon Asia is uniquely capable of producing rice and her inhabitants are rice eaters. Corn does very well in large parts of North America and her inhabitants manage to make good use of it, mostly in indirect ways via hogs, beef cattle, dairy cows, etc. Northern Europe builds her diet around the potato and its derivatives. The Hawaiian depends on his taro and the South Sea Islander on coconut and fish. And so on.

---

[1] In this case, roughly in terms of calorie intake.

[2] National Resources Committee, *Consumer Expenditures in the U.S.A.*, Washington, 1939, p. 25.

[3] See Karl Brandt, "Foodstuffs and Raw Materials," chap. 5 of *War in Our Time*, W. W. Norton and Co., New York, 1939, p. 106. "Fortunately peoples have developed their diets in conformity with their environments and their ability to secure supplies."

Moreover, not only do people adjust their diets to regional productive capacities but, by and large, they grow and multiply where the food supply is ample and expansible; they tend to stagnate when the limits of food production have been reached. In short, it may be said generally that in regard to food man shows an unusual willingness to adapt his wants to the whims of nature. This can hardly be surprising if one considers (1) the enormous quantities required to sustain a person or family and the saving that results from dependence on nearby sources of supply, (2) the perishability of some foodstuffs, (3) the possibility of concocting fully adequate diets out of highly diverse combinations of foodstuffs, and (4) the subjective and changeable nature of the taste for different foods. The result is that foodstuffs do not play in international trade a part anywhere nearly approaching the importance of their role in the general scheme of things.

The situation is wholly different in the case of fibers. In the first place, the production of fibers is even more rigidly regionalized than is the production of foodstuffs. Cotton, the leading fiber in the world, is produced in many countries, but four countries supply over 80 percent. Similarly, wool is produced over wide areas, but five countries supply the bulk of apparel wool. Many fiber-yielding plants are even more restricted in their habitat. Thus jute production is largely concentrated in a small area of Bengal, that of abacá in sections of the Philippine Islands, of henequen in Yucatán, of sisal in British East Africa, of silk in Japan and China, and so on down the line. Fiber plants seem to be more selective in their environmental requirements than foodstuffs. Perhaps man, needing food more urgently than fibers, pushed the quest of suitable habitats more vigorously in the case of foodstuffs than he did in the case of fibers. Moreover, in many densely populated parts of the earth the land cannot be spared from food production even if it can produce excellent fiber crops.

Similarly, on the demand side, one notes much stronger insistence on particular fibers for particular uses than is generally true of foodstuffs. Wearing apparel such as suits and dresses is made almost exclusively from cotton, rayon, and wool, the first two being dominant in warm countries and wool in colder countries.

In western countries, most hosiery and undergarments are made from rayon, nylon, or silk. Jute goes mainly into bagging, abacá into rope, sisal and henequen into twine, hemp into cordage. To be sure, a certain amount of substitution is possible, but it is far more limited than is true of foodstuffs.

The combined result of these two facts—regional concentration of fiber production and limited substitutability—is that fibers play an exceptionally great part in international trade. The aggregate value of world cotton exports frequently exceeds that of wheat exports. Wool exports rank very high on the lists of raw-material exports and fibers as a group constitute the largest single item among agricultural raw-material exports. Many fibers are produced in agricultural countries but consumed in industrial countries either because of the high per capita purchasing power characteristic of industrial countries or because the fibers serve industrial needs. The industries that prepare raw fibers for consumption are concentrated in industrial countries.

Table 18.1 shows the high degree of geographical concentration of the production of major fibers for the world market.

TABLE 18.1. Shipments of Fibers from the Chief Exporting Countries as Percentages of World Exports, 1934-1938 Averages[4]

Fiber	Chief Exporting Countries	Percentage of World Exports
Cotton	United States, India, Egypt, Brazil	84
Wool	Australia, Argentina, New Zealand, South Africa	80
Silk	Japan	77
Flax	U.S.S.R., Belgium	54
Jute	India	98
Abacá	Philippine Republic	95
Sisal	British East Africa	50
Henequen	Mexico	92

CLASSIFICATION OF FIBERS

In order to understand why the production of a given fiber is geographically concentrated, it is necessary to analyze more fully how fibers are produced, what their properties are, and to what uses they are put. This analysis calls,

[4] Tables 18.1 and 18.2 from Food and Agriculture Organization, *World Fiber Survey*, 1947, p. 6.

TABLE 18.2. Natural Fibers

		Vegetable Fibers			Animal Fibers	
Seed	Bast	Leaf	Fruit Husk	Whole Parts of Plant	Wool and Hair	Excretion
Cotton	Jute	Abacá	Coir	Rattan	Sheep's wool	Silk
Kapok	Flax	Sisal		Spanish moss	Hair of	
	Hemp	Henequen			Camel	
	Ramie	Istle			Alpaca	
	Sunn	Cantala			Llama	
	Meshta	Garoa			Vicuna	
	Urena	Phormium tenax			Goat	
		Palm leaf fibers			Rabbit	
					Horse	
					Cattle	

first of all, for a classification of fibers on the basis of origin.

Fibers fall into two main classes: natural fibers and man-made or artificial fibers. Table 18.2 shows a classification of the most important natural fibers.

Generally speaking, seed and bast fibers are soft fibers and leaf and fruit husk fibers are hard fibers. Most soft fibers can be spun and woven; most hard fibers go into cordage, rope, twine, upholstery, and similar articles. Kapok cannot compete with cotton as a textile fiber but, because of its resistance to water, finds special applications. Among animal fibers, wool and silk are most widely used as textile fibers, but fine textures can also be achieved with camel, vicuna, and goat hair (mohair).

Fig. 18.1 shows the classification of man-made fibers. It will be noted that three chief groups are distinguished: regenerated natural polymers,[5] mineral base fibers, and synthesized polymers. In the early stages of the synthetic fiber industry the first group was by far the most important. The natural polymers most widely used at present for "regeneration" are wood pulp and cotton linters, both being desired for their alpha cellulose[6] content. As yet,

the rayons are by far the most important group of regenerated natural polymers and, as the figure indicates, all of them are derived from cellulose or from cellulose esters or ethers. The others in the group make a good showing in terms of diversity of source—clam shells, seaweed, milk, eggs, feathers, soybeans, peanuts, corn—but as yet they are not too important quantitatively.

Among the synthesized polymers, i.e., polymers built up by man from building blocks similar to or like the ones used by nature, nylon at present is by far the most important. Of the mineral fibers, glass fiber has had a phenomenal career of late.[7]

In terms of main uses the most important fibers may be divided into two groups: (1) Apparel and household fibers: cotton, wool, silk, flax, rayon filament and staple,[8] nylon. (2) Industrial fibers: hemp, jute, abacá, sisal, henequen.

Economic Implications

This genetic classification of fibers into vegetable and animal, natural and artificial is more than a mere exercise in taxonomy. It has economic implications of far-reaching importance.

[5] A polymer is a large complex molecule.

[6] "Alpha or resistant cellulose is that portion which is not dissolved by treating pulp or linters with 17½ percent caustic soda at room temperature for 30 minutes. Cellulose from cotton linters has an alpha content which averages over 98 percent in the purified state. Wood pulp manufacturers have succeeded in making highly purified rayon pulp with an average alpha content of 90-91 per-

cent which is adequate for its intended use. A few super-purified sulphite wood pulps have also been developed with alpha contents running as high as 98 percent. The alpha cellulose content from wood pulp can be increased but only at a considerable increase in cost." FAO, op. cit., p. 154.

[7] "Class Now and Tomorrow," Fortune, March, 1943, pp. 123 ff.

[8] See the discussion of the rayon industry.

MAN-MADE FIBERS

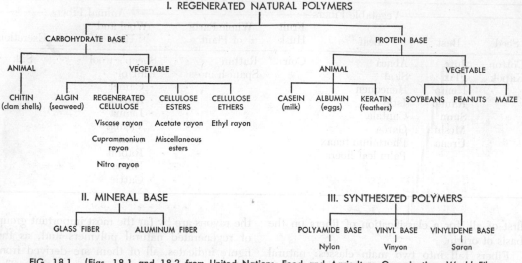

FIG. 18.1. (Figs. 18.1 and 18.2 from United Nations, Food and Agriculture Organization, *World Fiber Survey*, 1947.)

It so happens that, throughout the world as a whole, the production of vegetable fibers, with few exceptions, requires labor—in fact, a great deal of labor. There is cotton with its almost insatiable demand for labor for the cultivation of the young plant ("chopping") and especially for picking. All the bast fibers require lots of labor more or less all along the line, but especially in processing the fiber preparatory to spinning and weaving. This is not surprising in view of the nature of bast fiber. Bast fibers are tubes lined with woody substances on the inside and surrounded by woody substances on the outside. Bast, then, is the middle of three layers. These three layers are held firmly together by gluey substances. To separate this middle layer is a tremendous task which, in the absence of successful machine processes, requires endless and often backbreaking labor under most trying conditions. As will be shown later, in specific instances progress has been and is being made in the mechanization of these processes. Similarly, the removal of fibers from leaves—abacá, sisal, henequen, etc.—is being mechanized to some extent. But even so, a great deal of labor is still required in connection with harvesting, feeding leaves to crushers, and so on. In short, one could go almost so far as to call vegetable fibers *labor fibers*, suggesting by the term that

labor constitutes the chief bottleneck to expansion or that an adequate supply of labor is the *sine qua non* of their successful production.

The situation as regards animal fibers is quite different though not quite so clear-cut. By far the most important fiber-bearing animal is the sheep. Sheep are produced in conjunction with farming or on a ranch or range basis. The largest number of wool sheep are produced by the latter method. Although the care of flocks and shearing require labor, it is land, vast stretches of cheap land, which constitutes the main basis of a successful wool-producing enterprise. Wool, therefore, may rightly be called a *land fiber*. This term also fits other animal fibers more or less, with the exception of silk.

Silk most definitely is a *labor fiber*. The intensive cultivation of the mulberry bushes which supply the feed for the silkworms requires very large amounts of labor. The care of the silkworm requires even more. The final step, reeling the silk from the cocoons, is one of the most tedious tasks performed by human labor.

The production of artificial or man-made fibers rests primarily on *capital* in the form of scientific knowledge, "know-how," machines, laboratory equipment, etc. One might rightly refer to them as *capital fibers*.

Thus the genetic classification of fibers has

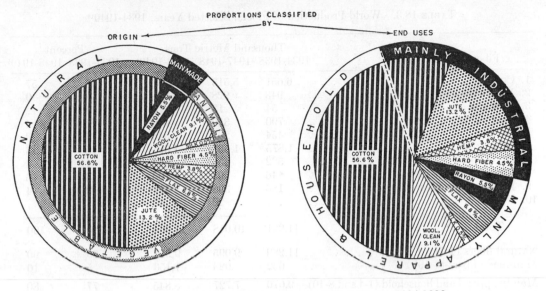

FIG. 18.2. World Production of Major Fibers and Fiber Groups, 1934-1938.

definite economic implications; it suggests which of the three production agents—land, labor, and capital—is the most vital in the production of specific fibers. This economic implication, in turn, permits further deductions. It goes far to explain where different fibers are produced.

Wherever cotton is produced successfully, exclusive of the areas in which mechanization has been introduced, one finds plenty of labor.[9] If sufficient labor was not there to start with, it was brought in. Where labor is scarce, cotton culture will remain a precarious venture until mechanization is introduced and the necessary capital equipment provided. The plethora of labor in our own South is in part a hand-down from slavery days, in part an aftermath of the Civil War which turned many farmers into so-called poor whites and gave rise to tenancy and sharecropping. The Nile valley is teeming with humanity, so are India and China. The government of the U.S.S.R. can direct labor where it is needed—to the irrigated cotton fields of Turkestan and Uzbekistan if that seems desirable. In Brazil, immigrants and coffee plan-

tation labor are available. In Peru it is the peon. Wherever cotton is produced by hand methods, there *must* be abundant cheap labor.

Jute, by far the most important bast fiber in terms of quantity produced, is unthinkable without the lowly Hindu ryot toiling endless hours for low returns, standing ankle-deep in mud under the blazing sun of the tropics. Flax grown for fiber is at home where rural population density is high and opportunities to grow other crops are sharply limited. Ramie or China grass, if anything, is even more dependent on labor than the other basts. The following quotation drives home the truth of this statement:

The pith and bark of the stalks must be separated from the fiber by a process called "stripping," which is merely the ripping of the bark and fiber from the pith, and is quickly done. Most of the labor is involved in the scraping process.

Before scraping, the stripped ribbons are soaked in water from two to three hours. Then three or four strips of peel are laid on a board at one time. The strips are scraped a few times on the inner side from bulb to point and then turned over and scraped on the outer side. The scraping removes the bark and pith and is done with dull steel or bamboo knives. After scraping, the fiber is dried and then done up in 40-pound bales. These bales constitute the finished China-grass fiber product handled by the native Chinese.

One laborer can strip from 10 to 13 pounds per

---

[9] There is increasing evidence that, at least in the semi-arid West of the United States, the mechanical revolution is extending more and more to cultivation. This point will be discussed more fully in the next chapter.

TABLE 18.3. World Production of Fibers, Selected Years, 1934-1949[10]

| Fiber or Fiber Group[a] | Thousand Metric Tons | | | Percent | |
	1934-1938	1947-1948	1948-1949[b]	1934-1938	1948-1949[b]
1. Cotton	6,651	5,513	6,281	56	57
2. Wool (clean)	943	928	948	8	9
3. Raw silk	54	13	13	1	...
4. Flax	790	350	450	7	4
5. Hemp	454	267	345	4	3
6. Jute	1,875	1,568	1,391	15	13
7. Hard fibers[c]	522	456	483	4	4
8. Rayon filament yarn	446	595	706	3	6
9. Rayon staple fiber	186	308	417	2	4
10. Nylon[d]	...	20	30	...	...
Total	11,921	10,018	11,064	100	100
Natural fibers (1-7)	11,289	9,095	9,911	95	90
Man-made fibers (8-10)	632	923	1,153	5	10
Mainly apparel and household (1-4 and 8-10)	9,070	7,727	8,845	77	80
Mainly industrial (5-7)	2,851	2,291	2,219	23	20

[a] Data for cotton, wool, and jute relate to production seasons; those for silk, flax, hemp, hard fibers, rayon, and nylon to calendar years.
[b] Preliminary figures.
[c] Abacá, sisal, and henequen.
[d] Approximate estimates.

day, but can scrape only 2 to 6½ pounds of fiber per day.[11]

And so on down the line. Kapok in Java, sisal in Indonesia, abacá in the Philippines, henequen in Yucatán—the theme is the same, though its development varies in each case. The color of the laborer's skin may differ, the methods of production may vary, but the leitmotif never changes—abundant and cheap labor.

Similarly, the geographical distribution of the production of animal fiber can be explained in terms of abundance of cheap land. It is not true—in fact, it would be wrong to imply—that abundance of one agent of production is the sole requirement for success. Other elements must help. But the explanation of success can well be built around a single factor.

Where do we find rayon and nylon mills? The answer is simple. Where capital resources are sufficient to support such mills. However, an important difference between labor and land, on the one hand, and capital, on the other, must be noted. Land is immobile. In general, labor too prefers or is compelled to remain in its wonted habitat. If the owner of a rayon mill gets tired of what he considers uncalled-for labor domination in Country A, he may conceivably move the mill—lock, stock, and barrel—by means of freight cars, trucks, planes, or ships, to a place where he thinks labor and perhaps market conditions are better. But this is rare. What is not rare, however, is the practice of capitalists in one country erecting rayon mills in other countries. Capital-fiber industries, therefore, do not tend to be as rigidly regionalized as labor- or land-fiber industries. Labor-fiber production thrives where there is abundant labor. Land-fiber production thrives where there is abundant land. But capital-fiber production thrives either where capital is or where the capitalist wants to put it.

RELATIVE IMPORTANCE OF FIBERS

Fibers differ widely in relative importance in terms of both quantity produced and value of output. The position of the most important fibers at selected intervals from 1909-1948 is shown in Figs. 18.2 and 18.3. In Fig. 18.2, the fibers are arranged on the basis of both origin

[10] FAO, *Fibers*, Commodity Series Bulletin No. 14, August, 1949, p. 3.
[11] J. F. Gillen and J. O. Hayes, *Ramie or China Grass*, U. S. Department of Commerce, Trade Information Bulletin No. 166, p. 4.

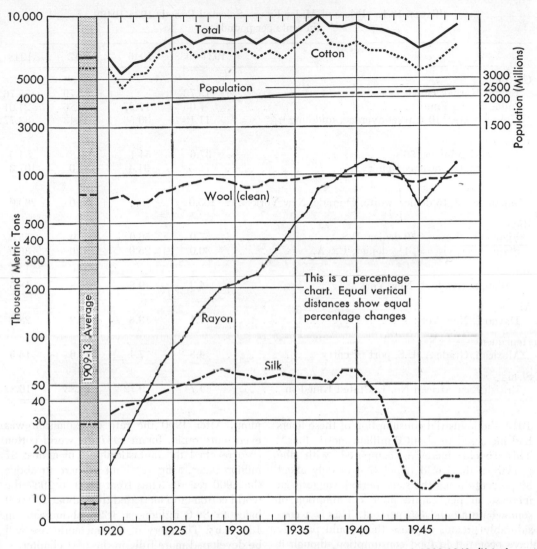

FIG. 18.3.   World Production of Major Apparel Fibers, 1909-1913 average, and 1920-1948. (United Nations, Food and Agriculture Organization, Commodity Series, *Fibers*, Bulletin No. 14, August, 1949, p. 7.)

and chief end uses. Fig. 18.3 shows the shifts in the relative position of the different fibers; in particular, the meteoric rise of rayon and the equally meteoric decline of silk are clearly brought out. Production figures both before and after World War II are given in Table 18.3.

The relative position of these fibers in terms of value is naturally quite different. How great this difference is may be deduced roughly from Table 18.4, which lists prices of some of the fibers for the five-year period 1934-1938 and the years 1946, 1947, and 1948.

PRODUCTION AND PRICE TRENDS

These quantitative and price relationships are not constant, but subject to drastic changes. The relative importance of textile fibers in terms of world output has shifted violently during the past 150 years. For one thing, there has been a very large increase in fiber production. Although our knowledge of the field is limited, it is estimated that in 1800 the world's textile industries used just over 1 million metric tons of wool, flax, and cotton. This is in addition to the unknown quantity used in homes. By 1909-

TABLE 18.4.   Prices of Major Fibers, Selected Periods 1934-1948[12]
(in cents per pound)

	1934-1938	1946	1947	1948
Cotton				
Egypt, Karnak Good	15.73	. . .	37.79	75.76
India, Jarilla Fine	7.05	17.27	16.86	24.01
United States, 10-market average, middling $^{15}\!/_{16}''$ . . .	11.18	30.56	34.43	33.77
Wool (clean basis)				
British Dominions, 56's	37.6	54.1	66.8	84.5
United States, 56's, combing	72.5	91.4	107.0	107.3
Silk				
Japanese, 13/15 denier, white, D grade, New York . .	165.0	. . .	455.0	260.0
Rayon				
Filament, viscose, 150 denier, U.S.A.	57.0	56.0	67.0	75.0
Staple fiber, viscose, 1½ denier, U.S.A.	30.0	25.0	32.0	36.0
Jute				
Indian, native first, New York	4.3	9.8	15.8	18.5
Abacá				
Davao I, New York	7.1	13.8	24.2	28.1
Henequen				
Mexican, Grade A, U.S. port of entry	4.8	7.4	14.6	15.5
Sisal				
British East African No. 1, United Kingdom	4.74	9.72	13.83	16.82

1913, the industrial consumption of these fibers had increased to about 6 million metric tons.[13] This sixfold increase, compared with the growth in the world population of only about 80 percent during the same period, suggests an increase in per capita fiber consumption of somewhere around 3.5 percent. This is a considerably greater increase than could possibly have occurred in food consumption, though it is dwarfed by the increase in mineral consumption (see p. 425).

It is believed that, at the end of the eighteenth century, wool provided the bulk, probably around 78 percent, of textile raw materials —at least in the West—with flax a poor second, with around 18 percent, and cotton bringing up the rear, with only 4 percent. Then followed the meteoric rise of cotton to first place among the fibers—a rise which lifted cotton production from about 200,000 bales in 1800 to about 20 million bales a century later, a hundredfold

[12] *Ibid.*, pp. 100-102.
For footnotes and further details, see source.
[13] See FAO, *World Fiber Survey,* 1947, p. 7.

jump. After 1900 the rate of expansion was even more rapid, for in 1937 the world cotton crop reached the fantastic figure of almost 37 million bales, a figure about 83 percent above the 1900 record. Thus from 1800 to 1937 the world cotton crop increased from about 200,000 bales to 36.6 million, a 183-fold increase in 138 years. The story of this meteoric rise will be developed more fully in the next chapter.

But cotton was not the only miracle worker. The opening up of the southern hemisphere and the invention of refrigeration made available to the woolen and worsted industries of the West vastly larger supplies of wool. Perhaps most spectacular is the story of rayon, which between 1909-1913 and 1939-1943 managed to widen its wedge into the world fiber supply from a bare 0.2 percent to 13.9 percent. Then rayon was followed by nylon, and nylon by orlon. And there is no reason to believe that the triumphal march of man-made fibers, products of science, has come to a halt, or soon will.

Rayon's gain was a loss for silk. Stagnating

from 1929 to 1940 while rayon climbed to dizzy heights, silk was practically eliminated by World War II. The wartime dip in rayon production is unquestionably merely an episode in a brilliant career that has by no means reached its zenith. The outlook for silk is dark.

BIBLIOGRAPHY

"Glass Now and Tomorrow," *Fortune*, March, 1943.

National Bureau of Economic Research, *Textile Markets*, New York, 1939.

United Nations, Food and Agriculture Organization, *World Fiber Survey*, Washington, 1947.

Weindling, L., *Long Vegetable Fibers. Manila, Sisal, Jute, Flax and Related Fibers of Commerce*, New York, Columbia University Press, 1947.

Chapter 19

COTTON

COTTON'S METEORIC CAREER

Although hard pressed by upstart rivals such as rayon and nylon and afflicted with manifold difficulties of its own, cotton is still the world's leading fiber. In terms of weight, it still constitutes over half of all fiber and almost three-fourths of all apparel fiber production in the world.

Cotton's career as the world's premier fiber was indeed meteoric. From modest figures attained after eighteen centuries or more of slow upward plodding, world production increased by leaps and bounds until in 1937 it reached what for long may remain its peak, a crop of 36,615,000 bales (of 478 pounds net weight per bale), or almost 18.5 billion pounds—over 7 pounds for every man, woman, and child on this planet! Even the five-year average for 1934-1938 approached 30 million bales, or over 15 billion pounds. Jute, its nearest rival, only once passed the 5-billion-pound mark; its output usually ranges around 3 or 4 billion pounds. Furthermore, jute is cheap stuff, not an apparel fiber. Other fibers, such as wool, flax, hemp, and rayon, are left far behind.

That a tiny fiber ranging from less than half an inch to seldom over two inches in length[1] should reach such stature is a miracle indeed. Flax, hemp, jute—all the bast fibers—are much longer; they range from 2 to 9 feet in length. Spinning fibers of such length into a thread is obviously not beset with the difficulties inherent in spinning an even, strong thread from the tiny cotton fibers. Indeed, cotton could never have aspired to world leadership, perhaps not even to commercial importance, had not both nature and man performed miracles which endowed it with great utility and value.

Nature performs her miracle in the cotton plant, in the ripe boll, as the fruit pod is called, where the seeds lie softly embedded in the rich white plant hair. This plant hair, while still fed by the sap that circulates through the plant, resembles a blown-up rubber tube. After the plant has reached maturity, the sap recedes, whereupon the tubular plant hair collapses into a flat ribbon with a twist or "kink." And this ribbon, precisely because it is *flat* and has a *twist,* is as spinnable as other fibers many times its length.

---

[1] The actual range is from ¼ inch to 2½ inches, the latter being Sea Island cotton.

Men in the earliest recorded times learned to spin this tiny plant hair into thread. At first the thread was coarse, but eventually the spinner's skill reached such heights that threads of incredible fineness were spun.

For many centuries the use of cotton was largely confined to tropical countries. Its real success, however, came after the West had not only adapted cotton for its own use but usurped world leadership in its manufacture and in the trade in its finished products. It was western ingenuity, drive, and purchasing power which gave cotton its global significance as a major item of world commerce.

The cotton plant is native to many parts of the tropics and subtropics. There are many species and innumerable varieties. Some cotton in the tropics grows on perennial shrubs with woody stems which reach such heights that one speaks of tree cotton. More often, it is a much smaller annual plant. One species has slick seeds which are easily removed from the lint, as the plant hair is called. In another the seed is covered with a fuzzy growth called linters. The removal of these so-called green seeds from the lint is so difficult that it was more or less impractical until Eli Whitney in 1793 invented the modern saw gin—another miracle without which cotton might never have become king.

Until then only the slick seed cotton was cultivated on a large scale. The history of cotton up to the Industrial Revolution was written mainly by the variety grown mostly in India and other oriental countries. The supply was sufficient to meet the demand, which at that time was limited largely to tropical countries and the international luxury trade. But with the coming of the Industrial Revolution, when the white race overflowed to all parts of the earth and the Occident attained global dominion and unprecedented wealth, the linen and wool which, together with silk and leather, had long filled Europe's apparel needs, could no longer supply the growing demand. A newcomer was sorely needed, and cotton entered the picture.

At first only weak cotton threads could be spun on machines, threads too weak for use as warp[2] in woven fabrics and hence relegated to use as woof or weft. But with the invention of the "water frame,"[3] cotton attained its manhood; and when Whitney's cotton gin opened the bottleneck that had kept the production of green seed cotton down to negligible quantities, the stage was set for the New World to become the leading purveyor of raw cotton to the modern textile industry.

Cotton growing as it has developed since 1800 is truly the child of the Industrial Revolution. Not only did power-driven machinery make cheaper the production of cotton goods and progress in chemistry make possible revolutionary improvements in bleaching and finishing, but machine industry also furnished the instruments of world trade. It also made possible, or at least contributed to, important irrigation works such as the Aswan dam across the Nile in Egypt and the Sukur barrage across the Indus in India. Finally it supported an increase in the world's population, especially rapid in the case of the white race, and a rise in living standards which go far to account for the phenomenal growth of cotton culture.

Cotton culture expanded because it was profitable. It was profitable because conditions created by the Industrial Revolution made it so. And now that cotton culture in the leading producing country, the United States, is facing grave difficulties, it is again the power-driven machine and science which hold out the best hope of salvation. In the meantime, although cotton culture owes its rise to industry, its methods, on the whole, still remain extremely primitive. Production is still based on human labor, little aided by science and machine technology, except in certain areas and until recent years. Primitive methods mean inefficient methods, inefficiency brings low productivity, and low productivity spells poverty.

KING COTTON'S TARNISHED CROWN

As a result, the glory of cotton is tarnished. To this day, cotton growing in most parts of the earth carries the stigma of degrading poverty for the millions who do the actual work

---

[2] The warp consists of the stouter threads extending lengthwise in the loom and crossed by the woof, or filling threads.

[3] In the water frame—its name is as meaningless as its function is vital—the thread is guided over two successive rollers that revolve at different speeds, thus regulating the tension to which the emerging thread is subjected and thereby making possible the spinning of stronger threads. With its invention, cloth could for the first time be manufactured entirely from cotton.

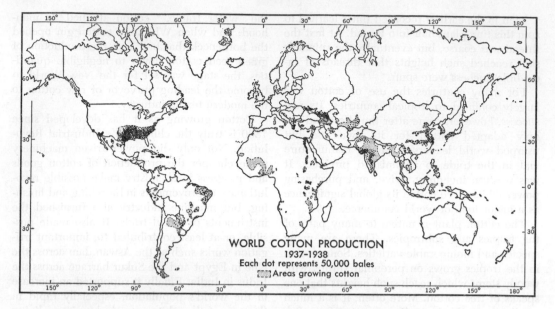

WORLD COTTON PRODUCTION
1937-1938
Each dot represents 50,000 bales
▨ Areas growing cotton

FIG. 19.1. (Figs. 19.1 and 19.2 from U. S. Department of Agriculture, Bureau of Agricultural Economics.)

in the fields—the planting, cultivating, and picking. In the United States, the cotton-growing states make up the nation's lowest-income group. The statistical correlation between cotton growing and poverty is startling.

It is true that, throughout the modern history of cotton growing, there have always been individuals and even minority classes who derived considerable income from cotton. It is likewise true that the total value of the cotton crop reaches a most impressive figure; but when this is divided by the number of people whose aggregate effort made the crop possible, the result is shamefully puny—or was until governments did something about improving conditions.

Unfortunately, the labor angle is not the only aspect of cotton culture awaiting correction; the situation regarding the land itself is almost as bad. As Jonathan Daniels put it, "Flesh and earth are often sold with the staple as gold is sold from the mine."[4] Cotton culture has two harmful effects on the soil: (1) depletion of soil fertility, i.e., the removal of minerals by the cotton plant, and (2) the damage done by erosion resulting from faulty methods or badly

located plantings. Of these the second is by far the more important. Minerals can be replaced by the application of commercial fertilizers so long as there is soil to absorb them. Erosion damage, however, is often irreparable; if restitution is possible, it generally is costly and slow. All this is realized clearly now, but it was not understood and appreciated in the nineteenth century—the century that measured success in dollars and cents at the expense of lasting assets.

GEOGRAPHY OF COTTON CULTURE

Today cotton is produced in many countries. The major portions of the world's cotton area lie between 35° north and 25° south latitude.[5] But there are several cotton-producing regions beyond these limits. Thus, in South America, both Argentine and Peruvian cotton areas lie farther south. In Asia, both the Chinese and the Russian (Uzbekistan) cotton regions extend farther north. In the latter area some cotton grows as far north as the latitude which, in the western hemisphere, runs through Hudson Bay. In Africa a more or less continuous cotton belt stretches all the way from the Nile delta

---

[4] Jonathan Daniels, *A Southerner Discovers the South*, The Macmillan Company, New York, 1938, p. 253.

[5] In the western hemisphere this means between the latitude of Memphis, Tennessee, and that of São Paulo, Brazil.

to Mozambique. As yet its continuity is fictitious rather than real, reflecting potentialities based on climate rather than actualities based on a realistic appraisal of the overall situation.

Fig. 19.1 shows world cotton production as of 1946-1948. This map does not show all the areas within which natural conditions are satisfactory for cotton culture, for only small portions of such areas actually produce cotton. It takes a great deal more than the right climate-soil combination to make cotton culture successful. If other conditions—labor, capital, market, transport facilities, etc.—are exceptionally good, even mediocre or slightly deficient natural conditions may prove no deterrent to cotton cultivation. Vice versa, the best natural conditions do not make cotton culture possible in areas where there is an insufficient labor supply or which are too inaccessible or suffer from other handicaps sufficiently great to overcompensate the natural advantages.

Most cotton regions are in preponderantly agricultural countries. The United States and the U.S.S.R. are the chief exceptions, both being countries that extend from cold or temperate latitudes to subtropical latitudes and both including under one form of government important agricultural and industrial areas. In a free democratic system such heterogeneity of enterprise and such wide geographical dispersion present serious problems of national harmony not felt to the same extent under a closed or controlled economy.

Natural vs. Cultural Factors and World Cotton Geography

Throughout this book the theme has been stressed that nature provides opportunities and sets limits to human success, but does not determine what man will make out of these opportunities and how hard he will struggle to reach these limits. How far he will go depends on the state of the arts, the availability of capital, complex economic interrelations, human attitudes, social institutions, and political considerations—in short, on "natural" *and* economic *and* technological *and* social *and* political factors.

Cotton illustrates this basic truth with unusual clarity. The water frame and the cotton gin have been mentioned. The one made possible the successful manufacture of all-cotton goods by power-driven machines; the other gave green seed cotton the go-ahead signal. One might be inclined to argue therefore that our cotton culture rests not on a natural but on a technological basis. But technological determinism is as one-sided as is natural determinism. It takes many factors and causes to explain complex phenomena of human history.

Obviously, cotton is a labor-fiber, but how much labor is required depends on diverse conditions of the natural environment, of technology, of management, etc. However, the amount far exceeds the labor required for grain crops. The problem of providing adequate labor for cotton culture is aggravated by the fact that there are three distinct seasonal peaks: (1) preparing the seed bed, (2) hoeing and thinning out or "chopping"[6] the rows of young plants, and (3) picking. Of these, the last, in the absence of mechanical pickers, is the most critical, because if cotton is not picked when ready, it tends to lose grade and this is costly.

Slavery once solved these labor problems. How much cotton our South could grow was, before the Civil War, a function not only of acres but, to a large extent, of the number and productivity of the available slaves. When the slaves were freed, tenants and sharecroppers took their place. As late as 1921 a U. S. Department of Agriculture report on cotton contained this statement: "With one mule a man can plow, chop and hoe from 10 to 20 acres, from which 5 to 10 bales of cotton can be produced and this is ordinarily all one family can pick. Therefore, one mule implements are used over the greater part of the eastern portion of the cotton belt."

So, at least in that portion, labor requirements go far to determine the size of the farm, the nature of the implements, and the methods of production. If cotton must be picked by hand by labor that must live on the plantation, there is no incentive to introduce mechanical means of plowing, cultivating, and chopping. But if, as in many parts of our western cotton belt, migratory labor is available for picking, mechanization can proceed piecemeal even

---

[6] Hoeing means removing weeds with a hoe. "Chopping," which is also done with a hoe, means removing excess plants from the row so that clusters about 14 inches apart are left.

TABLE 19.1.   Cotton: Acreage, Production, and Yield, by Major Producing Countries, Five-Year Averages, Selected Periods, 1909-1948[7]

	1909-1913	Percent	1924-1928	Percent	1934-1938	Percent	1944-1948	Percent
			Acreage in million acres					
United States	32.9	50.1	41.9	50.4	28.4	34.6	19.7	33.1
India[a]	22.3	33.9	26.0	31.3	24.7	30.1	14.6	24.5
China	3.8	5.8	5.4	6.5	7.4	9.0	5.9	9.9
U.S.S.R.	1.2	1.8	1.7	2.1	5.0	6.1	3.3	5.5
Egypt	1.7	2.3	1.8	2.2	1.8	2.2	1.2	2.0
Brazil	0.8	1.2	1.5	1.9	5.2	6.5	5.3	8.9
Others	2.9	4.4	4.8	5.9	9.4	11.6	9.5	16.0
Total	65.7	100.0	83.1	100.0	82.0	100.0	59.6	100.0
			Production in million bales[b]					
United States	13.0	60.5	15.0	56.0	12.7	41.3	11.3	46.9
India	3.8	17.9	4.9	18.3	5.3	17.3	3.3	13.7
China	1.5	7.0	2.6	9.7	3.1	10.1	1.9	7.8
U.S.S.R.	0.7	3.3	0.9	3.4	3.0	9.8	2.1	8.7
Egypt	1.5	7.0	1.5	5.6	1.8	5.9	1.3	5.4
Brazil	0.4	1.8	0.5	1.9	1.8	5.9	1.4	5.8
Others	0.7	3.3	1.4	5.2	2.9	9.4	2.9	12.0
Total	21.5	100.0	26.8	100.0	30.7	100.0	24.2	100.0
			Yield in pounds per acre					
United States	188.3		171.3		212.4		273.6	
India	81.2		89.2		102.2		106.7	
China	190.9		227.5		203.2		157.1	
U.S.S.R.	266.8		237.3		284.1		310.1	
Egypt	398.8		403.3		478.3		521.2	
Brazil	237.3		167.7		163.9		125.6	
Others	108.0		149.9		147.6		146.0	
World average	156.1		154.3		178.9		193.7	

[a] Subcontinent of India.
[b] Bales 500 lb. gross, 478 lb. net.

though mechanical pickers have not yet been perfected.

An adequate labor supply is just as vital for successful cotton production as are proper climate and soil. However, human attitudes—social institutions as well as "politics"—have much to do with the availability of labor. Attitudes toward labor are not static; they undergo significant changes. Labor conditions more or less taken for granted at one time may be frowned upon two or three decades later. In

[7] Converted from Food and Agriculture Organization, *World Fiber Survey,* 1947, p. 49, and supplemented by the Bureau of Agricultural Economics of the U.S. Department of Agriculture (October 28, 1949).

other words, the conditions determining the cost of producing cotton are not static; a region which has enjoyed low costs because of an excessively low wage scale may lose this advantage when society is no longer willing to countenance the exploitation of its members.

To say, therefore, that a country should produce cotton simply because it has the right soil and climate is dangerously wrong. Cotton should be produced only where nature ("land"), labor, and capital—in short, *all* cost-determining factors—are right. The idea of perpetuating sharecropping and tenancy under conditions bordering on peonage is no longer considered sound. The strongest advocates of our country's keeping its lead as a grower and exporter of cotton are now urging the speedy mechanization and the wholesale rationalization of cotton culture. Such policies will, however, raise the grave problem of finding employment for the hundreds of thousands of farm families whom mechanization will displace (see p. 333).

Political considerations likewise affect cotton culture. When our Civil War drastically reduced this country's cotton production, English cotton spinners in self-defense vigorously supported the huge irrigation program for Egypt which helped to make the Nile valley one of the chief cotton-growing regions in the world.[8] France and Germany, equally desirous of reducing their dependence on American cotton, likewise encouraged cotton production in their African colonies, but the results were not too successful. Even so, this goes far to show how inadequate is any attempt to explain world cotton production in terms of purely natural geographic conditions.

WORLD PRODUCTION BY COUNTRIES

During the past half-century about half the cotton crop of the world has been produced in the United States. Most of the remainder has come from five countries: India, China, the U.S.S.R., Egypt, and Brazil. Table 19.1 tells the story of four decades of production, its division among producing countries, and the acreage and yield in the different countries. The table reveals a number of significant facts and trends.

1. A decline in cotton acreage in the United States—from 50.1 percent in 1909-1913 to 33.1 percent in 1944-1948—and in production—from 60.5 percent to 46.9 percent respectively for these same two periods. This decline is largely the result of national curtailment policies aimed at raising the profitableness of cotton growing.

2. An increase in cotton acreage and production in China, the U.S.S.R., and Brazil. However, China's advance was halted and partially reversed by war.

3. A slight decline in production in both India and Egypt. This is explained in part by the growing pressure of the population on the food supply, in part by disturbances in India, and in part by the general uncertainties of the period in both countries.

4. The wide range in yield—from a little over 100 pounds per acre in India to over 500 pounds in Egypt. The master key to the high yield is irrigation, but in the United States heavier use of fertilizers and concentration on better land are contributory factors. The decline in Brazil's yield is explained by the expansion of cotton growing into new lands and a resort to primitive methods of cultivation.

These points will be developed more fully as each of the important cotton-growing countries is studied separately.

COTTON IN THE UNITED STATES
Geography

The main area in which cotton is grown in the United States is the so-called cotton belt, comprising parts or all of the following states: Virginia, North Carolina, South Carolina, Georgia, Florida, Tennessee, Alabama, Mississippi, Louisiana, Texas, Oklahoma, and Arkansas. Its area is about 700,000 square miles, or about 23 percent of the total area of continental United States. Less than 5 percent of the total area of the cotton belt is cultivated in cotton; the present acreage is about 20,000,000 acres, or 31,250 square miles. The cotton belt is so called partly for historical reasons, and partly because cotton is still predominant in many areas throughout this region, gives employment to more people than any other branch of agriculture, and is the most valuable cash crop in the entire area.

As Fig. 19.2 shows, cotton production is most heavily concentrated in the bottom lands of the Mississippi—the delta country—extending from about Memphis, Tennessee, to Vicksburg, Mississippi. This delta country contains some of the richest and deepest soil in the world, alluvial accretions of many centuries. Top-notch growers have had yields of 600 to 700 pounds per acre over large areas. However, the

---

[8] After World War I, as the result of the growing movement for independence in Egypt, Britain could no longer depend on Egyptian long-staple cotton. Hence the Lancashire Cotton Spinners Association, in its quest for a dependable source of supply, started a giant plantation near Scott, Mississippi. However, because of the boll weevil their hope of growing long-staple cotton was thwarted, although the plantation itself, under expert management, has thrived as a cotton-growing center. See *Fortune*, March, 1937, pp. 125 ff.

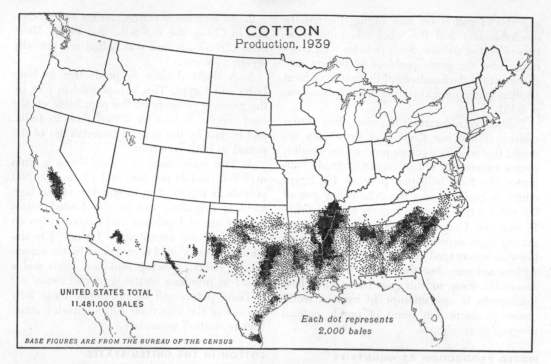

COTTON
Production, 1939

UNITED STATES TOTAL
11,481,000 BALES

Each dot represents
2,000 bales

BASE FIGURES ARE FROM THE BUREAU OF THE CENSUS

FIG. 19.2.

Mississippi occasionally rolls destructive flood waters over a strip of land up to 200 miles wide, carrying whole sections of land with it down to the sea.

North central Texas is another important cotton-growing area. Both it and the delta country are relatively flat, making mechanization possible; but the extent of mechanization depends on other factors than topography (see pp. 333 ff.).

Recently an increasing amount of cotton has been grown, under irrigation, outside the cotton belt—in New Mexico, Arizona, and California, and in a small section of southwestern Texas. Irrigation cotton has several advantages over rainfall cotton. It has a longer staple,[9] the growing season is likely to be longer, and the supply of water can be more carefully controlled. However, although less risky, it is sometimes costlier than rainfall cotton.

California grows the largest amount of irrigation cotton, as Fig. 19.2 shows, and the de-

velopment of this method of cotton growing has been particularly spectacular there.[10] Her production, in thousand running bales, increased from 319.6 in 1944 to 772.0 in 1947 and to 975.0 in 1948. Corresponding figures for the other two irrigation cotton states are: Arizona, 132.0 in 1944 and 234.0 in 1947; New Mexico, 113.2 in 1944 and 179.0 in 1947. But the total output of cotton for these three states —564.8 thousand running bales in 1944 and 1185.0 in 1947—is a relatively small though fast-growing proportion of our total crop of 11,839.4 running bales in 1944 and 11,857.0 in 1947; their output was less than 10 percent of the total in 1947. Fig. 19.3 shows cotton production in this country by states.

History of Cotton Production

The history of cotton growing in the United States may be divided roughly into a period of expansion, which reached its peak in 1925 when nearly 46 million acres were planted in cotton, and a period of contraction that set in

---

[9] All western cotton-growing centers dependent on irrigation grow only one variety of cotton each. All varieties so grown are relatively long-staple varieties.

[10] See *Fortune*, May, 1949, summarized in *Reader's Digest*, August, 1949, pp. 127-131.

thereafter.[11] Several causes account for the decline in acreage from the 1925 peak: (1) the boll weevil, (2) increased foreign competition, (3) the Great Depression and the New Deal, (4) the disastrous effect of World War II on international trade in general and on trade in cotton in particular.

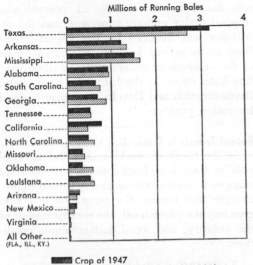

Millions of Running Bales

■ Crop of 1947
▨ Ten-year Average Period 1937-1946

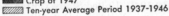 FIG. 19.3. Cotton Ginnings, United States, by States, 1947 Crop and Ten-Year average, 1937-1946. (U. S. Department of Commerce, Bureau of the Census, *Cotton Production and Distribution, Season 1947-1948*, Bulletin No. 185, 1948.)

The Boll Weevil. The Mexican boll weevil crossed into Texas in 1892 and in thirty years covered practically the entire cotton belt, except for certain scattered sections.[12] Largely as the result of its invasion, cotton production in the United States declined from 13.4 million

---

[11] Since 1948, what may appear to some as the beginning of a new chapter in our cotton history has been evident. As a result of the increased yields encouraged by the government's liberal crop support policies, our cotton crops are making an upward climb toward the higher brackets reminiscent of the best crop years in our history. But already there is talk of acreage curtailment and marketing quotas; furthermore, the carry-over is assuming disquieting proportions.

[12] The pink boll worm which infests cotton in India, Egypt, and other areas is said to be even more destructive; but the Mexican boll weevil devastated the world's premier cotton-growing region and was responsible for a great curtailment of cotton culture. See A. B. Cox, "Cotton," *Encyclopædia of the Social Sciences.*

bales in 1920 to less than 8 million in 1921, and there was a corresponding drop in yield—from 178.4 pounds per acre in 1920 to 124.5 in 1921. It virtually wiped out the Sea Island crop, which was grown chiefly on the islands off the coast of South Carolina and Georgia and which had the longest staple—nearly 2½ inches—of any cotton grown.

That such damage materially raises the costs of production is self-evident, but it also increases the risks. The unpredictability of the weather, always a direct factor in the hazards of the cotton industry, now became an indirect factor as well, because weather affects the hibernation and breeding habits of the pest.

The results of this increased cost and greater hazard were manifold. It encouraged crop diversification throughout the cotton belt, which on the whole proved advantageous in the long run. It stimulated cotton production in other parts of the country such as Texas and Oklahoma, and New Mexico, Arizona, and California.

Increased Foreign Competition. Another cause of the decline in acreage from the high of 1925 was competition from abroad, in which the boll weevil was a major, but not the sole, causal factor. When the damage done to our crops by the weevil raised doubts as to whether the United States could continue to supply the world demand, foreign cotton acreage, excluding the U.S.S.R., rose 45 percent—from 28.2 million acres to 40.8 million, mainly in India, Egypt, Peru, and Brazil.

Another powerful force behind this increased foreign competition was economic nationalism born of the bitter experiences of World War I and nourished by the failure to reestablish world commerce on its former level. The U.S.S.R. is a striking example of this; the redoubled efforts of the European colonial powers to expand cotton culture in Africa also belong in the same category.

The Depression and the New Deal. Cotton, like all apparel fibers, felt the brunt of the catastrophic collapse of demand during the Great Depression. Expenditures for food could be cut but not eliminated, for people have to eat even during a depression. But other, less urgent expenditures were cut to the bone. Hence cotton prices suffered a disastrous drop.

The New Deal, through the AAA, sought to

lift the price of cotton by means of acreage curtailment. Of the 40.2 million acres cultivated in 1933, only 29.4 million were harvested; the rest was plowed under. From then on, the cultivated acreage was held permanently under 30 million. When the first Agricultural Adjustment Act was declared unconstitutional by the Supreme Court, acreage control was linked up with soil conservation. The beneficial effects of this constructive policy were soon felt in increased yields and in the generally higher prosperity of the agricultural South.[13]

World War II and Cotton. The two World Wars affected cotton in the United States in far different ways. World War I did not stop our cotton exports; World War II did. Domestic cotton consumption was moderate during World War I; during World War II it reached unprecedented heights—11.0 million running bales in 1941, as against 5.6 and 6.7 for 1937 and 1938 respectively. Foreign consumption showed a fairly steady decline, from a high of 6.3 million running bales in 1935 to lows of 1.2 in 1941 and 1.3 in 1942 and 1943. Thus, in the face of dwindling foreign sales, our cotton more than ever before came to depend on the domestic market. Foreign countries could not buy it for several reasons. What little dollar exchange they could command was soon spent on food and other materials even more vital than cotton. Furthermore, their mills and machinery were destroyed by the war, and transportation facilities were disrupted. That our tariff policy and the exorbitant price of our cotton were contributing factors goes without saying.

But it is almost as vital for a cotton-growing country to export its surplus as for a cotton-importing country to have raw materials for its textile mills. There are three main ways in which this difficulty can be solved, even in the face of the importing countries' virtual financial bankruptcy. (1) The exporting country can donate the cotton, (2) it can ship on credit, (3) it can enter a processing agreement under

which the importing country pays for the raw cotton by delivering a certain portion of the goods manufactured from it. All three methods were used.

Of the 3.7 million bales exported by the United States in 1945-1946 (total world exports were 9 million bales), 27 percent was probably lend-lease shipments and 19 percent was financed by UNRRA; 11 percent was shipped under military programs, and the remainder was financed by the Export-Import Bank or by private lenders. In addition, some of the proceeds of general-purpose reconstruction loans made by the International Bank for Reconstruction and Development may be used for cotton purchases.[14]

Recent Trends in Production

As the result of world events and national policies, there have been a number of important changes in cotton culture in the United States, changes that involve the geography of cotton growing, the plant itself, the mechanization of the industry, and social and economic conditions.

TABLE 19.2. United States Cotton Acreage, Yield, and Output[15]

	1909-1913	1924-1928	1934-1938	1946	1947	1943-1947
Harvested area (million acres)	33.2	41.9	28.4	17.6	21.3	19.4
Yield (pounds per acre)	189.0	171.0	214.0	235.7	267.3	262.0
Crop (million bales)	13.0	15.0	12.7	8.6	11.9	10.6

A number of geographical shifts have taken place. As a result of the decline in acreage, some of the old cotton-growing areas were eliminated. In general, the shift was away from the poorest submarginal land to land offering distinct advantages in terms of fertility, accessibility, and mechanizability. As a result of the shift to better land which rigorous curtailment policies greatly encouraged—total cotton acreage which reached its peak in 1925 was cut virtually in half—and because of more intensive cultivation, there has been a striking increase

---

[13] Some features of the New Deal agricultural policy may have been excusable politically, but economically they were inexcusable. Furthermore, not all the economic progress made by southern agriculture can be credited to the New Deal, for in our complex economic life causes are never simple.

[14] See "A Business Venture to Speed World Recovery," *Reader's Digest*, August, 1949, pp. 105-108; and FAO, *World Fiber Survey*, 1947, pp. 64, 65.

[15] *Agricultural Statistics, 1948.*

in yield per acre. Table 19.2 shows this clearly. This higher yield is due in part to increased use of fertilizers as well as to unusually favorable weather. Part of it is due to the use of better seed and the development of superior strains. Soil conservation may also have contributed its share. On the other hand, it may be partly fictitious, for whereas the farmers themselves were formerly depended on for yield and acreage figures, inspectors now estimate these figures by means of sampling measurements.

The plant itself has been improved by years of patient seed selection and hybridization. One result has been an increase in the length of the staple from around ⅞ inch to 1 inch. But this has been offset by a loss in quality, for mechanical picking and such short-cut hand-picking methods as stripping or snapping,[16] which are prompted by labor shortage, raise the content of the dirt and other foreign matter in the lint.

Mechanization. The mechanical revolution has been slow in reaching cotton growing, although our other two leading crops, wheat and corn, were mechanized earlier. Why has cotton held out so long? There are several causes, some of which have already been brought out. In brief, they are as follows: (1) The abundance of "cheap" labor in the South does not encourage the introduction of expensive labor-saving devices. (2) The South as a whole is only now emerging from the impoverishment that followed the Civil War, and poverty means shortage of capital and lack of buying power. (3) Social conditions—the prevalence of tenancy and sharecropping, and the social unrest stirred up by race conflict—have discouraged the outside investment necessary for mechanization.

But besides these economic and social causes, cotton culture posed technological problems that seemed insuperable. Human judgment is called for at two stages of cultivation—in chopping, which involves discrimination between healthy and weak plants, and in picking, which calls for the selection of only fully mature bolls. Selection in picking is vital to successful cotton growing; hence any mechanical picker must be selective. In spite of the fact that exercising judgment is the last thing a machine can be expected to do, the mechanical pickers now coming on the market are doing just that!

It took almost a century to develop a successful picker. The first patent for such a machine was taken out in 1850, and by 1937 the total number issued by the Patent Office exceeded 900.[17] Improvement followed improvement, down to the elaborate devices of today.[18] Of these, apparently the most successful are those having moistened rotating spindles to which the lint adheres as the machine moves over the plants.

As work on a successful picker reached its final stages, important corollary developments took place in other phases of cotton culture. Plant breeders succeeded in developing new varieties that are better adapted to machine picking than the older ones; important factors here are height and time of maturity of the plant, and the rate at which the bolls open. Defoliation was found to be important in machine picking, and calcium cyanamide proved to be a good defoliant. Defoliation has many advantages. It hastens the maturing process by enabling sunlight to reach the immature bolls, and it diverts the growing energy of the plant away from the leaves, which have outlived their usefulness, to the bolls, which grow larger and larger. It exposes the bolls more freely to the machine picker and it reduces the danger of their being stained by tiny leaf particles. Ginning techniques are being improved to remove the "trash" that is likely to be collected in larger amounts in machine picking. The problems involved in preparing the soil and the seed bed and in chopping and hoeing by machine are also being solved.[19] The importance of the revolutionary improvements in tractors during the twenties and thirties in all these developments can hardly be exaggerated.

Mechanization was accompanied by what might be called a social revolution.[20] For one

---

[16] Snapping off the entire boll.

[17] Roman L. Horne and Eugene G. McKibben, *Mechanical Cotton Picker*, WPA, *Studies of Changing Techniques and Employment in Agriculture,* Report No. A.2, 1937, p. 5.

[18] See Oscar Johnston, "Will the Machine Ruin the South?" *Saturday Evening Post,* May 31, 1947.

[19] For interesting details, see *ibid.*

[20] According to Oscar Johnston (*ibid.,* p. 93), mechanization was the result, rather than the cause, of this social revolution. Perhaps it is safer to say that it is both cause and result, for the interactions are reciprocal.

thing, the hitherto abundant labor available for cotton growing was cut sharply early in the 1940's, for there was a veritable exodus of labor from the South. Other people in large numbers were drawn from cotton growing to the rapidly expanding industries of the South. Cotton growing lost both land and labor when the war-born demand arose for southern crops other than cotton. Wages in southern agriculture rose under the double impetus of the economic law of supply and demand and of social laws designed to strengthen the position of labor, and made cost reduction imperative if cotton was to compete with the cheaper synthetic fibers. At the same time, the price of cotton rose to new heights, and this in turn put into the pockets of cotton growers the money with which to buy machines.[21]

The present progress of mechanization thus seems to belie the fears of those who foresaw such problems as the wholesale displacement of labor by machines. Such problems seem to have lost some of their terror. Topography is an important factor in mechanization, which means that not all of the cotton belt can be mechanized. Hence remnants of old-fashioned cotton culture seem destined to survive, as do small semimechanized farms in hilly sections, provided they can keep their laborers at work the year round, the key to efficient labor productivity. Nor is mechanization likely to displace as much labor as was feared. The operation and maintenance of machine equipment calls for a considerable labor force. Moreover, on at least some plantations the first two pickings will probably continue to be done by hand because of the premium price paid for cotton picked with special skill and care. Under such a procedure the plants would be defoliated and picked by machine only after these two pickings.

There is also the fact that national and world pictures have changed, relieving the South's dependence on one crop and pressing for diversification of her entire economy, industrial as well as agricultural. It now seems that the South is not the only region that needs

to worry about the results of the mechanization of cotton, for the land and labor freed from cotton culture will create competition for farmers in other parts of the country. The South will grow more wheat, corn, soybeans, and peanuts, and will produce more meat and dairy products. In short, she will reduce her dependence on northern agriculture while at the same time competing with northern producers.

Perhaps the greatest threat to the South inherent in the mechanization of cotton is the possibility of its spread to foreign countries, such as parts of Argentina, Paraguay, Brazil, and Africa, that have vast level areas suitable for cotton growing but lack the labor necessary for hand culture. Even here there are grounds for hope, for in one sense there has never been overproduction of cotton. True, more cotton is often produced than people can afford to buy at prices remunerative to the grower, but here the trouble lies, at least in part, with purchasing power; underconsumption rather than overproduction is involved. If the world-wide per capita demand for cotton matched the per capita demand in the United States, cotton production would grow by leaps and bounds.

COTTON IN OTHER COUNTRIES
India

Cotton culture in India is of ancient origin, which means hoary traditions that perpetuate primitive production methods and worn-out

FIG. 19.4. (Figs. 19.4, 19.5, 19.6, and 19.7 from Agricultural Adjustment Administration, *Round the World with Cotton*, 1944.)

soil. Furthermore, the teeming millions of people press hard against the means of sustenance; hence food crops generally enjoy preference

---

[21] It should be borne in mind that all these developments did not take place at an even pace throughout the entire cotton belt. Furthermore, the South's high birth rate in part offsets the decreased pressure on the supply of labor.

over others in their claim on the land. The cotton yield is deplorably low, for much of the seed is sown broadcast and the climate is kind to insect pests and plant diseases against which the farmer is more or less helpless. Nevertheless, India ranks second among cotton-growing countries. Most of her cotton is short-staple. Efforts to improve the crop are under way.

The political independence which India and Pakistan attained in 1947 granted them full autonomy in the control of their resources, and may point to a further drift toward economic nationalism. One manifestation of this is the five-year plan for cotton production designed to give both countries a larger output of cotton with a staple considerably above the United States average. How political upheavals in that part of the world will affect such ambitious plans is anyone's guess.

China

The situation in China in some ways resembles that in India. Here too nonfood crops compete with food crops for the land. Here too

FIG. 19.5. Cotton-Producing Areas of China and Korea.

the length of the cotton staple is typically short; in fact, China is known for growing some of the shortest cotton in the world. But in China, especially in the northern part, the winters are severe and fuel is scarce. Hence cotton wadding is widely used for clothing to give the body more protection against the cold. Short-staple cotton is adequate for this wadding.

For a time during the thirties, China's cotton production expanded and an improvement in staple quality was noticeable. This was largely the result of Japanese efforts toward increasing

China's output of raw cotton and expanding the cotton textile industry, especially in the large coastal cities. But war and revolution have changed all this. The Japanese are gone from China, and food comes first in times of internal struggle and social revolution.

The U.S.S.R.

Before World War I, Russia was one of the more important importers of cotton, producing about 3 percent of the world crop. Before World War II, however, production had increased until the U.S.S.R. ranked fourth as a producer—after the United States, India, and China.

Today the U.S.S.R., self-sufficient as far as cotton is concerned, is working hard to push production up to new heights. The 1946-1950 five-year plan aims at close to 5 million bales as the national goal, as against less than 3 million in 1934-1938. The yield per acre is to be raised materially, and production is to be shifted more and more from nonirrigated areas in the Crimea and the Caucasus to the irrigated areas of Uzbekistan. The irrigated area is itself to be extended by means of huge dams that are to be built.

Egypt

For many centuries Egypt—in other words, the Nile valley—was one of the great granaries of the Mediterranean world. During our Civil War, however, she became one of the leading cotton producers in the world and the leading producer of long-staple cotton. British leadership provided the know-how as well as the necessary capital for irrigation dams. Egypt faces the same problem of food vs. nonfood crops as India and China do; the problem was clearly manifest during World War II when laws were passed sharply curtailing her cotton acreage.

Before World War II Egypt's annual output averaged 1.8 million bales. This dropped to around the million-bale mark during the war and is now hovering around 1.3 million bales. The Egyptian government has taken over the unsalable surplus of extra-quality long-staple cotton. The world is still so busy catching up with the demand for coarser grades of cotton cloth that the disposal of this superior grade of raw cotton represents a real problem.

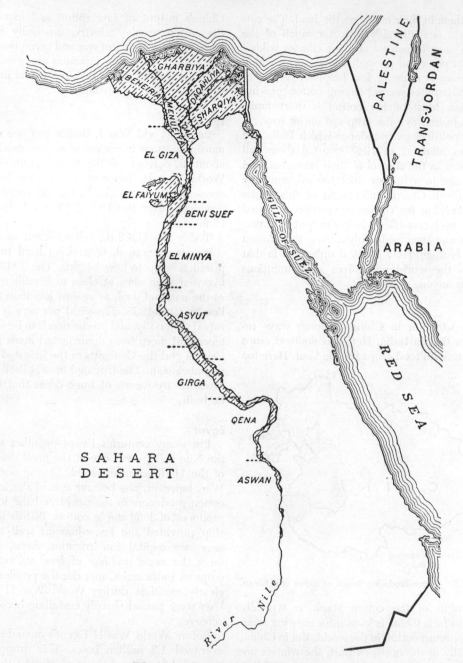

FIG. 19.6. Cotton-Producing Areas of Egypt.

Brazil

Brazil is both old and young as a cotton-growing country. Cotton has been grown for centuries in the tropical northeast; in fact, in this region, with its truly tropical climate, the cotton plant becomes a perennial woody shrub

that ranges up to as much as 9 feet in height. The tree is cut down after harvest as a precaution against insect pests, but it resprouts the next year.

Two things that happened in the 1920's caused Brazil to introduce cotton growing in

Flame cultivator used in weeding and cultivating cotton. (Standard Oil Co. (N.J.), photo by Roberts.)

Mechanical cotton pickers, developed after more than a century of experimentation. (Standard Oil Co. (N.J.), photo by Roberts.)

Hoeing cotton in Louisiana. (Standard Oil Co. (N.J.), photo by Webb.)

Picking cotton in Egypt. The population is very dense, labor is cheap, and mechanization does not yet pay. (U.S.D.A. photo.)

Cotton spinning mill in Tashkent, Uzbekistan. (Sovfoto.)

Sisal mill at Msanan in Tanganyika. (By Deane Dickason, from Ewing Galloway.)

Bucket spinning machine which reels rayon threads into so-called "cakes." (E. I. du Pont de Nemours & Company.)

Man-made fibers. Liquid forced through the holes of a spin-neret becomes separate filaments which form rayon thread. (E. I. du Pont de Nemours & Company.)

Continuous rayon process. (Photo courtesy of Industrial Rayon Corporation.)

The plant at Camden, S.C., that manufactures Orlon acrylic fiber, a new synthetic fiber. (E. I. du Pont de Nemours & Company.)

Weaving rayon. (Photo courtesy of Industrial Rayon Corporation.)

The Sabine River Works of the du Pont Company at Orange, Texas, which manufactures chemical intermediates for nylon. (E. I. du Pont de Nemours & Company.)

Drying coffee in Brazil. (From Ewing Galloway.)

Mule train of coffee in Colombia. (Standard Oil Co. (N.J.), photo by Collier.)

Automatic coffee roasting machines in San Francisco. (By Ewing Galloway, N.Y.)

Gathering wild rubber in Bolivia. (By Ewing Galloway, N.Y.)

Guayule plantation in California. This desert plant yields rubber after a four-year growing period. (By Ewing Galloway, N.Y.)

A synthetic rubber plant at Port Neches, Texas. (From Ewing Galloway.)

Fordlandia, the former Ford rubber plantation 700 miles from the sea on a tributary of the Amazon. (From Ewing Galloway.)

Natural rubber plantation in Sumatra. (By Cowling. From Ewing Galloway, N.Y.)

Track-mounted drilling machine that bores a hole for an explosive coal-loosening charge. (U.S. Steel Corporation.)

A giant shovel loads coal from a stripped coal seam near St. Charles, Ky. (Bucyrus-Erie Company.)

Coal cutting machine, operated by two men, that can slice nine feet into the coal seam. (U.S. Steel Corporation.)

Strip mining. This stripper rides along on the Kansas coal seam it has exposed. (Bucyrus-Erie Company.)

Fushun open-pit mine in Manchuria, probably the largest open-pit coal mine in the world. (From Ewing Galloway, N.Y.)

Coal washing plant, where coal is cleaned and sorted before moving down the Monongahela River. (U.S. Steel Corporation.)

A forest of derricks. Under the "rule of capture," offset well drilling led to waste of capital and oil, as this California scene suggests. (© Spence. From Ewing Galloway, N.Y.)

The 40-acre spacing of oil wells seeks to avoid waste caused by the crowding of wells. (Standard Oil Co. (N.J.), photo by Rotkin.)

the southeast part of the country. One was the decline in our own production, and the consequent rise in price, because of the havoc wrought by the boll weevil; the other was the fact that Brazil's coffee-growing industry had run into serious difficulties. In other words, to

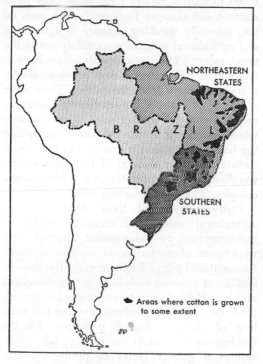

FIG. 19.7. Cotton-Producing Areas of Brazil.

the Brazilian planter, cotton looked better and coffee looked worse, so he naturally tried his hand at cotton. Similarly, in the thirties, when the New Deal curtailed cotton acreage and raised prices, the Brazilian was again far from slow in taking advantage of the tempting ratio of cotton to coffee prices.[22]

Brazil had plenty of land and, within limits, an adequate labor supply, but she was short of capital and technical know-how. Coffee planters must be taught how to raise and prepare cotton for the market, gins must be built, and experts must be available for "classing" the cotton. Brazil's efforts to put herself on the map

as a modern grower and exporter of cotton have been supported by foreign capital and her own government. The best way to build up a reputation for Brazilian cotton is to assure uniformity of both staple length and quality, and this can be accomplished through seed control; hence the government has taken over seed distribution.

Brazil has a cotton textile industry that she protects by a high tariff wall and by giving preference, in her export policies, to manufactured goods over raw cotton.

Other Producing Countries

The six countries just discussed—the United States, India, China, the U.S.S.R., Egypt, and Brazil—produce the bulk of the world cotton crop. In 1909-1917 their production constituted 96.9 percent of the world total, but since then there has been a persistent decline—to 94.6 percent in 1924-1928 and on down to 86.5 percent in 1945-1947. Smaller producers are creeping up. They make up a long list but may be grouped for convenience as follows: (1) Latin America (excluding Brazil), (2) the British Empire (excluding India), (3) the French colonial empire, and (4) Turkey, Korea, and the Belgian Congo.

The Latin-American group includes Mexico, Peru, and Argentina. Both Mexico and Peru were growing cotton when the Spanish *conquistadores* landed on their shores centuries ago. All the Peruvian cotton and most of the Mexican is grown under irrigation. Some of Peru's crop is long-staple cotton; both Egyptian and native varieties are grown. Much of the Mexican cotton is grown near the United States border; the industry has been helped to some extent by capital from this country. Argentina's cotton is grown in the northernmost part, in the so-called Chaco, by squatters from many parts of Europe—especially the eastern part—who lead a precarious existence trying to grow cotton under rather adverse conditions.[23]

There is hardly a British possession in Africa where cotton growing has not been attempted, nor have Australia and the British West Indies

---

[22] As a matter of fact, both cotton and coffee can be grown on one plantation, because the coffee trees usually occupy the hillsides above the frost line, leaving the more level valley bottoms free for cotton.

[23] There is talk of 50 million acres of "cotton land" in this part of the world. After all, what is "cotton land"? Land that *could* grow cotton if . . . , or land on which *people can* grow cotton and *live decently*?

been overlooked. Yet only two regions—the Anglo-Egyptian Sudan and Uganda—have shown appreciable results. The output in the other areas not only is small but fluctuates rather sharply. The combined output of all these regions has never run as high as ¾ million bales and it is now little better than half a million—a far from impressive figure against a world cotton crop of 25 or 30 million bales.

Even less impressive have been France's efforts to grow cotton in her colonies and mandates. The best year on record was 1944, when output reached 153,100 bales.

Nor have Korea, Turkey, and the Belgian Congo managed to produce much above 300,000 bales. Generally their output ranges between this figure and 100,000 bales.

PRODUCTION OF TEXTILES FROM COTTON
Agricultural vs. Nonagricultural Industries

The cluster of activities extending from the cotton field through the textile mill is sometimes referred to as "the cotton and cotton textile industry," but use of the term "industry" in this case is somewhat misleading. It tends to obscure the degree of integration, the vital characteristic that differentiates typical agricultural industries, engaged in processing agricultural products, from other manufacturing industries, engaged in processing nonagricultural products. Typically a modern steelworks owns everything at every stage of the production process, including the sources of its raw materials—ore, coal, timber, etc.—some of the means of transporting them, and the various plants—blast furnaces, coke ovens, rolling mills, etc.—through which the raw materials pass on their way to the finished product. In other words, the steelworks is highly integrated in the sense that the entire range of activities from raw materials to finished product is under one ownership. Such integration is as atypical of agricultural industries as it is typical of nonagricultural industries. It is doubtful whether there is a single cotton mill in the whole world that grows the cotton it processes.

This contrast in industrial structure reflects the fundamental differences between agriculture, as analyzed in Chapters 11 and 12, and manufacturing industry, as developed in Part III; ultimately it goes back to the basic dualism of nature developed in Part I. These basic differences in turn account for the fact that agriculture is typically a highly individualized and, in the absence of government controls, a highly competitive enterprise whose risks are far different from those affecting nonagricultural manufacturing enterprises. The forces that in many industries render large-scale units more efficient and cheaper than small-scale units do not, generally speaking, operate in agriculture and agricultural industries—certainly not to the same extent. The agricultural industries can secure their raw materials most economically by purchasing them from the farmer. Since most products of nature are extremely heterogeneous, a complex market mechanism develops whose function is to turn the heterogeneity into the homogeneity that is essential to the manufacturer. Further division of functions—credit, warehousing, transportation, etc.—adds to the complexity of the marketing structure.

Partly because of their dependence on agricultural sources of supply, agricultural industries are to some extent affected with weaknesses characteristic of agriculture itself. Raw-material prices fluctuate violently; the difficulties of assuring truly homogeneous stocks of raw materials are great; working with agricultural, i.e., organic, products involves full mastery of many technical problems. Finally, the human element in the form of labor constitutes a greater factor in production and hence in cost than is the case in nonagricultural industries. It is not surprising, therefore, that agricultural industries—and the cotton textile industry in particular—are far more decentralized as to both physical plant and control, and more competitive, than many nonagricultural industries.

Location of the Textile Industry

The manufacture of cotton textiles is one of the most widely diffused industries in existence. Several reasons account for this diffusion. In the first place, cotton is neither perishable nor weight-losing; hence the industry is not tied to the source of its raw material. Sugar cane, as we have seen, has to be processed near the source of the cane because of perishability and the heavy weight loss in processing—it does not pay to haul large amounts of worthless ingredients, such as the water and pulp in the cane, to distant processing plants. The same principle applies to other industries—canning of perishable produce and smelting of low-grade ores, for example. But cotton is nonperishable and its processing does not entail any considerable weight loss. In the second place, in the United States at least, freight charges are usually higher on manufactured goods than on raw materials. Thus, if cotton goods for the Far Eastern market are to be manufactured from Texas cotton, it would be far cheaper, other things such as labor, etc., being equal, to ship the raw material to China or Japan and have the actual fabricating done there. Thus the cotton textile industry is footloose as far as raw material is concerned.

Other factors, however, strongly influence the location of textile mills. Labor constitutes an unusually high percentage of the total production costs and therefore is probably the most important direct factor. Hence the mills tend to be located in areas where abundant labor can be recruited, such as the Piedmont regions of the Carolinas and Georgia.

Availability of labor is not, however, the only determinant of location. Regional differences are important indirect factors—at least they were until recently. Thus the almost virtual absence of labor unions once gave the Southeast a distinct advantage over New England. So also did the more lax state laws regulating labor. New England's labor laws prohibited night work for women, which meant that the mills could work only during the day; a night shift was out of the question because of the higher wages that had to be paid men operators. Furthermore, such restrictions produce cumulative effects in the form of higher overhead costs which, together with higher total production costs, must be reflected in higher prices; this in turn restricts the market and thus reduces the number of hours of work for the mill—a veritable vicious circle! But the southern mill owners were not hampered by such restrictions. The significance of such regional differences is now more historical than real, as the result of the widespread extension of labor unions throughout the entire country and the New Deal legislation regulating hours and wages. But in the meantime the cotton textile industry definitely established itself in the South and gained considerable momentum of its own.

The Production Process

The various stages in the growing of cotton have already been described in some detail. One fact that should, however, be brought out at this point concerns the relation between landlord and tenant farmer. Usually the two coöperate in growing the cotton, the contribution made by each varying in relation to the farmer's status as sharecropper, share tenant, or cash tenant.[24]

Ginning. After the cotton is picked, it goes to a gin where the seeds are removed from the lint by means of circular saws. The cotton gin usually buys all the seed from the farmer; he receives cash for part of it, the balance of the seed being payment for the ginning. Frequently the money received from the sale of the seed is the only actual cash the farmer receives for his crop. Although the seed constitutes about two-thirds of the crop by weight (one objective in cotton breeding is to reduce the seed constituent), in 1945 it sold for less than one-sixth of the price paid for the entire cotton crop.

The number of gins in the United States has been constantly declining. In 1902 there were 32,735 but by 1945 there were 11,048, of which only 8632 were active. The number of bales handled by each gin has been increasing; the average number per gin was 342 in 1902 and 1021 in 1946. The ownership of cotton gins varies; some are owned independently, others are owned by farm coöperatives, and still others by independent producers, merchants, banks, etc. In Oklahoma gins are regulated public utilities; and in the Southwest many gins belong to cottonseed mills which hope thus to assure their supply of raw materials.[25]

Spinning. When the cotton leaves the gin

---

[24] The sharecropper contributes his labor and the necessary fertilizer and is responsible for the cost of ginning; in return he receives half of the crop he has helped "make." The share tenant's contribution is the same as the sharecropper's but in addition includes work animals and their feed; for this he receives three-fourths of the cotton crop and two-thirds of the other crops, and the landlord pays one-third of the fertilizer and ginning costs. The cash tenant is more independent than either of the other two classes of tenants; he rents a certain amount of land and pays the rent either in cash or in kind.

[25] For a discussion of the cottonseed industry, see pp. 280-282.

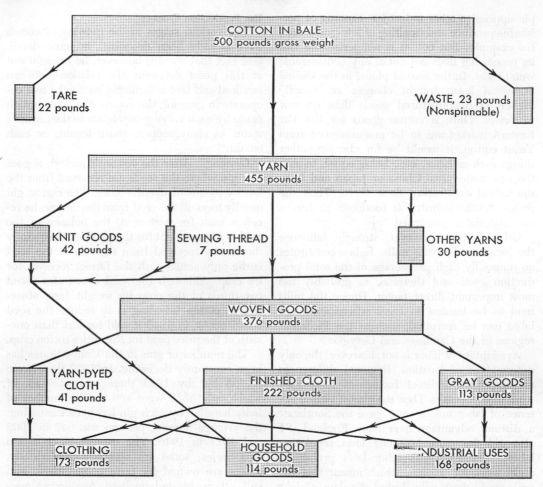

FIG. 19.8. Approximate Distribution of a Typical Bale of Cotton, 1930. (Association of Cotton Textile Merchants of New York.)

it passes through a labyrinthine maze of mercantile agencies ranging from local buyers to giant firms; it may change hands several times in the process.[26] This complex mercantile setup converts the chaos of heterogeneous cotton produced by individual farmers into the orderly and homogeneous raw material required by the cotton mill. In the milling end, integration has

[26] For a description of the cotton market, see W. H. Hubbard, *Cotton and the Cotton Market*, Appleton-Century-Crofts, Inc., New York, 2nd ed., 1924; A. B. Cox, *Cotton Prices and Markets* and *Services in Cotton Marketing*, U.S. Department of Agriculture, Bulletin Nos. 1444 and 1445, 1926; Federal Trade Commission, *The Cotton Trade*, Washington, 2 vols., 1924; National Bureau of Economic Research, *Textile Markets, Their Structure, Relation to Price Research*, New York, 1939.

been on the increase; some large concerns are wholly integrated, handling all the processes from opening the bales through knitting or weaving and finishing. Less than 20 percent of the spinning is done by independents who then sell the yarn to knitting or weaving mills. Where style is involved, mill operations are frequently controlled by commission houses. After the cotton is spun into yarn and the yarn is woven or knitted into textiles, it undergoes further finishing involving bleaching or dyeing. These processes are frequently done by independent concerns.

Types of Cotton

So far, cotton has been discussed mainly as though it were a homogeneous commodity. As

TABLE 19.3. Types of Cotton and Their Uses[27]

Type	Typical Material	End Use
Strict middling, 1⅛″	Sateens	Men's topcoat or overcoat lining
" " "	Brassière fabric	Women's brassières or bandeaux
" " "	Lawn, print	Blouses, waists, skirts
Middling, 1¹⁄₁₆″	Prints, broadcloth	Men's handkerchiefs
" "	Broadcloth, poplin	Men's dress shirts
" "	Broadcloth, print	Pajamas, night shirts
Middling, 1″	Knit 80/2 to 120/2	Women's full-fashioned hosiery
" "	Bed ticking, jacquard	Bed ticking (mattress)
" "	Terry toweling	Turkish and terry towels
Middling, ⅞″	Knit 12s to 14s	Men's athletic socks
" "	Knit 26s	Shirts and drawers
" "	Knit 12s	Union suits
Strict low middling, 1″	Flannel	Work gloves
" " " "	Seersucker, gabardine	Suits
" " " "	Flannel, terrycloth	Women's bathrobes
Strict low middling, ¹⁵⁄₁₆″	Denim drill	Overalls, jackets
" " " "	Outing flannel, broadcloth	Children's pajamas
Low middling, 1″	Seersucker, piqué	Women's suits, ensembles
Low middling, ¹⁵⁄₁₆″	Whipcord	Riding, hunting, and camp trousers
" " "	Corduroy, gabardine	Women's coats and jackets
" " "	Birdseye	Infants' diapers
" " "	Woven	Blankets
" " "	Sheeting	Oiled rainwear garments
Low middling, ⅞″	Chenille, tufted	Bath mats
Strict good ordinary, ⅞″	Osnaburgs	Fertilizer bags
Good ordinary, ¹³⁄₁₆″	8/3 carded yarn	Rugs, carpets (warp yarn)
" " "	Cotton batts	Thermal insulation

a matter of fact, it is nothing of the sort. No two bolls are alike; they differ in length and composition of fiber, in color, in strength, in freedom from foreign matter, in general appearance, etc. Heroic attempts have been made to arrange this infinite variety into a manageable number of classes or types.

The staple length largely determines the fineness of the yarn that can be spun; the longer the staple, the finer the yarn, i.e., the smaller the number of filaments in the diameter of the yarn. Yarns are classified by "counts,"[28]

i.e., the number of hanks of a standard length in a pound. Most Indian cotton yields low-count yarn; United States cotton yields medium-count, and Egyptian cotton yields high-count. Sea Island cotton had an even longer staple than the Egyptian, and was reputed to yield yarns of 300 counts; in other words, one pound of yarn spun from Sea Island cotton would be 756,000 feet long! The secret lies in the fact that longer staples possess far greater cohesion than shorter staples.

The different types or classes of cotton are

---

[27] This table is a highly condensed and completely rearranged extraction from a larger table prepared by the National Cotton Council and published in a *Study of Agricultural and Economic Problems of the Cotton Belt,* Hearings Before Special Subcommittee on Cotton of the Committee on Agriculture, House of Representatives, Eightieth Congress, First Session, July 7 and 8, 1947, Government Printing Office, Washington, 1947, pp. 369-373.

[28] The "count" system is used in classifying yarns for cotton, wool, and linen. It expresses fineness in

terms of length of yarn per pound of weight. The standard hank lengths differ for different fibers—840 yards for cotton, 560 for wool, and 300 for linen.

The denier system used for silk and rayon expresses fineness in terms of weight in grams per unit of length, the unit being 9000 meters. Thus a 150 denier rayon is a yarn 9000 meters of which weigh 150 grams.

Under the count system, higher numbers indicate greater fineness. Under the denier system, higher numbers indicate greater coarseness.

TABLE 19.4. Suggested Classification of the Commercial Cottons of the World by Competing Groups[29]

Group	Normally Suited for Spinning Yarns of English Counts	Typical Goods Made from These Counts	Staple Length of American Cotton Normally Used	Typical Cotton	Countries Representing the Principal Production of These Cottons
1	Barely spinnable	Blankets, wadding, and felts	None grown in the United States	Tientsin	North China, India, Dutch East Indies
2	0 to 15s	Very coarse goods	Under $7/8''$	Indian Oomra	India, China, United States
3	15s to 25s	Sheetings	$7/8''$ to $1''$	American Bowed	United States, Mexico, India, Russia, South Brazil, Argentina
4a	25s to 40s	Print cloths	$1''$ to $1\frac{1}{16}''$	Texas Staple	United States, Russia, Brazil, Argentina, South Africa, West Africa
4b	40s to 60s	Shirtings Medium tire yarns	$1\frac{1}{16}''$ to $1\frac{1}{8}''$	Memphis	
5a	60s to 75s	Dress goods Tire yarns	$1\frac{1}{8}''$ to $1\frac{3}{16}''$	Egyptian Uppers	Mississippi Delta, Carolinas, Egypt, Peru, North Brazil, Sudan, East Africa, Haiti
5b	75s to 80s	Fine knitting yarns Fine insulating yarns	$1\frac{3}{16}''$ to $1\frac{3}{8}''$	Longest Delta Staples	
6	Above 80s	Laces and lawns Sewing thread Best tire yarns	$1\frac{3}{8}''$ and longer	Sakellaridis Sea Island	Arizona, Egypt, Sudan, Peru, British West Indies

used for different purposes. Table 19.3 lists typical materials and their uses, together with the type of cotton most suitable for each.

Table 19.4, although older, is still useful because of the inclusion of foreign types of cotton.

Cotton Textile Manufacture in the United States

Cotton textile manufacturing in this country began in New England in 1790, when Samuel Slater built from memory a cotton mill like the one he had worked in as a mechanic in England. The industry flourished in New England for almost a century, much of the time behind a tariff wall that protected it from foreign

[29] W. G. Reed, "Competing Cottons and United States Production," *Economic Geography*, July, 1932, p. 296.

competition. In the 1880's, however, interest in cotton mills began to develop in the South, and it soon became apparent that cotton goods could be produced more cheaply there than in the North. The result was a rapid increase in the southern industry, and a gradual decline in the northern.

Ebb and flow in the textile industry can be measured readily in terms of active spindles and cotton consumed. These two criteria are used in Table 19.5, which shows developments in the industry in New England and the South for various years from 1840 to 1949. On the basis of active spindles, New England was far in the lead in 1840, with 1.6 million out of a total of 2.3 million. The situation remained relatively unchanged until 1880, when the South began to forge ahead. In the next half-century

TABLE 19.5.   Cotton Spindles and Cotton Consumed in the United States, by Regions, Specific Years from 1840 to 1949[30]

| | Active Cotton Spindles (millions) | | | | Cotton Consumed (million bales) | | | |
Year	New England	Cotton-Growing States	Others	Total	New England	Cotton-Growing States	Others	Total
1840	1.6	0.2	0.5	2.3	0.2	0.1	...	0.3
1850	3.0	0.3	0.8	4.0	0.4	0.1	0.1	0.6
1860	3.9	0.3	1.1	5.2	0.6	0.1	0.2	0.8
1870	5.5	0.3	1.3	7.1	0.6	0.1	0.2	0.8
1880	8.6	0.6	1.5	10.7	1.1	0.2	0.3	1.6
1890	10.9	1.6	1.9	14.4	1.5	0.5	0.5	2.5
1900	13.2	4.4	1.9	19.5	1.9	1.5	0.4	3.9
1910	15.7	10.5	2.0	28.3	2.0	2.2	0.5	4.6
1920	18.3	15.2	2.0	35.5	2.4	3.6	0.4	6.4
1930	11.4	18.6	1.3	31.2	1.1	4.7	0.2	6.1
1940	5.3	17.8	0.7	23.6	0.9	6.6	0.2	7.8
1941	5.1	17.7	0.6	23.4	1.1	8.3	0.3	9.7
1942	5.1	17.8	0.7	23.6	1.3	9.5	0.3	11.2
1943	5.0	17.7	0.6	23.4	1.2	9.6	0.3	11.1
1944	4.8	17.7	0.6	23.0	1.0	8.7	0.3	9.9
1945	4.5	17.6	0.6	22.7	0.9	8.5	0.2	9.6
1946	4.4	17.0	0.6	22.0	0.9	8.1	0.2	9.2
1947	4.3	17.0	0.5	21.4	1.0	8.8	0.3	10.0
1948	4.1	16.8	0.4	21.3	0.9	8.2	0.2	9.3
1949	3.1	15.6	0.3	19.0	0.6	7.0	0.2	7.8

she outstripped New England by a wide margin, and she has maintained this position down to the present.

The South's lead is even more striking when measured in terms of cotton consumed. There are three reasons for this. (1) Until fairly recently, southern mills made coarser yarns than those spun in the North, and coarser yarns use up cotton more quickly. (2) Much of the southern equipment is newer and therefore faster than the older northern machinery; even when the same yarn counts are spun, the new machines use more cotton per spindle-hour than the old ones do. (3) Southern spindles on the average are operated more hours per day than are northern spindles.

World Cotton Textile Manufacture

Our cotton textile industry is surpassed only by that of the United Kingdom, and then only

[30] U. S. Department of Commerce, Bureau of the Census, *Cotton Production and Distribution*, Bulletin 185, Washington, 1947; 1948-1949 figures from National Cotton Council of America.

if the measurement is made in terms of spindles rather than of cotton consumed. In 1900, Great Britain had 45.5 million spindles, as against 32 million for the continent of Europe and 19.3 for the United States. This situation has undergone a complete change since 1900. The first phase ended in 1939, with the beginning of World War II.

Table 19.6, which covers this first phase, reveals the major shifts. By far the most striking is the "de-Europeanization" of the cotton textile industry between 1914 and 1939. From a mill consumption of cotton that averaged 47.3 percent of the world total in 1905-1913, Europe, including Britain, dropped to an average of 29.6 percent during 1934-1938. The western hemisphere held its own. Asia shows the major gain, Japan and China together gaining 12.2 percent of the world total; the U.S.S.R. gained less than 3 percent. The labor factor goes far to explain the shift to Asia; national self-sufficiency is clearly evident in the case of the U.S.S.R.

World War II brought with it a sharp reduc-

TABLE 19.6.   Spindles in Place and Mill Consumption by Countries, Selected Periods, 1900-1939[31]

Country	Spindles in Place (millions)			Spindles in Place (percentage of world total)			Mill Consumption of Raw Cotton (million bales)[a]		Mill Consumption of Raw Cotton (percentage of world total)	
	1900	1914	1939	1900	1914	1939	1909-1913	1934-1938	1909-1913	1934-1938
United Kingdom	45.5	56.0	36.3	...	38.7	25.0	4.1	2.8	20.2	10.0
Continental Europe										
France	...	7.4	9.9	...	5.1	6.8	1.0	1.2	4.9	4.3
Germany	...	11.4	10.9	...	7.9	7.1	1.8	1.0	8.9	3.6
Italy	...	4.6	5.3	...	3.2	3.6	0.8	0.7	3.9	2.5
Belgium	...	1.5	2.0	...	1.0	1.4	0.2	0.4	1.0	1.4
Spain	...	2.0	2.0	...	1.4	1.4	0.3	0.2	1.5	0.7
Other	...	9.6	11.4	...	6.6	7.8	1.4	2.0	6.9	7.1
Total	32.0	36.5	40.9	...	25.2	28.1	5.5	5.5	27.1	19.6
U.S.S.R.	...	7.5	10.3	...	5.2	7.1	1.7	3.1	8.4	11.1
Asia										
Japan	...	2.4	11.5	...	1.7	7.9	1.2	3.4	5.9	12.1
India	...	6.4	10.1	...	4.4	7.0	1.8	2.6	8.9	9.3
China	...	1.4	4.5	...	1.0	3.1	0.4	2.2	1.9	7.9
Other	...	...	0.9	...	...	0.6	...	0.5	0.0	1.8
Total	...	10.2	27.0	...	7.1	18.6	3.4	8.7	16.7	31.1
Western hemisphere										
United States	19.3	31.5	25.3	...	21.8	17.4	4.9	6.4	24.1	22.9
Canada	0.5	0.9	1.1	...	0.6	0.8	0.1	0.3	0.5	1.1
Brazil	...	1.4	2.8	...	0.9	1.9	0.3	0.7	1.5	2.5
Mexico	0.4	0.7	0.9	...	0.5	0.6	0.1	0.2	0.5	0.7
Other	...	...	0.7	...	...	0.5	0.2	0.2	1.0	0.7
Total	20.2	34.5	30.8	...	23.8	21.2	5.6	7.8	27.6	27.9
Africa	...	...	...	...	...	...	...	0.1	...	0.3
World total		144.7	145.3		100.0	100.0	20.3	28.0	100.0	100.0

[a] Bales of 500 lb. gross, 478 lb. net.

tion in cotton textile manufacture in Europe, including Britain. The industry was largely wiped out in China and Japan. Recovery has been slow because of food, labor, and fuel shortages. Japan was the worst sufferer, the government having destroyed most of her

spindles in its desperate attempts to advance the war effort. Only 2.1 million spindles were being operated in 1947, as against the 11.5 million in 1939. The magnitude of the catastrophe is shown by the fact that in 1937 Japan supplied about 40 percent of the world's cotton textile exports.

[31] FAO, *World Fiber Survey*, August, 1947, p. 67.

BIBLIOGRAPHY

Agricultural Adjustment Administration, *'Round the World with Cotton,* Washington, 1944.

Alderfer, E. B., and Michl, H. E., *Economics of American Industry,* New York, McGraw-Hill, 1942.

"British Cotton," *Fortune,* August, 1946.

Burgy, J. H., *The New England Cotton Textile Industry,* Baltimore, Williams and Wilkins, 1932.

Copeland, M. T., *The Cotton Manufacturing Industry of the United States,* Cambridge, Harvard University Press, 1912.

Cotton Textile Institute, *Cotton from Raw Material to Finished Product,* New York, 1940.

Cox, A. B., "Cotton," *Encyclopædia of the Social Sciences,* New York, Macmillan, 1931.

Daniels, J., *A Southerner Discovers the South,* New York, Macmillan, 1938.

"Delta and Pine Lands," *Fortune,* March, 1937.

Dodd, W. E., *The Cotton Kingdom, Chronicles of America Series,* New Haven, Yale University Press, 1920, vol. 37.

Garside, A. H., *Cotton Goes to Market,* New York, Stokes, 1935.

Horne, R. L., and McKibben, E. G., *Mechanical Cotton Picker,* Philadelphia, Works Progress Administration, 1937.

Hubbard, W. H., *Cotton and the Cotton Market,* New York, Appleton-Century-Crofts, 1924.

International Institute of Agriculture, *The Cotton Growing Countries, Present and Potential,* London, King, 1926.

International Institute of Agriculture, *Studies of the Principal Agricultural Products on the World Market,* No. 1, *World Cotton Production and Trade,* Rome, 1934.

Johnston, O., "Will the Machine Ruin the South?" *Saturday Evening Post,* May 31, 1947.

Lepawsky, A., *State Planning and Economic Development in the South,* Washington, National Planning Association, 1949.

McIsaac, A. M., "The Cotton Textile Industry," in Adams, W., (ed.), *The Structure of American Industry,* New York, Macmillan, 1950, chap. 1.

Malott, D., and Martin, B. F., *The Agricultural Industries,* New York, McGraw-Hill, 1939, chap. 4.

Markham, J. W., "Integration in the Textile Industry," *Harvard Business Review,* January, 1950.

Murchison, C. T., *King Cotton Is Sick,* Chapel Hill, University of North Carolina Press, 1930.

National Cotton Council of America, *Cotton Statistics and Related Data* (loose-leaf, mimeographed), Memphis (annual).

Orchard, J. E., *Japan's Economic Position,* New York, McGraw-Hill, 1930.

Reed, W. O., "Competing Cottons and United States Production," *Economic Geography,* July, 1932.

Richards, H. L., *Cotton and the A.A.A.,* Washington, Brookings Institution, 1936.

Scherer, J. A. B., *Cotton as a World Power,* New York, Stokes, 1916.

Smith, B. B., *Factors Affecting the Price of Cotton,* Technical Bulletin No. 50, Washington, U. S. Department of Agriculture, 1928.

Smith, T. R., *The Cotton Textile Industry of Fall River, Massachusetts,* New York, King's Crown Press, 1944.

Stern, B., *Mechanical Changes in the Cotton Textile Industry, 1910-1936,* Philadelphia, Works Progress Administration, 1937.

"The Comers and Their Cotton Mills," *Fortune,* May, 1944.

U. S. Department of Agriculture, *The World Cotton Situation,* Parts I and II (mimeographed), Washington, 1936.

U. S. House of Representatives, Eightieth Congress, 1st session, *Study of Agricultural and Economic Problems of the Cotton Belt,* Hearings Before Special Subcommittee on Cotton of the Committee on Agriculture, Washington, July 7 and 8, 1947.

Vance, R. B., *Human Factors in Cotton Culture,* Chapel Hill, University of North Carolina Press, 1929.

Woofter, T. J., and others, *Landlord and Tenant on the Cotton Plantation,* Washington, Works Progress Administration, 1936.

"Will Clayton's Cotton," *Fortune,* November and December, 1945.

Chapter 20

OTHER NATURAL FIBERS

WOOL

Characteristics of Wool

Among apparel fibers sheep wool ranks second in value and third in quantity of output, having been surpassed by rayon in 1941.

Not all wool is fit for apparel use. About a third of the Argentine clip is generally classified as "carpet wool" and probably over half the wool produced in the U.S.S.R. falls into this category of coarse-grade wool used primarily in carpet making. Most of the Asiatic wool that enters world trade is in the same category.

Just as a sharp distinction must be made between seed cotton and lint cotton, so raw wool "in the grease" must be distinguished from scoured wool from which the grease, together with dirt and other foreign matter, has been removed. The weight loss resulting from the two refining processes—ginning cotton and scouring wool—are comparable, though more uniform in cotton and somewhat larger on the average—nearly two-thirds. The weight loss in wool, which is called shrinkage, ranges from 20 to 80 percent and probably averages under 50 percent. Although cottonseed has become a by-product of considerable value, the grease

removed from wool is worth much less. Its uses and the demand for it are quite limited, at least in normal times.

Whereas cotton is ginned near the field where it is picked, most wool is shipped "in the grease." According to a recent estimate, only about 7 percent of the wool exported from Australia and only about 5 percent of that from New Zealand is scoured. In the case of Texas, the largest wool-producing state in the United States, the ratio of scoured shipments to total shipments appears to be about the same.

There are several reasons for this seemingly wasteful procedure of shipping hundreds of millions of pounds of waste, near-waste, and low-value by-products halfway around the globe. The first and most important has to do with what may be called the anatomy of wool. Under the microscope the scoured wool fiber shows fine scales on the sides which give it an appearance not unlike a slim, elongated, and rather closely packed pine cone. These scales are as vital to the spinnability of wool as "the flat ribbon and the kink" of the cotton fiber are to its spinnability. The grease is a natural protection for these scales. If wool were scoured at the point of export, say Australia, and then packed in high-density bales, it would "felt"; i.e., the scales would interlock and thus produce a mesh of compressed fibers which are no longer spinnable.

In shipping scoured wool, therefore, it is necessary to safeguard the scales against damage. This is done by carding the wool, i.e., pulling it through teeth which lay the fibers parallel in loose slivers; these are carefully rolled up on large spools, which must then be carefully packaged. The process may be carried a step further by combing, whereby the "tops," i.e., the long fibers used for making worsted fabrics,[1] are separated from the "noils," i.e., the short fibers which may be used in making felt. The safe shipment of tops requires as careful spooling and packaging as does the shipment of carded wool.

Carded wool and tops, therefore, require considerable space. Moreover, the extra weight of the spools and boxes partly offsets the weight-reduction benefit gained by scouring. Finally, carded wool and tops do not enjoy the cheap freight rates generally accorded by both land and water carriers to basic raw materials such as raw wool.[2]

---

[1] Worsted fabrics have a smoother, wirier touch than woolen fabrics. The latter are softer and sometimes fuzzier, e.g., tweeds. Worsted fabrics are made of extra strong yarn spun from tops, whereas woolen fabrics are made of woolen yarn to which cotton, rayon, shoddy (re-used wool), carpet wool, and other matter are often added. Not all wools can be converted into tops and noils. Hence one may speak of woolen wools, meaning wools from which woolen yarns and woolen fabrics are made; and of worsted wools—wools from which the tops are combed and from which worsted yarns are spun. The distinction between woolen and worsted goods, therefore, is one involving both technical processes and the type of wool used.

[2] There are those who claim that, in general, such processes as carding and combing are best carried on in the same establishment in which the other processes take place, or at least in the same locality, thus assuring close personal contact between processors and manufacturers. The woolen and worsted mills of the United States and Europe do practically all their own carding, whereas "topping" is frequently done by separate firms but in close contact with the spinning and weaving mills that use the tops. A worsted mill may prefer to buy tops from independent top makers because it may thus be able to shift part of the inventory risk, or because the specialist may possess superior

Wool is either shorn from the live animal or "pulled" from the skin of the slaughtered animal. Most shorn wool is sold either "in the grease," or on a "scoured basis" or "clean basis." The same wool may sell for 60 cents a pound "in the grease" or for around $1.20 a pound on a "scoured basis." In the latter case the price relates to the number of pounds which the raw wool is expected to yield after ordinary commercial scouring and which here is assumed to be about half the weight of the raw wool. Pulled wool, chiefly a packing-house by-product, is generally quoted "scoured."

Classification

Wool is virtually unclassifiable. Wools may be divided into broad categories such as carpet and apparel wools or into the so-called woolen wools or worsted wools, i.e., raw wools which lend themselves to the manufacture of woolen and worsted yarns respectively.

TABLE 20.1. World Production of Raw Wool by Major Quality Categories, Prewar, 1947-1948, and 1948-1949[3]

	1934-1938		1947-1948		1948-1949	
	Metric Tons	Percent	Metric Tons	Percent	Metric Tons	Percent
Merino	645	37	553	33	595	34
Crossbred	682	40	749	44	741	43
Apparel type	1327	77	1302	77	1336	77
Carpet type	388	23	386	23	388	23
Total	1715	100	1688	100	1724	100

Beyond these broad categories more detailed classifications have been set up. A system long used in the United States was based originally on the blood of the sheep. Certain breeds of sheep, especially the Roman-Spanish Merino and in some areas the French Rambouillet, are known for their high yield of fine-quality wool. A full-blooded Merino sheep yielded so-called "fine" wool. The wool from a sheep with only

equipment and know-how. Hence tradition as well as vested rights may help to perpetuate long-established practices. This may, in part, account for the slow progress made by those who for some time have been trying to transfer scouring operations from the point of delivery to the country of origin.

[3] Food and Agriculture Organization, *Fibers*, Commodity Series Bulletin No. 14, August, 1949, p. 44.

half Merino blood was designated as ½ blood wool, and so on down to ¼ blood and low ¼ blood. The coarsest, and incidentally the longest, wools were designated "common" and "braid."

In England the so-called Bradford system classifies wools on the basis of the number of hanks of 560 yards each which one pound of wool will yield. The finest wools, i.e., those with the smallest diameter, give the most hanks of yarn per pound. Now the two systems are used interchangeably in the United States.

TABLE 20.2.   Relationship of Bradford and Blood Classifications, and Percentage of Apparel Wool Consumption in the United States, Three-Year Average, 1936-1938

Grade		
Bradford	Blood	Percent
64s, 70s, 80s	fine	38.6
58s, 60s	½ blood	13.6
56s	⅜ blood	21.6
48s, 50s	¼ blood	15.6
46s	low ¼ blood	
44s	common	10.6
36s	braid	

Table 20.2 shows the relationship of the classes in the two systems, together with United States mill consumption of apparel wool by these grades in 1936-1938.[4] But these are only rough divisions, little more than rallying points in an infinite array of classes and subclasses, types and subtypes.[5]

The inadequacy of wool classification has serious repercussions. It affects the wool trade and through it the manufacturing industries depending on wool. In the first place, future trading, i.e., the buying and selling of contracts calling for future delivery of wool of a specified class or type or quality, is more or less out of the question.[6] As a result, manufacturers of

woolen and worsted goods are exposed to the risk of fluctuating raw-material prices far more than are the manufacturers of cotton textiles or wheat flour and many other processed or manufactured foodstuffs.

In the second place, as an aid to classification, great importance is attached by the wool trade to the region in which the wool originates. The geographical features and customary practices in a region have a definite bearing on quality and help to identify wools, thus supplementing or aiding classification. Thus, in the United States wools are known as (1) Texas wools; (2) territory wools, those grown in the range area west of the Mississippi, other than Texas; and (3) domestic or fleece wools, those grown in the farm-land areas mostly east of the Mississippi. This third group includes Ohio delaine, the finest wool grown in this country.[7]

Similarly in the case of carpet wools quality is to some extent associated with the point of origin. Thus, East Indian wools are carefully subdivided into regional classes, such as the highly prized Bikaneres that come from the state of Bikaner and the adjoining territory of the Punjab, and the Joris wools that come from Cutch and western India.[8]

Probably the most telling effect of lack of dependable standards is the resort to public auction sales as the most satisfactory method of selling the bulk of the world's wool clip. By far the most important wool auctions are held in London and this city has thus retained, in the case of wool at least, part of the preëminence as an entrepôt that she long enjoyed but later lost as regards many other commodities. As a result, a large share of the world's wool clip is physically concentrated at one point of the globe to which buyers from many wool-manufacturing countries are attracted. That this has contributed greatly to maintaining England's position as a leading manufacturer of

---

[4] National Bureau of Economic Research, *Textile Markets*, New York, 1939, p. 20.

[5] The difficulties of standardizing wool types are illustrated by the fact that the British government's purchase plan in force during World War II made it necessary, for purposes of appraisal, to draw up tables of limits that showed 1500 classified types of Australian wool, 950 of New Zealand wool, and 350 of South African wool; relatively few types of any one Dominion's clip were common to another's. See FAO, *World Fiber Survey*, August, 1947, p. 82.

[6] Attempts have been made to introduce future

trading in wool but they were limited in scope and never fully successful. Since wool tops are much more uniform and hence can be classified more easily, they lend themselves much better to future trading. Actually future trading in wool tops is carried on in such leading wool trading centers as New York, Antwerp, Belgium, and Tourcoing-Roubaix, France.

[7] See National Bureau of Economic Research, *op. cit.*, p. 21.

[8] See FAO, *World Fiber Survey*, p. 86.

woolen and worsted goods goes without saying.[9]

Wools of British, including Dominion, origin predominate at the London auctions. The political setup may thus reinforce, or help to maintain, a commercial or economic development. That United States and Russian wools do not reach the London auctions is only natural, for neither country exports wool to any extent; their wools are consumed at home. But the fact that, since World War I, the bulk of the South American wools have been marketed without recourse to the London auctions suggests that political solidarity may have something to do with maintaining London as the trading center for wools of British origin.

Moreover, changes on the demand side may also have had an effect on the decline of the London market. The London auction sales were at their height at a time when the bulk of wool was sold to British, United States, and continental European manufacturers and merchants. As Australia, Japan, and other nations entered the list of wool-manufacturing countries, London proved less satisfactory as a global collecting point and auction sales in the Dominions disposed of part of the clip.

Geography of Wool Production

Some wool is produced in nearly every country in the world, but the bulk of the apparel wool is produced in relatively few countries. The leading producers of both apparel and carpet wool during selected periods from 1934 to 1947 are shown in Table 20.3.

An analysis of the apparel wool producers reveals the following facts: (1) The southern hemisphere is represented by five countries, all of them raw-material exporting countries. Their aggregate contribution to the world's total wool clip was over 900 thousand metric tons, or almost 60 percent. Australia alone contributed over one-fourth of the world total. (2) The British Commonwealth of Nations is represented by five countries aggregating almost half of the total apparel clip. This makes wool the most British of all the major agricultural staples

and recalls the time long ago when the British were predominantly shepherds. Britain's economic influence over Argentina and Uruguay, which continues strong into the present, reinforces this impression. (3) The leading wool-manufacturing countries—the United States, Great Britain, Germany, and France—all maintain domestic sheep flocks either because this fits into their agricultural pattern or because they value sheep for mutton and lamb as well as for wool or because they wish to cut down their dependence on outside supplies in favor of a domestic sheep industry.

The latter applies in particular to the United States, in 1934-1938 the second apparel wool-producing country in the world. (During World War II, however, her production declined and the ranking of the wool-growing countries changed accordingly.) As was pointed out in Chapter 18, wool is essentially a *land fiber;* i.e., abundant cheap land is usually the first prerequisite of a successful wool-growing industry. This country has large areas of such land, though not in the same abundance as has Australia or Argentina or South Africa. But the United States is at the same time the leading manufacturing nation of the world. This strange dualism in her economic life—the fact that she is at one and the same time the leading manufacturing and the leading agricultural nation—has created many economic dilemmas. A highly mature industrial country, especially if it is the world's leading creditor, cannot afford to try to compete with less mature economies, especially if they are debtor countries. Even though the United States has land that can support wool sheep, she may have to leave that particular enterprise to other countries who can only produce wool or at least little else and cannot produce automobiles and electric appliances as cheaply as she can. Her price level and wage standards, which take their cue from the industrial character of her national economy, pervade her entire system and adversely affect the cost basis of her agriculture, especially the segments that cannot be mechanized or are dependent on extensive methods. The nation is thus torn between consideration for its welfare as a whole, and consideration for the welfare of specific regions. National and regional interests clash. So long as, and to the extent that, the national government is a conglomerate of

---

[9] Incidentally, this gathering of wools from half the world for personal inspection, fleece by fleece, batch by batch, by international buyers probably has as much to do with forestalling the transfer of the scouring business from the manufacturing countries to the raw-material producing centers as any one single factor.

TABLE 20.3. Apparel Wool and Carpet Wool Production, by Main Groups of Producing Countries, Selected Periods, 1934-1947[10]

Groups of Wool-Producing Countries	1934-1938	1939-1943	1945-1946	1946-1947[a]	1934-1938	1939-1943	1945-1946	1946-1947[a]
	(1000 metric tons, greasy)				(percent of world total)			
Apparel wool (merino and crossbred)								
Five main surplus countries								
Australia	451.78	504.39	398.25	453.59	26.2	28.5	24.6	27.6
Argentina[b]	171.46	211.37	230.42	210.92	9.9	11.9	14.2	12.8
New Zealand	135.62	146.96	160.12	167.83	7.9	8.3	9.9	10.3
South Africa	113.40	116.12	88.45	86.18	6.6	6.6	5.5	5.2
Uruguay	50.35	57.15	62.14	72.57	2.9	3.2	3.8	4.4
Total	922.61	1035.99	939.38	991.09	53.5	58.5	58.0	60.3
Five main deficit countries								
United States	205.48	201.85	175.09	154.22	11.9	11.4	10.8	9.3
United Kingdom	49.89	44.45	38.10	27.22	2.9	2.5	2.4	1.7
France	24.49	19.05	15.42	9.07	1.5	1.1	1.0	0.6
Germany	17.69	21.32	13.61	13.61	1.0	1.2	0.8	0.8
Canada	8.62	7.71	8.62	6.80	0.5	0.4	0.5	0.4
Total	306.17	294.38	250.84	210.92	17.8	16.6	15.5	12.8
Other countries	147.42	105.69	116.12	113.40	8.6	6.0	7.1	6.9
Apparel wool total	1376.20	1436.06	1306.34	1315.41	79.9	81.1	80.6	80.0
Carpet wool								
Three main producing countries								
U.S.S.R.[b]	95.26	133.36	104.33	117.93	5.5	7.5	6.5	7.2
China	49.89	40.82	40.82	40.83	2.9	2.3	2.5	2.5
India	45.36	36.74	36.29	36.29	2.6	2.2	2.2	2.2
Total	190.51	210.92	181.44	195.05	11.0	12.0	11.2	11.9
Other countries	156.49	122.92	132.90	132.90	9.1	6.9	8.2	8.1
Carpet wool total	347.00	333.84	314.34	327.95	20.1	18.9	19.4	20.0
Grand total	1723.20	1769.90	1620.68	1643.36	100.0	100.0	100.0	100.0

[a] Preliminary estimates.
[b] Based on classifications adopted in *U.K. Dominions Wool Disposals*, Board of Trade, Cm. 6855, His Majesty's Stationery Office, London. According to U. S. Department of Agriculture standards, approximately one-third of the Argentine clip is classified as "carpet," and 40 to 50 percent of the U.S.S.R.'s clip as "apparel." Slightly different classifications were adopted tentatively in the *Report of the First Meeting of the International Wool Study Group*, London, March-April, 1947. New standards for the classification of main types of wool are now being worked out by a technical subcommittee and will be considered by the next full meeting of the Wool Study Group. FAO's decision concerning standards of classification will await the outcome of the Study Group's work. Pending this decision, it is considered convenient, for the purpose of this summary table, not to split up the clips of main producing countries but to arrange the country-totals according to main categories.

[10] FAO, *World Fiber Survey*, p. 83.

regional pressure groups that lack a strong uni-fied viewpoint, regional pressure groups will win through logrolling and horsetrading and national interests will be subordinated to local interests.

The United States was able to maintain her place as a leading wool-growing country only by keeping out, by means of scandalously high tariffs, the cheaper and often superior wools from the natural sheep regions of the earth, especially the southern hemisphere. Even while her representatives at Geneva were fighting for sounder principles of international trade, the wool lobby was again trying to turn the screw of protectionism one thread higher. Fortunately President Truman vetoed the bill, which he called "a tragic mistake."

As far as carpet wool is concerned, about one-fifth of the world's commercial wool clip is considered carpet wool (see Table 20.3). Of this, about three-fifths comes from Asia, the rest from South America. Some carpet wool finds its way into the apparel market, where it is used to obtain special effects as in tweeds or is mixed with "woolen" wools for other woolen weaves. But the bulk goes into carpets, upholstery, and similar uses calling for coarser fiber and lower prices.

Production Problems

The economics of wool production is infi-nitely more complex than that of cotton. The fact that cotton is an annual crop renders feasible, within reasonable limits, adjustment of the supply to predictable demand by means of acreage control. To be sure, the adjustment is far from perfect, as the discussion of cotton clearly revealed. But sheep are perennials, i.e., organisms whose life span extends over a num-ber of years.[11] In general it holds true that the longer the life cycle the greater the difficulties of adjusting supply to demand.

The situation is complicated by the fact that the sheep yields not only wool but also meat—mutton and lamb—and such minor products as skin, tallow, fertilizer, etc. The sheep flocks throughout the earth vary widely in regard to the relative importance of these various prod-ucts as sources of income.

The situation in wool is quite different from

that in cotton. Cotton too gives several prod-ucts—lint, and seed which yields oil, hulls, meal, and linters. But lint is always *the chief* product; the others are never more than by-products. Sheep are different. Some yield pri-marily meat with wool as a by-product. Still others are about equally valued for wool and meat, the two constituting joint products rather than main and by-products.

By breeding, through the ages, definite wool and meat types of sheep were developed and during the nineteenth century a third, the crossbred, was developed. Among the wool types the merino, which may be traced back to the Spain of Roman times and which laid the basis of the Australian wool-growing indus-try, is the most famous. Among the meat types English breeds like the Cotswold, the Shrop-shire, and the Lincoln are probably best known. Until improvements in ocean transportation, especially the introduction of refrigeration in the 1880's, rendered feasible the shipment of meats over such long distances as from South America or even Australia and New Zealand to Europe, mutton types of sheep were pre-ferred in the areas closest to consumption cen-ters; the distant overseas territories specialized in wool types. When industrialization and mechanization created in Europe, and espe-cially in Great Britain, large markets for over-seas food imports, refrigeration offered these distant countries the opportunity to add meat to their list of exports, and a wholesale shift from wool types to crossbred types took place in New Zealand, Argentina, and Uruguay. To-day possibly 98 percent of the New Zealand wool clip and 86 percent of that of Argentina and Uruguay comes from crossbred sheep.[12]

Conditions in Australia and South Africa are not nearly so favorable to the maintenance of crossbred flocks and the development of mutton exports as they are in the other sheep countries of the southern hemisphere. On the whole, the crossbred sheep has proved a far better invest-ment than the pure wool type; returns are greater and more stable. This greater profit-ability in turn accounts for the forging ahead during the second half of the past century of the southern hemisphere as the world's sheep center.

---

[11] This theme of annuals versus perennials will be systematically developed in chap. 22.

[12] See FAO, *World Fiber Survey*, p. 84.

Not only did flocks increase rapidly, but through breeding and care of the pasture the yield of wool was increased in spite of the shift from wool to crossbred types in much of this area. The yield was doubled in about sixty-five years, a remarkable achievement in animal breeding and improved husbandry.

The dual dependence of the crossbred sheep industry on the wool and the meat markets creates problems. The demand for mutton is subject to consumers' whims; people apparently tire of mutton from time to time. These unpredictable ups and downs not only render the meat business uncertain but have repercussions on the wool market. For the lower price for mutton in these "doldrums" of demand tends to be reflected in a stiffening of wool prices. If the wool market cannot stand this pressure, perhaps because of style changes or interfiber competition or depression conditions in the textile market in general, the economic basis of the sheep economy will be undermined, i.e., marginal production will drop out and flocks will be reduced. Because sheep are "perennials," such maladjustments are felt over far longer periods than is generally the case of annuals such as vegetable fibers.

Nor need this cycle of disturbance start from the mutton side. It may just as readily originate in the wool market, for it too is subject to unpredictable ups and downs which may be even more violent than fluctuations in the demand for mutton. On the whole, however, it may be assumed that the dual dependence on meat and wool is preferable to a more one-sided dependence on one or the other of the two joint products. For, while each at times is a disturbing element in the supply and demand situation of the other, the general effect of the sheepman's double basis of income is, in the long run, likely to be beneficial not only in greater aggregate returns but even in more stability.

One of the factors affecting future wool supplies is soil erosion and consequent deterioration of pastures due to overgrazing. This problem to a considerable extent lies beyond the control of the individual stockman or outside the scope of remedial action by him. Fortunately, a fuller realization of this deadly long-run danger seems to be developing in wool-raising countries, and it is to be hoped that this will lead to effective concerted action. To be effective, it *must* be concerted. Erosion control is one area where sole reliance on private initiative falls short of offering a solution.

Actually the sheep situation is more complicated than the foregoing account in terms of three basic types may lead one to assume. The following gives an idea of the complexity of the sheep business.

While using the customary and convenient broad division between "merino" and "crossbred" production, it should be borne in mind that, in reality, the classification of types of sheep by returns is more gradual and more complex. J. E. Nichols, in *A Study of Empire Wool Production*, Leeds, 1932, states: "Sheep may be grouped into eight main types according to the nature of the return secured by the breeder; Australia furnishes examples of most of them. In general, the progression from one type to another follows that of the zones of origin and is imposed upon the progression from pastoral to agricultural conditions. Thus in the merino zone occur sheep, chiefly wether, which are kept as wool producers only (type 1), and breeding sheep, which return profit by the sale of their castrated male offspring as potential wool producers (type 2). These are succeeded largely within the 'come-back' and quarterbred zone by animals which are bred for the purpose of producing wethers' offspring as potential wool and mutton producers (type 3) and which have a greater rate of increase (or higher fertility . . .) and so supply surplus stock, of both sexes, for breeding and for wool and mutton production (type 4). In all these the production of wool is the main issue and the stock is predominantly of merino kind, but successive crossing with Long Wool and then Down Stock, leads gradually to the higher developed mutton forms, such as wool-producing 'half-bred' ewes, whose offspring are largely used as a basis for mutton-production (type 5); wool-producing ewes whose wether lambs are sold for early mutton and fat lamb, and whose ewe lambs are kept to breed fat lamb (type 6); and cross-bred ewes themselves finished for mutton after their useful life as the mothers of early-maturing lambs is ended (type 7). The incidence, in Australia, of the eighth type of pure-bred mutton ewes producing cross-bred lambs, is small. It will be noted that the progression is also towards early maturity of offspring."[13]

World Trade in Raw Wool

The world trade in wool is dominated on the export side by the five sheep countries of the

---

[13] *Ibid.*, p. 89, footnote 6.

TABLE 20.4.   Distribution of World Wool Exports[14]
(1000 metric tons actual weight, and percentages)

Importing Countries	Shipments from Five Chief Exporting Countries			
	1909–1913	1924–1928	1934–1938	1945–1946[a]
United Kingdom (retained)	174.6	180.5	221.3	214.5
	26.6%	24.5%	26.6%	22.0%
France	149.2	170.5	147.4	87.3
	22.8%	23.1%	17.8%	8.9%
Belgium	79.8	75.7	102.0	49.6
	12.1%	10.3%	12.3%	5.1%
Germany	156.5	137.4	93.4	0
	23.9%	18.6%	11.3%	0
Rest of Continental Europe	20.9	53.5	99.3	138.6
	3.2%	7.3%	12.0%	14.2%
European Continent, excluding U.S.S.R.	406.4	437.2	442.1	275.5
	62.0%	59.3%	53.4%	28.2%
United States	58.0	68.9	52.2	436.1
	8.9%	9.3%	6.3%	44.7%
Japan	5.0	35.8	84.8	. . .
	0.8%	4.9%	10.2%	. . .
Others	10.9	14.5	29.0	49.4
	1.7%	2.0%	3.5%	5.1%
Total (100%)	654.9	736.8	829.4	975.6

[a] Preliminary.

southern hemisphere. During the period 1936–1938 these five countries supplied about 86 percent of all wool exports. Except in the case of Argentina, whose agriculture is highly diversified—it includes wheat, corn (maize), cattle, linseed, fruit, wine, and quebracho—wool constitutes a major item in the export trade of these countries, for Uruguay almost half, for Australia and South Africa over a third, and for New Zealand over a fourth.

It is a peculiarity of the wool export trade that it shuns carry-overs from one clip year to the other. This means that wool prices fall sharply in times of contracting demand. This is particularly true of crossbred wools whose producers rely on the less erratic behavior of meat prices as a partial hedge. They can afford, therefore, to take serious punishment in the wool market and still survive, being subsidized more generously, as it were, by the mutton market. That violent fluctuations of wool prices are a bane to the manufacturer who in the

[14] Ibid., p. 95.

absence of a futures market cannot protect himself by hedging goes without saying.

Table 20.4 shows the pattern of distribution of world wool exports for the five leading exporting countries.

Since the period covered by the table includes two world wars the pattern shows marked changes. About the only market area that seems to have survived more or less intact is that of the United Kingdom. (Note that the data cover only "retained" wool imports, which means that reëxports are excluded. In other words, the table shows ultimate market destinations and not physical movements of trade. If the latter were shown, the United Kingdom market would loom much larger.) Throughout the period of about thirty-seven years that country absorbed around one-quarter of the wool exports. On the other hand, continental Europe tumbled from 62 percent in 1909–1913 to 28.2 in 1945–1946. Naturally, for Germany is wiped off the map for the time being, and she was the biggest buyer in the pre-World War I period. France was not yet back on her feet, nor was Belgium. The increase from 3.2 to 14.2 percent for the rest of Europe indicates that during the past three decades the woolen and worsted industries that were once centered in Europe and the United States have been greatly decentralized—a reflection of the political changes wrought by Versailles and after.

Equally dramatic is the jump of United States imports from 6.3 percent in 1934-1938 to 44.7 in 1945-1946. This increase is first of all a logical aftereffect of our enormous wool consumption during wartime. But it also reflects the sudden recovery, actual or anticipated, of civilian demand for woolen and worsted goods as well as the decline of the domestic wool clip during the war, caused by labor scarcity and the fact that cropping, cattle raising, and dairying proved more profitable than wool production.

Nor are the figures any less dramatic for Japan, with her increase from 0.8 percent in 1909-1913 to 10.2 in 1934-1938. The blank for 1945-1946 is not surprising. The pall of atomic smoke had hardly cleared from Hiroshima and Nagasaki.

Wool Control During and After World War II

Wool is a strategic commodity of the first order. The armed forces are voracious consumers of it. The uncertainty of the shipping situation in wartime, particularly serious in the case of overseas supplies of wool which come from distant sources, renders difficult the adequate procurement of wool supplies for the armed forces. In order to make certain that their needs are met and to prevent a runaway market from raising prices to fantastic heights, governments in wartime take stringent measures to control the wool market.

Thus, two weeks after the outbreak of World War II the British government announced the conclusion of agreements to purchase the entire Australian and New Zealand wool clip for the duration of the war and one wool year thereafter. Six weeks later a similar agreement was concluded with the South African government. Prices at first were held about one-third above 1938 prices and later raised to just over 50 percent above the prewar average.[15] Since wool was rationed and its manufacture curtailed, the

ordinary marketing process, built chiefly around auction sales, was revamped and the complex lists of quality types mentioned above (see p. 348) were drawn up. In the United States the government at first guaranteed the domestic wool clip and in 1943 actually took it over. The law required that fabrics purchased by the armed services should, so far as practicable, be made from home-grown wool. The Commodity Credit Corporation (CCC) acted as the marketing agent.

In spite of the fact that wartime wool consumption in the United States and in several newly industrialized countries such as Australia, Argentina, and India rose rather sharply, only about two-thirds of the current supplies of apparel wool available in the chief exporting countries were absorbed during the war, and a total of about two years' supply was left over. This is explained by the decline of consumption, especially in Europe but also in Great Britain.

Just as after World War I a similar carryover was liquidated by a special agency, the BAWRA (British-Australian Wool Realization Association), set up for the purpose, so again after World War II a special agency was created to perform a similar function, though on a wider scale. The main object was to relieve Britain of the sole responsibility for the wartime accumulation. Her stock was therefore transferred to a joint organization, the U.K.-Dominions Wool Disposals, Ltd., a private registered company that was given wide powers to see the British wool economy through the difficult period of postwar adjustment. To facilitate the task it was decided to resume the London and Dominion auction sales as soon as practical; they were resumed in September, 1946.

Wool vs. Synthetics

Clean or scoured wool sold in the United States in 1949 at prices more than four times as high as those for "wool" types of rayon staple[16] and for cotton. This price relationship

---

[15] See *ibid.*, p. 97.

[16] Rayon staple is rayon fiber chopped up into short lengths similar to that of cotton and wool fibers. "Wool" types of rayon staple are those which in diameter, length, and other respects are patterned after wool; they are used mainly as an admixture to or an adulterant of wool.

suggests two thoughts: (1) that wool may be in a vulnerable position in interfiber competition and (2) that it must possess properties for which a heavy premium is being paid. All commodity competition rests on two sets of considerations: (1) the peculiar uses and properties of the commodity and (2) its cost in comparison with that of other commodities serving similar uses and having similar properties.

The chief superior qualities of natural wool are warmth-giving properties, reversible elasticity, felting properties, and water repellence. So long and in so far as these qualities are sought in preference to other qualities of other fibers for a sufficient number of sufficiently important uses, wool is safe in its lofty castle of high prices. To what extent this condition prevails depends on a complex set of circumstances. Thus, for example, improved heating and improved diets may have a tendency to cut down the physical need for warmth-giving clothing. On the other hand, high incomes may enable a larger number of people to indulge in unnecessarily large wardrobes selected for style appeal. Thus a shift such as that from Japanese cotton and silk to wool after World War I and the countershift after World War II cannot fail to leave their imprint on the wool market situation.

The advance in the scientific knowledge of diverse competing fabrics and the technical know-how of their treatment has much to do with their competitive stamina. The synthetic fibers are the true offspring of science. The research laboratory is the very heart of the synthetic industry. Compared with the modern synthetic industries, agriculture ranks little above the time-honored rule of thumb. But under the competitive impact of synthetic fibers, those who depend on natural fibers for their economic existence are turning to science as their savior. The results are encouraging. Thus, recent progress in efforts to evolve a nonshrinkable and mothproof wool proves how greatly science can improve on a natural product. Recent research into the molecular structure of wool may yield revolutionary results.

Wool not only faces the competition from other natural fibers and synthetic fibers, but more than any other fiber it faces the problem of re-use. Virgin wool is beset by competition from shoddy or mungo, as re-used wool is called. Moreover, woolen goods containing not only shoddy but possibly carpet wool or cotton or rayon staple compete with worsteds made from pure wool tops. The argument sometimes advanced, that the lower cost and hence lower prices of adulterated woolen goods will widen the market, is none too strong. For the raw-material cost constitutes but a minor element, say 7 to 15 percent, of the retail price of the finished product, such as a man's suit. The cost reduction through adulteration constitutes a still smaller amount which cannot possibly stimulate demand sufficiently to offset the reduction in the use of virgin wool. Moreover, consumer education in the wearing qualities of different fibers may remove the little price appeal that adulteration offers.

SILK

The Debacle of Silk

In turning from cotton and wool to silk one instinctively feels the need of changing the tense from the present and future to the past. For, while more or less all natural fibers are beginning to feel the competitive pressure of man-made products, while both cotton and wool are yielding ground especially to rayon and nylon, silk, at present at least, looks like a "has-been."

Silk is one of the oldest fibers known to man. The silkworm has been cultivated in China for many hundreds, perhaps thousands, of years. Sometime around 300 A.D. the secret of silk production leaked out of China; and sericulture, as the cultivation of silk is called, spread over a broad region—westward over India, Afghanistan, Iran (Persia), to Syria, and into the Mediterranean region as far as the Rhone valley of France and the Po valley of Italy where Lyons and Milan respectively became centers of the silk industry.

As recently as the 1920's silk was still one of the leading apparel fibers known to man, not in quantity to be sure, but in the aggregate value of its commercial output. Average annual raw silk production during the period 1925-1929 was slightly less than 90 million pounds. But while cotton and wool were "cents" fibers, silk was quoted in dollars per pound. During the wild speculative boom of the twenties its price went as high as $9.00 a pound. Even at

$5.00 a pound 90 million pounds bring $450 million. In fact, the 1929 silk imports of the United States alone were valued at more than $427 million. And this is more than a whole jute crop of 4 billion pounds brings at 4 cents a pound.

This boom resulted from a strange interaction of events on both sides of the Pacific. In Japan Commodore Perry had forced the doors of Nippon and ushered in that strange era of pseudo-westernization which sought to mix old-fashioned Samurai feudalism with modern machine capitalism. In the United States rising standards of living and especially the wild stock market boom of the 1920's had created a huge demand for Japanese silk. Clerks and laborers sported ten- and fifteen-dollar silk shirts made, perhaps, from silk costing $9 a pound, and stenographers preferred silk hose at $3 a pair to a square meal.

On this side of the Pacific our insatiable demand was driving silk prices to fantastic heights and seeking ever-larger imports, mostly from Japan. Across the Pacific, bank directors and corporation chairmen held in feudal or quasi-feudal bondage vast numbers of peasant families who raised the mulberry shrubs and tended the cocoons, and equally vast numbers of filature[17] girls, paying next to nothing for the peasants' exacting labor and the mill girls' highly skilled work. Thus a price that was soaring skyward because of the speculative craze of a capitalism gone mad was commanded by a commodity produced at costs deflated by a feudalistic pseudo-capitalism. The hundreds of millions of dollars of profits that poured into the hands of Japanese bankers, industrialists, and merchants had much to do with building up not only Japan's industrial strength but her military and naval power as well.

But the Wall Street boom collapsed, ushering in the Great Depression. Ten-dollar silk shirts went out of fashion and silk was going begging at $2 a pound, or some such price. In the meantime, the rayon industry had forged ahead, offering ever better products at ever lower prices. And much later came nylon, not a substitute for silk but its equal if not its superior in some respects, not bought, as much of rayon was bought, because it was cheap.

World War II dealt a further blow to silk. Japan's mulberry plantations gave way to cropped fields that would produce food for her armies; her filatures were destroyed for the scrap metal that could be used in her war effort, and the workers were herded into munitions plants. No chapter in the history of any industry that has ever existed is more dramatic and more tragic. In a few short years Japan's silk industry plunged from fantastic prosperity to almost unbelievable, perhaps unredeemable, hopelessness. When the MacArthur regime tried to sell Japanese silk after the war, any illusion it may have had about silk's capacity to recapture its market position was soon shattered on the realities of a most disappointing market price.

Technology[18]

The silkworm has four stages of growth: (1) the egg, (2) the worm, (3) the chrysalis, which lives inside the cocoon spun by the worm, and (4) the moth, which breaks the cocoon as it emerges and lays the eggs which start the cycle again. The cocoon *is* the silk; it consists of about a thousand yards of silk. Of this, about half is discarded as waste (but utilized as a waste product). For the innermost layers are too fine and weak and the outermost layers, which anchor the cocoon to the leaf and tree, are coarse, tough, and frequently broken.

The processing of silk preparatory to weaving or knitting is done in two stages: (1) the preparation of *raw* silk for shipment, especially export; and (2) the making of *thrown* silk yarn or thread ready to be woven or knitted. The first operation takes place in a reeling mill, or filature. Filatures are located near the centers of sericulture and hence may be viewed as processing appendages to this industry. The preparation of thrown silk, on the other hand, is closely associated with the silk-weaving and silk-knitting industries where it is manufactured into fabrics, hosiery, underwear, etc.

In preparing raw silk, the filature girls and women, standing before individual basins of water in which the cocoons are floating, un-

---

[17] A filature is the mill in which the cocoons are unwound and the cocoon fiber reeled into so-called raw silk.

[18] This discussion is based largely on National Bureau of Economic Research, *op. cit.*, pp. 29-32.

ravel the cocoons and feed generally from 5 to 10 fibers[19] into a strand which is reeled on revolving drums. The reeling replaces spinning, the length of the cocoon fiber obviating the need for the spinning which is necessary to combine shorter fibers into yarn. However, broken pieces of cocoon fiber (they are called schappe) must be spun. Thus the product of the filature consists of skeins of raw silk ready for shipment.

Raw silk is converted into thrown silk after it has been shipped to where it will be knitted or woven. There are three steps in preparing thrown silk: (1) the "boil off," (2) "weighting," and (3) "throwing." The purpose of the boil off cannot be understood without some knowledge of how the silk is secreted by the silkworm. The silkworm has two silk glands, each of which leads to an orifice located below the mouth of the worm. In spinning its cocoon, the worm secretes one filament of silk, or fibroin, through each of these two orifices. These two filaments are cemented together by another secretion called sericin which, like the silk itself, hardens on contact with the air. The boil off removes the sericin and leaves the two filaments separated and exposed. The sericin weighs roughly one-fifth of the weight of standard raw silk; it was this weight loss that led to the practice of weighting, i.e., restoring the original weight by the addition of tin salts. In actual practice, weighting frequently exceeds this modest limit.

Historically silk is tied up with royalty and caste, with aristocrats and nabobs. To say that it does not go as well with democracy as it did with the snobbish display of the privileged classes may be putting it too strong. But when silk became a mass-consumption good of the masses in industrialized centers, its scanty supply had to be stretched; hence many a shiny garment contained more of the metal used for "weighting" than of silk itself.

The weighted silk consists of loose bundles of fibers. These bundles are subjected to a twisting operation known as throwing; firms that do this operation are known as throwsters. The throwing process converts the silk into a yarn which is now ready for the weaving or knitting mill; several yarns may be combined into a thread.

Geography of Sericulture

Like most vegetable fibers and unlike most animal fibers, silk is definitely a *labor fiber*. As was explained in Chapter 18, this means that labor is the key to its location. Silk production involves hard, exacting, and, in part, highly skilled labor. Sericulture can thrive only where an adequate supply of cheap labor—i.e., *really*, not spuriously, cheap—is available. It gravitates toward "the marginal coolie" and this means in general the densely populated centers of Asia.

Sericulture as it was practiced during the nineteenth century in the Rhone and Po valleys was really not much more than a seasonal supplementation of intensive agriculture. The mulberry tree culture of these areas was strictly seasonal; there was one crop of leaves and one crop of silkworms a year. But in large sections of Asia, especially parts of China and Japan, the mulberry can be cultivated as a shrub which yields fresh leaves during most of the year. This, however, requires a great deal of labor, more probably than the French and Italian peasants could spare from their general chores. While, therefore, in Europe the *Bombyx mori* was the mainstay of sericulture, in Asia, especially in Japan, the *Bombyx polyvoltina*, which can be bred successfully during the larger part of the year, became the mainstay. Moreover, sericulture in Europe was geared to a rational crop rotation system.

When Europe's silkworm production suffered serious ravages from disease, Japan took over in earnest. Mulberry trees replaced cotton and their culture came to occupy approximately 10 percent of her cultivated land. No less than 2,200,000 Japanese peasants were partially or wholly occupied in sericulture in 1929.[20] In 1933-1937 cocoon production constituted 12

[19] The number of cocoons combined in the reeling process depends on the yarn to be made from the raw silk. The natural silk filament is 1¼ to 1½ denier (i.e., 9000 meters of it weigh 1¼ to 1½ grams). Hosiery yarns are usually 13/15 denier and are thrown from raw silk reeled from 5 or 6 cocoons (each cocoon fiber consists of two filaments). Weaving yarns are usually 20/22 denier and are thrown from raw silk reeled from 9 or 10 cocoons.

[20] Ruth E. K. Peterson, "Raw Silk," *Japanese Trade Studies*, Special Industry Analysis No. 10, mimeographed, quoted in FAO, *World Fiber Survey*, p. 111.

percent of the total value of Japan's agricultural production. In addition, about 800,000 workers were engaged in reeling and weaving.[21]

When the all-important United States market for Japanese silk collapsed in 1929, it did not take the Japanese long to realize that something had to be done to stave off disaster. A broad program of rationalization looking to increased yields and lower costs was instituted. Improved mulberry seedlings and high-yield egg strains were distributed among farmers; the latter were licensed and held to strict accountability. Similarly the silk-processing industries were ruthlessly "rationalized"; i.e., inefficient filatures were scrapped, small weaving mills were closed, labor productivity was stepped up all along by surprising amounts. How well Japan succeeded in not only maintaining but even enlarging her production and considerably increasing her share of the world output is shown in Table 20.5. Thus Japanese production increased from 14,100 metric tons in 1911-1915 to 34,100 in 1924-1928, two-thirds of the world production, and to 42,500 tons in 1934-1938,

TABLE 20.5.   Raw Silk: Estimated Production by Countries, Selected Periods, 1911-1946[22] (1000 metric tons)

Country	1911-1915	1924-1928	1934-1938	1947	1948
Japan	14.1	34.1	42.3	6.7[b]	8.1[b]
Korea	0.1	0.9	...	...	...
China	9.0[a]	9.0[a]	4.7[a]	0.5	0.4
Italy	3.6	4.6	2.6	2.3	1.0
U.S.S.R.	...	0.8	1.5	1.5	1.5
Others	2.5	1.5	2.8	1.5	1.5
Total	29.3	50.9	53.9	12.5	12.5

[a] Exports.
[b] Commercial production only.

three-fourths of the world total. Her poor showing in 1946 is not surprising considering the times.

As was mentioned before, efforts to sell Japanese silk in the United States in 1946 and 1947 proved most disappointing. A program was drawn up calling for the sale of 8400 tons in 1946, this to be increased to 11,300 tons by 1950. Actually 5000 tons were shipped to the

United States in 1946, approximately three-fourths of which was still unsold at the end of the year. Even though the price had dropped to $4.40 a pound in 1947 and to $2.60 in 1948, the silk was hard to move. Hosiery seemed to be the best hope for silk, but apparently that field has been preëmpted by nylon in the upper brackets and by rayon in the lower. In 1946 only 4 percent of the hose sold in the United States were silk, as against 76 percent in 1940.[23]

FLAX

Production

The flax plant *linum* is valued for two widely different products, the oil-bearing seed and a bast fiber from which linen is made. In spite of vigorous efforts, the attempt to make the same plant yield both of these products in commercial amounts has not succeeded. To bear a rich crop of seeds the plant must have many branches; to yield satisfactory fiber it should be as nearly nonbranching as possible. Flaxseed, the seed of the latter plant, is relatively poor compared to linseed, the seed of the former plant. Apparently the two objectives are mutually exclusive.

The sharp separation in the culture of the two plants rests also on economic grounds. Linseed production lends itself readily to mechanization and is therefore found in such countries as Argentina, the United States, and Canada. India is also an important producer, though for different reasons.

Flax production for fiber even today calls for such large amounts of labor that it is concentrated in areas of relatively cheap labor. The U.S.S.R. is the leading producer, with 70 to 80 percent of the world output to her credit. Other important countries are the Baltic States —Lithuania, Latvia, and Estonia—as well as Poland, Germany, Belgium, the Netherlands, and France. As a result of World War II, production was greatly increased in countries which formerly had produced very little, such as Great Britain, Egypt, Northern Ireland, and Australia. The inclusion of Australia suggests that mechanization has made progress.

Table 20.6 shows flax fiber production and trade during 1934-1938.

[21] *Ibid.*

[22] Figures for 1911-1928 from FAO, *World Fiber Survey,* p. 110; figures for 1934-1948 from FAO, *Fibers.*

[23] See FAO, *World Fiber Survey,* p. 114.

Of particular interest is Belgium's position as a custom processer of flax straw for orders received from her two neighbors, France and the Netherlands. The southwest corner of Belgium has long been known for the excellence of its flax retting and scutching. Some of the yarn made in French mills from French-grown flax but Belgian-processed fiber is shipped to the Netherlands for weaving. In that part of the world international boundaries do not seem such formidable barriers after all.

TABLE 20.6. Flax Fiber: Area, Production, and Trade, by Countries, 1934-1938 Average[24]

Country	Area (1000 acres)	Production (1000 metric tons)	Trade[a] Exports (1000 metric tons)	Imports (1000 metric tons)
U.S.S.R.	5128	556.0	52.9	...
Poland	324	37.1	14.4	...
Lithuania	193	28.0	14.7	...
Germany	86	22.4	...	20.1
Belgium	59	19.6	42.2[b]	15.8
Latvia	156	20.8	10.0	...
France	79	20.7	5.0	34.7[c]
Netherlands	32	12.0	7.4	0.7
Yugoslavia	32	11.3	9.6	...
Estonia	67	8.8	5.9	...
Rumania	59	8.8	[d]	...
Czechoslovakia	37	7.8	[d]	16.3
Japan	42	5.4	[d]	...
United Kingdom	22	4.8	1.8	60.4
Others	173	18.7	10.8	22.8
Total	6489	782.2	174.7	170.8

[a] Exclusive of exports and imports of straw as such.
[b] Includes fiber produced from straw imported from France and the Netherlands.
[c] Includes fiber from domestic straw exported to Belgium for processing and returned in fiber form.
[d] Not reported separately; included under "Others."

Technology

To avoid injuring the bast, fiber flax must be pulled from the ground. This was done by hand until very recently, when flax-pulling machines were introduced, especially in the U.S.S.R. The pulled stalks are then retted and scutched. In retting, the stalks are soaked in water so that the woody and gummy sections will rot and thus loosen up. In scutching, the bast is separated from the vegetable matter that has been loosened in retting. Formerly

[24] *Ibid.*, p. 118. (Area in 1000 hectares converted to 1000 acres by multiplication factor 2.47109.)

done by hand with comb-like rasps, scutching can now be done by mechanical beaters and pullers.

The scarcity of hard fibers in Italy, Germany, and Great Britain during World War II led to an expansion of flax production and to the use of part of the crop as a substitute for jute and for such hard fibers as sisal and henequen, used primarily as binder and baling twine, sacking, wrapping, etc. Because this sudden expansion of the flax acreage created a serious bottleneck in retting facilities, green scutching —i.e., mechanical decortication (removal of the bark and bast from unretted stalks)—was resorted to. It proved feasible for lower-grade fiber, but not for fiber to be used for linen.

Consumption

Flax, one of the oldest and formerly one of the most important fibers, has lost ground to cotton in the apparel and household-goods field and to jute in the industrial field. Synthetic fibers have made further inroads on its market. The large amount of hand labor required and the higher wages it commands raised costs and prices, and removed linen from all but a limited luxury market. This applies to the part of the flax crop that enters international trade and is processed and manufactured in the leading industrial countries. It does not apply to the lower grades of linen used in eastern countries where house or cottage industry still predominates. Home-grown flax and home-made linen is likely to be cheaper than cotton goods manufactured in mills from imported cotton; at any rate, it does not call for an outlay of cash.

HEMP

True hemp, that obtained from *Cannabis sativa,* is a bast. A number of fibers obtained from plants not remotely related to *Cannabis* are loosely referred to as hemp. Thus abacá, which is obtained from a species of banana cultivated in the Philippines, is known as Manila hemp. Sisal, another leaf fiber, is often called sisal hemp, and so forth. Both abacá and sisal are hard fibers, whereas all basts are soft fibers.

Hemp in general is coarser than flax and it lacks the whiteness that accounts for much of the economic significance of fiber flax. Like flax, it is grown for both seed and fiber, but hempseed oil is of decidedly secondary importance. It is strictly a by-product of the fiber. Hemp is used primarily for strong twines and for ropes up to one inch in diameter. The oakum used for calking may be considered a waste product of hemp.

Like all bast fibers, hemp is a *labor fiber*. It is produced in the U.S.S.R., in densely populated sections of Italy, in the Balkan countries, and in parts of Asia. The U.S.S.R. is by far the largest producer (see Table 20.7) and Italy the largest exporter.

TABLE 20.7.   True Hemp: Area and Production, by Countries, 1934-1938 Average[25]

Country	Area[a] (1000 acres)	Production (1000 metric tons)
U.S.S.R.	1544	186.7
Italy	188	89.6
Yugoslavia	121	46.5
Rumania	121	26.8
Korea	64	17.8
Poland	84	11.8
Hungary	30	10.7
Manchuria	62	10.6
Others	131	48.0
Total[b]	2345	448.5

[a] Area refers to hemp grown for fiber and seed.
[b] Exclusive of China, for which comparable data are not available.

While most basts are labor fibers by necessity, i.e., for the simple reason that machinery has not yet been perfected, hemp can be cultivated and harvested and scutched mechanically. If, nevertheless, the fiber continues to be produced by hand labor, it is because wage scales in the regions where it is produced are too low to warrant mechanization.

JUTE

Jute fiber is a bast and therefore a soft fiber; however, it is very coarse. Hence it is used almost exclusively for bags and bales for agricultural products and for such wrapping materials as burlap and hessian. Some jute is used in the manufacture of linoleum and carpets.

As in the case of hemp, jute production could be mechanized. A mechanical scutcher and decorticator has been developed and cultiva-

[25] FAO, *World Fiber Survey*, p. 126. (Area in 1000 hectares converted to 1000 acres by multiplication factor 2.47109.)

tion and harvesting could be done by machine. But, as is true of hemp, the low labor cost precludes its mechanization. Jute sells for a few cents a pound and therefore is too cheap to tempt financiers into trying to wrest it from its present producers.

All basts are several feet long and for that reason none of them are particularly difficult to spin. The jute manufacturing industry has long been concentrated in Bengal, which produces about 90 percent of the world's jute crop. The political reorganization of India has cut Bengal's jute area in half, the major portion going to the Moslem area of Eastern Pakistan. The effect of this political development on the world's future jute output cannot yet be appraised.

India normally processes about two-thirds of her output, the rest being exported to Great Britain and continental Europe. In 1946 the work week in the Calcutta jute mills was reduced from 54 to 48 hours.[26] Whether tightening labor regulations will result in the industry's shift to the reputedly more efficient European mills remains to be seen. Dundee in Scotland has long been the leader in Britain's jute manufacture and her products are typically of higher quality than those produced in Calcutta.

During World War II the necessity of expanding the acreage devoted to food production in India cut sharply into her jute acreage. The result has been a shortage of jute and a sharp increase in price. Early in 1947 jute was selling at a price almost five times higher than the 1934-1938 average and over twice as high as the 1939-1943 average. Ordinarily such high prices would greatly stimulate production. The Indian government, however, has taken stringent measures to prevent overproduction through acreage control. In 1947, India's exports of jute products were rationed by a quota system.

HARD FIBERS

Of the large number of fibers constituting the hard fibers, only the three that are most important in world trade—abacá, or Manila hemp; sisal, sometimes called sisal hemp; and henequen—are discussed here. As the use of

[26] *Ibid.*, p. 134.

the term hemp suggests, these hard fibers compete with hemp in its use as cordage, twine, and rope. However, they are not completely interchangeable, for each fiber has specific properties that give it first claim to a particular segment of the market. Thus, as has been said, most hemp is used for cordage and twine and for ropes up to one inch in diameter. The best quality of abacá goes into marine hawsers, this fiber excelling in its resistance to the corroding effect of salt water. Moreover, its tensile strength permits its use in heavier rope with a larger diameter. Sisal and henequen are exceptionally well suited to use as binder twine in grain harvesters.

All three of these fibers are herbacious perennials. The abacá is a native of the Philippine Islands and the bulk of the abacá of commerce is produced there. Only in very recent years have efforts been made to start plantations in other parts of the world, primarily Central America. Both sisal and henequen are natives of the Yucatán peninsula of Mexico. Although henequen production is still concentrated in Yucatán and production has recently been pushed in Cuba, the center of sisal production has shifted to British East Africa, Portuguese East Africa, Indonesia, and Haiti.

Though these plants are all perennials, they vary in the length of time required to grow to full strength and in the bearing period. "Abacá is first harvested for fiber two or three years after the plant stock is set out, and under favorable conditions it will bear commercial grades of fiber until it is 15 to 20 years old. The life cycle of the sisal plant is six to ten years; fiber yields begin two to four years after planting. Henequen plants live 10 to 20 years, but as a rule the leaves are not cut for fiber until the fourth to seventh year."[27]

Table 20.8 shows the estimated world production of abacá, sisal, and henequen.

RAMIE, A TANTALIZING PROMISE

One of the oldest fibers known to man is ramie, or China grass, a perennial bast fiber. It is nature's masterpiece among the fibers, for it combines the strength of hemp with the whiteness of linen and the luster of silk, and it is easily spun. Being a perennial, its cultivation

[27] *Ibid.*, p. 139.

requires far less labor than do cotton and other annuals. It could be grown successfully on an acreage far larger than that now devoted to any fiber. Actually, however, only moderate amounts are produced.

TABLE 20.8. Hard Fibers: Estimated World Production, by Countries, 1934-1938 Average, 1946 and 1947[28]
(1000 metric tons)

Fiber and Country	Average, 1934-1938	1946	1947
Abacá			
Philippine Islands	170[a]	50	75
British North Borneo	1	...	1
Netherlands East Indies	[b]	...	...
Central America	...	6	19
Total	171[b]	56	95
Sisal			
Netherlands East Indies	84[b]	...	...
British East Africa	120	135	126
Portuguese Africa	25[c]	30	33
Haiti	6[c]	17[d]	22[d]
Others	4	...	...
Total[b,c]	239	182[f]	181[f]
Henequen			
Mexico[e]	96	100[g]	100
Cuba	12	14	15
Total[f]	108	114	115
Grand Total	518	365[h]	410

[a] Data based on balings reported by the Fiber Inspection Service, converted at 278 pounds per bale. (Cf. Bureau of Census and Statistics, *Yearbook of Philippine Statistics*, 1940, Manila, pp. 141-142.) Loose or unbaled fiber consumed locally is not reflected in these totals.
[b] Statistics on hard fibers published in the prewar period by the Netherlands East Indies Government related to total hard fiber exports. Data adequate for estimating the abacá component are not available. As the bulk was sisal, total hard fiber exports from this source have been shown as sisal in this table.
[c] Exports.
[d] Includes waste.
[e] Data on Mexican production of sisal are not reported separately but are included in henequen totals.
[f] Very rough estimates for the Netherlands East Indies and countries grouped under "Others" bring the sisal totals for 1946 and 1947 up to 195 and 200, respectively.
[g] Estimated on the basis of statistics for Yucatán.
[h] Includes sisal totals referred to in note f above.

Egyptian mummies were wrapped in ramie. Mandarins wore clothing made from it.[29] Millionaire yacht owners had sails made from it. Only the very rich could afford to pay for this miracle fiber. The reason is simple—the high cost of decortication. It takes many hours of strenuous labor to separate enough bast from

[28] *Ibid.*, p. 141.
[29] The Chinese ramie industry was, and perhaps still is, centered around Hankow on the Yang-tze.

the ramie stalk to produce even one pound of the fiber.

What the world has long been waiting for is a mechanical device which will remove the bast cheaply and thus make available this masterpiece of nature for mass consumption. The discovery of such devices has been announced repeatedly with loud fanfares, but up to now they have been premature—based on wishful thinking—or downright fraudulent. But now it looks as if, at long last, the final obstacles are being overcome and ramie will come into its own as the ideal fiber it is. This is brought out in the following:

For many years the ramie fiber industry stood on the threshold awaiting an entrance into the industrial empire of the nation. That it had not taken its rightful place was due chiefly because integra-

tion of its component parts had not been fully achieved. Now, the unlimited quantity of the plants from which ramie fiber is obtained is not only assured but its quality and consistency is continually being improved. The demand for the finished products is surpassing even the most fanciful earlier expectations. And in its third essential, the practical decorticating and degumming process, the kinks are being fast ironed out by the mechanical genius to which we owe the vastness of our industrial power.

The industrialization of ramie fiber daily becomes more imminent, and its success inevitable, as the last arc of the cycle is being rapidly bridged and narrowed to completion.[30]

---

[30] W. B. Granger, *The Latest Triumph in Fibers, the History, Culture, Processing and Marketing of Ramie in Florida*, State Department of Agriculture, Tallahassee, New Series No. 130, July, 1948, p. 4.

BIBLIOGRAPHY

"American Woolen Company," *Fortune*, June, 1935.

Blau, G., "Wool in the World Economy," *Journal of the Royal Statistical Society*, vol. 9, part 3, London, 1946.

Ellsworth, R. S., "Watch Out for the Raw Silk Bonanza," *Reader's Digest*, November, 1947.

Gillen, J. F., and Hayes, J. O., *Ramie or China Grass*, Trade Information Bulletin No. 166, Washington, Department of Commerce, 1923.

Granger, W. B., *The Latest Triumph in Fibers, the History, Culture, Processing and Marketing of Ramie in Florida*, New Series No. 130, Tallahassee, State Department of Agriculture, 1948.

International Institute of Agriculture, *Studies of the Principal Agricultural Products on the World Market*, No. 8 *Sericulture in the World*, Rome, 1947.

Peterson, R. E. K., "Raw Silk," *Japanese Trade Studies*, Special Industry Analysis No. 10 (mimeographed), Washington, U. S. Tariff Commission, 1945.

Rawlley, R. C., *Economics of the Silk Industry*, London, King, 1919.

Smith, M. A., *The Tariff on Wool*, New York, Macmillan, 1926.

Chapter 21

MAN-MADE FIBERS

NATURE AND MAN AS RIVAL CREATORS

Primitive man is largely dependent on nature. He satisfies his wants with the few things that she places within the reach of his native abilities, aided perhaps by simple tools and abetted by a few rules of thumb. As man progresses his tools improve; he learns to harness inanimate energies; he tampers with nature in an effort to make her more amenable to his will. The natural landscape becomes the cultural landscape. Yet, in spite of all these man-made changes, up to a certain point civilization rests squarely on nature and is, more or less, an elaborate scheme embodying modifications of nature. There comes a time, however, when science and techniques have advanced sufficiently to dare man to try his own hand at creation. Nature's work no longer seems good enough; it has flaws; it does not go far enough. So the age of synthesis, or creative chemistry, dawns.

This creative effort develops in stages. First man takes cotton and "mercerizes" it, i.e., gives it a silk-like luster—a modest improvement on nature.[1] Next he watches the silkworm and endeavors to imitate it.[2] Again he starts with an advanced product of nature, cellulose—as does the silkworm for that matter—but this time he is a little bolder and converts it chemically into raw material for his artificial substitute. That is how rayon started, from cotton linters and wood pulp. Finally, he goes a step further and probes to the very bottom of nature's mysteries and, like her, builds complex molecules, polymers, from the same simple building blocks that nature uses—hydrogen, oxygen, carbon, and so forth. Thus nylon is popularly said to be made from water, air, and coal (see p. 372). As man penetrates deeper into the mysteries of matter and gains mastery over ever-larger quantities of energy, his creative effort will more and more take over the

---

[1] Similarly during World War II the Germans "cottonized" flax, hemp and other bast fibers.

[2] Similarly, the French chemist Mège-Mouriez' discovery that unfed cows continued for days to deliver milk rich in butterfat but lost their animal fat in the process led him to conclude that the cow converts some of her own fat into butterfat. (See *Fortune*, December, 1947, p. 207.) This keen observation eventually led to the manufacture of artificial butter, or margarine.

work which once was nature's exclusive domain.

This urge to take over the arduous duties of nature is in part the inevitable corollary of scientific progress. The inventive urge in man drives him forward; science is a dynamic force which cumulatively feeds on its own achievements. To man, with his insatiable desire for new and better things, nature seems niggardly. She does not supply enough of the good things; therefore, they seem expensive. Or they are hard to get at, their production is costly; again, the price seems high. Or else, the products of nature seem defective; they lack desirable properties or possess undesirable ones. So the scientist searches for a better substitute. Perhaps the drive is not equally strong in all segments of humanity, but it is peculiar to a particular nation or society which war or other difficulties have cut off from its supply of natural products.

Whatever the motives behind this effort to supplement nature's handiwork, it is one of the outstanding features of our age. In many instances man now has the choice of either turning to nature to supply certain needs or trying his own hand. Nature at long last has a rival, a competitor. That puts many industries on the spot which today, as of old, depend on nature. If they want to survive, they must put their house in order, or else the scientist, backed by the capitalist, will take over.

In no other field is this rivalry between man-made and natural products felt more keenly than in the fibers. Silk may already have received its knockout blow. Cotton is hard pressed. Wool is on the defensive. So it goes, and the end is not yet in sight, for every year brings reports of new scientific triumphs reflected in still better products and still lower prices.

THE FOUR RAYONS[3]

The work of the silkworm has long fascinated man. As early as 1664 the noted physicist Robert Hook prophesied that one day man would learn to imitate the mechanical and chemical achievements of the silkworm as it takes cellulose from the mulberry bush, digests it, and squirts two filaments through the ori-

fices in its head. A century later the French naturalist Réaumur, of thermometer fame, repeated the prediction.

Nitrocellulose Rayon

In 1884 the prophecy was fulfilled when Count Hilaire de Chardonnet patented the first commercially successful process for transforming a liquid into a solid textile thread. After more than a decade of experimental vicissitudes, his factory in Besançon went into actual operation around the turn of the century. Chardonnet used an ether-alcohol solution of nitrocellulose, as had the long line of scientists before him who had worked with nitrocellulose —or pyroxylin as it is also called—demonstrated the action of different solvents on it, and developed various derivatives such as celluloid, filaments for incandescent light, and so forth.

Cellulose Acetate Rayon

Another root of the modern rayon industry reaches back to 1865, when cellulose acetate was discovered. Its one great advantage over nitrocellulose, noninflammability, gave research in cellulose acetate a great impetus especially until around 1901, when the perfecting of the denitrating process rendered nitrocellulose likewise noninflammable.

Cellulose acetate found many uses, but its commercial development as an artificial textile filament did not begin until 1902, when a patent was granted in the United States. Its experimental production began in Boston in 1914. But the real acetate rayon industry was not born till after World War I, when the Swiss chemists Henri and Camille Dreyfus began the manufacture of acetate filaments in England.

Cuprammonium Rayon

Another drawback of the Chardonnet, or nitrocellulose, process was the high cost of the alcohol and ether that were used as solvents. To overcome this handicap, scientists turned to a hydrated cellulose called cuprammonium. First made in 1890, it was not commercially successful till the turn of the century, when factories using the process were erected in France, Germany, and England. Of late, it has lost ground as the result of the progress made in perfecting the acetate and, especially,

---

[3] This account of rayon is based largely on a preliminary report published by the United States Tariff Commission in 1944.

the viscose processes. The last has become the most important of the rayon processes.

Viscose Rayon

The discovery of viscose, or cellulose xanthate, in 1892 is responsible for the bulk of rayon made today. At first, viscose was used to make cellophane, a transparent wrapping material. The revolutionary discovery of the centrifugal spinning pot by C. F. Topham in 1900 paved the way for the exploitation of viscose filament on a commercial scale. The viscose process was first used in 1905.

FILAMENT AND STAPLE RAYON

Originally rayon[4] was known as artificial silk. This term suggested the expectation that rayon would replace silk. And so it did to some extent. But as new types of rayon were developed, as the quality improved, and especially as the cost and price dropped and total production increased far beyond the maximum total output ever reached by silk, rayon inevitably began to make inroads into the market areas of other fibers, especially of cotton. At first, this took the form of competition between rayon fabrics and cotton fabrics. These rayon fabrics were woven from rayon filament yarn, i.e., yarn reeled from long filaments. (Like silk, rayon comes in such lengths that reeling, rather than spinning, is the technique used in producing the yarn.) Later, however, the displacement took a new form, when rayon filament was cut up into lengths corresponding to those of cotton. This chopped-up filament, which came to be known as rayon staple, was mixed with or added to cotton[5] as it was fed into the spinning machine. Thus, a mixed cotton-rayon staple yarn was spun. Rayon staple can also be spun by itself.

The production of rayon staple was stimulated beyond all normal limits by the preparations for World War II, reaching its fullest development in Germany, Italy, and Japan during the thirties. These countries, which used to be among the leading importers of cotton, needed whatever foreign exchange they could put their hands on to buy minerals and other strategic war materials; hence they turned to rayon staple with a view to reducing their cotton imports to a minimum. Later on, as Japan deliberately destroyed her textile industries to make labor and materials available for war industries and as the industries of Germany and Italy were subjected to progressive destruction, the world output of rayon staple declined almost as fast as it had risen. It is now in process of postwar readjustment.

To conclude from this account that rayon staple is an inferior material would be a grave error. It has made a definite place for itself and will be used freely even if other fibers such as cotton are in ample supply. That the high price of cotton in the United States had something to do with the rapid increase in her production of rayon staple is more than likely.

WORLD RAYON PRODUCTION

The first year that rayon yarn production was recorded was 1900. At that time about 2,000,000 pounds were produced. In 1923 the

---

[4] The name *rayon* was officially adopted as a generic term describing diverse cellulose filaments in 1922. Not all rayon producers accepted it. Thus cuprammonium rayon continued to be sold under the trade name of Bemberg. At first, there may have been some thought that "rayon" could be applied to all artificial filaments. But as the number increased and especially as diversity of origin led to an even wider range of properties and to general heterogeneity, new names such as nylon were readily accepted.

[5] Rayon staple is also used to supplement wool, but this has not yet proved fully successful. In December, 1947, some periodicals in this country carried full-page advertisements, the upper half of which consisted of a picture of three rayon yarns. The lower half carried this text: "Now *Rayon* Can Have a Permanent Wave. Years of research . . . the very rearrangement of rayon's molecular structure . . . went into this picture. At the top are some crimped rayon fibers. Next you see them after they have been wet and dried under tension. Finally you see what happens when they are re-wet and re-dried under no tension. At last, . . . scientists have given man-made rayon the additional quality of a *permanent* wave when desired. Textile manufacturers and . . . engineers . . . have already fitted crimped rayon into the needs of luxurious, inexpensive blankets. Blended, or used alone, it is going into warmer, lighter coats, robes and sweaters; crisper skirts and suits. Entirely new fabrics are on the horizon. Some say this is one of the greatest developments in rayon since rayon itself." That this announcement may sound ominous to wool producers and wool processors is quite possible.

| | Millions of Pounds | | | | | | | Percent of Total | | | | |
| | Rayon | | | | | | 4-Fiber | | | | | |
Year[a]	Yarn	Staple	Total	Cotton	Wool	Silk	Total	Rayon	Cotton	Wool	Silk	Total
1890	...	...	...	5,975	1,600	26	7,601	...	79	21	...	100
1900	2	...	2	6,975	1,610	38	8,625	...	81	19	...	100
1905	11	...	11	8,050	1,600	42	9,703	...	83	16	1	100
1910	18	...	18	9,500	1,770	51	11,339	...	84	16	...	100
1911	19	...	19	11,000	1,750	54	12,823	...	86	14	...	100
1912	20	...	20	10,450	1,780	59	12,309	...	85	14	1	100
1913	25	...	25	10,950	1,730	60	12,765	...	86	14	...	100
1914	20	...	20	11,975	1,720	49	13,764	...	87	13	...	100
1915	19	...	19	9,000	1,700	52	10,771	...	84	16	...	100
1916	23	...	23	9,075	1,630	60	10,788	...	84	15	1	100
1917	24	...	24	8,825	1,670	59	10,578	...	83	16	1	100
1918	26	...	26	8,950	1,680	55	10,711	...	83	16	1	100
1919	28	...	28	9,600	1,740	60	11,428	...	84	15	1	100
1920	33	...	33	9,850	1,780	46	11,709	...	84	15	1	100
1921	48	...	48	7,250	1,830	65	9,193	...	79	20	1	100
1922	74	...	74	8,825	1,820	70	10,789	1	81	17	1	100
1923	102	...	102	9,125	1,800	88	11,115	1	82	16	1	100
1924	139	...	139	11,500	1,920	97	13,656	1	84	14	1	100
1925	185	...	185	12,800	2,010	104	15,099	1	85	13	1	100
1926	212	...	212	13,400	2,140	111	15,863	1	85	13	1	100
1927	295	...	295	11,200	2,170	118	13,783	2	81	16	1	100
1928	361	...	361	12,400	2,250	129	15,140	2	82	15	1	100
1929	434	7	441	12,600	2,250	135	15,426	3	82	14	1	100
1930	451	6	457	12,100	2,210	130	14,897	3	81	15	1	100
1931	500	8	508	12,700	2,230	126	15,564	3	82	14	1	100
1932	517	17	534	11,200	2,200	116	14,050	4	80	15	1	100
1933	666	28	694	12,500	2,170	122	15,486	4	81	14	1	100
1934	771	52	823	11,000	2,120	125	14,068	6	78	15	1	100
1935	935	139	1,074	12,600	2,160	121	15,955	6	79	14	1	100
1936	1,021	300	1,321	14,700	2,230	119	18,370	7	80	12	1	100
1937	1,197	626	1,823	17,600	2,280	120	21,823	8	81	10	1	100
1938	996	928	1,924	13,200	2,350	109	17,583	11	75	13	1	100
1939	1,145	1,095	2,240	13,050	2,460	135	17,885	12	73	14	1	100
1940	1,186	1,285	2,471	13,725	2,500	130	18,826	13	73	13	1	100
1941	1,265	1,552	2,817	12,250	2,540	107	17,714	16	69	14	1	100
1942	1,200	1,456	2,656	12,225	2,490	80	17,451	15	70	14	1	100
1943	1,153	1,392	2,545	11,725	2,480	50	16,800	15	70	15	...	100
1944	1,033	1,052	2,085	11,295	2,370	30	15,780	13	72	15	...	100
1945	897	501	1,398	9,510	2,270	24	13,202	11	72	17	...	100
1946	1,103	574	1,677	9,660	2,290	30	13,657	12	71	17	...	100
1947	1,318	694	2,012	11,150	2,230	33	15,425	13	72	15	...	100
1948	1,557	920	2,477	13,060	2,240	36	17,813	14	73	13	...	100

[a] Rayon figures are on a calendar basis; the three natural fibers are shown seasonally. Cotton: 1890-1948, New York Cotton Exchange Service, converted on basis of 478 pounds per bale. Wool: 1890, estimated; 1900 forward, estimates by U. S. Department of Agriculture; grease equivalent figures converted to scoured basis shown at 60% of grease. Silk: 1890-1920, "Rohseide" by Dr. Eva Flugge; 1923-1940, League of Nations Statistical Year Book; 1941 forward, our estimates; baleage data have been converted by us to a poundage basis using the factor of 132¼ pounds per bale. Rayon: Filament yarn and staple data from *Rayon Organon*, June, 1949, pp. 88-89.

[6] *Rayon Organon*, June, 1949, p. 86.

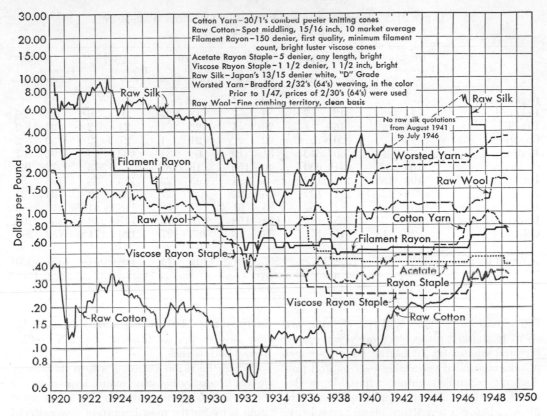

FIG. 21.1.   United States Rayon (Fiber and Yarn) Prices, Monthly, 1920 to June, 1949, ratio scale. (*Rayon Organon*, July, 1949, pp. 104-105.)

100-million-pound line was crossed. In 1929 rayon staple made its first appearance, with about 7,000,000 pounds. In 1935, total rayon production, filament and staple, crossed the 1-billion-pound line, reaching an all-time high of 2.8 billion pounds in 1941. It dropped to a recent low of 1.4 billion pounds in 1945 but it was recovering by 1948, when it was 2.5 billion pounds.

In Table 21.1 rayon production figures are shown with those for cotton, wool, and silk, both total and percentage figures being given. It will be noted that rayon stood at 1 percent for the first time in 1922, rose to 16 in 1941, only to drop back during World War II to 11. But by 1948 it was back to 14 percent. It is also worthy of note that in 1941 rayon output rated higher in percentage than wool—16 as against 14 percent. That same year the cotton output was only 4.3 times as large as the rayon output;[7] in 1948 the ratio was 5.2 to 1.

Spectacular indeed is the rise of the staple industry. In 1929, 7 million pounds of rayon staple were produced, as against 434 million pounds of filament. In 1940, little more than a decade later, staple production outstripped filament—1285 million pounds as against 1186 million. Staple held the lead until 1944, when the two branches produced almost identical amounts, 1052 million pounds of staple and 1033 million of filament. After that, the destruction of the Axis rayon mills, or damage to them, tipped the scales sharply in favor of filament.

---

[7] In comparing rayon with cotton it must be kept in mind that rayon filament compares with cotton *yarn* and that raw cotton suffers a loss of around 10 percent or more in conversion to yarn. Rayon staple compares to cotton as it is fed into the spinning machine after certain preparatory steps have been taken. Rayon staple is uniform in length; cotton is not.

This difference in the two fibers has been appraised by experts as being worth 4 cents a pound.

TABLE 21.2.   World Rayon Production, by Countries, 1935-1948[8]
(in million pounds)

| | 1935-1939 Filament | | 1940-1944 Filament | | 1945 Filament | | 1946 Filament | | 1947 Filament | | 1948 Filament | |
	Yarn	Staple	Yarn	Staple	Yarn	Staple	Yarn	Staple	Yarn	Staple	Yarn	Staple
Argentina	3	...	8	...	9	1	9	1	10	...	10	...
Belgium	14	1	12	7	4	7	18	27	20	26	22	25
Brazil	8	...	16	1	20	1	23	1	24	2	24	2
Canada	14	...	20	...	22	...	21	1	27	2	30	2
France	61	12	60	40	31	19	68	34	82	43	96	67
Germany	105	227	161	600	40	150	18	89	33	73	72	161
Italy	100	138	102	177	3	4	65	29	115	48	105	39
Japan	258	173	111	192	6	22	9	21	16	19	34	35
United Kingdom	109	30	82	52	85	51	107	68	118	81	146	82
United States	289	24	455	137	624	168	678	176	747	228	856	265
Others	98	13	141	141	53	78	85	127	126	171	152	239
World total	1059	618	1168	1347	897	501	1104	574	1318	964	1557	920
	1676		2475		1398		1678		2012		2477	

The reasons for this rapid rise of rayon are clear. In the first place, since rayon is a manufactured commodity, it has all the advantages of man-controlled processing over natural production: controlled output adjustable to demand, predictability of supply, uniformity of quality. Being a recent invention, rayon benefits from constant improvements which the financially strong and on the whole progressive industry can afford to promote. In so far as the supply can be adjusted to demand, the violent crop and price fluctuations characteristic of natural products are avoided. A manufacturer of rayon goods generally knows what price to expect. Moreover, the price has been steadily going down (see Fig. 21.1). In the United States, the price in 1920 ranged from $2.50 to $6.00 a pound for rayon filament. It fell below 50 cents a pound in 1938 and rose slowly during the war years to about 70 cents in 1947, to 76 in 1948, and 78 in 1949. Of particular interest is the fact that the rayon filament price dropped below the wool price in 1933 and below the cotton yarn price in 1944. The rayon staple price fell from 60 cents a pound during 1927-1931 to 26 cents during 1937-1946. Toward the end of 1946 it rose, reaching 42 cents early in 1947 and 47 cents in 1948. But the raw cotton price rose faster

and rayon staple is selling almost as much below raw cotton as filament rayon is selling below cotton yarn.

When the rayon industry was in its infancy it was necessary for some manufacturers to use cotton linters as raw material. Nowadays wood pulp is by far the most important raw material of rayon manufacture. From an average of 41 percent linters in 1930-1934, the rate dropped to 20 percent from 1941-1945. The extremes ranged from 44 percent linters in 1934 to 12 percent in 1942. These changes are largely due to changing price ratios of the two raw materials, for, other things being equal, a short cotton crop tends to send the price of linters up. Since cotton linters are also used in other industries such as plastics, lacquer, explosives, and paper, the demand situation no less than the supply situation is very complex. In general, linters are preferred as raw material for high-tenacity yarn.

About three-fourths of the world's rayon, filament and staple, is made by the viscose process, about 23 percent by the acetate process; the remaining 2 percent is divided in the ratio of about 2:1 between cuprammonium and nitrocellulose. These figures reveal a tremendous drive behind acetate which, as late as 1936, constituted only 10.2 percent of all the rayon made in the world. At that time, viscose represented 86.1 percent. The present ratio is

[8] *Rayon Organon*, June, 1949, pp. 88-89.

TABLE 21.3.   Rayon Plants in the United States[9]

Name	Process	Location[a]
American Bemberg Corporation	Cuprammonium	Elizabethton, Tenn.
American Enka Corporation	Viscose	Enka, near Asheville, N. C.
" " "	"	Lowlands, Tenn.
American Viscose Corporation	Viscose	Front Royal, Va.
" " "	"	Lewiston, Pa.
" " "	"	Marcus Hook, Pa.
" " "	"	Nitro, West Va.
" " "	"	Parkersburg, West Va.
" " "	"	Radford, Va.
" " "	"	Roanoke, Va.
" " "	Acetate	Meadville, Pa.
Beaunit Mills, Inc.	Viscose	Coosa Pines, Ala.
Celanese Corporation of America	Acetate	Cumberland (Amcelle), Md.
" " " "	"	Narrows (Celco), Va.
" " " "	"	Rockhill, S. C.
" " " "	"	Rome, Ga.
" " " "	Viscose	Rome, Ga.
E. I. Du Pont de Nemours and Co., Inc.	Viscose	Buffalo, N. Y.
" " " " " " " " "	"	Old Hickory, Tenn.
" " " " " " " " "	"	Richmond (Ampthill), Va.
" " " " " " " " "	Acetate	Waynesboro, Va.
Industrial Rayon Corporation	Viscose	Cleveland, Ohio
" " "	"	Covington, Va.
" " "	"	Painesville, Ohio
North American Rayon Corporation	Viscose	Elizabethton, Tenn.
Tennessee Eastman Corporation	Acetate	Kingsport, Tenn.

[a] Plants of smaller corporations are located at Newcastle, Del.; Rocky Hill, Conn.; Cleveland, Ohio; New Bedford, Mass.; Utica, N. Y.; Woonsocket, R. I.; and Brooklyn, Conn.

little better than 3:1. Table 21.2 shows world rayon production by countries, 1935-1948.

THE RAYON INDUSTRY OF THE UNITED STATES

As has been said, the rayon industry—both rayon filament and rayon staple—began in Europe. During the period between the two World Wars, Japan became an important producer of both rayon filament and rayon staple. One would hardly expect that the United States, which leads in so many lines of industrial progress and is the world's leading producer of raw materials, would foster the development of an industry which produces substitutes for silk and cotton. For her high purchasing power permitted her to absorb the bulk of Japan's silk exports; furthermore, she is the leading producer of cotton. It seems logical to assume that the desire to find substitutes

is strongest where the ability to procure "the real stuff" is most limited. There is also the fact that the rayon industry, a chemical industry, developed at a time when the United States was still preoccupied with opening up her vast continent and had not yet launched on her spectacular career as the leading chemical producer, a career which began in earnest only after World War I had forcefully demonstrated the danger of being dependent on other countries for basic chemicals.

As a result of this situation, the American rayon industry began as an economic colony or exclave of Europe. European rayon manufacturers controlled the patents and had the technical know-how. The high import duties levied by the United States made it necessary for these European producers to build branch plants in this country from which to supply the bulk of the domestic market. The history of the leading rayon manufacturers of the United States clearly reveals the importance of the

[9] *Ibid.*, pp. 89 ff.

European background of what is today one of our leading industries.

The rayon industry of the United States is located in the eastern part of the country. Most of the 28 plants in operation in 1947 were scattered along the Appalachian Mountains from New York to Georgia. The rest are located in three subareas: (1) the Cleveland-Buffalo area, (2) southern New England, and (3) the Philadelphia area. Table 21.3 lists the concerns that make rayon in the United States, and gives their plant locations.

Among the factors determining the location of rayon plants, the following are important: ready access to an adequate supply of water of the proper quality; ready access to fuel and service materials such as sulfuric acid, caustic soda, and acetic anhydride; proximity to the market, i.e., to finishing plants, textile mills, tire factories, and style centers.[10]

The viscose plant at Elizabethton, Tenn., will illustrate how these factors are taken into account in choosing mill locations. This plant has an excellent water supply right in its backyard, so to speak—abundant Appalachian Mountain stream water of just the right quality. Coal can be obtained from West Virginia or Virginia, caustic soda from Saltville, Va., and sulfuric acid (obtained from pyrites) from Pulaski, Va. All these sources of supply are close by and transportation facilities are excellent. Labor can be recruited from nearby mountain areas or from the cities in the region. Moreover, Elizabethton is located favorably as regards both the textile centers of the South and the finishing plants and style centers of the North.

The rayon industry of the United States is a highly compact industry that includes only fifteen independent companies; four of them control three-fourths of the entire industry. These fifteen concerns, in 1945, produced goods valued roughly at $400 million. That this compactness rules out competition of the old-fashioned cutthroat variety may be expected. To be sure, there is competition, but it is not the blind type that is subject to impersonal

forces like those found in the automatic market. It differs materially from the competition under which, in the absence of government controls, a cotton grower has to operate.

As a result of this difference in the nature of the competition, and for other reasons,[11] rayon prices tend to be far more stable than those of natural fibers. This is a strong point in favor of synthetic fibers, although organized futures exchanges, by permitting "hedging," mitigate to some extent the disadvantages inherent in natural fibers. Besides price stability, the rayon industry has also enjoyed persistently profitable prices. During most of its existence the young industry has operated in a sellers' market. Consequently, it has been enabled to build up reserves with which to expand and improve plants, do research work, advertise extensively, etc. A less compact industry might be able to do likewise, but only under much more difficult circumstances.

The Continuous Process

By the end of World War II, the rayon industry in the United States had virtually ceased to be an economic colony of European capital. Not only did the United States absorb into her own economy the plants that were established here as foreign-controlled branch factories, but she also made a great contribution to the technology of the rayon industry—the "continuous process" of making viscose yarn.

The significance of this revolutionary improvement lies in the fact that the time of production is cut down from 5½ days required for the viscose process, still used in most mills in the United States, to 4½ hours.[12] Theoretically, the equipment should turn out about thirty times as much rayon under the new process. Furthermore, the equipment needed is far more compact and hence saves much space. But it is far costlier. The net result, however, is a remarkable saving in cost. In addition to this saving, the new process offers the advantage of improved quality resulting from less

---

[10] Access to labor, formerly very important, is now relatively unimportant because production processes have become more and more semi-automatic as the result of such control devices as the electric eye.

[11] Among other reasons, the uninterrupted operation of plants throughout the year ranks high. All-year-round operation is in sharp contrast to the concentration of harvest in a short period of the year.

[12] See an article on the Industrial Rayon Corporation of Cleveland, in *Fortune*, October, 1946, pp. 101 ff.

handling. For it reduces, if indeed it does not eliminate, breakage of the yarn and thus precludes costly loom stoppage. Furthermore, the uniform tension possible with this process is said to give the yarn superior dyeing quality. It also cuts down the quantity of "seconds" produced in weaving.

To understand the continuous process it is necessary to describe briefly the old system of making viscose yarn.[13] Viscose, as was stated above, is spun from cellulose xanthate which is squirted through spinnerets into a spin-bath where it is converted into solid filaments. The spinneret corresponds to the orifices below the silkworm's mouth. But the rayon process has three great advantages over nature's handiwork. (1) Whereas the silkworm produces only two filaments in one strand (the seracin which surrounds them makes necessary the bothersome "boil-off" procedure; see p. 357), a rayon spinneret can have as many orifices as the number of filaments that are to be combined in a single yarn. A typical yarn is 150-40, meaning that the yarn is 150 denier and is made up of 40 filaments; the spinneret for this rayon has 40 orifices. (2) The width of the orifices can be controlled to produce filaments of varying diameter. (3) Each filament is separately treated by chemicals, thus eliminating any process corresponding to the boil off.

From the spin-bath the strand of filaments passes over two glass wheels into an enclosed rotating pot in which it is thrown by centrifugal force against the walls. This process, which takes eight hours, gives the filaments the twist which justifies applying the term yarn.

The yarn is then placed in aging and steaming cabinets where fumes are removed; this takes a minimum of three hours. Next, 400 to 500 yards of damaged yarn are removed. The rest of it is then wrapped in a protective "stocking" and passes through a machine 235 feet long, where it is washed, desulfurized, bleached, and oiled; these operations take place at forty-eight different stations, each requiring a four-minute stop, or a total of three hours and twelve minutes. Next the yarn is placed in a centrifugal machine which removes excess moisture. Finally, the yarn goes into a 175-foot tunnel, where it is dried for 114 hours by hot air.

This description clearly brings out two facts: the time and space required and the numerous handlings involved. In the continuous process all these steps are combined in one huge machine operation. From the spin-bath, located at the top of the machine, the liquid drips by gravity down on the uppermost set of rollers. The filaments then descend to eight additional rollers, each successive set being underneath the preceding one. The size and speed of the rollers are so arranged that the yarn stays long enough on each set for each successive step to be completed. The steps[14] are as follows:

1. Reeling the yarn as it comes from the spin-bath.
2. Bathing in dilute acid.
3. Washing with warm water.
4. Desulfurizing.
5. Again washing with water.
6. Bleaching with hypochlorite.
7. Again washing with water.
8. Spraying with oil emulsion.
9. Throwing off excess oil.
10. Drying.

These ten steps take 4½ hours as compared with the 5½ days for the old process.

High-Tenacity Yarn

In the late thirties another important innovation, high-tenacity viscose yarn, was introduced in rayon production. This yarn is 80 percent stronger than the ordinary rayon yarn used for clothing textiles and hence makes possible the manufacture of rayon tire cords and fabrics which are equal or superior to cotton cords and fabrics. So far, the rayon industry has confined itself to producing for the tire market. The other possibilities of high-tenacity viscose yarn are great but have not yet been exploited.

During and after World War II, under a government-sponsored program, the production of rayon tire cords and fabrics expanded from 9,000,000 pounds in 1939 to more than 200,-000,000 in 1946. In the latter year rayon cord constituted over 40 percent of all tire cord made in this country. This sensational develop-

---

[13] The following description is based on *ibid*.

[14] As described in *ibid*.

ment shows what a dynamic and therefore dangerous competitor rayon really is.

RAYON VS. COTTON

At first it was silk which felt the terrific competitive impact of rayon; it could hold on to its market only by making price concessions which came close to being ruinous. Now it is cotton which has to stand the brunt of this commodity competition. To be sure, for certain uses—as when great wet strength is required—cotton still has superior advantages. But rayon has captured much of the United States market for women's apparel, because it seems to possess advantages in draping, appearance, and other style characteristics. What is more, in recent years, it has had a strong talking point—a lower price!

How the expanding sale of rayon in this country cuts into the cotton market is easily realized when one considers that the 380 million pounds of rayon produced here in 1939 were the equivalent of 895,000 bales of cotton and the 1124 million pounds produced in 1948 equaled 2,650,000 bales. The peak of world rayon production was reached in 1941 with 2834 million pounds, the equivalent of 6.7 million bales of cotton, or roughly one-fifth of the world crop.

So long as the economy of the United States is expanding by leaps and bounds, equivalence does not necessarily mean actual replacement of cotton by rayon, but it certainly means a curtailed market for cotton. Moreover, if this expansion in our economy should cease and if the world resumes rayon production at the prewar level or higher, the pressure on cotton will be strong.

TRUE SYNTHETIC FIBERS
Nylon

Nylon is the name given one of scores of truly synthetic fibers developed by the Du Pont research chemists working under the late Wallace Hume Carothers. His tragic death in 1937 occurred less than three weeks after he had filed, for Du Pont, historic patent No. 2130948, the key patent for the true synthesis of fibers.

The work on nylon, which began in 1928, was based on the observation that natural fibers consist of polymers which lie parallel to each other. The task was to invent practical processes of polymerization and to develop poly-

mers from which useful fibers that would be equal if not superior in desirable qualities to natural fibers, especially silk, could be produced.

The chemists knew that the polymers of nature are constructed from such universal building blocks as carbon, hydrogen, oxygen, and nitrogen that occur in coal (carbon), water (hydrogen), and air (oxygen and nitrogen). To say that nylon is made from coal, water, and air is not wholly false, but it suggests, to the layman at least, a gross simplification of what is actually a highly complex chemical process.

The process of making nylon involves two separate steps: (1) the preparation of the intermediate raw material which chemists call an amide salt, and (2) the actual making of nylon.[15] The intermediary raw material is shipped, mixed with water, in tank cars.

The fiber-building polymers are produced in giant autoclaves under heat and pressure controlled by electronic tubes. The polymer mass is hardened under a stream of ice water and then broken up into small chips which are mixed under pressure with hydrogen and then melted down. The liquid is forced through the tiny holes of spinnerets which produce the actual filament—fine filament for textile purposes, and the coarser monofilaments for such uses as toothbrush bristles. Nylon can also be rolled into transparent sheets resembling cellophane.

At first, nylon was used mainly for full-fashioned ladies' hosiery, but since the war its uses have been expanding at an astounding pace. The manufacturer of nylon is anxious to avoid exaggerated claims for its properties but expects it to do at least as well as silk, the most elastic fiber made by nature. Its severe blow to Japan's silk industry was powered mainly by its price appeal, which should grow even stronger as more experience and new knowledge accumulate and as the unit cost decreases with expanding volume of produc-

---

[15] The amide salt is prepared either from coal, as in the Du Pont ammonia plant at Belle, West Virginia, or, as at their plant in Orange, Texas, from gaseous hydrocarbons obtained as by-products in petroleum refineries.

The actual making of nylon was first confined to Du Pont's Seaford plant about 80 miles from Wilmington, Delaware.

tion. Nylon prices to hosiery mills have already been materially reduced, from $3.52 a pound prior to October, 1940, to $2.15 beginning in February, 1947, for 40 denier 13 filament yarn. The price is not expected to drop as low as rayon prices.

Commercial production of nylon was begun in 1939. By 1946 the output had been stepped up to 25,000,000 pounds, with further expansion in the offing. In addition, several million pounds of nylon polymers went into monofilaments and plastics. New plants at Martinsville, Va., Chattanooga, Tenn., and Orange, Texas, were expected to step up the volume of production still further. The 1948 output amounted to more than 60,000,000 pounds.

Other Synthetic Fibers

Three other groups of synthetic fibers deserve mention, not because of their present volume of sales but because of the promise they hold for the future and the proof they furnish of the vitality of chemical research. These three groups are: (1) fibers made from synthetic resins, (2) protein fibers, and (3) glass fibers.[16]

Fibers Made of Synthetic Resins. There is a growing list of fibers that are made from synthetic resins. One of the oldest of these fibers is Vinyon, made by the American Viscose Company from a synthetic resin produced by the Carbide and Carbon Chemical Corporation. Another is Saran, produced by the Dow Chemical Company. Many other companies are active in this promising field, among them the B. F. Goodrich Company, Du Pont, and the Monsanto Chemical Company.

Synthetic resins possess widely differing

properties and this diversity is communicated to the fibers derived from them. The process of determining these properties, establishing prices in keeping with their utilities, and finding the markets to which they are suited is both painstaking and time-consuming, but definite progress is being made. The prospects that fibers made of synthetic resins will in time furnish a respectable part of the total fiber supply are good.

Protein Fibers. The oldest protein fiber known is the Italian "Lanital," made from casein or milk protein as early as 1936. More recently a casein fiber known as Aralac was produced in the United States, and in 1946 commercial production of fiber from soybean protein got under way. Work on a fiber derived from peanut protein has been proceeding in England for some years. These examples suggest the range of future activities in this field.

Protein fibers, however, present several problems. When first introduced, they lacked strength and were therefore used primarily in the form of "staple" mixed with rayon staple. Moreover, it seems reasonable to assume that the cost of proteins normally exceeds that of cellulose, which means that protein fibers have to be sold on the basis of properties different from, and presumably superior to, those of cellulose-derivative fibers. Modern scientific research has removed far greater stumbling blocks than the ones currently limiting the production and sale of protein fibers.

Glass Fibers. As yet, the main use to which glass fibers are put is as so-called mineral wool for insulating purposes. The production of glass-fiber wool has reached considerable proportions, about 150 million pounds being sold as early as 1946. Textile-type fiber made of glass is limited to special uses where neither resiliency nor ability to stretch is called for, such as laminated plastics, decorative draperies, and filters. Glass fiber is both strong and noninflammable.

---

[16] See *Study of Agricultural and Economic Problems of the Cotton Belt,* Hearings Before Special Subcommittee on Cotton of the Committee on Agriculture, House of Representatives, Eightieth Congress, First Session, July 7 and 8, 1947, pp. 378-379.

BIBLIOGRAPHY

"American Viscose Corporation," *Fortune,* July, 1937.

Avram, M. H., *The Rayon Industry,* New York, Van Nostrand, 1927.

"Celanese Corporation of America," *Fortune,* October, 1933.

"Glass Now and Tomorrow," *Fortune,* March, 1943.

"Nylon," *Fortune,* July, 1940.

Rayon Organon, New York, Textile Economic Bureau, Inc. (monthly).

U. S. Tariff Commission, *Preliminary Report on Rayon,* Washington, 1944.

UNIT 4. TREES AND TREE CROPS

Chapter 22

TREE CROPS

GROWING IMPORTANCE OF TREE CROPS

Traditional Predilection for Annuals

Both plants and animals vary widely in length of life span, but plants vary more widely than animals. There is no counterpart to the sequoia in the animal kingdom.

When man lived by gathering wild seeds and fruit—free gifts of nature—the age of the plant furnishing the food was of no concern. It made no difference to him whether the food came from a young plant or an old tree. To this day many primitive people, especially in the tropics, depend on wild tree crops for much of their living. But when man came to depend on plants which he himself planted, cultivated, and harvested, the time which elapsed between planting and harvesting became crucial, for on it depended whether the new crop would come in before the old one gave out. All of us know the story of the Pilgrim Fathers whose lives may have been saved by an early corn crop, the gift of the red men.

Primitive men were much on the move. They were always in a hurry, impatient, worried about tomorrow's food supply. They could not afford to plant trees and wait years for them

to bear edible fruit. As one writer puts it: "Man was tied to an ancient apron string of nature."[1] Hence man developed a definite predilection for annuals, i.e., plants—particularly the cereal grasses—with a life cycle of one year.[2] To this day, therefore, the bulk of human food comes from annuals—wheat, ryè, rice, corn, barley, the sorghums and millets, etc.

There is another reason for the dominant position of annuals in man's food economy. Whether annuals or perennials, especially trees and shrubs, thrive in a given area depends mainly on climate, soil, and topography. As a rule tree growth needs more water per acre than annuals; hence trees thrive in regions of medium and heavy rainfall, for they can tap

---

[1] J. R. Smith, *Tree Crops: A Permanent Agriculture*, Harcourt, Brace and Company, New York, 1929, p. 11.

[2] A borderline case is the biennial, whose life cycle resembles that of the annual but is divided by a dormant season into two periods covering parts of two successive years. Such a plant is the sugar beet (see chap. 15), which stores sugar in the first year to restart the life process the following season. The case of winter wheat is somewhat similar.

ground water which annuals cannot reach. They may do well on hillsides too steep for cropping. Moreover, while annuals fit better into the climatic scheme of things in the temperate zones with their sharply divided seasons, perennials fit more generally into the climatic system of the tropics. As has been brought out before, the cereal grasses, the most important food crops, do best in the great plains and prairies which were opened up for settlement by the railroads. Thus the Industrial Revolution in the earlier phases did much to foster the cultivation of annuals.

While there can thus be no question of man's predilection for annuals as sources of food, the by no means unimportant role of perennials throughout history must be recognized. There is first of all the forest which through the ages has furnished wood for fuel and construction work, and under special conditions served as a major grazing area. There are the tropical perennials such as sugar cane, cassava, bananas, plantain, taro, sago palm, coconut palm, cacao, and many others which have long contributed to the support of people in the torrid zone. There are the olive trees and orange trees, the date palms and the grapevines which have long been of major importance, especially in the Mediterranean region. There are the fruit trees—apple, pear, cherry, plum, walnut, etc.— which have long thrived in many parts of the temperate zones. This list, though far from complete, suffices as a warning against letting the prominence of annuals mislead one in underestimating the early and widespread importance of perennials.

Increasing Importance of Perennials

While there is no gainsaying that perennials have long been of great importance to man, it is equally true that their importance has vastly increased as the result of a series of significant developments in modern history, especially within the past hundred years. These developments will be briefly discussed.

Conquest of the Tropics. The tree crops which play the most important role in modern world commerce are rubber, coffee, tea, cacao, coconut, palm and palm-kernel oil, bananas, sugar cane, citrus fruit, grapes, Brazil nuts, pecans, and walnuts, apples, pears, and other temperate-zone fruit, abacá, sisal, and cinchona.

Two facts about this list stand out as particularly significant: (1) the strong predominance of tropical products (all but citrus fruit, grapes, and temperate-zone fruits and nuts) and (2) the growing importance of plantation products—coffee, tea, cacao, bananas, sugar cane, citrus fruit, abacá, sisal, cinchona, grapes, almost all the rubber, most nuts (except Brazil nuts), and an increasing amount of coconut and palm and palm-kernel oil.

As was pointed out before, climatic conditions in the tropics favor the perennial flora. For ages the tropical perennials were wild plants superficially and destructively exploited by primitive people. Then with the commercial revolution and the great discoveries the white man went on a rampage which brought most of the tropics under his sway. Thus the perennials of the tropics were pressed into the service of the West; they became commodities of commerce and their exploitation was pushed with a vigor incomprehensible to the easygoing natives. The wild plants were first savagely and destructively exploited with the aid of slaves. But as the white man's rule was strengthened and the wild stands were depleted, the jungle yielded to the plantation and eventually brutal force yielded to rational management and scientific control. The Spanish and Portuguese brought sugar cane to South America and the Caribbean. The British and later the Dutch built up a vast empire of rubber plantations in the Middle East. Coffee brought from Arabia became one of the chief plantation products of Latin America. Cacao plantations spread from South America to Africa. The British, followed later by the Japanese, built up vast tea plantations. The Dutch transferred cinchona from its wild habitat in the Andes to Java and built up a global monopoly in quinine. The Japanese in Formosa shifted from destructive exploitation of camphor trees to more conservational methods. And so on down the line, to tung trees in China and our own South, sisal in Mexico, Africa, and Indonesia, to abacá in the Philippines, etc.

Establishment of Law and Order. Whatever else one may think about the white man as a colonizer, the fact must be conceded that, in his fumbling way, he managed to establish law and order, tranquillity, and stable institutions, and in doing so made possible the cultivation of perennials. All perennial culture, but particularly the planting of trees, rests on the stability of social institutions. No one would be foolish enough to spend a decade or more and the effort, thought, and expenditure required to build up an olive grove which can bear fruit for a century, unless he feels reasonably sure of a reward for himself and his descendants.

This close association between law and order on the one hand and planted tree crops on the other is well brought out in Knight's enlightened study of tree culture in Africa.[3] "Tree and vine areas are more closely restricted by climate because of the initial delay in returns on the investment; requiring time to recover, they are more sensitive to disorder and can reach their full development only in a particular kind of administrative and economic atmosphere." This particular atmosphere is that of law and order and stable institutions. Knight goes on to say: "The introduction of European (especially French) administrative and economic organizations has at least doubled the populated and cultivated areas—and increased their wealth to an incalculable degree." The tree to which he refers particularly is the olive tree, and to prove his point he gives the following account of olive tree culture:

Olive trees, especially in dry regions, require expert care. They must be grafted, watered, weeded, and protected from animals, among which the worst is the camel, a huge beast capable of reaching even the upper branches with his sharp teeth. There must be a market for the oil, and a financial organization of society able to carry the enterprise during five or six years with no fruit at all, and seven or eight before the returns equal the annual cost of exploitation. In ten or twelve years, the cost of establishing the grove is covered, and the height of productivity is reached in about ten more. A grove will last a century if properly pruned and otherwise methodically cared for, but goes to pieces very quickly otherwise, especially in a camel country.[4]

This relation between law and order and the cultivation of perennials is of the utmost importance at present, for the stabilizing influence

of occidental capitalistic powers has for a century spread to remote parts of the earth, thus creating an institutional atmosphere in which tree culture is being carried on successfully on an ever-increasing scale.

Accumulation of Surplus Capital. Ordinarily, the establishment of a plantation of perennials requires capital to tide over the nonremunerative period before returns begin to come in. As we have seen, the mechanical revolution, by raising labor productivity with the aid of the power-driven machine and of science, greatly contributed to the accumulation of surplus capital, some of which was available for plantation ventures overseas, especially in the tropics. The same process of capital accumulation also aided the rapid increase of population and the equally rapid increase of per capita purchasing power in the industrial countries of Europe and North America and thus created an expanding market for plantation products. Furthermore, this capital made possible the scientific research in plant breeding which attained its most spectacular results in Java's famous P.O.J. 2878 (see p. 234) and in the miraculous rubber trees of the Middle East whose yield literally dwarfs that of their natural ancestors in the jungles of the Amazon.

Thus, in diverse ways, the availability of surplus capital contributed vastly to the growth and improvement of plantations of perennials. This growth is by no means confined to the tropics; it embraces such significant developments as citrus groves in the United States— the oranges, grapefruit, lemons, tangerines, limes, and kumquats grown in California, Florida, and Texas, our expanding nut-growing industry including walnuts, pecans, and cashews, the tung oil industry of our South, etc.

It led to another important development: the rise of the specialized fruit farm. Whereas formerly small orchards constituted parts of diversified farmsteads, now large portions of the apple and pear crops come from monocultural or single-crop farms. The same thing applies in different degrees to many other fruits. This development would not have been possible had not the greater availability of capital encouraged greater risk taking and had not science with its superior breeding techniques and pest and disease control lowered certain risks materially.

---

[3] M. M. Knight, "Water and the Course of Empires in North Africa," *Quarterly Journal of Economics,* November, 1928, p. 56.

[4] *Ibid.,* p. 61.

TABLE 22.1. Some Characteristics of Selected Perennials[5]

Crop	Age at Which Bearing Begins (years)	Age Commercial Bearing Begins	Age at Which Maximum Yield Is Reached	Duration of Yield	Nature of Yield: Seasonal, Continuous, or Sporadic	Average Yield per Tree or Shrub	Remarks
Apple	4 to 7	8 to 12	16 to 25	20–35	Biennial	1 bu. per tree	Yield depends upon age, variety, and locality of tree
Orange	3 to 4	5 to 8	15 to 20	20–35	Annual	2 boxes per tree	
Persian walnut	4 to 6	6 to 10	...	35–40	Annual	43.4 lbs.	1000 to 1200 lbs. per acre, average yield
Grapes (bunch)	3	4	5	30–40	Annual	11.1 lbs. per vine	
Grapes (raisin)	3	4	5	35–50	Annual	2⅛ lbs	
Pecan	5	8 to 12	35 to 40	...	Biennial or sporadic	12 lbs. per tree	
Coffee	3 to 4	5 to 6	...	20	Harvest 7 mos. after blossom, when berries are red	1 lb. dried coffee per tree at 6 yrs., or 6 cwt. per acre	Each berry contains 2 seeds (beans). About 850–1000 fresh seeds to a lb., so that 1½–1¾ lbs. should plant an acre
Coconut	7 to 10	10	...	60	6 crops a yr. every 2 mos.	45–50 nuts a tree, or 3000 per acre	
Cocoa	5	10 to 12	...	...	Continuous	4–5 cwt. cured beans per acre	
Cinchona	6	7	...	...	......	2 lbs. per tree at 7 years	
Camphor	3 to 6	...	...	...	Clippings 3 or 4 times a year	15–20 lbs. clippings per tree, or 120–130 lbs. distilled camphor	Clippings, 6–10 in. yield 1½–2½% distilled camphor oil

[5] This table was prepared, at the author's request, by the Division of Pomology, U.S. Department of Agriculture.

In all these developments the increased demand for tree crops must be kept constantly in mind. The huge rubber plantation industry of the Middle East is unthinkable without the automobile and the rubber tire. The enormous sales of sugar, coffee, cacao, bananas, etc., are equally unthinkable without a correspondingly large purchasing power generated by modern industry, trade, and science, especially in the United States.

CLASSIFICATION OF PERENNIALS

While perennials as a class share certain characteristics and face certain common problems associated with these characteristics, they also differ considerably among themselves. So significant are these differences (see Table 22.1) that, in behavior, some perennials differ from others more sharply than they differ from some annuals. The most important classes of perennials will therefore be discussed from three points of view: (1) the characteristics of the plants themselves, such as wild or cultivated, etc.; (2) the method of production, i.e., monoculture or diversified farming; (3) the nature of the demand for them.

Wild and Cultivated Perennials

As was pointed out earlier in this chapter, the economic problems which plague the cultivator of perennials are wholly unknown to the collector of the "free gifts of nature" from wild perennials. The latter has his own serious problems, but they are not associated with the time that elapses between planting and harvest and between the appearance and death of the tree.

In spite of the definite shift toward cultivated perennials that has been mentioned, wild perennials continue to play an important role. As yet the bulk of the world's timber stands are wild perennials, but lumber is not a tree crop as the word is used in this chapter and hence it will be discussed in the next chapter. Rubber obtained in the Amazon region is wild rubber, as is most African rubber except that produced by the Firestone plantations in Liberia. A large portion of the oil-bearing palms of the tropics—the coconut, the elaeis, the oiticica, the babassu—still occurs in wild stands. The carnauba palm of Brazil from which wax is extracted, the chicle-yielding sapodilla

of Mexico, the camphor trees of Formosa, and several trees that yield tanning agents such as the quebracho of Paraguay, the dividivi of Venezuela and the valonia of Turkey are likewise wild. As is to be expected, wild perennials occur less frequently in the temperate zone. The perennials that yield the big money crops—coffee, tea, cacao, rubber, cane sugar, and bananas—are cultivated. Their aggregate value dwarfs the total proceeds from the sale of wild perennial crops.

Woody and Herbaceous Perennials

The classification of plants into annuals and perennials is based mainly on the duration of life of the underground stem. There are perennials whose underground stems survive for a number of years but whose growth above ground dies down periodically much like that of annuals. It is only when the above-ground growth turns woody as in trees and shrubs that it too lives on "through the years" *(per annos)*. Thus a sharp distinction must be made between woody and herbaceous perennials.[6]

By far the most important commercial herbaceous perennials are the sugar cane and the banana. When these plants are harvested the above-ground herbaceous growth is cut off near the ground, but the root systems in the ground survive and under proper climatic conditions resprout voluntarily. This resprouting is called ratooning (see p. 239). Ratoon crops are distinguished from planted crops by the fact that the latter behave like annuals. In general, herbaceous perennials do not live as long as trees and palms, nor do they take as long to reach commercial bearing age. Hence herbaceous perennials as a rule are not affected by the serious economic problems which beset most cultivated tree crops. However, in areas such as Cuba, where cane may ratoon for as long as ten years or more, problems definitely similar to those of tree planters do arise.

Natural and Man-Induced Tree Crops

From the economic standpoint it makes a great deal of difference whether a tree crop is a natural product of the tree or a man-

[6] There are woody annuals such as the cotton plant in our South, but this is really a variant produced by cultivation from the original tropical ancestor, the cotton tree (see p. 336).

induced crop. Most tree crops are natural products—nuts, berries, fruit, etc. But there are several important tree crops which are produced not spontaneously but in response to human interference.

By far the most important of these is the latex of the rubber tree (*Hevea brasiliensis*). Like other trees the *Hevea* produces leaves, flowers, fruit, etc. It also maintains for its own biological needs a certain amount of a particular sap known as latex.[7] But this amount is a mere fraction of that harvested when a tree is tapped for latex. Man deliberately wounds the tree by cutting into certain layers of the bark; the tree's response to the wound is the production of extra amounts of latex. Other examples of the same type are maple sugar, turpentine and resin obtained from certain pine trees, and cork obtained from one species of oak. Tea is similar, for man can decide more or less at will how many leaves he will pluck from the tips of the branches of the shrub. The production of camphor under present methods comes in the same category, as does the production of quinine.

The distinction between these two types is very important because it indicates the wide difference in man's control over the size of the crop. The great threat for the coffee planter is a bumper crop or, even worse, two bumper crops in succession. His great hope may be for a frost that will keep the supply in bounds and the price up to expectations. Whatever his fears and hopes, there is no denying that violent year-to-year crop fluctuations constitute a major problem (see p. 387). In sharp contrast to the coffee planter's helplessness in the face of the uncontrollable forces of nature, the rubber grower, in theory at least, has almost as much control over the output of his trees as the automobile manufacturer has over the output of his assembly lines. As will be brought out later (see p. 394), actually the control is not as complete as it seems to be on paper.

Dual-Crop Perennials

A minor distinction can be made between perennials on the basis of another aspect of the crop. Most perennials are grown or exploited

for only one crop. However, in a few instances, two or more crops are obtained.

A few trees are exploited both for the wood itself and for a product obtained from the tree. Walnut and cherry trees are examples more familiar to the older generation, accustomed to walnut furniture and show pieces of cherry wood, than to the younger generation, for styles in furniture have changed. The outstanding example of dual-purpose trees is seen in the naval stores industry, which taps southern pines for resin from which turpentine and rosin are obtained. The duality of purpose, however, depends on the care with which the tapping is done. Careful tapping has been carried on in France for many decades. Its practice is spreading in the piney woods of our own South largely as the result of rising lumber prices which have put a premium on greater care. The term "dual purpose" must not be taken too literally as applying to only two uses; it is also used in the case of trees utilized for more than two purposes, as, for instance, the cork oak of Portugal and western Spain which yields not only cork and timber but also acorns as fodder for swine and fallen branches for fuel.[8]

Perennials in Monoculture and Diversified Farming

Whether the grower of perennials faces serious problems associated with the time element of production depends in large measure on the circumstances under which the trees are grown. If a farmer engaged in mixed money crop farming maintains a small apple orchard on his farm, the economic problems involved in tree crop production are still present but have lost much if not all of their "sting" because he is not wholly dependent on the return from

---

[7] The latex contains the rubber which is extracted by a simple process of coagulation.

[8] The related term "institutional perennials" deserves mention. By this is meant a plant whose continued production rests not on its biological nature but on the institutional setting in which it is grown. The term may well be applied to annuals grown in one-crop regions where the opportunity to switch to alternate crops is entirely absent, or at least remote. There are frontier regions in which the entire system of distribution, physical as well as technical and financial, is so one-sidedly adapted to a single crop—generally wheat—that this one crop must be produced year after year with almost the same regularity as an oak tree yields acorns or a coffee tree bears coffee berries.

the orchard. While he is waiting for it to reach bearing age he can rely on the proceeds from his other crops to sustain him. The cultivation of small stands of rubber trees by Indonesian peasants is a similar case.

The situation is wholly different in the case of the owner of tree plantations maintained as his sole source of support. As was mentioned before, with the accumulation of capital and the growth of urban markets made possible by the mechanical revolution, a definite trend toward specialized one-crop farming set in, and monoculture in the tropics—coffee, cacao, tea, rubber, etc.—grew by leaps and bounds. This specialization has greatly increased the risks faced by tree plantation owners.

Nature of the Demand

Finally, some basic aspects of demand must be brought out. Problems of adjusting supply to demand may arise as much from the demand side as from the supply side. The adjustment of a recalcitrant supply may be eased by an elastic demand which responds freely to price changes reflecting variations in the relative supply. Then again, it may be seriously aggravated by virtual inelasticity of demand.

The demand for various tree crops differs widely, from the habit-governed rather inelastic demand for coffee, and the demand for rubber—almost as inelastic but for different reasons (see p. 393)—to the highly elastic demand for such luxury consumption goods as raisins and walnuts. Any analysis of the problems confronting planters of perennials must carefully consider these differences in the demand for the respective products.

THE ECONOMICS OF PERENNIALS

The difference in the time factor of production is by far the most important distinction between annuals and perennials. Practically all other variations in their behavior and in the problems involved in their production are traceable to this basic difference. The life of perennials varies materially, from a few years in the case of peach trees, to several decades in the case of coffee and rubber trees.

Gestation Period

The life cycle of the perennial can be divided into two distinct phases, the gestation period and the bearing period. By gestation period is meant the period preceding bearing. A difference is frequently made between physical bearing and commercial bearing. The meaning of commercial bearing is not quite clear; it may be defined either as that which pays the out-of-pocket expenses of picking, or that which pays its share of all expenses, including overhead. The gestation period for rubber is eight to ten years; and for coffee, four to six years.

The economic effect of this gestation period is twofold. In the first place, it entails periods of unremunerative waiting. Whoever starts a rubber plantation or a similar enterprise must be prepared to wait possibly ten years before he can expect worth-while returns on his investment. Moreover, during these ten years he must advance considerable sums of money, the amount varying with the size of the plantation and many other factors. In the second place, the prolonged waiting period necessitates a long-range anticipation of demand. The rubber planter who began in 1912 had to make a guess as to the market of 1922, and in a young dynamic industry "there's many a slip 'twixt the cup and the lip." It is natural that the financial aspects of a rubber plantation are indirectly adjusted to these economic handicaps. This adjustment involves partly the wide distribution of the stock of rubber planting companies among the public to whom speculative profits are alluring, and it also affects the rate of profit that is expected. An authority on the financial aspects of the rubber plantation industry placed the "stimulating profit rate"[9] at 15 percent.

This unremunerative waiting period, however, does not entirely lack compensatory aspects. In the first place, the power of speculative gain notwithstanding, capital can hardly be expected to flow as freely into rubber plantations in faraway tropical lands as into more ordinary ventures which promise more immediate returns. This may tend to forestall too rapid expansion under normal conditions. The second and more important point is that the gestation period affords temporary protection from competition. If it takes ten years to bring

---

[9] By "stimulating profit rate" is meant a rate sufficient to attract new capital in amounts large enough to assure the growth called for in the industry by the demand.

a rubber plantation to commercial bearing and if no young trees are about to reach bearing age, the existing plantations will be immune from this new competition for a period of several years. Fortunately or unfortunately, things do not ordinarily work out that way. If, by chance, conditions approximate this assumption, extreme swings from fantastic profits to appalling losses, from famine prices to the low return from a flooded market are the inevitable results of the lagging adjustment of supply to demand. Plantations of perennials are thus good examples of the proverbial "prince and pauper" type of economic enterprise.

Various devices are used to alleviate the difficulties involved in this prolonged waiting period. Young peach trees are frequently grown in nurseries before they are set out in the orchard, thus reducing the period during which the orchard land is not earning a return on its investment. Another device, used in the Lower Rio Grande valley, is to start the perennial plantings piecemeal, step by step, and in the early stages utilize the acreage not yet planted for the purpose of raising annual cash crops. In other cases catch crops are resorted to. In the coffee regions of Brazil, for instance, except in periods of extraordinary prosperity, it is common practice to permit the laborers to grow food and feed crops among the young coffee trees. This can be done not only during the gestation period but also in mature plantations in times of financial strain. However, since using plantation land for other crops may adversely affect the yield of the coffee trees, the effect on supply as well as on cost must be taken into account. Generally speaking, the demand remaining stationary, a reduction in supply tends to raise the price; but, on the other hand, a poor yield tends to raise the unit cost of production. Needless to say, the extent to which the hardships of the unremunerative waiting period can be reduced varies materially with the region and the form of management.[10]

Bearing Period

So far the discussion has been confined to the economic effects of the gestation period. We now turn to the second period in the life of a perennial, namely, the bearing period. As Knight well points out, the producer of tree crops is handicapped not only by the initial delay in returns but also by the fact that his is an investment which can and must yield returns over a considerable period of time. As has been said, the length of the bearing period varies considerably. Plantations are examples of overhead economy; they experience a reduction of unit cost as their output approaches the potential maximum.

With the exception of a few aforementioned perennials whose output is man-controlled as in the case of latex, maple sugar, rosin, and turpentine, plantations share with other branches of agriculture the risks and uncertainties inherent in organic substances and biological processes. A coffee tree, in bearing berries, obeys the laws of nature infinitely more readily than its owner's will, whereas a machine in a factory is a man-made mechanism which listens more closely to its master's voice. In a certain sense, therefore, a plantation may be said to combine the risks of overhead economy with the biological risks of agriculture. Moreover, in the face of unfavorable market developments, the plantation owner lacks the one great remedy available to the farmer who is producing annual crops—acreage adjustment. The owner of a plantation should not be expected to parry the swift strokes of adverse market changes with the destruction of tree capacity any more than the owner of an automobile factory is expected to tear down his buildings and smash his machines simply because the market is going against him. Naturally, short-lived perennials such as peach trees present fewer difficulties in the way of acreage adjustment than do long-lived perennials such as rubber and coffee trees.[11] It would be folly to expect the grower

---

[10] It is well to keep in mind the fact that not all producers of tree crops have to start with clearing a jungle or planting a barren expanse of land. When a plantation industry is once established, the purchase of tree stands at different stages of maturity becomes increasingly important as a method of entering the field. The California orange industry has reached such a stage of development that buying a ready-made grove is a far more common way

of starting in the business than developing a new orchard from the ground up.

[11] In response to violent price drops caused by overproduction, during one period the coöperatively organized peach growers of California ripped millions of healthy trees out of the ground, the cost of this colossal work of destruction being defrayed out of the increased returns traceable to the reduced supply.

of trees whose bearing age may exceed half a century to follow blindly the example set by the grower, the bearing age of whose trees extends over a mere fraction of that time.

Tree Crops and Price Control

The law of supply and demand operates smoothly only when supply can be adjusted to demand with speed and accuracy. This adjustment can be satisfactorily achieved under conditions either of a static or elastic demand or of a highly flexible supply. Practically all producers of perennial crops suffer from the absence of one or the other of these conditions, and some from both. It is not surprising, therefore, that these producers have long felt compelled to resort to artificial price control. The following raw materials (perennials are indicated by an asterisk) have been subjected to artificial price control:[12]

*Camphor (natural)	Potash
*Chinchona bark (for	*Pulpwood
quinine)	*Quebracho
*Citrate of lime	*Rubber
*Coffee	*Sandalwood oil
Cotton (long staple)	Silk
*Currants	*Sisal
Kauri-gum	*Sugar
Mercury	Sulfur
Nitrate	Tin
Pearlshell	

In view of what has been said about the nature of perennials, the fact that eleven of the twenty commodities in this list are perennials is not surprising. It should be pointed out, however, that camphor, pulpwood, quebracho, and sandalwood are generally obtained from wild perennials and hence are not directly subject to the theory here propounded—that *cultivated* perennials can hardly survive without some interference with the spontaneous forces governing supply and demand. Since this list was compiled, other perennials have come under price control. Cacao comes to mind. Wool, though an animal product, could be included. In the United States, nuts, especially walnuts, have been subjected to strict marketing control which could not help reacting on prices.[13]

[12] B. B. Wallace, and L. R. Edminster, *International Control of Raw Materials*, The Brookings Institution, Washington, 1930, p. 13.

It is not claimed here that the law of supply and demand always works smoothly in the case of annuals. Other factors besides the character of the plant must be considered. What is claimed here is that the law affects each commodity according to its characteristics and the circumstances under which it is produced and consumed. Furthermore, in the case of *cultivated* plants, it is claimed that the fact of being a perennial is one of the most potent characteristics affecting the manner in which the law operates. While "annuality" does not preclude interference with the smooth functioning of the adjustment process as generally conceived, "perenniality" constitutes a strong presumption in favor—in fact, an almost infallible sign—of trouble. Hence, so far as cultivated perennials are concerned, the best hope seems to be not absence of interference or control, but reasonable and constructive control.

PROBLEMS OF TREE CULTURE

Anticipation of Demand

The main cause of the economic difficulties that beset the growers of tree crops, and to some extent also the growers of herbaceous perennials such as cane sugar, is the length of

[13] It is worthy of note that only one agricultural annual appears on the list, long-staple cotton, which is generally grown under irrigation and hence is affected by problems of overhead. However, soon after the above book was published, a number of annuals came under government control under the New Deal. In fact, our agricultural reform and parity legislation regulated a large number of annual crops in one way or another. Moreover, the trend was not confined to the United States.

This wholesale governmental control over the production and marketing of annuals is a reflection of abnormal conditions, especially the dislocation of agricultural production brought on by world wars and depressions. It is also a defensive measure by which small-enterprise agriculture tries to protect itself from the dangers stemming from industry, commerce, and finance that are no longer fully competitive.

This type of agricultural price control of annuals is altogether different in causation and justification from that being discussed in this chapter. This chapter deals with price control applied to privately produced tree crops. It has its roots in the fact that the very nature of perennials rules out the smooth operation of the law of supply and demand and tends to destroy the industry in the absence of interference.

the production process, including the preparatory or gestation period. The length of this process robs supply of flexibility, thus aggravating the difficulty of keeping it aligned with demand, and renders more difficult the 'anticipation of demand. This difficulty increases not proportionately with the length of the time involved but at a far higher rate. If economic life were a placid stream flowing at a constant velocity and volume through a pleasant valley, the inflexibility resulting from long production cycles might not cause serious trouble. But economic life, especially today, is a turbulent mountain torrent whose behavior is subject to violent and unpredictable changes without notice.

Demand in general is subject to cyclical fluctuations in business activity. This difficulty tends to be more pronounced in the case of producers' goods such as rubber than in consumers' goods such as coffee or sugar. It is particularly pronounced in the case of commodities devoted largely to a single use such as rubber tires and tubes, especially if the market is concentrated in a single country.

If cyclical fluctuations reach the violence of the Great Depression, the problem posed by the catastrophic collapse of demand is staggering for the owners of long-lived tree capital. Defensive measures are not readily taken because the gravity of the situation reveals itself only gradually and because the duration of the blight is problematical. As it is, the plantation owner hopes from month to month, from year to year, that the bottom has been reached and the turn for the better has come, only to be plunged ever deeper into despair.

Similar in the violence of its force is war. Twice in a generation world wars have closed the all-important European market more or less tightly for years at a time to the growers of coffee, cacao, rubber, and other tree crops. Because of the inflexibility of the long-lived one-product tree plantation, such wholesale excisions of large segments of the market present more or less insoluble problems, that is, insoluble in terms of orthodox remedies.

Demand is also affected by political events. Puerto Rican coffee growers had long been able to sell the bulk of their crop at remunerative prices in Spain. But that was before 1898, when the United States took the island over

and alienated it politically from its former mother country. Tariff laws, quota regulations, empire preference, embargoes may strike with sudden force, throwing the cumbersome tree plantation off balance far more than typical producers of annuals.

Crop Fluctuation

The disturbances which afflict the growers of perennials stem from the same general sources which cause economic instability in general. It is in the violence of the impact that the difference lies. These disturbances afflict both the supply and the demand side of the equation.

The size of agricultural crops in general is greatly affected by weather. Tree crops, as a rule, are not exempt. For example, the crop of coffee berries from a given stand of trees fluctuates violently from year to year in response to the vagaries of the weather. The extent of this fluctuation varies with the location of the coffee plantation; it is far more violent in São Paulo, the leading coffee state in Brazil, and in neighboring regions than in the tropical highlands of Colombia or Costa Rica. Indeed, the fact that a vast portion of the earth's entire coffee tree capacity is concentrated in this one subtropical region of southern Brazil is in large part responsible for the coffee problem and goes far to explain why it was Brazil that had to take the initiative in attempting to solve it. The weather's effect on tree crops is further accentuated by the tendency of trees to rest after bearing a bumper crop. A frost that hits a tree thus weakened is apt to do severe damage.[14]

Vulnerability of Trees as Capital

Another source of trouble that afflicts perennials more than annuals is hurricanes. They are confined to specific areas, particularly the Caribbean. The damage which a hurricane inflicts on a tobacco field is as nothing compared with the havoc it plays with a coffee plantation. Recovery from hurricane damage may be surprisingly swift in the case of annual field crops. But if coffee trees are actually uprooted, the damage cannot be repaired for five to seven

---

[14] As was pointed out, several tree crops, especially rubber and, to a lesser extent, tea are exempt from these violent crop fluctuations.

years, and tree capital which might have been good for perhaps decades more is irreparably lost.

Scientific Progress

Scientific discoveries and technological changes may affect crops adversely by aiding or creating rival crops or regions or better varieties which reduce the competitive vigor of the old crops and cause their obsolescence. Here again the high overhead makes tree plantations more vulnerable to such changes. Even herbaceous perennials such as sugar cane are not immune. Perhaps the most striking examples of this are the introduction of P.O.J. 2878 and its impact on the world sugar situation (see p. 234), and the development of bud grafting and later of seed improvement based on work with clones, which affected the supply of cultivated rubber. Such revolutionary boosts to productive capacity have at least a twofold impact on the industry involved. In the first place, the rather sudden spurt in productive capacity poses grave problems of adjusting supply to demand. In the second place, the wholesale obsolescence of older plantations may create a problem for which the industry is utterly unprepared. The lower cost of producing the crop which is almost sure to follow may eventually prove a blessing, but the transition from the old to the new basis may be both bewildering and painful.

Government Policies

Perennials share with other crops the risks from arbitrary interference in their market by national governments prompted perhaps by political motives as much as by economic considerations. Here again the less flexible, more cumbersome nature of long-lived tree plantations tends to aggravate the difficulty. The artificial fostering of beet sugar industries in country after country is one of the main causes of the sugar surplus.

Whatever one may think of the relative merits of laissez faire, it is self-evident that this philosophy offers no solution for the problem faced by the owners of tree plantations and, to a lesser extent, the producers of herbaceous perennials—especially sugar cane and bananas. It is not surprising, therefore, that the records of the past half century are replete

with one price control scheme after another involving cultivated perennials. If a crop escaped, it escaped unnoticed. Coffee, cacao, rubber, quinine, camphor, citrus and other fruit trees, nut-bearing trees, sugar are but the better-known examples of this wholesale desertion from free-market economics. This drift toward artificial control of economic activity which, of course, engulfs ever wider segments of the world is one of the most significant phenomena of our time. It must be studied objectively and scrutinized for its effects, good or bad, on the body economic.[15]

Of the long list of price control schemes involving tree crops, two are chosen for brief discussion: (1) Brazilian coffee valorization and defense; and (2) the price control of rubber, exercised first by the British alone and later jointly by all important countries engaged in the production of cultivated rubber. These two commodities are chosen because they loom large on the list of United States imports, and consequently any effort to raise prices artificially touches a tender spot in our body economic. They are chosen also because, although both are tree crops, coffee and rubber are very different in significant respects. They therefore prove the point that, though all cultivated tree crops have certain fundamental characteristics in common, a specific plant's peculiar nature and other factors account for notable variations in the general theme. It is just as important to be able to appreciate the variations as it is to recognize the theme.

COFFEE AND PRICE CONTROL
The World Coffee Situation

"Coffee is primarily a Western Hemisphere product and problem. Over 85 percent of the

---

[15] Fortunately the literature on this subject has been greatly enlarged in recent years. In particular, the Food Research Institute of Stanford University under the able direction of Joseph S. Davis has contributed valuable volumes. Two particularly relevant books are K. E. Knorr, *World Rubber and Its Regulation,* and V. P. Wickizer, *The World Coffee Economy with Special Reference to Control Schemes,* both published by the Stanford University Press in 1945 and 1943 respectively. A third book in the same series, also by Wickizer, is *Tea Under International Control,* which came out in 1944. References to pertinent literature are cited in all three volumes. The following discussion leans heavily on these three books.

world supply comes from Latin America, mostly from Brazil and the countries bordering on the Caribbean. The United States constitutes by far the greatest market, absorbing more than half the entire world ouput."[16] Before World War II the countries of continental Europe took about 40 percent of all the coffee exported, but it may be some years before they will again be able to absorb so large a share of the world supply.

Brazil is by far the largest producer of coffee. Production is concentrated in the state of São Paulo and parts of neighboring states. The climate is such that frost is a real factor, occasionally cutting the crop to a fraction of its potential. More recently droughts and pests have added their share of trouble. For about a century coffee was a frontier crop in Brazil. As the need arose, she expanded production by planting new regions, but their limit has been reached; furthermore, the older regions are in need of soil restoration if they are to continue as economic producers. Soil erosion following removal of the forest cover is beginning to cause considerable concern.

Brazilian coffee furnishes the base of blends which contain so-called mild coffee—*cafe suave* —from other parts of Latin America, notably Colombia; these are added for aroma and flavor.

TABLE 22.2. Value of Coffee Exports in Percent of Total Commodity Exports for Selected Countries[17]

	1929	1944
Brazil	71	36
Colombia	61	73
Costa Rica	62	58
Dominican Republic	10	4
El Salvador	93	84
Guatemala	77	65
Haiti	77	43
Nicaragua	54	23
Venezuela	17	2

Coffee plays a very important though declining part in a number of Latin-American economies. Table 22.2 shows the relation of coffee exports to total commodity exports for selected countries in 1929 and 1944.

[16] V. D. Wickizer, *The World Coffee Economy,* p. 3.

[17] Inter-American Coffee Board, *Study of the World Coffee Situation,* 1948, p. 2.

Table 22.3 furnishes some basic facts regarding the world coffee situation during the period 1920-1949. Of particular importance is the rapid increase in Brazilian production during the decade beginning in 1925. The steady increase of coffee production in the so-called mild countries (included under "Other Countries") is no less notable.

Brazilian Coffee Valorization

During much of the nineteenth century, coffee production in southern Brazil centering in the state of São Paulo proved highly profitable on the whole. The industry grew rapidly, and Brazil became by far the most important source of coffee in the world. Both climate and soil favored the crop and the land opened up by railroads and highways seemed almost unlimited.

This increase in production coincided with the rapid industrialization of the United States and of Germany and other European countries which provided an expanding market. Populations grew fast and per capita purchasing power rose considerably.

Around the turn of the century the first serious threat of imbalance appeared between the supply of coffee and the demand for it, when an unusually large number of trees happened to come into bearing. By 1900-1901 the number of bearing trees in São Paulo alone was more than three times as great as it had been in 1890-1891. Brazil's coffee production doubled within a decade.[18] As a matter of fact, supplies began to accumulate in the middle nineties and would have proved extremely burdensome had not the sharp drop in the price of coffee in foreign markets been neutralized, so far as Brazilian exporters were concerned, by the equally rapid decline of Brazilian foreign exchange which followed the overthrow of the empire in 1889 and the establishment of a republic. By 1900 the outlook began to be ominous. The price of coffee fell alarmingly and the governments of the coffee-growing states of Brazil, meeting at Taubaté in 1901 to discuss possible remedies, banned the new planting of coffee trees.

[18] See V. D. Wickizer, *The World Coffee Economy,* p. 139. For a clear analysis of the cyclical nature of tree culture, see Inter-American Coffee Board, *op. cit.,* p. 12.

TABLE 22.3. The World Coffee Situation, 1920-1949[19]
(Production and consumption in million bags of 60 Kg.; prices in cents per lb.)

	Production							Prices		
		Brazil						Wholesale (N. Y.)		Retail Roasted, U. S.
Year[a]	World Total[b]	Total	São Paulo	Other States	Other Countries	Consumption[c]	Destruction in Brazil	Santos No. 4	Mani-zales	
1920	14.0	7.5	4.2	3.3	6.5	18.5	. . .	19.0	21.5	47.0
1921	22.4	14.5	10.2	4.3	7.9	20.3	. . .	10.4	15.6	36.3
1922	20.7	12.9	8.2	4.7	7.8	19.5	. . .	14.3	17.4	36.1
1923	18.3	10.2	7.0	3.2	8.1	20.7	. . .	14.8	18.8	36.9
1924	24.2	14.9	10.4	4.5	9.3	21.4	. . .	21.3	25.5	42.6
Average	19.9	12.0	8.0	4.0	7.9	20.1	. . .	16.0	19.8	39.8
1925	24.3	14.6	9.2	5.4	9.7	20.7	. . .	24.5	27.9	50.4
1926	26.6	15.5	10.1	5.4	11.1	22.3	. . .	22.3	28.5	50.2
1927	26.4	15.8	9.9	5.9	10.6	22.9	. . .	18.7	25.1	47.4
1928	39.4	27.1	18.0	9.1	12.3	23.2	. . .	23.2	27.3	48.2
1929	26.1	13.6	8.8	4.8	12.5	23.9	. . .	22.1	22.8	47.9
Average	28.5	17.3	11.2	6.1	11.2	22.6	. . .	22.2	26.3	48.8
1930	40.8	28.2	19.5	8.7	12.6	25.4	. . .	13.2	17.2	39.5
1931	29.4	16.6	10.1	6.5	12.8	26.9	2.8	8.7	15.6	32.8
1932	41.3	28.3	18.7	9.6	13.0	23.8	9.3	10.7	11.4	29.4
1933	34.0	19.8	15.0	4.8	14.2	24.6	13.9	9.3	10.5	26.4
1934	42.9	29.6	21.8	7.8	13.3	24.0	8.2	11.2	13.7	26.9
Average	37.7	24.5	17.0	7.5	13.2	24.9	8.6	10.6	13.7	31.0
1935	31.5	18.2	11.7	6.5	13.3	26.3	1.7	8.9	10.3	25.7
1936	36.5	20.9	13.5	7.4	15.6	26.2	3.7	9.5	11.3	24.3
1937	42.6	26.4	17.8	8.6	16.2	26.4	17.2	11.1	11.6	25.5
1938	38.6	23.5	15.9	7.6	15.1	29.8	8.0	7.8	11.0	23.2
1939	37.8	23.1	15.6	7.6	14.7	29.2	3.5	7.5	11.8	22.5
Average	37.4	22.4	14.9	7.5	15.0	27.6	6.8	9.0	11.2	24.2
1940	34.3	19.1	12.4	6.7	15.2	24.4	2.8	7.2	8.4	21.2
1941	31.8	16.5	10.2	6.3	15.3	21.6	3.4	11.4	15.2	23.6
1942	32.0	15.8	9.3	6.5	16.2	17.2	2.3	13.4	15.9	28.3
1943	29.4	13.6	8.5	5.1	15.8	20.7	1.3	13.4	15.9	29.9
1944	28.2	12.2	5.9	6.3	16.0	24.5	0.1	13.4	15.9	30.1
Average	31.1	15.4	9.3	6.1	15.7	21.7	2.0	11.8	14.3	26.4
1945	26.0	8.3	3.9	4.4	17.7	26.7	. . .	13.4	15.9	30.5
1946	24.0	12.2	6.5	5.7	11.8	25.8	. . .	18.5	21.7	34.4
1947	28.5	14.6	7.5	7.1	13.9	25.8	. . .	26.7	30.1	46.6
1948	36.5	18.9	11.0	7.9	17.6	29.6	. . .	26.8	32.5	51.4
1949	40.5	22.3	11.3	5.7	18.2	32.5	. . .	30.2	35.6	53.7
Average	31.1	15.3	8.0	6.2	15.8	28.1	. . .	23.1	27.2	43.3

a For production, marketing year begins with the preceding calendar year; for all others, with the calendar year.
b Data not equally comprehensive for all years.
c Consumption = world net imports.

[19] 1920 through 1939 average from V. D. Wickizer, *The World Coffee Economy*, Food Research Institute, Stanford University, pp. 248, 249; figures for 1940 through 1947 supplied by Mr. Wickizer; 1948 and 1949 data supplied by U.S. Department of Commerce.

TABLE 22.4. Extent of Variation of Coffee Yields in Brazil, Measured from Five-Year
Average Yields, 1920-1924 to 1940-1944[20]
(million bags of 60 kg. each)

| Marketing Year | Average Annual Exportable Production | Crops Above Five-Year Annual Average | | | Crops Below Five-Year Annual Average | | | Interval of Range for Period: High-Low Crop |
		No. of Crop Years	Range	Interval of Range	No. of Crop Years	Range	Interval of Range	
1920-1924	12.0	3	12.9-14.9	2.0	2	7.5-10.2	2.7	7.4
1925-1929	17.3	1	27.1	...	4	13.6-15.8	2.2	13.5
1930-1934	24.5	3	28.2-29.6	1.4	2	16.6-19.8	3.2	13.0
1935-1939	22.4	3	23.2-26.4	3.2	2	18.2-20.9	2.7	8.2
1940-1944	15.4	3	15.8-19.1	3.3	2	12.2-13.6	1.4	6.9

At this point must be mentioned a characteristic of the coffee tree which tends to interfere with the orderly marketing of the crop. Especially in a latitude such as that of São Paulo where frosts are by no means unknown, the crop is subject to violent fluctuations from year to year. The violence of these fluctuations varies inversely with the size of the area under consideration (see Table 22.4). Coffee consumption, on the other hand, is strongly affected by habit. Short-run demand is highly inelastic, especially in the United States, the largest market for coffee; even considerable wholesale price reductions do not materially encourage retail sales. A bumper crop, therefore, cannot be marketed, in the sense of getting it into actual consuming channels, before the next crop is ready for harvest. A large part of it must be stored. "Green" coffee prepared for the market can stand prolonged storage without undue loss in quality. Traditionally, coffee merchants in the importing countries assumed this storing function as a matter of routine. So long as demand over the years grew apace with supply, the excess stored supplies could be liquidated during the off-crop years. Naturally, the held-over stocks tended to keep down the price at which short crops could be sold; but, by and large, the system seemed to work to the satisfaction of all concerned.

As was mentioned earlier, several developments occurred soon after the turn of the century which caused a drastic change in the system. In the first place, the 1901-1902 crop[21] was the largest on record—over 16 million bags, almost three times as large as average crops a decade earlier. Prices collapsed, and panic gripped both planters and export merchants. In spite of this, Brazil's general credit position was materially improved, with two results. As was mentioned before, the milreis had been falling for over a decade. Now it began to recover; in other words, a coffee exporter who wished to convert his dollar and sterling credits into milreis received fewer milreis per dollar or pound sterling. The exchange situation now favored the importer as against the exporter. This aggravated the plight of the export industry. But it also meant that Brazil could borrow at more reasonable rates of interest than had formerly been the case. So long as the French coffee importer in Le Havre, for example, could borrow against negotiable warehouse receipts for stored coffee at 3 or 4 percent whereas in Brazil the rates ran as high as 10 or even 15 percent, this importer was the only logical person to assume the storing function, for interest rates largely determine storage costs. Under such conditions, storage in Brazil, financed in Brazil, was clearly out of the question. But when Brazil's state and federal governments discovered that they could borrow large sums in London against stored coffee at 8 percent or less, the possibility of Brazil's taking over in part or in full the storage function formerly performed by foreign merchants was clearly envisaged.

---

[20] Inter-American Coffee Board, *op. cit.*, p. 15. Based on compilations made by the U.S. Department of Commerce.

[21] The crop or marketing year runs from July 1 to June 30.

The result was that in 1905, when another bumper crop loomed, the government of the state of São Paulo officially adopted a policy of *valorização*, or valorization. As originally conceived, this is a presumably temporary marketing policy intended to raise the price, by government intervention, above unduly low levels, *but not above the level which free competitive market forces would bring about.* Destruction of part of the surplus was considered but not carried out. São Paulo, aided financially by the federal government, bought up over 8 million bags by the end of 1907, and later, with the aid of a foreign loan of £15 million, raised the total amount removed from the market to just under 11 million bags. A vital feature of the scheme was the prohibition of new plantings for a period of ten years after 1902. Partly because of this drastic curtailment measure and partly because of the increased demand during the relative prosperity that preceded World War I, the first price control measure may be declared a success, in spite of the failure of Brazil's minor coffee-producing states to cooperate with São Paulo. Prices rose to remunerative levels and by 1914 all but 3 million bags of the valorized stock had been sold. The bankers' loan was paid off in 1914, and Brazil was indemnified at the peace conference for stocks seized by Germany in World War I.

The main reason for success is the fact that consumption caught up with production, or, to put it differently, production was curtailed to a point where consumption could catch up. An accurate appraisal of the efficacy of this first valorization scheme is impossible, for there is no way of knowing what might have happened in its absence. It is possible that under laissez faire plantations with large coffee-bearing capacity would have reverted to jungle, thus creating a scarcity as great as, or perhaps even greater than, that brought on by the curtailment of new planting. Perhaps the most significant aftereffect was psychological, in that it conditioned the Brazilians to favor interference with the free market.

This effect was greatly reinforced by the enormous financial success of the second valorization scheme undertaken by the state of São Paulo, with the aid of the federal government, to bring the supply (1917-1918 was another bumper crop year) in line with the demand that was seriously curtailed by the war then raging in Europe. This time, and from then on, surplus stocks were stored in Brazil, not in the importing countries as had been the case under the first valorization scheme. Just as a *force majeure*—the war—had brought on the difficulty, so another *force majeure*—in fact, an act of God, frost—saved the day. Though many planters were ruined, valorization proved a huge success.

When, in 1921, world prices tumbled from the high perch reached during the war and its aftermath, the coffee market was again thrown into panic. Again the government intervened, but this time the federal government took the lead, issuing paper money to finance the third valorization scheme. The result was a rather sharp decline in the value of the milreis which, while it encouraged coffee exports, was not without drawbacks for the Brazilian economy as a whole. Again frost came to the rescue and the scheme again proved a success.

Summing up the net results of these three valorization schemes,[22] one may say that they prevented a severe drop of prices in 1906-1907, resulted in higher prices than might otherwise have been expected during 1910-1912, and resulted in moderate price fluctuations during World War I and the postwar recession. In general, these measures benefited producers if not consumers. But there was one serious flaw in this serene situation. Brazilians became unduly impressed with their capacity to cope with whatever trouble might come along—be it bumper crops, frosts, wars, or depressions—and had acquired an optimism even greater than that for which they had long been known. This optimism proved their ultimate undoing, for it made them forget the importance of the ban on tree planting from 1902 to 1912 in the success of the first valorization scheme and it led them to count too freely on God's aid in the shape of timely frosts and other crop-damaging acts.

Brazil's Coffee "Defense" Policies

While the third valorization scheme was still in progress, Brazilian coffee policy underwent a radical and ominous change. Encour-

[22] See also B. B. Wallace and L. R. Edminster, *op. cit.*, pp. 136-150, quoted also in V. P. Wickizer, *The World Coffee Economy*, p. 143.

aged by the success of three strictly temporary market interventions, coffee people came to look upon intervention as a normal feature of coffee marketing and turned to what came to be known as "permanent defense of coffee." Instead of having an eagle eye on new plantings in terms of their delayed though inevitable effect on later harvests, the price controllers, no longer content with taking bumper crop supplies off the market, now turned their attention to the irregularity with which all coffee crops were shipped from the interior to the port of Santos for export—huge amounts during the peak of the harvest season and little more than a trickle during the off months. There is no annual peak in coffee consumption, so why should there be one in its shipment? These conditions appeared to offer another chance to "stabilize" the price and perhaps divert another slice of revenue from the merchant to the grower.

A policy aimed at this purpose was initiated by the federal government in 1923. To permit the storage of coffee held back from the rail haul to Santos, the government built a series of special warehouses and purchased others. In 1925, São Paulo took over the task of market control through its newly created semiofficial São Paulo Institute for the Permanent Defense of Coffee, which was responsible for administering the policy of regulated shipments to Santos. A special bank was set up to finance the supposedly seasonal withholding of the crop. But the Institute went further. Through purchases of coffee it turned price control from a sporadic to a regular procedure; every serious price dip became a signal for market interference. These operations were financed partly through a transportation tax on coffee shipments and partly through foreign loans.

The 1927-1928 crop was a real "whopper"— 27.1 million bags! Weather conditions were ideal not only in São Paulo but in the neighboring coffee areas as well. So ominous did the situation seem that the usually noncoöperative neighboring states joined the São Paulo Institute in its efforts to ward off the shock of so large a crop. Prices were maintained, but at the expense of a large increase in carry-over stocks. The next year brought an even larger crop, but again prices held up amazingly well. These favorable prices, in the absence of re-

striction on new plantings, encouraged heavy outlays in new trees. Coffee trees in Brazil take four to five years to reach commercial bearing age, after which yields tend to rise to a peak. This means that new plantings cannot affect the volume of the harvest until four or five years later, but from then on the total crop will expand at an alarming but relentless rate. The recklessness of the planters in the face of this certain day of reckoning was paralleled by that of the financial institutions whose directors seemed to be equally blind regarding the inevitable outcome. Bad as the situation was because of what the Brazilians had done or failed to do, it became infinitely worse with the onset of the Great Depression in the fall of 1929. Thus, an utterly unmanageable supply situation was vastly aggravated by the havoc wrought in demand.

As if to make the cup flow over, another difficulty arose. Encouraged by Brazil's price-stabilizing and price-raising efforts, other Latin-American countries greatly expanded their coffee areas—in particular Colombia and certain sections of Central America, where coffee is grown in the shade in high altitudes of tropical highlands. This coffee is known as mild coffee, is rich in aroma, and sells at a considerable price above that paid for the coarser and harsher Brazilian coffee. Coffee roasters in consuming countries came to rely increasingly on admixtures of these mild coffees in their expensively advertised blends. To supply these blends and thus safeguard their heavy investments in good will they must continue to buy this coffee even at exorbitant prices. These mild coffees, therefore, are indeed formidable rivals of Brazilian coffee.

Collapse, Revolution, and Recovery

The storm struck São Paulo with full fury. Once more the state government tried the old tricks; it borrowed £20 million from foreign banks. But by that time the situation was so completely out of hand that the federal government had to come in—not to take over where the smaller unit had failed but to adopt entirely new and far more drastic policies. The economic collapse brought on a political revolution, and a new regime was in power; Vargas, a strong man from the South, a *gaucho* from Rio Grande do Sul, now headed the government. A new phase of coffee defense began.

As was to be expected in view of the new plantings now reaching bearing age and the depression going from bad to worse, the surplus problem grew progressively worse in the following years. In a way, the new government was called upon to pay the penalty for its predecessor's errors; but beyond that it tried to regain as much as possible the position of leadership in world coffee long held by Brazil.

The first step the new government took was to renew the ban on new plantings. The excess supply of 25 million bags left by the old regime was increased by the 1931-1932 crop of 28.3 million bags and the 1933-1934 crop of 29.6 million—the result of the vast new plantings in the late twenties. The low demand made two things inevitable—prices fell to new lows and unsalable surplus stocks had to be destroyed, which in turn meant drastic taxes. In spite of the destruction of around 57 million bags by 1937, the supply was still not low enough; furthermore, "milds" were selling at prices hardly higher than Santos prices and in amounts which threatened to dislodge Brazil permanently as the world's premier coffee country. Finally realizing that other countries were reaping the benefit of her sacrifices and after vainly attempting to bring the countries that produced the mild coffees into the control scheme, the government abandoned the policy of permanent defense, first adopted in 1925, in favor of free competition.

The result was immediate and striking. Prices dropped from an average of 11.1 cents for Santos 4's in New York in 1937 to 7.5 in 1939; exports rose during the same period from 12.1 to 16.5 million bags. In the meantime destruction continued, 8 million bags in 1938 and 3.5 million in 1939, and so on, until by 1944 a total of 79,215,000 bags—10.5 billion pounds—had been destroyed.[23] At 10 cents a pound, this would be worth $1 billion—a fearful penalty to pay for lack of foresight, bungling, and, one might add, an untamed desire to get rich quick.

---

[23] Burning coffee may seem highly reprehensible. But in judging this economic vandalism, one should not forget that apples rotting on the ground and tomatoes dumped into the Hudson River are just as effectively lost to the consumer as is coffee burned by the producer. The ways and means differ; the effect is the same.

Coffee in World War II and After

Just as Brazil by means of drastic measures was ready for a fresh start as the leading purveyor of coffee to the world, World War II broke out and once more robbed her of her European market which normally accounts for about 40 percent of the world demand. Again destruction had to be resorted to in order to keep even a normal supply from swamping an abnormally small market.

But by this time the situation had changed in two respects. In the first place, there seemed to be a profitable means of disposing of excess coffee, for an inventor had discovered how to convert coffee into a thermosetting plastic, with caffeine and coffee oil as by-products. A pilot plant was built by the Brazilian government in São Paulo in 1941, and others were in the blueprint stage. In 1949, however, the commercial success of this plan was still problematical and some of the early enthusiasm had worn off.

In the second place, not Brazil alone, but all the coffee countries were faced by the same problem, more or less. But the bulk of the coffee supply comes from Latin America, which is closest to the United States geographically as well as politically and economically. In the face of the Nazi threat, western hemisphere solidarity became a powerful slogan and the Good Neighbor Policy had a ready appeal. Out of this background there emerged an institutional set-up unique in the annals of economic control—the Inter-American Coffee Agreement of 1940, which remained in operation as a market control device until 1948.

Under this agreement, fourteen Latin-American coffee-producing countries and the United States agreed to regulate not only the shipment and sale of Latin-American coffee to the United States but also the latter's imports of coffee from nonsignatory countries, as well as shipments from signatory countries to countries other than the United States. In so far as coffee prices were thus raised by voluntary action on the part of the United States, one may speak of political subsidies to Latin America. Fortunately, the tremendous expansion of the economy of the United States and, with it, of purchasing power, led to an unprecedented increase in coffee consumption in that country that went far to offset the impairment of other markets. At the same time weather conditions in Brazil were unfavorable and short crops were harvested. As a result, the average New York coffee price for Santos No. 4 rose sharply from 11.8 cents in 1940-1944 to 26.7 in 1947, and much higher in 1948 and 1949. In 1950 retail prices of coffee in the United States approached $1.00 a pound.

Looking back on the ill-fated efforts of São Paulo and Brazil to control their coffee industry, we may draw some conclusions.

1. A crop with the characteristics of coffee—violent variations in yield plus inelasticity of short-term demand—cannot be marketed without the storing of surplus supplies. If the merchant performs this function, he may be overly pessimistic; if the grower undertakes it, he may be overly optimistic. No control scheme is economically sound which does not make the careful alignment of *anticipated* demand and *anticipated* supply the very keystone of its structure. To avoid the influence of selfish pressure groups, control and its enforcement should be entrusted only to impartial experts.

2. Control schemes tend to treat high-cost producers too generously. They should be so administered that the efficient low-cost producer has as much chance to forge ahead *at the expense* of the high-cost producer as he would under free competition. Not only does fair play for the consumer demand this, but the long-run interest of the industry itself is better served. Here again impartial judgment must prevail, for the low-cost producer is only too happy to let the high-cost producer survive so long as it means huge profits for himself.

RUBBER

Brief Historical Review

The story of rubber is a drama in three acts. Moreover, it is an allegory which illustrates or symbolizes man's material progress on this earth. Just as man first depended on the wild products or free gifts of nature, then turned to agriculture to go into partnership with nature, and finally learned to imitate nature and occasionally "go her one better," so people first collected rubber from wild trees, shrubs, and vines, later cultivated the trees on plantations, on farms, and in gardens, and finally learned to make rubber synthetically. In some instances, notably in dyestuffs, the synthetic products have managed to wipe out the natural proto-

types, but in the case of rubber the issue is still hanging fire. For the time being it looks as though cultivated and synthetic rubbers will share the market.

The first region to produce wild rubber on a large commercial scale was the Amazon basin, which occupies the major part of Brazil and portions of Venezuela, Colombia, Ecuador, Peru, and Bolivia. Here, following Charles Goodyear's discovery of vulcanization in 1843 and the subsequent development of a commercial demand for crude rubber, merchants enrolled the aid of natives to collect rubber in the jungle, mainly from the tree known to botanists as *Hevea brasiliensis*, but also from the castilloa tree and other plants. By 1850 the volume of shipments of rubber from South America had reached the 1000-ton mark. Interest in rubber spread to other parts of the globe, especially to Africa—more particularly to the Congo, rendered infamous by the "Red Rubber Scandals" centering around King Leopold II of Belgium. By 1900 wild rubber production from all sources totaled about 54,000 tons. It reached its all-time peak in 1912 with 70,000 tons, of which Brazil furnished 42,000.

Throughout this period the rubber price in London averaged around 75 cents a pound, but it went over $3.00 a pound in times of short supply, and *averaged* $2.09 a pound in 1910! The price tended upward as demand increased and as the search for rubber had to be pushed to less accessible spots in the interior of the jungle. Wild rubber evidently had passed the point of diminishing return. Even if it had not, it could never have met the needs of the age of motor and air transport, in which rubber is one of the most widely used and strategic raw materials, ranking alongside of steel, copper, and petroleum in the machine civilization of today. In 1948, the capacity to produce rubber, crude and synthetic, was estimated to be in the neighborhood of 3 million tons, or over forty times the peak output of wild rubber, and consumption was running at about half that rate.

The second act of the rubber drama starts with "the great seed snatch" of 1878 when, in violation of Brazilian law, the Englishman, Henry A. Wickham, later knighted by his grateful Queen, removed thousands of seedlings from the Amazon region, which, eventually transferred to Ceylon, started what probably is the greatest venture in tropical agriculture, the Asiatic rubber plantation industry.

The first plantations were started in the 1880's, but the real push began around the turn of the century, rapidly gained momentum under the impact of rising prices, and developed into one of the wildest speculative crazes ever witnessed. By 1914, plantation rubber exports for the first time exceeded wild rubber shipments, reaching the 400,000-ton mark in 1922 and close to a million tons in 1939 (see Table 22.5). At that time wild rubber was practically on the way out, though it

TABLE 22.5. World Production of Natural Rubber by Major Regions, 1900-1948[24] (thousand long tons)

	Southeast Asia	Other	Total
1900-1904	1	46	47
1905-1909	5	63	68
1910-1914	38	72	110
1915-1919	206	51	257
1920-1924	351	28	379
1925-1929	609	38	647
1930-1934	853	15	868
1935-1939	938	32	970
1940-1944	826	70	896
1945-1948	707	65	772

was revived during World War II by the desire of the United States to have a nearby source of crude rubber, wild or planted. In 1939, total production of rubber other than wild was as follows: 976,000 tons from planted trees, 75,000 tons synthetic, 100,000 tons reclaimed.

Just as the high price of wild rubber had encouraged the growth of the plantation industry, so during the twenties British price control gave a strong impetus to the use of reclaimed rubber as a limited substitute and to efforts to produce rubber synthetically.[25] Work in synthetic rubber had, to be sure, begun earlier, especially in Germany during World War I;

in fact, it was there that the foundation of the synthetic industry was laid with the development of buna rubber, so named after butadiene, a derivative of benzene and sodium (Na). Except for Germany, the U.S.S.R. was the only country to develop a synthetic rubber industry before World War II.

The synthetic phase marks the third act of the rubber drama. Its climax was reached during World War II, when opposing belligerents on both sides of the Atlantic resorted to synthetic rubber. By far the most important development was the almost overnight creation, in the United States, of a gigantic synthetic rubber industry. This almost rivaled the plantation industry in volume of output. Whereas Germany had to rely on benzene, a coal-tar derivative, petroleum and natural gas served as the raw materials of the new product in the United States. Table 22.6 shows the output of synthetic rubber by countries. The creation of this giant industry is one of the wonders of this age of science.[26]

TABLE 22.6. Production of Synthetic Rubber, All Types, by Countries, 1938-1948[27] (in thousand long tons)

	United States	Canada	Germany	Total
1938	1.0	...	5.0	6.0
1939	1.8	...	22.0	23.7
1940	2.6	...	39.8	42.4
1941	8.1	...	69.4	77.5
1942	22.5	...	98.1	120.2
1943	231.8	2.5	115.8	350.0
1944	764.1	34.8	101.6	900.5
1945	820.4	45.7	...	866.1
1946	740.0	51.0	15.6	806.6
1947	508.7	42.4	8.2	559.3
1948	488.3	40.5	3.4	532.2

Problems of Rubber Culture

The gestation period of *Hevea* is considerably longer than that of the coffee tree, for *Hevea* should not be tapped until it is six or seven years old, and it reaches maturity and maximum yield at twelve or thirteen years. This alone poses a difficult problem of demand anticipation which is rendered even more difficult by the nature of the demand for rubber.

[24] *Rubber Statistical Bulletin* (London), April, 1949.

[25] A minor result of these high prices was the entrance of American capital, especially that of Ford and Firestone, into the field of plantation rubber. Whereas the Ford plantation on the banks of the Tapajós, a southern tributary of the Amazon, was opened in 1926 and given up in 1947, the Firestone plantations are going concerns. In 1934 the Goodyear Tire and Rubber Company opened up rubber plantations in Panama and Costa Rica.

[26] For a valuable account of the American synthetic rubber industry, see *First Report of the Inter-Agency Policy Committee on Rubber*, pp. 16 ff.

[27] *Rubber Statistical Bulletin*, April, 1949.

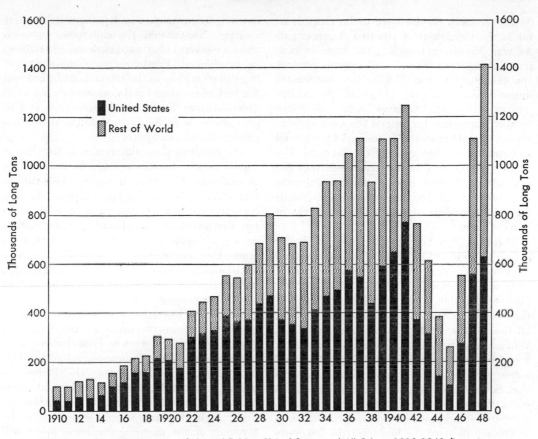

FIG. 22.1.   World Consumption of Natural Rubber, United States and All Others, 1910-1948. (Inter-Agency Policy Committee on Rubber, *First and Second Reports*, 1946, p. 91; 1940-1948 figures from *Rubber Statistical Bulletin*, April, 1949, p. 40.)

The United States is the chief market for rubber, as is shown in Fig. 22.1. The bulk of her rubber imports goes into tires and tubes. The sale of rubber, therefore, is highly dependent on one country and one use. Tire sales in the United States, in turn, are greatly affected by the business cycle.

The relative newness of the tire industry presents an additional difficulty. Tires undergo periodic changes reflecting technical innovations. Their lifetime has been extended at least tenfold from the few thousand miles a tire was good for in 1910. Higher speeds tend to cut down the lifetime, but better roads prolong it. In short, there are diverse forces at work which affect the tire needs per car owner per year, and this renders demand anticipation highly problematic. An industry which must spend a decade or more to build up its productive capacity and which has to face such great problems of demand anticipation is indeed in a difficult position when it tries to keep demand and supply in reasonable balance.

Moreover, demand is highly inelastic; i.e., it responds only little to price concessions or price advances. The price of tires could easily double, which means that the price of crude rubber could rise much faster without seriously discouraging the purchase of new motor cars, provided other items in the cost of the car remained constant or declined. It is true, though, that appreciable increases in the price of crude rubber encourage a greater admixture of reclaimed and virgin rubber. In other words, one must distinguish between two levels of demand: that of the rubber manufacturer who buys the crude, and that of the consumer who buys the finished product.

Rubber trees do not have to be tapped, so far as the physiology of the tree is concerned. As was pointed out earlier, the latex crop is not an ordinary crop, a biological product spontaneously produced by the tree, but a man-induced tree product.[28] This gives the rubber grower definite advantages over the coffee grower. Latex can be tapped the year around. Its flow is only moderately affected by seasonal changes in the life process of the tree. The rubber planter is thus largely freed from the violent year-to-year crop fluctuation inherent in a product affected by the weather. Nor is there the problem of seasonal labor peaks at harvest time.

Theoretically, therefore, the rubber planter is free to regulate the output from his trees all the way from zero to the maximum compatible with sound tapping practice. Actually, however, several difficulties curtail this freedom, if they do not destroy it. In the first place, almost all the rubber not tapped is irretrievably lost. While rubber trees do produce more latex after a rest period, the practice, if extended beyond a few months, results in a net loss of production. Secondly, a plantation has heavy overhead costs. When prices go down, the temptation is great to step up production in order to make up in volume of sales the loss from the lower return per unit of output. Of course, if enough growers succumb to this temptation, the result is apt to be disastrous. The labor situation, at least in certain regions of southeastern Asia, adds to this trouble. A considerable portion of the laborers on rubber estates in Malaya are migratory contract labor brought in from foreign countries, especially China and India, and therefore they cannot be laid off at will. But no one wants to pay wages for labor not done, and this may lead owners to tap even though market conditions indicate otherwise, for tapping is by far the most important task labor performs on plantations. So, actually, the freedom which looks so bright in theory may be rather dim in practice.

The southeast Asia rubber-growing industry is by no means a homogeneous unit; on the contrary, it is made up of definitely heterogeneous elements. In particular, the contrast between corporation-owned plantations and native garden patches and peasant holdings is striking. Nor should the difference between absentee-owned and native-owned plantations be overlooked. Furthermore, plantation practice differs widely in the Dutch East Indies and the rest of southeast Asia, as witness the crop diversification found on Dutch East Indian plantations and the monocultural plantation pattern found elsewhere.

The result of these differences as they affect supply may be summarized as follows: In terms of elasticity of short-run supply, i.e., rubber tapped, as against long-run supply, i.e., tree capacity, the small native growers lead. Having the lowest overhead and growing rubber as a cash crop that supplements their food crops, they can respond most readily to price fluctuations. When prices are high, they are willing to work harder and even to hire labor. Low prices mean a holiday for the peasant grower, and hired labor is laid off. Next in elasticity of short-run supply are the diversified plantations of the Dutch East Indies; then come the native or Chinese-owned plantations of Malaya and other areas. The European-owned plantations, having the highest overhead, show the least elasticity of supply. Indeed, their short-run supply may actually be inversely elastic, meaning that lower prices will elicit heavier tapping to maintain aggregate income and meet fixed charges.[29]

On the supply side, the rubber-growing industry thus suffers from two great difficulties. In the first place, the long-run adjustment of tree capacity to demand is difficult because of the length of the time lag and the unpredictability of demand. The result is that high prices generate overoptimism and lead to excessive plantings. In the second place, low prices do *not* lead to a contraction of tree capacity. One does not rip out trees that may still have an undefined but considerable future as productive agents just because, momentarily, the

---

[28] See p. 379.

[29] Incidentally, tree capacity around 1940 was divided between the different areas roughly as follows: Malaya and the Dutch East Indies each had about 40 percent, the remaining 20 percent being scattered in Ceylon, French Indo-China, Thailand, etc. Since, in general, natives work their trees harder, plant closer, and control about half the acreage in rubber trees, they may now possess over half the rubber-producing capacity of Southeast Asia.

TABLE 22.7. Production of Natural Rubber in Principal Territories, 1938-1948[30]
(thousand long tons)

	Malaya			Indonesia			Other		Central and South	
	Estates	Small Holders	Total	Estates	Small Holders	Total	Asia	Africa	America	Total[a]
1938	246	114	360	174	145	319	201	12	19	910
1939	244	116	360	193	183	376	230	15	20	1000
1940	334	214	547	277	265	542	283	16	26	1415
1941	370	230	600	300	350	650	341	17	26	1000
1942	55	100	155	100	100	200	219	30	35	640
1943	35	40	75	50	50	100	203	45	42	465
1944	25	...	25	25	25	50	179	56	50	360
1945	...	9	9	5	5	10	128	54	48	250
1946	174	230	404	...	175	175	172	47	40	838
1947	361	286	646	13	265	278	261	39	29	1255
1948	404	295	698	13	24	37	325	42	24	1520

[a] Includes negligible production of Oceania.

market situation is unfavorable. Nor do low prices assure a correlated reduction in tapping.

The situation is further seriously aggravated by the unpredictable impact of science. The *Hevea* tree in the jungle is a wild product of nature. The present *Hevea* stands in southeastern Asia are highly cultivated products of scientific plant breeding. In improving the wild tree, the plant breeder proceeded along two distinct lines: bud grafting, and seed selection or the use of so-called clonal seeds. Bud grafting, which was used first and was confined to large plantations, raised the average annual latex yield from about 5 pounds for unselected stock to 10 pounds for bud-grafted stock; the output has run as high as 25 pounds. Clonal seeds, which are available to and widely used by small native operators, became of practical importance only in the late 1930's. The implications of these improvements in the productive powers of *Hevea* are fantastic. They presage a veritable revolution in technique, may spell a drastic shift in cost relationships among different producing groups, and threaten tremendous overproduction once their application becomes widespread. At the same time they should materially bring down costs and thus not only open up the possibility of new uses but also improve the competitive position of natural rubber vis-à-vis both synthetic and reclaimed rubber. The uncertainties of the world political situation with its implications for the economic outlook must not be ignored.

Rubber Prices

One result of this abnormal and bewildering supply and demand situation is extraordinary instability in the price of rubber (see Fig. 22.2). These price fluctuations are most conveniently discussed if the time covered in the diagram is divided into definite periods. In the first period, 1913-1920, plantation rubber was just beginning to come into its own, the peak in 1913 indicating what the wild rubber brought. But as plantation rubber steadily invaded the world market, prices dropped gradually. The period 1920-1922 is marked by the disastrous price drop after World War I, when the price fell to about 15 cents from the earlier average of 75 cents. This terrific slump led to the adoption of the British price control scheme, the Stevenson Plan, which was in force from 1922 to 1928 and was limited to British possessions and protectorates. However, new plantations in uncontrolled areas, especially the Dutch East Indies, led to the eventual collapse of this artificial control scheme after rubber prices had hit a preposterous peak in 1925. The period 1928-1934 was marked by competitive dumping in the absence of control, which, together with the Great Depression, sent prices down almost to the zero point. The next period, 1934 to the end of World War II, saw the establishment, in 1934, of an international price control scheme, the International

---

[30] *Rubber Statistical Bulletin*, April, 1949, p. 3.

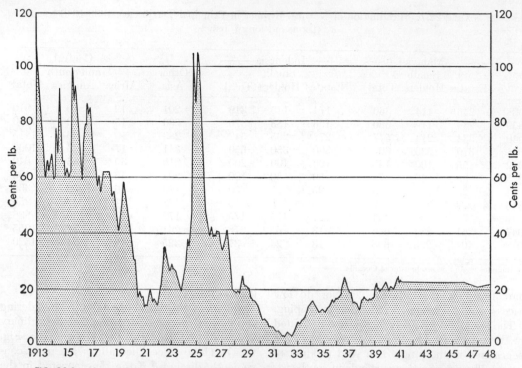

FIG. 22.2.   Natural Rubber Prices, Ribbed Smoked Sheets, New York, Spot Price 1913-1948. (Inter-Agency Policy Committee on Rubber, *First and Second Reports,* 1946, p. 94; 1943-1948 prices from *Rubber Statistical Bulletin,* April, 1949.) Note: In mid-1950 rubber prices skyrocketed.

Rubber Regulation Agreement,[31] which was signed by all the important rubber-growing areas in southeast Asia. On its expiration in 1938 it was renewed for another year; but before the year was up, all plans were disrupted by World War II, with its government purchas-

---

[31] Commenting on this control scheme, the *First Report of the Inter-Agency Policy Committee on Rubber* (pp. 13-15) brings out these points: (1) Under the Stevenson Plan no provision was made for the restriction of new plantings which higher prices encouraged. (2) Under the same Plan prices were allowed to get completely out of hand in 1925 and the authorities in control yielded to the temptation of increasing the price goal when the chance for doing so seemed to offer itself. (3) Both the Stevenson Plan and the International Rubber Regulation Agreement encouraged increased use of reclaimed rubber. (4) The price objectives were set high enough to yield a profit for practically all producers; since costs vary widely, mainly because of differences in efficiency and managerial setup, this price policy assured excessive profits to low-cost producers. (5) In the assignment of quotas, the control agreement discriminated against the small native growers, many of whom are low-cost producers.

ing and stock-piling and, above all, the Japanese conquest of the rubber-producing areas. The end of the war found the world too poor to buy even half the potential supply of rubber; the major problem was what to do with the huge synthetic capacity of the United States.

Postwar Problems

After World War II the United States found herself with a huge war-born synthetic rubber industry on her hands. It was decided to keep the most efficient half of this capacity in operation, to maintain some of the next best plants on a stand-by basis for emergency use, and to scrap the rest. In reaching this decision, the responsibility of this country as the largest buyer of plantation rubber from the rest of the world in terms of promotion of international trade and good will was definitely recognized. A less enlightened policy might well have aggravated the postwar troubles of a sad world engaged in a "cold war," with one-half struggling to restore world trade and the other half fighting against it.

That the orderly marketing of rubber can hardly be accomplished without occasional resort to interference and control is now conceded by most competent observers. Attention is now focused on rendering such interference and control as constructive as possible. Much thought was given to this problem at the Havana Conference devoted to the establishment of the International Trade Organization (ITO) sponsored by the United Nations.

The problem of artificial price control of tree products is part of a much larger problem which is variously referred to as the end of laissez faire, the decline of competition, concentration of economic power, relative inflexibility of industrial prices, monopoly, government in business, etc. The ultimate solution of the specific problem discussed in this chapter will come only as the broader problems of which it is a part are faced without fear and attacked with energy and wisdom.

BIBLIOGRAPHY

Barker, P. W., *Rubber Industry in the U.S.A., 1839-1939*, Trade Promotion Series No. 197, Washington, U. S. Department of Commerce, 1939.

George, H., *Kautschuk*, Vol. 9 of Schumacher, H. (ed.), *Wandlungen der Weltwirtschaft*, Leipzig, Bibliographisches Institut, 1938.

Howard, F. A., *Buna Rubber*, New York, Van Nostrand, 1947.

Inter-Agency Policy Committee on Rubber, *First and Second Reports*, Washington, 1946.

Inter-American Coffee Board, *First Annual Report 1941-1942*, Washington, U. S. Department of State, 1942.

Inter-American Coffee Board, *Study of the World Coffee Situation*, Washington, U. S. Department of State, 1948.

International Institute of Agriculture, *Studies of Principal Agricultural Products on the World Market*, Nos. 4 and 5 *Oils and Fats*, (1939), No. 6 *Olives*, No. 7 *World Rubber Production and Trade, Economic and Technical Aspects, 1935-1939* (1940), No. 9 *The World's Coffee*, Rome, 1947.

Jacob, H. E., *Coffee, the Epic of a Commodity* (translated by Paul, E. and E.), New York, Viking, 1935.

Kepner, C. D., Jr., and Soothill, J. H., *The Banana Empire*, New York, Vanguard, 1935.

Knight, M. M., "Water and the Course of Empire in North Africa," *Quarterly Journal of Economics*, November, 1928.

Knorr, K. E., *World Rubber Under Regulation*, Stanford University, Food Research Institute, 1945.

Lawrence, J. C., *The World's Struggle with Rubber, 1905-1930*, New York, Harper, 1931.

Lewis, R., and Holt, E. G., *Rubber Regulation and the Malayan Plantation Industries*, Trade Promotion Series, No. 159, Washington, U. S. Department of Commerce, 1935.

Orton, W., "Rubber: A Case Study," *American Economic Review*, December, 1927.

Rowe, J. W. F., *Studies in Artificial Control of Raw Supplies*, No. 2 *Rubber*, No. 3 *Brazilian Coffee*, Royal Economic Society, Memoranda No. 34 and 35, London, 1932.

Rowe, J. W. F., *Markets and Men*, New York, Macmillan, 1936.

Russell, J. A., "Fordlandia and Belterra, Rubber Plantations on the Tapajos River, Brazil," *Economic Geography*, April, 1942.

Secretariat of the Rubber Study Group, *Rubber Statistical Bulletin*, London (periodical).

Shaw, E. B., "Banana Migration and Sigatoka," *Journal of Geography*, December, 1941.

Smith, J. R., *Tree Crops*, New York, Harcourt, Brace, 1929.

Strain, W., "The Florida Citrus Crop," *Economic Geography*, January, 1942.

"Trouble in Synthetic Rubber," *Fortune*, June, 1947.

Ukers, W. H., *All About Coffee*, New York, Tea and Coffee Trade Journal Co., 2nd ed., 1935.

Ukers, W. H., *All About Tea*, New York, Tea and Coffee Trade Journal Co., 2 vols., 1935.

Wallace, D. H., and Edminster, L. R., *International Control of Raw Materials*, Washington, Brookings Institution, 1930.

Whittlesey, C. R., *Governmental Control of Crude Rubber: the Stevenson Plan*, Princeton, Princeton University Press, 1931.

Wickizer, V. D., *The World Coffee Economy, with Special Reference to Control Schemes*, Stanford University, Food Research Institute, 1943.

Wickizer, V. D., *Tea Under International Control*, Stanford University, Food Research Institute, 1944.

Wolf, H., and Wolf, R., *Rubber, a Story of Glory and Greed*, New York, Covici, Friede, 1936.

Chapter 23

THE FOREST AND ITS PRODUCTS

IMPORTANCE OF FORESTS

Size of the Forest

Where soil, climate, and topography permit vegetation to take the form of trees, the forest is one of the major forms of the natural landscape. Originally, over two-fifths of the land area of the earth, exclusive of the polar regions —or about 23 million square miles—is supposed to have been covered with primeval forest. About one-third of this once forested area has been robbed by man of its natural protective cover and been turned into barren desert.[1] About 15.4 million square miles of forest are now left.[2]

Forest Products

Roughly two-thirds of the total forest area is classified as productive. This is slightly more than 10 million square miles, or considerably more than three times the land area of the United States. Glesinger[3] estimates that under reasonable management the productive area could be raised to 8 billion acres and could yield one ton of forest products per acre. This 8 billion tons would be far more than twice the weight of all the fuels, metals, foods, and fibers now produced on the face of the earth. At present the utilization of the forest falls far short of this, the output of coal alone now exceeding the total world output of wood.

The direct current usefulness of the forest as a source of commodities is indicated by Table 23.1, which shows the total yield of the world's forests by major categories.

Old as the use of wood is, mankind is only on the threshold of the full scientific exploitation of this major resource. It is only during recent decades that real insight into the nature of wood has been gained and that we have begun to treat it as we do petroleum and coal— not as a fuel, but as a raw material from which

---

[1] Sir John Boyd Orr in the preface to Egon Glesinger, *The Coming Age of Wood*, Simon and Schuster, Inc., New York, rev. ed., 1949.

[2] Food and Agricultural Organization of the United Nations, *The Forest Resources of the World*, Washington, 1948, p. 6. The total area of the forests of the world is here given as 3978 million hectares. Using the conversion ratio of one hectare = 0.003861 square mile, the equivalent is 15,440,000 square miles.

[3] Egon Glesinger, *op. cit.*, p. 11.

science and technology can extract many valuable substances which in turn can be converted into many others. Most of the world's forests are still being exploited in the most primitive and wasteful fashion, with mere fractions of the natural substance reaching the consumer. Moreover, the bulk of them are as yet mere "neutral stuff," waiting for human ingenuity, capital, and need to convert them into one of the greatest resources at man's disposal.

TABLE 23.1.   World Wood Production by Major Uses[4]

	Million Metric Tons	Percent
Industrial uses		
Construction	400	33.0
Paper	60	5.0
Railroads	25	2.0
Mines	20	1.6
Rayon	5	0.4
All other	50	4.0
Total Industrial	560	46.0
Fuel	640	54.0
Grand total	1200	100.0

The potential significance of the forest for the future of mankind is particularly great because of the renewability of the forest cover. Properly treated, timber is a crop, a "flow" resource, a perpetual mainspring of varied utilities. The forest in this respect is like soil. *If properly treated by man,* it can be a dependable, inexhaustible, almost universal resource which will work for him long after oil wells are forgotten and mines are deserted.

Role in Welfare Economy

The significance of the forest is further enhanced by its influence on the natural environment far beyond the limits of the forest itself. Forests indirectly affect climate, stream flow, and soil conditions especially in the areas of drainage basins, and thus exercise a beneficial influence on agriculture and grazing, recreation and wildlife.[5] The destruction of the forest not only puts an end to these benign indirect effects but lets loose highly destructive forces which manifest themselves in floods and soil erosion and the ultimate catastrophe, the desert.

THE FOREST PROBLEM
Threat of Exhaustion

At the present time most of the forests of the world are so used—or abused and disused—that experts predict dire calamities in the not too distant future and irreparable damage on a catastrophic scale. They are emphatic in their assertion that at long last man now possesses the knowledge requisite to turn forests into perpetual treasure troves, and that, unless this knowledge is applied, unless forests are managed and cropped, put on a sustained-yield basis, one of man's greatest resource possibilities will soon be lost beyond recovery and be converted into a menace instead.

Why does man seem determined to destroy one of nature's greatest gifts? Until not so long ago the answer lay largely in one word: ignorance. Man knew neither the nature of the forest as a dynamic organism, nor the nature of wood and its great promise as one of the richest storehouses of things useful to him. In many parts of the earth ignorance is still the chief cause of mismanagement. This applies particularly to regions more or less inaccessible to the white man and inhabited by primitive people living in cultural darkness. Unfortunately, in their ignorance they do great harm. The primeval forest is not immune to the attack of human folly. The tropical forest of Africa, one of the last great stands of original forest, is said to be disappearing or deteriorating.[6] The primitive tribes constantly burn out new clearings for their little agricultural plots and this is said to open the door to destructive forces which are gradually transforming the tropical rain forests into savannah.[7]

---

[4] From Egon Glesinger, *The Coming Age of Wood,* Simon and Schuster, Inc., New York, rev. ed., 1949, pp. 13-14. The main use of wood by railroads is for ties or sleepers. In mines, the pit props which support the ceilings of excavations are the most important articles made of wood.

[5] See Raphael Zon, *Forests and Water in the Light of Scientific Investigation,* Senate Document No. 469, 62nd Congress, Second Session, 1927. See also Forest Service, U.S. Department of Agriculture, *Forests and National Prosperity,* Miscellaneous Publication No. 688, Washington, 1948, especially pp. 69-77.

[6] See André Marie A. Aubréville, "The Disappearance of the Tropical Forests of Africa" in *Unasylva,* July-August, 1947, pp. 5-11. See also H. L. Shantz in *ibid.,* March-April, 1948, p. 67.

[7] Savannah is a type of landscape marked by sparse, intermittent tree growth.

Even in our own Pacific Northwest the original forest stands of Douglas fir, Sitka spruce, redwood, etc., are subject to natural destructive forces. The woods there dry out thoroughly during a three-month drought, and frequent thunderstorms and high winds assure a maximum of damage from fire. In addition, the single-species stands of that region are exceptionally vulnerable to insect attack.[8] If such primeval forests are not taken in hand by man, they gradually are reduced in size and deteriorate in quality. Canada, whose forests are largely virgin timber stands, is credited with an annual gross growth of 86.7 million cubic meters (roundwood) of wood, and debited with a loss of 24.2 million from natural causes; this leaves a net growth of 62.6 million which is less than the annual cut of 69.3 million.[9]

But, unfortunately, man is a far more ferocious enemy of the forest than is nature. Speaking of the forests of the United States, Glesinger says, "For decades this area has been devastated as brutally as if by enemy invasion."[10]

Reasons for Abusive Practices

Many facts help to explain this vandalistic attitude of the lumbermen of the United States. For one thing, there is the psychological and perhaps ideological hangover from our frontier past when the pioneer, faced with a hostile forest, fought it with every force at his disposal, chiefly fire. To him the forest was an arch enemy that harbored ferocious wild beasts and even more ferocious wild men, and it preempted the ground from which he sought to draw his livelihood by farming. To be sure, it also furnished him with fuel, building material, and other valuable things. There was also the lingering idea of inexhaustible wealth—the forest seemed so big that nobody could ever destroy it. Those were growing pains, so to speak, childish ideas the nation gradually outgrew.

But there are more persistent ideas which are hostile to proper forest treatment. They stem mainly from the peculiarities of the forest itself. Trees are perennials; and once man tackles the job of managing the forest he is confronted by the "perennial" problem (discussed in the preceding chapter) in its most acute form. Proper sustained-yield management of forests may call for reproduction cycles of as many as 100 or even 200 years. Projects involving a distribution of costs and benefits over so long a period appear to be definitely outside of the profit calculus of the ordinary business enterprise. Fortunately, some forest enterprises such as pulpwood growing can be managed properly on the basis of a much shorter growth cycle. Broadly speaking, however, proper forest management does not fit readily into the rationale of ordinary private business enterprise because it calls for extraordinary procedures and institutions which are slow in developing.

There is another peculiarity of the forest over which the private entrepreneur is apt to stumble—the fact that a forest is a multiple joint-product proposition. It yields many direct products as well as material for many others—construction lumber, barrels, pulp for paper, resin and turpentine, the raw material for masonite, alcohol from sawdust, wood sugar from the waste liquor of paper mills, etc. Furthermore, a forest usually contains many species of trees, and the trees almost always vary as far as age, size, strength, straightness, etc., are concerned.

If this complex dynamic organism is to yield the maximum results *in the long run*, cutting must be planned far ahead so as to correlate the diversity of standing timber and its future needs with the diversity of the market requirements, which may change with technological progress. Modern science searches tirelessly both for new uses for trees whose commercial value is already well known and for ways of putting other trees to commercial use. In short, sound forest management calls for overall coordination, interindustry as well as external, including protection of forests, reforestation, and the marketing of forest products at prices which will make forest culture a profitable enterprise. All these factors are associated with the intricacies of the market process, and accordingly this coördination is a tremendous task

---

[8] See Anon., "Forestry in the Northwestern United States of America," *Unasylva*, November-December, 1947, pp. 28-38. (The writer is a European forestry expert.)

[9] FAO, *op. cit.*, p. 21. Roundwood is wood in the log, i.e., previous to being sawn or otherwise processed.

[10] Egon Glesinger, *op. cit.*, p. 24.

whose size and nature are only now being grasped—but fortunately to a greater extent than ever before.[11]

Obstacles to Solution of the Problem

The forest is a *national* resource; like a river system, it is a *multiple-purpose* resource (see pp. 409-412); it constitutes a social asset of the first magnitude; and it yields a great social profit which lies wholly outside the realm of business. The proper safeguarding of group interests requires that these facts be recognized; only within the frame of these basic principles should private enterprise be allowed to operate.[12]

But selfish pressure groups are doing all in their power to fight the measures needed if forests are to be protected. They are unconcerned about the exhaustion of our forest resources because we now have substitute materials—steel, cement, brick—far better than wood. But these people ignore the fact that ore deposits, for example, are exhaustible, whereas properly managed forest resources are not.

Another argument concerns the "threat" of superabundance. While the immediate problem in this country is a shortage of timber, there are some who claim that the restoration of the forest cover in an amount sufficient to protect the soil, the water supply, etc., would result in such vast supplies of timber that the price would collapse and private enterprise be driven out of the field. But such arguments grossly underestimate the demand-stimulating force of low prices, especially if they go hand in hand with improvements in quality.

In essence, the forest problem is one of institutional adjustment. Society must discover the particular blending of private and public action which will suit the peculiar needs of a forest.

NATURE AND PROPERTIES OF WOOD

Structure

Wood is composed largely of cellulose and lignin. Cellulose consists of long carbohydrate fibers that chemically are related to sugars. They constitute the portion of the living wood through which the life processes function. Lignin is the natural stabilizing agent which holds trees up; it is the scaffolding around the cellulose building. About two-thirds of the weight of wood is cellulose, one-third lignin. In most pulp manufacture the lignin is wasted; it contributes its share to stream pollution.

Properties

Wood possesses considerable unidirectional strength, i.e., in the direction of its grain. Compressed to one third of its size, it can attain a strength approaching that of mild steel. Wood is easily worked. Relatively simple equipment can prepare lumber properly for use in construction work. Lumbering, therefore, is one of the first industries to spring up wherever there are forests. Wood burns readily. The greatest use of wood is still as fuel, either in the raw form or as charcoal. Charcoal is the great fuel of primitive peoples; it is clean, does not smoke up a hut, and is ideally suited for food preparation since it calls only for the simplest kind of brazier.

This inflammability is at the same time one of the great disadvantages of wood compared with steel, cement, brick, etc. Where conflagration is a particular menace, as in densely built cities, wood is avoided as a construction material if builders can afford safer materials. Skyscrapers cannot be built of wood because

---

[11] For a development of the idea of interindustry coördination, see *ibid.*, pp. 243-255.

[12] A decision handed down by the Supreme Court of the United States on November 7, 1949, may well prove a milestone in the history of private property in general and of forest conservation in the United States in particular. As reported in the New York *Times* of November 11, 1949, an owner of timberland in the state of Washington had appealed to the United States Supreme Court from a ruling by the Washington State Supreme Court declaring constitutional a state law requiring the owner of timberland to reseed or restock land to maintain sufficient forest reserves and cover. The landowner took the position that the land was his and that therefore he could use it as he saw fit. In reply to this hoary misinterpretation of the true nature of private property the Supreme Court wrote: "We do not think that a State is required under the Constitution of the United States to stand idly by while its natural resources are depleted." Reference was made to "constitutional morality" and to "that great unwritten compact which exists between the dead, the living and the unborn." The opinion stressed that "private enterprise must use its property in ways that are not inconsistent with public welfare. . . . We must leave to the unborn something more than debts and depleted resources."

they exceed the limits set by the comparatively modest strength of wood.

A particular disadvantage in building is its dimensional instability. Wood absorbs moisture and swells as the moisture content of the air increases. It also warps and thus cannot keep the dimensions to which it was cut. Moreover, it is apt to rot when exposed to moisture.

For all these defects there are at least partial remedies; better ones will be found as the science of wood preparation progresses, and the market for wood may again expand. The wider market will depend largely on price per unit of utility. This, in turn, will depend largely on the extent to which our entire forest resources are used, as well as to the extent to which the problem of forest preservation and improvement is solved.

HISTORY OF FOREST RESOURCES

As was said before, a virgin forest is usually inimical to human culture. In its less dense fringes it serves to supplement the meat supply as both hunting ground and pasture. Until the potato became a staple of European agriculture, the virgin hardwood forests of central Europe furnished feed for hogs. It was a common practice to base the valuation of forest lands on their capacity to carry or to fatten hogs and other meat animals. As agriculture spread, the forest was viewed chiefly as the reservoir of potential farm land and thus, as frontier, it dominated both land and labor policy. Moreover, the forest was important as a source of fuel, especially charcoal. As the relative importance of these different functions varied, public policy gyrated between the extremes of the rather ruthless exploitation of forests in the interest of expanding agriculture and of careful social measures designed to safeguard the fuel supply and to supplement the food supply of the population. As a result of the rise and expansion of mining and metallurgy, fuel became the most valuable forest product until coal was substituted first for domestic heating and then for industrial purposes.[13] In countries bordering on the sea,

forests became the foundation of shipbuilding industries, maritime expansion, and naval prowess.[14] So important were turpentine and rosin in the building and operating of ships that to this day these forest products are known as "naval stores." For a time lumber for building, furniture making, and similar purposes became the chief commercial product of the forest industries.

But the change in forest utilization is continuing in our time. For example, the art of making paper from wood pulp was developed during the nineteenth century; and the manufacture of rayon, cellophane, and other cellulose products is almost entirely an achievement of the twentieth century. Within each forest-using industry constant changes in technology occur which forever call for a reappraisal of the part which the forest can and must play in our lives. When a successful solution of the problem of making paper from the common species of southern pine was found in the twenties, not only the southern pine region, but also the forest lands which had furnished the raw materials of the paper industry had to be revalued.

To sum up, the forest, once an enemy of man, has become a resource of the first magnitude. Its function changed with every shift in civilization. Expanding agriculture and animal husbandry replaced it as a major source of feed and food; coal superseded wood as the major source of heat; steel, cement, and brick are making heavy inroads on lumber as the premier building material. Steel has replaced wood in shipbuilding. But, in the meantime, new uses are developing and wood is valued as a source of cellulose. Moreover, the effect of the forest on climate and stream flow, as well as its recreational value, is now more fully appreciated.

Viewing this evolution from the standpoint of individual countries, details of shifting demand and supply relations assume added importance. The depletion of domestic resources, changes in transportation costs, shifting population centers, industrialization, and similar developments materially affect the part that forests play in the life of nations.

---

[13] In the United States iron making definitely passed through three stages: the charcoal stage, the anthracite stage, and the coke stage. Cf. J. R. Smith, *The Story of Iron and Steel,* D. Appleton and Company, New York, 1920, pp. 41 ff.

[14] See R. G. Albion, *Forests and Sea Power; the Timber Problem of the Royal Navy, 1652-1862,* Harvard University Press, Cambridge, 1926.

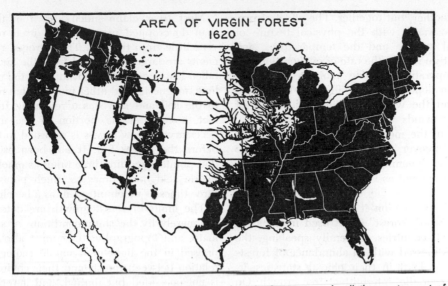

FIG. 23.1. When the early colonists settled along the Atlantic coast, nearly all the country east of the Mississippi River, and much land to the westward, notably in Arkansas, Louisiana, Texas, and the Pacific Northwest, was covered with a vast virgin forest—about 820 million acres in all. (U. S. Department of Agriculture, Forest Service.)

Broadly speaking, most industrial countries pass through three stages of forest history. The first is marked by energetic and often ruthless exploitation of local virgin forests. This is generally followed by a period of increasing dependence on foreign supplies. When, or if, the importation of foreign forest products proves financially burdensome, the third chapter is frequently begun with the effort to rehabilitate or partially restore the domestic forest resources.

In general, the forestry history of the United States runs true to form, but with one important deviation. Being of continental expanse and possessing several distinct forest areas, the United States has not one forest history, but several.[15] Moreover, her various forest areas produce different species.

The early settlers depended on local supplies. Consequently, the first large-scale commercial exploitation occurred in the northeastern part, especially in Maine, New York, and Pennsylvania. As the population increased and the Erie Canal permitted long-distance transportation, the Lake states were subjected to systematic exploitation. This was encouraged

and accelerated by the shift from water to rail transportation. In the nineties the piney woods of the South supplemented the vanishing supplies of the Lake region; and for several decades the South gained in ascendancy, only to be replaced as the nation's premier timber source by the Pacific Northwest. In 1944, 14.2 billion board feet of lumber were cut in the South, as compared with 15.3 billion in the West and 4.9 billion in the North.[16] These regional changes were accompanied by progressively increasing distances between source of supply and market and by corresponding rising freight charges.

DISTRIBUTION OF FORESTS
Natural Basis

Before man became the powerful geomorphologic agent that he is today, the forest cover of the earth was spread out in direct response to natural—that is, geographical and ecological—conditions.

Temperature, precipitation, altitude, contour, distance from sea, and thickness of humus are only some of the factors which account for the general distribution of the original forest cover. These factors operate not independently

[15] W. B. Greely, "The Relation of Geography to Timber Supply," *Economic Geography*, March, 1925, p. 4.

[16] Forest Service, *op. cit.*, p. 30.

of one another, but together. The effect of precipitation varies with the physical texture of the land surface and the temperature, high temperature raising the rate of evaporation and low temperature turning moisture into ice; mountain slopes function differently on the leeward and the windward sides; the effect of planetary winds varies with the geographical location of the mountain chains lying in their path. Moreover, all these factors must be studied as dynamic forces operating over periods of time, not as isolated phenomena of the moment.

In this connection it should be mentioned that the word "forest" is not used in the same way in all countries. Generally speaking, the countries blessed with an abundance of forests exclude—at least in their official statistics—irregular, sporadic, intermittent tree growth. On the other hand, in countries where the climate does not favor forest growth or where the forests have been destroyed, this irregular growth is usually counted as forest. Thus the Mediterranean *macchia*, a landscape somewhat similar to the North American *chaparral*, is frequently included in forest census figures of the Mediterranean countries, although similar regions would not be counted as forests in the United States.

The forest is one of the major forms of natural vegetation. It does not make great demands on soil fertility, but it is more exacting in its moisture requirements, as to both amount and distribution—absolute, and relative to temperature changes—than prairie grass or bush vegetation. Forest growth is not subject to the same topographical limitations as agriculture, for trees can grow well on mountain slopes where other forms of vegetation can seldom attain the status of crops. Hausrath[17] gives a slope of 20 degrees as the limit for agriculture, 30 degrees as the limit for meadow and pasture, and 40 degrees as the limit for general tree culture for timber purposes. However, much tree growth is found on slopes exceeding even this figure. Because of the capacity of trees to hold on to steep hillsides and mountain slopes, the forest plays an important role in the struggle against soil erosion.

[17] H. Hausrath, *Forstwesen*, vol. 7, part 7, of *Grundriss der Sozialökonomik*, J. C. B. Mohr, Tübingen, 1922.

Most trees claim much less from the soil than do cropped plants. Wood itself requires very little from the soil. The nitrogen requirements are largely obtained from the air. If the fallen leaves are not removed from the ground, lime, magnesia, and other minerals are restored to the soil and serve as a revolving fund. In fact, a considerable portion of the minerals necessary to grow leaves is returned to the soil before the leaves fall. It has been estimated that potatoes require three times as much phosphoric acid, nine times as much potash, and three times as much nitrogen, as a beech forest.

The limits of forest growth are determined not merely by the static conditions of soil, climate, and topography; they must also be appraised in the light of dynamic ecology. The relation between forests and their environment is not one-sided but mutual, and it represents a nice balance of the right and obligation of all living organisms found in its confines. Nature strives toward ecological equilibrium. It took man ages to understand this. In the meantime he crashed into the finely balanced structure like a bull into a china shop.

The violation of the laws governing the extent of the forest cover is one of the most tragic examples of human folly in the face of nature's wisely ordered system. As continuous waves of migrants swept over Europe and the pressure on the land increased, it was only natural that the forest should be pushed back with ax and fire. Perhaps it was equally natural that man, unconscious of the laws of ecology, went too far and tried to use the hoe or the plow where only trees could grow. Blasted hopes and abandoned farms revealed his error. In some places the forest returned; in others it was gone forever—the work of human destruction had been done too well.

Cultural Influences

As culture matures and civilization becomes more complex, cultural—that is, social, economic, technical, and institutional—forces tend to gain in importance over natural forces. In the absence of the steam engine and railroads, of laissez faire and rugged individualism, and of similar aspects of our national life, the forest resources of the United States would in all probability be infinitely larger than they are today.

Similarly, a study of the forest situation in the leading European countries reveals the extent and importance of cultural influences on forest resources. They reflect not only the marked natural heterogeneity of Europe, but also the contrasting diversity of her institutional development.

In Germany and other parts of central Europe, climatic conditions are favorable to forest growth. Throughout wide sections the forest possesses a natural superiority over other forms of vegetation. But it is nature materially affected by culture which accounts for the present forest reserves of this part of Europe; for while nature favors deciduous or hardwood trees, especially various beeches and oaks, coniferous or softwood trees, especially pines, firs, and hemlocks, predominate at present, as a result of artificial reforestation. The fact is that as early as the thirteenth century forests formed a definite object of public policy in central Europe. The late survival of feudalism; the powerful position held by the crown until the fall of the Hohenzollerns and by entailed estates even after that; the widespread support given to federal, state, and communal policies of forest preservation, support which is partly explained by the integrity, honesty, and efficiency of the old bureaucracy in general and of forest administration in particular; the early development of scientific forestry; a leaning among some groups toward state socialism which is in such striking contrast to the emphasis on private property rights and individualism in the United States—all these and many other similar elements in the make-up of the central European economic and social complex must be carefully considered in any attempt to explain the present expanse of forest in Germany, Austria, and the other countries of central Europe.

The situation in England is quite different from that in Germany. England's early dependence on domestic forests for shipbuilding material, and, later on, her dependence on mineral fuels as a substitute for wood; the rapid development of the iron industry; the accessibility of foreign sources of supply—especially Scandinavian, Finnish, and other Baltic countries; the control over colonial forest resources; and, above all, since the repeal of the Corn Laws, the sacrifice of agricultural and forestry interests on the altar of the expanding and dominating machine industries—all these account for the practical absence of forests in the British Isles.

Similarly complex are the reasons for the paucity of forests in the Mediterranean countries.[18] As was stated previously, the climate of these countries is less favorable to forest growth than that of northern and central Europe. In addition to this, however, the forest stands of most Mediterranean countries, at one time or another, were systematically gutted. Hoe culture is carried on intensively to this day on hillsides to which American agricultural methods could not possibly be applied. The extent of horticulture, especially the growing of grapes, olive trees, fig trees, and citrus fruit trees, also accounts for the absence of forests, for in more northern latitudes similar hillsides would be densely wooded. The demand side of the situation must not be overlooked. In the warm climate of the Mediterranean, man does not need the forest as urgently as he does in colder regions. For various reasons he may prefer to build his home of stone or other mineral materials. His fuel requirements are smaller and are met, at least partly, by the by-products of horticulture. Thus there is less incentive to forest preservation, especially in such countries as Italy and Greece whose coastline readily permits the importation of foreign forest products or their substitutes. Finally, in many parts of the Mediterranean basin, man would have to choose between the forest and the goat —those familiar with Mediterranean life can easily guess what the choice would be.

Distribution Statistics

The first comprehensive attempt to estimate the forest resources of the world was undertaken by the Forest Division of the U.S. Department of Agriculture, and the findings were published in 1922. Further investigations were made in 1928 and 1931 by professors in Finland and Sweden respectively. The International Institute of Agriculture in Rome published annual reports from 1933 to 1938 which were summarized in a comprehensive study by

---

[18] See E. C. Semple, *The Geography of the Mediterranean Region; Its Relation to Ancient History,* Henry Holt and Company, Inc., New York, 1931.

TABLE 23.2. Forested Areas of the World

Continent	Population (millions)	Total Land Area (million hectares)	Productive Forests (million hectares)	Other Forests (million hectares)	All Forests		
					Area (million hectares)	Percentage of Total Area (percent)	Productive Forest Area per Capita (hectares)
Europe and U.S.S.R.							
Reporting countries	278	332	92	6	98	30	0.3
Nonreporting countries	300	2,405	635	313	948	39	2.1
Estimated totals	578	2,737	727	319	1,046	38	1.3
North America							
Reporting countries	167	1,854	465	203	668	36	2.8
Nonreporting countries	34	493	42	18	60	12	1.2
Estimated totals	201	2,347	507	221	728	31	2.5
South America							
Reporting countries	90	1,487	561	78	639	43	6.2
Nonreporting countries	13	268	103	13	116	43	7.9
Estimated totals	103	1,755	664	91	755	43	6.4
Africa							
Reporting countries	138	2,245	290	527	817	36	2.1
Nonreporting countries	53	815	16	16	32	4	0.3
Estimated totals	191	3,060	306	543	849	28	1.6
Asia (excluding U.S.S.R.)							
Reporting countries	990	1,609	264	124	388	24	0.3
Nonreporting countries	234	982	94	38	132	13	0.4
Estimated totals	1,224	2,591	358	162	520	20	0.3
Oceania							
Reporting countries	10	802	24	16	40	5	2.4
Nonreporting countries	2	53	26	14	40	76	13.0
Estimated totals	12	855	50	30	80	9	4.2
Estimated totals (six continents)	2,309	13,345	2,612	1,366	3,978	30	1.1
Antarctica	...	1,388	...	...	...	...	...
Grand total	2,309	14,733	2,612	1,366	3,978	27	1.1

the Food and Agriculture Organization of the United Nations in 1946. In the same year appeared an independent study in Great Britain, *Empire Forestry Handbook.*

However, all these studies suffered from various handicaps, chief among which were incomplete statistical coverage and the lack of uniform definitions of important forestry terms. To resolve these difficulties as far as possible, the FAO conducted a further study based on the use of questionnaires and embodying uniform definitions of terms.[19] The results were published by the FAO in 1948 under the title *The Forest Resources of the World,* a comprehensive survey covering such aspects of forests as type of ownership, species composition, etc. The most important findings are contained in the two tables included here (see Tables 23.2 and 23.3).[20]

Here only a few outstanding facts are mentioned. Of the total forested area of 3978 million hectares (about 15.4 million square miles

or 9.8 billion acres), almost exactly one-third was unproductive in the sense defined above. In Africa, the proportion is reversed, almost two-thirds of the total forest being listed as unproductive.

Of the 2612 million hectares (about 10.2 million square miles or 6.5 billion acres) of productive forests, 942 million hectares, or 36 percent, are softwood forests (conifers), and 1670 million hectares, or 64 percent, are hardwood (broadleaved) forests. About 58 percent of the softwood and 52 percent of the hardwood forests are classed as accessible.

The total consumption of wood is about equally divided between softwood and hardwood forests, but 70 percent of the softwood yield goes to industrial uses; the remaining 30 percent is burned. The situation is reversed as regards hardwood, for over 70 percent is burned and less than 30 percent goes into industrial uses.

In view of the present preference for softwoods for industrial uses and the fact that they constitute only 36 percent of the total productive stands, and that only 58 percent of these stands is considered accessible, we see how misleading are totals of forest figures as a starting point for calculations of the adequacy of the world's supply of wood.

The limited softwood forests have to bear the brunt of the demand for wood for industrial uses. Since this is a critical situation, it is important to know how the softwood forests are standing up as regards sustained production capacity.

The three great conifer-producing regions of the world are Europe, the U.S.S.R., and North America. Europe is the classical land of scientific forestry, for her yields range all the way from a high of 7.3 cubic meters (roundwood) per hectare for Denmark to less than 2 per hectare for some other countries. This is to be expected in a continent that differs so strikingly in both natural and cultural conditions affecting forest growth. The average for Europe is 2.2 cubic meters (roundwood) per hectare, but it is hoped that this can be raised to 3 without too much difficulty. The U.S.S.R. is credited with a growth rate—this indirectly affects yield—of 2 cubic meters (roundwood); the corresponding figures for the United States and Canada are 2.3 and 1 respectively. The

---

[19] The following definitions of forestry terms are shortened versions of those used in the FAO survey; the sequence followed is roughly that of the column heads in Tables 23.2 and 23.3.

Yield—The quantity of products taken from the forest.

Sustained yield—The annual or periodic output of a constant volume of products in perpetuity. This is possible only if sustained growth is maintained within the forest.

Productive forest—Forests which lend themselves to sustained-yield management.

"Other" forests—Forests that are too submarginal to warrant sustained-yield management.

Accessible and inaccessible forests—A distinction designed to separate actual present forest resources from potential resources. The classification is flexible, and changes in it will occur as the result of such factors as improved transportation, population increase, and shifts in demand.

Conifers—The softwood trees: pine, fir, spruce, larch, Paraná pine, and ginkgo.

Broadleaved species—The hardwood trees: oak, beech, maple, lignum vitae, ebony, balsa, and poplar.

Overexploitation—The felling of the forest at a rate too high to be sustained indefinitely. The distribution of age classes is the determining factor. If this distribution is normal, the rate of felling may approximate the growth rate; but if younger trees predominate, the felling rate should be considerably lower than the growth rate.

[20] *Ibid.*, pp. 6, 7.

TABLE 23.3. Classification of Productive Forests
(million hectares)

Continent	Accessible Forests			Inaccessible Forests		
	Conifers	Broadleaved	Total	Conifers	Broadleaved	Total
Europe and U.S.S.R.						
Reporting countries	60	30	90	2	...	2
Nonreporting countries	256	78	334	210	91	301
Estimated totals	316	108	424	212	91	303
North America[a]						
Reporting countries	175	127	302	130	26	156
Nonreporting countries	5	27	32	5	12	17
Estimated totals	180	154	334	135	38	173
South America						
Reporting countries	8	248	256	4	301	305
Nonreporting countries	2	49	51	1	51	52
Estimated totals	10	297	307	5	352	357
Africa						
Reporting countries	1	136	137	...	153	153
Nonreporting countries	1	12	13	...	3	3
Estimated totals	2	148	150	...	156	156
Asia (excluding U.S.S.R.)[a]						
Reporting countries	24	98	122	36	93	129
Nonreporting countries	7	45	52	7	48	55
Estimated totals	31	143	174	43	141	184
Oceania						
Reporting countries	3	13	16	...	8	8
Nonreporting countries	1	7	8	4	14	18
Estimated totals	4	20	24	4	22	26
Estimated grand totals	543	870	1,413	399	800	1,199

[a] The total area of productive forest in Table 23.3 corresponds with that in Table 23.2. However, because a few countries reported productive area but did not report details given in Table 23.3, there are slight differences between the tables with respect to reporting and nonreporting countries.

predominance of virgin forest and the northern latitude of much of Canada readily account for the low growth rate in that country.[21]

Of the broadleaf forest area, only 21 percent is located in the temperate zone; the other 79 percent is in the tropics. The forests of the two zones are exploited in very different fashion. Hardwood forests in the temperate zone are exploited in much the same way as softwood forests, except that in the United States at present they are probably not being fully exploited. In the tropics only a few species pay removal; hence cutting is highly selective. Although in some regions this cutting may exceed the rate of growth of these species, the real danger to the tropical forest stems from fire and the destructive practices of the nomadic agriculturalists.

That the solution of the world forest problem does not lie in ownership, as such, is made clear by another table in the FAO's *Forest Resources of the World*, showing the distribution of the world's forest land on the basis of public vs. private ownership. No definite conclusion can be drawn from this table as to the superiority of one type of ownership over the other as far as the efficiency of forest management is concerned. The efficiency of management depends on the quality of the management in both cases. For example, some private corporations in the United States have as high a record in this respect as any public agency in the country; on the other hand, there are cases of utter neglect under both private and public ownership.

FOREST UTILIZATION[22]
Fuel

It is estimated that 54 percent of all the wood used in the world is used as fuel. Uses of wood as fuel range all the way from such primitive ones as the open fire of the camper and the open fireplace in the home to highly

efficient ones such as the automatic continuous-feed gas-consuming furnace and generator. Although a number of municipal wood-burning gas systems had been installed in southern Germany by the late nineteenth century, the more primitive and wasteful methods of wood burning unfortunately predominate.[23] The use of wood as fuel, especially in the form of charcoal, is responsible for many denuded mountainsides and for the widespread resulting erosion.

Structural Material

Until recently there has been great waste in the use of wood as a structural material. Standard factors of strength and working stresses were either unavailable or, if available, not applied. Consequently much wood was wasted because of overdesign for strength and stiffness or the absence of any design, larger pieces than necessary being used to carry a specified load.

The importance of wood for sleepers (or ties) on which railroad tracks rest and for pit props in mines can hardly be exaggerated. These uses of wood make it a key commodity which opens up entire segments of world economy by means of railroad transportation and mining.

By far the most important industrial use of wood is as construction material for houses, factories, bridges, churches, etc. However, it has had to yield ground to other structural materials such as metals, cement, brick, etc. If wood is to continue as a major structural material, constant improvements in its preparation and application will have to be made. Fortunately, considerable progress along these lines can be reported.

New Techniques

Except in Canada and Scandinavia where short forest rotations are being planned on an exclusive pulpwood basis and in regions where the forest serves as the source of fuel, the lumber market largely determines silvicultural practices. The high prices offered for high-quality lumber encourage selective cutting of superior species and individual trees to the eventual detriment of the forest. The result is deterioration of both species and individual

---

[21] In comparing the figures for other countries with those for Europe, one must keep in mind that in Europe the figures refer to the annual harvest. In other countries, however, they generally refer to the volumes that can be harvested at the end of a certain period; they make little allowance for intermediate yields which in Europe would be harvested during the life of the stand. See *ibid.*, p. 8.

[22] This section is based largely on J. Alfred Hall, "Forest Utilization," *Unasylva*, July-August, 1947.

[23] See Egon Glesinger, *op. cit.*, chap. 16.

tree quality. The great problem of modern wood technology is to broaden the supply base to include species and qualities of trees not hitherto used. This will permit fuller exploitation of the forest and hence cheaper production of wood. In addition, the utility of lumber must be increased by eliminating as many of the difficulties as possible.

The present waste of wood is appalling. Glesinger uses striking diagrams to drive home the magnitude of this waste.[24] The waste varies with the use, ranging from 10 percent in trees used for fuel, 30 percent in pulp logging, 50 percent in lumbering, to 70 percent in veneer logging. The industrial or processing waste is 85 percent in the case of fuel, and 50 percent for saw mills, pulp mills, and veneer mills. The total waste, i.e., forest plus industrial or processing, thus amounts to 90 percent in fuel uses, 85 percent in veneer manufacture, 75 percent in lumber manufacture, and 65 percent in pulp-mill operations. These wastes can be reduced, if not eliminated, by technological improvements and by fuller coördination of all forest-exploiting activities.

One technological advance in this direction is the widespread use of controlled drying machinery. In seasoning particularly refractory species of wood, chemicals are now used with good results, and the use of solvents for this purpose seems promising. Fuller exploitation of by-products such as oils, fats, resins, and certain sugars seems a definite possibility. The generation of heat inside the wood by high-frequency electric current may prove important as a drying process in regions where electricity is cheap.

The durability of wood can be increased by the use of chemicals. Coal-tar creosote has long been used for this purpose. Railroad ties treated with creosote last for thirty or forty years, as against the ten years for untreated ties. However, creosote has definite limitations because of its odor, color, and stickiness. Research to find more satisfactory protective agents is going on and has already led to great improvements.

Modern techniques of impregnating wood with fireproofing chemicals have produced substantially fireproof wood. As yet the processes are costly, but they permit the use of fireproof wood in particularly strategic places in a building. Science still has a virtually open field here, for not even the underlying principles are now known.

Perhaps the greatest weakness of wood is its dimensional instability, i.e., its tendency to swell, shrink, warp, etc. This characteristic is due largely to the fact that wood is hydroscopic; i.e., it absorbs water readily and eagerly because its cellulose component has a tremendous affinity for water. Several methods have been devised to overcome this weakness. In one inexpensive modern process in which wood is heated at high temperatures—short of charring—under moisture-controlled conditions, shrinking and swelling are reduced by as much as 40 percent. Two other methods, however, are now used more widely.

The first, the so-called "impreg" method, is aimed at plugging the pores of the wood by means of such substances as wax or paraffin-like materials which are applied either by impregnation in liquid form under pressure or by diffusion in a solvent that is later evaporated. This method, however, merely slows down the warping and shrinkage and hence does not have any permanent effect on the wood. The use of synthetic resins of the phenol-formaldehyde or Bakelite type has been found to lower shrinkage and swelling permanently by as much as 30 percent, but to reduce the resistance of the wood to impact.

In the second method the wood is compressed under 1000 pounds' pressure per square inch; hence its name, the "compreg" process. It is not a substitute for the "impreg" process, but rather an extension of it, for the wood is first treated with the synthetic resin and then subjected to pressure. Except for highly resinous wood and wood that is relatively impermeable to liquids, almost any kind can be compressed by this method to about one-third of its original thickness. Wood so treated takes a high polish; but, more important, it absorbs almost no water, which means that its dimensional instability is overcome. One very important implication of this process is the possibility of successfully using wood—for example, tropical forests—that is now considered unsatisfactory for lumber. "Compreg" wood approaches mild steel in strength and can be

[24] *Ibid.*, pp. 120-121.

machined easily with metal-working tools. The chief drawback to the method is the high cost of the resin used for impregnation. Although attempts are being made to find a substitute, the results as yet have not been wholly satisfactory.

Probably the most widely used method of overcoming dimensional instability is the manufacture of plywood. This received a tremendous boost when waterproof glues were produced by chemists; for these glues, when applied to wood under controlled heat and pressure, permit the manufacture of highly satisfactory plywood. Plywood manufacture is based on the veneer industry, i.e., the industry which turns the branchless butts of trees into long strips of thin wood. Pieces of strips are laid one above the other and laminated into a solid multiple layer of plywood. By laying the different veneer strips so that the grains of successive layers are set at an angle to each other, the warping and shrinking tendencies of the different layers are compensated or neutralized, giving the entire plywood a remarkable degree of dimensional stability. Plywood has another important advantage. Since only the outer veneers are visible, inferior wood—wood that is discolored or has an unattractive grain—can be used in the interior of "the sandwich."

The use of waterproof resin glues has also made possible the production of larger laminated or "scarfed" pieces of lumber. Thus the gap between the demand for wide boards and the supply of narrower boards which the inferior second-growth stands yield can be at least partially bridged by artificial wide boards made by gluing together the narrower natural boards.

The recovery of wood wastes by grinding them up and reassembling them in various forms of "synthetic" lumber or "plastic" is still in its infancy. Although complete recovery is still far from achievement, progress in this direction has already been made. At present, the so-called "synthetic" boards do not possess the "oriented strength" of normal wood; moreover, their high manufacturing cost precludes buying the waste materials at a price sufficiently high to contribute materially to maintaining forest operation.

Another method of increasing the usefulness of wood is to subject it to chemical processing, such as destructive distillation. The products of this are methanol (wood alcohol), acetic acid, and tars. This industry received a serious setback in the twenties when Germany succeeded in producing cheap synthetic methanol from coal. However, modern methods of vacuum distillation promise to yield entirely new products which may put the wood-distilling industry back on its feet.

Pulp and Paper

Of great importance in industrially advanced countries is the pulp and paper industry. While formerly confined to paper making, the pulp industry now furnishes raw materials for the rayon and similar industries. This is a new and rapidly growing field whose limits are as yet not in sight.

At present the pulp industry consumes only about one-fourth as much wood as the lumber industry, but it is growing rapidly—something that cannot be said of the lumber industry.[25]

The pulp and paper industries originated in the coniferous forests of northern Europe and the earlier processes were therefore based on the use of softwood; in fact, most wood pulp is still produced from softwood. The principal pulping processes are: (1) acid processes, exemplified by the sulfite process, used principally with spruce, fir, and hemlock; (2) alkaline processes, exemplified by the "Kraft" or sulfate process, formerly used principally with pine; also included is the soda process, applicable to hardwood; (3) the semichemical process, originally used with hardwood but apparently quite broadly applicable; and (4) the mechanical or "ground-wood" process, generally applied to light-colored softwood.[26]

Acid and alkaline processes have in common the fact that they dissolve the lignin component of wood but leave the cellulose in a more or

---

[25] In the United States wood pulp production increased from about 1.2 million tons in 1899 to 5.9 million in 1938 and 10.1 million in 1944. See C. F. Korstian and Lee M. James, *Forestry in the South*, Dietz Press, Inc., Richmond, Virginia, 1948, p. 51. The use of paper and paper board in the United States expanded from about 57 pounds per capita in 1899 to 119 pounds in 1919, 243 pounds in 1939, and 317 pounds in 1946. The peak has probably not been reached. See Forest Service, *op. cit.*

[26] *Unasylva*, July-August, 1947, p. 22.

less purified condition in the form of a fiber. The waste liquors from the mills can be used as softening agents. These processes yield a vast variety of products and can be used for a wide range of timber conditions; the sulfate process, which is being actively developed along these lines, can be used with both hardwood and softwood and combinations of the two. The time seems near when "run-of-the-woods" billets can be pulped satisfactorily without regard for species. There is a highly dynamic interplay between forest composition, pulping technology, and market requirements.

The other two processes—the semichemical and the mechanical—were developed mainly because of the high cost and low yield of the acid and alkaline processes. In the semichemical process wood chips are mildly cooked in a softening medium and then broken up into fibers by mechanical means. In the mechanical process billets of wood are ground up by being held against rapidly revolving stones. Both of these processes have a much higher yield than the other two, and the semichemical process can be applied to a wide range of species and qualities of trees.

An entirely new process, the holocellulose process, was recently developed in the United States. In this, all the cellulose is separated from the lignin by means of a very mild process, and fractionation of cellulose and hemicellulose is possible. This holds out high promises of industrial development.

Another recent development which likewise promises much is the manufacture of "papreg," or impregnated and laminated paper that is compressed under heat. It can be bonded to metals or coated with lacquer. Paper has thus become a structural material.

Wood Sugar

Wood can be converted into sugar by hydrolysis.[27] Sugars obtained from wood are mixtures of hexose ($C_6H_{12}O_6$) such as glucose, and pentose ($C_5H_{10}O_5$) such as xylose. Pentose as a rule cannot be converted into alcohol by fermentation with yeast. But as the chemistry of wood becomes clearer as the result of fur-

ther research we may reasonably expect wood to make considerable contributions to the supply of industrial alcohol, cattle feed, and even human food.

So far the most successful wood sugar process seems to be the Schöller process developed in Germany and improved in the United States. It yields about 1100 pounds of sugar per ton of dry softwood waste and from 500 to 600 pounds of lignin as a by-product. The transformation of the lignin into useful chemicals seems a definite possibility. This enhanced usefulness of lignin has been called the key to the wood sugar problem. If the lignin can be made to pull its own weight as it were, the cost of wood sugar could be reduced to a point where it would definitely compete with alcohol from such other sources as blackstrap molasses and petroleum.

The development of the wood sugar industry holds out great promise for an integrated forest-range industry, especially in rugged territory too poor to maintain a normal number of animals. The wood sugar converted into high-protein cattle feed could raise the carrying capacity of such land to a highly satisfactory level. Lignin can also be used as a soil builder, thus making possible a further contribution to the solvency of backward areas.

A great deal of space has been devoted to the discussion of forest utilization. It is a very important topic. As was pointed out earlier, in forestry the manner of harvesting determines the size and quality of future yields. The manner of harvesting, in turn, depends on what can be disposed of profitably. The technology of wood use is therefore the key to the solution of the forest problem. It not only determines the out-of-pocket cost of each article but, what is more, it lowers the burden of the overhead cost by spreading it over a wider variety of forest products. Once a forest can be completely utilized, its products may be expected to become so cheap that there will be little question of a market.

Forest resources are particularly important for remote areas not yet drawn into the present orbit of industrialization. New colonies can spring up in the forest and they can be almost self-sufficient by virtue of the near-universality of the products of the forest.

---

[27] The molecular structure of cellulose differs from that of sugar only by the absence of one molecule of water.

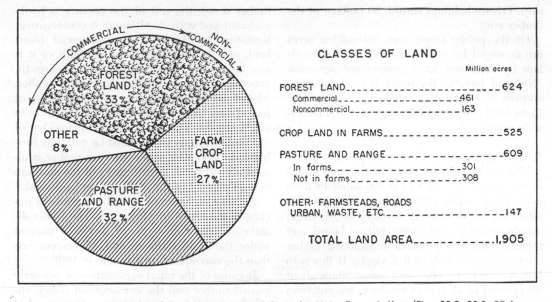

FIG. 23.2. Land Area of the Continental United States by Major Economic Uses. (Figs. 23.2, 23.3, 23.4, and 23.5 from U. S. Department of Agriculture, Forest Service, *Forests and National Prosperity*, Miscellaneous Publication No. 668, 1949.)

THE FOREST SITUATION IN THE UNITED STATES[28]

Forest Land and Its Uses

Of the more than 1.9 billion acres which make up the land area of the United States, over 900 million acres were forested when Columbus discovered America (see Fig. 23.1). Now 624 million acres of forest land remain, about two-thirds of the original forest and almost exactly one-third of our total land area. Fig. 23.2 shows the land area of the United States (exclusive of Alaska) by major economic uses.

This forest area of 624 million acres varies widely in character and productiveness. About three-fourths, or 461 million acres, is classed as commercial forest land, indicating that on it merchantable timber can be produced profitably. The noncommercial forest includes "the open-grown mesquite and pinyon-juniper of the Southwest, the chaparral woodland in southern California, high alpine forests, and oak-cedar breaks of Texas and Oklahoma."[29] It also includes 13 million acres of better sites set

apart as parks and game preserves. At least three-fourths of the forest acreage has a major or moderate influence on watersheds.

In the south from Virginia to east Texas and in the Douglas fir subregion of the Pacific Northwest, climate and other factors are especially favorable for the renewal and rapid growth of forests. These regions contain 45 percent of the commercial forest land. Seventy-five percent of the commercial forest land, generally including the most productive and accessible stands, is privately owned. Thirty percent of this, or 139 million acres, is in farms.[30] Nonfarm ownership accounts for 206 million acres; of this, 51 million acres are held by the basic wood-using industries—the lumber and pulp companies. The remaining 116 million acres of commercial forest land are publicly owned.

Of the privately owned land, 261 million acres are held in 4¼ million separate properties averaging 62 acres. These small properties predominate in all sections of the country. Many of the forest problems of the United States stem from this parcelization of forest owner-

---

[28] This section is largely based on Forest Service, *op. cit.*
[29] *Ibid.*, p. 4.

[30] Much depends on the definition of the term farm.

ship. Private holdings furnish 90 percent of the timber cut.

Of the public forest area, 89 million acres are managed by federal agencies, and 27 million by state and local government agencies. "National forests," the major federal category, consists of a total of 73 million acres, most of them in the west and in remote and inaccessible areas.

Timber Resources

The original timber stand of the area which now is the United States is estimated to have been about 8000 billion board feet. Of this total, which was made up largely of virgin stands centuries old, 1800 billion board feet remain after 300 years of destructive timber operations; only half of it is virgin. If this is to last, it must be cropped, not mined. Since about 80 percent of all timber products are cut from trees of saw-timber size, it is important to think of the timber crop primarily in terms of saw timber.

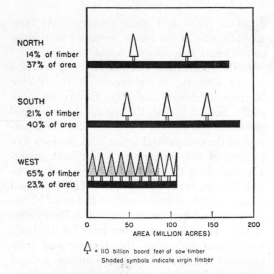

NORTH
14% of timber
37% of area

SOUTH
21% of timber
40% of area

WEST
65% of timber
23% of area

0   50   100   150   200
AREA (MILLION ACRES)

= 110 billion board feet of saw timber
Shaded symbols indicate virgin timber

FIG. 23.3. Distribution of Saw Timber in the United States, 1945.

At the beginning of 1945 the stand of saw timber in the United States was estimated at 1601 billion board feet. This sounds like a lot, but there is cause for concern. For one thing, the geographical distribution is poor. Whereas the Pacific Northwest and California, with *less than one-seventh* of the commercial forest land of the nation, have *more than half* the saw-

timber stand, the rest of the country is badly understocked with it. Although it contains over three-fourths of our total commercial forest land, only a little more than one-third of it is saw timber, and this is largely second growth, generally poorer in quality than virgin timber. Almost 80 percent of the 1043 billion board feet of saw timber in the western regions is in virgin stands. This is an important backlog of our timber supply which must be carefully husbanded. Moreover, while western timber is almost all softwood, three-fourths of the northern and 43 percent of the southern are hardwood.[31]

Another disturbing fact is the continuous decline of the forest growing stock. The 1945 estimate of 1601 billion board feet is 9 percent under the 1938 estimate and 43 percent less than the corresponding estimate in 1909.[32]

Because of the rapid exploitation of privately owned timber and the conservation policy applied to publicly owned timber, 43 percent of our present saw timber is on the 25 percent of publicly owned commercial forest land; the 75 percent of the forest land belonging to private owners has only 57 percent of the saw-timber supply. As was stated before, public timber lands are generally less accessible than private forest lands.

Moreover, the age composition of the nation's forests is far from satisfactory. "High-grading," i.e., cutting out the best trees and leaving the poor ones, destructive cutting, and fire have resulted in the replacement of superior trees by stands inferior in both the species and the quality of individual trees.[33] This shrinkage and deterioration of the nation's timber resources is at the heart of our forest problem. It is responsible for the rapid increase of lumber prices which has materially reduced the marketability of wood and its products.

Use of Timber Resources. The forests of the United States are now growing at the yearly rate of 13.4 billion cubic feet for all timber, including 35.3 billion board feet of saw timber. Over 57 percent of the saw-timber growth is in the South; only 24 percent is in the North, al-

[31] Forest Service, *op. cit.*, p. 19.
[32] These estimates are not entirely comparable. The actual decline is probably larger than the figures indicate.
[33] For a detailed discussion of this process of deterioration, see Forest Service, *op. cit.*, pp. 24 ff.

though that region has as much commercial forest land as the South. The remaining 19 percent is in the West. This growth record is made possible in part by the willingness of wood industries to use trees, particularly hardwoods and especially in the South, which formerly would have been rejected.

TABLE 23.4. Forest Drain in 1944[34]

	All Timber[a] (billion cubic feet)	Saw Timber (billion board feet)
Timber cut	12.18	49.66
Fire losses[b]	0.46	0.86
Insect and disease[c]	0.62	1.93
Windstorm and other losses	0.40	1.44
Total	13.66	53.89

[a] Excluding bark.
[b] Lumber tally.
[c] Average value destroyed yearly in 1934–1943.

Against this growth must be placed the drain on the forests by timber cutting, fire, insect and disease, and windstorm and other losses. The figures for 1944 are shown in Table 23.4. The saw-timber drain during 1942, the peak war year, rose to almost 60 billion board feet and reached that same level again in 1947. Nearly half the timber drain is in the South, which has only 28 percent of the nation's timber; about one-fourth occurs in the North and in the West, which have 21 and 51 percent of the timber respectively.

Lumber accounts for 70 percent of the saw-timber drain and 55 percent of the total cutting drain in cubic feet. Fuel wood accounts for 18 percent of the cutting drain; however, 55 percent of this is covered by utilization of wastes and hence does not actually constitute a drain. Two-thirds of the fuel now cut is hardwood. Table 23.5 shows the drain by commodities.

Comparing forest growth with forest drain shows that in 1944 the total drain of all wood, 13.7 billion cubic feet, nearly balanced the total growth of 13.4 billion cubic feet. However, the total drain in softwoods exceeded their growth by 21 percent, and in hardwoods the growth exceeded the drain by 17 percent. But even more serious is the fact that saw-timber drain exceeded saw-timber growth by 50 percent. These facts are shown graphically in Fig. 23.4.

Future Needs. The Forest Service has estimated that during 1950–1955 annual market requirements will call for production of a total of 61 billion board feet of timber. Lumber will require 44.3 billion board feet; pulpwood, 5.8 billion; fuel wood, 3.1 billion; veneer logs and bolts, 2.8 billion; and all other, 5.0 billion.

Where these amounts will come from is a serious question. Foreign sources of supply do not appear too promising. For one thing, Europe will have to import wood for years to come, for she has an appalling housing shortage

TABLE 23.5. Forest Drain, by Commodities Cut, 1944[35]

Commodity	Saw-Timber Drain			All-Timber Drain		
	Total (billion bd. ft.)	Softwoods (billion bd. ft.)	Hardwoods (billion bd. ft.)	Total (billion cu. ft.)	Softwoods (billion cu. ft.)	Hardwoods (billion cu. ft.)
Lumber	34.39	26.13	8.26	6.71	4.78	1.93
Fuel wood	3.86	1.96	1.90	2.20	0.72	1.48
Pulpwood	4.76	4.50	0.26	1.31	1.17	0.14
Hewn ties	1.64	0.78	0.86	0.36	0.15	0.21
Fence posts	0.23	0.08	0.15	0.22	0.06	0.16
Veneer logs	1.97	0.94	1.03	0.39	0.16	0.23
Mine timbers	0.32	0.07	0.25	0.23	0.04	0.19
Cooperage	0.75	0.20	0.55	0.17	0.04	0.13
Shingles	0.33	0.33	. . .	0.07	0.07	. . .
Other	1.41	0.60	0.81	0.52	0.16	0.36
Total	49.66	35.59	14.07	12.18	7.35	4.83

[34] *Ibid.,* p. 28.

[35] *Ibid.,* p. 29.

and some of her forests were overcut during the war. The German forests, once a model of systematic silviculture, are being badly overcut at present. Little softwood can be expected from the tropics, except for the Paraná pine of Brazil and certain softwoods of Mexico; moreover, it seems unlikely that a large export trade can be built up with tropical sources. Canada is in much the same plight as the United States; for there, too, shrinkage and deterioration are the rule. From a realistic view of the world situation, it seems more sensible to plan for exports from, rather than imports to, the United States.

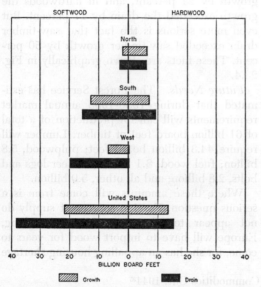

FIG. 23.4. Annual Growth and Drain of Saw Timber, United States, 1944.

Taking all contingencies into account, our Forest Service advocates that total timber growth be increased 50 percent and that sawtimber growth be doubled. To reach these goals will take at least half a century, or thereabouts. Such a program would imply, among other things, "that all the forests would be well protected, that destructive cutting would be stopped, that at least 400 million acres would be managed so as to build up growing stock and output, that from 20 to 25 percent of the land would be under very intensive management, that planting of nonproductive lands would be undertaken on an unprecedented scale, and that access road construction in the West would be continued on a large scale."[36]

[36] *Ibid.*, p. 41.

In the meantime, the virgin stands of the Pacific coast will have to stand the brunt of market requirements. The only way to solve the nation's timber problem is by improved and intensified forest management.

WOOD INDUSTRIES OF THE UNITED STATES
The Lumber Industry

Lumber manufacture is by far the largest of our wood-using industries, accounting for 70 percent of the saw timber cut in 1944. Its 39,000 establishments employed the equivalent of an estimated 442,000 full-time workers that year, and paid wages estimated at $774,000,000.

There are 213 large mills, most of them in the West; each of them cuts more than 25 million board feet (32.3 percent of the total cut) per year. Each of the 791 medium-sized mills accounts for between 5 and 25 million board feet (22.4 percent of the total cut). The 45.3 percent remaining is accounted for by the 37,891 small mills whose output is under 5 million board feet each. Most of them are primitive portable mills that are generally in need of repair. They are usually owned by people of modest means who own no timberland but buy stumpage in small lots as they need it. As the result of their damaging cutting practice, the countryside is denuded and remains unproductive for years to come. Furthermore, competition is keen, accounting systems are inadequate, and there is a high proportion of business failures among these small mills.

Such conditions render difficult the development of the more substantial mills. Inefficiency makes for high costs and high costs contract the market. The vicious circle thus created leads to overcutting and low returns throughout the industry—conditions which militate against sound forest practices. Moreover, the industry is being progressively hampered by the shortage of timber. Fortunately, however, its leaders are coming to realize more and more that good forest and cutting practice is the only basis on which a sound lumber industry can be built.

The Pulp and Paper Industry

In contrast to the 39,000 lumber mills, there are only 237 active pulp mills, all but 25 of them integrated with paper mills. In 1944 they employed the equivalent of 175,570 full-time

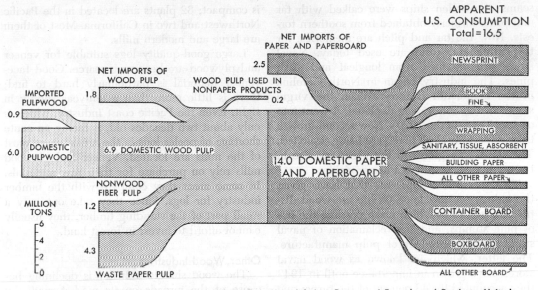

FIG. 23.5. The Flow of Pulpwood and Other Raw Materials into Paper and Paperboard Products, United States, 1939 (in million tons of wood pulp).

workers and paid total wages of $316,000,000. The high degree of integration and the heavy plant investment—it runs to over $200 million in the south alone—give the pulp industry an entirely different viewpoint of the forest. Moreover, because of the rapidly expanding demand for its products the industry is running at full capacity. It is undoubtedly the most stable of our forest industries. Fig. 23.5 shows the flow of pulpwood and other raw materials into paper and paperboard products made in the United States.

In 1944 the pulp mills owned 15 million acres of forest land in the United States. Affiliated mills owned additional acreage in Canada, part of which was acquired to obtain raw materials for the mills in this country. Much of the mill-owned land is well managed and under sustained-yield production.[37]

Of particular interest is the rapid growth of the pulp industry in the South, mainly the sulfate (alkaline) process for making Kraft paper.[38] Mills that make excellent alphacellulose

---

[37] Unfortunately, considerable amounts of pulpwood are secured from small wood-lot operators who sell through contractors. As in the lumber industry, these small-scale operations are in some cases actually destructive to timber resources.

[38] See C. F. Korstian and Lee M. James, *op. cit.,* pp. 47-52.

for rayon are also located in the South, and there is one newsprint mill in Luftkin, Texas. From 10 percent of the country's total wood pulp output in 1920, production in the South expanded to 16 percent in 1930 (760,000 tons), leaped to 40 percent in 1940 (3,560,000 tons), and continued to increase its leadership, producing 48 percent in 1944. The 51 mills scattered throughout the region have acquired over 6 million acres of land which supplies one-third of their requirements; the balance is supplied by small landholders.

Theoretically, there should be a harmonious balance between the lumber and pulp industries of a particular locality. For one thing, the lumber industry is interested in trees larger than those needed for pulpwood. Furthermore, pulpwood should be a by-product of properly managed lumber forests; thinning out the growing stands should provide it. Actually, however, there is often unreasonable competition between the two industries. The situation is aggravated by the fact that the pulpmills cluster in certain locations, especially on the coast, that are particularly accessible to their markets. This enhances the danger of overcutting.

The Naval Stores Industry

The naval stores industry, important to the South, takes its name from the fact that the seams of wooden ships were calked with tar and pitch formerly obtained from southern forests. Now the tar and pitch are memories, for turpentine and rosin are used today. Naval stores are obtained from longleaf and slash pines. The industry began in North Carolina in the eighteenth century. When the virgin stands of the South were depleted, it went into eastern Texas in the 1920's. Now second-growth trees, especially slash pines, are being exploited. The slash pine grows to the necessary size in twenty-five years and is a heavy yielder.

Two recent developments that have given the industry a new lease on life are wood distillation processes which make possible the use of pine stumps, and the reclamation of naval stores as a by-product of pulp manufacture. The latter, which are known as wood naval stores, have grown in importance until in 1943 they accounted for 43 percent of the turpentine and 46 percent of the rosin produced.

The Veneer and Plywood Industry

The veneer and plywood industry has grown rapidly in the past twenty-five years. It uses about 4.2 percent of the saw-timber cut, and in 1944 employed the equivalent of 54,170 full-time workers. There are three main types of products: "1. Face veneers, made chiefly from high-quality hardwoods and used in furniture, cabinetmaking, paneling, and similar manufactures; (2) container veneers, made from southern pine, ponderosa pine, sweetgum, tupelo, birch, beech, maple, elm, cottonwood, etc., and used for orange and egg crates, baskets, hampers, and boxes for shipping fruits, vegetables, and other commodities, and crating for refrigerators, radios, etc.; and (3) plywood, made chiefly from Douglas-fir, and used for construction, door panels and other millwork, small boats, refrigerator cars, and hundreds of other purposes."[39]

In 1944, 58 percent of the timber cut for veneer was hardwood. Over half the softwood veneer was for containers. Hardwood veneer plants vary widely in size and are scattered throughout the east; there are about 600 of them. Container production is centered in the south, and face-veneer production in the central and Lake regions. The softwood industry

is compact; 32 plants are located in the Pacific Northwest and two in California. Most of them are large and modern mills.

Large good-quality logs suitable for veneer and plywood are becoming scarce. Good face-veneer material is particularly hard to find; there is little more than a ten-year supply in sight. Even the Pacific coast industry, which is only about two decades old, is facing an acute shortage of peeler logs in the areas where most of the mills are located. Veneer and plywood mills rely on purchase for their raw materials. In some areas they compete with the lumber industry for logs. Since they take out only a small part of the standing timber, they usually cannot afford to invest in forest land.

Other Wood Industries

The wood shingle industry is declining because of the inroads on its market made by asphalt roofing and similar products. It is based almost entirely on western red cedar and is concentrated in the Douglas fir subregion. The output in 1944 was only one-third of the peak production about thirty-five years earlier. British Columbia now supplies about one-fourth of the demand.

The cooperage industry is likewise declining because of the depletion of suitable timber stands. The price of white oak, the chief wood used for this purpose, is so high that it virtually prohibits its use.

FORESTS AND DEMOCRACY

In a totalitarian state the difficulties of scientific forestry are mainly the difficulties inherent in the science itself. The forest is a complex dynamic organism whose most effective utilization requires a vast knowledge of facts and a high degree of managerial skill. Given that knowledge and skill, the forest service of a totalitarian state has few other obstacles to consider unless it be inadequate funds with which to carry out the policies that have been decreed. There are no institutional resistances; the politbureau does not consider the rights and whims of individual owners that conflict with state policy.

In a democracy, the government has the difficult task of convincing individuals of the wisdom and need of measures designed to safeguard the welfare of the group. Democracy can

[39] Forest Service, *op. cit.*, p. 57.

succeed only to the extent that the majority of the people can be induced to exercise the social self-control necessary for group welfare; in some cases this goes counter to the popular notion of individual liberty.[40]

Such a government's policies regarding a primary social asset—the forest—are a test of

[40] For a discussion of the fundamental issues underlying the concept of liberty, see John Stuart Mill, *On Liberty.*

real democracy. Failure to carry out a forest policy based on disinterested scientific analysis, designed to assure the welfare and security of the group, and approved by the majority of the people reveals a fatal lack of social self-discipline and disregard for group welfare. The forest is outstanding proof of the fact that group welfare is not an automatic by-product of a laissez-faire scramble for individual privileges.

BIBLIOGRAPHY

Ahern, G. P., *Deforested America,* Washington, U. S. Forest Service, 1928.

Albion, R. G., *Forests and Seapower,* Cambridge, Harvard University Press, 1926.

Anderson, S. A., "Trends in the Pulp and Paper Industry," *Economic Geography,* April, 1942.

Brown, N. C., *Timber Products and Industries,* New York, Wiley, 1935.

Brown, N. C., *A General Introduction to Forestry in the United States,* New York, Wiley, 1938.

Buck, C. J., "Definition of Sustained Yield," *Journal of Forestry,* February, 1937.

Chapman, H. H., *Forest Finance,* New Haven, Tuttle, Morehouse and Taylor, 1926.

Gaer, J., *Men and Trees: the Problem of Forest Conservation,* New York, Harcourt, Brace, 1939.

Glesinger, E., *The Coming Age of Wood,* New York, Simon and Schuster, 1949.

Glover, K., *America Begins Again,* New York, McGraw-Hill, 1939.

Greely, W. B., "The Relationship of Geography to Timber Supply," *Economic Geography,* March, 1925.

Grothian, W., *Holz,* Vol. 14 of Schumacher, H. (ed.), *Wandlungen in der Weltwirtschaft,* Leipzig, Bibliographisches Institut, 1938.

Gustafson, A. F., Guise, C. H., Hamilton, W. J., Jr., and Ries, H., *Conservation in the United States,* Ithaca, Comstock Publishing Co., 1949.

Hall, J. A., "Forest Utilization," *Unasylva,* July-August, 1947.

Hausrath, H., *Forstwesen,* Vol. 7, of *Grundriss der Sozialökonomik,* Tübingen, Mohr, 1922.

Havemeyer, L., *Conservation of Our Natural Resources,* New York, Macmillan, 1930.

Hiley, W. E., *The Economics of Forestry,* Oxford Manuals of Forestry, London, Oxford University Press, 1930.

Ise, J., *The United States Forest Policy,* New Haven, Yale University Press, 1924.

Jenks, C., *The Development of Government Forest Control in the United States,* Baltimore, Johns Hopkins Press, 1928.

Kendall, H. J., "The Lumberman's Attitude Toward Forestry," *Journal of Forestry,* October, 1919.

Korstian, C. F., and James, L. M., *Forestry in the South,* Richmond, Dietz Press, 1948.

Lillard, R. G., *The Great Forest,* New York, Knopf, 1947.

Pack, A. N., *Our Vanishing Forests,* New York, Macmillan, 1926.

Pack, A. N., *Forestry: An Economic Challenge,* New York, Macmillan, 1933.

Parkins, A. E., and Whitaker, J. R., *Our National Resources and Their Conservation,* New York, Wiley, 2nd ed., 1948.

Reed, F. W., "Public Forest Conservation and Private Timber Growing," *Journal of Forestry,* March, 1928.

Renner, G. T., *Conservation of National Resources,* New York, Wiley, 1947.

"The New Age of Wood," *Fortune,* October, 1942.

"Trees," *Agriculture Yearbook, 1949,* Washington, U. S. Department of Agriculture, 1949.

"Trees, the New Crop," *Fortune,* October, 1946.

United Nations, Food and Agriculture Organization, *Yearbook of Forest Products, Statistics,* Washington, 1948.

U. S. Department of Agriculture, Forest Service, *Report on the Forest Problem of the United States* ("Copeland Report"), Washington, 1933.

U. S. Department of Agriculture, Forest Service, *A Reappraisal of the Forest Situation,* Washington, 1946.

U. S. Department of Agriculture, Forest Service, *Forests and National Prosperity,* Miscellaneous Bulletin No. 668, Washington, 1948.

U. S. Tariff Commission, *Softwood Lumber,* War Changes in Industry Series No. 25, Washington, 1947.

Van Hise, C. R., *The Conservation of Natural Resources in the United States,* New York, Macmillan, 1914.

Wackerman, A. E., "Sustained-Yield Forestry," *Journal of Forestry*, February, 1937.

Woodbury, T. D., "Definition of Sustained Yield," *Journal of Forestry*, February, 1937.

Zimmermann, E. W., "Wood Industries," *Encyclopædia of the Social Sciences,* New York, Macmillan, 1935.

Zon, R., "Forests," *Encyclopædia of the Social Sciences,* New York, Macmillan, 1931.

Zon, R., and Sparhawk, W. N., *Forest Resources of the World,* New York, McGraw-Hill, 2 vols., 1932.

Zwnuska, J. A., "Some Aspects of the Economic Theory of Forestry," *Journal of Land and Public Utility Economics,* May, 1949.

PART III

RESOURCES OF INDUSTRY

UNIT 1. MINERALS, ORES AND RESERVES

Chapter 24

MINERAL RESOURCES AND MODERN MACHINE CIVILIZATION

MINERALS IN HISTORY

As has been pointed out,[1] the mechanical revolution neither innovated the use of inanimate energy—it merely increased its use by means of newly invented machines—nor initiated the use of minerals. The use of minerals, particularly metals, goes back to the earliest days of recorded history. Superior knowledge of metals and better control over their supplies were at all times major factors in determining the course of history.[2]

Yet, clear as the record seems to be regarding the importance of minerals, especially metals, in history, here as elsewhere one-sided determinism must be condemned. The Roman legions may have had better armor and weapons, but they also surpassed in discipline and in many instances enjoyed the benefit of superior leadership. Furthermore, the personal element must not be ignored—perhaps the Roman soldier felt pride in the system of law and order which he helped to set up. On the other hand, the wealth

---

[1] See chap. 5.

[2] "Egypt became a world power coincident with the acquisition of the Maghara copper deposits of the Sinai Peninsula about 4000 B.C." (B. Adams, *The New Empire*, The Macmillan Company, New York, 1912, p. 4.)

"The knowledge of the source of tin, said to have been carefully guarded for more than 260 years, and the monopoly in the trade so acquired by the Phoenicians, materially aided in building up their supremacy and in part enabled the Carthaginians to control the tin commerce of the world." (G. Smith, *The Cassiterides*, Longman, Green, Longman and Roberts, London, 1863.)

"The Roman Empire reached its supremacy after it attained political and industrial control of the mineral resources of Spain." (J. W. Furness, *et al.*,

---

Mineral Raw Materials, Bureau of Foreign and Domestic Commerce, U.S. Department of Commerce, Trade Promotion Series No. 76, 1929.)

"It was the possession of iron-tipped spears that enabled the Assyrians 'to come down like a wolf on the fold,' and to lay under tribute great, peaceful, prosperous cities of the coast whose merchants and artisans knew brass and bronze but were unacquainted with iron." (H. F. Bain, "Place of Minerals in a Power-Controlled World," *Proceedings of the World Power Conference*, Berlin, 1930.)

The Biblical story of the Philistines who held the Jews in submission by depriving them of the use of metals is another case in point. Many other examples are cited in W. T. Thom, Jr., *Petroleum and Coal, the Keys to the Future*, Princeton University Press, Princeton, 1929.

and power which metals brought to these ancient people may have corrupted their morals and degraded their social institutions, thus contributing to downfall no less than to ascendancy.

Because of their usefulness, beauty, or scarcity, metals—particularly the precious metals—have at all times aroused the cupidity of man. Moreover, because of their durability, they often encouraged the accumulation of wealth beyond current needs and thus promoted an interest in private property. Bain points to the revolutionary effect on the ideas of property among certain African tribes which followed the shipment of the metal trunks used for safekeeping: "Possession of such a safe and fireproof container gives the Kaffir almost his first opportunity to break with an age-long system of village communism and to store up individual goods for the future."[3] There is a close connection between the use of minerals, especially metals, and pleonexy,[4] the desire for more for its own sake.

MINERALS IN MODERN TIMES

While the use of minerals is as old as human civilization, the way in which they are used today and the magnitude of this use are absolutely novel. The mechanical revolution is completely tied up with the use of minerals. Just as it is the great divide in human history, so it also marks a great divide in the use of minerals. Ancient uses of minerals were largely confined to tools, weapons, and utensils, to road building, and the construction of buildings, aqueducts, sewer systems. All these uses continue today, but they constitute only a part—perhaps a minor part—of the total use of minerals. Today the bulk of the minerals goes into the making and operation of power-driven machines which emancipate man from drudgery, put wheels under him, and, by raising his productivity to the nth power, hold out a promise of security and comfort.

As Lewis Mumford points out in *Technics and Civilization*, the ancient world was not wholly ignorant of machines. It remained for the modern age so to multiply their number

that they came to form a coherent mass which he calls "The Machine"—a quasi-demonic being that controls man or threatens to. Moreover, many minerals in use today were either wholly unknown in ancient times or not available for use.

Increased Use of Metals

The most obvious aspect of modern mineral development is the pace at which men in many parts of the earth are drawing upon the mineral endowment of the earth. Table 24.1 shows world production of some important metals in 1800, 1929, and 1944.

TABLE 24.1. World Production of Some Important Metals[5] (million short tons)

	1800	1929	1944
Pig iron	0.50	110.0	125.0
Steel	...	130.0	170.0
Copper	0.02	2.1	2.9
Lead	0.03	2.0	1.5
Zinc	...	1.6	1.9

Rogers and Tryon[6] cite the following facts to illustrate the difference in the size of ancient and modern mining industries. When Alexander the Great took Susa and Persepolis, he is reported to have seized precious metals valued at $190 million, the accumulation of a thousand years or more. The gold mines of the South African Rand have produced that much in less than a year. It is estimated that modern mines could equal the entire output of the Athenian silver mines in Laurion in less than a year. Modern blast furnaces would take less than one day to produce the world's total output of iron in 1750. It is further estimated that 90 percent of present-day mining has come into existence during the past 150 years.

It is clear from these figures that modern use of minerals is of a magnitude altogether different from that of earlier times and that the

---

[3] H. F. Bain, *op. cit.*, p. 10.

[4] Cf. F. C. Müller-Lyer, *The History of Social Development* (translated from the German by E. C. and H. A. Lake), G. Allen and Unwin, Ltd., London, 1920, pp. 292-295.

[5] Figures for 1800 from Alfred Marcus, "Metals (Modern)" in *Encyclopædia of the Social Sciences;* 1929 figures from *U. S. Minerals Yearbook;* 1944 figures partly estimated and partly based on American Iron and Steel Institute, *Statistical Yearbook, 1947* (pig iron and steel), and American Bureau of Metal Statistics, *Yearbook, 1948* (nonferrous metals).

[6] H. O. Rogers and F. G. Tryon, "Mining," *Encyclopædia of the Social Sciences.*

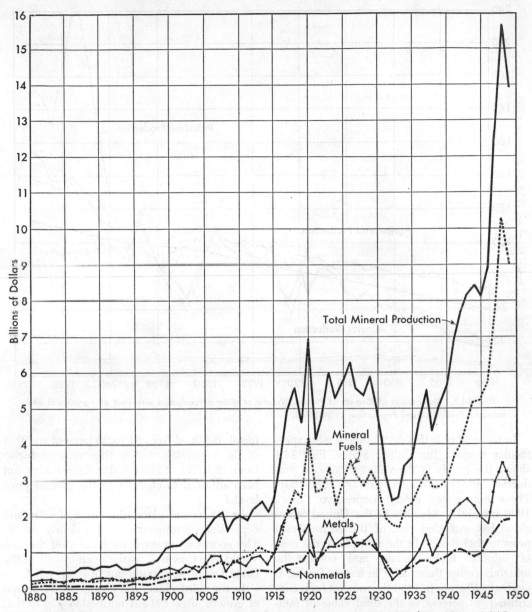

FIG. 24.1.   Trends in Value of Mineral Production in the United States, 1880-1949. (Figs. 24.1 and 24.2 from U. S. Department of the Interior, Bureau of Mines.)

nineteenth century marks little more than the prelude to the real performances that start with the twentieth century. "The burst of industrialization now sweeping the world is calling for mineral supplies on a scale without precedent in history. Mechanized world wars are making equally great demands. Production in the United States has quadrupled since the open-

ing of the century. It has been estimated that if the rest of the world were to become industrialized on the scale of the United States, world requirements for minerals would be multiplied seven times."[7]

[7] G. K. Leith, in *Raw Materials in War and Peace*, Department of Social Sciences, United States Military Academy, West Point, 1947, p. iii.

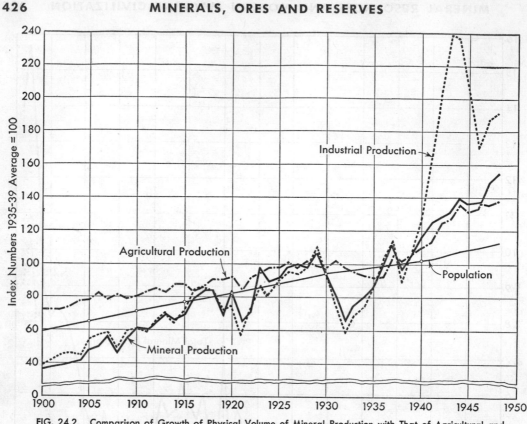

FIG. 24.2. Comparison of Growth of Physical Volume of Mineral Production with That of Agricultural and Industrial Production and Population, 1900-1948.

In no country is this development more spectacular than in the United States. Fig. 24.1 shows the trends in the value of mineral production in this country during 1880-1948. These figures are indeed impressive. "Since 1900 mineral production in the United States alone has exceeded that of the entire world prior to that time."[8] In the first place, the rank of mineral fuels, metals, and nonmetallic minerals (other than fuels) in terms of value is evident. Whereas in 1880 the mineral fuels constituted 33 percent of the total value of minerals produced in this country, they made up 61 percent of the total in 1944. This gain is due entirely to the rapid growth of the petroleum and natural gas industries. The value of coal was 26 percent of the total in both these years, while the value of petroleum and natural gas rose from 7 percent in 1880 to 35 percent in 1944. In the same period the value of the

metals declined from 51 to 28 percent and that of the nonmetals (other than mineral fuels) from 16 to 11. (These value figures have not been adjusted to changes in the general price level.)

In the second place, the effect of wars and depression on mineral output is clearly shown. The enormous upward surges during the two World Wars, as well as the deep trough of the Great Depression, stand out in sharp relief.

In the third place, the change in the tempo of growth after 1914 is noticeable. Up to that time aggregate values of our minerals had increased from less than $400 million to a little over $2 billion. From then on, they began to shoot up, reaching $7 billion in the late twenties, over $8.5 billion in World War II, almost $9 billion in 1946, $12.4 in 1947, and $15.6 billion in 1948. This accelerated rate of growth is by no means dissociated from the World Wars and the sense of global tension they engendered. But it is not altogether a political phenomenon.

[8] E. W. Pehrson, "The Mineral Position of the United States and the Outlook for the Future," *Mining and Metallurgy*, April, 1945.

These values were produced by about 500,000 persons in 1900, over a million in 1923, and about 600,000 in 1943. This decline in number of workers after 1923 reflects an amazing increase in labor productivity. While the preceding data are in dollar values, Fig. 24.2 shows the physical output of minerals and permits its comparison with that of agriculture and with the growth of our population.[9]

The rise of mineral production from 68 (1935-1939 average=100) in 1932 to 141 in 1944—better than double—is remarkable, particularly when compared with the rise in agricultural output from about 93 to 133, an increase of less than half. For the entire period 1900 to 1944 the comparative figures are from 36 to 141 for minerals, about a fourfold increase, and from 55 to 135 for agricultural production, slightly over a twofold increase.

But neither aggregate dollar value nor index number of physical value tells an accurate story. In fact, no real insight into the rise of the mineral industry, its magnitude and significance can be had except through a thorough and detailed analysis of all the important phases. Much of the story will be told in the remainder of this volume, but a preliminary survey will be attempted at this point.

TABLE 24.2.   Mineral Work Energy vs. Animal and Human Energy[10]
(in percent)

	Mineral Fuels and Water Power	Work Animals	Human Energy
1850	5.8	78.8	15.4
1950 (est.)	94.0	3.0	3.0

One effective way of showing the scope of the mineral revolution, i.e., the extent to which, during the past century or more, our civilization has shifted from a vegetable to a mineral basis of production, is to trace the source of physical work energy—what makes the wheels go around, actually and symbolically, as is done in Table 24.2. (See also Fig. 5.1.) From a modest begin-

ning in 1850, the output of mineral work energy increased to almost 400 billion horsepower hours, while that traceable to animals sharply declined and that traceable to human toilers increased at a rate far less than the population. The percentage figures in Table 24.2 are impressive. The shift from muscular energy derived from food and feed to mechanical energy derived from mineral fuels and from falling water is almost complete. Since mechanical power must be harnessed by metals, the shift in energy sources implies a shift from wood to metals. As machine-powered industry advances, the nonmetals are also used increasingly.

Table 24.3, covering the period since World War I, breaks down mineral production in the United States into its constituent parts—mineral raw materials, refined metals,[11] mineral fuels, and nonmetallic minerals (exclusive of fuels). To these are added water power, total electric power, and manufactured gas.

It is not easy to draw clear-cut conclusions from this table, mainly because it covers such a stormy period in our political and economic life. Yet the rapid and consistent rise of electric power and the almost as rapid increase in the use of water power stand out. Truly amazing is the expansion all along the line after 1940 in response to war needs and the rapid growth of our "cannon *and* butter" economy. It is clear that war calls for metals more loudly than for fuels or nonmetallic minerals, and loudest of all for electrical power. A 59.2 percent increase in five years is amazing, as is the 53.2 percent increase in refined metals.

What this table does not reveal is the vast qualitative improvement in the performance of both metals and fuels. A pound of coal did more work in 1944 than in 1919, in fact considerably more work. The 1944 barrel of crude oil yielded far more valuable fuel and other products than its 1919 predecessor. The typical metal of 1944 was a far better harnesser and general performer than that of 1919. Hence, in a way, these index numbers do not tell the whole story; this will be brought out in the following chapters.

Implications.   The most important contribution that minerals, both fuels and metals, have

---

[9] The rise of the industrial output curve after 1937 is surprising. To be sure, it reflects the cumulative effect of the increasing agricultural and mineral production. It is pointed out that some duplication of material processed by industry distorts the statistical picture.

[10] J. W. Dewhurst *et al.*, *America's Needs and Resources*, Twentieth Century Fund, New York, 1947, p. 787.

---

[11] Gold is omitted as having a mainly indirect bearing on industry.

TABLE 24.3. Indexes[a] of Production for Minerals, Water Power, Total Electric Power for
Public Use, and Manufactured Gas, 1919-1944[12]

(1940 = 100)

Year	Total Mineral Raw Materials	Refined Metals[b]	Mineral Fuels	Non-metallic Minerals[b]	Water Power	Total Electric Power	Manu-factured Gas[c]
1919	58.5	70.1	56.3	48.3	34.0	26.8	108.7
1920	67.7	78.9	65.2	59.0	37.0	29.9	118.1
1921	50.3	38.1	56.3	46.9	34.7	28.2	113.5
1922	57.9	60.2	56.1	61.4	39.1	32.8	113.5
1923	79.5	88.0	77.0	75.6	43.4	38.3	116.1
1924	74.1	75.9	72.0	79.2	44.5	40.6	125.1
1925	78.5	85.5	73.4	87.2	49.2	45.4	129.9
1926	84.5	90.5	80.6	90.0	56.9	50.8	139.2
1927	84.9	85.5	82.4	93.7	64.4	54.8	136.8
1928	86.0	89.5	81.9	96.1	74.1	59.7	140.3
1929	93.8	98.8	90.3	99.3	73.6	66.1	136.3
1930	81.6	74.6	82.3	89.9	70.8	65.3	128.2
1931	65.1	46.5	72.2	67.6	65.7	62.6	118.3
1932	50.9	24.5	62.2	45.5	72.5	56.8	102.7
1933	56.0	31.4	68.5	46.8	73.7	58.4	93.9
1934	61.1	37.4	72.6	54.8	72.4	62.6	95.1
1935	67.3	49.6	76.9	58.6	84.2	67.9	94.7
1936	82.2	72.2	86.5	81.2	86.1	77.4	95.3
1937	91.9	88.4	94.6	87.1	93.4	84.0	93.4
1938	75.8	54.2	85.3	73.8	94.1	80.5	90.6
1939	88.1	78.2	91.7	90.6	92.5	89.9	93.1
1940	100.0	100.0	100.0	100.0	100.0	100.0	100.0
1941	113.2	118.5	106.9	129.1	107.0	116.0	103.6
1942	121.5	133.9	112.5	136.6	133.0	130.5	112.1
1943	127.5	153.2	119.0	118.7	152.6	152.4	117.1
1944	130.2	145.3	130.2	105.8	152.5	159.2	120.5

[a] In arriving at the composite indexes, 1939 values were used to weight the data on physical volume of production.
[b] Excluding gold.
[c] Excluding fuels.

made to the development of modern civilization is the increased efficiency in human productive effort. A modern worker with the aid of power-driven machinery can produce many times the amount which the slave could and would produce. The use of such machinery makes possible division of labor, both occupational and regional, to an extent formerly impossible. Furthermore, the availability of large concentrated amounts of energy permits large-scale manufacturing and cheap mass transportation, with all the benefits they imply. This increased efficiency, in turn, has made possible the accumulation of a surplus over and above current requirements, thus laying the founda-

tion of modern capitalism, and has brought increased purchasing power and expanding markets.

Next to the all-important increase in labor productivity, increased mobility is the most significant implication of the modern machine age. Minerals as such have always lured men to move about the face of the earth in search of treasure, and the lure of gold and silver has led to migrations on a large scale. In the western world coal fields have become the bases on which the lofty structures of modern industry are reared. More recently, oil and gas fields have supplemented coal fields as sources of inanimate energy, but they have not attracted masses of people as the coal mines have. Capital goods in the form of machinery, railroad equipment, etc., have migrated to the mineral-

[12] Adapted from J. W. Dewhurst, et al., op. cit., p. 578.

ized sections of the earth. Hundreds of millions of dollars' worth of such equipment have been exported from industrial countries for installation in copper mines, tin mines, oil wells, and so forth, in the most inaccessible parts of the most backward continents.

But, more important, the power-driven machine applied to locomotion put whole societies on wheels, so to speak, and in doing so made possible the interdependent social exchange economy characteristic of modern times. This trend toward increased mobility gained momentum when internal-combustion and Diesel engines, and, more recently, jet propulsion made it possible for automobiles and airplanes to take their place beside the railroad and the steamship. Far more than is generally realized, this mobility lies at the root of the high labor productivity of modern machine industry, for it is this factor that accounts chiefly for the size of the modern market, which, after all, is the basis of modern large-scale production methods.

Selective vs. Mass Mining

Next to this phenomenal growth of the mineral industries of the world, the shift from selective to mass mining is perhaps the most outstanding development. This shift rests on what may be termed a technological "law" which says: The richness of the mineral deposit that will pay exploitation is in inverse proportion to the state of the arts, the level of technological development, the availability of capital, and the extent of know-how, with particular reference to mining, smelting, and transportation. In less formidable language, this means that primitive explorers and exploiters must select the rich, easily mined ores that lie near the surface and are near the market. They must lean heavily on nature's bounty, relying on it to make up for the deficiency of their own abilities and capacities. But as technology advances, as bigger and better machines and equipment become available, as more inanimate energy harnessed by this equipment comes to his aid, man can profitably exploit huge masses of progressively lower grades of ore.[13]

Economic and Political Implications. That

this change in mining methods has far-reaching implications goes without saying; it reflects a radical shift in the proportion of land, labor, and capital called for in mining. The little man who can afford a pick and shovel, a pan and a bag of beans, and perhaps a burro has little chance to enter the modern game of mass mining. The ante is too high; in many cases millions of dollars are involved. The result is that mining, especially successful mining, tends to be concentrated in firmer and stronger hands.

This is particularly true when mass mining becomes inseparably linked with large-scale smelting operations as in the case of copper and other metals. It does not pay to haul ores that contain less than 1 percent of copper. Such ores must be smelted at the mine, and the scooping operation is a mere preliminary to the smelting operation. Furthermore, mass mining may involve a radical shift in mining methods, as from shaft mining to open-pit operations. Mining, one might say, is absorbed in the industrial operation and thus removed from the reach of the old-fashioned miner. Moreover, as was pointed out above, lean ores require far more elaborate treatment and far more expensive equipment than rich ores.

Even prospectors are coming under the spell of this supercapitalism. Gone are the days when outcroppings pointed the way to some rich mother lode. These lucky strikes have been made, and the lodes have been explored and exploited. Now the search is for deeper deposits perceptible only to the highly trained scientist equipped with costly apparatus. The geophysical and geochemical exploration[14] which is becoming increasingly necessary in the search not only for oil, but also for other minerals, requires precision instruments and expert knowledge and skill. Billion-dollar corporations can afford such experts so equipped, but the little fellows cannot. Some of these methods are so complex that the federal government may be the logical agency to apply them.

---

[13] This is a parallel to the observation made in chap. 6 (p. 71) with regard to agriculture—that the horsepower support a farmer has determines the quality of the soil that he can farm.

[14] This change in methods of exploration is not another instance of the shift from selective to mass operation. It is brought up at this point for two reasons. In common with this shift, it requires more capital and more science; and it helps to reinforce the effect of this shift on the control of mining operations.

The implications of this shift from selective to mass mining reach far beyond national boundaries; they are global in extent. For just as within nations men and groups differ widely in their control over capital and credit, so also do nations differ. Moreover, men and nations differ also in their possession of, or access to, know-how and scientific knowledge. As a result, mineral deposits not only in the United States but also in many other parts of the world are exploited by corporations domiciled in the United States and representing United States stockholders. Other countries such as Great Britain, France, Belgium, and the Netherlands participate to a lesser extent in this global control of minerals. (The U.S.S.R. constitutes a world of its own in this respect.) Thus, practically all the copper deposits of Latin America are being exploited by United States capital. Almost all the oil deposits in the world, except those in the Russian sphere, are in the hands of either United States or British corporations; Dutch and French interests hold minority shares.

This global tendency is reinforced by several forces. In the first place, there is the all-important question of markets. The markets for minerals—especially crude oil, metals, and ores—are highly concentrated in the industrialized areas of the world. The oil-refining capacity is highly localized and a large portion of the scattered outposts are held by the representatives of industrial centers. The crude oil producers in outlying areas tend to become integrated with or agents of the oil-producing and -refining structure of the United States and Great Britain. The market for tin, alloying metals, nickel, etc., is highly concentrated in the same areas.

Thus, a large portion of all the mineralized areas of the globe come under the control of outside interests; they become economic exclaves, so to speak. This applies to the copper mines of South America and Africa, to the oil fields of South America, the Middle East, and the East Indies, to the gold and diamond mines of South Africa, and so down the line.

And here another point—the colonial situation—must be mentioned. The uneven distribution of political power is a further element that must be taken into account if the naked facts of mineral geography are to have real meaning. A significant element of this power is control over the sea and air lanes. A realistic approach to the question of access to mineral raw material must include all the pertinent factors which help to determine the actual working of the international situation. It must not be one-sided, pointing solely to one factor favoring one side of the argument and ignoring others unfavorable to it.

Governmental Control and Minerals

Another significant trend in recent mineral developments is that toward increased governmental control. Although this will be taken up in some detail in connection with the specific minerals most affected, here an attempt will be made to throw light on some of the causes responsible for this shift.

The causes vary widely with the different minerals. Thus, labor problems may be a cause. Coal, for example, is largely produced by hand labor, and coal miners constitute one of the largest groups of labor in the world. The low productivity of the hand labor in the case of coal, as against the more efficient methods used for petroleum and natural gas, leads to labor problems of such vast social significance that in many countries the state has taken over the coal mines. In other cases, coal mining has ceased to be profitable; hence, private capital has pulled out and left the state to hold the fort. Coal is so important to the entire economy that mere unprofitableness must not decide its destiny.

Mineral industries are sometimes taken over by the government because of their strategic importance and because private capital is not prepared to undertake projects that may be necessary.

In part, the trend toward government control is closely related to the general drift toward socialism and communism in many areas of the globe. The U.S.S.R., the outstanding exponent of communism that implies state control over all the means of production and over all the natural wealth on which they draw, is too well known to need elaboration. As the political control of the U.S.S.R. extends to ever wider areas, nationalization of mineral enterprises proceeds apace.[15]

---

[15] More will be said about this trend in the section on minerals and law. See pp. 435-436.

CLASSIFICATION OF MINERALS

Terminological Confusion

To the laymen the literature of mining and metallurgy is somewhat bewildering, partly because of his inadequate understanding of the terminology. The word mineral itself is not quite clear. Of course, it is drawn from mine and mining and therefore suggests getting something from the ground by digging. But is the same substance a mineral when it is obtained in one fashion and not a mineral when it is obtained in a different manner? Thus, is nitrogen a mineral if it is dug out of the ground in Chile and not a mineral when it is extracted from the air? Is iron a mineral when it is mined, but not when it is present in the blood or in spinach?

The answer is simple. Nitrogen is an element which is present in the air as well as in portions of the crust of the earth. These portions, e.g., the caliche along the north coast of Chile, are minerals containing the element nitrogen. Likewise iron is an element which is present in many forms, some of which are minerals. The ores of iron such as hematite and limonite are minerals. The iron ore that is mined is a mineral; the iron in spinach is an element, not a mineral. Whether water should be included in the list of minerals is a debatable point. It would hardly do, however, to call pumping water from a well a form of mining.

Another source of confusion is the fact that in the case of some minerals it is customary to speak of the refined products—iron, copper, lead, zinc, aluminum, gold, silver, etc.; whereas in other cases a lower, less pure stage is ordinarily referred to. Thus, one frequently reads of phosphate rock rather than phosphorus, the essential element in phosphate rock, nitrate instead of nitrogen, chromite instead of chromium. This terminology reflects trade practice. The United States imports Chilean nitrate; this term is applied to several chemical compounds, all of which contain nitrogen. Some chromites may be used as such; other chromites may yield the metal chromium. Magnesite may be used in the raw state as a flux, or magnesium may be extracted by metallurgical processing.

The terminology is even more confusing in such cases as ilmenite and rutile, for the name of the mineral does not suggest the name of the element because of which it is mined. Il-menite and rutile are both ores of titanium; wolframite and scheelite are both ores of tungsten. Sometimes one speaks simply of iron ore; then again, specific terms such as hematite and limonite are used to indicate specific characteristics of the ore. Pyrites is an iron compound generally valued more for its sulfur than its iron content. Calcium is another illustration of the layman's difficulties. Generally, in speaking of calcium, one thinks of such coarse materials as lime, limestone, chalk, etc. Only recently have scientists succeeded in extracting the "metallic salt" calcium from these baser sources.

Petroleum is a broad generic term for a vast array of hydrocarbon compounds containing impurities, from which various refined products such as gasoline, kerosene, gas oil, etc., are derived. The names of these products are themselves generic terms. The situation with coal is similar, except that scientists do not know yet what it is; they do know that it contains carbon, hydrocarbon, impurities, etc. The trade and most laymen recognize coals when they see them, but as yet the true nature of this mineral, one of nature's most valuable gifts to man, is unknown.

With these points in mind, we now proceed to the classification of minerals.

Classification by Major Use

On the basis of use, minerals may be divided into several categories, such as (1) energy minerals (coal, petroleum, and natural gas); (2) construction minerals (especially the metals) which go into machines, buildings, and transportation and communication systems; and (3) chemical minerals, such as sulfur, nitrates, phosphates, limestone, and many others.

Such a classification seems quite simple; actually it involves difficulties. For many minerals do not serve one purpose but several, perhaps many. Furthermore, the diverse purposes to which a single mineral is put may be scattered over a whole list of uses. Thus, the carbon in coal may be joined with iron to form steel. Synthetic rubber is made from derivatives of petroleum and natural gas, and so are nylon and many other products. Petroleum yields paraffin which may go into candles; it yields coke which may be used in electrodes. Nitrates go into explosives which release energy. Magnesium, when powdered, is highly explosive. Sulfur yields sulfuric acid which digests wood pulp, thus substituting for mechanical grinders.

However, since the bulk of the mineral fuels serve as sources of heat and energy, since the bulk of the metals go into construction, and since other minerals serve primarily as raw materials for the chemical industry, this classification retains much of its usefulness.

Underlying all modern industry is the power-driven machine. This gives the power resources and the metals that go into machine construction, the so-called machine resources, a position of unique importance.

Energy and machine or construction resources—i.e., the fuels and the metals—differ sharply in nature and hence in their rate of use. Machines and machine tools, power lines, pipe lines, telephone and telegraph lines, railroad tracks and rolling stock, ships and planes are made chiefly of metals. They are durable goods; they last for years, perhaps decades. To be sure, progress renders obsolescence inevitable and hence may call for renewal or change long before physical wear and tear demand it. Yet there is a tendency toward saturation in durable goods which is absent in the energy minerals. Even if not a single new machine or machine tool were built, if not another mile of rail or power line were laid, the need for energy minerals would continue almost unabated, because a machine without a constant supply of energy to drive it is dead, useless. Just as an individual may build himself only one house in a lifetime or buy only one car in a decade or one suit of clothes in a year but must eat every day—preferably several times—so the demand for metals for construction is far less continuous than the demand for fuels and other sources of energy.

Interdependence of Energy and Machine Resources. Higher temperatures demand furnaces built of materials capable of resisting such heat, and at the same time they render possible the production of better and stronger metals and alloys. Harnessing the concentrated amounts of energy generated by modern turbines requires stronger metals and alloys; these larger amounts of energy, in turn, are instrumental in providing the materials requisite to their own control. Coal fields are opened up and exploited with machine equipment, both

below and above ground; the coal, in turn, is needed to make the iron and steel and other metals which go into that machinery. Coal hoists and moves coal; steel helps to make more steel. Thus, the supplies of mineral fuels and machine materials must be viewed not as a dead mass of inert materials, but as parts belonging to a living organism that possesses dynamic powers of its own, even though they are subject to man's will and control.

Basic and Contributing Minerals

Functionally the minerals may be divided into basic and contributory minerals. The three basic minerals are coal, "the reducer and energizer," iron, "the harnesser and magnetizer," and copper, "the conductor of electrical energy." These three, "by combining and coordinating their peculiar properties, lay the foundations of human control of the forces of nature."[16] They are the star performers, behind which stands a strong supporting cast, the contributory minerals. Thus, petroleum and natural gas, although endowed with unique properties of their own, in general serve to supplement coal as the chief source of energy. Among other contributory minerals the ferro-alloys, particularly chromium, nickel, molybdenum, and manganese, deserve special mention. Although added in small—sometimes only minute—amounts, they materially affect and generally improve the character of iron and steel. Still other contributory minerals, especially platinum, function as catalysts, indispensable in chemical synthesis. The fertilizer minerals—potash, phosphate, and nitrate—form another group.

Expendable and Nonexpendable Minerals

Another important division is that between *expendable* and *nonexpendable* minerals, or, to be more accurate, between minerals having expendable and nonexpendable uses. Expendable minerals disappear in use; the nonexpendable do not. In fact, many metals are virtually indestructible. Generally speaking, the energy materials or fuels are expendable, and the machine materials or metals are not. Coal when burned ceases to exist as a solid; it disappears in the

---

[16] See W. H. Voskuil, *Minerals in Modern Industry,* John Wiley and Sons, Inc., New York, 1930, p. 23.

form of gases. Similarly, magnesium when used in flares and incendiary bombs is dissipated almost instantaneously. Other metals often survive in use. The precious metals, valued chiefly as the basis of credit and currency, as mediums of exchange and standards of value, are primarily nonexpendable. Gold is one of the most imperishable of metals. "Probably there is now in the Treasury vaults gold that was mined before America was discovered. There may well be there gold that passed as currency among the Romans, or was paid as tribute in Babylon."[17] Iron is much more destructible, although its lasting qualities can be much improved by alloys and paints and in other ways.

Perhaps it would be more accurate to speak of dissipative and nondissipative uses of minerals. For the expendability of a mineral depends largely on its use. Thus lead used in batteries may be re-used again and again, whereas lead in paint is dissipated, especially if used outdoors. Expendable minerals are definitely fund resources. Re-used minerals may be called revolving fund resources; they resemble flow resources.[18]

Metals and Nonmetallic Minerals

Probably the most widely used division of minerals is that between metals, fuels, and nonmetallic minerals other than fuels. The following list is not complete:

1. Metals
   a. General utility metals, long known to man—iron, copper, lead, zinc, tin, nickel, mercury.
   b. Light metals, relative newcomers on the scene, vital in the air age—aluminum, magnesium, titanium.
   c. Precious metals—gold, silver, platinum, palladium, etc.
   d. Metals used mainly for alloying, especially with iron—chromium, manganese, molybdenum, tungsten, vanadium, beryllium.
2. Fuels
   a. Coals—including anthracites, semibitu-

minous, bituminous, subbituminous, lignite, brown coal.
   b. Petroleum.
   c. Natural gas.
   d. Shale (potential source).
3. Nonmetallic minerals other than fuels
   a. Sulfur and pyrites—source of sulfuric acid.
   b. Nitrates, phosphates, and potash, the fertilizer trio.
   c. Fluorspar, dolomite, magnesite, cryolite; used largely as fluxes in metallurgical processes.
   d. Lime, limestone, chalk.
   e. Kaolin, china clay.
   f. Asbestos, mica, graphite, gypsum, etc., nonmetallic minerals having special uses.

USES OF IMPORTANT MINERALS

Our modern machine civilization is inconceivable without coal and iron. In a cruder form it could exist on these two basic minerals. (The lubricating oil that machines require could, if necessary, be distilled from coal.) For its higher development, however, a machine civilization requires additional materials. Printing presses need antimony; high-speed automatic machine tools depend on tungsten, vanadium, and chromium; without molybdenum, which gives steel the power to resist endlessly repeated shocks, automobiles would be less reliable; the electrical industry is unthinkable without copper, as is the canning industry without tin; catalysis calls for such agents as platinum or nickel; batteries require lead; no brass without zinc, no kodak films without silver; airplanes need aluminum, fountain pens call for iridium; aluminum reduction depends on carbon and cryolite, and so on, almost *ad infinitum*. If we consider electricity, gasoline engines, and aviation as essential features of our civilization, we would have to add copper, petroleum, and aluminum as indispensable prerequisites.

How great the dependence is on the so-called auxiliary minerals may well be illustrated by the telephone. From an interesting book published by the Western Electric Company, which manufactures telephone equipment, we learn that of all the raw materials required in the modern telephone system the following—all of them minerals—are essential: copper, iron

---

[17] H. F. Bain, "The Rise of Scrap Metals," in F. G. Tryon and E. C. Eckel (eds.), *Mineral Economics*, McGraw-Hill Book Company, Inc., New York, 1932, p. 161.

[18] See p. 82.

(e.g., soft iron for magnets); platinum (in switchboard lamps); gold, silver, platinum (a combination of these three goes into contact springs); lead (in cables and fuse wires); antimony (in the protective sheath covering cables and in condensers); tin (in solder, a lead and tin alloy); nickel (for plating to protect delicate parts against atmosphere, and for springs); zinc (for galvanizing iron to protect it from moisture and rust, and in brass); coal (granular carbon in transmitter is made from selected coal that must not exceed 1/100 cc. in size); aluminum (diaphragm); mica (as insulation in the transmitter); and asphalt (as a finishing on the transmitter and in cable terminals). No less than fourteen minerals!

Each of these metals is carefully selected because of its specific properties. The aim is always to produce the desired effect at the lowest cost; and, paradoxical as it may seem, the precious metals—gold, silver, and platinum —"are least expensive over a long period of time, for they resist the corrosive effect of the atmosphere which otherwise would in time put your telephone out of order."[19] Platinum is used in the switchboard lamps "because heat and cold affect it in about the same degree as glass and therefore the wires do not shrink away from the glass and let the air into the lamps."[20] Lead does not rust and it bends easily; hence the lead pipes and cables. Moreover, iron is often coated with lead paint to protect it against rust. The addition of 1 percent of antimony hardens lead and protects it against breaks and wear. Nickel resists the action of sulfuric and other acids and gives a smooth surface, agreeable to handle. Carbon translates the modulations of the human voice into varying electrical vibrations and thus makes voice transmission possible.

Interchangeability

While there are many cases in which no substitution can be made for the particular mineral called for, "to a surprising degree metals may be substituted for each other, and one will, when necessary, take on the work of another. They form a family group of sturdy

brothers."[21] Actual substitution, however, frequently involves an economic loss resulting from the sacrifice or nonuse of the peculiar and unique property. One should not conclude from the above quotation that petroleum may be substituted for coal in the same way that potatoes may be substituted for corn, or rye for wheat, or nuts for meat. The unique utility of petroleum rests on the low specific gravity of gasoline as an energy carrier. One can substitute crude oil for coal under a boiler, but in so doing he sacrifices the unique utility of petroleum. Vice versa, a high-grade coking coal possesses properties lacking in petroleum.

The extent to which, in actual practice, minerals are substituted one for another is largely a matter of price relation. Copper may be superior to aluminum as an electric conductor; but if, perhaps because of price manipulations, the price of copper is disproportionately high, aluminum may be substituted. Such a substitution may also be made if superiority in one respect overcompensates inferiority in other respects.

PECULIARITIES OF MINERALS

Although minerals are vital to modern industrial civilization, the literature on minerals and mineral economics is far more limited than that on agriculture. One of the first systematic attempts in the United States to compile what may be called the principles of mineral economics was made by the Brookings Institution in Washington and the Association of American Mining and Metallurgical Engineers.[22] This study listed four peculiarities of minerals as essential to an understanding of their nature.

1. Compared with the resources of agriculture, minerals are highly localized in occurrence and of strictly limited availability.[23]
2. Owing to the "hidden" nature of most minerals, their discovery is largely a matter of chance. This goes far to explain the speculative character of many mining enterprises. The risk is especially great in the case of the so-called "fugitive" minerals like oil and

---

[19] Western Electric Company, *From the Far Corners of the Earth*, p. 17.

[20] *Ibid.*, p. 15.

[21] H. F. Bain, "Place of Minerals in a Power-Controlled World," p. 7.

[22] F. G. Tryon and E. C. Eckel (eds.), *op. cit.* The famous classic, *Principles of Mining*, by former President Hoover should also be mentioned.

[23] Cf. chap. 11, especially p. 153.

gas. Uncertainty besets the discovery of new —supplementary or rival—deposits, as well as the extent and persistence of known deposits.

3. Mineral deposits are exhaustible. The continued exploitation of a mineral deposit is frequently accompanied by increasing difficulties which may be temporarily or partly neutralized by an improvement in the art of producing and utilizing minerals.

4. Most metals are durable and hence metal stocks tend to accumulate; the supply of these "secondary"[24] metals creates problems which are peculiar to the mining industry.

While these statements are valid and perhaps constitute as good an appraisal of the peculiarities of minerals as may be found, their interpretation must be based on reason.

SOME LEGAL ASPECTS OF MINING[25]

Mining laws vitally affect the manner, direction, and tempo of mineral developments. Modern mining laws, like all laws, are the outgrowth of a continued struggle between tradition and current needs. They reflect the history of a civilization, its present needs and its hopes for the future. Basic to an understanding of them are the concept of property rights and the facts of property holding.

While Roman law recognized unlimited irrevocable private property, in antiquity mining was carried on almost exclusively either by the state or by its concessionaires and lessees. On the other hand, Germanic law was feudal in its conception of real property. The "landowner" merely enjoyed the right of usufruct, i.e., the right to use the land for farming, homesteading, etc.; this right went no deeper than the plow. The king was the residual owner of the land; hence, subsoil mineral wealth underlying all the land, not merely the public domain, belonged to the crown and all mining was a "royal prerogative." But throughout the Middle Ages there prevailed in Germany the system of free mining under which prospecting for minerals was open to all and the principle of "finder's keeper's" applied to minerals discovered by successful prospectors. In the U.S.S.R., the means of production belong to the state; but this does not prevent the state from decreeing that the discoverer of a new mine is entitled to a concession covering its life. Thus, general concepts and principles of law are frequently at loggerheads with actual practice.

In actual practice mineral laws change with the times. In mercantilist days, marked by the strong power of absolute monarchs or by highly centralized state control, the tendency was toward royal prerogatives and state supervision. When liberalism became the dominant economic philosophy, with its faith in laissez faire and its emphasis on private property rights, individual enterprise, freedom of contract, etc., mining laws were liberalized. This trend was particularly noticeable during the early nineteenth century in both Germany and France when codified mining laws, first passed in the late eighteenth century, were radically revised to attract private capital into mining ventures. The state realized that if private capital was to flow freely into mining, not only must it keep hands off, but clear title had to be granted either in perpetuity or for several decades. The more capital is required for mining operations, the more are governments faced with the alternative of either taking on "the whole works" or granting the private risk taker adequate protection.

Under the Normans, Great Britain operated under the principle of royal prerogative; at first it applied only to gold and silver, but later it extended also to the ores of baser metals which contained gold and silver. The royal prerogative was later restricted to gold and silver. Since there were almost no deposits of these precious metals, the practical effect of these laws was to establish the principle that private property of the surface of the land reached down to the center of the earth and included all mineral wealth beneath this surface. Since after the Norman conquest much of the land in Great Britain was held in large blocks by powerful landlords who commanded considerable capital and in general were leaders of economic and cultural progress, the ancient controversy over the incompatibility of agricultural and mineral use of land never came up. For the really big landlord could easily

---

[24] Primary metals are obtained from the processing of ore; secondary metals are recovered from scrap.

[25] This section is based on Rudolf Isay, "Mining Laws," *Encyclopædia of the Social Sciences*, vol. 5, pp. 513-517.

combine the two functions without one interfering with the other. Had the land been held by large numbers of small farmers who had the right to forbid prospectors to trespass on their land—not to mention scarring it with holes—mining enterprises might have been seriously retarded by shifting the prerogative over mineral subsoil wealth from the crown or the state to private owners of the surface. As it was, the English surface ownership was such as to encourage rather than retard such enterprises.

Latin-American mining law basically follows the state-prerogative principle, but at times and in particular areas the dependence on foreign capital has led to considerable modifications. In fact, under Porfirio Diaz Mexico went so far as to shift by constitutional amendment from the state-prerogative principle to the principle of landowner control, at least so far as hydrocarbons were concerned. The Revolution of 1917 undid this legal legerdemain. In general, the trend in Latin America at the present time is neo-mercantilistic. The people are awakening to national consciousness and they look upon mineral wealth as a national and natural patrimony that is not to be sold like wares in the market place.

In Africa, which is largely colonial in status, the mining laws of the mother countries apply. In the Union of South Africa most of the mining areas are public domains. Asia, outside of the U.S.S.R., is very much in flux. In general, the trend is toward rising nationalism and away from colonialism.

The United States, the greatest mining country in the world, adheres to the principle of private landowner control over the subsoil mineral wealth. The situation is complicated by the fact that large areas of the country are in the public domain. Originally, the principle of state prerogative was applied. Thus, the ordinance of 1785 reserved to the federal government one-third of all gold, silver, lead, and copper from mines deeded by it in the public domain. In 1807, the lead mines of Missouri were specifi-

cally exempted from sale to private owners; only leases extending over brief periods were issued. The leasing system, however, proved unsatisfactory and outright sale was more and more resorted to. The law of 1866 abolished royalty payments to the government even by mines operating in the public domain. Now a prospector who has made a strike merely stakes out his claim, reports it to the authorities, receives a "possessory claim," and after working the claim for a stipulated period acquires title to the mine.[26]

In fact, in the United States the encouragement of private prospecting and mining has pushed even beyond the limits generally applied to the rights of private landowners. Two examples come to mind. Under the "rule of capture" (see p. 533) the owner of an oil well is legally entitled to whatever petroleum he can draw up through his well without regard to the limits of his surface property rights. In the mining of solid minerals, so-called extralateral rights permit the owner of a lode claim to pursue beyond his own boundaries into adjacent plots a vein whose apex is located within his own plot.

The United States at this period of history appears to be the last stronghold of free capitalistic enterprise. Her militancy seems to grow as her unique position in a world of rising socialism and spreading communism becomes increasingly clear. The controversy regarding the mineral rights over the continental shelf (see p. 505) is a case in point. The survival of the system, however, would seem to hinge less on the militancy of its proponents than on ability to divest it of abuses and to demonstrate its superiority by actual performance.

---

[26] During the hearings before the subcommittee of the Committee on Public Lands, May 15, 16, and 20, 1947, the issue was raised whether this simple procedure was still adequate under modern scientific prospecting covering huge areas. A new law was prepared in the Bureau of Mines, but has not yet been submitted to the Congress for action.

BIBLIOGRAPHY

Army Service Forces Manual, M 101-103, Army Service Forces, Washington, 1943-1944.

Bain, H. F., "Place of Minerals in a Power-Con-

trolled World," Berlin, Second World Power Conference, 1930.

Bain, H. F., "The Rise of Scrap Metals," in Tryon,

F. G., and Eckel, E. C. (eds.), *Mineral Economics*, New York, McGraw-Hill, 1932.

Bain, H. F., *Ores and Industry in the Far East*, New York, Council on Foreign Relations, 1933.

Barger, H., and Schurr, S. H., *The Mining Industries, 1899-1939*, New York, National Bureau of Economic Research, 1944.

Bateman, A. M., *Economic Mineral Deposits*, New York, Wiley, 2nd ed., 1950.

Bosqui, F. L., "Twenty Years Progress in Flotation," *Minerals and Metals*, November, 1940.

Bureau of Mines, *Minerals Yearbook*, Washington, U. S. Department of Interior (annual).

Cates, L. S., and Bancroft, H., "Techniques of Mineral Exploitation of the Future," in Parsons, A. B. (ed.), *Seventy-five Years of Progress in the Mineral Industry 1871-1946*, New York, American Institute of Mining and Metallurgical Engineers, 1947.

DeMille, J. B., *Strategic Minerals*, New York, McGraw-Hill, 1947.

Dolbear, S. H., and Bowles, O., *Industrial Minerals and Rocks*, New York, American Institute of Mining and Metallurgical Engineers, 1949.

Eaton, L., "Seventy-five Years of Progress in Metal Mining," in Parsons, A. B. (ed.), *Seventy-five Years of Progress in the Mineral Industry 1871-1946*, New York, American Institute of Mining and Metallurgical Engineers, 1947.

Elliott, W. Y., and others, *International Control in the Non-ferrous Metals*, New York, Macmillan, 1937.

Finley, J. R., *The Cost of Mining*, New York, McGraw-Hill, 2nd ed., 1910.

Fraser, C. E., and Doriot, G. E., *Analysing Our Industries*, New York, McGraw-Hill, 1932.

Hewett, D. F., "Cycles in Metal Production," Technical Publication No. 183, New York, American Institute of Mining and Metallurgical Engineers, 1929.

Holmes, H. N., *Strategic Materials and National Strength*, New York, Macmillan, 1942.

Hoover, H. C., *Principles of Mining*, New York, McGraw-Hill, 1912.

Isay, R., "Mining Laws," *Encyclopædia of the Social Sciences*, New York, Macmillan, 1932.

Jeffries, Z., "Metals and Alloys of the Future," in Parsons, A. B. (ed.), *Seventy-five Years of Progress in the Mineral Industry 1871-1946*, American Institute of Mining and Metallurgical Engineers, 1947.

Kiessling, O. E., and Corry, A. W., *Mineral Technology and Output Per Man Studies*, National Research Project on Reemployment Opportunities, Report E-6, Philadelphia, Works Progress Administration, 1937.

Killough, H. B., and L. W., *Raw Materials of Industrialism*, New York, Crowell, 1929.

Leith, C. K., *Economic Aspects of Geology*, New York, Holt, 1921.

Leith, C. K., Furness, H. W., and Lewis, C., *World Minerals and World Peace*, Washington, Brookings Institution, 1943.

Lovering, T. S., *Minerals in World Affairs*, New York, Prentice-Hall, 1943.

Marcus, A., "Metals (modern)," *Encyclopædia of the Social Sciences*, New York, Macmillan, 1932.

Mersereau, S. F., *Materials of Industry*, New York, McGraw-Hill, 1941.

Parsons, A. B., "Metals and Fuels: The World Has Enough," *Journal of the Franklin Institute*, June, 1945.

Parsons, A. B. (ed.), *Seventy-five Years of Progress in the Mineral Industry 1871-1946*, New York, American Institute of Mining and Metallurgical Engineers, 1947.

Pehrson, E. W., "Seventy-five Years of Progress in Mineral Production: the Statistical Record," in Parsons, A. B. (ed.), *Seventy-five Years of Progress in the Mineral Industry 1871-1946*, New York, American Institute of Mining and Metallurgical Engineers, 1947.

Read, T. T., *Our Mineral Civilization*, Baltimore, Williams and Wilkins, 1932.

Rickard, T. A., *Men and Metals*, New York, McGraw-Hill, 2 vols., 1932.

Rickard, T. A., *History of American Mining*, New York, McGraw-Hill, 1932.

Rickard, T. A., *Romance of Mining*, Montreal, Macmillan, 1944.

Rogers, H. O., and Tryon, F. G., "Mining," *Encyclopædia of the Social Sciences*, New York, Macmillan, 1932.

Roush, G. A., *Strategic Mineral Supplies*, New York, McGraw-Hill, 1939.

Royal Institute of International Affairs, *Raw Materials*, Information Department, Papers, No. 18a, 1939.

Royal Institute of International Affairs, *World Production of Raw Materials*, New York, Oxford University Press, 1941.

Salzmann, L. F., "Metals," *Encyclopædia of the Social Sciences*, New York, Macmillan, 1932.

Sampson, E., "Mineral Resources and International Strife," Princeton University, Alumni Lectures, 1938.

Simonds, F. H., and Emeny, B., *The Great Powers in World Politics*, New York, American Book, 1939.

Spurr, J. E., *Political and Commercial Geology*, New York, McGraw-Hill, 1920.

Spurr, J. E., and Wormser, F. E., *The Marketing*

of Metals and Minerals, New York, McGraw-Hill, 1925.

"The Race for Metals," *Fortune,* March, 1942.

Thom, W. T., Jr., *Petroleum and Coal, the Keys to the Future,* Princeton, Princeton University Press, 1929.

Tryon, F. G., and Eckel, E. C. (eds.), *Mineral Economics,* New York, McGraw-Hill, 1932.

Tryon, F. G., and Mann, L., "Mineral Resources for Future Populations," in Dublin, L. I. (ed.), *Population Problems,* Boston, Houghton Mifflin, 1926.

Tryon, F. G., and Schoenfeld, M. H., "Mineral and Power Resources," in *Recent Social Trends in the United States,* New York, McGraw-Hill, 1933, chap. 2.

Tryon, F. G., Heald, K. C., Read, T. T., and Rice, C. S., *Technology and the Mineral Industries,* Philadelphia, Works Progress Administration, 1937.

Tyler, P., *From the Ground Up,* New York, McGraw-Hill, 1948.

U. S. Military Academy, Department of Economics, History, and Political Science, *Raw Materials in War and Peace,* West Point, U. S. Military Academy, 1947.

Van Wagenen, T. F., *International Mining Law,* New York, McGraw-Hill, 1918.

Vosburgh, F. G., "Metal Sinews of Strength," *National Geographic Magazine,* April, 1942.

Voskuil, W. H., *Minerals in Modern Industry,* New York, Wiley, 1930.

Wallace, D. H., and Edminster, L. R., *International Control of Raw Materials,* Washington, Brookings Institution, 1930.

Yeatman, P., and others, *Choice of Methods in Mining and Metallurgy,* New York, McGraw-Hill, 1932.

Chapter 25

MINERAL RESERVES

THE SPECTER OF MINERAL EXHAUSTION

The most disconcerting feature of minerals is their exhaustibility. They are wasting assets. They are completely consumed in use if they are fuels; they are at least partially dissipated if they are minerals other than fuels. Therefore, the questions, "How large are the reserves? How much is left in the ground? What will happen when it is gone?" are vital, questions of life and death. For ours is truly a mineral civilization, a civilization which stands and falls on its capacity to produce staggering amounts of some minerals and varying quantities of many others.

One does not necessarily have to think of the end of all human civilization to feel deep concern over the approaching exhaustion of minerals, some sooner, others later. Even if atomic energy, directly as a substitute for the mineral fuels, and indirectly through the transmutation of elements, thus providing a source of metals and other minerals, could create a new basis on which to rebuild our civilization, we should still be facing the end of our particular brand of civilization and the colossal task of building a new one on an entirely different foundation.

There is no country on earth which owes more to minerals than does the United States. If, today, she is the richest and the most powerful nation of all, that position of pre-eminence to a large degree is due to the fact that we produce about half the coal, almost two-thirds of the petroleum and most of the natural gas, between half and two-thirds of the steel, and almost half the copper that are drawn annually from this planet; and that, in addition, we produce a host of other minerals and have access to virtually any mineral for sale anywhere on the globe, with the possible exception of the U.S.S.R. and her satellites. Moreover, there is no country on earth which has allowed its material culture and way of life to become as completely dependent on an uninterrupted flow of minerals as we have. Our proudest scientific achievements are tied up with minerals. Our greatest successes in business rest on a profligate use of minerals. Our military and naval prowess derives largely from unequaled control over, and use of, minerals. No country, therefore, is more vitally concerned over the question of mineral exhaustion than the United States.

At present there is much confusion about

this problem. On the one hand people read such headlines as: "Our petroleum reserves good for only 13 more years." "In a few years we'll scrape the bottom of our lead mines." "Copper will be gone in less than twenty years," and so forth. On the other hand they are told that there is nothing to worry about; that we are producing more oil than ever before. What is more, if we should run out of oil there is coal and shale from which to extract more oil; if our metal reserves are gone the scientists will find substitutes as good as they were, if not better. Faith in the new bonanza of science, the eternal horn of plenty!

So the people—that is, intelligent, thinking people—are bewildered. Their worry over the future may gnaw on their minds, but, not understanding the situation, they cannot decide what precautions or remedial measures to adopt.

TERMINOLOGY

In discussing the adequacy of mineral raw materials a number of terms recur again and again. Their exact meaning must be firmly grasped if misunderstandings are to be avoided. Among the most important are deposits, ores, reserves, and resources.

Deposits

Deposits is a natural science term pertaining to physical facts, to "neutral stuff." It fits into the physical inventory approach. Knowledge of deposits, i.e., of physical presence, must precede all appraisal of adequacy of reserves or availability of resources.

Ores

The concept of ore is totally different.[1] It is functional. It reflects the findings of the economic geologist and the mining engineer who report to their employer on the feasibility of profitable operation. Ores are those parts of deposits that pay exploitation. Two different aspects are involved, technical feasibility and profitableness. Two questions are asked and answered: Can we do it—do we possess the necessary knowledge, technique, skill, know-

how? Will it pay—is it worth the investment in equipment, machinery, working capital?

Since both costs and prices fluctuate seasonally, cyclically, and secularly as well as fortuitously, it follows that ores are a most elusive concept—"Now you see it, now you don't." If *costs* remain constant, a mining concern is apt to have more ore when the *price* of its product goes up. If *prices* are constant, the firm can write up its ore holdings if a technical innovation or some other development reduces *costs*.

Inasmuch as both costs and prices move up and down, the concept of ore may be rendered more realistic if one imagines the actual, currently "paying" ore body to be surrounded by imaginary layers of subores or near-ores, meaning additional segments of the deposit which are bound to become ore if either prices rise or costs go down; naturally the process works also in reverse. In this connection, it makes little difference how the terms subores and near-ores are used. Beyond the subores and near-ores lies the non-ore, the part of the deposit which, *at the prevailing state of the arts and at prices and costs within the range of reasonable expectation,* cannot be mined at a profit. The term "prevailing state of the arts" in this case is to be interpreted loosely to include reasonable improvements, but it does include revolutionary technical discoveries not now foreseen.[2]

In its customary usage the term ore refers only to metal-bearing minerals. One speaks of iron ore, copper ore, lead ore, etc., or of argentiferous, i.e., silver-bearing, ore. Strictly defined, a silver ore is one that is exploited for the sake of silver; silver is the economic determinant that justifies the term ore. Argentiferous ore, on the other hand, may be exploited for metals other than silver, or for silver. Some complex ores yield several pay metals none of

---

[1] See Alan M. Bateman, *Economic Mineral Deposits,* John Wiley & Sons, Inc., New York, 1942. pp. 22 ff. A second edition was published in 1950.

[2] It should be understood that the functional appraisal is itself relative to the yardsticks of time and space that are applied. If the appraisal of mineral adequacy is conceived in terms of years, the concepts used need to be interpreted somewhat differently from the way they would be in an appraisal covering decades or longer. Similarly, the criteria suitable to the present analysis vary with the size of the area under investigation, as for example whole nations or the properties of individual operators.

which alone warrants exploitation but which in combination yield a rewarding aggregate return.

One does not speak of coal ore or petroleum ore or marble ore or fluorspar ore. The reason is that these are mined as coal, petroleum, marble, fluorspar, etc., and not as ingredients in chemical compounds. The chemical compounds themselves constitute the commodities. If dirt containing from 1 to 70 percent coal were mined, it might conceivably be called coal ore. But what miners mine is coal, coal as pure as it can be extracted. The metallurgist is after iron, copper, lead, zinc, in the purest possible form. Usually the only way he can get these pure metals is by extracting them with the aid of fire or by other means from ores, i.e., compounds carrying among many other ingredients the metal he wants. Petroleum is expelled by gas pressure from the "sand" or rock in which it occurs or brought to the surface by pumping. The sand or rock itself is not mined. If it were, it might perhaps give rise to the term oil ore.

In the case of fuels and nonmetallic minerals, the counterpart to the term ore, which is largely confined to metal-bearing mineral compounds, is such terms as mineable coal, workable oil sands, commercial grades of phosphate rock, etc.

Reserves

Probably the greatest confusion arises in connection with the use of the word reserves because of the many meanings this term has. There are several approaches in terms of which the discussion of the word may be presented.

The Physical Inventory Approach. In seeking an answer to the question of how long our minerals will last, it seems logical to inquire into their physical occurrence. In what amounts do minerals occur in the earth's crust?

By the earth's crust is meant a surface layer ten miles deep that includes the hydrosphere (the ocean) and the lithosphere (the land). No one knows the exact composition of this crust, but scientists have made conjectures as to what it should be in the light of certain known facts and assumptions. Table 25.1 lists 32 elements and the percentage of each that the earth's crust is supposed to contain. These 32 elements make up somewhat more than

half the weight of the crust as defined above. Much of the remainder is taken up by oxygen, which is supposed to constitute about 46.59 percent of the weight of the crust.

What strikes the eye immediately and forcibly is the wide difference in rare and abundant metals. Silicon is 277,200,000 times as abundant as gold. Aluminum is 813 times as abundant as copper and 4065 times as abundant as lead. Magnesium is 20,900 times as abundant as tin. Evidently, there is such a thing as absolute scarcity; there simply is very little of certain elements in the crust of the earth.

TABLE 25.1. Content of the Crust of the Earth, Including the Lithosphere and the Hydrosphere, in Percentage of Sundry Elements[3]

Silicon	27.720	Tungsten	0.005
Aluminum	8.130	Lithium	0.004
Iron	5.010	Zinc	0.004
Calcium	3.630	Columbium and	
Sodium	2.850	tantalum	0.003
Potassium	2.600	Hafnium	0.003
Magnesium	2.090	Lead	0.002
Titanium	0.630	Cobalt	0.001
Manganese	0.100	Boron	0.001
Barium	0.050	Beryllium	0.001
Chromium	0.037	Molybdenum	0.0001
Zirconium	0.026	Arsenic	0.0001
Nickel	0.020	Tin	0.0001
Vanadium	0.017	Mercury	0.00001
Gerium and		Silver	0.000001
yttrium	0.015	Selenium	0.000001
Copper	0.010	Gold	0.0000001[a]

[a] This is equivalent to 24,500,000,000 tons of gold.

Functional or Operational Approach.[4] How realistic is it to count on man's ability to exploit minerals that lie ten miles below the land surface? To point out that oil wells already reach a depth of more than 20,000 feet and that mining at depths three or four times greater is

---

[3] A. B. Parsons, "Metals and Fuels: The World Has Enough," *Journal of the Franklin Institute*, June, 1945, pp. 437-444. The figures in this table are based on the calculations of F. W. Clarke, of the U.S. Geological Survey.

[4] One of the best expositions of this approach is found in *The Mineral Position of the United States*, a report prepared by the joint staffs of the U.S. Geological Survey and the Bureau of Mines and published as an appendix to the hearings before a Subcommittee of the Committee on Public Lands, United States Senate, Eightieth Congress, First Session, 1947, pp. 186-187.

therefore within the realm of the feasible seems to reveal a bit more than ordinary optimism. After all, are not petroleum and natural gas unique among the minerals in that they propel themselves up to the surface under their own pressure? Cannot oil be pumped up by machines or the pressure be restored when the original gas pressure is gone? And are not almost all the other minerals solids[5] which must be pried from their underground location and brought to the surface by men working below ground? And do not pressure and temperature rise rapidly as deeper layers of the earth's crust are tapped? At present, the bulk of the solid minerals are obtained from a rather thin upper crust; relatively few miners in the world work at levels below a few thousand feet.[6]

At best, the percentage distribution of minerals in the earth's crust to a depth of ten miles is of purely academic interest; it hardly belongs in the realm of workaday realities. Since this distribution can hardly be uniform, the practical appraiser of mineral reserves would have to know something, in fact a great deal, about how the minerals are distributed at the various depths. If all the gold were concentrated in the top 100-foot layer and all the aluminum lay at a depth of 9 miles or more, Table 25.1 would be dangerously misleading. The supply ratio of 81,300,000 to 1 for the two metals would have no practical meaning—at least not for a very long time to come.

Not only is vertical or *geological* distribution, in the sense of distribution *in depth*, of great significance for the practical meaning of data on the minerals in the earth's crust, but horizontal or *geographical* distribution is equally important. If the Pittsburgh coal bed were located in the Antarctic it would still be untouched by human hands instead of having helped to shape the economic destiny of North America. If the equivalent of the Pittsburgh coal bed were within hailing distance of the Itabira iron deposits of Minas Geraes, Brazil might today, perhaps in partnership with other sections of South America, occupy an economic and political place similar to that held by the United States.

Finally, careful attention must be given the *qualitative* aspects of mineralization. Few elements ever occur in the pure state; they occur as compounds physically and chemically combined. Moreover, such mineral compounds are generally found in an admixture of impurities, called gangue or waste. Thus a lead ore will contain (1) gangue or waste materials, and (2) lead ore minerals such as galena (PbS), cerussite ($PbCO_3$), or anglesite ($PbSo_4$). This means that the ore mineral must first be separated from the gangue, and then the metal must be separated from the other elements with which it is chemically compounded. The nature of the compounds and the character of the impurities, both physically and chemically considered, go far to determine the availability of minerals for human use.

In the final analysis, the question of the adequacy of mineral reserves is merely a phase of the broader question of the adequacy of all reserves. Seen in this light, the analysis of mineral reserves is merely an illustration of the fundamental principles underlying the functional nature of resources which constitutes the central theme of this book. Just as resources emerge from the totality of "neutral stuff"—in response to human needs and human abilities —so the availability of minerals for human use not only depends on physical presence but is also a function of human needs and wants and the willingness and capacity to pay for them, on the one hand, and of human abilities, the state of the arts, the supply of capital, labor skills, know-how, scientific personnel, etc., on the other.

Whether one thinks in terms of prices and costs expressed in monetary units or in more basic terms such as the intensity of man's need for minerals and his physical, mental, spiritual capacity to meet this need, the final answer to the question regarding the world's reserves of mineral raw materials is the same. Intensity of need and the state of the arts largely determine to what depth the crust of the earth can be exploited, what use can be made of the sea and the air. The physical make-up—the original natural as well as the man-affected make-up—of that particular horizontal segment of the crust which at a given time is subject to

---

[5] The process of gasifying coal *in situ* is still in the experimental stage.

[6] In chap. 26 it will be shown that the bulk of the coal produced in the United States comes from deposits less than 200 feet below ground and most of it does not require shaft mining.

human exploitation sets the outer limits to the production of virgin earth materials. But the portion of that maximum that is actually available for human use is a matter of cost and price, these terms being used as symbols of capacity to produce and of intensity of demand.

It follows that the appraisal of mineral reserves, as of all resources, cannot proceed along the lines of a physical inventory alone but must follow operational methods. A realistic analysis rests on the perfectly simple principle, "The proof of the pudding is the eating." How much "pudding" mankind eats ultimately may depend on social organization and capacity, the solution of the broad social and political issues of war and peace, even more than on the state of natural science and the progress of engineering and chemical industries.

Company Reserves and National Reserves. The meaning of the word reserve differs somewhat with the mineral to which it applies; it varies with the general frame of reference within which it is used. Thus, when one speaks of the iron ore reserves of the United States Steel Corporation, he uses the word in one sense; when he speaks of the iron ore reserves of the United States, the meaning is different. A corporation knows reasonably well what its ore reserves are. It must know, if its long-term investment problems are to be tackled intelligently. A steelworks is no stronger than its accessible raw-material supply, and this generally means, or at least includes, the ore supply. But no one knows what the mineral reserves of the United States are. Many parts of the country have never been surveyed adequately and thoroughly. Much of what surveying was done was superficial, relying largely on outcroppings. Little countries like Belgium or Holland can be surveyed, but to survey countries the size of the United States or the U.S.S.R. or Brazil is so huge a task that it has not yet been done successfully. The only way it can be done is slowly, piecemeal, the most promising area first, and so on. National reserves, therefore, are largely a matter of conjecture. At least their determination rests on conjecture to a higher degree than do private corporate reserves.

In general, in the United States mineral prospecting and mining are left to private enterprise. This has two significant implications for the state of knowledge concerning mineral reserves. In the first place, it means that the area chosen for prospecting depends on the private profit interests of individuals. Private prospecting is excellent so far as it goes, but it is not likely to lead to a systematic survey of the entire country. In the second place, in many instances, the private individual who has discovered valuable deposits has acquired valuable knowledge which he is loath to share with others for fear of competitors and interlopers. Even the government is often kept in the dark, with the result that there are big gaps in whatever systematic geological surveys are being attempted.

These remarks apply by no means uniformly to the entire field of minerals. The present system works exceptionally well in the case of petroleum. So unquenchable is the thirst for petroleum, so stupendous are the rewards an oil-thirsty world pays those who meet this imperative and still expanding need, that private exploitation has been carried on with as much expediency and ingenuity and on as large a scale as could be hoped for under any system. Indeed, it is doubtful whether any other system would have worked as well.

The situation is totally different in the case of certain strategic minerals such as tungsten. In normal times private enterprises can buy tungsten ores at relatively low prices from China and other countries. Private business has no particular interest in national self-sufficiency in times of emergency; the interests dependent on an ample supply of cheap tungsten far outweigh those concerned about the exploring and exploiting of domestic deposits. In such cases governmental initiative and expenditure can pay handsome dividends, as the experience of World War II showed. The way the present system works depends largely on the extent to which dominant private profit-seeking interests happen to coincide or conflict with the nation's interest in finding out about its mineral reserves. In general, the knowledge of mineral reserves varies inversely with the size of the area under study, the time which the study is to cover, and in particular with the funds available for the study.

Reserves of Specific Minerals. The meaning of the reserves also varies with the mineral to which it applies. For example, reserves mean one thing to the man interested in aluminum or magnesium, of which there is a generous supply in nature and whose exhaustibility or abundance depends chiefly upon the ingenuity of the technologist, and another thing to the man interested in copper, lead, or zinc, the known supply of which is more measurably finite. They mean something else to the man interested in tin or quartz crystals, of which the United States has virtually none, or to the man interested in such by-product metals as cadmium, bismuth, or silver.

A comparison between coal reserves and petroleum reserves will throw further light on this question. Fairly complete studies of the coal reserves of the United States have been made by the U. S. Geological Survey, and government agencies in other countries have reported their coal reserves.[7] The coal deposits recorded do not, as a rule, go beyond a depth of 3000 feet. The determination of their contour and general character is not a particularly difficult task for the geologist. Hence, our general knowledge of coal reserves is fairly complete though probably not too reliable. At any rate when one speaks of coal reserves of the United States he means total reserves.

The situation with regard to petroleum reserves is totally different. For one thing, the petroleum industry is a much younger industry. Furthermore, the demand for oil is so dynamic that even huge exploitation efforts costing many millions could hardly keep up with it; new methods of exploration had to be developed. Vast amounts had to be spent on exploration both by large corporations engaged in more or less all the phases of the petroleum business and by wildcatters whom the hope of chance discoveries lured into the twilight zone of uncertain stratification.

But all that these gigantic efforts can hope to accomplish is to assure the refining companies a certain margin of safety by supplying the increasing amounts of the crude oil needed to meet the insatiable demand for petroleum products. Thus, while national coal reserves presumably are *total* reserves, national oil reserves are only *proved* reserves, i.e., working reserves that are blocked out for current and immediately prospective needs. At best, the

explorers manage to keep between ten and twenty years ahead of production.[8]

Measured, Indicated, and Inferred Reserves. When attempts are made to ascertain mineral reserves on a scale more ambitious than determining proved working reserves (as of petroleum), it is of the utmost importance to indicate clearly the intensity and degree of accuracy of the work. For this reason, the U. S. Geological Survey and the U. S. Bureau of Mines differentiate between measured, indicated, and inferred reserves, suggesting a decreasing scale of accuracy and trustworthiness.[9] Here are the definitions given for these three categories:

Measured reserves are those for which tonnage is compared from dimensions revealed in outcrops, trenches, workings, and drill holes and for which the grade is computed from the results of detailed sampling. The sites for inspection, sampling, and measurement are spaced so closely and the geologic character is so well defined that size, shape, and mineral content are well established. The computed tonnage and grade are judged to be accurate within limits which are stated, and no such limit is judged to be different from the computed tonnage or grade by more than 20 percent.

Indicated reserves are those for which tonnage and grade are computed partly from specific measurements, samples, or production data and partly from projection for a reasonable distance on geologic evidence. The sites available for inspection, measurement, and sampling are too widely or otherwise inappropriately spaced to permit the mineral bodies to be outlined completely or the grade established throughout.

Inferred reserves are those for which quantitative estimates are based largely on broad knowledge of the geologic character of the deposit and for which there are few, if any, samples or measurements. The estimates are based on an assumed continuity or repetition, of which there is geologic evidence; this evidence may include comparison with deposits of similar type. Bodies that are completely concealed may be included if there is specific geologic evidence of their presence. Estimates of in-

---

[7] As will be brought out later, these surveys are proving less reliable than they were long considered to be. See pp. 461 ff.

[8] This will be developed further; see pp. 506 ff.

[9] Conceivably this method could be applied to petroleum, as, in fact, in a sense, it is; but the popular saying, "Oil is where you find it," still contains more than a germ of truth. The best that can be done for petroleum is to block out areas where oil cannot be found, where it may possibly be found, and where it probably will be found.

ferred reserves should include a statement of the special limits within which the inferred material may lie.[10]

This distinction between measured, indicated, and inferred reserves becomes increasingly important as prospecting is carried on, on a larger scale, not only by private corporations interested in a specific locality but also by agencies charged with plotting the nation's general reserve position with regard to selected materials, especially the critical and strategic minerals. If the degree of national sufficiency in minerals is to be ascertained, it will be impossible to wait for detailed reports on every locality, for the task could never be done in time to meet the need for information in an emergency. A certain amount of estimating and deducing on the basis of all the scientific data available must supplement accurate measurements based on drilling and similar exact procedures.

Reserves and Governmental Control. In peacetime available reserves are also known as commercial reserves in capitalistic countries because availability is measured by commercial standards, i.e., in terms of profitableness reckoned in money. But in war, when victory and the lives of many hinge on certain mineral supplies, the cost-price relationship drops more or less out of sight and availability becomes a matter of geological realities and of technical proficiency, scientific know-how, and availability of capital and labor determined not by a free and automatic market but by government decree. Under these conditions the government takes a hand in mineral procurement, either by subsidies to private enterprise or by direct participation in prospecting, mining, and processing.

To some extent, this applies even in a "cold" war. When peace hangs delicately balanced, considerations of national security demand that mineral reserve problems be approached not solely from the standpoint of business profit but also with due regard to their vital significance for national security. In some countries, especially those with totalitarian governments, the thought of impending war is so ever-present

that mere commercial considerations never determine the appraisal of reserves.

To assume, however, that in such countries availability is merely a matter of technological feasibility applied to existing physical endow-

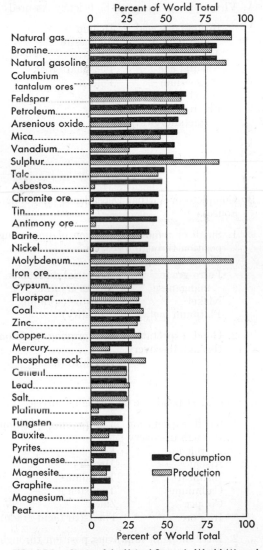

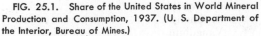

FIG. 25.1. Share of the United States in World Mineral Production and Consumption, 1937. (U. S. Department of the Interior, Bureau of Mines.)

ment—with due regard, of course, to depletion by use—overlooks the important fact that even in totalitarian states labor and capital equipment are "scarce," in the sense of being limited, and that even there a choice must be made between competing and conflicting uses. The

---

[10] *The Mineral Position of the United States*, p. 185.

TABLE 25.2. Mineral Position of the United States[a]—Actual, Impending, and Potential[11]

Actual and Impending Position[b]	Potential Position[c]

A. Virtual Long-Time Self-Sufficiency Assured

Bituminous coal	Helium
and lignite	Magnesite
Anthracite	Nitrates
Natural gas	Phosphate rock
Magnesium	Potash
Molybdenum	Salt
Fluorspar	Sulfur
(metallurgical)	

A. Virtual Self-Sufficiency

Bituminous coal	Titanium
and lignite	Vanadium
Anthracite	Fluorspar (all grades)
Natural gas	Graphite (flake)
Petroleum	Helium
Aluminum ores	Magnesite
Copper	Nitrates
Iron ore	Phosphate rock
Magnesium	Potash
Manganese	Salt
Molybdenum	Sulfur

B. Complete or Virtual Dependence on Foreign Sources

1. Small or remote expectation of improving position through discovery

Chromite	Tin
Ferro-grade	Industrial diamonds
manganese	Quartz crystals
Nickel[d]	Asbestos (spinning
Platinum metals	quality)

2. Good expectation of improving position through discovery

Cobalt[d]	Graphite (flake)

B. Complete or Virtual Dependence on Foreign Sources

Platinum metals	Quartz crystals
Tin	Asbestos (spinning
Industrial	quality)
diamonds	

C. Partial Dependence on Foreign Sources

1. Good expectation of improving position through discovery

Petroleum	Lead
Arsenic[d]	Mercury
Bismuth[d]	Tantalum[d]
Cadmium[d]	Tungsten
Copper	Zinc
Iron ore	Fluorspar (acid-grade)

2. Little hope of improving position through discovery

Antimony	High-grade bauxite
Vanadium	Strategic mica

C. Partial Dependence on Foreign Sources

Antimony	Mercury
Arsenic	Nickel
Bismuth	Tantalum
Cadmium	Tungsten
Cobalt	Zinc
Chromite	Strategic mica
Lead	

[a] Based on known "commercial" reserves, outlook for noteworthy discovery, and the possibility that known submarginal resources can be made available by technological progress and improved economic conditions.
[b] Based on present technological and economic conditions and on known "commercial" reserves.
[c] Dependent on whether technological and economic changes permit the use of known submarginal resources.
[d] Domestic production chiefly a by-product.

[11] *Mineral Position of the United States*, p. 183.

commercial appraisal in terms of money cost and money price implies this consideration of the relative scarcity of labor and capital, and cost and price figures reflect it. In totalitarian planning these factors must be measured in more direct fashion. But to appraise mineral reserves without regard to available manpower and capital equipment would be a fatal error.

MINERAL POSITION OF THE UNITED STATES

The foregoing discussion of the terminological and other problems of appraising mineral reserves is intended to provide a basis for estimating and understanding the mineral position of the countries of the earth. Because the United States is the leading producer and consumer of minerals and because her mineral-based economy is the largest and most vital element in the world economy today, that country is selected to illustrate the methods and problems of appraising a nation's mineral position.

Although the claim as to the supremacy of the United States hardly needs proof, statistics in support of it are presented in Fig. 25.1. In spite of the fact that later data would accentuate this preëminence, the year 1937 was chosen as being the last year before World War II in which world conditions had a semblance of normalcy. The fact that modern industry rests on minerals makes it axiomatic that the country whose total industrial output is probably almost as large as that of the rest of the world put together must produce and absorb a very large share of the minerals produced in the world.

No country, however, is completely self-sufficient as regards minerals; even the United States position shows definite gaps and deficiencies. Thus she is totally or virtually lacking in the following minerals:

Metals
Chromite
Ferro-grade manganese
Nickel
Platinum metals
Tin
Nonmetals
Asbestos (spinning quality)
Industrial diamonds
Quartz crystals

This list includes some of the most vital raw materials in peace or war. Ferro-grade manganese is essential to steel production. Tin is a key commodity of our food economy. Quartz crystals are vital to modern communication, especially in time of war.

If the minerals which the United States produces in respectable amounts but for which she is partially dependent on the outside are added, the list becomes considerably longer.

Antimony	Mercury
Arsenic	Strategic mica
Bismuth	Tantalum
Cadmium	Tungsten
Cobalt	Zinc
Lead	

There are others which she had to import in the past, but her domestic supply of them may be expected to increase as a result of technological progress and such inducements as higher prices, subsidies, etc. Table 25.2 gives a bird's-eye view of the mineral position of the United States, actual and potential.

Mineral Imports

The United States is a heavy importer of minerals. The countries from which the bulk of these imports are procured are listed in Table 25.3. Canada and Latin-American countries are italicized to bring out their dominance as sources of our mineral imports.

A comparison of the 1937 and 1943 alignment of sources reflects the effect of World War II—in particular, the concentration on nearby sources, the elimination of Japanese-occupied areas, the elimination of purchases from countries such as Belgium and the United Kingdom which normally act as go-betweens in the sale of the products of their colonial possessions and of other areas.

Our dependence on foreign sources for our mineral supplies is affected by several factors, one of which is the distance of the foreign source. Fortunately, the two neighboring countries are important sources of minerals. Canada leads the world as a producer of nickel and asbestos, and promises to become a major source of iron ore; she is also important as a producer of bismuth, cadmium, copper, lead, zinc, and the platinum metals, as well as gold and silver and fissionable materials. Mexico produces copper, lead, zinc, antimony, and bismuth, as well as silver and gold. Of our

TABLE 25.3.   Foreign Sources of Mineral Supplies of the United States, 1937 and 1943[12]
(Percentages are approximate.)

	1937	1943
Antimony	*Mexico* (63%), *Chile, Bolivia, Argentina*	*Bolivia, Mexico, Peru*
Asbestos	*Canada* (80%)	*Canada* (90%), South Africa
Bauxite (high grade)	*Surinam* (78%), *British Guiana* (15%)	*Surinam* (76%), *British Guiana* (22%)
Cadmium	Scattered sources	Belgian Congo (78%), *Peru* (22%)
Copper	*Chile, Mexico, Peru, Canada*	*Chile* (68%), Belgian Congo, *Mexico, Peru*
Industrial diamonds	Belgium, United Kingdom, Union of South Africa, *Canada*	South Africa (70%), Belgian Congo (20%)
Graphite	*Mexico* (46%), Ceylon, Japan, *Canada*	*Mexico* (75%), Madagascar (22%)
Kyanite	India	India
Lead	*Mexico* (30%), *Peru, Canada*	*Mexico* (70%), Australia, *Peru,* Africa
Manganese	U.S.S.R., Gold Coast, *Cuba, Brazil,* India	India, *Brazil,* Gold Coast, *Cuba,* South Africa
Mercury	Italy (50%), Spain (40%), *Mexico*	*Mexico* (63%), *Canada* (30%)
Mica	India (75%), *Canada,* South Africa	India (70%), *Canada, Brazil*
Nickel	*Canada* (98%)	*Canada* (90%), New Caledonia (5%)
Platinum	United Kingdom (72%), *Colombia,* U.S.S.R.	*Canada* (75%), U.S.S.R., *Colombia*
Quartz crystals	*Brazil*	*Brazil*
Tantalite	Australia	*Brazil* (60%), Belgian Congo (20%)
Tin	British Malaya (75%), United Kingdom (10%)	Bolivia (50%), Belgian Congo (48%)
Tungsten	China (70%), British Malaya	China (40%), *Bolivia* (30%), *Argentina, Brazil*
Vanadium	*Peru*	*Peru* (73%), South Africa (25%)
Zinc	Belgium, *Mexico, Peru, Canada*	*Mexico* (35%), Australia, *Canada*

noncontiguous neighbors, Cuba is a source of chromite (the refractory type), and of iron ore; she also produces manganese and nickel. Much of the Caribbean area seems destined to become a leading producer of high-grade bauxite. South America supplies several minerals which are lacking in the United States, especially quartz crystals (Brazil), vanadium (Peru), and tin (Bolivia). As the table shows, she also furnishes other minerals, some of them in large quantities. This array of minerals available in the western hemisphere leaves few important gaps in our supplies.

Another factor relating to our mineral imports is the fact that large sums of American capital are invested in important sources of minerals outside the country, especially in

[12] *Raw Materials in War and Peace,* Department of Social Sciences, United States Military Academy, West Point, 1947, pp. 145-149.

Latin America. One of our corporations owns and exploits the vanadium deposits of Peru; another has an interest in Bolivian tin; and almost the entire copper industry of Latin America is controlled by American capital. Furthermore, the United States as the leading buyer of many minerals enjoys a favorable market position.

Still another factor is foreign relations and naval and air power. The friendly relations of the United States with the British Commonwealth of Nations and Latin America, as well as with other nations, make remote the danger of political obstacles to her procuring of minerals. One of the most crucial elements in the procurement of foreign strategic and critical supplies is naval and military power. However, in view of recent developments in submarine construction and air power it is difficult to appraise the present status of any of the world powers. Furthermore, the "cold war" now being waged between East and West must also be taken into consideration.

Mineral Reserves

Although there is a connection between resorting to imports to supplement domestic supplies and the size of domestic reserves, import data cannot be relied on to indicate the size of these reserves. Too many factors are involved. For example, some minerals are imported free of duty, others are subject to duty or excise taxes (in lieu of import duties). The tariff often reflects business pressure, not concern for reserves. As was said before, imports may come by water from a nearby source more accessible than domestic sources which are far in the interior of the continent and can be reached only by rail. Nor, for that matter, are exports a sure sign that a country has ample reserves. Until World War II, international trade as a rule moved in response to business motives and reflected vanishing reserves only indirectly. Conservation is not the forte of private enterprise.

The difficulties besetting the appraisal of reserves were discussed at some length in the first part of this chapter. Table 25.4 must be studied with that exposition in mind. In order to make the meaning of reserves clearer, reserves may be expressed in terms of the relationship between the estimated reserves of a certain mineral and (1) its annual production and (2) its annual consumption. Thus, if petroleum output and consumption in a certain period are 1.5 and 1.0 billion barrels respectively and reserves are 15 billion barrels, the reserve situation can be expressed in terms of years of annual production and consumption. The reserve of 15 billion barrels will last for 10 years at the rate of 1.5 billion barrels annual production; the same reserves will last for 15 years at the rate of 1.0 billion barrels annual consumption. In other words, the 15 billion barrel reserves represent 10 years of annual production and 15 years of annual consumption. Similarly, if the annual production of copper is 1 million tons, annual consumption is 2 million tons, and reserves are 20 million tons, the reserves can be expressed as 20 years of production and 10 years of consumption.

It should be clearly understood that these figures indicating years are merely an arithmetical device to make unwieldly figures more meaningful; *under no circumstances should they be interpreted as predicting the length of time reserves can reasonably be expected to last.* The reasons for this are clear. For one thing, a single period of production and consumption does not reveal the all-important

TABLE 25.4. United States Mineral Reserves[13]

	Reserves[a] in Terms of Production Consumption (in years)	
Magnesium	Unlimited	Unlimited
Nitrates	Unlimited	Unlimited
Salt	Unlimited	Unlimited
Bituminous coal and lignite	4235	4386
Phosphate rock	470	600
Helium	232	235
Anthracite	179	187
Molybdenum	99	157
Rutile	283	124
Potash	113	99
Iron ore	78	76
Ilmenite	248	73
Arsenic[b]	120	55
Natural gas	55	55
Cobalt[b]	674	53
Sulfur	33	39
Bismuth[b]	56	36
Fluorspar	34	33
Bauxite	30	23
Zinc	24	20
Gold	19	19
Copper	25	19
Petroleum (proved reserves only)	14	15
Silver[b]	13	13
Cadmium[b]	18	11
Lead	15	10
Vanadium	13	8
Manganese	46	4
Platinum metals	18	3
Antimony[b]	18	3
Mercury	3	2
Tungsten	5	2
Tantalum	52	1
Chromite	10	Less than 1

[a] Estimated "commercial" reserves as of 1944 in known deposits, compared with 1935-1944 rates of production and consumption.

Figures indicate only magnitude of estimated reserves. They do not imply that production at the rates indicated could be maintained for the full period shown. Estimates do not include allowance for future discoveries.

[b] Obtained chiefly as by-products. Output depends on rate of production of associated metals.

[13] *Mineral Position of the United States*, p. 179.

TABLE 25.5. States and Their Principal Mineral Products in 1948[14]

State	Rank	Percent of Total Value for United States	Principal Mineral Products in Order of Value
Alabama	16	1.47	Coal, iron ore, cement, clay products.
Alaska	41	0.11	Gold, coal, platinum metals, sand and gravel.
Arizona	15	1.62	Copper, zinc, lead, silver.
Arkansas	22	0.99	Petroleum, coal, bauxite, natural gasoline.
California	3	9.44	Petroleum, natural gasoline, natural gas, cement.
Colorado	21	1.04	Petroleum, coal, zinc, molybdenum.
Connecticut	46	0.05	Clay products, stone, sand and gravel, lime.
Delaware	50	0.01	Clay products, sand and gravel, stone, raw clay.
District of Columbia	49	0.01	Clay products, raw clay.
Florida	28	0.43	Phosphate rock, stone, cement, sand and gravel.
Georgia	33	0.34	Raw clay, stone, clay products, cement.
Idaho	27	0.64	Lead, zinc, silver, antimony ore.
Illinois	6	4.21	Coal, petroleum, stone, clay products.
Indiana	18	1.34	Coal, cement, petroleum, stone.
Iowa	31	0.36	Cement, clay products, stone, coal.
Kansas	9	2.92	Petroleum, cement, natural gas, coal.
Kentucky	7	4.07	Coal, petroleum, natural gas, stone.
Louisiana	5	4.77	Petroleum, natural gasoline, natural gas, sulfur.
Maine	45	0.07	Cement, sand and gravel, stone, clay products.
Maryland	35	0.22	Coal, sand and gravel, cement, clay products.
Massachusetts	40	0.11	Stone, sand and gravel, clay products, lime.
Michigan	13	1.65	Iron ore, petroleum, cement, salt.
Minnesota	11	2.16	Iron ore, stone, sand and gravel, manganiferous ore.
Mississippi	23	0.96	Petroleum, natural gas, clay products, natural gasoline.
Missouri	24	0.91	Lead, cement, coal, stone.
Montana	25	0.83	Copper, petroleum, zinc, lead.
Nebraska	43	0.08	Cement, sand and gravel, clay products, stone.
Nevada	32	0.36	Copper, zinc, gold, lead.
New Hampshire	47	0.01	Sand and gravel, clay products, feldspar, stone.
New Jersey	29	0.41	Zinc, clay products, sand and gravel, stone.
New Mexico	12	1.78	Petroleum, copper, potassium salts, zinc.
New York	20	1.25	Cement, iron ore, petroleum, stone.
North Carolina	36	0.22	Clay products, stone, sand and gravel, talc and pyrophyllite.
North Dakota	44	0.07	Coal (lignite), sand and gravel, clay products, natural gas.
Ohio	10	2.64	Coal, clay products, stone, lime.
Oklahoma	8	4.05	Petroleum, natural gasoline, natural gas, coal.
Oregon	37	0.20	Sand and gravel, stone, cement, clay products.
Pennsylvania	2	11.31	Coal, cement, petroleum, stone.
Rhode Island	48	0.01	Sand and gravel, stone, graphite.
South Carolina	42	0.10	Stone, clay products, raw clay, vermiculite.
South Dakota	38	0.19	Gold, stone, sand and gravel, raw clay.
Tennessee	26	0.77	Coal, cement, stone, phosphate rock.
Texas	1	22.57	Petroleum, natural gasoline, natural gas, sulfur.
Utah	14	1.65	Copper, coal, lead, gold.
Vermont	39	0.13	Stone, slate, asbestos, talc.
Virginia	19	1.27	Coal, stone, cement, clay products.
Washington	30	0.41	Cement, coal, sand and gravel, stone.
West Virginia	4	8.10	Coal, natural gas, petroleum, natural gasoline.
Wisconsin	34	0.30	Stone, sand and gravel, iron ore, cement.
Wyoming	17	1.39	Petroleum, coal, natural gasoline, raw clay.

[14] Minerals Yearbook, 1949.

trends of production and consumption. Thus, coal production in the United States has been stable or even decreasing since 1918, whereas petroleum production has gone sharply upward from less than 400 million barrels in 1918 to over 2 billion in 1949. Furthermore, the nature of the reserves must be clearly understood. Coal reserves mean roughly all the coal in the ground down to a certain depth; petroleum reserves mean only known reserves. Vast new reserves of some minerals may be reasonably expected to be opened up as the result of great technological improvements, but experts hold out no such prospects in the case of other minerals. Many other pertinent facts and factors must be taken into account.

According to Table 25.4, the reserves of magnesium, nitrate, and salt are unlimited. The reason is simple. Magnesium and salt are found in sea water and the ocean may be viewed as an unlimited source of supply. Similarly, nitrogen can be obtained from the atmosphere, another source of unlimited supply. Actually, however, the situation is not quite so rosy, for none of these minerals can be extracted from their sources without vast expenditures of energy that nowadays is obtained mainly from coal, petroleum, and natural gas. And this energy can be harnessed only by means of metals whose supply is definitely "finite." The reserves themselves may be "unlimited," but actual availability is another matter.

The reserves of coal figured on this basis run into thousands of years. Although this may seem a cause for complacency to many people, early in 1948 a mining engineer of considerable reputation pointed out that, in the case of coal, gross overestimation of actual reserves and qualitative considerations called for a sharp reduction in the figures given for these reserves.[15] Instead of becoming less important, coal, in the absence of the complete reorganization of the energy scheme of man, may be called upon to step into the gaps left by other less durable energy carriers such as petroleum and natural gas. Engineers are already talking of a coal output in the United States of several billion tons. This would drastically reduce the years of coal reserves. The question of the quality of coal must also be considered. Metal-

lurgical coking coal is vital to our industrial structure; it constitutes the elite of the coal reserves. But a very large portion of the reserves is low-grade subbituminous coal and lignite. Location must likewise be considered—there are "the production states" of the East, with limited reserves, and "the reserves states" of the West, with larger reserves.

Rutile and ilmenite are ores of titanium, which is just beginning to come into its own. Our reserves of these two minerals look fairly impressive, mainly because our domestic production is so small, and also because we have been relying heavily on imports.

As is indicated in the table, arsenic, cobalt, bismuth, silver, cadmium, and antimony are produced chiefly as by-products. Consequently their production in this country depends on the rate at which the associated metals are produced. Their production cannot be stepped up in response to increased demand. In these cases the years of reserves furnish no reliable clue to the adequacy of the supply.

Of considerable significance are the figures for copper, lead, and zinc, three very important metals; for the figures indicate serious inadequacy. Some experts believe that there are large reserves of copper in submarginal deposits which will relieve the pressure in the case of that metal as technological and economic changes permit their use.

Table 25.5 gives a bird's-eye view of the mineral production of the United States, by states, and of the relative rank of the minerals produced.

It is evident from the foregoing that neither those who claim that the United States has more or less suddenly ceased to be the "have"-power *par excellence,* nor those who blindly belittle all warnings of actual or impending mineral inadequacy are in the right. As is usually true, reality in this case is neither as bad as the pessimists fear nor as good as the optimists hope. However, the situation is serious enough to call for courageous facing of the facts and for serious planning.

MINERAL POSITION OF OTHER LEADING POWERS

As Fig. 25.2 shows, the only other powers that can be compared to the United States as regards mineral endowment are the Soviet

---

[15] For further discussion, see pp. 464-466.

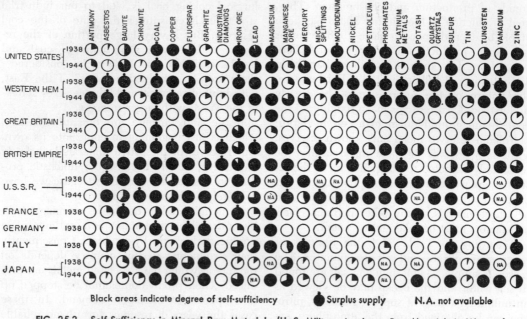

FIG. 25.2.   Self-Sufficiency in Mineral Raw Materials. (U. S. Military Academy, *Raw Materials in War and Peace*, 1947.)

Union, the British Empire, and the British Commonwealth of Nations. It is exceedingly difficult to give an adequate account of the U.S.S.R., and the British position has undergone such grave changes, especially following the loss of India and Burma, that available data are largely out of date. Moreover, no comparison of the mineral position of nations is of much value which does not take account of (1) foreign investments, (2) general financial position affecting purchasing power, (3) naval and air power, and (4) political conditions including the ability to win and hold allies. Hence the value of Fig. 25.2 as a source of detailed information is limited, but it does give a picture of the situation as a whole.

BIBLIOGRAPHY

Alderfer, E. B., and Michl, H. E., *Economics of American Industry*, New York, McGraw-Hill, 1942, Part II.

Bateman, A. M., "World Minerals—War and Postwar," *Mining and Metallurgy*, April, 1945.

Bateman, A. M., "Wartime Dependence on Foreign Minerals," *Economic Geology*, January, 1946.

Bateman, A. M., "America's Stake in World Mineral Resources," *Mining Engineering*, July, 1949.

Braden, S., "America's Mining Enterprise in Foreign Countries," in Parsons, A. B. (ed.), *Seventy-five Years of Progress in the Mineral Industry, 1871-1946*, New York, American Institute of Mining and Metallurgical Engineers, 1947.

Eckel, E. C., *Coal, Iron, and War*, New York, Holt, 1920.

Emeny, B., *The Strategy of Raw Materials*, New York, Macmillan, 1934.

Feis, H., *The Sinews of Peace*, New York, Harper, 1944.

Fuller, R. B., "U. S. Industrialization," *Fortune*, February, 1940.

Glover, J. G., and Cornell, W. B. (eds.), *The Development of American Industries*, New York, Prentice-Hall, 1941.

Hitch, C. J., *America's Economic Strength*, New York, Oxford University Press, 1941.

Kranold, H., *The International Distribution of Raw Materials*, New York, Harper, 1939.

Krug, J. A., "The Mineral Position of the United States," in Parsons, A. B. (ed.), *Seventy-five Years of Progress in the Mineral Industry, 1871-*

1946, New York, American Institute of Mining and Metallurgical Engineers, 1947.

Leith, C. K., *World Minerals and World Politics,* New York, McGraw-Hill, 1931.

Leith, C. K., and Lidell, D. M., *The Mineral Reserves of the United States,* Washington, National Resources Committee, 1936.

Pahl, W., *Weltkampf um Rohstoffe,* Leipzig, Goldmann, 1939.

Pehrson, E. W., "The Mineral Position of the United States and the Outlook for the Future," *Mining and Metallurgy,* April, 1945.

Rawles, W. P., *The Nationality of Commercial Control of World Minerals,* New York, American Institute of Mining and Metallurgical Engineers, 1933.

Roush, F. A., *Strategic Mineral Supplies,* New York, McGraw-Hill, 1939.

Spykman, N. J., *America's Strategy in World Politics,* New York, Harcourt, Brace, 1942.

Staley, E., *Raw Materials in Peace and War,* New York, Council on Foreign Relations, 1937.

U. S. Department of Interior, Bureau of Mines, *Mineral Raw Materials,* New York, McGraw-Hill, 1937.

U. S. Department of Interior, Bureau of Mines and Geological Survey, *Mineral Position of the United States* (published as appendix to *Investigations of National Resources,* Hearings before a Subcommittee of the Committee on Public Lands, U. S. Senate, Eightieth Congress, 1st Session, Washington, May 15, 16, and 20), 1947.

UNIT 2. ENERGY RESOURCES

Chapter 26

COAL—THE BASIS OF INDUSTRIAL CIVILIZATION

SIGNIFICANCE OF COAL

Just what share of the heat and energy supply of mankind must be credited to coal and what to the other sources—oil, natural gas, wood, and water power—can only be estimated. Not only is the world's total production of energy carriers not accurately known, but even more important is the fact that the efficiency of use of each one varies widely both from time to time and from place to place. Coal burned in an open fireplace is used far less efficiently than coal converted into electricity in a modern power plant. Much wood is burned in Africa in night-long outdoor fires to scare off wild beasts. But the mineral fuels and wood are used for other purposes than to supply heat and energy—e.g., carbon from coal is used in making steel, lubricating oil and wax are made from oil, carbon black comes from natural gas, etc.; hence estimates based on total production are misleading. Moreover, the rates of efficiency of use are in constant flux; the yardstick of 1913 does not accurately fit conditions in 1950. In the light of these facts, the reliability of the estimates in Table 26.1 may be appraised.

Several facts stand out. (1) Coal, though declining in relative importance (actual production figures for 1942 for the world were the largest on record), is by far the most important source of heat and energy in the

TABLE 26.1. Relative Importance of Sources of Heat and Energy in the World[1]
(percent)

	Coal and Lignite	Oil	Natural Gas	Fire-wood	Water Power
1913	74.1	4.5	1.4	17.6	2.4
1935	60.3	16.5	3.8	12.8	6.6
1948	54.8	24.6	7.3	7.2	6.1

world. (2) Oil and natural gas are forging ahead rapidly, but because their total reserves are much smaller than those of coal they are bound to lose in relative importance in the not too distant future. (3) Wood, theoretically a renewable resource, is actually being cut in many parts of the earth in a manner which

[1] Figures for 1913 and 1935 from R. Regul and K. G. Mahnke, *Energiequellen der Welt*, Institut für Konjunkturforschung, Berlin, 1937. Figures for 1948 from Nathaniel B. Guyol, United Nations, in a letter to the author.

precludes or jeopardizes regrowth; it is likely to decline even more in importance. (4) Water power, also a renewable or flow resource, is likely to gain in importance.[2]

World averages hide sharp regional differences in the use of energy. The interior of Brazil is dependent on wood for heat and energy; Venezuela has a high per capita consumption of oil; Texas depends heavily on oil and natural gas; the state of Washington, Scandinavia, and Switzerland depend on water power, etc. Each region of the earth makes use of whatever energy resources are available from local production or import. But the fact remains that coal is man's major source of heat and energy.

Coal is more than this. It is also the source of valuable materials such as gases, oils, tar, and pitch, from which in turn an infinite array of chemical products can be extracted. Coal was the main source of the ersatz materials which powered the Nazi machine. Carbon derived mainly from coke, a refined state of coal, is an indispensable ingredient of steel, the sinew of machine industry and of mechanized warfare.

The world output of coal is man's most colossal performance in material handling and mass moving. Much coal travels hundreds of miles by land and thousands of miles by water. It constitutes by far the railroads' most important payload and has played a vital role in the growth of the world's seaborne trade.

COAL IN MODERN HISTORY

As one surveys the part which coal has played in recent world history, it is difficult to escape the lure of one-sided determinism. However, to say that coal is and has been one of the most potent forces—perhaps the most important single factor—in shaping human destiny during the past two centuries is by no means the same as claiming that it alone has wrought the changes which have come about in economics and politics. One-sided determinism is amateurish and must be repudiated. Nevertheless, one would have to be blind to overlook the definite connection between British hegemony during the nineteenth century and England's pre-

ponderance as a producer, and especially as an exporter, of coal. Similarly, the causal nexus between Germany's ascendancy after 1870 and the development of her coal industry, and the connection between the rapid rise of the United States to a world power and the steep curve of her coal output, the basis of industrialization, are too obvious.[3] In general, the world dominance of the nations bordering the North Atlantic can hardly be explained without reference to the striking concentration of useful minerals within their borders, especially of major coal deposits and workable combinations of iron and coking coal.

Coal has been used for many centuries for household purposes and by individual craftsmen, such as smiths, brewers, and others. Locally, as in the trade from Newcastle to London and from the east coast of England to the continent, coal was important during the late sixteenth and seventeenth centuries.

As a major factor in world history, coal dates only from the eighteenth century. Its "coming of age" is accounted for by many factors, among which the following are the most important: (1) the depletion of the forests and the threatening scarcity of fuel—wood and charcoal—and of building material, especially for the shipbuilding industry; (2) the epoch-making discovery in 1708 of the practical application of coal to the smelting and manufacturing of iron; and (3) the perfection of the steam engine by James Watt in 1782. The first discovery meant the release of the iron industry from its dependence on charcoal. The effect of the steam engine is too complex to be appraised accurately in a few sentences. However, its importance to industrial production can be traced along two major lines. In the first place, it made possible the expansion of mining operations, for it solved the problem of water control and ventilation in coal mines and thus permitted deeper shafts and more economical exploitation. Until then only surface or near-

---

[2] The future of the energy economy of the earth is made more uncertain by the possibilities of direct solar radiation and atomic energy.

[3] It is true that this steep curve reached its apex in 1918 and from then on proceeded in irregular fashion until World War II, when the earlier peak was passed. By 1918 the industry of the United States, reared on coal, had reached sufficient strength to tap other energy sources, especially oil and natural gas, and had gained enough sense to use coal more economically, thus obviating the necessity of further expansion of production.

surface seams could be worked, and they were generally worked in such a way as to jeopardize the future exploitation of enormous underlying coal deposits. The steam engine also aided in underground hauling, in hoisting, and in the land transportation of mineral products.

In the second place, the steam engine brought about a phenomenal increase in the demand for mineral products. By cheapening coal it cheapened energy and, consequently, anything made with the aid of mechanical energy. Furthermore, it revolutionized transportation by land and sea and, in so doing, incredibly enhanced the usefulness of coal and immeasurably extended its market. Made of iron or steel, the steam engine itself depends on coal for both its manufacture and operation. The scarcity of wood drove one shipbuilding country after another to turn to metal, first iron and then steel, and again coal proved indispensable. Moreover, for decades the ships that scoured the Seven Seas to bring Europe food for her workers and raw materials for her machines were eager to carry coal on their outbound voyages, that being the one heavy bulk commodity moving away from northwestern Europe. Coal thus became the center pillar of British maritime supremacy and throughout the nineteenth century made history as no other commodity has ever done. When the iron ore of Lorraine was joined with the coal of the Ruhr through the Treaty of Frankfurt, the foundation of the most powerful industrial empire ever built on the continent of Europe was laid; and coal again wrote history which man will never forget so long as the story of the great World Wars lives. The history of the United States is railroad history. The iron and steel rails, the locomotives, are unthinkable without the coal of Pennsylvania and Ohio; and to this day, though hard pressed by Diesel oil, coal is a premier source of energy which keeps the wheels of the railroads moving; not only that, but coal also furnishes the railroads with their largest single item of revenue freight. Thus coal is the backbone of America's land

⁴ See E. W. Zimmermann, *Ocean Shipping*, Prentice-Hall, Inc., New York, 1921, chap. 12; also his articles, "Why America's Export Coal Business Should Be Built Up," *Coal Age*, December, 1920, and January, 1921.

transportation system, as it was, throughout critical decades, of the water transportation system upon which rests the British Empire. Coal has been "the key to the carrying trade"⁴ when that trade grew from its formative stage to its world-conquering manhood.

More recently, the Soviet Union, bent on rapid industrialization, has pushed coal production, the *sine qua non* of industrial prowess. Realizing the connection between industrial progress, economic well-being, and political power, many other nations have likewise made strenuous efforts to develop their coal resources. The story of Japan's attempts to erect a vast industrial structure on inadequate domestic coal supplies and the career of conquest on which she launched to accomplish her ends— a career which came to a tragic end at Hiroshima—is still too vivid to need recounting. Nor does the reader have to be reminded of the bitter struggle which has long been raging over Manchuria and northern China, regions abounding in coal. Equally well known is the spectacular success of India's iron and steel industry in drawing on the rich coal reserves of that country. Almost pathetic is the zeal with which Brazil is striving to overcome the handicap of inadequate coal supplies. Where there is any coal of reasonable quality in South America, plans are being laid to build industries on it. Chile, probably best endowed with coal of all the South American countries, is building a steelworks near its coal deposits; Peru and Colombia have similar plans.

Coal, Iron, and Industrialization

The connection between coal, iron, and industrialization is very close. Because coal, the Aaron, is inarticulate without iron, its Moses, coal mining reaches its full development only where iron is found accessible to coal. Without iron there can be no modern machinery, no steel rails; and without them modern industry and transportation can hardly exist. As the products of the blast furnace and steelworks are sent over the earth, they carry with them the demand for coal necessary for their operation and use—a demand which may be satisfied by tapping local supplies, as in South Africa, India, Australia, and other places, or by importing coal, chiefly from England—and, after World War II, from the United States—as in the case of Scandinavia, Italy, Argentina and some other parts of South America, Egypt, and many other sections of the world.

To be sure, in recent years petroleum, water power, and other forms of energy have made serious inroads in the field formerly held by coal. The fact that coal has lost some of its importance during recent decades is in part due to discoveries of new sources of heat and energy and to new developments affecting the use of fuels, and in part due to the fact that coal is less suitable for certain purposes than other fuels.

CLASSIFICATION OF COALS[5]
Types of Coals
Coals may be classified on several bases— for example, the physical properties of the coal itself, the diverse conditions under which it is found, and its use as affected by its specific properties. Coals reflect the wide variety of organic and inorganic substances which went into their formation as well as the widely varying conditions that governed it. They are not definite chemical compounds but mechanical mixtures of carbon, hydrogen, nitrogen, sulfur, etc. Coals are usually classified on the basis of descending carbon content, as follows:

A. Anthracite coal
   1. Meta-anthracite
   2. Anthracite
   3. Semi-anthracite
B. Bituminous coal
   1. Low-volatile bituminous
   2. Medium-volatile bituminous
   3. High-volatile bituminous A
   4. High-volatile bituminous B
   5. High-volatile bituminous C
   6. Subbituminous A
   7. Subbituminous B
   8. Subbituminous C
C. Lignite
D. Brown coal

The major difference between lignite and brown coal is the fact that lignite is consolidated whereas brown coal is powdery; also, the latter usually contains less carbon than lignite. Table 26.2 shows the characteristics of these different classes, or ranks, of coal. In this table, the term semibituminous includes both low- and medium-volatile bituminous.

In addition to the rank classification, which is based on their natural properties, coals may also be classified on the basis of grades. Grades result largely from the different sizes obtained when coals are broken up in mining and moving. Mechanical devices separate the various grades when the coal is being prepared for market.

Diversity of Occurrence
Not only do coal deposits differ widely in the nature of the coals they contain, they differ also as to conditions under which these coals are found. These factors go far to determine the mining methods which can be applied and the costs of production. Thus, "beds of coal show differences in thickness, depth, width, pitch, lamination and partings in the coal, nature of adjacent strata, especially roofs and floors, number of beds in an area, distance between successive beds, gaseousness of workings, amount of water, ease of drainage, extent of faulting and folding, accessibility of the bed for removal of coal, and location with reference to markets."[6]

These conditions are also largely responsible for the wide difference in labor productivity in the various coal regions of the earth. At least they account for much of the difference found between countries that are otherwise comparable as to economic and technical development. Mechanization itself depends a great deal on these conditions. Table 26.3 throws light on conditions in leading coal fields of the United States and Europe.

Specific Properties and Utilization
While to the layman technical details concerning the varieties of coal may seem superfluous, to the businessman who buys or sells coal they are of fundamental importance. A thorough knowledge of properties is not only vital to the intelligent interpretation of coal prices, but is indispensable to economical utilization. Thus, under most circumstances, it would be folly to burn gas coal under a boiler

---

[5] Like most substances of organic origin, coal is not a homogeneous product; hence the word coals is more accurate than coal.

[6] National Resources Committee, *Energy Resources and National Policy*, Washington, 1939, p. 57.

TABLE 26.2.   Characteristics of
As established by the International
the United States Geological Survey, 1921; and the Regnault-
(The several ranks of coal shade

Class (International Geological Congress, 1913)	Anthracite	Semi-Anthracite	Semibituminous	Medium Rank
	A_1	A_2	B_1	B_2
Calorific value:				
B.T.U.[a]	14,500–15,000	15,000–15,500	15,200–16,000	14,000–16,000
Calories[b]	8,000–8,330	8,330–8,600	8,400–8,900	7,700–8,800
Fuel ratio[c]	12 and over	6–12	4–6	3–5
or				
Split volatile ratio[d]	. . . . .	. . . . .	. . . . .	. . . . . .
Mean chemical composition (percent) of:				
C	93–95	90–93	80–90	75–90
H	2–4	4–4.5	4.5–5	4.5–5.5
O + N + S	3–5	3–5.5	5.5–12	6–15
Range (percent) of:				
Volatiles[e]	below 8	8–15	15–20	18–26
Fixed carbon[e] . .	above 92	85–92	80–85	74–82
Moisture[f]	. . . . . .	. . . . . .	. . . . . .	. . . . . .
Coking properties .	Does not coke, pulverulent		Weakly coking or non-coherent	Generally makes very dense coke
Color	Black, lustrous	Black, lustrous	Black, lustrous	Black, lustrous or dull
Flame	Very short, blue	Very short, somewhat luminous	Short, luminous	Medium to long, luminous
Smoke	Smokeless	Nearly smokeless	Very little smoke	Smoky
Fracture or cleavage	Conchoidal fracture	Conchoidal fracture	Distinct prismatic cleavage	Usually distinct cubical cleavage
Texture	Hard	Hard but friable	Friable	Soft to hard
Action on weathering	Very resistant, chemically and physically	Resistant, chemically and physically	Chemically resistant, often disintegrates rapidly into small prismatic fragments	Chemically little affected, but disintegrates slowly into prismatic fragments
Chief uses	Domestic and central heating; malting kilns; producer-gas	Steam raising; domestic heating; cement works	Steam raising; domestic heating; bunker fuel for steamships	Coke manufacture and steam raising

[a] Heat units to raise 1 lb. of water 1° F.
[b] Heat units to raise 1 lb. of water 1° C.
[c] $\dfrac{\text{Fixed carbon}}{\text{Volatiles}}$, ash-free, dry coal; of significance mainly for high ranks.
[d] $\dfrac{\text{Fixed carbon} + \text{volatiles}}{(\text{Hygroscopic moisture} + \frac{1}{2}\text{ volatiles})}$; of significance mainly for low ranks.
[e] Based on ash-free, dry coal.
[f] Of significance only for low ranks.

the Different Ranks of Coal[7]
Geological Congress, 1913;
Grüner grouping as modified•by Bone and Himus, 1936.
into one another imperceptibly)

Bituminous			Subbituminous	Lignite or Brown Coal
"Coking" Coal	"Gas" Coal	Low Rank		
B_2	C	B_3	D_1	D_2
....	12,000–16,000 6,600–7,800	12,000–14,000 6,600–7,800	10,000–13,000 5,500–7,200	7,000–11,000 4,000–6,000
2–3	1.5–2	1.2–1.5	below 1.2	below 1.2
.....	.....	2.5–3.3	1.8–2.5	below 1.8
84–89 5.0–5.6 5.5–11.0	80–85 about 5.6 10–15	70–80 4.5–6 18–20	60–75 6–6.5 20–30	45–65 6–6.8 30–35
26–32 68–74	32–40 60–68	40–45 55–60 (5–10)	above 45 below 55 (10–20)	above 45 below 55 (20–60)
Suitable for dense "metallurgical" coke	Suitable for soft porous "gas" coke	Generally does not coke, noncoherent	Does not coke, noncoherent	
Black, lustrous, or dull	Black, lustrous, or dull	Black, tending to dull	Brown or yellow streak, but sometimes black	Brown, dull, but sometimes black
Long, burns freely	Long, burns freely	Long, burns very freely	Long	Long
Smoky	Smoky	Smoky	Smoky	Smoky
.....	Resinous fracture	.....	Conchoidal or cubical fracture	Earthy and dull
Soft to hard	Soft to hard	Soft to hard	Soft	Soft
.....	.....	.....	Slacks into thin plates parallel to bedding with loss of heating value	Slacks very quickly in air, forming powder or thin platy fragments with marked loss of heating value
Coke manufacture	Gas making	Reverberatory furnaces; steam locomotives	Domestic heating; steam raising	

---

[6] International Labor Office, *Report on the World Coal-Mining Industry*, King, London, 2 vols., 1938.

TABLE 26.3. Comparison of Conditions in Leading European Coal Fields with Those Prevailing in the United States[8]

	United States	Great Britain	France	Belgium	Westphalia (Ruhr)	Upper Silesia
1. Coal seams	Large available reserves of coal in seams of suitable section for economic working lying at or near the surface. Large proportion of coal hard	Considerable proportion of coal worked from seams thinner than most economical section and lying at considerable depth below surface. Large proportion of coal hard	Seams worked on average thinner than most economical section and lie at considerable depth below surface. Coal rather soft	Seams worked on average thinner than most economical section and lie at considerable depth below surface. Coal rather soft	Seams worked on average thinner than most economical section and lie at considerable depth below surface. Moderately hard coal	Thick seams, some of them excessively so, lying at relatively shallow depth. Coal fairly hard
2. Roofs and floors	Generally good	Moderate (good, bad and indifferent)	Moderate (good, bad and indifferent)	Moderate (good, bad and indifferent)	Moderate (good, bad and indifferent)	Good
3. Faults	Relatively free from faults	Fairly numerous in the majority of districts	Very faulted	Very faulted	Very faulted	Relatively free from faults
4. Inclination of seams	Generally flat except in the anthracite region	As a rule fairly flat	Highly inclined	Highly inclined	Highly inclined	Moderately inclined
5. Inflammable gas	Relatively free from gas	Gas prevalent in the majority of districts	Gas fairly prevalent	Gas fairly prevalent	Gas prevalent	Little gas, but very liable to spontaneous combustion
6. Quality of coal	Fairly high	Generally high	Fairly good	Fairly good	High, particularly for coking purposes	Second class—high oxygen content
7. Drainage	Either free drainage or shallow pumping	Pumping demands heavy in many districts	Pumping demands fairly heavy	Pumping demands fairly heavy	Pumping demands fairly heavy	Fairly heavy pumping demands, but from relatively shallow depth
8. Sinking conditions for new developments	Generally easy	Generally difficult	Moderate	Difficult	Difficult	Generally easy

[8] Statement handed in to British Royal Commission (1925) by Dr. J. S. Haldane, F. R. S., on behalf of the Institution of Mining Engineers.

or to use steam coal for the manufacture of gas. Because of its cleanness, anthracite is ideally suited to household purposes; its use for purposes for which the less expensive bituminous coal would be as good, if not better, would obviously be economic waste. Relatively few coals lend themselves to the manufacture of metallurgical coke, that is, coke which can be used in a blast furnace.

Industrial conditions have generally adapted themselves to the suitability of coals. Thus, Pittsburgh owes much of its leadership as a center of the iron and steel industry to the proximity of both the world-renowned Connellsville coking coal and the high-grade steam coals suitable for power generation and heat production. The rise of the Hampton Roads ports as centers of the bunkering business and of the export coal trade in the United States is explained by the accessibility of Pocahontas coal and others mined in West Virginia and surrounding territories. Needless to say, the suitability of coals is purely relative. For example, the substitution of the modern by-product coke oven for the old-fashioned beehive oven has revised the definition of good coking coal. Changes in furnaces and boilers similarly affect the suitability of coals, the increasing use of powdered coal being especially noticeable.

COAL RESERVES OF THE EARTH

In view of the paramount importance of the size of the coal reserves for the destiny of individual nations as well as for mankind as a whole, the interest in reserves is very keen. The layman must understand that the actual size of the earth's reserves is not known. Three authoritative fairly recent estimates differ so widely in their aggregate results that all such figures must be treated with the utmost caution. If one estimate is two or three times as high as another, neither of them can be accepted without careful scrutiny as even approaching the actual facts.

The reasons for this uncertainty are not hard to find. A thorough survey of all the coal reserves in the world is an utter impossibility. It would bankrupt those who attempted it and, because of the limited number of experts and instruments available, it would take a very long time. One must therefore rely on the limited

data available. However, they differ widely in degree of dependability, comprehensiveness, and accuracy, and they are based on diverse methods of calculation. Some are recent, others are quite old.[9]

Reserves of the United States

To illustrate in a concrete way the difficulties in such a survey the coal reserve situation of the United States will be examined rather closely. On the one hand, unusual difficulties arise because of the size of the area involved. On the other hand, the government—both state and national—is apt to have access to greater than average funds and possibly better than average personnel. Moreover, the various parts of the country are all more or less accessible to the surveyor, a condition hardly true in such countries as the Soviet Union, China, and Brazil, which together constitute a considerable part of the earth's surface. How precarious is the task of measuring the coal reserves in even an advanced country like the United States becomes apparent in the following quotation from a report prepared by the National Resources Committee:

Total reserves of coal in the United States in minable beds are estimated to have been at the beginning of mining a little more than three trillion tons. The latest (1928) figure given by Marius R. Campbell, of the United States Geological Survey, is 3,214,898,600,000 net tons.[10] This estimate is a useful summary indicator of the magnitude of the reserves, although it needs to be interpreted with caution. It includes, on a tonnage basis, coals ranging from the highest-rank anthracite to the lowest-rank lignite. Coals with an ash content up to 30 percent are included, even though at the present time an ash content half as great sets the approximate limit for mining. A similar qualification applies to thickness and depth of the beds. In the Campbell estimate, 14 inches was adopted as the minimum thickness for bituminous coals and anthracite, two feet for subbituminous coals, and three feet for lignite. In practice, not many of the subbituminous and lignite deposits running to twice the minimum thickness adopted for the estimate are being mined in volume, and there is only

---

[9] Some were prepared for the Twelfth International Geological Congress held in Toronto in 1913.

[10] M. R. Campbell, *Coal Resources of the United States*, United States Geological Survey (multigraphed).

a small tonnage of the higher rank coals taken from beds less than two and one-half feet thick. There is some strip mining of beds 14 to 22 inches thick in Missouri, Kansas, Arkansas, and Oklahoma, and some mining, by the longwall system, of beds 17 to 24 inches thick in Missouri, Kansas, and Arkansas. Nevertheless, in Pennsylvania and West Virginia, which account for about half of the national total bituminous coal output, the bulk of the production is concentrated in beds of four feet or more thickness. The estimate of resources includes beds as much as 3,000 feet below the surface, whereas coal companies in this country seldom mine beds more than several hundred feet down, and a high percentage of the mines today do not require the sinking of vertical shafts to reach the coal, less expensive horizontal or sloping "tunnels" being sufficient.[11] Topography, of course, is an important factor in determining where coal is mined. Some foreign countries with small coal reserves operate coal mines at depths of more than 3,500 feet. Under the pressure of necessity, deeper beds in the United States could be worked, but, of course, at extremely high cost. It is estimated that an additional 604,000,000,000 tons of coal lie at a depth of from 3,000 to 6,000 feet. This amount added to the reserves at shallower depth gives a total of 3,818,898,600,000 tons at the outset of mining in beds of workable thickness. Nevertheless, owing to the unlikelihood of coal mining at depths of 3,000 feet or more for many generations, it appears advisable to revert to the previous estimate of three and two-tenths trillion tons as the basic figure for the bounds of available reserves. This figure does not include reserves in any of the United States' possessions. Alaska is known to have extensive reserves ranging in rank from lignite to anthracite.[12] Coal beds exist along the coast as well as in the interior of Alaska, but additional prospecting work will have to be done before the tonnage of recoverable coal can be estimated. Reserves in other possessions are probably negligible. Conditions on the island possessions generally have been unfavorable to the formation of coal. Hawaii, for example, although an important fueling station for vessels, has no native coal resources, the bulk of coal in the past having been supplied by Japan, Australia, and Great Britain[13]—an indication of the dearth of our continental supply along the Pacific

Coast and of the potential importance of the Alaskan deposits.[14]

One conclusion should be crystal clear from this estimate of the coal reserves of the United States: Unless truly fantastic improvements in the state of the arts are achieved, our descendants will have to pay far more for coal than the prices paid both in the past and at present. Large portions of the coal reserves listed by Campbell are of such poor quality, are located in such out-of-the-way corners (see Fig. 26.1), are so unfavorable as to thickness of vein, depth, etc., that only unheard-of ingenuity or desperate need will render them available for use. In other words, they are not commercial reserves now, and they may never be.

The United States has long been, and still is, the land of cheap coal, largely because of the low cost at which the cream of the high-grade coals of the Appalachian or eastern bituminous coal province can be mined. In spite of increasing wage rates, costs continue to be low compared with those in most other important industrial countries. Until recent years, when John L. Lewis drove labor costs to unprecedented heights, technological progress and mechanization were able to overcompensate higher labor costs. The mechanical proficiency of considerable portions of our coal mining industry is high. Favorable natural conditions, however, are probably the underlying cause of our low costs. Coal output per miner in this eastern bituminous coal province is very high. But the methods of recovery used are more wasteful than those employed in typical European countries. In the United States roughly one ton of coal is lost for every two tons mined. European recovery rates are much higher.

It will not do, therefore, to count on the 3.2 trillion tons of coal that are supposed to be in the ground as available for use. Actually, if our current wasteful methods of recovery are continued, little over 2 trillion tons will be available. Moreover, as was pointed out earlier, large portions of the reserves are low rank, i.e.,

---

[11] In West Virginia, for example, slope and drift mines outnumber shaft mines by more than 10 to 1. See *Annual Report of the Department of Mines, West Virginia,* 1936, pp. 54-90.

[12] National Resources Committee, *Regional Planning, Part VII, Alaska—Its Resources and Development,* Washington, 1937, p. 210.

[13] H. M. Hoar, *The Coal Industry of the World,* U.S. Department of Commerce, Trade Promotion Series No. 105, 1930, p. 240.

[14] National Resources Committee, *Energy Resources and National Policy,* pp. 49-50.

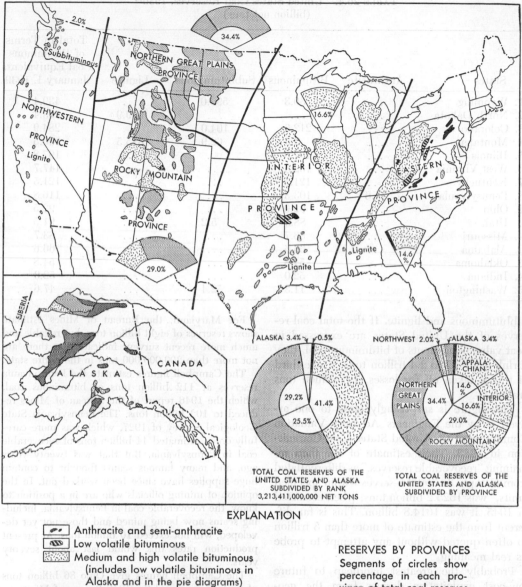

EXPLANATION

- Anthracite and semi-anthracite
- Low volatile bituminous
- Medium and high volatile bituminous (includes low volatile bituminous in Alaska and in the pie diagrams)
- Subbituminous (includes lignite in Alaska)
- Lignite
- Areas in Alaska underlain by rocks known to contain coal in places (not included in estimates of reserves)

RESERVES BY PROVINCES
Segments of circles show percentage in each province of total coal reserves of the United States and Alaska. The patterns show the rank of coal.

ALASKA 3.4%   0.5%

29.2%   41.4%

25.5%

TOTAL COAL RESERVES OF THE
UNITED STATES AND ALASKA
SUBDIVIDED BY RANK
3,213,411,000,000 NET TONS

NORTHWEST 2.0%   ALASKA 3.4%

NORTHERN GREAT PLAINS   34.4%

APPALACHIAN   14.6%

INTERIOR   16.6%

ROCKY MOUNTAIN   29.0%

TOTAL COAL RESERVES OF THE
UNITED STATES AND ALASKA
SUBDIVIDED BY PROVINCE

FIG. 26.1. Distribution of Coal Deposits of the United States and Alaska, 1944, by Types of Coal and Provinces. (U. S. Department of the Interior, Geological Survey and Bureau of Mines, *Mineral Position of the United States, 1947.*)

TABLE 26.4. United States Coal Reserves, 1936[15]
(billion net tons)

States	Anthracite	Bituminous	Subbituminous	Lignite	Total in Terms of Bituminous Coal Equivalents January 1, 1939
1. Wyoming	...	30.3	590.0	...	439.4
2. North Dakota	...	...	...	599.9	293.4
3. Colorado	...	212.6	104.0	...	284.9
4. Montana	...	2.6	62.9	315.5	200.5
5. Illinois	...	197.8	...	...	197.8
6. West Virginia	...	152.5	...	...	147.7
7. Kentucky	...	121.5	...	...	121.5
8. Pennsylvania	14.6	103.3	...	...	116.8
9. Ohio	...	92.0	...	...	92.5
10. Utah	...	88.0	5.2	...	91.5
11. Missouri	...	83.7	...	...	83.7
12. Alabama	...	66.6	...	...	66.6
13. Oklahoma	...	54.8	...	...	54.8
14. Indiana	...	52.0	...	...	52.0
15. Washington	...	11.3	52.4	...	47.6

subbituminous and lignite. If the total coal reserves of the United States are expressed in
heat value equivalents of bituminous coal, they
shrink from 3.2 to 2.4 trillion tons; if one-third
of this is taken off for losses, 1.6 trillion tons
are left.

This figure is surprisingly close to one arrived at by the Engineers' Advisory Valuation
Committee of the United States Coal Commission in 1923. Their estimate of the then remaining "recoverable reserves," as differentiated
from Campbell's "total reserves within specified
limits," was 1625.2 billion tons; when corrected
in 1945, it was 1614.8 billion. This is far different from the estimate of more than 3 trillion
so often quoted without any attempt to probe
its real meaning.

Probably the greatest handicap to future
low-cost exploitation derives from the geographical distribution of the coal deposits;
this is shown for the country as a whole in
Fig. 26.1. Table 26.4 lists the fifteen reserve
states in order of rank on the basis of bituminous coal equivalents.

There are those who believe that the estimates of coal reserves generally accepted in
this country are far too optimistic. Thus, Andrew B. Crichton has this to say:

[15] Compiled from several tables in *ibid.*

For Maryland, the Bureau of Mines estimate
shows reserves of eight billion tons, but reliable and
much more recent surveys indicate that there are
not more than 200,000,000 tons in the entire state.

The Campbell figures estimate the Pennsylvania
reserves at 112 billion tons of bituminous coal,
which the 1946 report of the Bureau of Mines reduced to 103 billion tons. The Pennsylvania State
Geological Survey of 1927, which was more carefully done, estimated 44 billion tons of recoverable
coal in Pennsylvania. But that was twenty years
ago, and many famous seams thought to contain
huge supplies have since been worked out. In the
opinion of mining officials who are in a position to
know, the recoverable coal in Pennsylvania, including seams now being mined and those not yet developed, will not exceed 10 billion tons. At present
production rates this would last about seventy
years.

The Campbell figures give Ohio 86 billion tons
of coal reserves, and the 1946 Bureau of Mines report has increased this to 96 billion tons. The
report of the Ohio Geological Survey, made some
years ago, estimated the state's reserves at 10 billion tons. To many mining experts who are familiar
with the Ohio fields, an estimate of six billion tons
would seem very high.

The estimates for West Virginia are even more
fantastic; apparently every black showing is called
a seam of coal. In one county, 31 different seams,
each estimated to contain millions of tons of coal,
are included in the astronomical figures. The 1946
estimates of the Bureau of Mines gives West Vir-

TABLE 26.5. World Resources of Coals, Brown Coal, Lignite, and Peat[16]
(million metric tons)

| | Date of Report | Coals | | Brown Coal and Lignite | | Peat |
		Proved Reserves	Probable Total Reserves	Proved Reserves	Probable Total Reserves	Probable Total Reserves
Europe						
Belgium	1913	11,000	. . .	. . .	. . .	. . .
Czechoslovakia	1932	6,450	25,000	12,500	. . .	. . .
France (including Saar) . . .	1935	6,000	17,000	1,600	1,600	. . .
Saar	1922	. . .	9,205	0	0	0
Germany	1922	71,240[a]	270,311	28,837	56,758	10,000
Netherlands	1913	212.5	4,474	. . .	. . .	. . .
Norway (Spitzbergen)	1933	. . .	8,000[b]	. . .	. . .	. . .
Poland	1934	13,988	47,793	1,500	5,000	5,500[b]
Spain	1913	4,500[c]	5,500[c]	. . .	. . .	. . .
U.S.S.R.	1933	295,900	998,000	12,890	202,000	72,330
United Kingdom	1933	129,500	176,000	. . .	. . .	. . .
North America						
Canada	1913	30,319	242,400	391,260	572,686	. . .
United States[d]	1928	. . .	2,040,640	. . .	852,128	13,380
Alaska	1913	. . .	3,544	. . .	16,559	. . .
Central and South America						
Chile	1913	2,116	. . .	. . .	. . .	. . .
Africa						
Union of South Africa . . .	1921-7	7,914	205,682	. . .	. . .	. . .
British Dependencies						
Nigeria[e]	1934	113	3,360	0	11,856	0
Asia						
China (excluding Manchuria) .	1913	. . .	10,112,000	. . .	600	. . .
Manchuria	1913	. . .	1,129	. . .	. . .	. . .
Japan proper	1932	5,895	16,218	66	473	. . .
India	1932	5,000	20,600	. . .	. . .	. . .
Australasia						
Australia	1927	20,900	139,000	10,621	. . .	. . .
New Zealand	1934	480	1,400	80	600	. . .

[a] Saar probably included here, but not in other figures.
[b] Approximate.
[c] Includes brown coal, lignite, and peat.
[d] Excludes Alaska and other noncontiguous territories.
[e] Included Cameroons under British mandate.

ginia reserves of 155 billion tons, but the West Virginia Geological Survey reduces this to 116.6 billion tons, an estimate which the state geologist admits is high.

Recent mine developments and diamond drill prospecting have shown in nearly every important

[16] *Statistical Yearbook of the First World Power Conference,* London, 1936, pp. 21-22.

coal-bearing area of the state that many seams estimated to contain millions of tons are either non-existent or too thin to be of any economic value. The New River and Winding Gulf fields are well on toward exhaustion. Few of the large producers have a life of more than twenty years, yet the Geological Survey credits them with reserves of six billion tons, enough for almost 200 years. There are very few operations in the state that have coal reserves for more than 75 years. The best information available indicates that the actual coal reserves of West Virginia will not exceed eighteen billion tons at most.[17]

So ominous were the doubts thrown on the reserve status of one of our most important resources that a National Bituminous Coal Advisory Council was set up. The preliminary report submitted by its Coal Resources Committee in December, 1948, is sobering, to say the least. It seems fully to support the pessimistic comments of Mr. Crichton, now a member of the Committee. The assumed underground continuity of important coal strata was proved nonexistent by further research. This applies to some extent even to the much-vaunted Pittsburgh bed.[18]

Coal Reserves of the World

The world-wide survey of coal reserves conducted in 1913 for the Twelfth International Geological Congress held in Toronto in 1913 remains the chief basis of calculations. However, a partial revision of this survey was published in *The Statistical Yearbook of the First World Power Conference*. Table 26.5 is from this revision.

Since then, on the basis of the revised data submitted by the National Geological Survey of China to the Third Power Conference held in Washington in 1936,[19] the figure for China— 10,112.6 billion tons—has been cut drastically to about 1.1 trillion tons. If this revision is incorporated into Table 26.5, the basic facts of the world's coal reserves in 1936 appear as shown in Table 26.6.

If these figures are reasonably dependable, it appears that North America has about 40 percent of the proved and probable anthracite

---

[17] Andrew B. Crichton, "Plight of Coal," *Collier's*, June 14, 1947, pp. 100-101. See also his provocative paper, "How Much Coal Do We Really Have? The Need for an Up-to-Date Survey," read before the American Institute of Mining and Metallurgical Engineers at the 1947 annual meeting.

[18] See National Bituminous Coal Advisory Council, "Report of the Coal Resources Committee in the Matter of Bituminous Coal Resources of Pennsylvanian Age East of the Mississippi River on the Basis of Information Now Available," Washington, 1948 (mimeographed).

[19] "Coal and Oil Resources of China," Third World Power Conference, Washington, 1936, Section IV, Papers 11 and 12.

and bituminous coal reserves, Europe about 35, Asia 20. The remaining 5 percent is scattered over the rest of the earth. South American data are incomplete. In addition, North America has the lion's share of the subbituminous coals and lignite.

TABLE 26.6.   World Coal Reserves by Continents[20]
(in billion metric tons)

| | Bituminous and Anthracite Coals | | Lignite and Brown Coals | | |
	Proved	Probable	Proved	Probable	Total
North America	30.3	2286.4	391.3	1441.4	4149.4
Europe	548.4	1561.8	60.1	270.6	2440.9
Asia	10.9	1155.5[a]	0.1	1.1	1167.6
Africa	9.3	209.7	...	11.9	230.9
Australia	21.4	140.8	10.7	0.6	173.5
Central and South America	2.1	1.1	...	...	3.2
	622.4	5355.3	462.2	1725.6	8165.5

[a] The figure for Asia has been reduced by 9 trillion.

In summary, the following points regarding reserves should be stressed:

1. Data are as yet incomplete and unreliable; considerable revisions upward and downward are to be expected.

2. There can be little doubt that North America has the largest reserves; and if the relatively small size of her population is taken into consideration, the reserve position of that part of the globe appears exceedingly strong.

3. Regardless of their inadequacy, the available data nevertheless give complete assurance that coal will be available in North America, in Europe, and in parts of Asia for centuries to come.

4. The geographical distribution, geological occurrence, and properties of the coal reserves point to greatly enhanced marketing difficulties and hence to sharply rising costs. But so dynamic is modern technology, especially that of energy production and distribution, that definite predictions are impossible.

FAMOUS COAL FIELDS

The major share of the coal produced to date has come from a rather small number of famous fields. Some of these will be described briefly.

---

[20] International Labor Office, *op. cit.*, vol. 1, p. 38. The figures for peat have been omitted.

The Pittsburgh Coal Field

Two-thirds of the coal produced in the United States comes from the Appalachian bituminous coal region, which stretches from Pennsylvania to Alabama, in general following the mountains that bear the same name. In the northern sector of this region is the famous Pittsburgh coal bed, which has been called the most remarkable coal bed in the world and has contributed a great deal to the economic development of the United States. It extends from north of Pittsburgh halfway into West Virginia and also into Ohio. Up to 1948 it had produced over $8 billion worth of coal.

The Pittsburgh coal bed is equally famous for its size, its ease of exploitation, and its quality and accessibility. Some of its seams of unexcelled coking coal crop out along the banks of the Monongahela at water level. The average thickness of minable coal is seven feet. Most of the iron ore which the coke prepared from this coal will turn into pig iron lies hundreds of miles to the northwest, but the interposition of the Great Lakes alleviates this situation. Excellent steam coal is found in Virginia and West Virginia—the Pocahontas and New River fields—hundreds of miles from tidewater; this means that the low price at the mine mouth is more than doubled at tidewater because of the transportation involved.

Because of the rarity of good coking coal needed in the form of coke in blast furnace operation, two regions stand out from the rest of the coal-bearing areas in the world; they are destined to be leaders in modern industrial civilization. The Connellsville region of the United States is one, and the Ruhr region of Germany is the other. England has coking coal, but not as much nor as good as either the United States or Germany has. Japan is worse off, and most of the other iron-producing countries are even more handicapped.

British Coal Fields

Great Britain has several famous coal fields which have made world history. Newcastle and Cardiff are names to conjure with. But more important than any one field is the amazing manner in which all the various fields form a well-correlated whole of diverse elements, each peculiarly suited, by the rank of the coal it contains, to serve the regions most accessible to it.

The value of a coal deposit depends on its availability for use. A region which possesses coals unsuitable to its needs may not be much better off than one which lacks coal. The coal deposits of the United Kingdom furnish a remarkable example of close harmony between specific properties of local supplies and regional requirements. The rapid progress made by

FIG. 26.2.   The Coal Fields of Great Britain. (L. D. Stamp, "Britain's Coal Crisis," *Geographical Review*, April, 1948.)

Britain's coal mining industry up to World War I is partly explained by the almost miraculous manner in which the various types of coal happened to fit the specific requirements of the markets they could most readily serve. Thus the major portion of the famous South Wales coal field consists of coal admirably suited for bunker purposes. A glance at Fig. 26.2 shows that the Bristol Channel cuts way into this region, making such ports as Cardiff and Newport easily accessible to the merchant fleets of the world, to say nothing of the British Navy. The coal of Durhamshire, on the other hand, is an excellent gas coal which could be

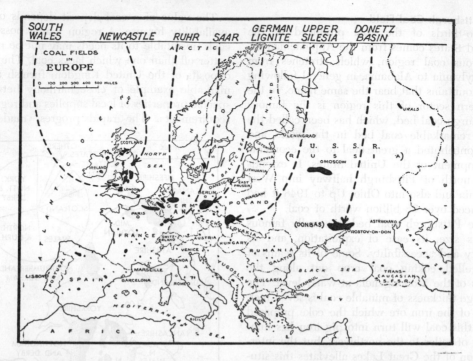

FIG. 26.3. (From H. S. Hoar, *The Coal Industry of the World,* U. S. Department of Commerce, Bureau of Foreign and Domestic Commerce, 1930.)

readily sold not only to English and Scottish gas works but also to those on the continent. It moved via Hamburg to Berlin, via Le Havre to Paris, up the Rhine to Cologne and all the way to Mannheim. Just to the north of this lies another field of excellent steam coal made famous by the expression, "Carrying coals to Newcastle." In the Black Country of the midlands region, coal suitable for conversion into metallurgical coke was found in close proximity to iron ore and limestone. It is indeed difficult to imagine a more ideal distribution of specific types of coal than that found in Britain.

Unfortunately, much of this advantage of location is offset by unfavorable working conditions which account for high pit prices and which have been aggravated by prolonged exploitation. In the United States the argument is occasionally heard that the British fell behind in the technical proficiency of coal mining, especially behind the United States and Germany. Since the government has taken over the coal mines, however, some efforts to raise the efficiency of Britain's coal mines have been made.

The Ruhr

On the continent of Europe (see Fig. 26.3) one coal field, the Ruhr, stands out as exceptionally important not only for Germany but for the entire continent. The Ruhr acquired world-wide notoriety during the aftermath of World War I when France, believing herself forsaken by her Allies, marched into that section in quest of her own security. Its transcendent value to the European economy was again deeply and bitterly realized during the economic chaos and despair following World War II. More than one statesman pointed to the Ruhr as the focal point of European recovery.

The Ruhr district is the most important coal field in Europe; among world centers it ranks second only to the Pittsburgh district of the United States. In 1937 it produced 127.8 million metric tons of coal—three times as much as all France and more than the entire Soviet Union. Its coal of excellent coking quality formed the basis for chemical and metallurgical industries. The coal mined in the Ruhr in 1937 contained more power than was produced by all the hydroelectric installations in the world in that year (the equivalent of 200 billion kilowatt-hours, as compared with 172 billion kilowatt-hours).[21]

The Ruhr district possesses an unusual combination of favorable circumstances. It has the greatest coal reserves in Europe, the seams being, relatively, both thick and numerous. Its coal field is the best-located on the Continent; the Ruhr is near the North Sea, focus of world shipping, and is centrally located for the Western European markets. The deep and regular Rhine River provides a magnificent navigable waterway through the western part of the field, and adjoining canals lead through the district. A dense network of railroads connects the Ruhr with other parts of Germany and Europe. The high state of German technical development found expression in efficient mining and extensive use of coal products. A powerful national organization of production and sales stabilized exploitation.

The reserves of coal in the Ruhr constitute 90 per cent of the bituminous deposits of Germany (pre-World War II boundaries) and may equal the combined total for all other coal fields of continental Europe outside the U.S.S.R. The concessions being mined at the beginning of World War II had enough proved commercial reserves to depths of less than 4000 feet to last for 250 years at the peak rate of production. The possible physical reserves, more than 200 billion tons, would be enough to last for perhaps 2000 years.[22]

During recent decades, especially after World War I, Germany more than any country pushed the development of her brown coal deposits. Although this coal is of unusually poor rank,[23] it became the basis of vast chemical

---

[21] Figures for coal production are those of the Reichskohlenrat, *Statistische Übersicht über die Kohlenwirtschaft im Jahre 1938*, Berlin, pp. 23, 76, 125. The data on hydroelectric power production were kindly supplied by Nathaniel B. Guyol.

[22] Chauncy D. Harris, "The Ruhr Coal Mining District," *Geographical Review*, April, 1946, pp. 194-221. This is an excellent monograph.

[23] It is customary to figure 4½ tons of German brown coal as equal to one ton of average bituminous coal.

BIBLIOGRAPHY

See the bibliography at the end of Chapter 29.

industries and of electric power generation. The upper Silesian coal field, next to the Ruhr the largest and best one in Europe, is now in the hands of Poland and Czechoslovakia, satellites of the Soviet Union.

The Donets Basin

In point of output, the most important coal field of the Soviet Union is the Donets Basin, or the Donbas, located in the southeastern section of the Ukraine (see Fig. 42.4). Its importance springs in part from the excellence of its location close to the iron ore deposits of Krivoi Rog, a few hundred miles west of the Donbas, and of the Kerch peninsula to the south, and to the manganese deposits of nearby Nikopol. It is easily reached by pipe line from the oil fields of the north Caucasus and the refineries of Rostov-on-Don. It lies only a short distance east of the great hydroelectric center of the Dneprostroi.

It is Soviet policy to spread its industries over the entire area from Poland to the Pacific. In the course of the eastward push of heavy industry, important coal fields of Siberia have come into production—the Kizel field of the Urals, the Karaganda field in Kazakstan, the Kuznetsk field in central Siberia, and so on all the way to Komsomolsk. Vast coal deposits located in northeastern Siberia have not yet entered the picture but may play an important role in the future.

The Fushun Mines

The Fushun coal deposits near Mukden, Manchuria, have the thickest bed—417 feet—of bituminous coal in the world. From this mine comes most of the coal produced in Manchuria, which in 1941 amounted to about 20 million tons. Fushun coal supplies the steelworks of Anshan, which constituted the backbone of Japan's steel industry on the mainland, producing 1,750,000 tons of pig iron and one million tons of steel.

Chapter 27

WORLD COAL PRODUCTION

Since coal is the basic fuel of industry, the world-wide urge to industrialize brings with it a global diffusion of coal production. In the nineteenth century coal production was largely confined to the countries around the North Atlantic. Today coal is produced also in both the European and Asiatic sectors of the Soviet Union, in India, Japan, Manchuria, China, Australia, South Africa, Chile, Peru, Brazil, Mexico, and many other countries.

World coal statistics, especially those covering a considerable period of time, are complicated by the changes in national frontiers which have resulted from two World Wars. This complication, however, is largely confined to Europe. Thus the Silesian coal field, which until 1919 was one of the mainstays of German industry and perhaps her largest coal reserve, is now in possession of Poland and Czechoslovakia, and, indirectly, of the U.S.S.R. The great lignite deposits of Saxony, which supported much of Germany's chemical industry and contributed materially to her power supply, now lie in the Russian zone. The Ruhr has been internationalized. The Saar, under French control for fifteen years after World War I and

then reverting to Germany in 1934, has been ceded to France. Manchuria, for many years under Japanese occupation, has come under the control of the Chinese Communists, as have also the most important coal fields of China proper. These facts must be borne in mind if the tables of world coal production are to be interpreted properly.

WORLD PRODUCTION STATISTICS

The total world coal production[1] increased as follows:

1880	365 million short tons	
1890	564 " " "
1900	846 " " "
1910	1279 " " "
1920	1455 " " "
1930	1559 " " "
1940	1980 " " "
1947	1803 " " "

[1] The figures for 1880 to 1930 are from C. K. Leith, J. W. Furness, and C. Lewis, *World Minerals and World Peace*, Brookings Institution, Washington, 1943, p. 213. Those for 1940 and 1947 are from Bureau of Mines, *Bituminous Coal and Lignite in 1947*, Mineral Market Series, No. 1664, p. 76. Metric tons have been converted into short tons. Lignite and brown coal have not been corrected to the bituminous coal equivalent.

The rapid rise from 365 million short tons in 1880 to 1279 in 1910, an increase of 914 million in thirty years, is truly remarkable. However, the increase in the next thirty years amounted to only 700 million. A better than threefold increase during the first thirty-year period is in sharp contrast to the modest increase of less than two-thirds in the next period. The reasons for this slowing down will be discussed later.

During the seventeenth and eighteenth centuries England was the only important producer and exporter of coal; at the beginning of the nineteenth century Belgium was her only rival. Because of its relatively well-developed coal industry, the Borinage, as the coal mining region of southern Belgium is called, was the object of covetous designs on the part of the ruling powers of that period. Not until the last decades of the nineteenth century did Great Britain yield to the United States her position as the leading coal producer of the world.

Statistical material on coal production is inadequate up until 1860, and what has happened since then can be told very briefly in terms of the production figures shown in Tables 27.1 and 27.2.

TABLE 27.1. Production of Coal in Principal Countries 1860–1913[2] (in million metric tons)

Year	Belgium	France	Germany	United Kingdom	United States
1860	9.6	8.1	12.3	80.0	15.2
1871	13.7	12.9	29.3	117.4	42.5
1880	16.9	18.8	47.0	147.0	64.8
1890	20.4	25.6	70.2	181.6	143.1
1900	23.5	32.7	109.3	225.2	244.6
1913	22.8	40.8	190.1[a]	292.0	571.1

[a] Exclusive of 87.2 million tons of brown coal.

Much human history—triumph and tragedy—is packed into these figures. The meteoric rise of the United States as a coal producer—from a mere 15.2 million metric tons in 1860, less than a fifth of the British output in that year, to about 620 million metric tons in 1948—is outstanding. The United States passed Great Britain around the turn of the century. After

[2] Figures for 1860 to 1900 from I. Lubin, "Coal," *Encyclopædia of the Social Sciences;* figures for 1913 from Bureau of Mines, *Mineral Resources of the United States,* 1913.

World War I both the British and our own figures started to level off, but while our output reached a new peak in World War II, bombed Britain, short of the manpower and capital sorely needed for overdue mechanization, dropped temporarily even behind Germany but came back strongly after World War II. Germany is the only country in which lignite and brown coal are intensively exploited. Though poor fuels in their natural state, they can yield electric power at unusually low cost, and can be converted into gas, gasoline, synthetic rubber, etc. The peak of Germany's war performance in 1942—252.0 million metric tons of coal and 244.6 million metric tons of lignite and brown coal—is impressive. Compared with these three giants, other countries, including such industrial nations as France and Belgium, make but a modest showing. The remarkably rapid increase of production in the Soviet Union, from 36 million metric tons in 1913 to approximately 175 million in 1947, reflects the expansion of coal production into the heart of Asiatic Russia. Poland possesses one of the richest and best coal fields in the world, that of Upper Silesia. It is of great economic and political importance for eastern Europe. The rapid increase in Chinese coal production was largely the result of military needs during the Japanese occupation.

COAL PRODUCTION IN THE UNITED STATES

By far the greatest coal producer in the world, the United States is the only country whose production of anthracite is so large that it is customary to cite figures for anthracite and bituminous coal separately.

Anthracite Coal

The anthracite industry is almost completely confined to eastern Pennsylvania in the area around Wilkes-Barre, including the Wyoming, Schuylkill, and Lehigh regions. There is some anthracite in Virginia, Arkansas, Colorado, and Washington, but production in these states is of minor importance. Pennsylvania is credited with 94.64 percent of the nation's anthracite reserve, Virginia with 3.17 percent, and Arkansas with 1.44. Anthracite production in the United States first passed the million-ton mark during the 1840's and exceeded bituminous production until about 1870; the average an-

TABLE 27.2.   Total Production of Coal in Selected Countries for Selected Years[3]
(thousand metric tons)

	1923	1929	1932	1937	1942	1944	1947	1948
United States	596,837	552,306	326,190	451,220	583,335	619,855	624,044	641,170
United Kingdom	280,430	262,046	212,083	244,268	208,231	195,839	202,948	210,841
Germany[a]	88,713	202,209	131,996	225,299	313,767	186,627	121,414	...
U.S.S.R.[b]	11,272	37,791	60,071	110,500	...	...	175,000[g]	...
Poland[c]	36,170	46,163	28,793	36,222	...	...	60,199	...
France[d]	47,163	67,758	57,042	44,686	42,521	25,686	45,928	43,872
Czechoslovakia	21,915	30,018	20,319	27,301	36,971	39,030	29,460	31,626
Belgium	22,922	26,940	21,424	29,859	25,055	13,529	24,390	26,679
Netherlands	5,299	11,634	12,798	14,369	12,423	8,394	10,262	11,032
Japan[e]	...	...	...	45,334	55,183	50,775	28,094	...
Union of South Africa	11,253	13,018	9,921	15,491	20,408	22,987	23,127	...
China[f]	24,552	15,186	18,858	22,520	41,214	37,002[g]	20,000[g]	...
Canada	15,281	15,697	10,381	14,048	16,720	15,031	12,622	16,204

[a] Data for 1935-1942 include the Saar.
[b] Data for 1923 and 1929 on fiscal year basis, October-September.
[c] Data for 1942 and after represent production from Polish mines and from former German Upper and Lower Silesian mines under Polish control.
[d] Data for 1923-1932 include the Saar.
[e] Data for 1942 and 1944 for fiscal year, April-March.
[f] Excludes Manchuria, Formosa, and Kwantung leased territory.
[g] Estimated.

nual output of anthracite in 1871-1875 was 23.4 million net tons as against 28.8 million for bituminous. From then on, the two coals part company, bituminous shooting up to a total of almost 600 million tons in 1918 and anthracite reaching its peak in 1917, with 99.64 million tons. Anthracite dropped below 50 million tons during the depression and never rose above 63.7 during World War II. (Instead of the metric tons used in international coal statistics, short tons are used in United States coal statistics.)

Because of its smokelessness, anthracite holds a preferential position in the household and commercial markets, though of late it has faced increasing competition from natural gas and fuel oil. It sells at prices considerably above those of bituminous coal. Average pit-head prices for the two kinds of coal are shown in Table 27.3.

In point of aggregate value, therefore, anthracite greatly exceeds its significance, measured in tons. Thus, while 63.7 million tons of anthracite were produced in 1944 as against 619.6 million tons of bituminous, a ratio of approximately 1 to 10, the respective aggregate values were $354.6 million for anthracite

and $1810.9 million for bituminous coal, a ratio of approximately 1 to 5.

One might say that anthracite is a specialty which can demand a price in keeping with its peculiar qualifications but which cannot invade other markets without losing its price advantage. Bituminous coals enter many markets and therefore have to fight it out with both rival fuels and hydroelectricity.

TABLE 27.3.   Average Annual Prices of Anthracite and Bituminous Coal[4]

	Anthracite	Bituminous
1890	$1.43	$ .90
1900	1.49	1.04
1910	1.90	1.12
1920	4.85	3.75
1930	5.11	1.70
1940	3.99	1.91
1945	6.26	3.06
1946	7.25	3.44
1947	7.65	4.16
1948	8.67	4.95

Moreover, the cost structure of the two branches of the industry is quite different. Whereas a large portion of the bituminous output can be produced cheaply because of unusually favorable conditions regarding occur-

[3] Bureau of Mines, 1948.

[4] Bureau of Mines, Minerals Yearbook.

rence and location, Pennsylvania's anthracite industry in general is an old industry that is definitely up against the law of increasing cost. The anthracite region has been exploited for a long time and approximately a third of its original coal endowment has been taken out or lost in the process—about 7 billion tons out of 21 billion. Although natural conditions are not as favorable to the mechanization of anthracite mines as they are in many bituminous mines, in recent years the output per man has been sharply increased by mechanical improvements. Thus, during the seven years 1927-1933, the output of anthracite per man per year was under 500 tons; under the impact of wartime conditions it rose as high as 815 tons in 1944. For the same seven-year period, bituminous output averaged slightly less than 900 tons per worker per year and rose to 1575 tons in 1944.[5]

As a result of this difference in labor productivity, the anthracite industry employs a far larger number of miners than its share of the nation's total coal output would indicate. The average number of employees in the Pennsylvania anthracite industry was 126,000 in 1890, 157,783 in 1923, and 77,591 in 1944. The corresponding figures for the bituminous industry are 192,204 in 1890, 704,793 (peak) in 1923, and 393,347 in 1944. In 1890 the number of Pennsylvania anthracite miners was about three-fourths the number of the bituminous miners. In 1944 the worker ratio was about 1 to 5, while the output ratio was nearer to 1 to 10.

The Pennsylvania anthracite industry is often cited as an example of natural monopoly, or something as close to that theoretical concept as one can hope to find today. For many decades anthracite was the only smokeless fuel available, and in some cases this favorable market situation was strengthened by city ordinances. The anthracite reserves are concentrated in a very small area, and their ownership was similarly concentrated in a few hands, especially the "hard-coal railroads"—the Lackawanna, Philadelphia and Reading, Erie, and Lehigh.

But anthracite's formidable position was attacked by that deadly enemy, commodity competition. Fuel oil and natural gas sapped the market and forced the industry to retreat from its peak output of almost 100 million tons during World War I to somewhere between half and two-thirds that amount after 1930, a retreat that brought painful adjustments in its train.[6] From a peak of almost 180,000, the number of miners dropped to less than 80,000. Some of the 100,000 who lost their jobs went into the "bootleg anthracite business"—one of the strangest fruits on the tree of our economy. Bootleg anthracite is coal dug by squatters from other people's property; in some years its output ran to several million tons.

Bituminous Coal

When our Civil War broke out, this country's output of bituminous coal had not yet reached the modest figure of 20 million tons, but after 1865 production climbed steadily and steeply until during World War I it reached the remarkable figure of 568.7 million net tons. Thereafter the output began to falter, seesawing up and down during the twenties and dropping to a low of 310 million tons in 1932, during the Great Depression. But it recovered during World War II and hit a new peak of 619.0 million tons in 1944. This was exceeded in 1947, when 630.6 million tons were produced. In 1948 and 1949 strikes reduced the output by considerable amounts.

Table 27.4 shows coal production, both anthracite and bituminous, in the United States from 1821-1948.

Fig. 27.1 shows capacity, production, average value per ton, and net income of the bituminous and lignite coal industry during the period 1905-1947. It depicts more than the recent trend, for it sheds light on two grave aspects of this country's bituminous coal industry—overcapacity and unprofitableness. Assuming 308 days of work during the year, i.e., excluding Sundays and holidays, the industry had a full-time capacity of close to one billion tons in 1923, whereas output during the period 1921-1927 inclusive averaged slightly under half a billion tons.

The enormous overcapacity in 1923 was due

---

[5] Incidentally, around 1948, bituminous coal mines in the United States averaged close to 6 tons per worker per day, as against about 1 ton in Great Britain.

[6] See the revealing account of the anthracite industry in George R. Leighton, *America's Growing Pains*, Harper & Brothers, New York, 1939, chap. 1.

TABLE 27.4. United States Coal Production, 1821-1948[7]
(Quantity in thousand short tons; value in thousand dollars)

Year or Yearly Average	Quantity Total	Anthracite	Bituminous
1821-1830	140	66	75
1831-1840	1,032	722	310
1841-1850	4,535	2,697	1,837
1851-1860	12,513	7,645	4,868
1861-1865	20,538	11,142	9,396
1866-1870	31,706	16,281	15,425
1871-1875	52,179	23,407	28,773
1876-1880	62,261	25,800	36,461
1881-1885	107,291	36,198	71,093
1886-1890	138,398	43,952	94,446
1891-1895	178,822	53,405	125,416
1896-1900	227,123	55,625	171,498
1901-1905	339,357	66,854	272,503
1906-1910	454,555	81,142	373,413
1911-1915	529,189	89,233	439,956
1916-1920	626,386	92,741	533,645
1921-1925	558,947	77,648	481,299
1926-1930	595,497	76,619	518,878
1931-1935	405,108	53,674	351,434
1936-1940	468,860	51,101	417,758
1941-1945	635,606	59,195	576,519
1918	678,212	98,826	579,386
1919	553,952	88,092	465,860
1920	658,265	89,598	568,667
1921	506,395	90,473	415,922

Year	Quantity Total	Anthracite	Bituminous	Value Anthracite	Bituminous[a]
1922	476,951	54,683	422,268	273,700	1,274,820
1923	657,904	93,339	564,565	506,787	1,514,621
1924	571,613	87,927	483,687	477,231	1,062,626
1925	581,870	61,817	520,053	327,665	1,060,402
1926	657,804	84,437	573,367	474,164	1,183,412
1927	597,859	80,096	517,763	420,942	1,029,657
1928	576,093	75,348	500,745	393,638	933,774
1929	608,817	73,828	534,989	385,643	952,781
1930	536,911	69,385	467,526	354,574	795,483
1931	441,735	59,646	382,089	296,355	588,895
1932	359,565	49,855	309,710	222,375	406,677
1933	383,172	49,541	333,631	206,718	445,788
1934	416,536	57,168	359,368	244,152	628,383
1935	424,532	52,159	372,373	210,131	658,063
1936	493,668	54,580	439,088	227,004	770,955
1937	497,387	51,856	445,531	197,599	864,042
1938	394,644	46,099	348,545	180,600	678,653
1939	446,342	51,487	394,855	187,175	728,348
1940	512,257	51,485	460,772	205,490	879,327
1941	570,518	56,368	514,149	240,275	1,125,363
1942	643,021	60,328	582,693	271,673	1,373,991
1943	650,821	60,644	590,177	306,816	1,584,644
1944	683,278	63,701	619,576	354,583	1,810,901
1945	630,934	54,934	576,000[b]	323,944	1,777,336[b]
1946	584,429	50,507	533,922	413,417	1,835,539
1947	687,814	57,190	630,624	413,019	2,622,625
1948	651,140	57,140	594,000	467,052	2,940,300

[a] Excludes selling expenses through 1936 and for 1939. Data for other years include selling expenses.
[b] Preliminary (recent years).

[7] Statistical Abstracts, 1948. Figures for recent years from U.S. Bureau of Mines.

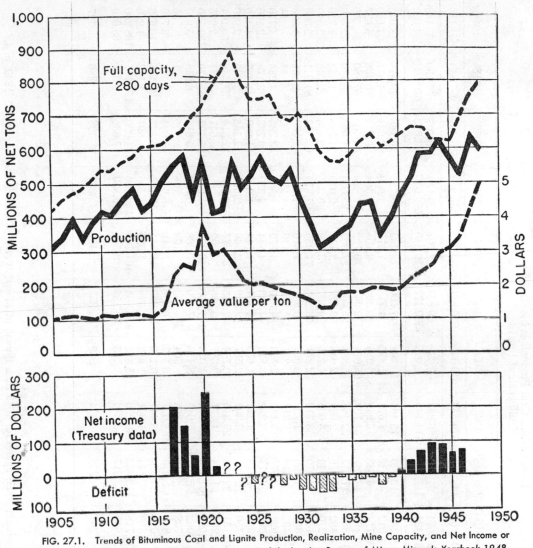

FIG. 27.1. Trends of Bituminous Coal and Lignite Production, Realization, Mine Capacity, and Net Income or Deficit, United States, 1905-1948. (U. S. Department of the Interior, Bureau of Mines, *Minerals Yearbook 1948*, 1950.)

mainly to two facts. (1) During World War I and immediately afterward, coal prices rose to great heights, almost quadrupling by 1920 and bringing wartime prosperity to a starving industry. This led to an enormous expansion of capacity. (2) No one at that time foresaw the drastic downward trend in the demand for bituminous coal resulting from the incredible rise of oil, natural gas, and water power and the spectacular advances made in using coal economically.

Bituminous Production by States. Before going further into the analysis of the over-capacity that constitutes the crisis in the coal industry, which incidentally is by no means confined to the United States, attention is drawn to some significant geographical shifts in bituminous production in this country (see Table 27.5). The most significant shift is that from the northern states—Pennsylvania, Ohio, Indiana, and Illinois—to the southern states, West Virginia, Virginia, and Kentucky. From 1913 to 1939 the four northern states showed a loss of 112.2 million tons, and the three southern states a gain of 64.8 million tons. Peak production in the old fields was reached during World

Table 27.5. Coal Production by States[g]
(million short tons)

State	1921–1925	1926–1930	1931–1935	1936–1940	1941	1942	1943	1944	1945	1946	1947	1948
Total quantity	558,947	595,497	405,108	468,860	570,518	643,021	650,821	683,278	630,934	594,429	687,814	651,140
Anthracite (Pa.)	77,648	76,619	53,674	51,101	56,368	60,328	60,644	63,701	54,934	60,507	57,190	57,140
Bituminous	481,299	518,878	351,434	417,758	514,149	582,693	590,177	619,576	576,000	533,922	630,624	594,000
Alabama	18,097	18,380	9,252	12,620	15,465	19,301	17,160	18,752	18,737	16,183	19,048	18,040
Arkansas	1,261	1,579	1,012	1,387	1,574	1,985	1,718	1,972	4,600[a]	1,631	1,871	1,660
Colorado	10,049	9,665	5,711	6,435	6,949	8,086	8,324	8,168	7,668	5,914	6,358	5,627
Illinois	68,523	57,310	40,198	48,367	54,703	65,071	72,631	76,792	72,525	63,469	67,860	66,500
Indiana	21,677	18,467	14,386	17,232	22,484	25,388	25,065	27,962	25,500	21,697	25,449	22,500
Iowa	4,952	3,879	3,492	3,376	2,939	2,948	2,771	2,141	2,010	1,788	1,684	1,750
Kansas	3,927	3,215	2,270	2,949	4,008	4,230	3,437	3,369	6,995[b]	2,493	2,745	2,615
Kentucky	43,743	61,116	38,130	44,970	53,710	62,231	63,211	71,356	67,875	66,553	84,241	82,000
Maryland	2,033	2,700	1,654	1,496	1,701	2,001	1,933	1,870	1,765	2,003	2,051	1,596
Michigan	976	705	492	510	311	231	169	140	125	80	14	14
Missouri	3,011	3,538	3,624	3,577	3,145	3,520	4,310	4,779	... [c]	3,733	4,236	4,470
Montana	2,881	3,139	2,396	2,871	3,254	3,829	4,833	4,844	4,550	3,723	3,178	2,800
New Mexico	2,772	2,612	1,338	1,378	1,251	1,669	1,851	1,744	1,500	1,280	1,443	1,420
North Dakota	1,221	1,622	1,750	2,161	2,309	2,537	2,500	2,366	2,523[d]	2,555	2,760	2,990[d]
Ohio	31,590	21,111	19,151	22,188	29,319	32,764	32,255	33,877	32,715	32,314	37,548	36,104
Oklahoma	2,741	3,346	1,368	1,444	1,771	2,387	2,838	3,209	e	2,647	3,421	2,925
Pennsylvania	133,721	137,038	86,592	101,556	130,240	144,073	141,050	146,052	131,650	125,497	147,079	132,550
Tennessee	5,078	5,544	4,062	5,197	7,045	8,158	7,179	7,266	6,600	5,618	6,258	5,910
Texas	1,084	1,107	738	816	353	304	153	109	108	56[f]	61[f]	56
Utah	4,593	4,683	2,846	3,373	4,077	5,517	6,666	7,119	6,644	5,994	7,429	6,716
Virginia	10,648	12,521	8,923	13,324	18,441	20,136	20,280	19,514	18,105	15,527	20,171	19,620
Washington	2,626	2,513	1,555	1,744	1,841	1,953	1,528	1,524	1,376	991	1,118	1,210
West Virginia	97,044	136,315	95,748	112,932	140,250	155,882	158,804	164,704	152,200	144,020	176,157	168,200
Wyoming	6,812	6,526	4,545	5,617	6,646	8,133	9,155	9,540	9,890	7,635	8,051	63,000
Other states and Alaska	239	246	201	238	364	359	356	407	339	407	386	427

[a] Includes Oklahoma.
[b] Includes Missouri.
[c] Included with Kansas.
[d] Included with South Dakota.
[e] Included with Arkansas.
[f] Lignite only.

[g] Figures for 1921–1947 from *Minerals Yearbook, 1948*; figures for 1948 from Bureau of Mines, *Weekly Coal Report*, February 25, 1949, p. 4.

War I or immediately thereafter while in the newer fields it was reached during World War II. There are many reasons for this shift.

The Northern Appalachian fields as a group continued to dominate the markets, increasing spectacularly in production until about the time of World War I. On the other hand, the middle and southern fields, when once started, increased even more rapidly than the northern group. Of the several reasons for this development, probably the most important is the increase in railroad facilities.[9] The last quarter of the nineteenth century and the first two or three decades of the twentieth century witnessed a great expansion of the rail net of the middle and southern Appalachians. The lines constructed to connect the middle Appalachians with the Great Lakes cities and with Norfolk and thence by water with New England and New York City were designed especially to carry coal;[10] they did a highly efficient job of it. Availability of these railroads opened the gates for a flood of easily mined coal destined for New England and the rising industrial area along the Great Lakes.

There were other contributing causes for the relative rise of the middle and southern Appalachians. The coal seams were, on the average, thicker than those still undeveloped in the North, and superior roof and other physical conditions in the middle Appalachians made mining easier than in the northern fields. The requirements of by-product coking, which largely replaced the use of beehive ovens in the 1920's, could be met by blending several coals. This fact reduced the premium value of coal from the Pittsburgh bed relative to coal from other areas and loosened the grip of the Pittsburgh District on both coke manufacture and the iron and steel industry. Unionization of labor did not become widespread in much of the middle and southern fields until the 1930's; consequently labor costs have in general been lower than in the North. These same fields, where they are in competition with the northern fields, have enjoyed freight rates to the Atlantic coast and to the Great Lakes that northern operators have contended are more favorable than they should be. Certain of the fields of southern West Virginia and western Virginia produce high-grade steam coals that have been in

much demand. Also, in the newer fields of southern West Virginia and eastern Kentucky coal lands have been acquired at relatively low prices, whereas the high valuation put upon coal lands in Pennsylvania and Ohio has burdened their owners with high depletion and often with high interest.[11] And, finally, the rise of the middle and southern Appalachians was promoted by the repeated strikes that shut down the northern mines during the decade following World War I.[12]

But probably the most important reason of all, as the authors of the above statement point out, is the fact that the older areas have been exploited much longer and have therefore lost some of the advantage of "cream skimming," whereas the newer fields still possess that advantage to a large degree.

During World War II the northern area temporarily regained some of its earlier lead. This is largely explained by the rapid expansion of industrial output, especially steel production, in that area. Coke production in particular increased in response to wartime needs.

The seven states covered in this discussion of geographical shifts constitute the core of this country's bituminous coal industry. In 1913, their aggregate production was 388.5 million tons out of a total of 478.4 million tons, or over 80 percent. In 1939 the figures were 341.1 million tons out of a total of 394.9, or not far below 90 percent. By the end of 1946, each of these states, except Virginia, had produced close to or over one billion tons; their aggregate was 18,676.8 million tons, or slightly over 80 percent of our total production of 23,196.0 million. The only other states producing an average of over 10 million tons were Alabama and Colorado, both of them states in which iron and steel industries are located.

Coal Production and Coal Reserves

It is evident from this discussion of production by states that there is a sharp contrast

[9] F. G. Tryon and B. W. Allin, "The Southern Appalachian Coal Plateaus," in Carter Goodrich and others, *Migration and Economic Opportunity*, Philadelphia, 1936, p. 94.

[10] For details of these coal movements in 1937, see W. H. Voskuil, "Bituminous Coal Movements in the United States," *Geographical Review*, vol. 32, 1942, pp. 117-127.

[11] C. E. Fraser and G. F. Doriot, *Analyzing Our Industries*, McGraw-Hill Book Company, Inc., New York, 1932, p. 369.

[12] See E. R. Murphy and H. E. Spitta, "Movements of the Center of Coal Mining in the Appalachian Plateau," *Geographical Review*, October 1945, pp. 628-629. The authors confine their discussion to the northern portion of the northern coal region.

between the eastern states, which lead in production, and the western states, which lead in reserves. Whatever correlation there may be between reserves and output would be definitely negative. Production thrives near the market when the right kinds of coal are available to meet existing demands at the right price. In

TABLE 27.6. United States Bituminous Coal Consumption 1937, 1946, and 1947[13] (million net tons)

Uses	1937	1946	1947[a]
Industry	216.7	218.2	247.0
Coke	74.5	83.3	104.6
Iron and steel, including coke	87.4	96.9	114.6
Railroads	88.1	110.2	109.3
Retail deliveries[b]	80.1	100.6	99.2
Electric power utilities	42.9	68.7	86.0
Colliery fuel	3.1	2.0	2.5
Foreign bunker[c]	1.8	1.4	1.7
Total uses accounted for	432.6	500.5	545.7
Total coal produced	445.5	533.9	619.0

[a] Preliminary.
[b] Mostly for space heating.
[c] Coal used under boilers in steamships engaged in foreign trade.

[13] *Minerals Yearbook, 1948.*

BIBLIOGRAPHY

See the bibliography at the end of Chapter 29.

other words, the deposits that are exploited first are those which are near the hub of the country's industrial life—i.e., the Northeast, near the centers of population—and which yield the most suitable coals at the lowest costs.

MAJOR USES OF COAL IN THE UNITED STATES

The consumption of bituminous coal in the United States can best be shown in tabular form, as in Table 27.6.

The year 1937 saw an encouraging business upswing; 1946 was a year of unusual general business activity but was marred by a serious coal strike. This may account for the relatively poor showing of industrial coal users. Evidently they were turning to competitive fuels and relying more heavily on central power-station electricity. In general, coal consumption falls far short of reflecting the enormous expansion of economic activity which took place during this decade. The reasons will be explained more fully later.[14]

[14] Early in 1949 it was reported that in 1948, for the first time, the utilities had exceeded the railroads as consumers of coal. While the steam locomotive is yielding to Diesels, the utility industry is in the midst of a large expansion program.

Chapter 28

THE BITUMINOUS COAL INDUSTRY OF THE UNITED STATES

STRUCTURE

The structure of the bituminous coal industry reflects (1) the heterogeneous nature of coal as it occurs in the crust of the earth and the resulting diversity of coal operations, and (2) the ideologies and institutions of the United States.

As has already been brought out, coals occur under highly diverse conditions. Some lie near the surface, some deep below. Some crop out on hillsides or river banks, some can be reached only by driving shafts down to the seam. Some seams cover large areas and are of considerable thickness, some are small and lean. Some lie near the market, some far away; and so forth.

The industry clearly reflects this diversity of natural conditions under which it operates. It is made up both of giant concerns that produce many millions of tons and are capitalized as high as $100 million and more, and of a huge army of small or middle-sized mines, not to mention the thousands of fly-by-night "snowbirds" and "wagon mines."[1]

Classification of Mines

The census divides coal mines into five classes on the basis of annual output. Table 28.1 shows this classification, and the number of active mines of commercial size[2] in each class in 1945. The total number is probably much higher because the unknown number of small "mines" that produce less than 1000 tons a year are excluded from the classification. Coal mines are scattered over thirty states.

Small coal mines survive for many reasons. They may be operated as a side line in primitive fashion, with little overhead and low return for the labor and capital put into them. They may be operated although they would not show profits if orthodox accounting methods were used. They may lie in a remote section protected by the high transportation charges on fuel brought in from the outside. Over-

---

[1] "Snowbirds" are operators who produce coal during the winter months when the demand for domestic fuel is strong. "Wagon mines" are so called because their main equipment is a wagon with which coal is hauled from "a hole in the ground."

[2] Any mine producing over 1000 tons a year is called a mine of commercial size. This term must not be confused with the term commercial mine used in the next section.

head is apt to be low, hence costs may be low even if production methods are not very efficient. They may supply a small local market and thus not have to resort to heavy sales campaigns. They may happen to tap a small pocket of good coal that is easily mined.

TABLE 28.1. Census Classification of Mines, and Number of Mines in Each Class in 1945
(Source: *Minerals Yearbook, 1947*)

Class	Annual Output (tons)	Number of Mines
1	200,000 and over	753
2	100,000–200,000	591
3	50,000–100,000	629
4	10,000– 50,000	1920
5	1,000– 10,000	3140

Commercial vs. Captive Mines

Two groups of coal mines must be sharply distinguished: the so-called commercial mines, which sell in the open market, and the so-called captive mines, which are owned by industrial concerns such as the large steel corporations, the leading automobile manufacturers, etc. The line of cleavage is not clear cut. Thus the Koppers Company, one of the largest owners of captive mines, is perhaps the largest seller of coal in the commercial market. The reason is simple. The mining properties which yield the types and grades of coal the company needs for its by-product coke ovens and chemical plants also yield other types and grades for which it has no use but which can be marketed elsewhere.[3]

It is estimated that roughly one-fourth of our bituminous coal output is produced by captive mines. This virtually withdraws from the commercial mines a sizable portion of the market and more or less deprives them of the heavy industrial demand which might otherwise serve as a backlog for them.

The motives behind the acquisition of captive mines vary. An industrial firm may be in search of a dependable source of a particular variety of coal—good metallurgical coking coal, high-grade steam coal, etc. Or the opportunity of acquiring large coal lands at bargain prices may be the determining factor. In the past, some companies have felt that this was a means of safeguarding against interruption of coal

supplies because of strikes in commercial mines. This argument had particular appeal when unionization of coal mines stopped at the Mason-Dixon line—many captive mines are located in Kentucky, Tennessee, Virginia, and West Virginia, just across the line—but it is hardly applicable today.

Railroads are largely barred from owning coal mines by the commodity clause of the Interstate Commerce Act, which forbids public carriers to haul the products of their own mines. This clause was primarily directed at the monopoly which the hard-coal roads had acquired in the Pennsylvania anthracite fields. Nor do the electric power companies own mines, for they require special grades of coal which can be produced most cheaply as joint or by-products of other grades. Railroads and public utilities often purchase coal under long-term contracts.

MINING METHODS

The heterogeneity of coals affects mining methods as well as the structure of the industry. Under certain conditions, strip mining can be used, but under other conditions only underground mining is suitable.

Strip Mining

A coal seam that is thick enough to warrant exploitation, is fairly horizontal, and has only a thin or moderately thick cover of earth—or overburden, as it is sometimes called—may be worked by a comparatively new method known as strip mining, in which the overburden is stripped off by giant shovels and the coal itself is then scooped up. This method has several advantages. It is likely to be economical, and the usual mining problems—water control, ventilation, and the danger of explosion—are more or less absent. However, although labor productivity is usually high,[4] strip mining may require a fairly large investment for preparatory work and mechanized equipment.

The first official records which include strip mining are those for 1914, when 0.3 percent of the bituminous coal and lignite produced in the United States was mined in that way.

---

[3] See "Koppers," *Fortune*, April, 1947.

[4] In 1947 strip mines averaged 15.93 tons per man per day, as compared with 5.49 tons for underground mines and 6.42 for all mines. Bureau of Mines, *Bituminous Coal and Lignite in 1947*, p. 22.

In 1947 the corresponding figure was 22.1 percent; in other words, of the total of 630.6 million tons of bituminous and lignite produced that year, strip mining accounted for 139.4 million, as against 491.2 million for underground mines. Progressive technology and the high wage rates paid to the members of the United Mine Workers have encouraged this supermechanized labor-saving process.

Underground Mining

When coal lies underneath an overburden that is too expensive to remove, underground mining must be used.

There are three methods: (1) If the coal seam is horizontal and outcrops on a hillside or a river bank, the coal can be reached and removed by a tunnel driven right into the seam. (2) If the coal seam slants and outcrops, so-called stopes are driven into it. (3) If the seam is deep and does not outcrop, vertical shafts are driven down to the seam, which is then opened up by various methods.

Although shaft mining is widely believed to be the most typical form of coal mining, this is not the case in the United States. The bulk of the coal which is not "stripped" is removed by tunnel or stope mining. Shaft mining is the exception rather than the rule, especially in the fields which contribute the major share of our total bituminous coal output. This fact goes far to explain the relatively low price of the coal in this country.

The customary method of removing coal from the mine in the United States is the "room-and-pillar system," under which pillars of coal are left to support the roof and thus prevent cave-ins. In Europe "the long-wall system" is more prevalent. Under that system more or less all the coal is removed from a continuous working surface, the mined-out space being filled with rock and sand, either by hand or by means of pneumatic, hydraulic, or other mechanical devices. The fact that under our system a good deal of coal remains unmined is responsible to a considerable extent for the loss of roughly one ton for every two tons mined in this country. Our system saves labor but not coal; the European system saves coal but not labor. In other words, the United States is long on coal and short on labor; the reverse is true in many parts of Europe.

COMPETITIVE NATURE OF THE INDUSTRY

A business in which a Mellon-dominated concern can manage to lose $35 million in less than twenty years and a Rockefeller-controlled company can go bankrupt is indeed a rare phenomenon.[5] The fact is that, in the absence of government regulation, the bituminous industry —both mining and marketing aspects—is keenly competitive. The structure of the industry helps to turn business rivalry into cutthroat competition. But several other factors likewise contribute. They will be discussed under the two headings of supply and demand.

Supply Aspects

A coal mine serves only one purpose, the production of coal. Whatever investment is sunk in the mine can be recovered only by mining and selling coal. There are no alternative uses for the property to which the management can turn if the going gets rough.

The danger of miscalculation of both costs and market opportunities lurks behind every hill hiding a coal seam, behind every tipple and every breaker. It takes a long time, perhaps several years, to open up, equip, and bring large coal mines into operation. During this "gestation" period the market may shrink or shift and leave the new mine without an outlet for its coal.

It is to the interest of railroads for whom coal constitutes one of the richest prizes in the freight-carrying business to open up coal mines within their reach.

Moreover, a coal mine is inevitably compelled to produce joint products. No mine can produce only one size of coal; it necessarily produces several. There may be a brisk demand for some of them but not for others. This means that some coals are produced which are a drug on the market; to get rid of them the operator resorts to the questionable practice of consignment sales, i.e., consigning them to an agent with instructions to sell them at whatever the market is willing to pay. Coal loaded in railroad cars on the sidings at the coal mine is a costly luxury, for demurrage charges soon

[5] This refers to the Pittsburgh Coal Company and the Consolidated Coal Company, which were recently merged into the Pittsburgh Consolidated Coal Company. See *Fortune*, July, 1947.

eat up the profit the coal may have promised when it was first dumped from the tipple.

One of the worst features of the supply side of coal mining is the heterogeneity of the mines themselves. Some are wonderful, others are hopeless. Some have never skipped a dividend.[6] Others have never earned one. The difference is not necessarily entirely or even mainly a question of management. No one can tell exactly how a coal property will behave in the course of operation. Some seams get better, others worse. The operator may run into unforeseeable dips and fractures, laminations and what not. The coal from the good seam which costs perhaps 50 cents a ton to produce competes with coal from the bad seam which costs perhaps three or four times that much.

Most coal mining methods still call for considerable amounts of manual labor, but some mines are being mechanized. But here again, managerial choice is not the sole deciding factor, for nature has much to say. Furthermore, mechanization may lower costs when the equipment is in full or reasonably steady use, but it also adds to the overhead and hence to the rigidity of the supply.

The dominant role which labor plays in coal mining has a vital effect on the supply of coal. Labor still constitutes by far the largest cost factor, and coal miners constitute one of the largest single groups of homogeneous man power. The history of coal mining can be told in terms of endless labor struggles, the backdrop of which is the general institutional setting of our country. It too changes as the battle rages on. There was a time when coal operators could exploit hordes of immigrants, playing one national or ethnic group against another—the Irish or Welsh against English, Slavs against Teutons, and so forth. When immigration ceased and the labor supply became stabilized both numerically and economically, the unionized North was pitted against the nonunionized South until finally, under the New Deal, the coal mining industry of the whole nation was unionized.

The coal supply is thus subject to unforeseen interruptions by strikes, a fact no consumer

---

[6] See "Coal at a Profit: Island Creek," *Fortune*, March, 1938, pp. 87 ff.

will long overlook if he can switch to a less erratic fuel. The labor situation also tends to raise the cost of mining and thus affects coal's competitive position in the fuel market.

The supply of bituminous coal is one-sidedly elastic on the positive side; i.e., it responds readily to increasing prices with a rapidly expanding output, particularly in wartime—the 1914 output of 422.7 million tons rose to 579.4 million in 1918; again, the 1938 output of 348.5 million tons rose to 619.6 million in 1944. And prices tend to go up with volume of output. On the negative side, the adjustment to a shrinking demand is far slower and much more painful, for mines are abandoned only after a desperate struggle to save the investment. Incidentally, abandonment is generally accompanied by heavy losses of minable coal.

Demand Aspects

In general the demand for coal is erratic. Its demand for household and commercial space-heating purposes is seasonal. Storage is costly and, in the case of lower-grade coals, not without danger. The demand for industrial coal as well as for railroad fuel follows the business cycle. This means that from half to two-thirds of the coal industry is afflicted with cyclical disturbances. Coal also plays a major role in war, the output and capacity tending to expand rapidly without assurance that peacetime requirements will support the expansion.

The worst feature of the demand for coal at present, particularly in the United States, is the long-term downward trend in demand. During the five-year period 1910-1914 the United States produced an average of 434.8 million tons of bituminous coal per year. For the five-year period 1935-1939 the corresponding figure was 400 million tons, or almost 10 percent lower. In the meantime the population had increased by 34.9 percent. If coal output per capita had held its own, it would have risen to an average of 587 million tons per year instead of dropping to 400 million. But the per capita output dropped from about 4.5 tons to about 3.1, a decrease of over one-third.

DECLINE OF COAL IN THE ENERGY ECONOMY OF THE UNITED STATES

This decline in the demand for coal by no means reflects a lessened demand for inanimate energy. On the contrary that demand has increased. It is coal that is singled out; the other energy sources are forging ahead. Indeed it is to a large extent the phenomenal expansion in the demand for these other sources that accounts for coal's poor showing.

In order to show statistically the comparative rate of production of different sources of energy —coal, petroleum, natural gas, and water power —it is necessary to express all of them by some common term, such as the British thermal unit (B.T.U.), the amount of heat required to raise the temperature of one pound of water one degree Fahrenheit.

For purposes of comparison the following heat values are chosen:

Anthracite	13,600 B.T.U. per pound		
Bituminous and lignite	13,100	" " "	
Petroleum	6,000,000	" "	barrel of 42 gallons
Natural gas	1,075	" "	cubic foot

Calculating a fuel equivalent of water power is difficult. In the first place, while the generating capacity of private water-power plants is known, the output of private plants, i.e., plants other than those owned by public utility corporations and public agencies, is not known. It is therefore estimated by assuming that they produce 40 percent of their theoretical rating. When the output of electricity in kilowatthours is known, the question of its fuel equivalent arises. In 1899 it took an average of 7.05 pounds of coal to generate 1 kw.-h. of electricity in a central-station power plant; so for that year the coal equivalent of one hydroelectric kw.-h. is 7.05 pounds. The corresponding figures for 1920 and 1946 were 3.0 and 1.29 pounds respectively. This hydroelectric energy is equated with a constantly declining amount of coal. For certain purposes it is desirable to show the output of hydroelectricity in terms of a constant fuel equivalent.[7] In this case 4.02 pounds, the fuel consumption in 1913, is sometimes used. Both series of figures are given in Table 28.2. This table reveals a number of important facts.

1. Total production of fuels and water power, expressed in their B.T.U. equivalents, increased from 4.3 quadrillion B.T.U. in 1889 to

35.4 in 1946, almost an eightfold increase in just under sixty years. The figures reveal the stimulating effect of wars and business booms and the opposite effect of depressions. The drop in 1944-1945 is explained by reconversion.

2. The rate of increase in the output of the several fuels and of water power varies widely. Thus Pennsylvania anthracite reached its peak of production during World War I (in 1917) and never even approached it afterwards. Bituminous coal reached a similar peak during World War I (in 1918), but exceeded this during World War II, though only by a slight margin, and again in 1947. Petroleum output (plus imports) increased from 382 trillion B.T.U. in 1900 to 12,462 trillion in 1948. The increase was both steep and unusually steady; in only three years was the figure smaller than in previous years. The increase in the output of natural gas was from an estimated 254 trillion B.T.U. in 1900 to 5543 trillion in 1948. But production has been gaining momentum of late and may soon put on a really spectacular performance. The increase in the output of water power, measured in terms of a constant fuel equivalent resembles that for natural gas. It was a little slower at the start but, from about 1920 on, the increase has been quite similar. In short, the total production of energy materials has increased rapidly. Coal alone is lagging behind, anthracite actually declining and bituminous doing little more than holding its own.

It cannot be emphasized too strongly that these figures do *not* show the amount of energy obtained from the fuels and from water power. They merely express the output of energy materials in B.T.U. so as to permit statistical comparisons. In the first place, the amount of energy actually obtained from these sources depends on the efficiency of their utilization. During the period from 1889 to the present this efficiency has been improved in a most impressive fashion, though much more so for some uses than for others; some of these improvements will be discussed in some detail later on. If it is arbitrarily assumed that the energy actually available for use and converted into work was 5 percent of the total B.T.U. figures listed above in 1889 and 25 percent in 1945, the energy supply of the United States, instead of increasing fivefold as did the supply

---

[7] Water power expressed in terms of a constant fuel equivalent.

TABLE 28.2. B.T.U. Equivalents of Major Sources of Energy Produced in the United States, 1889–1949[s]

(trillion B.T.U.)

| | Total Energy | | Water Power | | Mineral Fuels | | | | | |
| | Water Power at Constant Fuel Equivalent | Water Power at Prevailing Central-Station Equivalent | At Constant Fuel Equivalent[a] | At Prevailing Central-Station Equivalent[b] | Total | Coal Total | Bituminous and Lignite | Pennsylvania Anthracite | Petroleum (Total Crude, Including That Refined)[c] | Natural Gas |
Period										
1889	4,316	....	91	....	4,225	3,746	2,507	1,239	211	268[d]
1899	7,426	7,529	135	238	7,291	6,708	5,065	1,643	342	240[d]
1900	7,905	8,009	146	250	7,759	7,123	5,563	1,560	382	254[d]
1901–05 avg.	10,102	10,216	209	323	9,893	8,958	7,140	1,818	612	323
1906–10 avg.	13,867	13,974	369	477	13,498	11,990	9,783	2,207	1,037	470
1911–15 avg.	16,722	16,743	591	611	16,132	13,954	11,527	2,427	1,559	619
1916–20 avg.	20,648	20,505	851	708	19,797	16,504	13,981	2,523	2,473	820
1921–25 avg.	21,308	20,856	1,105	653	20,203	14,722	12,610	2,112	4,457	1,024
1926–30 avg.	25,002	24,006	1,781	785	23,221	15,679	13,595	2,084	5,782	1,760
1931–35 avg.	19,988	18,777	1,931	719	18,057	10,667	9,207	1,460	5,566	1,824
1939	24,620	23,035	2,423	838	22,197	11,745	10,345	1,400	7,789	2,663
1940	27,327	25,587	2,620	880	24,707	13,472	12,072	1,400	8,375	2,860
1941	29,549	27,679	2,804	934	26,745	15,004	13,471	1,533	8,717	3,024
1942	32,069	29,720	3,485	1,136	28,584	16,908	15,267	1,641	8,394	3,282
1943	33,900	31,205	3,999	1,304	29,901	17,113	15,463	1,650	9,117	3,671
1944	36,451	33,635	4,160	1,344	32,291	17,966	16,233	1,733	10,336	3,989
1945	36,030	33,009	4,463	1,442	31,567	16,628	15,134	1,494	10,726	4,213
1946	....	31,839	....	1,406	30,433	15,526	13,989	1,537	10,574	4,333
1947	....	35,674	....	1,426	34,248	17,975	16,522	1,453	11,347	4,926
1948	....	36,674	....	1,481	35,154	17,158	15,707	1,451	12,462	5,534
1949	....	31,786	....	1,552	30,234	12,481	11,397	1,084	11,572	6,181

[a] Assuming 4.02 lb. of coal per kilowatt-hour, average of central-station practice in 1913, base period.

[b] Assuming average central-station practice for each year; declined from about 7.05 lb. of coal per kilowatt-hour in 1889 to 1.29 lb. in 1946.

[c] Includes imports.

[d] Based on amount of coal displaced by gas, as estimated by gas companies.

[s] *Statistical Abstracts, 1948*, p. 491. Figures for 1946–1949 from U.S. Bureau of Mines, *Weekly Coal Reports*, March 31, 1950.

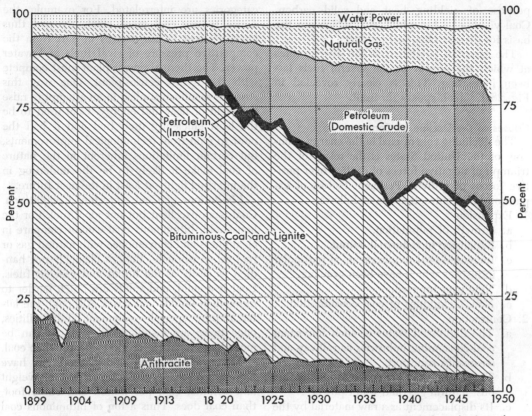

FIG. 28.1. Fifty Years of United States Fuel History. (Fuels and water power in British thermal units and equivalents.) (U. S. Department of the Interior, Bureau of Mines, *Minerals Yearbook, 1948*, supplemented by *Weekly Coal Reports*, March 31, 1950, p. 9.)

of energy materials, increased from 215 trillion B.T.U. in 1889 to 8971 trillion in 1945, a rate of increase five times as great. Such a figure gives a far more realistic impression of the progress in the use of inanimate energy matter than do the gross output figures. In other words, the statistical technique applied in arriving at the fuel equivalent of water power must be applied all along the line.[9] Nor should one overlook the fact that while the output of coal has no more than held its own, the energy obtained from this fuel has increased rapidly. For, like other fuels, coal today yields far more

---

[9] It seems unfortunate that the *Statistical Abstract*, in using the caption "Energy from Mineral Fuels and Water Power," is apt to mislead unwary users of this excellent work. It is not energy *from* these fuels, i.e., *available* or *obtained from* the fuels, which is shown, but merely a static theoretical thermal value imputed to the fuels.

actual heat and energy than it did thirty years ago.

In the second place, as was mentioned before, not all fuels are used solely for the generation of energy. Most anthracite, much bituminous, and a considerable amount of fuel oil and natural gas are used for space heating. While in physics heat may be considered a form of energy, it is quite likely that many readers will fail to give this meaning to the word energy.

Moreover, considerable and increasing amounts of the mineral fuels are used for purposes other than conversion into heat and energy. Thus carbon black is obtained from natural gas, coke and paraffin wax and lubricating oil from petroleum, and synthetic chemical products such as T.N.T., nylon salts, synthetic rubber, etc., from both petroleum and natural gas. Coal goes into coke which serves the dual purpose of yielding heat and solid carbon. Coal yields coal tar, pitch, etc., which are the basis for diverse chemical products.

The essential point here is the diverse rates at which the output of the several fuels has been increasing. This is clearly revealed in Fig. 28.1, which speaks for itself.

Causes of the Decline of Coal

The declining role of coal in the energy economy of the United States is the result of the triumph of negative forces of decline over positive forces of growth. Pertinent factors of expansion and contraction are as follows.

1. Expansion
   a. Growth of population.
   b. Expansion of industrial output.
   c. Increased coal requirements of particular industries which have been growing.
   d. New uses for coal.
   e. New techniques of coal consumption.
2. Contraction
   a. The depressed status of such important coal-consuming industries as railway and steamship transport.
   b. The displacement of coal as a fuel by fuel oils, natural gas, and water power.
   c. Its displacement as a raw material by the shift to a process whereby more steel is obtained through the remelting of scrap than through the smelting of iron ore.
   d. Higher fuel efficiency in the coal-consuming industries, particularly iron and steel manufacture, electricity supply, railway and steamship transport.[10]

The forces of contraction, which, as we have said, proved stronger than the expansion forces, fall into two distinct categories: (1) those stemming from outside the coal economy, especially competition from other fuels and of water power, and, indirectly, the greater reliance on scrap as a source of steel; and (2) those connected with the more efficient utilization of coal itself. It should be noted that these two

[10] Adapted from International Labor Office, *Report on the World Coal-Mining Industry*, P. S. King & Son, Ltd., London, 1938, p. 77. This list of causes was prepared during the middle thirties when certain effects of the Great Depression were still felt. Today, however, at least in the United States, the first of the contraction facors would probably not apply.

categories are interrelated. For example, the desire to use coal more efficiently and thus lower its cost in use derives in part from the competitive pressure of rival fuels and water power. The thermal power plant must compete with the hydroelectric plant. One way this struggle manifests itself is in an attempt to raise the yield of heat and energy. Coal used to be the least efficiently used fuel and it had the most to gain from technological improvements, but certain limitations inherent in the nature of coal make it likely to be the underdog in the interfuel fight—at least in the near future.

Limitations of Coal; Interfuel Competition. Coal is an excellent but not ideal fuel. For the household, bituminous coal cannot compare in cleanliness and convenience with natural gas or fuel oil. Anthracite, though clean, is not handled as easily as the liquid and gaseous fuels. Coal is a solid, and solids are much harder to move than liquids and gases. Although the latter require special equipment and facilities, once these are installed, oil and gas can be moved and handled far more cheaply than coal.

Moreover, both oil and natural gas have higher heat-energy values per unit of weight and volume, e.g., per pound and cubic foot, than coal does. Thus a ton of bituminous coal is rated at about 27,000,000 B.T.U., whereas a ton of crude oil, figured at 7.5 barrels, rates about 45 million, or over two-thirds higher. A cubic foot of average bituminous coal weighs 81.25 pounds and, at 13,500 B.T.U. per pound, rates about 1.1 million B.T.U., as compared with 1075 B.T.U. for a cubic foot of natural gas at ordinary pressure; however, a pound of natural gas contains considerably more heat value than a pound of coal, and natural gas can be compressed. What is more, both petroleum and natural gas yield their heat value more readily than does coal. Burning requires contact with oxygen, and the oxygen necessary for burning can be supplied to oil and gas more easily than to a solid fuel. Powdered coal behaves much like oil and gas.

As a result of this difference in heat value—especially in the field of transportation. With weight and volume, coal has been replaced by petroleum and natural gas for many purposes, especially in the field of transportation. With hardly any exceptions, the navies of the world now burn oil, whereas about a quarter century ago they still burned coal. Diesel locomotives are now in fairly common use, their greater thermal efficiency and secondary advantages overcompensating for the higher initial cost of the engine and the higher cost of the oil. Automobiles and airplanes have no use for coal; they depend on premium fuels which, at present, are obtained from petroleum. Fuel oil and natural gas have invaded the fields of domestic and commercial space heating. Even some industries have turned away from coal, taking advantage of the low prices of substitute fuels that happened to be available at the time or hoping for greater assurance of uninterrupted supplies of fuel.

The fact that coal is still used as widely as it is, is due to a number of reasons. In the first place, there is no substitute for metallurgical coke in extracting iron from ore. In the second place, industries have been built over or around coal fields; this means that, in many industrial areas, coal has the advantage of being on the spot or nearby, whereas other fuels must be brought in over considerable distances. Also, some industries tend to cluster around the iron and steel industry, which in turn is dependent on coal. Above all, coal near the mine is a cheap fuel; its low price is its strongest point. Premium fuels tend to sell at premium prices. Only as high transportation charges are added to a low mine price does coal lose its advantage of cheapness and therefore have to yield to more mobile and otherwise more desirable fuels. Furthermore, for years the price of coal has been rising faster than that of competitive fuels.

As a result of certain initial handicaps, coal was ill prepared for the fierce struggle which the younger fuels, petroleum and natural gas, entered with lusty vigor. The excess capacity with which the coal industry came out of World War I turned it into a tottering giant. Except in periods of exceptional demand, the industry as a whole has been operating "in the red" and hence has been unable to embark on the technological revolution which alone can save it.

It is true that, in response to the higher wages demanded by strongly organized union labor, remarkable progress in mechanization has been made. Thus, while in 1896 less than 12 percent of all bituminous coal was cut by machine, the figure for 1946 was over 90 percent.

In 1923, less than 1 percent of the bituminous mined underground was loaded mechanically, but in 1947, 61 percent was thus loaded. Strip mining, which is almost wholly mechanized, expanded so that its share of the bituminous output increased from 3 percent in 1914 to 21.1 percent in 1947.

All this is to the good and the coal-mining machine industry deserves much credit for its remarkable performance. But the upshot has been little more than the neutralization of higher wage costs. A far smaller number of miners—working much shorter hours, receiving much higher wages, and provided with far more equipment—produce about the same amount of coal as was produced during World War I. Wages still constitute about 60 percent of the cost of mining. Mechanization has lessened the dependence on large numbers of miners but not on labor as such, and at the same time it has added to overhead and thus reduced flexibility. It has played into the hands of larger, more heavily capitalized concerns.

Economies in the Use of Coal.   In the meantime the users of coal were tirelessly trying to squeeze ever more kilowatt-hours of electricity, more coke, more pig iron, more ton-miles of railroad service, out of every pound of coal they bought. Table 28.3 shows the progress made in this direction.

Implications

The rather sudden reversal of the trend of coal production which occurred after 1918 had serious implications for the bituminous industry of the United States. As was mentioned before, coal mines, especially large elaborate mines, require years for development, and once the work of opening up a property has progressed beyond a certain point, it is difficult to turn back. An unusually large number of such mines were being developed when the fateful turning point in trend was reached. The result was an amazing overcapacity (see Fig. 27.1), the reduction of which was painful not only for the mines that were discarded but for the entire industry. The peak of capacity was reached in 1923—four years after the armistice —with roughly 900 million tons. Against this capacity, the actual output of 500.3 million tons for the average year 1921-1930 does not look so impressive. By 1933 capacity had dropped roughly 30 percent, but the average annual production during 1931-1940 was only 384.6 million tons. After that it began to move slowly upward again, full capacity being reached during World War II.[12] Evidently it

TABLE 28.3. Fuel Efficiency of Coal[11]

	Pounds	Reduction from Base Period (Percent)
Steam railroads		
Pounds per 1000 gross ton-miles freight service		
Average		
1919-1920	170	...
1947	114	32.9
1948	111	34.7
Pounds per passenger-train car-mile		
Average		
1919-1920	18.5	...
1947	15.9	14.1
1948	15.7	15.1
Electric public utility power plants		
Pounds per kilowatt-hour		
1919	3.20	...
1947	1.31	59.1
1948	1.30	59.4
Iron and steel plants		
Pounds coking coal per net ton of pig[a]		
1918	3,194	...
1947	2,755	13.7
1948	2,775	13.1
Coke manufacture: Savings of heat values through recovery of gas, tar, light oils, and breeze by extension of oven coke in place of beehive, 1913-1914, expressed as percent of coal used for all coke in 1948[b]	...	19.0

[a] Includes only savings through higher yields of merchantable coke per ton of coal charged and lower consumption of coke per ton of iron and ferro-alloys. Excludes economies through recovery of coal chemical materials which are covered in next item.

[b] These coal chemical materials are used in part for boiler fuel, in part for metallurgical purposes, in part for domestic heating and cooking, and to a small extent for automotive fuel.

[11] Bureau of Mines, *Weekly Coal Reports*, April, 1949, p. 9.

[12] From the standpoint of the industry, such overcapacity is an undiluted evil, but for the country it is a vital safeguard. How could we win wars without the ability to step up coal production at will? This chronic overcapacity of our mining industry is one of the most important phases of preparation for war. The only other safeguards of this

takes a war, or preparation for and recovery from one, to put this country's most basic industry into the black.

PUBLIC INTEREST IN THE COAL MINING INDUSTRY

That the status of as important an industry as coal mining is a matter of grave public concern goes without saying. The industry is the steward, as it were, of one of the basic resources of the industrial age. It employs hundreds of thousands of men whose willingness to work may decide the fate of the nation. Nor has the public and its collective spokesman, the government, failed to show an interest in it. No industry has been investigated more, none has been the subject of more hearings and more reports. But action has not been quite so much in evidence.

The first important step in helping at least part of the industry was probably the Supreme Court decision of 1933 upholding Appalachian Coals, Inc., a sales agency organized in 1931 to market collectively the aggregate output of many mines. The decision clearly recognized the crucial fact that unbridled competition is fatal for an industry sick unto death when it exempted a segment of the industry from the competition insured by the Sherman Antitrust Act.

The next step was the Bituminous Coal Code of the NRA. This time the coal industry of the entire nation was organized for orderly marketing, and cutthroat competition was eliminated. The code flatly abrogated the philosophy of the Sherman Act. When the NRA was declared unconstitutional, a special law, the Coal Conservation Act of 1935—the first "Guffey Act"—was passed, but it too was declared unconstitutional. A new act two years later passed the scrutiny of the Supreme Court and was just beginning to bring order out of chaos when World War II broke out, bringing with it general price control legislation which included coal. When these wartime price control laws

type are (1) the Lake Superior iron ore mining industry with its vast open-pit mines which are ready to speed up production of that other vital raw material of war, iron ore—at least as long as the supply lasts—and (2) the excess capacity of our oil fields which are throttled down considerably below their maximum efficiency rate. (See p. 528.)

were rescinded in 1946, the coal industry found itself back where it had started—facing unregulated competition. So long as an expanded economy clamors for all the coal the mines can produce, there is no immediate problem. Although it is too much to hope that this will last, it perhaps is not too much to hope that science and technology will come to the rescue.

BIBLIOGRAPHY

See the bibliography at the end of Chapter 29.

Chapter 29

THE FUEL REVOLUTION[1]

Several weighty reasons justify the hope that before long a real change for the better will come over the coal industry of the United States. The cause of the industry's poor health lies not with coal but with the industry. Coal is one of the wonders of nature, but a wonder too little appreciated and too sorely abused. It is so abundant that its marginal utility is close to zero. It can be mined in primitive fashion and burned without benefit of either technique or science. The coal industry prides itself on being the biggest bulk-handling industry in the world. So it is. But precisely this "coal-in-the-lump" philosophy is what has brought coal to where it is today—a Goliath groggy from the slingshots of smaller but lustier and craftier rivals.

Most coal is still sold "in the raw," whereas hardly any oil is sold "in the crude." Oil is processed, refined, turned into countless products of science. To be sure, it has a head start, for its hydrogen-carbon ratio is about 10 to 6 and that of coal is 10 to 12; hence oil is a liquid, coal a solid. But this does not mean that while one product of nature can perform miracles, the other is not worth experimenting with.

Both oil and coal are hydrocarbons that consist of a vast number of different molecules. The chemist is best fitted to make full use of this array of diverse molecules, and he proceeds on two levels. On the lower level he confines himself to segregating the ingredients which make up the natural conglomerate. By fractional distillation[2] in a still he separates kerosene and gasoline, lubricating oil, gas oil, fuel oil, etc. In the by-product coke oven he separates coke (carbon) from gases and tar, ammonium sulfate, and so forth. But he goes much further. If the fractions thus obtained do not meet market needs or if higher utilities can be "built into" the products by further manipulation, the chemist takes matters into his own hands, breaks up what is too large, combines what is too small, adds or subtracts hydrogen, rearranges the atoms in the molecule—in short, creates new compounds. The future of coal lies in this type of chemical manipulation.

---

[1] Portions of this chapter are based on "The Fuel Revolution," *Fortune,* April, 1947.

[2] See chap. 33.

The By-Product Coke Oven

To a limited extent coal has been subjected to chemical manipulation for some time. In this country by far the most important form this manipulation has taken is associated with the production of coke. Coke is coal from which all ingredients other than carbon have been removed by combustion; it is essential in the making of iron in a blast furnace. Until the early 1890's coke was made in beehive ovens, simple brick contraptions in which the coal was burned in such a way that the volatile portion was distilled off and allowed to escape through the smokestacks. Until a demand for gas, tar, ammonium sulfate, etc., developed, there was no incentive to recapturing these gases.

The furnace designed for their recapture is popularly known as the by-product coke oven. While the first beehive ovens in this country were built in the early 1840's, it was not until 1893 that the first Selmet-Solvay by-product coke ovens were built near Syracuse, New York. In 1898 Heinrich Koppers of Essen built a new type of by-product coke oven for Hugo Stinnes, the German coal magnate, and nine years later he built the first Koppers ovens in the United States.

In 1919 the output of by-product coke for the first time exceeded the production of beehive coke and in the late thirties the latter practically disappeared. In 1938, 800,000 tons of beehive coke were produced, as against 31.7 million tons of "oven coke." However, during World War II, as in all periods of emergency demand, beehive coke staged something of a comeback, reaching a wartime peak of 8.3 million tons, as against 62.3 million of "oven coke." Beehive ovens are cheap and their operation is flexible; hence they are ideally suited for meeting unexpected peaks of demand.

The bulk of the by-product coke ovens are the property of steel companies and form an integrated part of the steelworks. By attaching them to blast furnaces, hot gases generated in the making of coke can be fed into any part of the iron-steelmaking processes which need them. In 1946, of the total of 85 active by-product coke oven plants, 53 were so-called furnace plants, i.e., plants tied in with steelworks, and 32 were "merchant plants." The furnace plants produced 77 percent of the total output of by-product coke that year.

The main advantage of the by-product coke oven over the beehive oven is obviously the recovery of by-products. As things work out, the coke just about pays for the coal, and the by-products pay for the plant and account for the profits, if any. In 1946, 85 active by-product coke oven plants produced 53.9 million tons of coke worth $450.1 million from 76.4 million tons of coal worth $440.5 million. The coke was priced at $8.35, the coal at $5.77.

The value of by-products is hard to ascertain because some are sold and others are used by the producer. The value, in millions of dollars, of the portion sold was as follows:

Tar	21.3
Ammonia liquor	1.4
Sulfate of ammonia	18.0
Light oil	1.1
Gas	48.7
Light oil derivatives	22.5
Naphthalene	1.6
Other coal chemicals	8.3
	122.9

In addition, the producers themselves used over $800 million worth of by-products.

Further advantages are the saving of heat, the possibility of using varieties of coals not suitable to the beehive oven, the saving on transportation costs (freight, spoilage, loss, etc.) that results because the coking coal is shipped direct to the steelworks. Beehive coke ovens generally are located near the mine to save the freight charges on the volatile portion of the coal.

Moreover, the value of the by-products depends on the market. As the chemical industry of the United States moves forward and expands, as new uses for by-products are discovered, the value tends to rise. However, there is danger of flooding the market with these chemical raw materials, and realization of this danger deters operators from hastily expanding the capacity of by-product coke ovens.

Manufacture of Gas from Coal

While most coke is produced from coking coals which yield large amounts of coke and limited amounts of gas, coke can also be obtained from gas coals which yield mainly gas along with some coke. England was the first country to produce "coal gas" on a large scale; it was used for the lighting of city streets and houses. In the English process of obtaining this gas, coal is only partially burned in a closed retort, thus becoming coke. If air is freely admitted, the carbon combines with the oxygen to form carbon dioxide (CO_2) and heat. If the air supply is carefully controlled, combustion can be checked to prevent the formation of carbon dioxide. The result is coke, and gases that can be burned in stoves and heaters. The Germans modified the English practice and obtained "producer gas," which consists mainly of carbon monoxide (CO) and inert nitrogen from the air and is used chiefly as an industrial fuel. Mixing coal gas and producer gas results in a fairly good fuel which was sold by the early gas industry.

CHEMICAL MANIPULATION OF COAL

The processes thus far described are on the first level of chemical exploitation: breaking the coal down into its constituent parts. A revolutionary change occurs when the chemist works on the second level—when he changes the molecules in coal by adding, subtracting, and rearranging the atoms.

"Water Gas"

The first step in that direction in the United States was taken in 1873, with the manufacture of "water gas." In this process coal or coke is heated to incandescence and then blasted with steam. In this reaction, carbon (in the form of incandescent coal or coke) plus water (in the form of steam) yields a mixture of carbon monoxide and hydrogen, or "water gas." This gas has a thermal value of 300 B.T.U. per cubic foot which can be raised to 500 B.T.U. by enriching the gas with a spray of petroleum oil (called "gas oil") which "cracks" or breaks down larger molecules into smaller fractions of gaseous hydrocarbon. This enriched "water gas" is the "city gas" sold by the gas companies today.

The Bergius Process of Coal Hydrogenation

At this point coal chemistry, so far as it concerned itself with problems of *fuel* supply, rested for a long time—in fact until 1910. In that year the German chemist Friedrich Bergius took the first step in a direction which

points toward the ultimate technical, though not necessarily economic, equivalence of all hydrocarbons—coal, petroleum, and natural gas.

Bergius proceeded from the basic fact that coal is a poor hydrocarbon because it is short of hydrogen when compared with natural gas or petroleum.[3] Hence the logical next step was to subject coal to hydrogenation, i.e., raise the hydrogen content of the hydrocarbon molecules.

Bergius accomplished this by preparing a paste of ground coal and running a blast of hydrogen gas into it at a temperature of 850° Fahrenheit and a pressure of 3000 pounds per square inch. In this manner he synthesized liquid hydrocarbons, light oils, heavy oils, and waxes—in short, products similar to those of the petroleum refinery. The difference is that in the case of petroleum nature did the synthesizing millions of years ago and all the refineries have to do is to separate the natural products by fractional distillation. Bergius laid the foundation of modern coal conversion and thus started the fuel revolution on its way.

The Bergius process was not an immediate commercial success because the catalysts[4] used in his original process proved unsatisfactory. When that problem was solved, the I. G. Farbenindustrie, the great German chemical concern which gained much notoriety in World War II, took over in 1927. It was the improved Bergius-I. G. process which supplied Germany with the bulk of the synthetic fuels without which the war would have ended sooner or perhaps never have been started.

The Fischer-Tropsch Process of Coal Conversion

While Bergius was working out the problem of synthesizing hydrocarbons, two other German scientists, Franz Fischer and Hans Tropsch, tackled it from a different angle. They started with the old-fashioned "water gas" reaction (see above) and modernized it (1) to make it a continuous rather than a batch process and (2) to raise its efficiency and thus cut the cost.

---

[3] As was mentioned before, the hydrogen-carbon ratio of coal is 10 to 12, as against 10 to 6 for petroleum and 4 to 1 for methane (CH_4), the main constituent of natural gas.

[4] A catalyst is an element or compound which by its presence accelerates or retards chemical reactions without becoming involved in them.

TABLE 29.1. The Conversion of Coal[5]

	"Producer Gas"	"Water Gas"	Lurgi Process	Bergius Process	Fischer-Tropsch Process
Aim	A low-B.T.U. industrial gas	Gas for your kitchen stove or heater; "city gas"	A high B.T.U. gas direct from coal without "enrichment"	Gasoline from coal (by hydrogenation)	Gasoline from coal (by gasification and synthesis)
Practical since	1839 in Germany	1873 in the U.S.	1936 in Germany	1927 in Germany	1933 in Germany
Basic reactions	$C + \tfrac{1}{2}O_2 \longrightarrow CO$	$C + H_2O \longrightarrow CO + H_2$ glowing coal or coke blasted with steam	$\begin{cases} C + H_2O \longrightarrow CO + H_2 \\ CO + 3H_2 \longrightarrow CH_4 + H_2O \\ C + 2H_2 \longrightarrow CH_4 \end{cases}$	$nC + nH_2 \longrightarrow (CH_2)n$	$C + H_2O \longrightarrow CO + H_2$ $nCO + 2nH_2 \longrightarrow (CH_2)n + nH_2O$
Temperatures Pressures	2500°F. atmospheric	1800°F. atmospheric	1800°F. 300 psi	850°F. 3000 to 10,000 psi	650°F. 250 psi
Efficiency	72%	62%	80%	42%	45-50%
Products	Carbon monoxide diluted with air's nitrogen (140 B.T.U./cu.ft.)	Carbon monoxide plus hydrogen (300 B.T.U./cu.ft. enriched with oil to 535 B.T.U.)	Carbon monoxide (23%), hydrogen (49%), methane (23%) (500 B.T.U./cu.ft.)	Gasoline, Diesel oils, lubricating oils, waxes	Gasoline, Diesel oils, lubricating oils, synthetic alcohols; waxes
Costs	9 cents/1000 cu.ft.	22 cents/1000 cu.ft.	No U.S. installations	15-18 cents/gal. (est.)	7-8 cents/gal. (est.)
Remarks	In limited industrial use where a lean gas is satisfactory.	The great basic conversion reaction; no longer an efficient end in itself, but a stepping stone to the future.	The linkage between the old water gas reaction and the modern world of coal conversion into gases and oils	Once a German triumph; now considered obsolete by most chemical engineers in U.S. oil industry.	The conversion process of the present day; basis on which U.S. engineers are constructing the fuel revolution.

[5] *Fortune*, April, 1947. Reproduced courtesy of *Fortune* Magazine.

The old-fashioned process calls for a succession of steam blasts on incandescent coals, each blast followed by a cooling-off period. This requires vast amounts of outside heat to raise the steam and to bring the coal to incandescence. The first problem, turning a batch process into a continuous process, was solved by the so-called Winkler process. The second objective, lowering the heat cost, was achieved by substituting oxygen for air, the oxygen being produced by the Linde-Fraenkl process of fractional distillation of liquid air. The Fischer-Tropsch process was coming into its own during the last stages of World War II. In 1944 Germany produced 4 million barrels of oil by this process, as against 27 million produced by the Bergius hydrogenation process.

The Lurgi Process

As if the Bergius and Fischer-Tropsch processes were not enough, Germany contributed a third important innovation to hasten the modern Fuel Revolution—the Lurgi process. Whereas Bergius, Fischer, and Tropsch were interested in liquids, gasoline, Diesel oil, lubricating oils, etc., Lurgi succeeded in turning the lowly brown coal into something comparable to natural gas.

Like Fischer and Tropsch, he too started with the basic "water gas" reaction. But he discovered that when pressure in the reactors was raised to 300 pounds per square inch, part of the carbon monoxide reacted with the hydrogen to produce methane, CH_4, the chief constituent of natural gas. The importance of this discovery lies in the fact that whereas carbon monoxide has a B.T.U. of only 317 per cubic foot, and hydrogen has 319, the figure for methane is 995. By blending methane with other products of coal conversion Lurgi produced a commerical gas of 500 B.T.U. which was piped considerable distances.

Table 29.1 shows the characteristic features of these various processes.[6]

The "Fluidized Bed"

The efficiency of the Fischer-Tropsch process was materially increased by the application of the "fluidized bed," an American invention perfected by petroleum engineers. By means of this device, reactions involving very high temperatures and catalysts can be greatly improved. Instead of reacting gases on solids in a "static" bed, the solids are pulverized, thus fluidizing them and permitting the gases to penetrate them more easily.

This Americanized version of the Fischer-Tropsch process is now being applied in a highly significant plant in the United States in Brownsville, Texas. It is designed to synthesize natural gas into gasoline. Its success may materially alter this country's fuel economy.

The modified Fischer-Tropsch process is also the basis of plans to produce synthetic hydrocarbons, oils and gases, from western Pennsylvania coals which cannot now be marketed at a profit. A pilot plant now under construction at Library, Pennsylvania, is expected to point the way to the erection of huge coal conversion plants, not only in Pennsylvania but, in the not too distant future, perhaps also in the western states—Wyoming, Montana, the Dakotas, Colorado, etc.—whose vast reserves of low-grade subbituminous coal and lignite have been barely scratched but which under the revolutionary methods of exploitation may become important links in our fuel economy.

---

[6] See also "The Fuel Revolution," *Fortune*, April, 1947; and C. A. Scarlott, "Bright New Future of Coal," *Westinghouse Inquirer*, September, 1947.

BIBLIOGRAPHY

Baker, R. H., *The Bituminous Coal Commission*, Baltimore, Johns Hopkins University Press, 1941.

Campbell, M. R., *The Coal Fields of the United States*, Professional Paper 100-A, Washington, Geological Survey, 1922.

Carlow, C. A., "World Coal Resources," in Parsons, A. B. (ed.), *Seventy-five Years of Progress in the Mineral Industry, 1871-1946*, New York, American Institute of Mining and Metallurgical Engineers, 1947.

"Coal at a Profit: Island Creek," *Fortune*, March, 1938.

"Coal: The Industrial Darkness," *Fortune*, March, 1947.

"Coal: The Fuel Revolution," *Fortune*, April, 1947.

Crighton, A., "Plight of Coal," *Collier's*, June 14, 1947.

Eavenson, H. H., "Seventy-five Years of Progress in Bituminous Coal Mining," in Parsons, A. B. (ed.), *Seventy-five Years of Progress in the Min-*

eral Industry, 1871-1946, New York, American Institute of Mining and Metallurgical Engineers, 1947.

Evans, C., Jr., "Seventy-five Years of Progress in the Anthracite Industry," in Parsons, A. B. (ed.), *Seventy-five Years of Progress in the Mineral Industry, 1871-1946*, New York, American Institute of Mining and Metallurgical Engineers, 1947.

Fritz, W. G., and Veenstra, T. A., *Regional Shifts in the Bituminous Coal Industry*, Pittsburgh, Bureau of Business Research, University of Pittsburgh, 1935.

Hamilton, W. H., *The Case of Bituminous Coal*, New York, Macmillan, 1926.

Hamilton, W. H., "Coal and the National Economy: a Demurrer," *Yale Law Journal*, February, 1941.

Hamilton, W. H., and Wright, H. R., *A Way of Order for Bituminous Coal*, New York, Macmillan, 1928.

Harris, C. D., "The Ruhr Coal Mining District," *Geographical Review*, April, 1946.

Hoar, H. M., *The Coal Industry of the World*, Trade Promotion Series No. 105, U. S. Department of Commerce, Washington, 1930.

International Labor Office, *Report on the World Coal Mining Industries*, London, King, 2 vols., 1938.

Interstate Commerce Commission, Board of Investigation and Research, *The Economics of Coal Traffic Flow*, Washington, 1945.

"Koppers," *Fortune*, April, 1937.

Lange, E. G., *Steinkohle*, in Schumacher, H. (ed.), *Wandlungen in der Weltwirtschaft*, Leipzig, Bibliographisches Institut, 1936, vol. 4.

Leonard, N. H., "The Bituminous Coal Industry," in Adams, W. (ed.), *The Structure of American Industry*, New York, Macmillan, 1950, chap. 2.

Lubin, I., "Coal Industry," *Encyclopædia of the Social Sciences*, New York, Macmillan, 1930.

Moore, E. S., *Coal*, New York, Wiley, 1940.

Murphy, R. E., "Wartime Changes in the United States Pattern of Coal Production," *Annals, Association of American Geographers*, December, 1947.

Murphy, R. E., and Spitta, H. E., "Movements of the Center of Coal Mining in the Appalachian Plateau," *Geographical Review*, October, 1945.

National Bituminous Coal Advisory Council, "Report of the Coal Resources Committee," Washington, December, 1948 (mimeographed).

National Industrial Conference Board, *The Competitive Position of Coal in the United States*, New York, 1931.

Parker, G. L., *The Coal Industry*, Washington, American Council on Public Affairs, 1940.

Report of the Committee on Prices of Bituminous Coal, New York, National Bureau of Economic Research, 1938.

Rostow, E. V., "Bituminous Coal and National Interest," *Yale Law Journal*, February, 1941.

Stamp, L. D., "Britain's Coal Crisis," *Geographical Review*, April, 1948.

Stutzer, O., *Geology of Coal*, Chicago, University of Chicago Press, 1940.

"The Pitt-Consol Venture," *Fortune*, July, 1947.

U. S. Department of Interior, Bureau of Mines, "Pennsylvania Anthracite," "Coal—Bituminous and Lignite," "Coke and Byproducts," in *Minerals Yearbook*.

Veenstra, T. A., and Fritz, W. G., "Major Economic Tendencies in the Bituminous Coal Industry," *Quarterly Journal of Economics*, November, 1936.

Voskuil, W. H., "Bituminous Coal Movements in the United States," *Geographical Review*, April, 1942.

Voskuil, W. H., "Coal and Political Power in Europe," *Economic Geography*, July, 1942.

Voskuil, W. H., *Coke—a Key Industrial Material*, State of Illinois Geological Survey Circular No. 127, Urbana, 1947.

Chapter 30

PETROLEUM:[1] ITS NATURE AND OCCURRENCE

There is an old saying, "Steam is an Englishman," and there was a time when that statement made sense. The steam engine was invented and perfected in Great Britain and that country long led in its production and sale. Likewise, it led in the production and sale of coal, for long the major source of steam-raising heat. Today one may appropriately paraphrase the statement to read, "Oil is an American."

Today the people of the United States, constituting 6 percent of the population of the earth, consume about 60 percent of all the petroleum produced in the world and American oil companies have a hand in the production of close to 80 percent of the world's total oil output. While Europe continues to rely on coal for possibly as much as 90 percent of her mechanical energy needs, in the United States the output of oil and of its sister fuel, natural gas, approximates that of coal in terms of heat equivalents, and the contribution of oil and gas to the total energy supply may eventually exceed that of coal.[2] It is just as natural for the

---

[1] Petroleum literally means "rock oil." Etymologically, therefore, the word suggests *liquid* hydrocarbons, *crude oil*. However, some experts insist that the word embraces all hydrocarbons other than coal and hence includes crude oil, natural gas, natural gasoline, and shale oil. Thus, in *Petroleum Facts and Figures*, the statistical annual of the American Petroleum Institute, a sharp distinction is made between *crude oil* reserves and *petroleum* reserves, the latter including, besides crude oil, also condensate or distillate and natural gas reserves expressed in crude oil equivalents (see 8th ed., p. 82). In the present discussion the word petroleum is used much as it is used in popular language, sometimes referring to oil only, and sometimes covering the entire range of hydrocarbons. The context will indicate in which sense it is used.

[2] In fact, the *Survey of Current Business* (U.S. Department of Commerce, July, 1948) stated that in 1947 oil and gas supplied 47.6 percent of domestic energy *consumption* in the United States, as compared with 44.2 percent for coal. In the same year, according to *Bituminous Coal and Lignite in 1947* (U.S. Department of the Interior, Bureau of Mines), coal constituted 50.2 percent of the total B.T.U. equivalent contributed by the fuels and water power *produced* in this country, as compared with 45.8 percent for oil and gas. The Department of Commerce reduces the share of coal by deducting fuel exports; both it and the Bureau of Mines include petroleum imports. In 1947 the United States was on a *net coal export* and a *net petroleum import* basis.

United States, a country of continental expanse, richly endowed with oil and gas reserves, to place such extraordinary reliance on these hydrocarbons as it was for Great Britain, the pioneer of the Industrial Revolution, the oil-poor but coal-rich island hub of world trade and world empire, to build her wealth and power on coal.

The American chapter of petroleum history starts with the internal combustion engine and its major application—the automobile. The automobile is as typically twentieth-century American as the collier and the coal-hauling tramp were typically nineteenth-century British. The automobile, including passenger car, truck, and bus, although known in most parts of the earth, continues to be a peculiarly American institution. In 1948, of all 58.0 million motor vehicles supposedly registered in the world, no less than 41.1 million, or 71.0 percent, were registered in the United States. Approximately 6 percent of the population of the world owned almost three-fourths of all the motor vehicles in the world.

There are two fundamental reasons for this. In the first place, the people of the United States *can afford* the luxury of an automobile and, in the second place, they *need* a car more than most other people. The United States is the only country of continental expanse which maintains a highly industrialized economy and a mechanized society with high per capita purchasing power on a population density of less than 50 people per square mile. At the same time her economy is thoroughly dependent on interregional trade. In such a situation, flexible transportation which, at a minimum cost, reaches every nook and cranny of her far-flung market area is of paramount significance.[8]

The railroads served to open up this vast territory in bulk, so to speak. But, especially in the West, the intervening spaces between the railroad nets, inadequately served by railroad and horse and buggy alike, constituted a challenge to the ingenuity of man. The automobile was the answer to that challenge. It became a vital organ of the American system. It remade the map of the country and reshaped the life of its people. It furnished the incentive for a vast network of highways, of tourist homes and camps, of service stations and garages, supply stores, etc. It altered the layout of cities and opened up the countryside. Above all, it created the modern oil industry and made it one of the towering giants of our economy. If all the ramifications of the impact of motor vehicles and motor fuel on the economy of the United States could be traced in the finest detail, its magnitude would be astounding.

This amazing transformation of the American scene contributed much to the mechanization of our economy and hence to its productivity and to the national wealth. This greater wealth, in turn, made possible the financing of the vast revolution in transportation and production and contributed to its continuity.

All this is fundamental. Many other facts and factors supported this development. The system of free enterprise which permits private citizens to exploit irreplaceable minerals without hindrance did much to step up the tempo and at times turned orderly progress into a mad scramble. The encouragement of—indeed the insistence on—wild competition played its part in placing speedy exploration and hasty exploitation ahead of the long-run interests of the nation. Faulty laws and unfortunate interpretations of laws put a premium on wasteful methods of production and use.

In retrospect many of these institutional aspects seem wasteful; but one should not judge developments outside the framework of their social climate and economic environment. Nor are all this wild scramble and tragic waste without their redeeming features and mitigating circumstances. Knowledge, know-how, techniques, and science thrive on wasteful haste perhaps as much as on careful systematic development. Would the United States today lead in all phases of petroleum science and practice had not the "rule of capture" (see p. 533) and other crazy schemes pushed the pioneer to frantic zeal? Would she today participate in producing four-fifths of the world's total output of oil if a desire to avoid waste had prematurely choked the enthusiasm and dynamism of the oil man and his industry?

Another reason why the United States is the leader today is the relative ease with which oil can be produced and marketed in this country. She is the only large industrial country

---

[8] See also chap. 10 for a more general discussion of this.

except the Soviet Union, a newcomer on the scene of modern industry, which possesses *within its own borders* huge deposits of mineral oil and natural gas. So far no other leading industrial country—again with the possible exception of the Soviet Union, like the United States a country of continental expanse—has discovered oil and deposits even remotely approaching those proved to exist in this country. In fact, current geological knowledge seems to preclude the possibility of such discoveries in Europe. The development of a strong petroleum industry in the United States, therefore, was definitely encouraged by the presence of vast deposits of petroleum within her borders. Moreover, these deposits happen to lie in highly accessible parts of the country. It is true that, unlike our coal, the bulk of our petroleum reserves are not located in the area of maximum concentration of fuel demand, i.e., the Northeast. But the vast reserves of the Southwest—Texas, Louisiana, Oklahoma, Kansas, Arkansas, New Mexico—are so situated that their products can be moved cheaply to the centers of demand either by pipe line and tanker or directly by pipe line.

California and the rest of the west coast are a world in themselves. They too are blessed with rich oil deposits, although perhaps not rich enough for the growing needs of this region. Current discussions suggest that this part of the country will soon be put on an import basis, drawing supplies from west Texas, the Rocky Mountains, and even South America.

In general, oil in the United States seems to be found where it is most needed. Oil, natural gas, coal, and water power seem to supplement one another regionally in an almost incredibly perfect pattern of energy sources. This too contributed to the success of the oil industry. But the primary cause of its success is still the fact that our oil industry operates in the greatest oil market in the world, in a region richly equipped with the paraphernalia of civilized intercourse—in sharp contrast to the deserts of Arabia and Iran and Iraq and the jungles of Venezuela and Colombia.

Once an industry is on its feet it tends to gain momentum. It realizes its own strength and becomes aware of its superiority over lesser rivals. Then it reaches out to the far corners of the earth—unless the sovereign power of other states blocks the way. To the three-fifths of the world's crude oil output it produces at home, the industry adds another fifth produced abroad.

As the industry expands to keep up with the demand for gasoline, other products are made available which, while perhaps at first a drug on the market, gradually gain in acceptability and usefulness and thus help to broaden the industry's economic basis. Thus, along with gasoline, the petroleum industry produces kerosene, various fuel oils, lubricants, wax, etc. Some of these, such as the lubricants, never had to beg for a buyer. Others, especially the fuel oils, were not always as salable as they are today. The oil engineer, the oil chemist, and the oil economist vied with each other in solving these sales problems, but at times the market took the solution into its own hands, so to speak. Thus when, after a long struggle, the Diesel engine broke down the early resistance and won a place for itself, this was a godsend to the petroleum refineries, for they could balance their production and sales programs better because the Diesel engine needed fuel oil no one else seemed to care for. Then too, after World War II, the American economy expanded as never before and many people for the first time could afford to switch from the dirty and troublesome coal burners to oil or gas burners that were clean and easy to operate. (Incidentally, John L. Lewis might be called the greatest oil salesman in the country, for his frequent strikes, called or uncalled, have rendered the nation's coal supply unreliable and thus made thousands of customers for the purveyors of oil and gas.) When opportunity knocked, the oil industry has been alert and ready to take advantage of it.

PETROLEUM IN THE MODERN WORLD
Petroleum in the Energy Economy of the United States

Commercial production of petroleum in the United States began in 1859, when the first oil well—"Drake's Folly"—was drilled near Titusville, Pennsylvania; but until the turn of the century Russia was the leading producer of petroleum and petroleum products. Today our petroleum industry produces annually over two billion barrels of oil of 42 gallons each, and sells about five trillion cubic feet of natural gas.[4] It owns pipe-line systems whose total mileage exceeds by a wide margin the railroad net that spans the continent. About a million and a quarter wells have been drilled in the United States to date, and every year tens of thousands more go down. Thus, in 1948, 38,803 wells were completed, with a total footage drilled of 134,659,093; the deepest one went down almost 20,000 feet. The products of the industry are marketed by retail outlets that dot the landscape and number literally in the hundred thousands.

Crude oil and natural gas produced in the United States in 1947 had a combined thermal value of 15,867 trillion B.T.U. as compared with 17,768 trillion B.T.U. for coal produced in that year. In percentage of the total energy imputed to the mineral fuels and water power,[5] this meant 45.3 percent of oil and gas as against 50.7 percent for coal.[6] By 1947 the newer energy carriers, oil and gas, were only 8.7 percent behind the old one, coal. As was mentioned before, the theoretical B.T.U. rating does not reveal the contribution to the amount of energy and heat actually generated, or the contribution made by specific energy carriers to the total amount of work done with the aid of that heat and energy. According to some estimates, the contribution of gas and oil to actual work done in the United States is nearer 70 than 50 percent. Similar estimates indicate that the corresponding figure for the world at large is around 30 percent.[7]

Oil the Great Mover[8]

Gasoline, the major product of petroleum, "packs a much bigger punch" in either a pound or a cubic foot than does coal. Hence in transportation, where a premium is placed on lightness and compactness and ease of storage, the high-power liquid, oil, is much preferred to the weaker and bulkier solid coal. Therefore, most motor vehicles—passenger cars, motorcycles, buses, and trucks—as well as airplanes, are run on gasoline. The more exacting demands of airplanes are met by superquality gasolines, power concentrates extraordinary. Of late, gasoline has been yielding some ground to other fuels. This is due to the introduction of new prime movers, especially the Diesel engine, installed in motor trucks, and the jet propulsion engine and gas turbine in airplanes.

The Diesel engine runs on light or distillate fuel oil. Such oil generally sells at prices considerably below those charged for gasoline. In fact, the price has been so low and the advantages of the Diesel engine so great that new railroad locomotives are almost all Diesels. An increasing number of motor trucks and buses are also equipped with Diesel engines. In 1950, almost 37,000 such vehicles were reported by trade journals (*Diesel Power Magazine* and *Bus Transportation Magazine*) to be registered. Thus, petroleum is invading another important field of transportation.

Practically the entire merchant marine and the navy have been converted from coal to oil. The power, cleanliness, and storability of fuel oil excel the properties of coal by so wide a margin, the advantages of operating on oil are so pronounced, that conversion was a foregone conclusion some time ago. Fuel oil is used either under boilers of steamships or in the Diesel engines of motorships. An oil-driven ship can travel three times as far without refueling as a ship using coal, and it can refuel on the high seas. The oil can be stored in odd places such as double bottoms.

Thus, oil is "the great mover," the chief means by which the miracle of modern mobility on land, on sea, and in the air is accomplished.

---

[4] In this discussion natural gas is frequently mentioned with petroleum because the two are closely related. Gas and oil often occur together. A wildcatter drilling a test well generally does not know whether it will be an "oiler," a "gaser," or a "duster," i.e., a dry hole. Both oil and natural gas are hydrocarbons and can be made to yield similar products. Yet the natural gas industry is sufficiently identifiable as an independent industry that an entire chapter is devoted to it and its problems.

[5] At prevailing central-station equivalent. See p. 483.

[6] Bureau of Mines, *Minerals Yearbook, 1947*, preprint. In 1948 oil and gas together exceeded coal by a modest margin. In 1949 because of strikes, coal dropped to 12.5 quadrillion B.T.U., and oil and gas rose to 17.8 quadrillion B.T.U.

[7] Figures provided in a letter from N. B. Guyol.

[8] This discussion is in part based on a publication of the Standard Oil Company (New Jersey) entitled *Petroleum in the World* and released in 1945. Ideas as well as some phrases have been borrowed from this pamphlet.

Possibly as much as half of all petroleum products serve the cause of transportation.[9]

Other Uses of Petroleum

Modern industry like modern transportation depends on machines. When wheels turn and machines move, metal parts rub together. Rubbing creates heat. The heat makes moving parts stick together and stop, unless they are lubricated.

Petroleum is by far the greatest source of lubricants. The introduction of petroleum lubricants in the form of oils and greases is another striking example of what, in this volume, has been referred to as the emancipation from the limitations of the organic.[10] Until petroleum refining yielded adequate supplies of lubricants for the wheels of modern industry, animal and vegetable products—beef and mutton tallow, lard, whale oil, palm oil, olive oil and castor oil—had to be used as lubricants. But their supply is so limited that, in the absence of something far more abundant to take their place, these lubricants would have completely throttled industrial progress. Moreover, animal and vegetable oils could hardly stand up under the heat of modern high-speed machines, nor can they meet the exacting demands of modern high-altitude flying. Scientifically controlled petroleum products can. It is difficult to find a meaningful scale of utility in terms of urgency of need, but one is tempted to name lubricating oil as the most vital contribution made by petroleum to modern civilization. It is the key that unlocks the door to all other achievements.

Until about 1910 the chief petroleum product was kerosene, used chiefly for illuminating purposes but also as a source of heat for cooking and in house heating. In the field of illumination, kerosene took over the work of an animal product—chiefly whale oil. Later on, when electricity proved superior, kerosene as an illuminant was driven back to less accessible areas of the earth not yet reached by electricity. Some kerosene is used as a fuel in tractor engines. From its position as the premier oil product of the nineteenth century, kerosene has been relegated to a definitely minor place. It constitutes about 6 percent of total refinery output in volume.

An increasing amount of fuel oil is being used to produce heat in private homes, commercial buildings, and industrial plants. In this field petroleum, chiefly in the form of heavy residual fuel oil, is competing with coal.[11] Residual fuel oil may be considered a byproduct. The quantity produced depends partly on the nature of the crude oil—some crude yields far more heavy residue than others—partly on the refining techniques applied. This, in turn, is largely governed by considerations of cost and price.

Certain crudes also yield paraffin, used in making candles, wax paper, etc. Such crudes are called paraffin-base crudes. Other crudes are asphalt-base crudes; they yield heavy products such as asphalt, roofing, and road oils. Almost all crudes yield a certain amount of coke, solid carbon; much of it is used in the manufacture of electrodes.

To an increasing extent refining gases are being turned to use, serving as the basis of important chemicals such as butadiene and styrene, the ingredients of a certain synthetic rubber; toluol, the basis of TNT; nylon salts, plastics, and so on.

This discussion of major uses of petroleum may be summarized by Table 30.1, showing the breakdown of the petroleum refinery output of the United States in 1946, 1947, and 1948. It is noteworthy that over 87 percent of the crude leaves the refinery as gasoline, fuel oil, and kerosene, and that the remaining eighth is divided among a list of quantitatively less important products. Again it is stressed that quantity does not necessarily reflect either money or use value. This depends largely on demand and the specific circumstances under which a given product is used. That the sig-

---

[9] A recent study estimated that as much as 62 percent of all petroleum was consumed in transportation, but by 1947 the figure had dropped below 50 percent. The increased use of fuel oil for space heating is one of the major reasons for this change. (Interstate Commerce Commission, Bureau of Transport Economics and Statistics, August, 1947.)

[10] Organic in this case refers to products obtained from growing plants and living animals rather than from organic minerals, derivatives of the vegetable and animal life of millions of years ago.

[11] In recent years natural gas has been gaining in the struggle against coal. See chap. 35.

TABLE 30.1. Petroleum Refinery Output of the United States, 1946-1948[12]

Product	1946 Thousand Barrels	Percent	1947 Thousand Barrels	Percent	1948 Thousand Barrels	Percent
Gasoline	748,411	41.7	814,841	42.4	819,676	40.4
Fuel oil (distillate and residual)	719,260	40.1	759,968	39.5	846,780	41.7
Kerosene	104,385	5.9	110,412	5.7	121,853	6.0
Still gas	88,136	4.9	85,564	4.4	81,159	4.0
Lubricating oil	45,645	2.5	51,765	2.7	51,416	2.5
Asphalt	44,911	2.4	49,286	2.6	51,919	2.6
Coke	10,621	0.6	12,077	0.6	14,494	0.7
Road oil	6,175	0.3	7,074	0.4	7,915	0.4
Wax	3,003	0.15	3,624	0.2	3,515	0.2
Miscellaneous	22,539	1.2	24,348	1.3	29,307	1.4
Shortage	1,695	0.15	4,222	0.2	2,636	0.1
Total	1,794,781	100.0	1,923,181	100.0	2,030,670	100.0

nificance of lubricating oil is hardly revealed by its 2.5 or 2.7 percent share of the total output goes without saying.

Oil in Everyday Life

Few people realize the extent to which petroleum enters everyday life, especially in the oil-rich United States. Many important uses have already been listed. The following mentions some of the less obvious end uses to which oil is put:

Look in your family medicine cabinet. You will likely see cold cream, vaseline, hand lotion, lipstick, perfume, hair tonic, mineral oil, rubbing alcohol, salves, and ointments. All may be made from petroleum or contain petroleum products.

Look at the floor under your feet. Is it covered with linoleum? Linoleum is made with oil. Is it covered with carpet? The wool was treated with oil before it was woven. Is the floor varnished? Oil went into the varnish. Is it waxed? The wax came from oil.

Look at your feet themselves. Are your shoes made of leather? Oil is used in treating leather goods. Look at your clothing. No oil there? But there is. Oil lubricated the strands of cotton or wool from which it was made. Oil may have helped to dye the cloth. Certainly oil removed the dirt, if you sent the garments to a cleaner.

Look around your house. Some part of oil prob-

ably went into the paint on your woodwork or furniture; the ink in your newspapers and magazines; the plastics in your telephone, your car, and your kitchen dishes; the film in your camera; the sprays that keep away moths and other insects. Some of the food you eat may have been ripened or preserved by oil. Certainly most of it was grown and carried to you with the aid of oil-driven machines.

Food, medicine, clothing, shelter, transportation— these things and many more the 4,500,000,000 servants freed from the rock now bring to man. Sunshine millions of years old is working for you today.[13]

Petroleum and War

In two World Wars the Allies, fighting first the Kaiser and his supporters and then Hitler and his Axis, "floated to victory on a flood of oil." Global war is war of great distances, with supply lines encircling the earth. Mobility is of the essence in modern strategy. There is not a branch of the armed services that can function properly without adequate supplies of oil and its products. Modern navies and merchant marines alike are propelled by oil. Superiority in the air based on 100-octane gasoline is vital to victory. Tankers were the premier target of marauding enemy submarines and $1.75 billion

[12] Bureau of Mines, *Mineral Industry Survey.*

[13] Standard Oil Company (New Jersey), *op. cit.*, p. 5.

was put into tankers built during the war to stave off defeat from that source. No less vital to the success of the Allied cause was the oil that went into synthetic rubber and high explosives.

Germany, and to a lesser extent Japan, made oil from coal but at a cost in man power and matériel which sapped their strength. The strategy of both those belligerents included the conquest of oil-rich regions as a major objective. Hitler's vain attempt to lay his hands on the Caucasus, a major source of oil, and Japan's overextension of her supply lines necessitated by her desperate need of oil from the Netherlands East Indies, were major causes of the collapse of the Axis. The incomparable superiority the Allies gained in having access to the oil resources of the earth must be considered a major factor in the outcome of the titanic struggle.

Of vital importance to that outcome was the capacity of the oil industry, especially that of the United States, to step up production of crude oil from about 1.25 billion barrels in 1939 to almost 1.75 billion in 1945. This was possible partly because of the excess peacetime capacity of the refining industry, partly because of the magnificent way in which all concerned rose to the occasion, but also partly because of the fact that for years, under the so-called conservation laws, this country's oil wells had been kept under a wrap to prevent overproduction from flooding the market. Moreover, large amounts of oil discovered during the thirties were kept under ground as a result of the control exercised under various proration laws.[14]

ORIGIN, NATURE, AND OCCURRENCE OF OIL
Origin of Oil

"Petroleum," writes Pratt, "literally rock oil, is the generic term for all natural hydrocarbon, gaseous, liquid, and solid (except coals)."[15] Most crude petroleum appears as an oil which, upon treatment by heat, pressure, or other means, yields diverse products ranging from gas through liquids to solids. Widely as crude oil may differ in character, properties, and behavior, it is all composed of hydrocarbon molecules made up of varying numbers of hydrogen and carbon atoms. The nature of the crude largely determines the products which can be derived from it by simple refining methods.

For long scientists disputed about the origin of petroleum, some upholding the inorganic theory, others defending the organic theory according to which petroleum is of animal and vegetable origin. As more and more evidence accumulated, the scale was tipped heavily toward the organic school. Today the issue is closed; it was decided in favor of the latter group, although the possible existence of inorganic oil is not categorically denied.

It is assumed that whatever the organic material from which petroleum developed, it was first deposited in clays and sands, along seacoasts, in swamps and lakes; and that its rapid destruction by oxidation was prevented by a covering of beds of other material.

Occurrence of Petroleum

This organic theory of the origin of petroleum is important because it furnishes the key to oil exploration. Experience lends support to the belief that only rocks of marine origin, sedimentary rocks such as sandstone, shale, and limestone, contain petroleum. Igneous rocks which have become solid after being melted by volcanic or similar action cannot ordinarily contain oil, and metamorphic rocks which are derived from either igneous or sedimentary types apparently do not normally contain oil.[16]

Before venturing upon a drilling operation that would cost, perhaps, one hundred thousand dollars, the operator must consider whether there is evidence that in the remote geologic age the necessary organic matter was deposited; whether nature provided a suitable storage reservoir, or porous rock that holds oil somewhat as a sponge holds water; whether the oil sands are covered by solid rocks which have prevented it from seeping to the surface or over too large an area under ground; and if there is the proper structure to have forced the oil within comparatively narrow limits to form a

---

[14] This is developed more fully later; see p. 535.
[15] Wallace E. Pratt, *Oil in the Earth,* University of Kansas Press, Lawrence, 1942, p. 9.

[16] According to L. T. Barrows of the Humble Oil and Refining Company, porous, igneous, and metamorphic rocks can absorb oil which has migrated from sedimentary rocks; there are actually a few oil fields producing oil from such rocks.

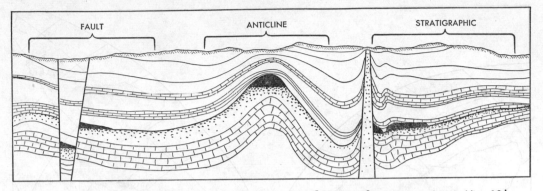

FIG. 30.1.   Three Kinds of Oil "Traps." (Standard Oil Company [New Jersey], *Petroleum in the World*, p. 13.)

pool; for sometimes breaks in the rocks allow oil to escape.[17]

Three structures are particularly favorable to the accumulation of oil: the anticline, the fault, and the stratigraphic trap (see Fig. 30.1). In addition, there are various combinations of these three types.

In the earlier stages of the industry, geologists strongly favored anticlines; only gradually did they recognize the importance of the other types of oil traps. The explorational methods and devices thus far developed are more effective in locating anticlines and faults than stratigraphic traps. Core boring designed to reveal the general geological layout is as yet the only reliable method for locating such traps.

Oil being a normal constituent of the sedimentary rocks of the earth, the first step in mapping the occurrence of oil in the world is to determine the occurrence of these rocks. They constitute roughly 40 percent of the land area of the earth, as Fig. 30.2 shows. Besides these potential oil-bearing areas, this map also shows the actual producing fields. The latter, of course, are all located within the zones of potential findings. These zones cover approximately 25 million square miles, an area about eight times larger than that of the United States. The potential areas lie mainly in Eurasia and the Americas. Africa is practically oilless except at the northeastern fringe and a few spots near the central portion of the west coast. Australia seems to be similarly deficient.

Our geological knowledge of the earth is still very incomplete. So far as our present knowledge permits an appraisal of the aggregate oil accumulation in the earth's crust, two regions stand out as the major areas of oil accumulation. Here is how a leading expert presents the situation.

When we peer into this obscurity surrounding the occurrence of oil, two regions gradually emerge as the principal reservoirs of oil in the earth. Or, in keeping with what Carl Becker so aptly designates as the "climate of opinion" prevailing in the world today, these regions might be described as marking the earth's "oil axis." One end of this axis is the environs of the Black, Caspian, and Red seas, the Persian Gulf, and the eastern end of the Mediterranean Sea in the Old World. Within this region lie the major oil fields of Russia, Iran, Iraq, Arabia, Roumania, and Egypt. The other end of this oil axis is the land margin which might be called the Mediterranean region of the New World: that geologically modern crustal depression now occupied by the Gulf of Mexico and the Caribbean Sea; here lie the great oil fields of Venezuela, Colombia, Mexico, and of the Gulf Coast of the United States. Of the proved oil reserve of the United States, itself, more than 9 billion barrels, or approximately one-half of the nation's total, lie within this region tributary to the Gulf of Mexico. Altogether, nearly 30 billion barrels of oil, or about two-thirds of the total proved reserve of oil in the earth, is contained in these two regions at the opposite ends of the earth's oil axis. Just as the modern ice cap at the South Pole exceeds that at the North Pole, so the Old World end of the axis, with some 16 billion barrels proved reserves, dominates the New World end and thus becomes the outstanding oil reserve in the earth.[18]

---

[17] Standard Oil Company (New Jersey) *Petroleum*, 1928, p. 8.

[18] Wallace E. Pratt, *op. cit.*, pp. 33-34.

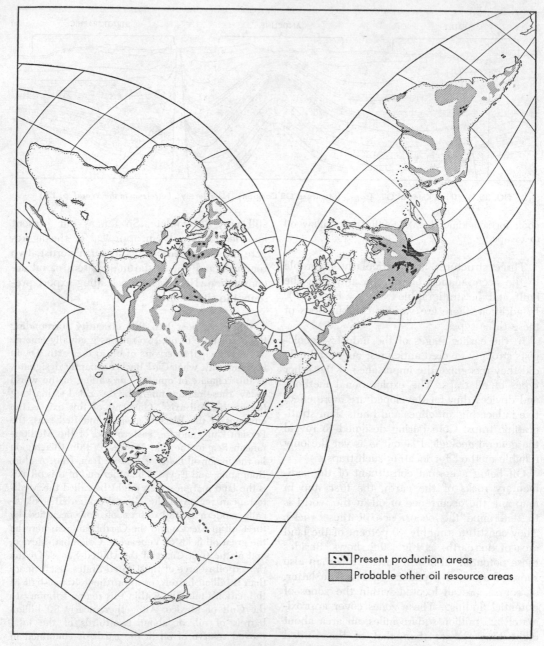

Present production areas

Probable other oil resource areas

FIG. 30.2.   World Oil for Today and Tomorrow. (*The Lamp*, June, 1944.)

Geologically this concentration of oil in these two major reservoirs of the earth may be explained by the following facts: Here are found the greatest segments of the earth's crust composed of very moderately deformed, geologically young marine rocks. Successive warpings have been sufficient to trap large amounts of oil but not too severe to prevent their preservation.

Besides these two major oil reservoirs there are several minor ones—or rather this is how the situation appears now in the light of our incomplete geological knowledge. Among the minor fields are those on both sides of the Pacific—in California and in the large islands of the Malay Archipelago, especially Borneo, Sumatra, Java and New Guinea. Another secondary group is the area around the North Pole, extending from northern Canada and Alaska around through northern Siberia and all the way to northern Europe.

Of late, keen interest has been focused on the continental shelf, the sea floor of the shallow marginal waters surrounding the continents. This shelf measures roughly ten million square miles, about a tenth of which adjoins the coasts of the United States and Alaska. It reaches far out from the northern shores of the Soviet Union and North America and is not negligible off Argentina and the east coast of Asia, but is less conspicuous elsewhere. What has attracted popular attention to this large submerged area of potential oil fields is the dispute between the federal government of the United States and the interested state governments over title to it.[19]

The continental shelf is of sufficient importance to call for awareness of its existence. To what extent it will contribute to the future supply of oil is a matter of speculative conjecture. Much will depend on the cost of underwater operations. At present, only a limited amount of such operations are in progress, but, to an extent, they are sufficient to suggest costs far in excess of typical land operation costs.[20]

Nature of Crude Oil

In preceding chapters the heterogeneity of coals was emphasized. Crude oils are equally heterogeneous and for the same reason—the wide variety of organic antecedents and of the geological, bacteriological, and chemical proc-

esses governing the formation and occurrence of the hydrocarbons. Three major types of crudes are distinguished: "paraffin base," "asphaltic base," and "naphthenic base." These types vary widely in their yield of gasoline under straight-run distillation. The paraffin-base crudes generally show the highest gasoline yields; some asphalt-base crudes yield no gasoline at all. Naphthenic-base crudes have an intermediary position. The most common varieties of crudes are combinations of the three.

These three types differ widely in specific gravity; low specific gravity indicates high gasoline yield, and vice versa.

Pennsylvania crudes generally have a predominating paraffin base and contain only a small percentage of asphalt compounds. The most familiar examples of asphaltic base crudes are Mexican and some of the California oils, which are black and heavy. The crude oils of Russia are in a large part naphthenic, and crude of this character is also found in California and in the coastal region of Texas. Mid-Continent crude oil has a mixed base, with characteristics pretty evenly balanced between paraffin and asphalt.[21]

In addition to the hydrocarbons which actually constitute petroleum, the oil as recovered from the ground contains small quantities of other compounds such as sulphur, nitrogen, oxygen, together with varying amounts of natural gas, water and dirt. Regardless of the base, the relative percentage of hydrogen and carbon remains nearly the same, i.e., about 85 per cent by weight of carbon content and 15 per cent hydrogen.[22]

The prices of crudes clearly reflect these differences. They are based on the value of the products which the refinery expects to obtain from the crude and the costs involved in conversion and in reaching the market. These costs, in turn, are affected by constantly changing refining practices and technology. The presence of sulfur tends to add to refining costs, for sulfur causes corrosion. Low viscosity also

---

[19] On June 23, 1947, the Supreme Court of the United States decided this question in favor of the federal government in so far as dominion and paramount rights over the continental shelf off California are concerned. For historical reasons the decision cannot be extended automatically to other states, notably Texas, whose entrance into the Union occurred under unique circumstances. Moreover, the question has been raised whether "dominion and paramount rights" includes title. In June, 1950, the Supreme Court decided that the rights of Louisiana and Texas are not essentially different from those held by California.

[20] The 1947 annual report of the Standard Oil Company (New Jersey) reports: "Humble Oil and Refining Company, a Jersey affiliate, has developed further its over-water drilling techniques. Of spe-

cial interest are preparations for the drilling of exploratory wells in the Gulf of Mexico, eight miles off shore. This will be the first well ever drilled in open water more than 30 feet deep and marks a significant step toward exploration of oil possibilities in the Continental Shelf" (p. 8).

[21] Standard Oil Company (New Jersey), *Petroleum*, pp. 26-27.

[22] *Ibid.*

tends to raise the cost of conversion, especially in cold weather when the free flow of crude stocks through the stills is impeded.

As will be shown later in the discussion of refining practices, the original character of the crude has lost much of its significance as a determinant of yields of specific products and of costs. The art of manipulation and chemical transformation has made great strides.

WORLD PETROLEUM RESERVES

As modern industrial civilization becomes progressively dependent on petroleum and the products derived therefrom, and as victory in global war, which through the rise of air power and the technical development of the submarine has become definitely three-dimensional, comes to depend more and more on superior command over petroleum supplies, the question of petroleum reserves becomes one of vital importance, especially to the people of the United States whose welfare and security rest largely on their prodigious output of oil. The question has become extremely acute in the very recent past mainly for two reasons: the unexpectedly rapid increase of world petroleum production from a little over 2 billion barrels in 1939 to over 3.4 billion in 1948—a 63 percent increase in nine years—and the ominous political situation of the globe marked by the growing tension between the East, led by the Soviet Union, and the West, championed by the United States.

Definition of Terms

In an earlier chapter considerable space was devoted to the general problem of reserve estimates, and great emphasis was put on the necessity for careful definition of terms. This applies even more strongly in the case of petroleum.

Perhaps the best way to open this discussion is to attempt to dispel popular misconceptions. The American Petroleum Institute, often referred to as the A.P.I., reported proved petroleum reserves in the United States on December 31, 1948, as 23,280,444,000 barrels of 42 United States gallons, the highest on record in the history of the industry.[23] If a layman takes this figure to represent all the petroleum known to exist in the ground in this country and is aware of the fact that our annual production exceeded 2 billion barrels in 1948, he may be tempted to conclude that the United States has barely enough oil in the ground to last another decade.

What the layman needs to know is the exact meaning of the term "proved reserves." This is perhaps best defined in the following quotation from a recent report:

The estimates . . . refer solely to proved or blocked-out reserves of crude oil (including condensate) *known to be recoverable under existing economic and operating conditions*. Therefore, they do not include any estimate of:

1. Oil under the unproved portions of partly developed fields.
2. Oil in untested prospects.
3. Oil that may be present in unknown prospects in regions believed to be generally favorable.
4. Oil that may become available by secondary-recovery methods from fields where such methods have not yet been applied.
5. Oil that may become available through chemical processing of natural gas.
6. Oil that can be made from oil shale, coal, or other substitute sources.

The committee again wishes especially to stress the fact that its estimates of proved reserves cannot be used as a measure of the rate at which these reserves can be produced with or without physical waste. Oil cannot be produced from the permeable rocks in which it occurs at any desired rate, because the flow of oil through the pores of the oil-bearing rocks is definitely controlled by physical factors of the reservoir. As a matter of fact, today's known oil can be recovered only over a period of many years and at gradually declining annual rates. This has been widely demonstrated by past performance under all kinds of operating conditions. Therefore, incorrect conclusions as to the life of these reserves can be obtained by dividing these reserves by the current rate of production.[24]

In other words, proved reserves constitute the working inventory which the oil companies have blocked out as the sources of the raw material with which to run the refineries. They

---

[23] This figure is exclusive of 3.5 billion barrels of natural gas liquids. If this figure is included, the total is more than 26.8 billion barrels.

[24] *Proved Reserves of Crude Oil, Natural Gas Liquids and Natural Gas, December 31, 1947*, published jointly by the American Gas Association and the American Petroleum Institute. Italics the author's.

TABLE 30.2. Composite Proved Petroleum Reserves, by States, December 31, 1949[25]
(thousand barrels)

State	Liquid Crude Oil	Natural Gas Liquids	Total Liquid Petroleum	Natural Gas[a] Equivalent	Total Petroleum
Alabama	3,547	. . .	3,547	. . .	3,547
Arkansas	297,463	55,642	353,105	145,698	498,803
California	3,822,751	320,275	4,143,026	1,665,272	5,808,298
Colorado	344,812	24,190	369,002	204,516	573,518
Illinois	468,138	26,666	494,804	38,865	533,669
Indiana	50,209	126	50,335	4,200	54,535
Kansas	738,390	106,405	844,795	2,348,260	3,193,055
Kentucky	56,168	13,245	69,413	224,899	294,312
Louisiana	1,909,769	596,422	2,506,191	4,447,968	6,954,159
Michigan	66,496	1,203	67,699	35,818	103,517
Mississippi	402,860	56,407	459,267	421,495	880,762
Montana	112,393	3,710	116,103	133,912	116,103
Nebraska	1,624	. . .	1,624	. . .	135,536
New Mexico	592,222	85,719	677,941	1,040,167	1,718,108
New York	62,900	. . .	62,900	11,114	74,014
Ohio	27,703	1,670	29,373	108,762	138,135
Oklahoma	1,329,918	234,030	1,563,948	1,937,663	3,501,611
Pennsylvania	103,356	2,643	105,999	103,613	209,612
Texas	13,509,732	2,143,711	15,653,443	16,528,400	32,181,843
Utah	15,831	208	16,039	10,930	26,969
West Virginia	37,992	12,831	50,823	285,872	336,695
Wyoming	691,602	43,863	735,465	362,280	1,097,745
Miscellaneous	3,613[b]	46[c]	3,659	3,851[d]	7,510
Total United States	24,649,489	3,729,012	28,378,501	30,063,557	58,442,058

[a] Estimated proved natural gas reserves converted at the rate of 6,000 cubic feet of gas equaling 1 barrel of crude oil.
[b] Includes Florida, Missouri, Tennessee, and Virginia.
[c] Includes Alabama, Florida, and New York.
[d] Includes Alabama, Florida, Maryland, Missouri, Nebraska, and Virginia.

are almost the exact counterpart of the blocked-out ore reserves of a concern that mines and refines metals. Just as ores are not physical quantities but economic magnitudes dependent on price-cost relationships, so are proved oil reserves not physical quantities. Just as rising prices and falling costs mean the invisible but nonetheless real expansion of ores, so proved oil reserves expand in response to increasing demand relative to supply and to improvements in production methods which lower cost or raise the rate of recovery.

In the early stages of the industry petroleum was produced by methods now recognized as incredibly inefficient and wasteful. Often as

[25] Courtesy, American Petroleum Industries Committee; authority, American Gas Assn., American Petroleum Institute.

little as only 10 percent and seldom more than 20 percent of the oil in a given reservoir was recovered. Now recoveries of 60 percent are being widely realized. If, therefore, forty or fifty years ago, 5 billion barrels of oil were discovered, this meant "proved reserves" of only half a billion or a billion barrels, whereas today one would be justified in recording a "proved reserve" of close to 3 billion. Proved reserves, i.e., reserves recoverable by known methods at prevailing cost-price relationships, today constitute a far larger percentage of total discoveries than was formerly the case. In terms of recoverable oil, each billion barrels of newly located oil is worth a multiple of what it was formerly.

Of equal significance are improvements in refining techniques. While during the early stages of the industry perhaps little more than 20 to 30 percent of the crude was sold as kerosene and gasoline, heavier fractions being discarded or put to uses which failed to take advantage of the values inherent in the oil, today it is technically feasible to convert almost the entire stock into desirable and useful products. Finally, the more economical use of these products must be taken into account in evaluating the true meaning and significance of reserves.

As was mentioned before, a distinction is made between oil reserves and petroleum reserves. The term oil refers only to liquid crude oil. Since some liquid petroleum is also recovered from natural gas,[26] liquid petroleum therefore includes both liquid crude oil and natural gas liquids. In addition to these two items, petroleum reserves include natural gas reserves converted into their crude oil equivalent at the rate of 6000 cubic feet of gas to one barrel of crude oil. Table 30.2 gives the composite proved petroleum reserves by states. It should be noted that the oil equivalent of natural gas exceeds the crude oil reserves by several billion barrels and that figures for natural gas reserves are rapidly being revised upward.

The true nature of these proved reserves as "running inventories" or as "a fund to support a certain optimum economic rate of withdrawal, the continuation of which depends on new accretions of proved reserves,"[27] is shown in Fig. 30.3. This figure indicates how each year new discoveries add to the accumulated discoveries and how, in spite of rapidly increasing production, proved reserves of crude oil on January 1, 1948, were almost 21.5 billion barrels, a figure which, though larger than any previous record, was surpassed by the 23.2 billion barrels at the end of that year. However, the current rate of production also is higher than at any previous time and the ratio of proved reserves to annual production is less reassuring today than it was some years back.

The figures for accumulated new discoveries

and new developments show that discoveries come in spurts. There was a tremendous wave during 1925-1930 which included the discovery of the unique east Texas field. During that period discoveries exceeded production by a wide margin. If we are to maintain similar margins of safety, future discoveries will have to be on an even larger scale proportionate to the higher rate of current production. When production in this country runs over 2 billion barrels a year, discoveries should run at over double the rate for the period when production was only 1 billion barrels. The crucial question is: Is such a rate of discovery possible?

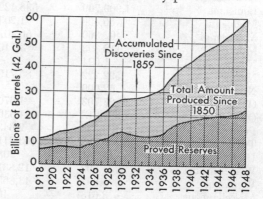

FIG. 30.3. Proved Reserves, Production, and Discoveries of Crude Oil in the United States, 1918-1948. This graph does not include natural gas liquids which in 1948 amounted to 3.5 billion barrels, raising reserves of total liquid hydrocarbons to 26.8 billion barrels in that year. (Oil Industry Information Committee, *Petroleum Industry Record 1918-1948*, 1949.)

One should not take the rather disappointing showing during the war years too seriously. Scarcity of man power and raw materials hindered exploration; furthermore, the "ceiling price" for crude oil was not high enough, relative to other prices, to encourage vigorous exploration. The test will come when conditions are more normal and thus more favorable to exploration.

It may be significant that in recent years additions to proved reserves have come less from the discovery of new fields than from the upward revision of the reserves in old fields. These revisions in part reflect more complete knowledge of reservoir conditions; in part, they result from better discovery practices. Reserves can be written up very fast by revising the expected recovery rate from 35 to 50 percent.

---

[26] At present this applies only to the recovery of liquids from so-called wet gas. The extraction of gasoline from natural gas by chemical processes is on the threshold of realization, one plant being on the point of starting operation.

[27] Bernard Brodie, "American Security and Foreign Oil," *Foreign Policy Report*, March, 1948, p. 302.

Proved Reserves, Indicated Reserves, Reserves, and Resources

The terminology on reserves is not yet clearly established. There is no question about the meaning of proved reserves, for this term has been accurately defined by the A.P.I. and their definition is universally accepted. Of late the expression, indicated reserves,[28] has been coming into use. This is a gradation just below proved reserves and may be defined as "virtually proved" reserves. Another term used in the recent literature is "reserves."[29] This term is broader than proved reserves and covers all the oil actually found by drilling. Since proved reserves, being recoverable reserves only, on the average include little more than half the total oil, "reserves" are roughly double the proved reserves. The justification for using this term is the possibility of improvements in recovery practices, especially the successful use of secondary recovery methods, i.e., the use of injected gas, water, or air to recover oil not recoverable with current methods.

The term "resources" has also been applied to potential oil reserves yet to be discovered.[30] However, in view of the special meaning given to the word resources in this volume, it seems more desirable to speak simply of future or potential reserves. The word "resources," as used by Mr. Holman, has both a narrow and a wide meaning. In the narrow sense it refers to the entire crude oil reserves including those yet to be discovered. In the wider sense it includes also the reserves of other materials such as natural gas, oil shale, oil sands, and even coal which are expected to be the source of such products as gasoline, kerosene, lubricating oil, fuel oil, etc., which now, in the United States at least, are extracted more or less exclusively from crude oil. It is when "reserves" is used in this wider meaning that talk of "oil enough to last us a thousand years" is heard. The layman must indeed be on his guard if he wishes to understand these intricate arguments about oil reserves.

Potential Oil Reserves of the United States

The topic of potential or future oil supplies is highly controversial. As yet, many of the relevant facts are so conjectural that even experts disagree widely and the utmost caution is called for lest false impressions be created.

There is complete agreement as to the fact that no one knows or can know the amount of crude oil still to be found in the United States. But rough calculations have been made which are intended to present at least a general idea of the approximate magnitude of the crude oil supplies still awaiting discovery. These calculations proceed from certain known facts: (1) the approximate extent of the geologic formations in which oil may be found (see Fig. 30.2), (2) the area that has been explored to date, (3) the percentage of the explored area that has proved productive, i.e., oil-bearing, and (4) the amount of oil that has been found under the average acre or square mile of this productive area. The figures for 1943 were as follows:

1. Total area in the United States rated as probably oil-bearing . . . . 1,500,000 sq. miles
2. Area explored to date . . 800,000 sq. miles
3. Percent on which oil has been found (8000 sq. mi.) . 1 percent
4. Amount of crude oil found to date . . . . 46.7 billion barrels[31] or 5.84 million barrels per sq. mi.

According to this calculation, in 1943 there were 700,000 square miles left to be explored; 7000 square miles of this should prove pro-

---

[28] Cf. *Preliminary Report of the Technical Oil Mission to the Middle East*, February 1, 1944. This mission was sent by the Petroleum Reserves Corporation, an agency of the United States government.

[29] See Petroleum Industry Research Foundation, Inc., *World Oil: Fact and Policy*, 1944, p. 8.

[30] See Eugene Holman, President of Standard Oil Company (New Jersey), in a letter to the editor of the New York *Times*, January 29, 1948.

[31] This figure is arrived at by adding to the "proved resources" of 20.1 billion barrels (January 1, 1944) the total accumulated production up to that date—26.6 billion barrels. This total should be increased by an unknown quantity representing additional oil yet to be proved either at greater depths or in new fields in areas already explored. According to the size of this unknown quantity, this calculation of reserves will be either reasonably accurate or too conservative. But in view of its general speculative character, this unknown factor need not be taken too seriously, for the result is at best a mere approximation.

ductive (if the 1 percent average is accepted as a basis of future discovery), and a little over 40 billion barrels of oil should be found. If this potential reserve of 40 billion barrels is added to the previously discovered 48.2 billion reserves (December 31, 1943), the total discovered and calculated future reserves of the United States as of 1943 amounted to about 87 billion barrels.

This is, of course, a very rough estimate. But it is rational, for it proceeds from known facts and makes logical deductions. It may prove too optimistic or too conservative. If, for some reason or other, the areas exploited thus far prove to have been the best areas in terms of oil content, which they well may be, the calculation will prove overoptimistic. On the other hand, in some regions in the United States the ratio of oil-bearing to total land runs as high as 2 or 3 percent. Luck may have reserved several such areas for future discovery, with the result that the future ratio may be nearer 2 percent than 1. This would make a tremendous difference in ultimate oil recovery.

It cannot be stressed too much that the calculation is made in terms of *proved* reserves, not total "reserves" discovered. The figures state that with present recovery practices about 90 billion barrels had either been produced or were in sight as *recoverable* reserves, not total reserves. Total reserves would be double, for, petroleum technology being as dynamic as it is, it would be deliberate pessimism to assume that recovery rates will not go up. Furthermore, proved reserves reflect current price levels. Changes in price relationships favorable to petroleum would warrant further upward revision. In conclusion, one may venture to say that an estimate of 100 billion barrels of total oil reserves, including the amounts already produced, is by no means unreasonable.

Whether this estimate will calm the fears of those who are deeply concerned over our oil reserves is another question. Perhaps these additional comments may increase their peace of mind: (1) We can expect to supplement domestic supplies by imports, surely from South America and perhaps the Near East. (2) According to present knowledge, our natural gas reserves exceed our oil reserves. That natural gas will yield increasing amounts of gasoline may be considered a foregone conclusion. (3)

Our crude oil reserves will not be exhausted suddenly, but will decline gradually, allowing ample time in which to perfect known processes or new and better processes of recovering from coal and lignite the entire range of products now obtained from crude.

Proved Petroleum Reserves Outside the United States[32]

The United States has been explored for oil far more thoroughly than any other country in the world. About 1.25 million wells[33] have perforated her soil—and there is no surer way to determine the presence or absence of oil than the actual drilling of wells. In no other country does the number of wells or the intensity of exploration approach that in the United States. On the whole, our knowledge of oil reserves outside this country is even less accurate and dependable than knowledge of our own reserves. This, of course, refers to total, including potential, reserves and not to proved reserves. However, certain basic facts regarding world oil reserves, current and future, appear fairly definitely established.

The most important of these is recognition of two major oil reservoir regions, the so-called *petroleum axis* of the earth, which were discussed earlier in this chapter (see p. 503)—the Mediterranean and Middle East, and the Mediterranean region of the New World. There are also two minor bases: one lying between Asia and Australia and the other surrounding the North Pole. The last-named region is still largely unexplored but holds great promises.

To get an approximate idea of the total oil reserves of the earth one can extend to the global scene the calculations of our own potential oil reserves made earlier in the chapter (see above). For the earth as a whole, the

---

[32] The word "proved" used in connection with world reserves does not have quite the same exacting meaning as it does when applied to reserves in the United States. There are "estimated proved" reserves and "proved and indicated" reserves.

[33] Many of these wells may be considered unnecessary for effective exploitation; in fact, they were detrimental to orderly development. But some of them may have contributed their share of evidence without which geologists could not have advanced as rapidly as they did. Many others, however, were too shallow to do even that.

figure corresponding to the 1.5 million square miles of the United States which might be oil-bearing is 22 million square miles, an area about 15 times as large. This yields an estimate for the world of 1500 billion barrels, of which about 58 billion had been produced by the end of 1948, leaving roughly 1442 billion barrels. Again it cannot be too much emphasized that this figure is arrived at by a very rough calculation. Undoubtedly, it is far away from the actual figure, but at least it will give some idea of the general picture.

A recent report contains the following estimates of oil reserves controlled by the major powers and others as of January 1, 1948:

	Million Barrels	Percent of Total
United States	43,095	60.4
British and Dutch	18,735	26.3
Russian	6,000	8.4
Others	3,482	4.9
Total	71,312	100.0

In this connection the factors of accessibility and availability must be mentioned. The two so-called poles of petroleum concentration happen to be ideally located for economic development. The highly articulated topography helps to make marketing easy, for they lie near the two largest markets for petroleum products, North America and Europe, respectively. In neither area does Anglo-American exploration face any great institutional obstacles in terms of hostile ideology or economic rivalry, a condition that can hardly be said to hold true of concentrations of petroleum reserves in other parts of the globe. Much of the rest of the oil is inaccessible and therefore unavailable for some time to come.

Another factor is strategic location. War has a strange way of demanding that things which

BIBLIOGRAPHY

See the bibliography at the end of Chapter 34.

in peacetime seem uneconomical be done. At present, the Near East is taking on increasing strategic importance; her oil, too, is increasing in immediate value. The Arctic seems far less remote to the strategist than to the peacetime purveyor of petroleum. The Near and Middle East and the New World Mediterranean region today assume special significance because of their superior accessibility to the greatest foci of economic and strategic demand.

It will be noted that regions under British and Dutch control—including the Near East—rank second to the United States. Actually, geologists familiar with the two regions hesitate little to put the Near East ahead of the United States in ultimate performance. The following quotation explains this attitude:

When one considers the great oil discoveries which have resulted from the meagre exploration thus far accomplished in the Middle East, the substantial number of known projects not yet drilled, and the great areas still practically unexplored, the conclusion is inescapable that reserves of great magnitude remain to be discovered.

The proved and indicated reserves of this area are comparable with those of the United States, yet all of the Middle East reserves have been discovered by the drilling of less than a total of 150 wildcat wells. In the United States we drill more than 20 times this number of wildcat wells each year.[34]

[34] Petroleum Industry Research Foundation, Inc., op. cit., pp. 10-11.

Speaking before the Scientific Conference on Conservation and Utilization of Natural Resources at Lake Success on August 25, 1949, a geologist, Professor A. I. Lavorsen of Stanford University, startled his audience by saying that an undiscovered 500-year supply of petroleum was waiting to be found and that even a 1000-year supply was not beyond the range of possibility. This extreme optimism took even the oil industry by surprise, one of its representatives labeling Lavorsen's statement " an exercise in metaphysics." See an editorial in the New York Times, August 26, 1949.

Chapter 31

WORLD CRUDE OIL PRODUCTION

For a bird's-eye view of the statistical development of world petroleum production the reader is referred to Tables 31.1 and 31.2, which show crude oil production by continents and countries, respectively, from 1857 to 1948. Since 1857, the first year for which statistics on world petroleum production are available, 58,329,733,000 barrels of oil had been produced as of January 1, 1949. Several significant facts should be noted:

1. The modern oil industry is a young industry; it is not yet one hundred years old.

2. Production has accelerated at a rate unmatched by any other major commodity of world commerce. In 1857, 2 thousand barrels were produced; in 1861, over 2 million; in 1877, over 15 million; in 1895, over 103 million; in 1923, over 1 billion; in 1948, over 3 billion.

3. The United States has a leading position in oil production, as Table 31.3 shows. Altogether she had produced, by January 1, 1949, a total of 37.1 billion barrels out of a world total of 58.3 billion barrels, or 63.6 percent, almost two-thirds of all the crude oil produced throughout the world.

PRODUCTION IN THE UNITED STATES

The oil-producing districts of the United States are shown in Fig. 31.1. Production by states is shown in Table 31.4, and by regions in Table 31.5. The regional shift during less than half a century is striking. In 1900 the Northeast produced almost 95 percent of the crude oil and California most of the balance. By 1935 the center of gravity had shifted to the Southwest, 71.7 percent, and California, 20.9 percent. In 1948 Illinois was petering out, and the Rocky Mountains were gaining slightly in importance. Production in Florida had not yet reached the point where it registered on the national scale. Mississippi, on the other hand, came strongly to the fore, producing over 35 million barrels in 1947 and at the rate of more than 120,000 barrels daily in July, 1948.

At present, Texas is by far the leading oil state in this country, in terms of both production and proved reserves. In 1948 she produced 903 million barrels out of a total of 2016 million, or 44.8 percent. By the end of 1948 she had produced 12,417 million barrels out of a total of 37,099 million, or 32.7 percent of the

TABLE 31.1. World Crude Oil Production by Continents, Selected Years, 1860-1948[1]

Year	North America Million Barrels	North America Per-cent	South America Million Barrels	South America Per-cent	Europe[a] Million Barrels	Europe[a] Per-cent	Asia Million Barrels	Asia Per-cent	Africa Million Barrels	Africa Per-cent	World Million Barrels
1860	0.5	100.0	...	...	...	...	...	...	...	...	0.5
1870	5.5	94.9	...	...	0.3	5.0	...	...	...	...	5.8
1880	26.6	88.7	...	...	3.4	11.2	...	...	...	...	30.0
1890	46.6	62.1	...	...	29.8	40.1	0.2	...	...	...	74.6
1900	64.5	43.3	0.3	0.2	80.1	53.4	4.2	2.9	...	...	149.1
1910	213.5	92.9	1.4	0.6	93.8	41.1	19.0	8.3	...	...	227.8
1920	600.2	87.0	7.1	1.0	39.2	5.7	41.4	6.0	1.0	...	688.9
1930	939.1	67.1	189.5	13.5	174.0	12.3	105.4	7.5	2.0	...	1,410.0
1940	1,406.0	65.4	268.7	13.3	280.1	13.4	188.4	9.0	6.5	...	2,149.8
1946	1,791.0	65.1	467.0	15.6	208.3	7.7	271.3	10.0	9.1	...	2,746.7
1947	1,920.3	64.0	518.7	17.3	236.3	7.9	338.1	11.2	8.7	...	3,022.0
1948	2,087.4	61.4	575.7	16.9	260.1	7.7	469.9	13.0	11.5	...	3,404.6
Total[b]	39,591.0	67.8	6,169.4	10.6	7,747.8	13.3	4,701.4	8.1	119.1	0.2	58,329.7

[a]Includes minor amounts produced in Asiatic Russia other than Sakhalin.
[b]Total production to date.

TABLE 31.2. World Crude Oil Production by Countries, Selected Years, 1860-1948
(in million barrels)

	1860	1870	1880	1890	1900	1910	1920	1930	1940	1946	1947	1948	Total[b]
Canada	...	0.3	0.4	0.8	0.9	0.3	0.2	1.5	8.6	7.6	7.6	12.5	141.3
Mexico	...	...	...	...	...	3.6	157.1	39.5	44.0	49.2	56.3	58.4	2,348.9
United States	0.5	5.3	26.3	45.8	63.6	209.6	442.9	898.0	1353.2	1733.9	1856.1	1201.6	37,098.7
Argentina	...	...	...	...	...	...	1.7	9.0	20.6	20.6	21.8	23.0	411.5
Colombia	...	...	...	...	...	...	...	20.3	25.6	22.5	25.9	23.8	442.7
Peru	...	...	...	...	...	1.3	2.8	12.4	12.1	12.6	12.8	13.8	371.4
Trinidad	...	...	...	...	...	...	2.1	9.4	22.2	20.2	20.5	20.7	372.4
Venezuela	...	...	...	...	...	...	...	136.7	185.6	388.5	434.9	491.4	4,523.0
Rumania	...	...	0.1	0.4	1.6	9.7	7.4	41.6	43.2	31.4	28.6	29.2	1,187.1
Soviet Union	...	0.2	3.0	28.1	75.8	70.3	25.4	125.6	218.8	157.7	187.5	210.0	6,051.3
Egypt	...	...	...	...	...	...	1.0	2.0	6.5	9.1	8.6	11.4	118.5
Bahrein	...	...	...	...	...	...	...	...	7.1	8.0	9.4	10.8	98.8
Iran	...	...	...	...	...	...	12.2	45.8	66.3	146.8	154.5	189.8	1,937.6
Iraq	...	...	...	...	...	...	...	...	24.2	35.7	35.8	22.6	407.1
Kuwait	...	...	...	...	...	...	...	...	...	5.9	16.2	46.1	68.3
Saudi Arabia	...	...	...	...	...	...	...	...	5.1	59.9	89.9	142.9	345.1
British Borneo	...	...	...	...	...	...	1.0	4.9	7.0	2.1	13.0	17.5	156.2
Indonesia	...	...	...	...	2.3	11.0	17.5	41.7	62.0	2.1	8.0	30.7	1,173.4
Total[a]	0.5	5.8	30.0	74.6	149.1	227.8	688.9	1410.0	2149.8	2746.7	3022.0	3404.6	58,329.7

[a]Includes others.
[b]Total production to date.

[1] Tables 31.1 and 31.2 are adapted from *World Oil*, February 15, 1949, pp. 230, 232, 234.

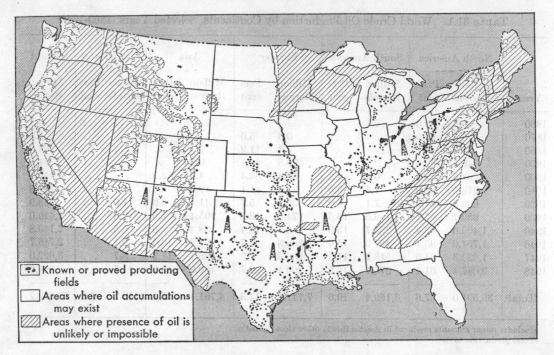

Known or proved producing fields

Areas where oil accumulations may exist

Areas where presence of oil is unlikely or impossible

FIG. 31.1. Present and Potential Oil-Producing Areas of the United States. (*The Lamp*, April, 1944.)

TABLE 31.3. Oil Production—The United States and the World[2] (in thousand barrels)

	World	United States	Percent of World Total
1860	509	500	98.2
1870	5,799	5,261	90.7
1880	30,018	26,286	87.6
1890	76,633	45,824	59.8
1900	149,137	63,621	42.7
1910	327,763	209,557	63.9
1920	688,884	442,929	64.3
1930	1,410,037	898,011	63.7
1940	2,149,821	1,353,214	62.9
1948	3,404,574	2,016,200	59.2
Total	58,329,700	37,098,700	63.6

total. California and Oklahoma rank next, with totals of 8.0 and 5.9 billion barrels, or 21.6 and 15.9 percent of our total output, respectively. In recent years, as Oklahoma's production declined, Louisiana came to the fore, ranking third in 1946 and again in 1947.

These enormous amounts of oil, running into billions of barrels, are produced in hundreds of fields and by hundreds of thousands of wells.

Formerly, the life of a typical field was very short; the typical production curve ran up sharply and came down equally fast. But fortunately the situation has greatly improved as a result of measures which will be discussed fully later. But it is still true today, as it was in the past, that the only way of maintaining production is by "producing" new fields or enlarging the output of the older ones.

The American Petroleum Institute has prepared a list of the 67 leading oil fields of the United States.[3] The east Texas field tops the list. Discovered in 1930, it still led the parade in 1946, producing 2.33 billion barrels in seventeen years—a record unapproached by any other field. In fact, no other field has ever neared the billion barrel mark. While ranking second in accumulated production, the field at Long Beach, California, discovered in 1921, is now a minor producer, with less than 10 million barrels a year.

Of special interest because of strategic possibilities is Navy Petroleum Reserve Number

---

[2] *Ibid.*

[3] See American Petroleum Institute, *Petroleum Facts and Figures*, 8th ed., 1947, p. 56.

TABLE 31.4. United States Crude Oil Production by States, Selected Years, 1860-1947[4]
(in thousand barrels)

	1860	1870	1880	1890	1900	1910	1920	1930	1940	1945	1946	1947
Alabama	...	...	...	...	...	...	...	...	...	181	380	398
Arkansas	...	...	...	...	...	...	...	19,702	25,775	28,613	28,375	29,609
California	...	...	40	307	4,325	73,011	103,377	227,329	223,881	326,482	315,179	332,958
Colorado	...	...	...	369	317	240	111	1,656	1,626	5,036	12,016	15,766
Florida	...	...	...	...	...	...	...	...	...	30	57	260
Illinois	...	...	...	1	...	33,143	10,774	5,736	147,647	75,094	75,297	66,440
Indiana	...	...	...	64	4,874	2,160	945	994	4,978	4,868	6,726	6,092
Kansas	...	...	...	1	75	1,128	39,005	41,638	66,139	96,415	97,218	105,072
Kentucky	...	...	...	6	62	469	8,738	7,389	5,188	10,325	10,578	9,469
Louisana	...	...	...	...	...	6,841	35,714	23,272	103,584	131,051	143,303	159,276
Michigan	...	...	...	...	...	...	...	3,911	19,753	17,267	17,074	16,283
Mississippi	...	...	...	...	...	...	...	...	4,400	19,062	24,216	35,163
Missouri	...	...	...	...	2	4	...	...	44	45	51	55
Montana	...	...	...	...	...	...	340	3,349	6,728	8,420	8,801	8,700
Nebraska	...	...	...	...	...	...	...	...	276	305	265	220
New Mexico	...	...	...	...	...	...	...	10,189	39,129	37,351	36,860	40,971
New York	...	211	1,041	1,658	1,301	1,054	906	3,647	4,999	4,648	4,863	4,787
Ohio	...	...	39	16,125	22,363	9,916	7,400	6,486	3,159	2,828	2,908	3,120
Oklahoma	...	...	...	...	6	52,020	106,206	216,186	156,164	139,200	134,497	141,325
Pennsylvania	500	5,050	24,987	26,800	13,258	8,795	7,438	12,803	17,353	12,515	12,996	12,563
Tennessee	...	...	...	...	...	...	14	21	24	8	10	8
Texas	...	...	...	...	836	8,899	96,868	290,457	493,209	754,710	760,505	817,087
Utah	...	...	...	...	...	...	...	...	3	...	...	...
Virginia	...	...	...	...	...	...	...	...	...	4	16	65
West Virginia	...	...	179	493	16,190	11,753	8,249	5,071	3,444	2,879	2,929	2,599
Wyoming	...	...	...	...	6	115	16,831	17,868	25,711	36,219	38,304	43,980

4, established August 7, 1944, near Point Barrow in northeastern Alaska, 200 miles north of the Arctic Circle.[5] This can hardly yet be called a field and information is naturally scanty, but its possibilities are considerable. The Naval Reserve covers about 35,000 square miles. Exploration has been going on at Umiat, about one hour by air from Point Barrow. The first exploratory work was done by Seabees, who withdrew in January, 1946, leaving the field to private contractors. There are geophysical exploration camps at Cape Simpson and on the Meade River. Hundreds of tons of oil field machinery have been flown in, some of it from New Guinea. Congress appropriated about $10 million to continue the work of exploration until 1950. If it is true, as some strategists believe, that the Arctic is the key to continental defense, this Alaskan oil drama is worth watching.

4 *World Oil Yearbook, 1948,* pp. 167, 168.
5 See G. N. Meyers, "The Struggle for Arctic Oil," *Saturday Evening Post,* April 19, 1947, pp. 26 ff.

PRODUCTION ELSEWHERE IN THE WORLD

The United States produces about three-fifths of all the oil in the world. Almost half of the remainder is produced in the western hemisphere. During recent decades this hemisphere has produced over 80 percent of the world total.

From the standpoint of ownership and management, foreign oil production falls into two distinct categories: (1) oil developed independently by the Soviet Union within its borders and by some European countries within their own territories, and (2) oil explored and produced by companies domiciled in the United States and Great Britain—with France and the Netherlands as junior partners, so to speak—in countries whose inhabitants have neither the knowledge nor the capital for the economic development of the vast oil reserves found within their boundaries. Moreover, their domestic market for oil products is small.

This division leaves out a few countries which, for historical or ideological reasons, do not fit into a simple classification. Among them

TABLE 31.5. United States Crude Oil Production by Districts, Selected Years, 1900-1948[6]

	1900 Million Barrels	1900 Per-cent	1935 Million Barrels	1935 Per-cent	1940 Million Barrels	1940 Per-cent	1946 Million Barrels	1946 Per-cent	1947 Million Barrels	1947 Per-cent	1948 Million Barrels	1948 Per-cent
Appalachians	36.3	57.1	32.4	3.2	33.8	2.5	34.2	2.0	32.8	1.8	32.0	1.6
Lima-Indiana-Michigan	21.8	34.3	16.7	1.7	20.2	1.5	17.3	1.0	16.4	0.9	17.0	0.8
Illinois-Indiana	...	...	5.1	0.5	152.6	11.3	82.0	4.7	72.3	3.9	71.4	3.5
Midcontinent	0.9	1.4	608.6	61.1	687.0	50.8	871.0	50.2	949.8	51.2	1063.8	52.8
Gulf coast	...	...	105.7	10.6	201.3	14.9	354.6	20.5	382.6	20.6	411.4	20.4
Rocky Mountains	0.3	0.5	20.3	2.0	34.4	2.5	60.1	3.4	69.1	3.7	80.6	4.0
California	4.3	6.7	207.8	20.9	223.9	16.5	314.7	18.2	333.1	17.9	340.1	16.9
	63.6	100.0	996.6	100.0	1353.2	100.0	1733.9	100.0	1856.1	100.0	2016.3	100.0

are Japan, whose career as an oil producer is temporarily suspended, and Mexico, whose government in 1937 appropriated foreign oil holdings and has for a number of years operated her oil industry as a government monopoly. There is Bolivia, which also closed down on foreign holdings and has since made a modest beginning on her own, though with the aid of outside technical advice. Brazil is in a somewhat similar position, and Argentina is now operating on a dual basis, i.e., partly government operation, partly with the aid of foreign capital. In the rest of Latin America, the Near and Middle East, the Far East, Africa, and Canada, oil development is undertaken almost exclusively by foreign capital.

In a world in which the East, led by the Soviet Union, is facing the West, led by the English-speaking countries, it is of interest to see how oil production is distributed between the opposing camps. Of the 3.4 billion barrels of crude oil produced in 1948, 241.1 million, or over 7 percent, were produced by the Soviet Union and her satellites, and about 100 million by what may be called "neutrals." The rest of it—3,064 million barrels, about 90 percent— was produced in the United States, in the British Empire, or in countries in which American or British capital, together with some French and Dutch capital, was dominant.[7] What the situation would be in case of war between East and West is a different matter.

[6] Figures for 1900 from R. Arnold and W. J. Kemnitzer, *Petroleum in the United States and Possessions,* Harper & Brothers, New York, 1931, p. 33; 1935, 1940, 1946 figures from Bureau of Mines *Petroleum Statements* (annual); 1947 and 1948 figures from Bureau of Mines, *Monthly Petroleum Statements.*

The Soviet Union

The Soviet Union sprawls over almost 8 million square miles, most of which has yet to be explored. Much of the land is in areas considered favorable to oil discoveries. Until recently her oil industry was largely confined to the region between the Black and Caspian Seas, including the rich oil fields of the Caucasus. More recently, the Emba fields east of the Caspian Sea and, farther north, west of the Ural Mountains, especially around Perm (Molotov), have been opened up. The Ob basin has been mentioned as an important oil prospect.

At present the oil output in the Soviet Union, still suffering the effects of World War II, is about half that of Venezuela. The Soviet oil industry is a state monopoly. The foreign capital which, before the 1917 Revolution, was engaged in exploiting Russian oil was expropriated. The main participants were Sweden (Nobel), France (Rothschild), British and Dutch concerns, and international bankers. A little oil is found in several of the Soviet Union's satellite countries.[8]

Western Europe

The January, 1948, issue of *The Lamp,* house organ of Standard Oil Company (New Jersey), carried an enlightening article on the

[7] In large parts of the world, foreign capital does not own the oil fields outright but holds concessions granting the right to produce and market oil under conditions laid down by the sovereign ruler of the area.

[8] Of interest as a curiosity rather than a major economic asset are the oil fields of Albania. The oil of the Devoli River Valley was known to Aristotle as an oil for lamps and medicine. Neither production nor reserves are sufficient to attract much attention.

crude oil industry of Europe, its achievements and prospects.

As part of their reconstruction programs, the relatively oil-less countries of western Europe have increased their search for oil to a scale never before known to their old civilizations.

Their geology is unpromising at best, and the volume of their new oil may prove to be insignificant when compared to the large scale of American oil resources. But oil in these impoverished countries has to be measured against their crippling shortages of fuel and foreign currencies. Even insignificant production can thus be of great importance to these shattered countries as they work their way out of the shadows.

Before the war, western Europe hardly produced enough oil to light the lamps in its cottages. To pave its roads with asphalt, to lubricate its machinery and to drive its land and air transport, it relied on ocean tankers which loaded their crude oil and products a thousand miles and more away in the eastern Mediterranean, the Persian Gulf, the East Indies and the Caribbean.

Its trickle of home-produced crude represented but 1½ per cent of its total consumption of liquid fuels. From the North Cape to Sicily, its populations aggregated some 275 millions. On an average day in 1938, they burned 777,100 barrels of liquid fuel. On the same day, they took out of the ground 12,300 barrels of crude oil.

Three countries were responsible for this meager production. By far the larger part of it came from Germany (excluding Austria), which produced 10,600 barrels a day, most of it by drilling on the salt domes of the north German plain. The French contributed 1,400 barrels a day, mainly from the old Pechelbronn field which was producing axle grease more than 200 years ago. Italy, whose Romans were great users of oil products 2,000 years ago, took 300 barrels a day from three small fields in the Po valley.

This was supplemented by a much larger production of liquid fuels from coal, shale, wood and potatoes. It was further supplemented by a still larger import of crude and products from Russia, Rumania and Poland in eastern Europe. But all of western Europe's home-produced supplies, both from crude oil and from other sources, plus the supplies it imported from eastern Europe, came together to only 134,000 barrels a day, or about one good tanker load. Western Europe was thus dependent on sources outside Europe for 643,000 barrels a day, or 83 per cent of its liquid fuel consumption.

The British in particular and the Dutch and French on a lesser scale had important oil interests of their own outside Europe. From these and other overseas sources, their deficits were made good as part of the massive flow of imports on which their economies were based; and as far as oil is concerned, the geology of western Europe offers no evidence that this established way of life can ever be greatly changed.

Surprises, of course, are not to be ruled out. It is never safe to overlook the precedent of Hungary in eastern Europe, which had to import all its oil as recently as 1936. But through the work of Magyar Amerikai Olajipari, R. T., an affiliate of Standard Oil Company (New Jersey), Hungary by 1941 was taking enough crude from its own soil to supply its own demands and leave a surplus for export.

Unlike eastern Europe, however, western Europe has never had a major oil field, and on the geological evidence now available, it seems likely never to have one. Small increases in oil production are possible; and in countries which are struggling to get back on their economic feet, the development of any new production at home, even small production, is of the utmost urgency.[9]

Fig. 31.2 will help the reader to orient himself. In Hungary, American oil companies have been active both in crude production and in refining and marketing. The present status of the modest known deposits and installations is in doubt. Poland is an old producer; oil was produced in numerous fields in Galicia in the south in 1870. The peak output was reached in 1925 with 6 million barrels. Reserves are estimated at 30 million barrels. French and American capital participated before World War II. Rumania is by far the most important oil country in the orbit of Soviet political influence. She has been producing for a longer time than the United States. The output reached its peak in 1936, with 64 million barrels. Reserves are estimated at less than 400 million barrels. There is evidence that the production peak has been passed. Before the war, American, British, Dutch, French, and Belgian capital exploited Rumania's oil resources.

Canada

For strategic as well as for economic reasons, the United States is particularly interested in the oil reserves that have been or may be found in the countries bordering her.

---

[9] "Oil-Hungry Europeans Seek Added Production," *The Lamp*, January, 1948, p. 29.

Existing producing fields
Sedimentary basins in which **new** production may be found

HEIDE
HANOVER   Berlin
SCHOONEBEEK   RUSSIAN ZONE
BRITISH
AND
FRENCH   *AMERICAN*
ZONE   *ZONE*
MIDLANDS
London
Paris
PECHELBRONN
ST. MARCET   GABIAN
PO VALLEY
Rome

FIG. 31.2.   Oil in Western Europe. (*The Lamp*, January, 1948.)

In Canada most of the drilling operations until recently were concentrated in the populous eastern section, although 90 percent of the oil-promising sedimentary marine rocks are in the west. Four oil-bearing areas have been located: (1) the Turner Valley field (see Fig. 31.3); (2) the fabulous Athabaska tar sands, rumored to hold a billion barrels of oil, southwest of Lake Athabaska; (3) the Norman wells in the Mackenzie River valley, south of the Arctic Ocean; and most recently, (4) the Leduc field, named after a small prairie town forty

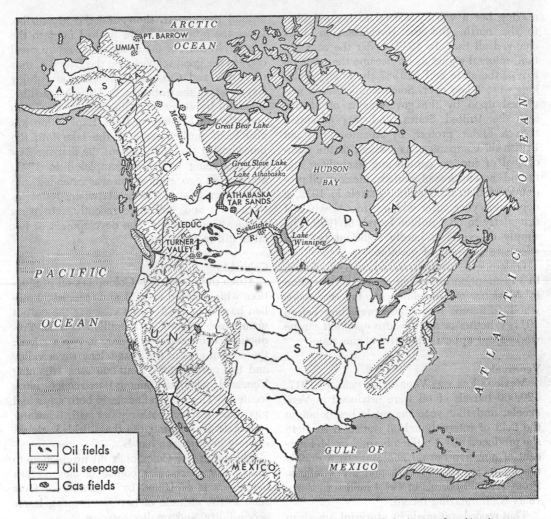

FIG. 31.3. Canadian Oil in the North American Scene. The white areas mark the basins of prehistoric seas whose sedimentary rock yields much of our oil and gas. Fields and seepages in the United States and Mexico are not shown. (*The Lamp*, June, 1947.)

miles south of Edmonton.[10] The Canadian fields lie in the northern section of the same basin of ancient seas of which Texas, Louisiana, and Mexico form the southern end.

Until now the Turner Valley field has proved most valuable, largely because of its accessibility; it is only thirty miles from Calgary. Up to 1947 it had produced almost 87.5 million barrels, but it is now on the decline. Fortunately, in 1949, it became evident that the area around Leduc is a major source of oil. So large are the proved reserves that a pipe line

to the Great Lakes is a probability. It now appears that Canada will become a major factor in the western hemisphere oil picture.

Mexico

Until 1911, foreign capitalists came close to enjoying extraterritorial rights and even the Mexican constitution had to bow to their will. Favored in such unprecedented fashion, these capitalists, especially those from Britain and the United States, were willing to risk considerable sums in the search for Mexican oil. So successful were their endeavors that in 1921 Mexico's output reached 193 million barrels,

[10] See *ibid.*, June, 1947, pp. 8, 9.

making her a worthy second to her neighbor to the north. But the Revolution in 1911 changed all that. In 1917, under the constitution, mineral rights again became the prerogative of the state and in 1937 the foreign holdings were taken over. Some compensation was agreed upon by the governments of Mexico and the United States, and was accepted, though under protest, by American but not British oil companies. As a result of the withdrawal of foreign capital and know-how and the subsequent loss of markets, Mexican oil production fell to 32.8 million barrels in 1932, a depression year, after which it rose slowly and irregularly to 58.4 million barrels in 1948. The supply of crude is hardly sufficient to yield adequate amounts of gasoline.

Of late, conversations have begun which look to a resumption of foreign capital participation in Mexico's oil development, but on terms wholly different from those prevailing before 1911. Whether or not a *modus operandi* can be worked out appears doubtful at this time.

Venezuela

Mexico's loss was Venezuela's gain. In 1917, 120,000 barrels of oil were produced in Venezuela, and that year she made her debut in the field of international oil statistics. In 1948 she produced 491.4 million barrels, or 24.4 percent of our own output and more than double the figure for the U.S.S.R. and her satellites. From 120,000 barrels to 491.4 million in thirty years is an amazing record.

That record was made by powerful American and British oil companies who found the institutional climate of Venezuela much more to their liking than that of revolutionary Mexico. It is true that with the death of Gómez, the Dictator-President of Venezuela, there began a period of gradual change in favor of stricter supervision and somewhat more onerous terms. At no time, however, has a Venezuelan government lost sight of the tremendous advantages to be gained from the skillful development of its natural endowment in oil by foreign enterprises—advantages which are measured not merely in annual royalties but perhaps even more in the invisible benefits which a feudal agrarian country derives from the example set by industrial leaders.

The development of Venezuela's oil began

around the eastern shore of Lake Maracaibo. Later the operations were pushed far into the lake itself. Most of the crude is moved by small craft to the great refineries on the Dutch islands of Aruba and Curaçao. A refinery at Amuay Bay, east of the entrance to Lake Maracaibo, is served by a new pipe line, which went into operation in December, 1948. Exploration has also been pushed west of the lake into the limestone of the Mara region; the first successful producing well was completed in 1947. Some years ago, exploration was extended into the eastern area of Venezuela where refineries were built and, still more recently, into parts of the Orinoco llanos. The development of her oil is still in full swing.

Colombia

Much more modest is Colombia's oil production, which started in 1921 and reached 20 million barrels in 1928. In no year has the output gone much beyond 25.5 million barrels. Production is concentrated mainly in two sections: the central area of the Magdalena River valley and the northeastern mountain area adjoining Venezuela where the famous Barco concession is located.[11] There are refineries in both areas and pipe lines connect both regions with tidewater terminals. Development of these fields is almost entirely in American hands.

The failure of Colombia's oil production to follow the spectacular course of her eastern neighbor's is explained by a number of facts such as the attitude of her government, lesser accessibility, and smaller reserves.

Other Latin American Countries

Oil production in Peru dates back to 1896. A peak of over 17 million barrels was reached in the middle thirties, but since then production has been tapering off. It stood at 13.8 million barrels in 1948. Ecuador started to produce oil in 1917. The output reached the million-barrel mark in 1928 and in 1947 it amounted to 2.3 million barrels. Oil is found only in the Santa Helena peninsula, southwest of Guayaquil. The Standard Oil Company (New Jersey), through an affiliate, searched for oil in Bolivia, but after a rupture with the Bolivian "powers that be" preferred to lose its large investment

[11] See "The Fabulous Barco," *Fortune*, March, 1940.

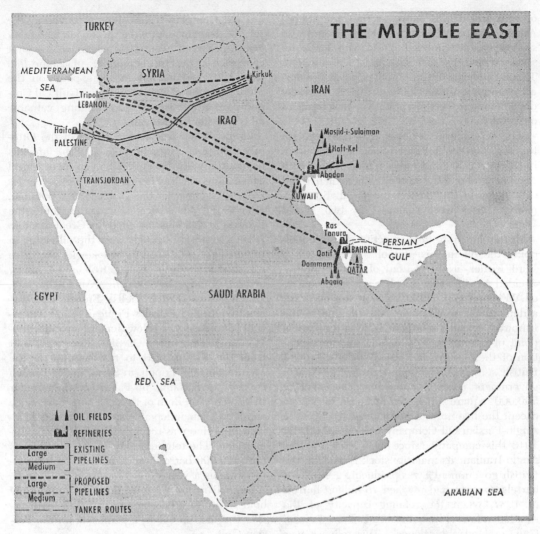

FIG. 31.4. (The Lamp.)

rather than continue operations under thoroughly unsatisfactory conditions; during World War II the State Department arranged for partial compensation. Brazil, at present, prefers "to go it alone"; her oil production so far is a mere trickle. Some predict a great future for the oil industry of that country, whose area is over half that of all South America. The government of Paraguay is looking for oil in her newly conquered strip of the Chaco. Argentina's output is about 20 million barrels a year. Much of it is produced by a state-owned operator who exploits mainly the deposits around Comodore Rivadavia on the southern coast. Foreign companies, under Argentine control, are help-

ing to develop the deposits in the north around Salta and Jujui and farther south in the foothills of the Andes. Trinidad, the British island off the east coast of Venezuela, was long famous for its asphalt lake and is now producing between 20 and 22 million barrels of crude. The most recent discovery of oil in South America was made in Chile, near the Straits of Magellan.

The Near East[12]

As was pointed out in the discussion of reserves, the Middle East is perhaps the richest

---

[12] The discussion of oil production in the Near and Far East is based to a great extent on the U.S. Tariff Commission's report on petroleum.

oil area on earth. It embraces Iran, Iraq, Saudi Arabia, Bahrein, Kuwait, and Egypt, and also several smaller political units with large reserves which are just getting into production. This is the heart of the Arab world and the desert country south of the Caucasus. It is wholly dependent on foreign capital for development of its oil.

The oil-hungry Germans had their eye on this region, their interest taking tangible form in the Berlin-Bagdad railway and in huge concessions granted by Turkey which then ruled over much of this part of the world. But Germany's hopes were shattered by two World Wars.

Britain began to take an active part in developing the oil in this part of the world when Lord Fisher, as First Lord of the Admiralty, decided to shift the British navy from coal to oil. Winston Churchill, realizing the need for a dependable source near "the life-line of the Empire," selected southern Iran as the logical point of operation. Fortunately for the execution of these plans, in 1901 William d'Arcy, a British subject, had obtained from the Persian government a sixty-year concession covering 500,000 square miles—in fact, all of Persia except the five northern provinces. In 1909 the Anglo-Persian Oil Company was organized. By 1913 this company (since 1935 known as the Anglo-Iranian; its majority stock is held by the British government) was producing 1.9 million barrels. Output had reached 75 million barrels in 1937, when the refining capacity of the Abadan refinery, near the head of the Persian Gulf, created a bottleneck. This refinery was enlarged during World War II to 440,000 barrels a day—it is now the largest in the world —and production was stepped up to double its former peak. It reached 189.8 million barrels in 1948, not far below the 210.5 million credited to the Soviet Union. A projected pipe line to the Mediterranean may encourage further expansion.

The activities of the Anglo-Iranian Oil Company are not confined to Iran. The company is part owner of the Iraq Petroleum Company (see below) and controls refineries and marketing facilities in Great Britain and western Europe, some of them jointly with the Shell interests. Recently the Anglo-Iranian Oil Company entered into an agreement with the Standard Oil Company (New Jersey) covering the sale of Iranian oil to the American company over a period of twenty-five years and the joint construction by both companies of a pipe line from the Persian Gulf to some point on the Mediterranean. Together with the Gulf Oil Corporation, Anglo-Iranian is exploiting valuable oil concessions in Kuwait.

Iraq. When Iraq was still part of the Ottoman Empire, German and British interests negotiated with the Turkish government for oil concessions there. This region, which occupies a large section of the former Mesopotamia, after World War I became a mandate under the League of Nations assigned to Great Britain. A keen and ugly struggle over the oil rights in this area ensued. When the smoke cleared, there emerged in 1928 the Iraq Petroleum Company owned jointly by British (Anglo-Iranian), Dutch (Royal Dutch-Shell), French (government-controlled Pétroles Français), and American (Standard Oil [New Jersey] and Socony-Vacuum) companies. A pipe line was built from the Kirkuk field to two termini on the Mediterranean—Tripoli, in Syria, under French control; and Haifa, in Palestine, then under British control. Both of these regions have since acquired their independence. This original 12-inch pipe line was recently paralleled by a 16-inch line. The total capacity of the two lines is now 270,000 barrels a day, or close to 100 million barrels a year.[13]

Subsidiaries of the Iraq Petroleum Company hold rights to other promising fields, both inside Iraq and in Qatar, a peninsula on the Persian Gulf.

Bahrein. The island of Bahrein, about 3000 square miles in area, lies in the Persian Gulf, close to the coast of Saudi Arabia. It is ruled by a sheik who has long been under British protection. After prolonged British efforts to find oil had failed, Standard Oil of California was allowed to take over in 1930, and two years later struck oil. In 1936 the Texas Company bought a half-interest in the venture. Conditions in general are favorable: the oil-yielding horizons lie near the surface, the crude has an unusually high yield of gasoline, and deep-sea tankers can load a short distance from a refinery built on the island. However, Bahrein's

---

[13] *World Oil,* October, 1949.

output is declining and the refinery is now in part devoted to processing crude piped in from nearby Saudi Arabia.

Saudi Arabia. In 1933 the Standard Oil Company of California acquired a sixty-year concession in the independent kingdom of Saudi Arabia. When the Texas Company entered the Bahrein agreement in 1936, the two companies formed the Arabian American Oil Company which holds the concessions in both Bahrein and Saudi Arabia. Oil exploration in Saudi Arabia was highly successful and a refinery was built at Ras Tanura. However, the bulk of the Arabian crude is piped to the large refinery on the island of Bahrein.

When in the thirties Axis agents tried to get a foothold in Saudi Arabian oil developments, the government of the United States took an active part in safeguarding the position of American corporations there. A plan under which our government through the Petroleum Reserves Corporation was to construct a pipe line from the Persian Gulf to some point on the Mediterranean aroused keen interest in 1944 but was so vigorously opposed by the oil industry that it was soon abandoned. Instead, private capital is now building this costly pipe line which will obviate the need of the long tanker voyage around Arabia and through the Suez Canal. In order to supply the capital for this stupendous venture and provide a broader basis for the development of oil in Saudi Arabia, the Standard Oil Company (New Jersey) and Socony-Vacuum in 1947 bought 30 and 10 percent respectively of the stock of the Arabian American Oil Company.

A serious difficulty in the marketing of Middle Eastern oil by American corporations developed when in 1949 the British government blocked the sale of "dollar area" oil in the "sterling area." This policy renders difficult the sale in Europe of not only Middle Eastern but also Venezuelan oil, with the result that increasing amounts are shipped to the United States. These heavy imports of foreign oil, in turn, lead to a progressive curtailment of our own production, especially in the Southwest, with serious implications for the producers of oil and the financial position of the state governments. The situation is aggravated by the phenomenal developments in Canada, as a result of which she not only will become self-sufficient but may ship surplus oil into the United States.

Kuwait. To the north of Saudi Arabia and bordering on the Persian Gulf lies the sheikdom of Kuwait, which, like Bahrein, has long been under British influence. Attempts on the part of American oil interests to obtain oil concessions in this, perhaps the largest single oil reserve in the world, met with tenacious resistance from British officialdom. However, in the thirties, under heavy pressure from the United States government, a more liberal attitude developed and in 1934 a company owned jointly by the Anglo-Iranian and the Gulf Oil Corporation began to search for oil. The results are clearly reflected in the rapid rise of oil production in that area (see Table 31.2). Shell interests have contracted to purchase large amounts of Kuwait oil.

Between Kuwait and Saudi Arabia lie two so-called "neutral" zones claimed by both adjoining states. Concessions to search for oil in these zones were granted to two independent American companies. One will pay royalties to Saudi Arabia, the other to Kuwait.

Egypt. So far as is now known, Egyptian oil reserves are not large compared with the vast deposits in the Arab countries to the east. However, even a moderate output of oil and gas is of great importance to the economy of that overcrowded country. As a result of new discoveries at Ras Chareb, production picked up considerably in 1938. Shell interests control the active oil concessions in Egypt.

Ethiopia. The Sinclair Oil Company has long held concessions in Ethiopia. Political disturbances delayed operations until 1949.

The Far East

Indonesia. The principal oil region of the Far East lies in the shallow basin between Asia and Australia that is studded with the large islands of Borneo, Sumatra, Java, and New Guinea, and generally referred to as Indonesia. This region is as yet largely unexplored. Politically it has long been under British and Dutch colonial rule, although recent political changes have materially weakened that hold. The entrance of American capital into this area was long resisted but was gradually allowed as part of a general policy of letting the United States take over an increasing share of the white man's

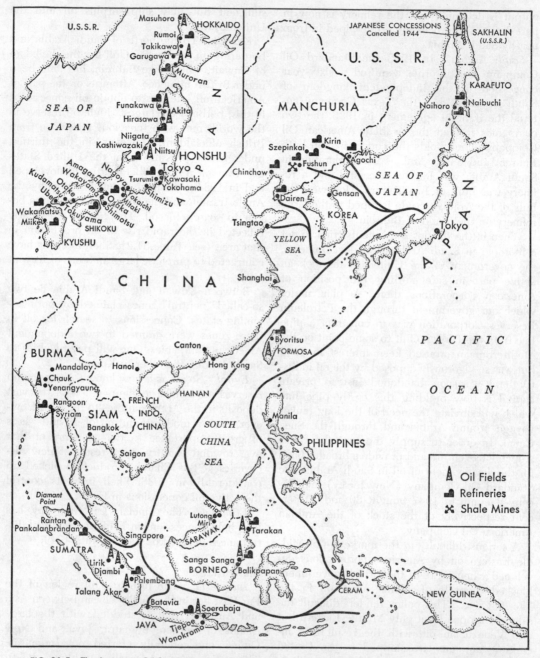

FIG. 31.5. The Japanese Oil System During World War II (until the spring of 1945). (*The Lamp*, October, 1945.)

burden which had become too heavy for the older colonial powers. This area was overrun by the Japanese during World War II and much damage was done to oil properties. Part of that damage has since been repaired.

Indonesia cradled one of the largest oil con-

cerns in the world, the Royal Dutch-Shell group, a merger of Dutch petroleum interests with the Shell, a British transport and trading company. In affiliation with the Paris Rothschilds, the Royal Dutch-Shell group reached into Rumania, since lost to the Soviet bloc. It developed the oil resources of Egypt and Trinidad, became the second largest producer after Venezuela, and through the Shell Oil Corporation (formerly the Shell-Union Oil Corporation) is one of the largest oil producers in the United States. Its share in the Iraq Petroleum Company was mentioned above. In the international field the Dutch-Shell group is the closest rival to the Standard Oil Company (New Jersey). In several parts of the world Dutch-Shell interests work hand in hand with American interests, generally through jointly owned subsidiaries like the Mene Grande in Venezuela.

India and Burma. The principal oil fields of India are located in the north along the Indus River, and in northeastern Assam. The oil fields of Burma, more prolific than those of India, lie along the Irrawaddy River. These fields were developed by British companies as were those of British Borneo in the regions of Brunei and Sarawak.

China. Oil has been discovered in the Kansu field which lies 1550 miles by rough road north of Chungking. The inaccessibility of the field militates against its early development. So far only negligible amounts have been produced. Oil has been produced in Sinkiang, the Chinese "Far West," which once was under Russian influence and may come under it again. Manchuria has shale deposits from which oil has been extracted by the Japanese. Some oil has been found on Formosa.

Japan. In spite of vigorous efforts, only minor oil deposits have been located on the islands of Japan.

Sakhalin. Sakhalin is a sparsely populated island off the coast of Siberia, north of Japan.

BIBLIOGRAPHY

See the bibliography at the end of Chapter 34.

For some time the southern portion of it was under Japanese control. Not finding oil in their part of the island, the Japanese produced some oil under Russian concessions in the north. Little is known of the size of these deposits. Japan lost Sakhalin in World War II.

RECENT SHIFTS AND TRENDS

As one tries to decipher the hieroglyphics of contemporary oil history, certain facts seem to stand out:

1. The unexpectedly rapid increase in the postwar demand for petroleum products in the United States.

2. The possible difficulty in meeting this need from domestic sources.

3. The consequent prospect of larger imports, especially from South America.

4. The need of putting western Europe, including Germany, back on her feet, and the "implied obligation" to provide the much-needed petroleum products.

5. The consequent effort to open up Middle Eastern sources from which European markets can be reached economically.

This, in rough outline, is the overall pattern of current development. It is heavily overlain with disturbing aspects stemming largely from a few lines of thought: (1) the resentment of the Soviet Union at whose doorsteps these Middle Eastern developments are taking place; and (2) the speculations of many people as to why virtually all the oil, except that in the U.S.S.R., should be developed by Anglo-American companies and their affiliates. We shall have more to say about this later when we come to discuss the political phases of the world oil problem.

Chapter 32

CRUDE OIL AND ITS TECHNOLOGY

Prospecting

The technique of petroleum in all its phases is one of the most advanced and most complex of all modern techniques. Here not much more can be attempted than to present some rather elementary information which will give the reader a general impression of the ingenuity and drive behind this vital phase of modern industrial development.

The most direct way of exploring for oil is to look for surface signs such as seepages. These naturally are the first to be exploited. But seepage is a rather rare occurrence. By far the largest portion of underground oil has no easily visible telltale contacts with the surface. The search for this invisible oil was at first largely a hit-or-miss proposition; people had a "hunch" and sometimes were lucky.

The experience gradually gained from this trial-and-error method of exploration served as the basis for ever-improving scientific methods. When the oil industry began in the United States, knowledge of the country's geology was very incomplete. Moreover, for long geologists had preconceived notions as to where oil could be found and where it could not be found. The

best way to learn about a country's geology is to drill holes; but no one, not even the government, can afford to drill many and deep holes merely to advance the knowledge and understanding of this science. It is only when the chance of rich rewards in the form of precious metals, useful minerals, and especially oil, beckons the explorer that large-scale drilling operations are undertaken. By the end of 1947, no less than 1,265,137 wells had been dug in the United States in the search for petroleum. The deepest hole drilled was 17,823 feet (a wildcat well in Caddo County, Oklahoma).[1] The footage drilled in 1947 alone ran to the staggering total of 113.2 million feet. This is the grandest geological laboratory imaginable.

And the wells *are* scientifically studied. Not only are the cores analyzed in every way known to the scientist, but electric logs—so-called Schlumbergers—are kept which help materially in interpreting the core samples. With the aid of this evidence the tectonics of an entire region

---

[1] Reports early in 1949 mention a well which passed the 18,000-foot level.

can be reconstructed with an accuracy hardly believable to the layman.

While drilling is still the most dependable method of determining the structure of the earth's crust and of locating oil, valuable supplementary methods have been developed. Five distinct geophysical methods of exploring are now recognized: magnetic, gravimetric, seismic, geochemical, and electrical. As yet the first three are by far the most important in actual practice, but the other two are gaining.

Looking for oil in areas in which as yet no proved reserves of petroleum have been located is called wildcatting.[2] According to the old definition, a wildcat well had to be two miles distant from the nearest proved area. The definition has been revised recently, so that any well more than one mile away from a proved area is a wildcat well. However, the depth of the deposit must also be taken into account; for example, a well located in an old field but pushed to a greater depth is also a wildcat. Because of this change in definition and for other reasons, statistics on wildcat wells must be interpreted with caution.

Wells

Current statistics differentiate the following seven classes of wells: oil, distillate, gas, dry, water input, gas injection, and salt-water disposal. Water input and gas injection wells are used in so-called secondary recovery. They are also known as service wells.

Another important distinction is that between flowing wells and pumping wells. Some pumping wells produce as much oil as flowing wells do; some produce even more. Pumping wells which produce small amounts such as less than a barrel a day are called stripper wells.[3] Flowing wells produce under the natural pressure of gas and/or water; pumping wells operate on the principle of the simple suction pump. Be-

tween these two types are wells which have lost part of their natural pressure and which produce in response to the artificial injection, under pressure, of water, gas, or air, or several of these combined. This is called secondary recovery. It has been brought to a high point of perfection in the Bradford field of Pennsylvania, an old field that produces high-quality crude. At the end of 1947 there were about 428,500 oil wells, of which all but 49,400 were pumping wells. Approximately 60,000 natural gas wells were in operation.[4] A relatively small number of wells produce a large share of the total output.

Depth and Cost. Ever since deep drilling opened up entirely new horizons of oil in the region in Louisiana and Texas along the Gulf of Mexico, way below the shallower reservoirs, of which Spindletop was one of the more spectacular, search for deep-lying oil has proceeded at an accelerated pace. There is a tendency for crude to become lighter with increasing depth. Just as is true in many phases of modern industry, oil drilling is a race between improved techniques and methods which *lower* costs and the ever greater performances demanded which tend to *raise* costs. Although drilling techniques have been improved constantly and remarkably, the greater depths mean greatly increased costs in spite of all technological progress. A well 10,000 feet deep still costs about three times as much as one 7000 feet deep, and a 15,000 footer is nearly twelve times as expensive. From depths of 7000 to 10,000 feet, drilling costs jump from about $10 a foot to about $100 a foot![5]

Of course, these are average costs. Much depends on the nature of the formation to be pierced. The reasons for these high costs are not hard to find. Progress slows down as temperature and pressure go up, the round trip of the tools and bits is longer and therefore takes longer, etc.

Most wells are drilled straight down, but there is such a thing as "directional drilling," i.e., slanting toward a specific goal. Directional drilling is used, for instance, in the areas adjoining the continental shelf to reach the submarine deposits. Horizontal drilling is becom-

[2] "Wild cat wells cost almost twice as much as the second and succeeding wells in a field. This is due to the greater amount of coring and survey work required, and delay, born of caution necessary when little is known about formations peculiar to that field." See "Deeper and Costlier," *The Humble Way*, December, 1947, pp. 6, 7.

[3] For an attempted definition, see Ronald B. Shuman, *The Petroleum Industry, An Economic Survey*, University of Oklahoma Press, 1940, pp. 49-50.

[4] Much natural gas is produced by oil wells.

[5] See "Deeper and Costlier," *The Humble Way*, December, 1947.

ing increasingly important.[6] Special devices are being developed to make this procedure more efficient.

Crude Oil Production and the Nature of Reservoirs

Oil is usually found in a trap below a cap rock. Oil mixed with water and gas under great pressure fills the crevices of the host rock such as sandstone, limestone, and shale. A gas cap frequently tops off the oil-bearing area. From underneath ground water often pushes against the oil, the water being under hydrostatic pressure. Oil, gas, and water are in an equilibrium determined by the laws of physics and chemistry. In many fields ground-water pressure is absent, gas furnishing the only drive.

When the cap rock is pierced, the pressure is released at the point of perforation, and oil, gas, and water are forced to move toward it. Unless this migratory action is carefully controlled, the tremendous reservoir energy is quickly dissipated, the gas from the gas cap enters the oil, and the gas in the oil escapes and renders the oil less fluid and hence more difficult to recover. At the same time water enters the pool, cutting off many sectors from access to the escape holes and thus making inaccessible many sectors of oil-bearing rock. The result is rapid dissipation of reservoir energy, speedy production of a portion of the oil—perhaps 10 to 25 percent—a rapid decline in the rate of production, and the early abandonment of the well or wells. Such uncontrolled production used to be typical in the United States; in fact, every known method was used to speed up production as much as possible. As a result, large portions of the earlier reservoirs were left untouched; they may be irretrievably lost, or at best only a portion may be recovered by expensive secondary methods.

Today, in many fields great care is taken to control the rate of flow so that the fullest use will be made of the reservoir energy. In some cases gas is returned to the reservoir to maintain its pressure. The goal is to "produce" the field at its maximum efficiency rate (M.E.R.). In attaining this rate it is important to watch the gas-oil ratio. It is also important to perforate the cap rock at the proper point, pref-

erably near the oil-water line as far from the gas cap as possible. Under proration, which will be discussed more fully later on, an attempt is made to give each reservoir a rating or "allowable" which permits operation at the M.E.R. Fig. 32.1 shows the effect of the gas-oil ratio on reservoir behavior.

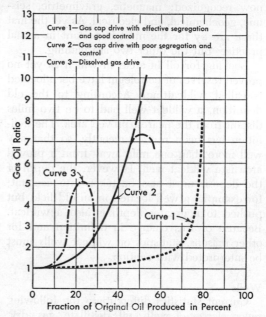

FIG. 32.1. Gas-Oil Ratio and Reservoir Behavior. (Standard Oil Development Company, *Joint Progress Report on Reservoir Efficiency and Well Spacing*, 1943, p. 28.)

Formerly many wells were spaced closely over a single field, with the result that the reservoir energy was tapped at many points, making control more or less impossible. Today, well spacing has become a science. Only after the reservoir has been thoroughly studied on the basis of all the available evidence is the decision reached as to the number of wells to be drilled, and their position. The forests of wells reminiscent of Spindletop or Oklahoma City or Long Beach are now considered obsolete, a reminder of the folly of ignorance.

Even though efforts are being made to control the rate of production of petroleum fields, many wells play out rather early and are either abandoned or else join the large army of "strippers."

Storage

Before the production of crude oil was controlled under proration laws, chance discoveries

---

[6] See *Fortune*, September, 1947, pp. 97 ff.

Fluid catalytic cracking units in a refinery at Baton Rouge, La. (Standard Oil Co. (N.J.), photo by Russell Lee.)

Refining scene. Light ends fractionators with Horton spheres for butadiene storage in the foreground. (Standard Oil Co. (N.J.), photo by Corsini.)

A gas cycling plant. (Standard Oil Co. (N.J.), photo by Libsohn.)

Oil refinery at Ras Tanura, Saudi Arabia. (Standard Oil Co. (N.J.), photo by Corsini.)

Oil gauges and valves. (Standard Oil Co. (N.J.), photo by Corsini.)

Pipe-line manifold system. (Standard Oil Co. (N.J.), photo by Corsini.)

Pipe-line control room. (Standard Oil Co. (N.J.), photo by Corsini.)

Checking pipe-line shipments. (Standard Oil Co. (N.J.), photo by Corsini.)

Loading a tanker in Sumatra. (Standard Oil Co. (N.J.), photo by Corsini.)

Oil barges on the Mississippi. (Standard Oil Co. (N.J.), photo by Russell Lee.)

Wheeler Dam, 6342 feet long and 72 feet high, crosses the Tennessee River. (Tennessee Valley Authority.)

Generating units in the Pickwick powerhouse. (Tennessee Valley Authority.)

TVA's Fontana Dam in western North Carolina. The dam is 2365 feet long and 480 feet above bedrock. Turbine generators have a capacity of over 200,000 kw. (Tennessee Valley Authority.)

Rebuilding the Dnieper Dam. (Sovfoto.)

A 100,000-kw turbine generator. (Public Service Electric and Gas Company, New Jersey.)

Triple compound power unit of the State Line Generating Company at Hammond, Ind. (By Ewing Galloway, N.Y.)

The first steam power plant to use steam at 1050 degrees Fahrenheit. (Public Service Electric and Gas Company, New Jersey.)

Control room in the Sewaren generating station. (Public Service Electric and Gas Company, New Jersey.)

Loading iron ore on Lake Superior. (U.S. Steel Corporation.)

Unloading an ore steamer on Lake Erie. (U.S. Steel Corporation.)

The twin blast furnaces of the South Works in Chicago (top center) are 235 feet tall and have a daily capacity of 1500 tons of iron each. In foreground, stores of ore and limestone. (U.S. Steel Corporation.)

Russian steelworks. Blast furnaces at Mariupol on the Sea of Azov. (Sovfoto.)

ORE DOCK & STORAGE

COKE OVENS
BLAST FURNACES

OPEN HEARTH

SOAKING PITS

SHEET & TIN MILLS

TOWN OF SPARROWS POINT

PIPE MILLS

PLATE MILLS

WIRE MILLS

RAIL MILL

SHIPYARD WAYS

COAL DOCK & STORAGE

The Sparrow's Point, Maryland, plant of the Bethlehem Steel Corporation. (Courtesy of Bethlehem Steel.)

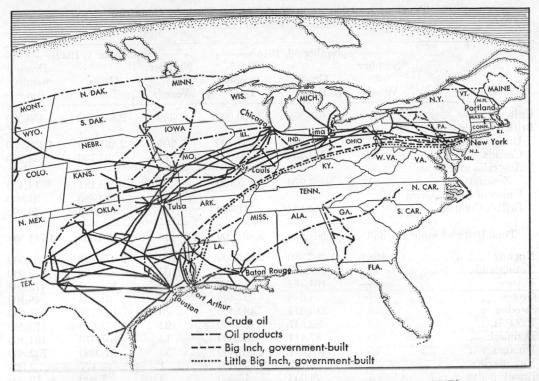

FIG. 32.2.   United States Interstate Oil Pipelines, 1946. (*The Lamp*, January, 1947.)

of large reservoirs would result in large surpluses of oil which the market could not absorb
in an orderly fashion. In those days vast storage lakes were built, but it was almost a case
of "jumping from the frying pan into the fire."
The large-scale storage of crude oil is very
apt to prove uneconomical. The best place to
store oil is in the ground; i.e., the best policy
is to avoid the necessity of excessive storage
by holding the supply to the level of demand.
However, a certain amount of storage is unavoidable in connection with refinery and marketing operations. The storage tanks used for
this purpose have been improved until now
they are quite satisfactory.

Transportation

Pipe Lines.   The petroleum industry is in a
unique position as regards transportation. Petroleum and its products being mainly liquid
or gaseous lend themselves to transportation by
pipe lines. Few people realize that the total
pipe-line network for crude oil, refinery products, and natural gas is larger than the entire
railroad net of the United States.[7] On January

1, 1945, the following pipe lines were operating
in the United States:

TABLE 32.1.   Miles of Pipe Lines Operating in the
United States[8]

Type of Product Carried	Miles
Crude oil	
Trunk lines	69,716
Gathering lines	56,203
	125,919
Refined products	14,278
Natural gas	218,440
Total	358,637

Of particular interest among the pipe lines
are the Big Inch and the Little Big Inch. These
large-diameter lines—24 and 20 inches, respectively—were built by the United States government in World War II, when German submarines were playing havoc with the tanker
fleet that carried crude oil and refinery prod-

---

[7] According to reports of the Interstate Commerce Commission, steam railroads in this country
owned 226,696 miles of first-line track. See *Statistical Abstract of the United States, 1947*, p. 507.

[8] *Petroleum Facts and Figures, 1947*, pp. 138 ff.

TABLE 32.2. Changes in World Tanker Fleet, by Countries[9]
(Between September 1, 1939 and September 30, 1945)

Country	September 30, 1945			September 1, 1939		
	Number of Vessels	Gross Tons[a]	Dead-weight Tons[b]	Number of Vessels	Gross Tons[a]	Dead-weight Tons[b]
United States[c]	949	8,658,859	13,820,000	389	2,836,792	4,450,500
British Empire:						
United Kingdom . .	347	2,450,640	3,591,100	406	2,861,679	4,258,200
Canada	30	164,236	226,600	11	93,736	133,500
Australia and New Zealand	1	3,976	5,100	2	10,181	14,400
Union of South Africa	. . .	. . .	. . .	2	23,395	31,600
British Colonies . .	8	50,124	71,400	25	187,916	276,800
Total British Empire	386	2,668,976	3,894,200	446	3,176,907	4,714,500
Norway	168	1,392,890	2,111,500	263	2,073,229	3,125,500
Netherlands	77	387,983	542,800	105	525,608	740,000
France	24	164,472	246,500	49	321,107	473,600
Greece	4	18,089	27,400	7	31,356	48,100
Sweden	36	316,074	482,400	20	168,519	257,000
U.S.S.R.	16	82,847	121,700	22	121,609	173,500
Denmark	10	87,411	135,800	13	105,370	164,400
Panama	66	478,541	753,400	53	468,060	732,800
Yugoslavia	1	3,177	3,300	1	3,177	3,300
Brazil	5	29,952	45,300	2	7,900	12,200
Belgium	4	28,641	41,900	10	70,429	101,100
Argentina	24	145,826	203,700	25	139,790	194,500
Turkey	1	6,134	9,000	1	3,723	6,200
Chile	3	9,341	12,100	2	7,586	9,600
Honduras	1	7,623	11,100	1	7,623	11,200
Venezuela	23	65,118	90,100	23	63,445	85,700
Peru	1	2,820	4,300	1	2,820	4,300
Mexico	6	32,559	48,600	2	9,540	14,500
Uruguay	1	6,599	10,700	. . .	. . .	. . .
Cuba	. . .	. . .	. . .	1	1,983	3,200
Total[d]	1,806	14,593,932	22,615,800	1,436	10,146,573	15,325,700

[a] The entire cubic capacity in "tons" of 100 cu. ft. each.
[b] The safe cargo capacity in long tons.
[c] Includes vessels owned by the Army and Navy.
[d] For 31 selected countries, a few of which had no tankers.

ucts from the Southwest, mainly Texas and Louisiana, to the big refineries and markets of the Northeast. Railroad tank cars were rushed into service but could take over only a small part of the burden. So something truly spectacular was done. Pipe lines of unheard-of dimensions, diameter and length, were laid all the way from Texas to New Jersey. During the war Big Inch carried a daily load of about

310,000 barrels of crude oil (113.2 million barrels a year) from Longview, Texas, to Phoenixville, Pennsylvania, a distance of 1252 miles. From there lines 20 inches in diameter carried the oil to refineries in Linden, N. J., and in Philadelphia. Big and Little Big Inch reach from Beaumont, Texas, to Linden, N. J., a distance of 1475 miles. Little Big Inch was built to deliver, per day, 225,000 barrels of gasoline or a smaller quantity of heavier oil products. After the war, a heated debate raged over the

[9] *Petroleum Facts and Figures, 1948,* p. 143.

disposal of these giant pipe lines. They were finally turned over to natural gas transport companies.[10]

Fig. 32.2 shows the portion of this country's pipe-line system that operates in interstate commerce. All gathering lines and all intrastate lines are omitted. This vast system handles one-ninth of the entire freight tonnage of the United States. The operation of pipe lines is approaching "push-button" performance. The dispatch of millions of barrels of oil and oil products a day proceeds with almost unbelievable smoothness, the reward of scientific progress and ingenuity.

Tankers. Next to the pipe lines, tankers, coastwise and ocean-going, carry the largest load. A large ocean-going tanker carries as much as 150,000 barrels (6,300,000 gallons) of crude oil or refined products.[11] The tanker fleet suffered fearful losses during the war. The United States spent as much as $1.75 billion to bring the fleet up to the point where it could do the work expected of it in wartime. Almost two-thirds of the war matériel shipped overseas were petroleum products of some sort.

Table 32.2 shows the world's tanker fleet by countries, September 1, 1939, and September 30, 1945. The figures include only sea-going iron or steel steam and motor tankers of 1600 gross tons and over. Note that while United States-owned tankers made up less than one-fourth of the deadweight tonnage in 1939, they constituted about 60 percent of the greatly enlarged fleet of 1945. In gauging the carrying capacity of the modern fleet its considerably improved speed must be taken into account. A fast tanker can make more turnarounds a year and thus move a considerably larger annual tonnage than a slower tanker of the same size.

Tankers constitute about one-third of our merchant marine tonnage, and tank shipments make up about one-third of all the water-borne foreign trade of the United States. Although tankers as a rule carry goods in only one direction, returning with ballast (water carried in the double bottom), they nevertheless have the lowest costs of all transport facilities handling crude oil and its products. The figures cited by Mr. Howard J. Pew, president of the Sun Oil Company, in his testimony before the Temporary National Economic Committee in September, 1939, give a good idea of comparative costs. They are shown in Table 32.3, together

TABLE 32.3. Comparative Transportation Costs, 1937 and 1946[12]

Type of Transportation	Million Ton-Miles	Percent	Cost per Ton-Mile, 1937	Cost per Ton-Mile, 1946
Water	10,378.7	87.92	$0.00063	$0.00082
Railroad	244.4	2.07	0.01640	0.01695
Pipe line (crude)	744.2	6.30	0.00477	0.00344
Pipe line (gasoline)	373.0	3.16	0.00527	0.00445
Truck	64.2	0.55	0.04873	0.06125
Total	11,804.5	100.00	0.00162[a]	

[a] Weighted average.

with the same company's estimated costs per ton-mile for 1946. The 1937 figures antedate the construction of the Big and Little Big Inch pipe lines. They have brought down pipe-line costs considerably.[13] But, as was mentioned before, many pipe lines now carry natural gas.

Tank barges are used on rivers and canals. Tank cars, moving on railroad tracks, hold 8000 to 10,000 gallons each. Large amounts of packaged petroleum products move by railroad. Tank trucks carry up to 5000 gallons in one load.

Retail Outlets

There were in 1946 about 214,100 service stations in operation in the United States. In addition, according to a Department of Commerce estimate in the *Survey of Current Business*, there were 179,700 other retail outlets such as motor vehicle dealers, automobile repair shops, parts and accessory dealers, and

---

[10] See chap. 35.

[11] In May, 1948, Standard Oil Company (New Jersey), in a full-page ad in the New York *Times*, announced that six 26,000-ton tankers with a speed of 16 knots were on order, the largest tankers ever operated by the company.

[12] The 1937 figures from TNEC, *Hearings*, p. 7178. The 1946 figures on cost per ton-mile from U.S. Department of Commerce, Office of Domestic Commerce, Transportation Division, *Industry Reports, Domestic Transportation: Petroleum Transportation*, 1949, p. 27. The percentage and ton-mile figures shown in the table are for 1937.

[13] See Wallace R. Finley, "The Big Inch Pipeline," *Mining and Metallurgy*, October, 1943, pp. 440-445.

country general stores, making a total of 393,-800 retail outlets for gasoline. However, this figure is believed to be a considerable underestimation.

WASTE ELIMINATION AND STABILIZATION

The petroleum industry, as has been said, is young. In spite of its spectacular growth, it has seldom been able to catch up comfortably with the seemingly insatiable demand of our modern industrial civilization for petroleum products. Under these conditions "growing pains" were, and to some extent still are, unavoidable.

In the United States, where petroleum after 1900 came to be a vital element of the economy, the pressure to produce as much oil as rapidly as possible was extraordinary. And haste makes waste—in crude oil production perhaps more than in most extractive operations. Moreover, the belief in the all-saving grace of competition, the emphasis on consumers' present benefits in the form of low prices as against careful husbanding of limited reserves of irreplaceable gifts of nature, and unfortunate legal interpretations conspired to turn the business of producing crude oil into a mad scramble that not only tolerated waste but actually encouraged it.

As was stressed before, the only economical and efficient way to produce crude is to take the fullest possible advantage of natural reservoir energies of gas and water pressure.[14] Three types of "drives" are distinguished: the dissolved gas drive, the gas cap drive, and the water drive. Many fields have combinations of these drives. The dissolved gas drive is not very satisfactory because it permits recoveries which seldom run higher than 20 to 40 percent of the original oil in place. The gas cap drive is from 50 to 100 percent more efficient. When a gas cap does not exist it is sometimes possible to create one. When the water drive is used, water is allowed to work up into the oil sand as oil and gas are withdrawn; "the displacing effect of the advancing water tends to maintain pressure in the reservoir by offsetting the fluid withdrawal and to cleanse the sand of oil up to the limit of the minimum residual oil satura-

tion."[15] The water drive is believed to be inherently the most efficient natural oil recovery mechanism in the majority of sand reservoirs. Most sand reservoirs are "water-wet" under natural conditions because of the presence of initial interstitial water, and the flushing action of the water can be very thorough.

Regardless of the type of drive used, it is of the utmost importance that the rate of withdrawal be carefully controlled. Pressure must be maintained constantly so that gas does not escape without performing its vital duties of (1) keeping up the viscosity of the oil and (2) forcing this viscous mass up to the surface.

The knowledge of the structure and behavior of reservoirs is quite advanced today. Instruments have been devised which accurately measure reservoir pressures, gas as well as water pressures. Hence it is now possible to "produce" an oil field rationally. But this knowledge is of fairly recent origin, it was learned the hard way by bitter experience, and the cost in wasted oil was considerable.

Not only did we not know the facts about oil reservoirs, we firmly believed in fancies. The early false conceptions, even more than lack of knowledge, contributed to waste. Petroleum has so many unique properties, behaves in such peculiar fashion that the regular principles and rules of law which apply to solid minerals and to water are more or less inapplicable.

As was explained in Chapter 24, in the United States the basic rule governing mineral rights is that subsoil mineral wealth belongs to the owner of the surface. Suppose that an oil reservoir lying beneath one square mile of surface land is owned by 100 separate owners. If one of these owners strikes oil and he alone taps the reservoir, he may, under favorable circumstances, be able to suck up most of the oil in the reservoir through a single well or a few wells at the most, tapping not only the portion below his own land but that underlying his neighbors' properties as well. The tendency of oil and gas is to move toward the point of least pressure, and this behavior created the notion that oil is "fugitive" or "fugacious" and therefore must be treated under the law like wild game which flees from the hunter. The game

---

[14] This refers to oil reservoirs of the sand type which consist of porous and permeable rock whose interstices contain oil and gas under pressure.

[15] Standard Oil Development Company, *Joint Progress Report on Reservoir Efficiency and Well Spacing*, 1943, p. xiv.

laws said that the owner of a piece of land may entice game to his property, and if he kills it on his land the game is his. This is "the rule of capture." This rule was then applied to oil, which meant that the landowner had no title to the oil under his land—unless he reduced it to possession through capture. A typical court decision of that day read as follows:

If, then, the landowner drills on his own land at such a spot as best subserves his purposes, what is the standing of the adjoining landowner whose oil or gas may be drained by this well? He certainly ought not to be allowed to stop his neighbor from developing his own farm. There is no certain way of ascertaining how much of the oil and gas that comes out of the well was once *in situ* under this farm and how much under that. What then has been held to be the law? It is this, as we understand it; every landowner or his lessee may locate his wells wherever he pleases, regardless of the interest of others. He may distribute them over the whole farm or locate them on only one part of it. He may crowd the adjoining farms so as to enable him to draw the oil and gas from them. What can the neighbor do? Nothing; only go and do likewise. He must protect his own oil and gas. He knows it is wild and will run away if it finds an opening and it is his business to keep it at home.[16]

"Out of possession there is not property." "The right of the owner of the land is a right not to the oil in the ground but to the oil he may find." These are typical expressions in the legal decisions pertaining to oil law. To be sure, courts are in disagreement and conflicting decisions have been handed down; but the weight of authority is apparently on the side of the doctrine of nonownership which seems to have found favor with the United States Supreme Court. Such faulty oil law did much damage to the industry and to society at large during the early decades of oil development. Since then, both the law and the courts have made much progress.

Physical and Economic Waste

There can be no denying that the "rule of capture" followed during the formative stages of the industry put a premium on haste. It goes

without saying that if a man assumes oil to be underneath his land and sees his neighbors dig wells just across his boundary line through which they can physically, and may legally, drain the oil from underneath his property, he will get busy and dig a sufficient number of wells to "offset" their drilling activities. The process works both ways—if he takes the initiative his neighbors will follow suit. The result is a hot race between various drilling crews to reach the oil sands first.

In the first place, this meant an enormous waste of the labor and material which go into drilling operations. It is staggering to think of the sums of money and the years of labor that could have been saved if oil fields had been developed rationally the way we can develop them now with our superior knowledge and understanding. As always, hindsight is better than foresight. In the second place, there was the waste of oil left in the ground by faulty production methods, much of which can never be recovered. This is a little like crying over spilled milk. But how we should treasure some of that "spilled milk" now!

Besides this physical waste there was economic waste. The hasty production that followed any oil strike meant production without regard to market needs. And overproduction meant unremunerative prices. So everyone lost in this mad battle for oil. Society lost, for there might have been much better uses for the steel and labor that went into useless derricks and pipes; certainly it would now know what to do with the oil that was formerly wasted. The producer lost the difference between what the oil would have been worth under orderly marketing and what he got when it was dumped on an unwilling market incapable of absorbing the flood of black gold.

This tendency toward undue haste in drilling was aggravated by the powerful speculative appeal which oil has for the average man. It is easier to sell bogus oil stock than almost any other security, for everybody thinks that he will be the lucky one who will grow rich overnight from some unprecedented gusher. The result is that where such conditions prevail there is no end to the amount which can be had for oil drilling—the failure of nine does not deter the tenth from risking his last penny on the speculative venture.

[16] L. M. Logan, Jr., in F. G. Tryon and E. C. Eckel (eds.), *Mineral Economics*, McGraw-Hill Book Company, Inc., New York, 1932, p. 231.

Under such conditions the oil "game" was more or less removed from the category of ordinary business enterprise. The average businessman ceases to produce when he finds the market flooded with his product. Not so the producer of crude petroleum, for he is driven by the fear that if he doesn't get the oil today, his neighbor will get it tomorrow. Moreover, business which proves unprofitable ordinarily tends to go down or even out, because no new capital will flow into it and the old capital will tend to flow out. Not so with the oil business, for failure is no deterrent.[17]

Uncontrolled Supply and Technological Improvements

As long as the refining industry confined itself to processing and marketing, the independent oil producers were the only sufferers from this chaotic state of affairs, unless we consider the loss to society in the rapid depletion of wasting assets and the undue acceleration of economic and social development. But when the refiners themselves entered the field of crude oil production, the damage spread.

Overproduction of crude oil is the deadly enemy of rationalized scientific large-scale capitalistic refining enterprises. What is more, every step forward in technological development increases the industry's sensibility to the disturbing and damaging influence of overproduction. This is due partly to the fact that technological improvements usually involve heavier investments; they increase fixed charges and lower the industry's flexibility in the face of changing market conditions. But technological improvements in petroleum refining enhance the danger of overproduction in an even more direct and definite manner. Thus, for instance, "cracking" permits much higher yields of gasoline from crude oil than can be obtained by simpler methods, and hydrogenation goes infinitely further. Gasoline can now be made either directly from crude oil, or in "cracking" stills from gas oil, a by-product of straight gasoline distillation, or from heavy crudes which without "cracking" would not lend themselves

to distillation for gasoline. A refining industry equipped with modern "cracking" stills can get along with much smaller quantities of crude oil. If the demand for gasoline sets the pace for total production, an increase in the gasoline yield from 20 to 60 percent will reduce the crude oil requirements of the industry to one-third; and under these conditions the overproduction of crude oil will damage the industry infinitely more than was the case before modern scientific improvements were introduced. It pays to operate a "cracking" plant only if the gasoline yield from "straight-run" or "topping" operations does not meet the market requirements. The industry is subject to a law somewhat akin to Gresham's law, according to which bad money drives out good money. If there is an oversupply of crude oil, the simpler and therefore cheaper processes get the business away from the more complex and therefore more expensive plants. In the final sense, "cracking," hydrogenation, isomerization, polymerization, alkylation, and other chemical manipulations are the scientist's answer to the threat of an early depletion of petroleum reserves. These ingenious methods are not found in a world about to drown in a deluge of oil.[18]

Remedial Measures

A number of developments have taken place during the past few decades which have reduced waste and point toward the ultimate solution of the problems discussed above. After a period of inadequate oil discoveries which gave rise to fears of the early exhaustion of our oil reserves, the situation was drastically changed in the middle twenties by the rapid succession of great discoveries such as Seminole, Oklahoma City, and east Texas. The pendulum swung all the way to the other extreme. The country was literally flooded with oil, and crude was selling in some places for as little as ten cents a barrel.

In the meantime, the larger oil companies that for long had confined their activities largely to refining and marketing began to enter

---

[17] Although this was true of much of the oil industry in the United States until the late twenties or early thirties of the present century, many of the evils have been remedied, as will be shown later.

[18] This situation was true of the early thirties, when the demand for crude oil was determined by the demand for gasoline. Since then, however, markets for other products—especially fuel oil and Diesel oil—have opened, and such products are no longer subsidiary to gasoline.

the crude production business on a large scale. They bought up producing companies and started on vigorous production campaigns. A large segment of the oil industry became integrated—from oil in the ground to the gasoline sold at a filling station. These giant corporations whose investments ran into hundreds of millions of dollars needed stability—protection from the danger of uncontrolled crude production, for erratic unpredictable production of crude is poison to large-scale manufacturers loaded down with heavy fixed charges.

At the same time the knowledge of reservoir conditions improved and the technique of controlling the flow from wells was progressively perfected.

Unit Pool Operation. The need for more rational procedure in oil production was recognized early. In 1924, President Coolidge created the Federal Oil Conservation Board which held hearings and issued reports. The unitization or unit pool operation proposed at one of the early meetings has remained to this day the most rational method of oil production ever discovered. In essence it considers and treats the interconnected oil pools or reservoirs underlying a given area as a unit. The owners of the surface agree on a single plan of "producing" the field as a whole, and each owner is allotted a share determined by as fair and just a method as human ingenuity can devise. (As yet, this ingenuity has apparently been unable to find a perfect solution.) Although very slow, progress seems to have been made, for it begins to look as if a "doctrine of correlative rights," suitable to the situation in oil with its conflicting interests of co-owners of a pool, were slowly emerging.

Proration and Stabilization. In the oil industry there is much talk of "conservation." Oil executives generally use the word to mean the avoidance of waste, physical and economic. Used in this sense it may have little to do with what the old conservationists like Pinchot and Theodore Roosevelt were talking about. Those old crusaders were thinking of posterity. Oil executives speak first of all for the living, for the here and now.[19] What they call conserva-

tion is largely a composite of two elements: (1) stabilization of earnings of the petroleum industry, especially the larger companies, and (2) economies which by lowering prices permit the consumer to buy more oil products today. Neither element has much to do with the old-fashioned idea of conservation.[20]

One of the most important features of this so-called conservation program is proration. Proration received a great boost by a historical accident, or rather coincidence—the simultaneous greatest boost of supply, in the discovery of the east Texas oil field in 1929-1930, and the severest curtailment of demand, in the Great Depression. Under the impact of this "double feature," the idea of stabilized production adjusted to reasonable demand expectations slowly won friends. The landowners or royalty holders who are most vociferous in advocating unrestrained production were decidedly in the minority and state after state passed proration laws, i.e., laws which regulated the total output of oil wells under the state's jurisdiction and allocated or prorated to each well its "allowable."

Since the demand for oil products is international in scope, isolated state acts soon proved inadequate. Three steps were taken to meet this situation. (1) The oil-regulating states entered into an Interstate Oil Compact that set up a joint commission to coördinate the activities of the several states. (2) The Connally "Hot Oil" Act was passed; it holds the federal government responsible for suppressing traffic in "hot oil," i.e., interstate traffic in oil produced in violation of state oil conservation laws. (3) The U. S. Bureau of Mines was charged with the duty of preparing forecasts of demand for crude oil by refineries and for petroleum products.

Perhaps because of genuine enthusiasm for conservation but more likely because of legal considerations, the proration laws have generally become known as conservation laws. Since in this case conservation is defined as the elimination of avoidable waste, the name is not wholly misleading, for in the attempt to stabilize the industry much waste has been eliminated. In fact, the conservation laws have materially aided in putting crude oil produc-

---

[19] It is true that as corporations increase in size, as their assets run into the billions, they develop a certain regard for posterity. But their first obligation is still to the present stockholders.

[20] See chap. 49.

tion on a far more efficient basis, and have resulted in far higher recovery records than those formerly achieved. Stabilization laws, as such, are hardly harmonious with the spirit of competition and of antitrust laws. There is some doubt as to what would happen if stabilization and waste-elimination objectives ever met in a head-on collision; that would be the test. But so long as conservation is defined as the elimination of waste which it pays to avoid, there is no conflict between long-run social interests and the short-run profit-seeking interests of business.[21]

Some people go so far as to argue that stabil-

ization laws are the enemy of true conservation. They maintain that the objective of stable earnings achieved by adjusting supply, at a price satisfactory to the seller, to demand, at a price which the traffic will bear, is by no means identical with the objective of conservation, even in the narrow sense of waste elimination, and at times may prove incompatible. They argue that unit pool operation is the only logical basis for the efficient development and production of reservoirs. At present, the situation seems only partially solved; much has been done that points in the right direction, but much still needs to be done.

---

[21] The Texas Supreme Court decision in the Seeligson Field case upholding the Texas Railroad Commission in its effort to enforce the elimination of the waste of gas is encouraging. This decision stated that the Railroad Commission had not only

the statutory authority but the duty to stop the flaring of gas *when the quantities are great enough in a particular field to make such requirements economically feasible and reasonable.* Flaring is the burning of escaping gas.

BIBLIOGRAPHY

See the bibliography at the end of Chapter 34.

Chapter 33

PETROLEUM REFINING; THE PETROLEUM INDUSTRY

As has been stressed repeatedly, the fundamental difference between the coal and petroleum industries is that most coal is sold in the raw, whereas crude oil reaches the market, via the refinery, in the form of numerous prepared products.

PETROLEUM REFINING

In general, the history of petroleum refining falls into two distinct, though overlapping, phases. During the first, the refiner contented himself with the physical separation of hydrocarbon molecules by heat treatment and distillation. During the second, he subjected the molecules to an increasing number of chemical processes which break up, combine, and otherwise change the original molecules.

Crude oil consists of numerous hydrocarbons, i.e., molecules made up of hydrogen and carbon atoms. Refining is the process of separating the different constituents, or fractions as they are called. But refining today does not stop there; it improves the fractions, recombines them at will, and, in general, manipulates the products of nature. Ideally the object of refining is to convert, at the lowest possible cost, crude oil into the combination of products that, in view of prevailing market demands, will yield the maximum net return to the refiner.

Petroleum Chemistry

The innumerable hydrocarbons differ widely as to their boiling points. Some boil at room temperature, others break up at higher temperatures, still others even before reaching the boiling point. Refining takes advantage of this important fact and in the fractionating bubble tower (Fig. 33.1) separates crude oil into numerous "fractions" by so-called distillation.

In order to gain a clearer understanding of the process, which to a layman is nothing short of magic, one must look a little more closely at crude oil. As was stated before, it is a mixture of hydrocarbons. Hydrocarbons can be classified. The chemist differentiates between saturated and unsaturated hydrocarbons.[1]

The simplest saturated hydrocarbon molecule is methane, CH_4, sometimes called marsh

---

[1] To understand saturation, one must understand valence. Any elementary textbook in chemistry contains a simple discussion of valence.

537

gas, a major constituent of natural gas. It is made up of one carbon atom and four hydrogen atoms, supposedly hooked up like this:

$$
\begin{array}{c}
H \\
| \\
H - C - H \\
| \\
H
\end{array}
$$

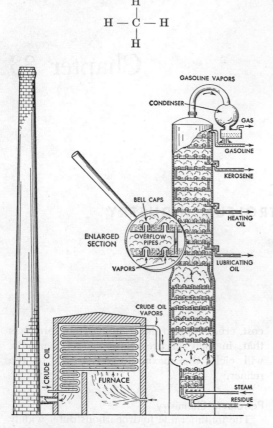

FIG. 33.1. Crude Oil Distillation: Pipe Still and "Bubble Tower." (*The Lamp*, June, 1945.)

Methane is the smallest molecule of a long series of hydrocarbons, each of which consists of a string of carbon atoms surrounded by hydrogen atoms, as follows:

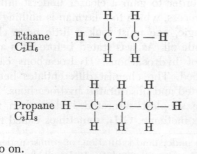

Ethane
C_2H_6

Propane
C_3H_8

and so on.

One more carbon atom, together with its pair of hydrogen atoms, is always added. So the series runs as follows:

Methane	CH_4
Ethane	C_2H_6
Propane	C_3H_8
Butane	C_4H_{10}
Pentane	C_5H_{12}
Hexane	C_6H_{14}
Heptane	C_7H_{16}
Octane	C_8H_{18}

Besides these saturated hydrocarbons there are many types of unsaturated molecules. A few are shown here.

The olefin type

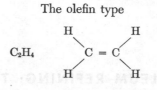

C_2H_4

The acetylene type

C_2H_2 $H - C \equiv C - H$

Straight chains such as those shown so far may double up and hook onto themselves, forming rings. Examples are the aromatic or benzol type of ring:

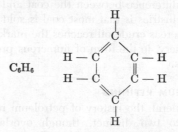

C_6H_6

And this two six-atom ring type called naphthalene:

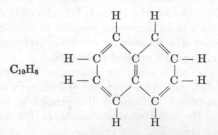

$C_{10}H_8$

These are just a few simple examples of hydrocarbon molecules. Actually there are many more types and numerous representatives of each type, running up to several hundred carbon atoms with correspondingly large numbers of hydrogen atoms.

One important point in connection with this discussion is that, in general, the boiling point rises as the number of carbon atoms relative to the hydrogen atoms increases. Molecules with 10 carbon atoms will in general boil off in the gasoline range (see Fig. 33.1); 30 or 40 carbon atoms will put the molecule into the lubricating oil range, etc.

Besides knowing something about the heterogeneity of crude oil molecules, the layman must know a few other elementary facts of petroleum chemistry.

1. An isomer is a molecule which has the same number of atoms of each element as another molecule but differs from the other in arrangement or structure.

Thus, butane is assumed to have the following structure:

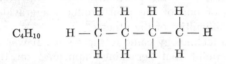

However, it can also look like this:

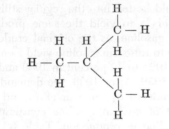

This is isobutane, also C_4H_{10}, but arranged in a forked chain. This is important because isomers have different properties; they behave differently. For example, octane may be very poor gasoline, whereas isooctane may be excellent. The refinery chemist has learned to "isomerize" molecules, thus turning water into wine, so to speak.

In general, the number of isomers increases with the number of atoms that make up a molecule. Pentane, C_5H_{12}, has 3 isomers; dodecane, $C_{12}H_{26}$, has 355.

2. A polymer is a string of like molecules. Some molecules are too light to be of practical use. If, however, they are arranged into "trains," as it were, they may become extremely useful. And the refiner has learned to "polymerize."

3. "Cracking" means precisely what the word suggests. The chemist has learned to break or crack heavy molecules into (a) lighter ones which can be handled by known refining techniques and (b) a residue of heavy, perhaps extra-heavy, ones which need further treatment before they can be put to effective use.

At first cracking was done by subjecting heavy molecules to carefully controlled combinations of heat and pressure, 200 to 3000 pounds per square inch at temperatures from 860° F. to 1200° F. This was called thermal cracking. Later it was found that the presence of a catalyst greatly facilitates the action of the heat-pressure combination.

The catalysts first used were solids; they were placed in a stable bed over which the vapors passed. This was done in the Houdry process. This method had serious drawbacks. The vapor could reach only the surface of the catalyst, not the entire solid. Moreover, the surface "fouled" very rapidly. The next step was to have two beds, one of which was used while the other was being cleaned; this helped the situation but added to the investment cost. A later improvement was the so-called moving-bed method, in which the bed was moved through the vapor. The final solution came during World War II when the so-called fluidized, i.e., vaporized, catalyst was perfected. Forcing the refinery vapor through a catalytic vapor, or a vaporous catalyst, effected the most complete interpenetration and contact of the two mediums, and a highly efficient continuous operation became possible. (This process was of the utmost importance in the wartime high-octane aviation gasoline program.)

4. Hydrogenation is the addition of more hydrogen atoms to a hydrocarbon molecule. (The Bergius process of coal hydrogenation was described in Chapter 29.) Before catalytic cracking and other chemical processes of manipulating petroleum were perfected, it looked as if petroleum hydrogenation might become as important in this country as coal hydrogenation was in Germany. Actually, it has not worked out that way. However, in hydrogenation, the petroleum chemist has another trick up his sleeve which he can play when the situation warrants.

Dehydrogenation is the opposite of hydrogenation. Thus butadiene (an important intermediary in the production of synthetic rubber) is butane from which two (di) pairs of hydrogen atoms have been removed by dehydrogenation.

5. Alkylation involves a chemical reaction which yields saturated molecules from a "mixture" of saturated and unsaturated gaseous hydrocarbons. The process is of vital importance in producing high-octane aviation gasoline,[2] for such gasoline must not contain unsaturated molecules.

Changing Demand and Technology

The history of petroleum refining reflects basic changes in demand. At first, the major commodity produced was kerosene, used mainly in "oil lamps." Some lubricating oils were also produced; the rest was residual fuel oil marketed as circumstances permitted. As kerosene lost ground to gas and electricity, its market shifted to "the provinces" and to the more primitive regions of the earth. Much kerosene was exported to Europe and especially to Asia —"Oil for the Lamps of China."

As the automobile came into general use, gasoline became the chief source of income and therefore the main objective of refining. In 1921 a typical "straight-run" refinery working up mid-continent paraffin-base crude produced the following products:

	Percent by Volume
Gasoline	28
Kerosene	11
Gas oil	40
Fuel oil	10
Lubricants	5
Other products (paraffin, coke, etc.) and loss	6
	100

In terms of financial results, however, the distribution was totally different. The gasoline brought in over half the total revenue, lubricating oils were in great demand and correspondingly valued, kerosene pulled a little more than its own weight, but the others, especially gas oil, were a drug on the market.[3] Gas oil brought in little more than 10 to 12 percent of the revenue.

In other words, the demand for and the supply of specific petroleum products were in a state of utter disequilibrium. The high price paid for gasoline and the prospect of a rapidly increasing demand for it stemming from the owners of motor vehicles which entered the market by the millions every year, was a great temptation to step up its production. But at the prevailing state of the arts and with the refinery equipment then in existence, more gasoline could not be produced without at the same time producing about twice as much of the little-wanted gas oil and fuel oil, the joint products of gasoline. The so-called law of supply and demand breaks down in the case of joint products, or at least does not function smoothly, for the price that solves the problems of one of the joint products aggravates the difficulties of the other.

So technology came to the rescue. It was at this point that "cracking" appeared on the scene. The gas oil was fed into cracking stills where it was broken up into lighter molecules that could be fed into the regular stills ("bubble towers") to yield the same products, including gasoline, as the original crude. It was possible to raise the gasoline yield from 28 percent in 1921 to 42 percent in 1930 and 45 percent in 1939. After 1939, the demand for fuel oil engendered by our war effort and the curtailment of civilian gasoline consumption led to a decline in production. Table 33.1 shows the main points of these developments.

Beginning with 1939, there is a division of gas and fuel oil into gas oil and distillates—i.e., light fuel oil, especially Diesel oil—and residual or heavy fuel oil. This reflects the growing importance of the light oil obtained in distillation processes as distinguished from the heavy residual oils which are left. Diesel oil fitted well into refinery schemes and helped to solve the problem of the gas oil surplus. The

---

[2] Octane rating indicates the antiknock quality of gasoline. The rating is expressed by the octane number, which shows the percentage of isooctane by volume in a mixture of isooctane and normal heptane that is the same as in the gasoline to be rated.

[3] As was mentioned in the discussion of coal, gas oil was so called because its chief buyers were the gas companies manufacturing water gas from coal, but willing to enrich this mixture by spraying it with vapors of gas oil.

TABLE 33.1.   Average Yields of Principal Petroleum Products per Barrel of Crude Run to Stills[4]
(percentage)

Year	Gasoline	Kerosene	Gas and Fuel Oil	Gas Oil and Distillates	Residual Fuel Oil	Lubricating Oil
1899	12.9	57.6	14.0	...	...	9.1
1909	10.7	33.0	33.6	...	...	10.7
1919	25.2	15.4	50.2	...	...	5.6
1929	39.3	5.7	45.5	...	...	3.5
1939	45.0	5.5	...	13.1	24.7	2.8
1940	43.2	5.7	...	14.2	24.4	2.8
1941	44.3	5.2	...	13.4	24.3	2.8
1942	39.9	5.1	...	14.7	26.9	2.9
1943	37.2	5.0	...	14.8	29.2	2.7
1944	39.5	4.7	...	14.4	27.7	2.5
1945	40.7	4.7	...	14.5	27.3	2.4
1946	39.6	6.0	...	16.6	24.9	2.6
1947	42.4	5.7	...	16.9	24.1	2.7
1948	40.4	6.0	...	18.7	23.0	2.5

flow chart in Fig. 33.2 traces crude oil from the well to the finished product.

The greatest achievements of the refiners, however, are to be seen not in their solving of the problem of the *quantitative* unbalance of joint products but in the remarkable *qualitative* improvements of their products. The art of chemical manipulation — catalytic cracking, isomerization, polymerization, alkylation, etc.— borders on the miraculous. As a result of this scientific advance, unsurpassed perhaps by any other industry, the public can buy better products and at lower prices.[5]

Types and Location of Refineries

Petroleum refineries differ in size and in the variety of their processed products. There are the small "prairie-dog" refineries which spring up overnight, so to speak, where wildcatters have struck it rich and disappear almost as fast when the nearby boom town starts to fold up.

There are large refineries, permanently located at strategic points. They may undergo internal changes to keep up with the progress in technology and science, and new units may be added to permit certain products to be made; but, by and large, they constitute permanent features of the landscape. Such refineries are those at Abadan, at the head of the Persian Gulf, and on Aruba and Curaçao.

The location of refineries is affected by (1) the center of crude oil production, (2) market centers, and (3) means of transportation. Favorable locations for large refineries are tidewater points fairly close to the center of crude production. Tankers are the cheapest transport facilities and tidewater location has the advantage of sending different products in different directions with a minimum of backtracking. If Texas crude is hauled to points on the Jersey coast, kerosene may have to be hauled back via the Panama Canal to China; but if the crude is refined at Baytown or Beaumont, Texas, the gasoline can be shipped by tanker to the Northeast, the kerosene to China, and Diesel oil to Europe or South America without any back haul. Similar advantages are gained by locating refineries on the various islands in the Indian archipelago—Java, Sumatra, New Guinea, etc. The refineries in Arabia, on the island of Bahrein, and on the coast of Palestine may be located in part with an eye to strategic objectives.

---

[4] Figures for 1899-1946 from *Petroleum Facts and Figures*, 7th ed., p. 116, and *ibid.*, 8th ed., p. 107; 1947 and 1948 figures from Bureau of Mines, *Monthly Petroleum Statements*.

[5] Incidentally, this splendid combination of better quality and lower price can hardly help but tempt the consuming public to use oil products in ever-greater quantities, thus rendering spurious any claim to old-fashioned bona-fide conservation to which the more economical use of crude oil might otherwise lead. One cannot eat one's cake and have it too. For fuller discussion see chap. 49.

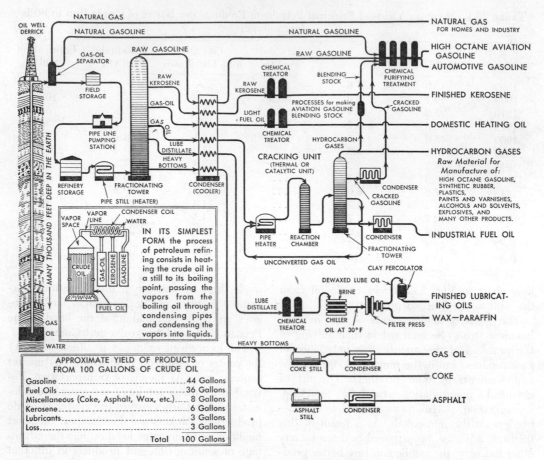

FIG. 33.2. Typical Flow Chart Tracing Crude Oil from Well to Finished Product. (American Petroleum Institute, 1944.)

The location of large refineries on the islands of Aruba and Curaçao may be explained in part by the shallow water of Lake Maracaibo which prevents the use of deep-draft tankers (see p. 531). Hence the crude is hauled to these islands by small shallow-draft vessels. There may have been a time when the Dutch flag waving from the flagpole of a $100-million investment looked better than the flag of a country whose government seemed far less stable than that of the Netherlands.

In exceptional cases the location of refineries may be influenced by legal fiat. Building at least a limited refining capacity may be one of the conditions laid down by the sovereign power in whose territory alien capital is permitted to exploit oil deposits. This is true particularly in South America. But there may be refineries in Europe which constitute a variation of the same theme. Thus the government of France has been eager to keep out imports of refined products so as to attract the refining industry to its own bailiwick.[6]

THE PETROLEUM INDUSTRY

The modern oil industry is Big Business with capital B's. Ordinarily it is carried on either by governments—the Soviet Union and her satellites, by Argentina, Mexico, and others—or by corporations, mostly giant organizations.

---

[6] For a full discussion of refineries of the United States and their location, see U.S. Department of Commerce, Office of Domestic Commerce, *United States Petroleum Refining, War and Postwar*, Industrial Series No. 7, 1947.

TABLE 33.2.   Leading Companies in Various Branches of the Oil Business[7]

Branch of Industry	Date	Number of Companies	Percent
Total investment	Dec. 31, 1938	20	66.7
Domestic producing oil wells	Dec. 31, 1937	20	23.7
Production of crude oil	1937	20	52.5
Crude oil-gathering pipe-line mileage	June 30, 1936	20	57.4
Crude oil trunk pipe-line mileage	Jan. 1, 1938	14	89.0
Total crude oil pipe-line mileage	June 30, 1936	20	72.0
Investment in pipe lines	Dec. 31, 1938	15	77.4
Pipe-line operating income	1938	15	86.4
Deadweight tonnage of tankers	Sept. 30, 1937	15	87.2
Stocks of refinable crude oil	Dec. 31, 1937	20	96.5
Daily crude oil capacity	Jan. 1, 1938	20	75.6
Daily cracking capacity	Jan. 1, 1938	20	85.2
Crude oil runs to stills	1937	20	82.6
Production of gasoline	1937	20	83.8
Stocks of finished gasoline	Dec. 31, 1937	20	90.0
Stocks of lubricants	Dec. 31, 1937	20	93.0
Six selected stocks figures	Dec. 31, 1937	20	94.2
Gasoline pipe-line mileage	Jan. 1, 1938	16	96.1
Domestic sales of gasoline	1938	18	80.0

The Independent Oil Man

It is a unique feature of the petroleum industry of the United States that independent producers have existed and survived alongside the big integrated companies, and this in every phase of the industry—crude oil production, refining, and marketing. This is probably due to our laws, which protect the small independent against the "big fellow" and which, in theory at least, give title to subsoil mineral wealth to the owner of the surface land but in practice permit individuals to draw oil from underneath a neighbor's land. The main reason, however, for the survival of the independent oil man is the fact that the United States is a highly mechanized economy and offers the greatest domestic market for petroleum products. Under these conditions the independent can make use of existing refining and transportation facilities and is within easy reach of the market. This does not mean that such conditions prevail everywhere in the United States; it means that independents survive in areas where these conditions exist. Independents could not survive a minute in the jungles of South America and New Guinea or the deserts of Arabia and Iraq because they cannot create the paraphernalia of civilization.

Importance of Large Companies

Large companies rule supreme in foreign countries where governments leave the field to private enterprise. They play a very great role in the petroleum business of the United States. Table 33.2 shows the position in terms of ownership of twenty leading companies in various branches of the oil business. It will be noted that the percentages are particularly high in the field of transportation. Of interest is the fact that while these leading companies owned only 23.7 percent of the domestic producing wells, they produced 52.5 percent of the crude oil; and while they owned 75.6 percent of the crude oil refining capacity, they owned 85.2 percent of the daily cracking capacity. Cracking units are costly.

These large companies are known as integrated oil companies, because they integrate or bring together, under one ownership, management, and control, properties and activities in all four of the principal branches of the oil business—crude production, refining, transportation, and marketing. If research were listed as a principal activity, the integration could embrace that too, for the leading companies

---

[7] TNEC, "Petroleum Industry," *Hearings,* 1940, p. 7103.

are as dominant here as they are in the other branches, if not more so. In recent years, chemical plants making such products as synthetic rubber and toluene have been added. This is another field in which only the big companies can thrive.

Some companies are engaged in both refining and marketing but are weak in the crude production branch of the industry, though making efforts to strengthen their position as a crude producer. Others are strictly marketers and have neither refineries nor oil wells. Some are engaged in transportation, refining, and marketing; others, primarily in crude oil production. Some are fully integrated.

The proportion of production by the large and small companies must be considered in relation to their ownership of reserves. For when production is regulated on the basis of oil in place for the purpose of bringing about uniform withdrawal and increasing ultimate recovery, there is bound to be a definite correlation between reserves and the output of different owners and producers. Under such conditions the share of the large companies owning large reserves tends to go up. In times of overproduction crude prices tend to drop faster than the prices of refined products. This is apt to play into the hands of independent refiners who purchase their crude. In order to protect independent producers from abuse by companies owning their own pipe lines, the so-called Common Purchase Act was passed in Texas.[8]

It is estimated that the number of independent oil producers in the United States increased from about 10,000 in 1919 to about 16,000 in 1930 but later dropped to less than 14,000.[9] This fact shows that although the large oil companies, heavily interested in refining and marketing, have made great inroads into the field of crude oil production, which originally—in the United States at least—was dominated by the small independent producers, the latter have by no means disappeared. The industry is thus divided into two camps. In one are the large corporations engaged in a keen competitive struggle with one another, but vitally interested in the stabilization of crude oil production. In the other are the large number of independent operators whose investments are much smaller and who therefore stress the short-run market interest at the expense of the long-run interests of a stabilized industry. The independent oil operator may have been a cattle man yesterday; and in many instances he views the business of crude oil production as a

---

[8] Section 8 of Article 6049a of Title 102, Revised Statutes of Texas, 1925 (as amended), reads:

"*Section 8. Defining Common Purchasers of Crude Oil and Preventing Discrimination in Purchaser.* Every person, association of persons or corporation who purchases crude oil or petroleum in this State, which is affiliated through stock-ownership, common control, contract, or otherwise, with a common carrier by pipe line, as defined by law, or is itself such common carrier, shall be a common purchaser of such crude petroleum and shall purchase oil offered it for purchase without discrimination in favor of one producer or person as against another in the same field, and without unjust or unreasonable discrimination as between fields in this State; the question of justice or reasonableness to be determined by the Railroad Commission, taking into consideration the production and age of wells in respective fields and all other proper factors. It shall be unlawful for any such common purchaser to discriminate between or against crude

oil or petroleum of a similar kind or quality in favor of its own production, or production in which it may be directly or indirectly interested, either in whole or in part, but for the purpose of prorating the purchase of crude oil or petroleum to be marketed, such production shall be taken in like manner as that of any other person or producer and shall be taken in the ratable proportion that such production bears to the total production offered for market in such field. The Railroad Commission of Texas shall have authority, however, to relieve any such common purchaser, after due notice and hearing as hereinafter provided, from the duty of purchasing petroleum of inferior quality or grade." (Railroad Commission of Texas, *Oil and Gas Circular*, No. 15, June 15, 1932.)

[9] See *Times Annalist*, January 30, 1931, quoted in C. E. Fraser and G. F. Doriot, *Analyzing Our Industries*, McGraw-Hill Book Company, 1932, p. 418. This estimate, however, includes about 10,000 owners of individual farms. Actually, there are not more than 5000 companies, partnerships, or other recognized corporate entities which might be described as oil producers. It is interesting to know that three-fourths of the United States output is produced by approximately 100 companies. The companies which produce 20,000,000 barrels or more annually produce 25 percent of our output; the companies which produce 10,000,000 barrels or more annually produce one-half of the output, and the 100 companies mentioned above are those which produce approximately 1,000,000 barrels or more yearly.

means of getting rich quick which he will quit as soon as he "makes his pile."[10] Therefore, two economic philosophies are at loggerheads in the oil industry: the old laissez-faire philosophy of unbridled competition, which stresses the right of private ownership at the expense of all other considerations, and the philosophy of control—corporate or social—which is an inevitable corollary of the evolution of giant corporations and of the growth of fixed investments which in the case of individual corporations may amount to billions of dollars. The clash is heard in the forum where the legal battle over the industry is being waged.

---

[10] It must be recognized, however, that as the oil industry matures, even the independents learn the desirability of "orderliness" and become strong proponents of "stabilization."

BIBLIOGRAPHY

See the bibliography at the end of Chapter 34.

Chapter 34

PETROLEUM IN WORLD AFFAIRS

INTERNATIONAL TRADE

It is the function of trade to move things from where they are to where they ought to be. In few cases is there greater need for international trade than in the case of petroleum and petroleum products. There are two phases of international trade in petroleum: (1) the movement of crude oil across international boundaries from wells to refineries and (2) exports and imports of refined petroleum products.

Movements Across International Boundaries

Significant instances of movement across international boundaries are the shipments of crude oil from the Lake Maracaibo region and other parts of Venezuela to the large refineries on the islands of Aruba and Curaçao, to the Atlantic coast of the United States, to Canada, and to Europe; and pipe-line shipments of crude oil from the Mosul and Kirkuk fields of Iraq to refineries in Syria and Palestine. When the pipe lines now projected or under construction are completed and in operation, such shipments will be made from Arabia and other Middle-Eastern sources of crude to refineries on the shores of the Mediterranean.

These movements of crude oil are not inter-national trade in the usual sense of the word. Ordinarily international trade consists of transactions involving a transfer of title from the national of one country to the national of another country. Thus the export of United States cotton to Japan presumably involves a transfer of title from a national of the exporting country to a national of the importing country. But most international crude oil shipments do not involve a bona-fide change of title. Much of the crude that leaves the Maracaibo region of Venezuela is the property of a subsidiary of the Standard Oil Company (New Jersey), the Creole Petroleum Corporation. Nominally it is "exported" from Venezuela and "imported" by the Netherlands West Indies. Actually, this boundary-crossing movement is merely an intra-corporate transaction, in which crude is shifted from the well of a corporate subsidiary of the Standard Oil Company (New Jersey) to a refinery belonging to another subsidiary of the same corporation. It is not trade in the ordinary sense; there is no sale-purchase, no transfer of title.

Basically, the international movement of crude oil is the result of what is largely a technical decision, i.e., where best to locate a refinery. The ordinary concepts of international trade which are based on the assumption of national business units—that is, business enterprises confined to one country in matters of ownership, control, and management—break down in the face of modern supernational holding companies.

But this does not mean that there cannot be bona-fide international trade in crude. If the Mexican government petroleum monopoly produced crude oil in excess of its refining capacity, it might sell the surplus abroad. If someone in Paraguay should strike oil but could not afford to put up refineries, the crude might well be exported to Argentina. Just as crude oil production and refining capacity are not balanced regionally within the United States, necessitating large interregional shipments of crude, so also the same imbalance internationally must result in crude shipments across national boundaries, some of which may constitute bona-fide international trade.

TABLE 34.1. Per Capita Consumption of Petroleum Products in Selected Countries, 1936 and 1947[1]
(barrels per year)

	1936		1947	
	Barrels	Rank	Barrels	Rank
United States	8.51	1	13.8	1
Canada	3.86	2	7.7	2
Union of South Africa	2.85	3	.....	.
Venezuela	2.38	4	.....	.
New Zealand	2.32	5	.....	.
Argentina	2.04	6	3.05	4
Australia	1.86	7	3.27	3
United Kingdom	1.71	8	2.24	6
Denmark	1.32	9	.....	.
Norway	1.31	10	.....	.
Scandinavian countries	....	..	2.87	5
Brazil	....	..	0.43	8
France	....	..	1.16	7

Consumption of Petroleum Products

Data on consumption of petroleum products in different countries are scarce. A few are presented in Table 34.1. Of the ten countries in the 1936 column, only the United States, Venezuela, and Argentina are important producers of petroleum. As producers, the United States and Venezuela rank first and second in the world, respectively. Venezuela is the world's

leading exporter of crude oil. Argentina's production is not quite adequate to meet her needs. The United States is now a net importer of oil and oil products.

Oil consumption tends to vary directly with general per capita productivity[2] and inversely with density of population per square mile. All the above countries, except Venezuela, are in the upper brackets of a list ranking countries according to general per capita productivity. The first criterion determines whether a country can afford to buy crude oil; the second materially affects the need.[3]

The absence of Germany, Italy, and Japan from the list is in part explained by the fact that by 1936 the Axis countries were doing their utmost to push synthetic oil programs. This applies chiefly to Germany, but Japan's efforts, concentrated largely in Manchuria, were by no means negligible. Italy largely depended on imports from Germany.

The international trade in petroleum and petroleum products looms large in both weight and value. In 1946, crude oil constituted about 44 percent of the world's total petroleum exports in terms of quantity, but in value it constituted a much smaller proportion of the total. International movements of crude oil that year amounted to 495.4 million barrels; the figure for petroleum products (gasoline, kerosene, distillate and residual fuel oil, and lubricants) was 628.4 million barrels. The largest item next to crude oil was residual fuel oil, 324.2 million barrels. Venezuela and the Netherlands West Indies (Aruba and Curaçao) led, with total exports of crude oil and oil products amounting to 593.7 million barrels. Next came the United States, with 199.2 million, and Iran, with 111.0 million; the other 219.8 million barrels were scattered among the rest of the exporting countries.[4]

---

[2] Venezuela's high rank is probably explained by the large consumption of oil by the oil industry itself.

[3] It must be remembered that the major uses of oil are in the field of transportation.

[4] Bureau of Mines, *International Petroleum Trade.*

For details on international trade in petroleum and petroleum products, see U.S. Tariff Commission, *Report to the House of Representatives on Crude Petroleum and Its Liquid Refined Products,* 1932, pp. 105-114.

---

[1] TNEC, *Hearings,* Part 14A, p. 7697. The 1947 figures are estimates of the Standard Oil Company (New Jersey).

During the thirties the Soviet Union pursued a rather aggressive oil export policy, exchanging petroleum products for much-needed machinery and other industrial products. At present she is hardly in a position to spare crude oil, for her war-damaged refineries are finding it difficult to meet the country's crying needs.

Although the bulk of the international trade in petroleum products can be explained in terms of geographical imbalances of production and consumption, there is another aspect which must not be overlooked—the fact that petroleum products are joint products. While, as was shown in the discussion of petroleum refining, modern refining techniques allow for considerable flexibility in the yield of various products, still a refiner sometimes inevitably produces "fractions" in excess of local or domestic needs. Kerosene illustrates this point. In general, as was pointed out earlier, the demand for kerosene tends to be greater in less-developed countries. Hence, exporting it to such countries is a logical solution to the problem created by the joint production.

United States Trade in Petroleum

The United States is both an importer and an exporter of petroleum and petroleum products. This is partly explained by the continental expanse of the country. In general, the Southwest ships to the Northeast, but the latter also draws on South America, especially Venezuela. California, on the other hand, because of her geographical location may find exporting to Asia more economical than shipping through the Panama Canal to the Northeast.

The natural pattern was somewhat distorted when in 1932, in response to pressure exerted especially by the independents, an excise tax (in lieu of an import duty) of 2.5 cents a gallon on gasoline and half a cent a gallon on other products including crude oil was levied. As a result, temporarily at least, the Northeast drew more heavily on California, and Venezuela instead of exporting to the United States made heavier shipments abroad. In 1939 the tax on products other than gasoline was cut in half, but for a limited quantity only; the old rate was retained for the rest. Shipments in bond for reëxport, whether before or after processing, continue to be duty-free.

The trade of the United States in petroleum products is subject to extraneous influences. Thus events in Mexico (see p. 520) cut off what during the twenties constituted a major factor in our petroleum economy, imports of Mexican crude. Even closer, however, is the nexus between this country's foreign trade in petroleum and our domestic petroleum situation. Thus during the early twenties when we faced a deficit in crude oil, imports exceeded exports by a wide margin; later, however, after the discovery of a series of large reservoirs reversed our position, exports jumped ahead and imports lagged behind.

During World War II, shipments abroad, especially to our armed forces, were made possible by increased production coupled with the artificial curtailing of domestic consumption through gasoline rationing. Production could be stepped up surprisingly quickly because under the proration laws output had been held down to demand. As a result, many fields had been producing below their maximum efficiency rate, but during the war they were allowed to bring production up to this rate.[5]

PETROLEUM AND WORLD POLITICS
Petroleum and War

"Petroleum is an outstanding source of fuel, lubricants and international friction."[6] Some writers have gone so far as to say that modern wars are fought with and for oil. That wars today are fought, and especially won, with oil, there can be no doubt. Whereas during World War I the navies of the world were still predominantly coal-propelled, subsequently they became wholly oil-driven. Whereas in World War I there were thousands of planes, in World War II there were tens of thousands and their unit fuel demands far exceeded those of their predecessors. Modern war is mechanized war and many troops are air-borne. A single American armored division required 75,000 gallons of motor fuel a day. An aircraft carrier used 18,000 barrels (756,000 gallons) of fuel oil for one round trip from a Pacific coast port in the United States to the Southwest Pacific.

---

[5] From this it appears that proration laws have a certain incidental strategic value.

[6] Joseph S. Davis in his foreword to Herbert Feis, *Petroleum and American Foreign Policy*, Food Research Institute, Commodity Policy Studies No. 3, Stanford University, 1944.

Global war is a war of supply lines encircling the earth. Oil alone can keep these lines open. It also takes oil to haul oil.

Oil today is strategic material No. 1 and the amounts of oil needed to fight any future war will be prodigal indeed.[7] Where the oil will come from is the grave question that occupies the minds of the strategists and statesmen of all the nations, especially the Great Powers, that cannot with certainty rule war out of the range of future possibilities.

Not only do the armed forces need prodigious amounts of petroleum products, but they are very particular about their quality and even more so regarding the location of the sources of these products. The sources must be safely within their reach, under their control. Thus, whether the United States should count on Middle-Eastern oil in time of war is a grave question and one that cannot be answered with complete assurance.

Besides the oil products actually needed by the armed forces, the men responsible for the conduct of a war are keenly interested in the oil needed to keep the war industries and domestic transportation lines open and to satisfy the civilian demand so that people can carry on their work in the wartime economy.

The amount and efficiency of crude oil production, the refining capacity, the refinery output in terms of specific products, the possibility of stepping up production all along the line, almost at a moment's notice, are problems of deep concern in the conduct of future wars.

One might reason that the United States, being the largest producer of oil in the world, has least reason to worry, but a little thought will quickly discourage such complacency. There is little doubt that because we lead in production we have dug into our reserves more deeply perhaps than any other country that is in a class with our own. No other country has allowed its entire economy to become as completely dependent on oil as has the United States. Because she is the most powerful nation in the world today, her responsibilities for world order and world peace exceed those of all the other countries. The needs for

oil are large and imperative; the sources from which to meet them show signs of diminishing returns.

And we are not the only country that feels the need of vast oil supplies for prosperity and security. This raises the question of how conflicting claims to the assuredly limited supplies of oil are to be reconciled. Thus a comprehensive and constructive oil policy becomes a primary requisite for world peace.

Oil the Troublemaker

Such a policy has been sorely lacking in the past, with the result that again and again oil became the bone of contention between Great Powers seeking to safeguard or strengthen their positions. Perhaps the two World Wars that Germany inflicted on mankind may be placed in this category. When the British navy, after 1907, systematically shifted from coal to oil, Germany, realizing the inferiority of her own coal-propelled navy, felt the lack of oil more keenly than ever. The fact that her nationals could buy petroleum products in peacetime at fair and nondiscriminating prices was of little if any consolation. The Bagdad railway and negotiations for oil concessions in the Near East were pushed with redoubled vigor. The British viewed the railway as a dagger pointed at their "lifeline of the Empire" and feared a powerful rival next door to their Iranian oil fields. To Germany it seemed that if Britain by unilateral action could acquire the oil of 500,000 square miles of Iran, her own efforts to secure concessions in Mesopotamia could scarcely be rejected as wholly unreasonable. A first-class conflict arose over oil; how it was decided is a matter of history.[8]

A rather acute, and in retrospect most regrettable, situation developed during the twenties when American oil companies, worried perhaps by the constant pessimistic predictions of the early exhaustion of our oil reserves, looked abroad for a means of supplementing their domestic sources of supply. It was bad enough when oil found within the British Em-

---

[7] Atomic energy will play an important role in future wars, but it is unlikely to eliminate oil as a major factor in the period of time with which we can afford to concern ourselves.

[8] It can be argued that Germany wanted the oil to wage war—in other words, that the decision to wage war preceded the quest for oil, that oil was merely incidental and not a major cause of the conflict. Which interpretation is more realistic can hardly be determined objectively.

pire was categorically declared to be British, to the exclusion of alien explorers. But the situation became desperate when the British tried to keep American explorers out of mandated territory such as Iraq and Palestine and persuaded the Dutch government to exclude American interests from the Djambi field of Java, granting exclusive rights to the newly founded Royal Dutch-Shell combination. While thus trying to exclude American interests from participating in the development of foreign oil fields, the Shell interests were vigorously pushing production in the United States, doing their best to accelerate the much-dreaded exhaustion of our reserves.[9] At this time, each side, in what in retrospect looks like an almost childish game of reciprocal accusations, claimed that it had but a few drops of oil whereas the other side was swimming in oil and hogging it all.

Sumatra

In fact, the British were active in the oil fields of India, which then included Burma, in the Dutch East Indies, Iran (still called Persia), Mexico, Colombia, Peru, Ecuador, Trinidad—in short, wherever prospects seemed to warrant investment.

It was then that Congress, provoked by the British intransigence, put into the Mineral Leasing Law of 1920 a clause which authorized the federal government to withhold concessions to parties whose governments failed to grant reciprocal rights to United States nationals. The matter came to a head when in 1920 Great Britain and France signed the San Remo oil agreement under which the oil of Iraq, a mandate under the League of Nations, was to be divided between those two countries. Seldom did the government of the United States protest more vigorously than in response to this flagrant violation of the rules governing mandated territories, and of the principles of the open door policy long championed by this country. The San Remo agreement came close to being a joint plundering plot.

The result of her protests was the formation of the Iraq Petroleum Company (I.P.C.), the shares of which were divided as follows: 5 percent to an Armenian who later became a British subject, the remaining 95 percent in four equal parts—23.75 percent each—to Anglo-

Iranian, Royal Dutch-Shell, French, and American interests. A pipe line was built from Kirkuk to Haidatha; here it forks, one branch going to Tripoli in Syria, then under French control, the other to Haifa in Palestine, then under British authority. A refinery was built in Haifa, 30 percent of whose capacity was to be held at the disposal of the American participants in the Iraq venture. How this arrangement satisfies the principle of the open door may not be quite clear to the layman not versed in the deeper meaning of diplomatic terms.

Typical of the spirit of the time was the Red Line agreement that was attached to the Iraq settlement. A red line was drawn on a map around adjoining areas to indicate that within the region thus marked exploration for oil was to be a matter of joint concern for all the participants to the Iraq settlement. This area among other sections includes all of Arabia, Syria, Palestine, and Qatar, a peninsula projecting from Saudi Arabia toward the island of Bahrein. Similarly smacking of cartel philosophy and discrimination was the arrangement between Anglo-Iranian and Gulf Oil for the exploration of Kuwait. Anglo-Iranian exacted from Gulf the condition that the latter could not market its products in areas where Anglo-Iranian oil was marketed. It is assumed that such anomalies of the spirit of fair play and nondiscrimination were outlawed by certain clauses in the Anglo-American oil argument of 1945.

In Latin America, too, oil stirred up considerable trouble. This does not mean that only the oil companies are to blame. Governments can be unreasonable too. Both sides suffered from growing pains and had to grope slowly toward fair and mutually advantageous arrangements, safeguarding alike the rights of those who invest capital at not inconsiderable risk and who place at the disposal of undeveloped countries the knowledge, experience, know-how, skills, etc., of their own civilization, and of those who offer their national heritage for exploitation by aliens.

The New Spirit

But it looks as if men, after all, were willing and able to learn. Even Harold L. Ickes, former Secretary of the Interior, stated before the

---

[9] This does not mean that exhaustion of our reserves was their major objective, but it certainly was an effect of their action.

American Petroleum Institute in Chicago in November, 1945:

Whatever may or may not have been the case in the past, the information available to me indicates that the more progressive American companies in recent years have gone even beyond their obligations in advancing the social and economic interests of the countries where they operate. They deserve sincere approbation for these activities. These fair, progressive companies will benefit by the official affirmation of the principle which they have voluntarily followed, while the unfair, the unprogressive company—the one that kills the goose —could scarcely, with grace, ask for diplomatic support for its improprieties.[10]

Under the title "World Oil Policy," one reads:

The world suffers today from the lack of an enlightened comprehensive policy with respect to the earth's resources of oil. We are confronted with an acute and growing need for oil; not alone for military activity in war but for economic and social advances in peace. The oil fields of the United States, which have supplied more than 60 per cent of the world's oil in the past, cannot be relied upon to maintain this record in the future. Our own peacetime demand already approaches, if it does not even exceed, our capacity to produce oil, efficiently.

But the rest of the world needs oil as badly as we do. Most of the Latin-American nations need more oil; China needs oil; India needs oil. Everybody's need is immediate. The world's merchant marine floats on oil. The wheels of modern industry everywhere are turned by oil. Standards of living can rise only as they are supported by cheap transportation—"the greatest economic and social revolution which has ever taken place"—and today cheap transportation exists only on a basis of cheap oil.

Our own high living standards, higher than any other people ever enjoyed, rest upon a productive capacity only possible because of our unrivaled system of motor transportation. Our motors are driven by oil, so cheap, so abundant as to be within reach of practically every family unit in the nation. If the world's standard of living, along with its per capita oil consumption, were lifted only half way to the levels of our own, the world's proved oil reserves would be exhausted within a decade.

The development of adequate sources of supply of oil for the world is an indispensable preliminary to the establishment of high standards of living over the world. Once developed, the oil resources of the earth can be made the foundation upon which to erect high standards of living in other nations, just as our own oil resources have been made the basis of our own high living standard.

The responsibility for devising and establishing an enlightened world oil policy rests on the United Nations. The fourth principle of the Atlantic Charter recognizes this responsibility:

"to 'further the enjoyment by all states, great or small, victor or vanquished, of access on equal terms, to the trade and to the raw materials of the world which are needed for their common prosperity.'"

No raw material is more important in this connection than oil and among the United Nations, Great Britain and the United States, the outstanding oil-finding and oil-producing peoples, must assume the leadership in establishing wise policy with respect to this raw material.[11]

Then follows a plea for rational exploitation of the oil fields, looking for optimum recovery and maximum life. This leads to what might be called a credo of the modern oil executive, stating what he expects from others and what he is willing to do for others. It reads as follows:

Our own government can contribute to the formulation and establishment of an enlightened world policy for oil by assuming leadership, in concert with Great Britain, in devising an acceptable policy and in persuading other nations to agree and to adhere to its provisions.

Our government can also lend active diplomatic support to American citizens and other nationals who seek, through legitimate methods, to negotiate, explore and develop oil concessions throughout the world, to produce and distribute oil and oil products, in free enterprise.

The assurances which American citizens have usually sought from a foreign government in undertaking the development of oil resources under a concession from that government are:

1. security of title to the property or rights acquired;

2. managerial control of their own operations; and

3. the opportunity to make a reasonable profit from the enterprise.

---

[10] John W. Frey and H. Chandler Ide (eds.), *A History of the Petroleum Administration for War, 1941-1945*, Government Printing Office, Washington, 1946, p. 285.

[11] *The Lamp*, December, 1943, pp. 1-3.

Given these assurances, concession contracts may take a variety of forms; they may provide a straight royalty to the government; they may share profits with the government; or they may become "mixed company" operations with the government. Local capital may be admitted to the enterprise if it desires to participate.

The foreign government which lets oil concessions to private individuals or companies will properly insist:

1. that an adequate participation in the proceeds from the enterprise come to the government;

2. that operations shall be so conducted as to contribute to the domestic economy of the nation;

3. that domestic demands for oil be fully satisfied at low prices before any oil is exported;

4. that development and production proceed in an orderly manner with no avoidable waste of the natural resource;

5. that the enterprise give to local citizens the maximum of training and employment at fair rates of compensation; and

6. that oil and oil products available for export move to market in fair volume at fair prices.

In considering the operations of American citizens engaged in the oil industry of foreign countries the government of the United States would wish to assure itself:

1. that American citizens are accorded the rights to which they are reasonably entitled by the terms of their contracts with foreign governments, judged by the laws of that government;

2. that American citizens live up to their obligations to foreign governments and so conduct their operations as to contribute to the national welfare of the country in which they operate;

3. that the operations are conducted in conformity with the best interest of the United States;

4. that the principles of conservation are adhered to in the development of the oil resources;

5. that the exportable surplus move efficiently, in orderly manner and at fair prices, into markets of consumer nations; and

6. that imports of oil or oil products into the United States be so regulated as to serve the best interest of our domestic economy, including our domestic oil industry.

The government of the United States should collaborate with other governments to establish and maintain orderly production from oil resources throughout the world for the benefit of the consuming nations. Withdrawals from all fields should be ratably adjusted to supply the demand if possible, but, in any event, they should not exceed the optimum rate. Exploration should be stimulated as long as any possible resources remain untested. Exportable surpluses should be efficiently and equitably distributed under the provisions of the United Nation's world oil policy.

Imports of oil or oil products into the United States must supplement domestic supplies to meet the national demand, without working a hardship on the domestic industry or stifling oil-finding at home. Imports should be admitted only to supply special products, or demand that cannot be met by withdrawals from domestic oil fields at rates not in excess of the optimum in each case.

The adoption of the policy proposed above will secure adequate petroleum reserves to meet the future needs of our own nation and of the other nations of the world more certainly and more rapidly than any alternative procedure. No more effective contribution to future world peace is likely to be devised.[12]

One cannot help contrasting this position with what he read about certain oil companies operating in foreign countries some decades ago. The old swashbuckling buccaneer is gone. In his place there is a fair-minded, far-seeing business statesman, aware of his duties to his stockholders—yes—but aware also of his duties to his country and to humanity at large. Of course, this is the only sane policy; it is the only policy which can safeguard the long-run interests of producer and consumer alike. It is the only policy under which civilization can survive.

---

[12] *Ibid.*

BIBLIOGRAPHY

Allen, R. E., "The Paradox of Proration," *Oil and Gas Journal*, October 30, 1941.

American Petroleum Institute, *Petroleum Facts and Figures*, New York, 8th ed., 1947.

Arnold, R., and Kemnitzer, W. J., *Petroleum in the United States and Possessions*, New York, Harper, 1931.

Bain, J. S., *The Economics of the Pacific Coast Petroleum Industry*, Berkeley, University of California Press, 2 vols., 1944.

Baker, H. H., "Achievements and Unsolved Problems in Oil and Gas Conservation," address before the American Petroleum Institute, Galveston, 1949 (mimeographed).

Ball, M. W., *This Fascinating Oil Business*, Indianapolis, Bobbs-Merrill, 1940.

Baum, A. W., "Now We Have Plenty of Oil," *Saturday Evening Post*, June 3, 1950.

Brodie, B., "American Security and Foreign Oil," *Foreign Policy Report*, March, 1948.

Deegan, C., "Proven Reserves—What Are They?" *Independent Petroleum Association of America Monthly*, September, 1949.

DeGolyer, E. L. (ed.), *Elements of the Petroleum Industry*, New York, American Institute of Mining and Metallurgical Engineers, 1940.

DeGolyer, E. L., "Seventy-five Years of Progress in Petroleum," in Parsons, A. B. (ed.), *Seventy-five Years of Progress in the Mineral Industry, 1871-1946*, New York, American Institute of Mining and Metallurgical Engineers, 1947.

Egloff, G., "Modern Energy Supplies," *Scientific Monthly*, April, 1936.

Ely, N., "The Interdependence of the States in Oil Conservation, a Survey of the Interstate Compact Plan," New York, American Institute of Mining and Metallurgical Engineers, Petroleum Division, September 30, 1932.

Fanning, L. M., *The Rise of American Oil*, New York, Harper, 1936.

Fanning, L. M., *American Oil Operations Abroad*, New York, McGraw-Hill, 1947.

Fanning, L. M. (ed.), *Our Oil Resources*, New York, McGraw-Hill, 1945.

Federal Oil Conservation Board, *Reports I-V*, Washington, 1926-1932.

Feis, H., *Petroleum and American Foreign Policy*, Stanford University, Food Research Institute, 1944.

Finney, W. R., "The Big Inch Pipe Line," *Mining and Metallurgy*, October, 1943.

Fraser, W., "International Aspects of the Petroleum Industry," in Parsons, A. B. (ed.), *Seventy-five Years of Progress in the Mineral Industry, 1871-1946*, New York, American Institute of Mining and Metallurgical Engineers, 1947.

Frechtling, L. E., "Oil and the War," *Foreign Policy Reports*, June 1, 1941.

Friedwald, E. M., *Oil and War*, London, Heinemann, 1941.

Frey, J. W., "The World's Petroleum," *Geographical Review*, July, 1940.

Giddens, P. H., *The Birth of the Oil Industry*, New York, Macmillan, 1938.

"Great Oil Deals," *Fortune*, May, 1947.

Hardwicke, R. E., "The Rule of Capture and Its Implications as Applied to Oil and Gas," *Texas Law Review*, June, 1935.

Hardwicke, R. E., "Oil Conservation: Statutes, Administration, and Court Review," *Mississippi Law Journal*, March, 1941.

Hardwicke, R. E., "Antitrust Laws et al. v. Unit Operation of Oil and Gas Pools," New York, American Institute of Mining and Metallurgical Engineers, 1948.

Hardwicke, R. E., "Market Demand as a Factor in the Conservation of Oil," *Tulane Law Review*, 1948.

Hardwicke, R. E., *Conservation of Oil and Gas*, New York, Mineral Section, American Bar Association, 1949.

Hardwicke, R. E., "The Tidelands and Oil," *Atlantic Monthly*, June, 1949.

Hardwicke, R. E., and others, *Legal History of Conservation of Oil and Gas, a Symposium*, American Bar Association, Mineral Section, 1939.

Heroy, W. B., "The Supply of Crude Petroleum Within the United States," Washington, Petroleum Administration for War, 1943.

Holaday, W. M., Albright, R. E., Apjohn, T. L., and Steffens, L. R., "Fuels—Their Present and Future Utilization," Annual meeting, American Petroleum Institute, Chicago, November, 1949.

Ickes, H. L., *Fightin' Oil*, New York, Knopf, 1943.

Illig, C., Patterson, C. P., and Hardwicke, R. E., "The Constitution and the Continental Shelf," *Texas Law Review*, April, 1948.

Ise, J., *The United States Oil Policy*, New Haven, Yale University Press, 1926.

Joint Progress Report on Reservoir Efficiency and Well Spacing, New York, Standard Oil Development Company, 1943.

Kemnitzer, W. J., *Rebirth of Monopoly*, New York, Harper, 1938.

Laidler, H. W., *Concentration of Control in American Industry*, New York, Crowell, 1931.

Leven, D. D., *Done in Oil*, New York, Ranger Press, 1941.

Levy, W. A., *The Rule of Capture in the Law of Oil and Gas, in the Absence of Unit Operation*, New York, Columbia University Press, 1938.

Meyers, G. N., "The Struggle for Arctic Oil," *Saturday Evening Post*, April 19, 1947.

"Middle Eastern Oil," *Fortune*, May, 1947.

Morgan, E. P., and Salisbury, H. E., "Oil Troubles Iran's Waters," *Collier's*, April 5, 1947.

Mouzon, O. T., "Petroleum Import Policy of the United States," *Economic Geography*, April, 1946.

"Mr. Ickes' Arabian Nights," *Fortune*, June, 1944.

National Industrial Conference Board, *Oil Conservation and Fuel Oil Supply*, New York, 1930.

National Petroleum Council, *U. S. Crude Petroleum Reserve Production Capacity*, Washington, January 26, 1950.

Osburn, C., *Oil Economics*, New York, McGraw-Hill, 1932.

Patton, W., *United States Petroleum Refining, War*

and Post-War, Industrial Series, No. 7, Washington, U. S. Department of Commerce, 1947.

Petroleum Industry Research Foundation, *World Oil: Fact and Policy*, New York, 1944.

Pogue, J. E., *The Economic Structure of the American Petroleum Industry*, Bulletin of the American Association of Petroleum Geologists, February, 1937.

Pogue, J. E., *Economics of the Petroleum Industry*, New York, Chase National Bank, March, 1939.

Pogue, J. E., and Coqueran, F. G., *Capital Formation in the Petroleum Industry*, American Institute of Mining and Metallurgical Engineers, February, 1940.

Pratt, W. E., *Oil in the Earth*, Lawrence, University of Kansas Press, 1942.

Rister, C. C., *Oil! Titan of the Southwest*, Norman, University of Oklahoma Press, 1949.

Rostow, E. V., *A National Policy for the Oil Industry*, New Haven, Yale University Press, 1948.

Shuman, R. B., *The Petroleum Industry*, Norman, University of Oklahoma Press, 1940.

Standard Oil Company (New Jersey), *Petroleum in the World* (no date).

Stocking, G. W., "Oil Industry," *Encyclopædia of the Social Sciences*, New York, Macmillan, 1933.

"The Big Gulf Gamble," *Fortune*, July, 1948.

"The Fabulous Barco," *Fortune*, March, 1940.

Thom, W. T., Jr., *Petroleum and Coal: The Keys to the Future*, Princeton, Princeton University Press, 1929.

T.N.E.C., *Petroleum Industry*, Hearings, 1940, vols. 14-17.

U. S. Senate, 79th Congress, 1st and 2nd Sessions, *Investigation of Petroleum Resources*, Washington, 1945-1946.

U. S. Tariff Commission, *Report to the House of Representatives on Crude Petroleum and Its Liquid Refined Products*, Report No. 30, Washington, 1932.

U. S. Tariff Commission, *Crude Petroleum*, Washington, 1942.

Watkins, M. W., *Oil: Stabilization or Conservation*, New York, Harper, 1937.

Weiss, H. C., "Some Current Problems in Oil Conservation," New York, American Institute of Mining and Metallurgical Engineers, Petroleum Section, 1939.

Wellman, P. I., "Bubble Beneath the Plains," *Saturday Evening Post*, December 12, 1942.

Whitman, W. G., "Liquid Fuel Supplies and National Security," Annual meeting, Petroleum Institute, Chicago, November, 1949.

Wilson, R. E., and Roberts, J. K., "Petroleum and Natural Gas; Uses and Possible Replacements," in Parsons, A. B. (ed.), *Seventy-five Years of Progress in the Mineral Industry, 1871-1946*, New York, American Institute of Mining and Metallurgical Engineers, 1947.

World Oil Atlas, Houston, Gulf Publishing Company, 1948.

Chapter 35

NATURAL GAS

EVOLUTION OF NATURAL GAS AS A COMMODITY

Natural gas, as distinguished from manufactured gas obtained from coal, occurs either in conjunction with oil in oil fields or, separate from oil, in gas fields, including condensate and distillate fields.[1] Gas occurring in conjunction with oil is generally known as casing-head gas, the casing-head being the top of an oil well.

The production of casing-head gas is as old as the oil industry itself. Most oil in the ground contains gas or mixes with gas as it is tapped. The vital function of this admixture of gas as the natural driving force which brings oil to the surface was not understood in the early days of the industry; hence most casing-head gas was either dissipated or used for purposes less vital than its natural function. At present, casing-head gas constitutes probably one-third of all the natural gas produced in the United States.

The exploitation of natural gas fields is a

---

[1] Condensate and distillate fields contain gas from which liquid hydrocarbons can be obtained by condensation or distillation.

development of relatively recent origin. In fact, the emergence of a national natural gas industry, approaching in size of market the oil industry itself, is still in process.

Chemically, all natural gases are similar if not more or less identical. Casing-head gas, after yielding its liquid or easily liquefiable ingredients, may be sold in the same market as gas obtained from a gas well. Gas drawn from gas wells may be used to repressure or to maintain pressure in oil wells just as casing-head gas is used. But even now, on the whole, most wells—oil, gas, and dry holes—are drilled in the hope of striking oil.

The ties between this comparatively new industry and the oil industry are far looser than those between casing-head gas and oil. Most of the natural gas produced today is not a by-product of oil, as was once the case, but an independent product of a largely independent industry. Conceivably, the production of natural gas from gas wells may increase while the oil industry is reaching a state of equilibrium.

More and more natural gas is entering the national market. Its interstate transportation is a public utility function controlled by the federal government under the Natural Gas Act of 1938. Since long-distance transmission requires heavy investments in pipe lines, compressor stations, communication systems, etc., a pipeline owner, in order to protect his investment, tends to enter the business of producing natural gas on a large scale. However, the close affiliation with a public utility function has cast a shadow of doubt on whether the production of natural gas is a strictly private enterprise. This has tended to sharpen the distinction and widen the division between the natural gas and the oil industries. In some cases oil companies have actually divested themselves of their gas holdings.

NATURAL GAS IN THE ENERGY ECONOMY OF THE UNITED STATES

The total amount of natural gas which comes to the surface in the United States is not known. An unknown amount of casing-head gas is lost by being vented or weathered, i.e., allowed to escape in the air, or flared, i.e., burned. Not all the gas used by the oil and gas industries is metered, hence its amount is not accurately known. The amount of natural gas *marketed* in the United States in 1948 is estimated at 5 trillion cubic feet. At ordinary atmospheric pressure (14.65 p.s.i.)[2] and at 60° F. the weight of this volume of natural gas is estimated at 120 million tons, or about a third greater than the weight of the nation's steel output. The heating value of a cubic foot of natural gas is about 1075 B.T.U., as compared with 13,500 B.T.U. for a pound of average-quality bituminous coal. On this basis the 5 trillion cubic feet of natural gas marketed in the United States in 1948 equals roughly 200 million tons of bituminous coal.[3]

The theoretical heat value of the total recorded production of natural gas in this country in 1947 was 4.9 quadrillion B.T.U. This compared with 18.0 for all the coal, 11.3 for oil, and 1.4 for water power (see p. 484). Natural gas constituted 13.8 percent of the total heat equivalent of all the mineral fuels and water power produced here that year.[4]

Of all the sources of heat and mechanical energy, the production of natural gas is increasing most rapidly. Fuel index figures for 1947 are as follows (1918 = 100):[5]

Natural gas	617
Domestic oil (produced in the U. S.)	521
Imported oil	264
Water power	203
Bituminous coal	109
Anthracite and lignite	58
All coal	101

The dollar value of the natural gas produced in 1946 was $885.0 million, as compared with $2441.8 million for crude oil, $1806.2 million for bituminous coal, and $413.4 million for anthracite. Largely because of its novelty and the sudden spurt of production, but also in part because of the by-product nature of the portion of the natural gas output which is produced along with oil, natural gas does not yet sell at a price commensurate with its intrinsic use value. As new uses for it are discovered and developed, as the pipe-line net expands and natural gas reaches all the markets to which its excellent properties entitle it, and as its market position reaches a point of equilibrium with competitive commodities, the aggregate value of its sales is bound to reach figures considerably above those currently registered.

The amount of natural gas marketed is probably five times as large as the total sales of manufactured gas, and the difference is growing bigger. The fact that a cubic foot of natural gas has a heating value of 1075 B.T.U., as compared with 540 for standard city gas, makes the preponderance of natural gas loom still larger. Here again a difference in markets must be recognized, for whereas fully two-thirds of all manufactured gas is sold to domestic consumers, at present the bulk of the natural gas is sold to industries.

[2] The weight of a cubic foot of gas varies with the pressure to which the gas is subjected and with the temperature. Weight per cubic foot increases with increasing pressure and with decreasing temperature.

[3] Since coal and natural gas differ widely in their uses and since the bulk of the natural gas is available in areas where coal is scarce, only a fraction of the natural gas marketed competes with or displaces coal.

[4] It must be remembered that not the entire output of fuel is used for the production of heat and the generation of power. In this case, B.T.U. is merely a common unit of measurement.

[5] Bureau of Mines, "Bituminous Coal and Lignite, 1947," *Mineral Market Report,* November 22, 1948, pp. 12-15.

Natural gas for mechanical reasons is not now suitable as a fuel for means of transportation—automobiles, planes, ships, locomotives. Therefore it does not compete with oil in its main market area. However, if current experiments in converting natural gas into gasoline prove successful, some competition between crude oil and natural gas as sources of gasoline may develop. So long as the well-nigh insatiable demand for gasoline continues, this may prove a boon to both industries, resulting in a division of functions between the two sister hydrocarbons, the liquid and the gaseous.

Everything that is done to help natural gas fill the role to which its unexcelled properties entitle it is bound to result in a gain not only to its producers, processors, and distributors, but to society at large. The enmity with which coal owners and miners alike now view its intrusion into the northern and eastern markets will then subside.

NATURAL GAS TECHNOLOGY

About 85 percent of typical natural gas is methane ("marsh gas"), CH_4. The rest is largely ethane, C_2H_6. The boiling points of methane and ethane are $-259°$ F. and $-128°$ F. respectively, and hence it is very difficult to liquefy them. This gas is known as "dry gas."

Besides methane and ethane, most natural gas, especially that occurring in conjunction with oil but also that obtained from the so-called condensate or distillate wells, also contains propane, butane, and the lighter gasoline fractions (see p. 538). The extraction of gasoline from casing-head and natural gas has long been practiced. More recent is the commercial extraction of propane and butane. Because at ordinary temperatures and pressures these gases are too volatile to stay with the gasoline, they formerly escaped into the atmosphere; but since the middle thirties they have been carefully recovered and compressed into liquid petroleum gas. This gas, the so-called L.P. gas, or L.P.G., is a valuable household fuel that is sold in steel bottles or tanks to people living beyond the reach of city mains. Propane, with a boiling point of $-44°$ F., is sold mainly in the North; it packs 2520 B.T.U. to a cubic foot. Butane has a boiling point of $+31°$ F. and is sold mainly in the South where frost is less frequent. It rates 3270 B.T.U. per cubic foot.

Liquid Petroleum Gas

How dynamic the natural gas business is, is well illustrated by what has been happening to L.P.G. In 1922, when records for liquid petroleum gas were first kept, total consumption was 223,000 gallons, or 8 million cubic feet. By 1936 this modest volume had grown to 106.7 million gallons and sold for $48 million. By 1946 sales reached 1.7 billion gallons,[6] worth $380 million at retail. About half this amount was sold to domestic customers; the rest went to gas manufacturers and to chemical and other industries.[7]

Natural Gasoline

As was stated before, besides propane and butane, lighter gasoline fractions are also extracted from so-called wet gas. All casing-head gas is wet gas. Gas drawn from gas wells may be either wet or dry. The average oil well in Texas produces about 15 to 20 barrels of oil a day, and about 17,000 to 30,000 cubic feet of natural gas if it has a normal gas-oil ratio. In Texas much of the casing-head gas from which natural gasoline has been extracted is vented or flared. As soon as markets develop and the price goes up, this waste will stop automatically. No such problem seems to exist in California because of the close proximity of the points where the gas is produced and consumed. The elimination of such waste is one of the chief problems of the industry and of the controlling agencies of both state and federal governments.

Fig. 35.1 shows the United States production of natural gasoline and the average value in cents per gallon. Natural gasoline is a high-

---

[6] A gallon of L.P.G. expands into from 30 to 36 cubic feet of gas, depending on whether the gas used is propane or butane or a mixture of the two. If an average expansion to 33 cubic feet is assumed, the 1.7 billion gallons were equal to 56.1 billion cubic feet. The steel bottles and tanks in which L.P.G. is marketed are tested for a pressure of about 450 pounds p.s.i., or 30 atmospheres. Working pressure seldom exceeds 220 pounds. The pressure varies with the outside temperature.

[7] See "L.P.G., the Gas That Flows from Bottles," *The Lamp*, June, 1947, pp. 26 ff.; "Bottled Gas," *Fortune*, March, 1948, pp. 121 ff. See also Federal Power Commission, *Natural Gas Investigations*, Part II, *Practices and Problems in Producing, Gathering and Processing Natural Gas*, pp. 55 ff.

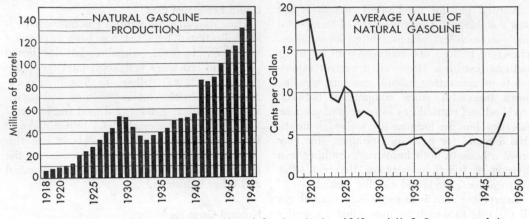

FIG. 35.1. (Federal Power Commission, *Natural Gas Investigation*, 1948, and U. S. Department of the Interior, Bureau of Mines.)

quality product that is too rich for ordinary motors; hence it is blended with other gasolines.

Cycling Plants

At present the demand for natural gasoline and other liquid or liquefiable ingredients of natural gas is greater than the demand for the gas itself. As a result, a peculiar practice called cycling has developed. As the word suggests, the gas is removed from the well, stripped of its "wet" fractions, and then returned to the reservoir in the hope that the time will come when it will pay to extract the now dry gas. This practice is largely the result of laws passed by several southwestern states, including Texas, which forbid the venting or flaring of gas from gas wells.[8] To a considerable extent the recent increase in the production of natural gasoline and L.P.G. is due to cycling operations.

Desulfurization

Besides methane, ethane, and commercially liquefiable hydrocarbons, natural gas may contain impurities, especially sulfur, usually in the form of hydrogen sulfide. The sulfur content may vary from a mere trace to several hundred grains per 100 cubic feet of gas. More than 1 grain generally disqualifies the gas for sale to domestic customers. Such gas is known as sour

---

[8] Cycling plants are sometimes incorrectly referred to as recycling plants. This term preferably applies to plants that inject gas into reservoirs which have lost their original gas pressure. Such plants are often called gas drive plants.

gas as distinguished from sweet gas, which is virtually free from sulfur.

Desulfurization processes have been developed which convert sour gas economically into sweet gas. If the sulfur content is high enough the recovery of the sulfur may pay; there is one field in Arkansas where 60 to 70 tons of marketable sulfur are produced a day. Ordinarily, however, the residual sulfur-bearing gas is dissipated into the air.

Extraction of Helium

Helium is a rare constituent of natural gas. Only in a few fields is the helium content sufficiently high to warrant extraction. The content usually runs from 1 to 2 percent but ranges up to 8 percent in a field in New Mexico. Being one-seventh the weight of air, helium is the lightest gas next to hydrogen. It is chemically inert and therefore is not inflammable. These two properties render helium the ideal gas for lighter-than-air aircraft, such as rigid airships of the Zeppelin type, blimps, balloons, etc. In addition, it has important uses in the cure of respiratory troubles, and it has revolutionized deep-sea diving. If used to inflate the tires of a large plane it reduces the overall weight by roughly 100 pounds. It is indispensable in some forms of welding. Whereas in 1917 helium, which was then extracted from radioactive minerals, cost above $2500 a cubic foot, its present price is less than one cent a cubic foot.

Its production is a monopoly of the federal government, which has invested about $16 mil-

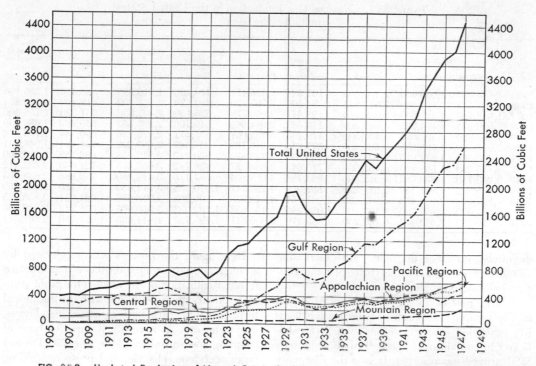

FIG. 35.2. Marketed Production of Natural Gas in the United States, by Regions, 1906-1947. (Federal Power Commission, *Natural Gas Investigation*, 1948, and U. S. Department of the Interior, Bureau of Mines.)

lion in plants. The gas from which helium has been extracted loses none of its market value thereby; in fact, its B.T.U. rating is slightly enhanced.

NATURAL GAS PRODUCTION IN THE UNITED STATES

As was stated before, the total production of natural gas in the United States is not known. The official statistics compiled by the Bureau of Mines cover only the marketed portion. Fig. 35.2 shows the production by regions from 1906-1947. These statistics do not include gas used in the repressuring of wells or in cycling plants.

The following facts stand out: (1) During the forty-year period total market production increased about twelvefold. (2) Since 1928 the average rate of increase was approximately 8 percent a year. (3) From 1939 to 1947 production almost doubled, indicating that the industry, in both its production and its distributive branches, has entered a new era of rapid growth. (4) Whereas in 1906 the Appalachian

region was responsible for the bulk of production and remained dominant until 1926, today the center of production is in the Gulf region of the Southwest. Its predominance should increase in the near future as plans for additional long-distance pipe lines from there to the east, north, and west are brought to completion.

Since 1935 additional statistical records have been kept that include the amounts returned to reservoirs, losses and waste, the amounts applied to field uses, and the amounts obtained from oil and gas wells respectively. These data are shown in Table 35.1.

The enormous increase in the amount of gas returned to formation is particularly noteworthy. It reflects the more scientific "producing" of oil fields as well as cycling operations. On the other hand, the amount lost and wasted, through flaring and otherwise, has also increased. The conservation laws of Texas recognize waste only if it is economically avoidable. This ties up the determination of waste with the elusive market factors of costs and prices. The trend of gas prices, however, seems to be

TABLE 35.1.　Natural Gas Production in the United States[9]
(million cubic feet)

Year	Gross Production			Returned to Formation	Net Production	Losses and Waste	Marketed Production (Incl. Field Use)	Field Use	Net Marketed Production (Less Field Use)
	Gas Wells	Oil Wells	Total						
1935	1,493,005	1,005,000	2,498,005	101,584	2,396,421	479,826	1,916,595	580,414	1,336,181
1936	1,483,595	1,161,240	2,644,835	84,505	2,560,330	392,528	2,167,802	618,468	1,549,334
1937	1,613,780	1,325,630	2,939,410	98,631	2,840,779	526,159	2,407,620	651,320	1,756,300
1938	1,566,975	1,494,225	3,061,200	116,532	2,944,668	649,106	2,295,562	659,203	1,636,359
1939	1,832,820	1,500,680	3,333,500	179,433	3,154,067	677,311	2,476,756	680,884	1,795,872
1940	2,095,180	1,598,920	3,694,100	377,911	3,316,189	655,967	2,660,222	711,861	1,948,361
1941	2,490,590	1,612,910	4,103,500	660,630	3,442,870	630,212	2,812,658	686,158	2,126,500
1942	2,885,090	1,568,810	4,453,900	773,643	3,680,257	626,782	3,053,475	721,063	2,332,412
1943	3,208,780	1,733,780	4,942,560	843,756	4,098,804	684,115	3,414,689	780,986	2,633,703
1944	3,649,830	1,964,390	5,614,220	882,979	4,730,241	1,010,258	3,711,039	855,180	2,855,859
1945	3,887,727	2,014,453	5,902,180	1,061,951	4,840,229	896,208	3,918,686	1,061,951	2,856,735
1946	3,807,500	2,382,700	6,190,200	1,038,242	5,151,958	1,102,033	4,030,605	1,038,242	2,992,363
1947	3,769,768	2,963,462	6,733,230	1,083,119	5,650,611	1,195,745	4,444,693	1,083,119	3,361,574

definitely on the upgrade. An increasing amount of gas should therefore become economically recoverable.[10]

A large part of all the natural gas produced in the United States comes from twelve leading gas fields (see Fig. 35.3), which are believed to contain over one-half of the country's total proved gas reserves. It was the discovery of these gigantic reservoirs, between 1916 and the present, that encouraged investors to make natural gas a national big business. To reach our large cities and the industrial markets of the Northeast and of California requires an investment of such magnitude that only correspondingly large reserves warrant the undertaking. There then began a fruitful interactive play between the widening marketing ventures and the search for new huge gas reserves, one encouraging and justifying the other. The process was further favored both by the rapid increase in total fuel needs engendered by the expansion of our economy during and after the war, and by the corollary increase in fuel prices, especially of coal and fuel oil. The chance of cashing in on the wide spread between local field prices of natural gas and the price distant consumers were willing to pay grew ever bigger and more tempting. The result was a rapid expansion of the interstate gas-transmitting pipe-line net of the United States.

Here again the process was accelerated by an interesting dynamic interplay of constructive forces. Realization of the chance for profit stimulated bold experimentation with the traditional technology of pipe-line construction, laying, operation, etc. As a result, a superior type of coupling was introduced—the so-called Dresser type; acetylene, electric, and pressure welding came into vogue; and high-pressure boosting stations, radio communications along the line, improved steel pipe of ever larger diameter and greater resistance to pressure were introduced.

RESERVES OF NATURAL GAS

The study of the reserves of natural gas presents the same problem as does the study of oil reserves. Experts apparently agree that our current "proved reserves" (the term being used in the same sense in which the oil industry uses it) are roughly 200 trillion cubic feet.[11] This is greater than our currently "proved oil reserves" in both weight and heating value. Large additions are confidently expected.

A striking feature is the rapidity and con-

---

[9] U.S. Department of the Interior, Bureau of Mines.

[10] In this connection the Texas Supreme Court's decision in the Seeligson Field case is worth recalling; see p. 536.

[11] Estimates are based on highly complex mathematical calculations and are derived by diverse methods. In comparing the different estimates, an attempt should be made to check on the methods and formulas used. In particular, it is important to know whether the estimates give reserves at the same or at different pressures and temperatures. For example, the well-known De Golyer estimates are in terms of 16.4 p.s.i. at 60° F., whereas those of the American Gas Association are in terms of ordinary atmospheric pressure at sea level, 14.65 p.s.i.

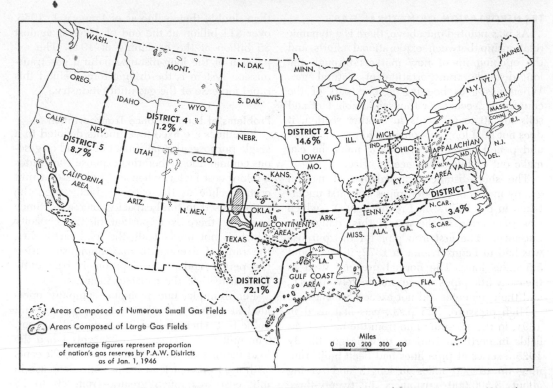

FIG. 35.3. Major Gas-Producing Areas of the United States, 1946. (Federal Power Commission, *Natural Gas Investigation*, 1948.)

sistent rate at which our natural gas reserves have increased—from slightly under 20 trillion cubic feet in 1920 to 200 trillion.

As is true of oil reserves, the life of gas reserves cannot be estimated by dividing total reserves by the amount currently produced. In the first place, the output curve is not level but climbs up sharply. In the second place, the amount of gas which is taken from the reserves in a year's time is physically limited by a fairly definite rate of production. The production-reserve ratio is more favorable for gas than for oil; in other words, the present annual output of natural gas in the United States constitutes a smaller portion of our reserves than is the case with oil.

Although it is impossible to predict the size and rate of future gas field discoveries and although the life expectancy of our reserves cannot be determined, the relationship between discoveries and net production can be established; it is a significant indication of future prospects. So long as this ratio goes up—it rose from 14 to 1 in 1919 to 31 to 1 in 1946—prospects of future supplies are favorable. The indication is that the natural gas industry is at present in a strong reserve position and that the rate of new discoveries is considerably in excess of the current rate of increase in output. The latter may pick up sharply when the pipeline projects currently planned or under construction have been completed.

New discoveries of gas will depend in part on the future development of oil discoveries. But since the bulk of the gas comes from gas wells, the outlook for the discovery of additional gas reserves is particularly significant. Additions to known gas reserves will be found (1) in deeper zones in currently producing fields, (2) in extensions of present fields, (3) in new areas between or near present fields, and (4) in regions not now in production. The first source is especially important because, as was mentioned earlier, it now appears that greater depth favors the presence of gas rather than of oil.

TRANSPORTATION OF NATURAL GAS

As was pointed out above, there is a dynamic relationship between explorational efforts and the opening up of new markets through the long-distance transportation of natural gas. When gas goes begging in one part of the country at 2 cents per thousand cubic feet and sells for 50 to 60 cents in another section, it does not take long for someone to get out paper and pencil and figure out how much he can make out of this difference in price.

The short-distance transmission of natural gas by means of wooden pipes was first undertaken in the 1820's, in Fredonia, N. Y., which was pioneering in the use of this "dangerous nuisance." The first iron pipe for this purpose was laid in Pennsylvania in 1872; it was about 5.5 miles long. The normal pressure used in the early iron pipes was approximately 80 p.s.i., and their diameter did not exceed 8 inches.

High pressure, 525 p.s.i., was first used in 1891, in the 120-mile line from the natural gas fields in northern Indiana to Chicago, Ill. By 1925 a series of pipe lines had been built, running up to 300 miles in length and serving about 3,500,000 customers in twenty-three states. The huge gas fields that were discovered in Louisiana and the Southwest between 1916 and 1922 put the industry on a new basis. The possibility of a nation-wide business appeared likely from the large reserve figure. Moreover, by about 1925 the technology of the high-pressure, long-distance transmission of gas had advanced far enough to warrant extending the length of the pipe lines to 1200 miles and increasing the diameter to 24 inches. Thus the stage was set for a dramatic boom in pipe-line construction which brought the total field, transmission, and distribution lines to 150,000 miles in 1934, to 218,000 by 1945, and to around 240,000 by 1948. Diameters have also been getting bigger. One line from the Arizona-California border to Los Angeles that transmits Texas and New Mexico gas to Los Angeles has a diameter of 30 inches.

There has been a tremendous postwar expansion of the pipe-line net, especially the long-distance lines. So rapid is this postwar expansion that, according to an estimate made in July, 1950, by the American Gas Association, by the end of 1954 the total investment in the nation's gas utilities will be considerably more than double their value as of January 1, 1945, over $11 billion at the end of 1954 as against $5 billion at the beginning of 1945. The expansion of the long-distance natural gas transmission system is the driving force behind this rapid increase of the gas utility industry.

Problems of Long-Distance Transportation

Pipe lines are fixed investments devoted to a single purpose—the movement of liquid or gaseous commodities. Operating expense constitutes a minor cost factor, whence it follows that unit costs decline as the capacity factor, i.e., the ratio of used to total capacity, increases. Since normally there is a portion of the capacity which is not used at all, the load factor—i.e., the ratio of average to maximum use during the period under consideration—is frequently used instead of the capacity factor.[12]

For example, one pipe-line company operated at a unit cost of 70 cents per thousand cubic feet when its load factor was 22 percent. The unit cost decreased to 28 cents when the load factor rose to 60 percent, and to 20 cents with a 94 percent load factor. The decrease in unit cost was much greater—from 70 to 28 cents—when the load factor increased from 22 to 60 percent than when the load factor increased from 60 to 94 percent. This pattern—an initial sharp drop in unit cost that definitely tapers off when the load factor reaches 60 percent or over—is fairly characteristic of all pipe-line companies.

The ownership and operation of gas pipe lines are beset with great risks and difficulties. Like petroleum pipe lines and electric power transmission lines, gas pipe lines are specialty carriers, dependent for their profitable existence on one industry and one commodity. The risks and difficulties are especially great in the case of the long interstate gas pipe lines that cost many tens of millions of dollars.

The chief risk lies in maintaining a level of pipe-line operation sufficient to meet expenses and earn a profit on the investment. The pipe-line operator must be sure that sufficient gas will be shipped through his line. The volume shipped depends on the demand for gas in the territory served by the pipe line; this demand,

---

[12] In other words, the load factor is a *used* capacity factor, whereas the capacity factor is a *total* capacity factor.

in turn, depends on the cost of the gas delivered compared with the cost of competitive fuels; the delivery cost of the gas is in turn affected by the charges made by the pipe-line operator.

In order to assure himself of sufficient gas, the pipe-line owner either enters into long-term contracts with producers of natural gas or leases or acquires title to gas fields himself. Often pipe-line promoters are owners of large gas properties. Thus contracts or integration of ownership assures delivery of gas to the pipe line.

The problem of an adequate market is more complex. The market varies with the ultimate use to which the gas is put. The sale of gas to individual householders for space-heating purposes is beset with difficulties of its own. Such sales come under public utility regulation, which requires that the needs of the public be met on demand. Unpredictable weather changes account for unpredictability of the load required to meet the demand; hence the seller must be prepared to meet exceptional peak demands. Moreover, the space-heating demand is highly seasonal. As a rule, the high rates chargeable for gas in this category make selling it an attractive proposition.

But it leaves the gas pipe-line operator with a poor load factor,[13] one in which there are many gaps, especially the deep one made by the summer months. In order to fill these gaps he seeks supplementary market outlets, particularly in industries which are willing to contract for interruptible service—i.e., grant him the right to interrupt service to them when the gas is needed for delivery to household consumers—and in industries whose peak demand for gas occurs in the summer, the slack season for the household demand.

Such industries are attracted by low rates. In his eagerness to acquire these supplementary industrial outlets, the gas pipe-line operator may be tempted to cut rates even below out-of-pocket expenses. In other words, he may be tempted to "dump" gas in order to maintain a satisfactory load factor.

To steer clear of such practices, the operator may resort to storage. In the Northeast, especially in Pennsylvania, Ohio, and New York, there are abandoned natural gas fields which can be used to store gas that is delivered during periods of slack demand and marketed during periods of peak demand. Furthermore, the sellers of natural gas may acquire local plants that produce manufactured gas and use them as stand-by facilities for periods of peak demand.

PROBLEMS OF PUBLIC CONTROL

The production and gathering of natural gas, like the production and interstate transportation of oil, is under the control of the states. On the whole, the problems involved are similar—avoidance of waste, protection of correlative rights, adjustment of supply to demand, etc.

The most striking difference in control develops from the fact that under the Natural Gas Act of 1938 the interstate transmission of natural gas is placed under the Federal Power Commission and is treated as a public utility function. The Commission issues certificates of necessity and convenience authorizing the construction of interstate natural gas pipe lines, and it regulates the rates charged for the interstate transmission of natural gas.

Section 6 of the Natural Gas Act of 1938 specifically exempts the production and gathering of natural gas from the control of the Federal Power Commission. These functions are left to the states. This exemption, however, applies only to gas produced by parties not identical or affiliated with those controlling the interstate pipe lines. Thus the gas must be sold "at arm's length"; the sale must be more than a mere bookkeeping entry on the books of buyer-seller subsidiaries belonging to the same ownership group. In other words, the production or gathering of gas by interstate pipe-line companies or their affiliates is subject to federal control. But, like all markets, the gas market constitutes an integral which cannot be neatly subdivided into compartments, some of which are free from federal control, others of which are subject to it. As a result, a serious controversy has arisen in connection with federal control over field prices of natural gas. On the one hand, it is claimed that without control over the gas produced by interstate pipe-line companies, the entire control exercised by the

---

[13] For a full discussion of the meaning of load factor as distinguished from capacity factor, see chap. 37, especially p. 604.

Federal Power Commission becomes illusory. On the other hand, it is argued that interference with the price of gas at the producing end is an unwarranted intrusion into the area of state control, an interference with private business prerogatives, and a danger to the conservation of oil and gas. In view of the close connection between gas and oil, it is not surprising to see the oil industry lined up with the gas industry in its opposition to federal control of field prices. In the spring of 1950 a bill was passed by Congress, the so-called Kerr Bill, which was intended to decide this issue in favor of the industry. However, President Truman's veto prevented its enactment.

In general, the Federal Power Commission seeks to protect the consumer's interests. If it interferes with prices, the chances are that it is trying to hold them down rather than to push them up. While, in general, such concern for the consumer is laudable, in the case of natural gas under certain circumstances more damage might be done by prices too low at the producing end than by prices too high at the consuming end. In the absence of government subsidies, it would seem axiomatic that a private profit-seeking business cannot afford to put into effect "conservation," i.e., waste-elimination measures which not only do not pay but on the contrary call for money to be paid out. If the field price for natural gas is so low that it does not pay to gather the gas, it will go to waste unless production can be stopped. Hence, every day billions of cubic feet of gas, especially casing-head gas, go to waste, are vented or flared because the price is too low to warrant gathering it. It is frequently argued that, at present, no measure can assure greater success in conservation than one resulting in a higher field price for natural gas, especially in the Southwest. At 2 cents per thousand cubic feet, natural gas will go to waste; at double the price, the same gas will sell easily in a profitable market. For that reason it is claimed that price-depressing actions on the part of the Federal Power Commission are, or at least can be, anticonservational. What the Commission is probing for, of course, is the price that will, on the one hand, protect the public against gouging by unscrupulous producer interests and, on the other hand, make possible an effective "conservation" program. But that price is hard to hit.

Another aspect of this problem of price interference deserves attention. Natural gas is a premium fuel, coal in the lump is an ordinary fuel. When the price of natural gas is unduly depressed gas will replace coal. In principle, a social loss occurs whenever a premium commodity displaces an inferior commodity in doing a task which the inferior commodity is capable of doing satisfactorily. In theory, in a free competitive market marginal utilities and marginal costs so interact that prices reflect the equilibrium at which all commodities perform the work for which they are best suited. Such ideal conditions may never exist, but the goal should not be lost sight of. Unduly depressing the price of natural gas is inimical to attaining this equilibrium.[14]

The people of the United States have reached a high level of material achievement partly because they have enjoyed relatively free trade within the national domain. There have been exceptions and anomalies that have marred the harmony of the national scene, but the fundamental fact stands virtually unimpaired. Our nation's strength derives from the strength of its parts, and the parts in turn derive strength from the whole. The argument that Texas gas should be reserved for a Texas chemical industry yet to be built, or any other Texas industry of the future, is a latter-day version of the old infant industry argument of the protectionists. It is a return to mercantilism and to a particularly primitive mercantilism at that. Any attempt on the part of one state or a group of states to reserve for local or regional use a national asset which inevitably is also a state and a regional asset is bound to bring down upon it a storm of protest and lead to retaliation which will play havoc with the very roots of this nation's strength.

In terms of geographical location, the water power of the Northwest is a regional asset; but the aluminum made with its aid helped to win the war. The same applies to steel made with the aid of the coal of Pennsylvania, West Virginia, Ohio, and so forth, and of the iron ore

---

[14] It must be recognized that, in so far as gas is produced as a by-product of oil and in so far as fortuitous discoveries play an important role in determining the rate of production, realities in the natural gas business depart widely from the assumptions of the marginal theorist.

of Minnesota and half a dozen other states. The know-how born in the industrial and academic laboratories of the nation is or should be freely at the disposal of all, not of the particular state or region in which the laboratories happen to be located. Provincialism is a menace to this nation, which has grown strong, in large part, because history saved it from this curse. We cannot afford to fight narrow nationalism in Europe and at the same time try to introduce a worse particularism into our own system.

USES OF NATURAL GAS

The clarification of the issues involved in the problem of public policy just discussed rests in part on a clear understanding of the present uses of natural gas and of those to which it may be put in the future as technological progress continues.

The outstanding feature of natural gas consumption is its concentration in (1) certain areas, (2) certain classes of industry, and (3) a relatively small number of individual industrial plants.

To a large degree, this pattern of consumption is the result of the geographical pattern of the pipe-line net which more or less governs the marketing of natural gas and exercises a powerful influence on both field and delivered prices. As the pipe-line network expands and changes, the marketing pattern and all its corollaries change with it.

At present, most natural gas is consumed in the states or regions where it is produced. In 1945 six states—Texas, Louisiana, California, Oklahoma, West Virginia, and Kansas—produced 87 percent of all the natural gas marketed in the United States. These same states consumed 68 percent of our total production, or a little under four-fifths of all the gas they produced. California consumed all the gas she produced; the other five supplied 60 percent of the gas "imported" by the rest of the nation.

Texas, which in 1945 produced 43.9 percent of the national output, consumed one-third of the national total. The other five states consumed another third, leaving the remaining third for the other 42 states. The Southwest consumed 58.2 percent, the Appalachian region 12.2, the Midwest 9.9, the Southeast 3.8, the Rocky Mountain area 3.0, and California 12.9. That this geographical pattern of consumption is undergoing material changes as the pipe-line net is being expanded goes without saying.

Distribution of Consumption by Uses

Table 35.2 shows the breakdown of United States natural gas consumption by major uses in 1945 and 1946.

TABLE 35.2. Natural Gas Consumption by Major Uses, 1945 and 1946[15]

Use	1945 (billion cubic feet)	1946	1945 (percent of total)	1946
Industrial				
Oil and gas field operations	917	960	23.5	23.6
Carbon black production	432	478	11.1	11.7
Petroleum refining	338	355	8.7	8.7
Electric public utilities	326	307	8.3	7.5
Cement plants	39	58	1.0	1.4
Other industrial	1010	1032	25.9	25.3
Total industrial	3062	3190	78.5	78.2
Domestic	608	650	15.6	16.0
Commercial	230	237	5.9	5.8
Total U. S. consumption	3900	4077	100.0	100.0

In 1946 no less than 44.0 percent of all marketed natural gas was used in oil and gas field operations, in carbon black production, and in petroleum refining. This simple fact goes far to explain the geographical concentration of gas consumption in the gas-producing states. About two-thirds of the marketed gas may be designated as "pipe-line gas." The greater part of this gas too is consumed relatively near the source. Interstate gas movements in 1945 amounted to only 28 percent of the total amount of gas marketed and to 43 percent of the pipe-line gas. Only negligible amounts were exported to Mexico and Canada —that is, negligible in terms of the total amount produced. In absolute figures the 18 billion cubic feet exported in 1945 look fairly respectable.

In 1945, 59 carbon black plants, 43 of which are located in Texas, used 432 billion cubic feet of natural gas.[16]

[15] Federal Power Commission, *op. cit.*, vol. 8, p. 96.

[16] Natural gas is the only major commercial source of carbon black, which results from the imperfect combustion of the gas. Texas law forbids the manufacture of carbon black from sweet gas (see p. 558); hence the bulk of the sour gas produced there is used for this purpose.

Carbon black is an indispensable ingredient of

The following trends in consumption are important:

1. Domestic and commercial consumption is declining. In 1920 domestic and commercial consumers used 286 out of a total of 798 cubic feet, or 36 percent. The corresponding figures for 1945 were 838 billion out of a total of 3900 billion, or 21.5 percent. So high are domestic rates compared with average rates that this 21.5 percent brought in half of the total revenues from all ultimate consumers.

2. Industrial consumption has increased correspondingly, from 64 percent of the total in 1920 to 78.5 percent in 1945. Field uses declined slightly. Carbon black users more than doubled their percentage share. Electric utilities increased their share from about 3 percent in 1920 to over 8 in 1945.

One use of natural gas which is of particular interest is its use in the chemical industry, especially for making synthetics. All natural gas can be manipulated chemically and made to yield products having an aggregate value far greater than that produced when gas is used as the fuel. But to extract this value requires investment and labor, and what such products will bring in the market depends on supply and demand. The conversion of natural gas into chemical end products, like all such conversion, is not merely a technical problem, but above all an economic one that centers around costs, prices, and profits.

As was shown above (see p. 557), natural gas differs in composition, but consists mainly of methane, ethane, propane, butane, and isobutane, and only to a minor extent of pentane and the heavier hydrocarbons. In addition it contains "inerts" such as carbon dioxide, nitrogen, and helium.

Natural gas can be made to yield, at reasonably low cost, certain relatively pure and chemically active hydrocarbon gases which are coming to have an increasing demand as raw materials—or, to use a technical term, feed stock—of chemical industries that make synthetics.[17] The organic synthetic industry in the United States is very young, hardly more than twenty years old; but it made great strides forward during World War II. Some of the synthetics now made from natural gas are entirely new substances; others are identical with substances previously made only from other feed stock. Both oil and natural gas companies are engaged in converting natural gases into synthetic.

During and right after World War I there was a great upsurge of chemical developments in this country based on coal-tar derivatives. After 1933 there was a similar advance based on noncoal-tar synthetic organic chemicals. Production increased from 1 million tons in 1936, valued at $100 million, to 6 million tons in 1945, valued at $650 million. This is exclusive of synthetic rubber, synthetic ammonia, and other wartime products. Indications suggest that in a few years the noncoal-tar organic industry will surpass its older sister, the coal-tar derivative industry. It may soon double the total value of our prewar chemical manufactures. In the offing are synthetic resins, plastics, fibers, solvents, insecticides, refrigerants, pharmaceuticals, paints, protective coatings, detergents and cleaning compounds, antifreeze, alcohols, synthetic ammonia, nitrates, fertilizer, rubber, and special components of motor and aviation gasoline—all from natural gas. Hundreds of compounds are already being produced, and the surface has hardly been scratched.

The raw materials needed for these ambitious, almost fantastic, programs may be considered by-products of methane, the chief constituent of natural gas. The programs rest on the fundamental fact that the value of these by-products—ethane, propane, butane, and isobutane—as feed stocks exceeds their fuel value by a wide margin. In the aggregate these by-products constitute only a fraction of the total volume of natural gas, less than 10 percent on the average. A million cubic feet of untreated natural gas typically yields about 82,000 cubic feet of hydrocarbon concentrates which are excellent feed stock for the chemical industry.

the tires without which our economy could not function properly in either war or peace. A standard 6.00 x 16 four-ply automobile tire requires a maximum of 5 pounds of carbon black if it is made of synthetic rubber, and 3.5 pounds if made of natural rubber.

[17] This word as here used includes all substances made by the artificial recombining of atoms. Organic synthetics are synthetics that contain carbon.

The heat value of the remaining residue gas is reduced only slightly, from 1136 B.T.U. per cubic foot to 1031 B.T.U.

The time is approaching when even dry gas —methane with some ethane—will be used as a raw material of the chemical industry. Already a plant is being built in which dry gas is used in the synthesis of gasoline by the modified Fischer-Tropsch process (see p. 492). This process will yield Diesel oil and alcohols along with the synthetic gasoline. Other chemists have even more ambitious plans for methane.

BIBLIOGRAPHY

A Study of the Natural Gas Industry, New York, Empire Trust Company, 1949.

Blackley, F. F., and Oatman, M. S., Natural Gas and the Public Interest, Washington, Granite Press, 1947.

"Bottled Gas," Fortune, March, 1948.

Federal Power Commission, Natural Gas Investigation, Washington, 1948.

"L.P.G., the Gas That Flows from Bottles," The Lamp, June, 1947.

Shuman, R. B., The Petroleum Industry, Norman, University of Oklahoma Press, 1940. (The last part of this volume is devoted to the natural gas industry).

U. S. Department of Interior, Bureau of Mines, Minerals Yearbook, chapter on natural gas (annual).

Chapter 36

THE NEW ERA OF WATER POWER

Next to the increasing importance of hydrocarbons as sources of energy, the rise of electricity is the most characteristic feature of the so-called second industrial revolution. One of the most valuable by-products of the development of the electrical industry is the new significance given to water power. Modern use of water power involves the water turbine, the dynamo, and the transmission system. These inventions of the nineteenth century have emancipated water power from the limitations of the old wooden water wheel and made possible the exploitation of such gigantic forces as Niagara Falls and the construction of such man-made wonders as the Grand Coulee Dam.

NATURE OF WATER POWER

An excellent treatise[1] on the energy resources of the United States refers to coal as the basis of our national welfare, to petroleum as the accelerator of progress, to natural gas as nature's bonus to America, and to water power as an unused annuity. These epithets strikingly characterize the four most widely used sources of mechanical energy. The characterization of coal brings out the relative longevity of its reserves and the fundamental significance which attaches to this all-important fossil fuel. The term applied to petroleum rightly emphasizes the fact that this liquid fuel can supplement but not supplant coal. In supplementing, it tends to accelerate the progress of economic development, in so far as that progress is based upon energy expenditure. The characterization of natural gas—nature's bonus to this country—requires no comment. In assaying the descriptive term applied to water power—an unused annuity—it is well to keep in mind that the expression was coined in 1920, and that a remarkable development has been going on since that time—at least the use of water power has begun in this country and in Europe.

As was pointed out before, the major defect of inanimate energy is the exhaustibility of the minerals from which it is drawn. From the standpoint of permanence, water power is the most desirable form of energy. Since water power is a function of solar radiation and

[1] C. G. Gilbert and J. E. Pogue, *America's Power Resources, the Economic Significance of Coal, Oil, and Water Power,* D. Appleton-Century Company, New York, 1921.

topography—two factors which, for the purpose of economic analysis, may be considered permanent—this source of energy is a "flow resource." In so far as the gravitational energy of which the flowing water is the carrier can be made available only through the work of man, such as dams, turbines, transmission systems, transformers, etc., the perishability of these structures to some extent communicates itself to water power. However, their rate of physical depreciation and obsolescence is fairly slow and they can be replaced; but coal, petroleum, and natural gas, when burned, are irretrievably lost.

It may be true that the benefits of permanence can be bought at too high a price. If a fuel power plant can deliver power at a price materially lower than that at which hydroelectricity can be sold, few people will want to burden the living generation with excessive charges in the hope of bestowing on posterity a blessing of doubtful value in the form of larger fuel reserves. By and large, hydroelectricity must compete with other forms of inanimate energy on the basis not of relative permanence but of current cost. That that cost is in turn affected by the permanent availability of water goes without saying.

INCREASED IMPORTANCE OF WATER POWER
Water-Power History

So rapid has been the technological progress in fuel electricity plants that for years observers have been proclaiming the obsolescence of hydroelectric plants. But they did not reckon with several important phases of the power situation, phases which have given water power a new lease on life.

Once before it looked as if water power were on the way out. The steam engine and later the steam turbine and other fuel-using prime movers were sweeping away the old-fashioned water wheels by which since time immemorial the operators of small mills (grist mills, sawmills, ore crushers, etc.) had harnessed the power of small streams, confining themselves to very modest "heads," as the drop or fall of the water is called. At this point, electricity rescued water power from oblivion. When, as the result of many inventions in diverse parts of the West, it became possible to harness the power of a Niagara Falls and similar masses of

falling water, to convert it into electricity, and to send it hundreds of miles overland, water power staged a remarkable comeback. This was during the first three decades following the opening of Edison's electric power plant in Manhattan in 1882, the first in the world.

Then fuel power plants started to gain on their hydroelectric rivals and talk of the obsolescence of water power was heard. One reason for this gain was that water wheels and water turbines and other basic hydroelectric installations had reached such a high state of technical perfection that little improvement was possible. This, however, applied less to transmission and distribution facilities. The extent to which fuel plants were gaining on hydro plants was manifest in the decreasing amount of fuel required to generate a kilowatt-hour (see footnote, p. 483). In the early stages of steam-power plants it took over 10 pounds of coal or its equivalent in oil or gas to generate a kilowatt-hour. By 1899 that figure had dropped to 7.05 pounds per kilowatt-hour so far as central power stations were concerned. A half century later it was down to less than 1.3 pounds. Such fuel savings indicate keen competition for water-power plants. In a widely publicized speech at the opening of a steam-power plant in California, one of the leading water-power states of the Union, Edison himself dwelt upon this increased competition and fiercely attacked the popular misconception of "cheap" if not "free" water power, singing the praises of the rapidly improving fuel plant.[2] It was then that many water-power sites which had long been considered promising were struck from the list of economically feasible projects, and water power seemed condemned to stagnation, if not for the limbo.

The Myth of "Free" Water

Lest there be any misunderstanding, let it be stated here that of course Edison was right in ridiculing the popular idea that just because water falls from heaven, therefore water power is free. The same creative power that made the winds and the clouds, the brooks and the rivers,

---

[2] Mr. Edison's speech was reproduced in a propaganda leaflet that was widely distributed by the National Electric Light Association, the predecessor of the Edison Electric Institute.

also made coal and oil and natural gas. All the natural endowment of our planet is free in one sense; precious little is wholly free in another. The idea of free water power would hardly occur to a generation that has had to foot large bills for hydroelectric developments—for dams, reservoirs, turbogenerators, transmission systems, and all the various paraphernalia through which alone the nature-given force of rushing or falling water can be rendered articulate. But those who impatiently declared water power to be obsolete were likewise thoroughly mistaken. They failed to consider certain elementary aspects of the energy situation and could not anticipate the revolutionary change in man's attitudes toward water power which was in the offing.

Regional Aspects of Water Power

An elementary aspect of the energy situation overlooked by the eager mourners is the fact that the world energy pattern is not a simple uniform pattern but one that resembles a crazy quilt. Each region has its own peculiar advantages and disadvantages. Hence, global generalizations as to the respective merits of water and fuel power have little meaning. Each area must be examined by and for itself. As was pointed out in a preceding chapter, coal, the main source of fuel power, cannot ordinarily be economically hauled overland for more than a few hundred miles; and even ocean hauls, though considerably cheaper than land transportation, cannot escape the law of diminishing returns.

It follows that the feasibility of developing water power in competition with fuel power depends largely on the distance of a given water-power site from the nearest source of fuel and the resultant cost of fuel in the area in which hydroelectricity is to be sold. It is true that, by and large, the great world centers of industry in the past have developed around coal fields and that some of the greatest water-power sites are located in thinly populated regions. But it is also true that as the world population grows, the urge to spill over from the densely populated older industrial centers into the blank spaces on the map increases, provided ways can be found to render these areas productive. In this connection, it is worth while noticing that many younger industries—

especially those making light metals, alloys, chemicals—can emancipate themselves from the hold that coal has long had on manufacturing industries and strike out for themselves in the newer fields of hydroelectric power. Power markets are no longer as firmly bound to certain areas as they once seemed to be. For certain industries the offer of cheap power is a surprisingly strong drawing card.

Lengthening Transmission Lines

But not all industries are so foot-loose or mobile. Above all, the great urban centers are stationary load centers. Power must come to them. Whether or not electricity generated at a given water-power site can reach such a market depends largely on transmission. At the present time, the longest transmission of electricity in the United States is from Hoover Dam (formerly known as Boulder Dam) on the Colorado River to Los Angeles, California, a distance of close to 300 miles. The power is transmitted at a "pressure" of 285,000 volts. During World War II, German experts were playing with the idea of transmitting hydro-electricity from Norway to Germany by cable at 500,000 volts. Experiments with 550,000 volts are now under way in the United States.[3] If one figures roughly on 1000 volts for every mile of transmission, 300,000 volts permit 300 miles of transmission; 500,000 volts, 500 miles. A circle with a radius of 300 miles has an area of about 430,000 square miles, or more than one-seventh of this country's total area. A circle with a 500-mile radius includes about 1,200,000 square miles, or considerably over one-third of the total area. It does not take too much imagination to appreciate the effect of longer, economical transmission lines on the marketability of hydroelectricity, and of all electricity for that matter. Cities that were formerly beyond the reach of a certain power plant might suddenly find themselves drawn into its orbit. Increasingly these market circles would overlap, and interregional competition of distant and diverse power sources would increase, promising rich rewards for those winning the technological improvement race and penalizing the laggards. The possibilities of such developments stagger the imagination.

---

[3] See *Business Week,* January 5, 1946, pp. 48 ff.

Increasing Fuel Costs

Another factor which has saved water power from limbo is the rising cost of fuel. It is true that the most efficient power plants can now generate a kilowatt-hour of electricity from less than a pound of coal. But it is also true that the cost of a pound of coal today is a multiple of what it was before union pressure and other forces raised miners' wages and other cost items to dizzy heights. From 1937 to 1947, power plants of public utility companies in the United States cut their fuel consumption from 1.42 pounds of coal (or the equivalent of other fuels) to 1.31 pounds, but the cost of fuel per kilowatt-hour generated rose from 23 to 37 cents, or almost 60 percent. The fuel bill rose from $164 million in 1937 (it dropped to $147 million in 1938) to $601 million in 1947.[4] Of course, this does not mean that water power is immune to cost increases; for it, too, is afflicted with higher costs. But the point here is that the particular technological advancement whereby fuel electricity was to give hydroelectricity the coup de grâce is not proving quite so powerful because its force has been blunted by the rising cost of fuel which overcompensates the savings.

In this connection, one must keep in mind that, temporarily at least, the rapidly increasing use of natural gas, described in the preceding chapter, is injecting a new factor into the competitive struggle between diverse sources of energy and may offset here and there the benefits that otherwise might accrue to hydroelectricity as a result of the rising prices of coal and oil.

THE FEDERAL GOVERNMENT AND WATER RESOURCES

The New Deal and the New Asset Consciousness

But the most powerful blow struck in defense of water power has come from another corner, not from technology, not from changing costs, but from changes in human attitudes, attitudes which imperceptibly emerge from the womb of social philosophy and take on tangible form in rewritten and reinterpreted laws and in revised public policies. In the United States these new attitudes with their tangible aftermath are largely identified with the New Deal. But that is not quite accurate. The roots of the new movement, the origin of the new way of viewing our natural and national endowment of basic assets, reach further back in time, to the conservationists of Theodore Roosevelt's day. One of the greatest of the new hydroelectric enterprises—the Boulder Canyon Project, the keystone of which is the Hoover Dam—was started under President Hoover, years before the phrase "the New Deal" was coined.

The crux of the new philosophy is the realization that, in the long run, the magnificent achievements made under private capitalistic enterprise are endangered by inadequate regard for the durable basic assets, natural and cultural, on which all economic life depends, and for the conditions, forces, and processes of nature which underlie all human endeavor. So-called laws of short-range profit-seeking market economics come into progressively serious conflicts with the laws of nature. A young continent can stand a great deal of punishment from men unaware of the mysteries of ecology. But inevitably the time comes when man must take account of the situation, call a halt to his destructive folly, and make his peace with nature. Few people not ideologically warped in their judgment will seriously question the glorious achievements of the free enterprise system which have helped to make the United States the richest, freest, most powerful country in the world. But one would have to be blind not to see the terrific cost in impaired basic assets—eroded soil, polluted rivers, gutted forests, overgrazed ranges, and, last but not least, blighted or frustrated humanity—at which this progress was bought.[5]

The natural basis of economic enterprise is the earth, meaning chiefly the soil, minerals, and water. Upon that basis man erects his handiwork, "culture" viewed as the sum total of human change wrought in nature; to it he applies his skills and energies. So rapid is the advance of cultural improvement and so slow

---

[4] Edison Electric Institute, *Statistical Bulletin No. 15* (covers 1947).

[5] This theme is eloquently developed in Fairfield Osborn's *Our Plundered Planet*, Little, Brown and Company, Boston, 1948, and in William Vogt's *Road to Survival*, William Sloane Associates, New York, 1948. For a discussion of these books see chap. 50.

is the rate of deterioration of this natural basis that for long periods of time it seems as if cultural progress may be overcompensating the impairment of the basic natural assets. The general impression is one of real progress when in reality the very ground on which man's civilization rests may be slipping. No technical achievement made so far warrants the belief that man through techniques and science can emancipate himself from his dependence on the earth as the source of food, raw materials, and fuels.

The collapse of the boom in 1929 and the Great Depression that followed shook people's faith to its foundations—faith in the bonanza of untrammeled private enterprise and undiluted laissez faire. A reaction was inevitable. The pendulum had to swing back. Men searched for the deeper meaning of economics and inevitably came face to face with ecology. Those who had long been market-conscious at last became resource-conscious.

Water a Keystone of the Resources Structure

In the ecological scheme of things water plays a vital part. If properly cared for, water is the bringer of life; if neglected, it can be the cause of disaster. And it has been neglected by the market-conscious leaders of our economy. Every year water-induced erosion ruins large amounts of topsoil. Every year floods destroy vast property values and take an intolerable toll of human life. Rivers are polluted with the sewage of a thousand cities. Wild life is suffering. Human health is endangered. Rivers are silting up and blocking navigation.

Here was a vast field in which governments—local, state, and federal—could perform prodigious feats without stepping on the toes of private business.[6] If government had not done

---

[6] As far back as 1926, Owen D. Young, Chairman of the Board of the General Electric Company, said before the convention of the National Electric Light Association: "There is a class of water powers which, in my judgment, must be separately considered. No suggestion has yet been made which adequately meets these needs. When vast rivers either on international boundaries or within the United States require development for general purposes, such as navigation, irrigation and flood control, as well as for power, there arises *a new kind of question which is wholly unrelated to the old controversy of government versus private ownership.*" (Italics mine.)

this long before, it was due partly to incomplete realization on the part of both experts and laymen of this vital necessity, partly to the failure of penny-wise and pound-foolish Congressmen to appropriate the necessary funds. But now all this changed. Business was unable —in the Depression—to take care of the livelihood of large portions of the population. The government had to step in. Here was the golden opportunity to make up for decades, perhaps a century, of neglect. Many of the "alphabet agencies" such as CCC and PWA helped to tackle the new task of saving and improving our basic assets, especially soil and water.

River System Control

For a long time the federal government, mainly through the Corps of Army Engineers, had been responsible for flood control in certain major river areas. But it was a long time before it was fully realized that the proper way to regulate and control water is by managing entire river systems. Much bitter experience and costly failures finally made it clear beyond doubt that building levees along the lower Mississippi was useless unless supported by carefully coördinated water control along the upper Mississippi, especially the headwaters. A river system is an indivisible whole, an integral. At last this elementary truth, which should never have been ignored, was universally accepted. Then it was realized that if the Mississippi floods were ever to be brought under control, its tributaries, like the Missouri and the Ohio, and the tributaries of the tributaries all the way back to the brooks and rills, would have to be brought under control. It was then that the Army Engineers Corps directed their attention to the Tennessee River, a tributary of the Ohio, and to the Clinch and the Holston, the French Broad and the Hiwassee and other tributaries of the Tennessee.

Realization of the integrity of a river system was only the first step. The inseparability of the river system from its watershed environment was equally important. The behavior of the water is not merely a function of rainfall—its intensity, character, seasonal distribution, etc. —and topography; it is vitally affected by the nature of the land surface. Rainfall soaks into forest soil and into fields well covered with vegetation, but it runs off freely from barren rock and naked hard-baked fields, especially in the channels prepared for it between rows of tobacco and cotton plants. The control of water does not stop at the river bank; it takes in the entire landscape and every activity that depends on and in turn affects that landscape—agriculture, forestry, grazing, etc. Thus water became a strategic key to full-fledged all-out river-valley watershed planning, i.e., planning for proper control of the water and all the other basic assets which affect its behavior.

The control of a river system requires many measures. There are different schools of thought on the subject of proper control. Some stress the vital need of proper care of the earth cover of the watershed area. Others emphasize the vital part played by dams in controlling river flow, avoiding floods, supplying irrigation water, improving navigation channels, etc. There are other schools, but these are the leading ones. As experience accumulates, it appears that all of them are right; all of these factors must be considered, though the relative importance of each varies with the area in question. In the upper Mississippi valley soil treatment to reduce run-off and afforestation in the headwater areas are probably far more efficient than they are in the lower valley. In the latter, on the other hand, flood control measures take precedence.[7] These two types of measures in the two segments of this river system of course supplement each other and must be coördinated.

A corollary of integrated watershed control is the multiple-purpose dam. Dams built by private power companies generally serve but one purpose, the generation of power. Only in rare exceptions is attention given to flood control and navigation—general welfare factors usually beyond the scope of ordinary business enterprise.[8] Probably in no case have the implications for wildlife been considered. Now when the government—the federal government when navigable streams were involved—built dams as part of a coördinated watershed control plan, it could not afford to concentrate on the clearly lucrative objective—the generation of electric power; it had to make every effort to accomplish as many purposes as possible, to construct dams so that they would meet as many exigencies as possible.

At first some people believed that the so-called multiple-purpose dam was a logical monstrosity, that flood control called for empty reservoirs ready to welcome the masses of flood water, whereas the generation of power required full reservoirs to furnish the necessary head. Similar arguments were advanced for the incompatibility of the various purposes of dams, such as providing a uniform depth in navigation channels. Some even went so far as to condemn all power generation at river dams, arguing that man should content himself with utilizing waterfalls, such as Niagara, provided by benevolent nature.

While perhaps the evidence is as yet insufficient, the experience with multiple-purpose dams, especially under the Tennessee Valley Authority, points toward their soundness provided they are fitted into a comprehensive scheme and are operated with skill and intelligence. Here are some of the reasons why the idea is gaining wider acceptance. In most watersheds, in fact almost everywhere, floods are seasonal phenomena. In the Tennessee River system they occur mainly from December to March. During the dry season the generation of water power lowers the level in the reservoirs so that they are ready to receive the flood water. The winter months in which heavy rains and snowfalls fill up the reservoirs are at the same time the period of peak demand for electricity.[9] The flood waters which are allowed to run down the spillways are not lost as sources of electric energy; they perform manifold duties as they reach the various dams downstream.

There was a time when water-power plants required a uniform head, but this is no longer true. The Kaplan adjustable water turbine has effectively solved the problem of varying heads.

---

[7] This difference in the work to be done is reflected in the fact that, whereas the Bureau of Reclamation is most active in the upper reaches of the Mississippi River system, in the lower the Army Engineers Corps has the initiative; the Engineers Corps has long been connected with flood control.

[8] For an account of a multiple-purpose development by a private power company, see *Reader's Digest*, April, 1950, p. 73.

[9] In regions where floods are caused by the melting of snow or glaciers in the summertime, as is the case in parts of the Pacific slope, a similar balance between supply of and demand for water may be struck where summer irrigation needs are considerable.

By means of floodgates which are raised above the level of the dam, enormous extra space for unusual flood waters can be provided at relatively little expense.[10]

It stands to reason that a multiple-purpose dam will not generate as much electricity as will a similar system of dams built exclusively for that purpose. But the Tennessee River system, where flood control and navigation are put far ahead of power generation, has shown definitely that remarkable contributions to the supply of electric energy can still be made. In 1947, the TVA, with a total installed capacity of 2,538,902 kilowatts (of which only 8 percent was steam and auxiliary power), generated 14,111,300,000 kilowatt-hours of electricity, about 4.7 percent of the nation's total output.

Government Control of Electric Power

Thus the government entered the field of electric power generation on a vast scale. That this step, which was merely incidental in a far vaster scheme of watershed control and regional resources development, was fought savagely by private utilities goes without saying. During its first years the TVA was engaged in a continuous struggle in the courts, the lower courts generally siding with the private power companies, and the Supreme Court with the government. The crux of the issue was whether society could afford to forego the enormous by-product benefits of vast amounts of electric energy that were generated in connection with the performance of legitimate government functions, simply because certain conflicts with private business interests were inevitable.

The struggle was sharpened by a number of circumstances associated with the economic and political atmosphere of the period—the early years of the New Deal and the Roosevelt administration, and the Great Depression. It was a time when, because of the business depression, demand for electricity was at a low point. At the same time the Federal Trade Commission was carrying on its investigation of the power industry (resulting in a monumental report of 84 volumes). This, in turn, led to strong legislative measures designed to stop the abuses

revealed in the report. Particularly prominent in this reform movement were the Public Utilities Act of 1935, Title One of which is the Holding Company Act containing the notorious death-sentence clause, and the act establishing the Securities and Exchange Commission. Feelings ran high. The cry of "economic royalists" was heard and "the Morgan sit-down strike" was one of the answers. It was not the ideal climate in which to begin a social experiment of unprecedented boldness.

Power Rates and the TVA

In particular the problem of rates charged for electric power generated much heat. Under regulation by state public service commissions, private power companies had been able, by and large, to do just about as they pleased. The laws governing the valuation of properties, on which the whole structure of rate regulation was based,[11] were extremely lax; the investor was usually favored, the consumer seldom. Now the Federal Power Commission was entrusted with the task of probing into the valuation of all power companies engaged in interstate commerce.

What perhaps caused as much bad blood as anything else done under the New Deal was the promotion of the yardstick idea. As we have seen, TVA was generating electricity incidental to its other functions of flood control, navigation, recreation, etc. The dam that served one purpose served all. This raised the question of cost allocation. There is no cost accountant living who can determine with accuracy what portion of the total cost should be allocated to flood control, what to navigation, and what to power. Even if it were possible to establish these costs for a given moment, they would change overnight. Therefore no one can say with assurance and accuracy how much the hydroelectricity generated by the TVA actually costs. Besides this question of costs, there were various controversial issues such as the adequacy of "in-lieu-of-tax payments" made by the TVA. Under the circumstances, it is thoroughly understandable that private power companies objected—violently—to the idea of having TVA

---

[10] In this connection, it should be noted that the storage capacity of the top layers of a reservoir is far larger than that of the bottom layers. Reservoirs taper toward the bottom.

[11] Under that system not the rates themselves but the return on investments was subject to control. Almost anything was allowed that could possibly account for swelling investment values.

power costs held up to them as a yardstick. They felt, and probably rightly so, that the yardstick idea had a punitive element to which they had every reason to object. Certainly not all the companies had been guilty of the abuses which the Federal Trade Commission brought to light. There were "good" power companies as surely as there were bad ones. And the yardstick idea did not differentiate between the sheep and the goats.

But there is more to the question of power rates than fussing over cost allocations. A fundamental philosophy of pricing is involved which cannot be brushed aside. Those responsible for TVA felt, or rather concluded from the evidence before them, that the private power industry was caught in a vicious circle of high rates, low consumption, and high costs. Private companies, in general, tend to be timid about reducing rates, knowing that once this has been done, perhaps experimentally, it is politically impossible to raise them again, for regulating commissions would not dare to face the uproar of public indignation. Some companies did experiment with "objective rates" and "promotional rates." But, with rare exceptions, they refused to "gamble" on the stimulating effect of low rates on use. TVA, on the other hand, perhaps influenced by Ford's magnificent success with his low-priced mass-produced mass-consumed car and impressed by the fact that electric power is one of the great blessings of mankind, struck out boldly with rates so low that consumption responded almost immediately. And just as surely as mass consumption of Ford cars made possible their mass production, and just as surely as mass production lowered unit cost and price and thus stimulated mass consumption, so that fortunate nexus between larger use, larger output, and low unit cost is equally operative in the case of electricity. The responsiveness of demand to lowered rates was skillfully prodded by energetic sales campaigns offering appliances at reduced prices.

Low rates for electricity attract industries, electrical machinery raises the productivity of labor, this in turn raises incomes and the standard of living, and this again calls for the use of more electricity. Similarly on the farm, the liberal use of electricity renders labor more productive and sets in motion a spiral of forces which raises the whole level of the economy.

A successful farmer takes care of his farm—he stops erosion, which in turn reduces run-off, which eases the task of flood control.

Thus TVA initiated what may be called an A-to-Z approach to the problem of regional development. Whether the success of the experiment had anything to do with the fact that private utilities later entered the rural areas with as much gusto as they had previously shunned them is a moot question. In recent years the private power industry has added millions of farmers to its lists of customers and has not lost money in doing so. The enormous improvement in the American farmer's economic status that resulted from the fantastically high prices for agricultural products undoubtedly had much to do with opening up rural America as a profitable field for the sale of electricity.

When the Roosevelt administration pushed the development of publicly controlled hydroelectricity in different sections of the country, first in the Tennessee Valley—the Hoover Dam had been started under the Republican administration—then in the Northwest (especially Bonneville and Grand Coulee), the Mississippi valley, California, and elsewhere, there went up a hue and cry against the "insane" enlargement of the nation's power supply beyond reasonable limits and the generation of power in parts of the country that seemed to offer no possible power market even in the future. The government was accused of the reckless spending of public funds. The administration, however, apparently took the position that there cannot be an oversupply of as vital a commodity as electrical energy, there can only be underconsumption. And sufficient rate inducements can create the demand.

Post-World War II Developments

Unfortunately, this question has never been really settled. For before normal conditions could prove one side right, World War II abolished normalcy and created a power demand which came close to being too much for government and private business working together in pushing power development to the utmost. The output of electricity increased from 161.3 billion kilowatt-hours in 1939 to 279.8 billion in 1944, or over 73 percent; and installed capacity was expanded from 49.4 to 62.1 million kilowatts, almost 28 percent. Facilities were expanded to the limits set by the availability of steel, copper, labor, and so on down the line of vital elements of the "military potential," but 28 percent was the best that could be done. Because of the coal shortage, water power was given preference. So, for once, TVA and other government projects were treated regally by an otherwise purse-tight Congress. Existing dams were rushed to completion, new ones started; generators were hurried to the installation sites and every kilowatt-hour that could be squeezed out was enlisted in the war effort. Without the power from the TVA and from Bonneville and Grand Coulee, it is doubtful whether the country could have attained an output of aluminum anything like the 2,000,000,000 pounds plus which were actually produced. But to do this it was necessary to push the output of electricity as never before. A 28 percent increase in generating capacity yielded a 73 percent increase in kilowatt-hours produced—there is the story in a nutshell! All production records were broken and reserve capacity dwindled to the vanishing point. Capacity and load factors climbed to dizzy heights, overhead costs fell apace.

In 1945 there was a slight letup in power consumption, about 8 billion kilowatt-hours, and the industry and the country were inclined to rest on their oars. But not for long. The miraculous postwar expansion of our economy soon called for more electric power than had been used even at the height of the war effort. The production figure passed the 300-billion mark in 1947. Was the low-rate policy paying? Did electrification of homes and farms know no bounds? Did electricity find new converts among industries?

One upshot of this postwar miracle is the greatest program of expansion that the private power industry of the United States has ever witnessed. This program which got under way during the second half of 1947 entailed the expenditure of approximately $6 billion. As a result of it, capacity was increased by 15 million kilowatts by the "business-managed" companies alone.[12] It is estimated that between August, 1945 (V.J. Day), and 1951—less than six and a half years—private power companies

---

[12] The figure for 1948 expansion exceeded by 0.8 million, or over 20 percent, the record for annual capacity expansion, 3.8 million in 1924.

will have put to work 18.5 million kilowatts and various government agencies an additional 4.5 million kilowatts, a total of 23 million kilowatts. The total installed capacity in 1945 was 62.9 kilowatts; hence the increase amounts to no less than 36.5 percent and probably exceeds the total capacity installed up to and including 1925.

Since a large portion of the newly installed capacity is and will be fuel power, it is possible that in spite of the remarkable comeback of water power rendered feasible by the publicly owned multiple-purpose dam, water power will lose some of its percentage share of the total power capacity.

To no small degree, power developments in the United States and elsewhere will depend on the political situation. Power is one of the main factors of our military potential. To be sure, no factor can be viewed by itself, apart from such other vital factors as steel, coal, oil, man power, etc. Economic expansion has become far more than mere economics. Never before in history has a depression in the United States been freighted with more dire calamity than in the present world situation. The West stands or falls with a strong or weak United States economy.

WORLD WATER POWER—DEVELOPED AND POTENTIAL

So far, the discussion has been confined to the United States. What about the rest of the world? Unfortunately information is far from adequate. The U.S. Geological Survey estimated that by the end of 1947 the total capacity of installed water-power plants in the world was 88.4 million horsepower, equivalent to about 64.8 million kilowatts. Of this, somewhat more than 18 million kilowatts are installed in the United States, leaving the rest of the world approximately 46.8 million. This country has probably a little more than 6 percent of the world population and a little over 28 percent of the installed water power of the world—in other words, a per capita water-power capacity about five times the world average.

But a world average does not mean much. Water power, both developed and potential, is very unevenly divided among the nations of the world. Some have none, others are richly blessed. Some have pushed the development

TABLE 36.1. Countries with One Million Horsepower or Over of Water Power Installed in 1947[13]

Country	Developed Water Power (million horsepower)	Area (thousand sq. miles)	Horsepower per Square Mile	Population, 1947 (in millions)	Horsepower per Capita	Output of Coal (million metric tons)	Output of Oil (million metric tons)
1. United States	24.2	3022.4	8.1	144.0	0.17	613.4	251.0
2. Canada	10.5	3694.9	2.8	12.6	0.83	13.0	1.7
3. Japan	8.6	147.9	57.3	78.0	0.11	27.0	0.2
4. Italy	6.3	119.7	52.5	45.9	0.14	1.3	...
5. France	6.1	212.7	29.1	41.0	0.15	44.5	...
6. Sweden	3.8	173.1	22.4	6.8	0.56	...	...
7. Norway	3.8	125.0	30.4	3.1	1.23	0.3	...
8. Switzerland	3.7	15.9	232.8	4.5	0.82	...	...
9. Germany	2.6	137.7	16.1	65.9[a]	0.04	85.8[c]	0.6
10. Soviet Union	2.2	8365.2	0.26	190.0[b]	0.01	[d]	[d]
11. Austria	2.0	32.4	61.8	6.9	0.29	0.1	...
12. Spain	2.0	190.8	10.5	27.5	0.07	10.6	...
13. Korea	1.8	85.2	21.1	27.2[a]	0.06	...	...
14. Brazil	1.5	3285.3	0.46	47.6	0.03	2.1	...

[a] 1946.
[b] Rough estimate.
[c] Exclusive of lignite.
[d] No data available.

of their resources to the utmost, others have not even touched theirs. The United States is unique in that she is by far the largest producer and consumer of coal, oil, and natural gas and *at the same time* one of the largest producers of water power. If all the power, heat, and light generated from both fuels and water power is taken into consideration, no matter whether it is used for lighting, manufacture, or locomotion, our use of water power is almost negligible—perhaps not more than 3 or 4 percent. But when the generation of electricity alone is considered, water power looms much larger—in fact, it accounts for between 30 and 40 percent of the total electricity generated in this country.

Geographical Distribution of Developed Water Power

The generation and distribution of hydroelectricity are symptomatic of an advanced stage of industrialization and for that reason are confined to areas of the earth which are themselves industrially advanced or in which industrially advanced countries are interested for political or economic reasons. In 1947 there were fourteen countries that had more than 1 million horsepower of installed hydroelectric capacity. They had an installed hydroelectric capacity of 79.1 million horsepower, or over 90 percent of the world total of 86.9 million. Eight of these countries, not counting the Soviet Union, are in Europe; three in the western hemisphere; two in Asia. The fourteenth, the Soviet Union, extends over parts of both Europe and Asia.

Table 36.1 lists these fourteen countries and their installed hydroelectric capacity, and also contains pertinent information which will help the reader to appraise intelligently the bare facts of the geographical distribution of hydroelectricity. The table throws light on factors, such as fuel production and the stage of industrialization, which aid in explaining the extent of hydroelectric development. Moreover, by giving figures showing hydroelectric horsepower per square mile and per capita it places the absolute figures in their proper perspective. These data are helpful in analyzing why countries vary widely in the extent or intensity of hydroelectric development. In using them it is well to remember that in 1947 the damage done to hydroelectric installations during World War II, especially in Germany and European Russia, had not yet been repaired.

Evidently hydroelectric development is most

---

[13] Figures on areas, from Goode's *School Atlas*, 1946 ed.; figures on population and on the output of coal and oil from *United Nations Monthly Bulletin of Statistics*, June, 1948.

advanced in countries like Norway and Switzerland which (1) lack coal and oil deposits of their own and therefore buy imported fuel, generally at fairly high prices; (2) are blessed with natural conditions—topography, rainfall, etc.—favorable to water-power development; (3) are industrially advanced, and consequently (4) have a high per capita income. France, which is rather poor in coal deposits and has no oil to speak of, has strongly favored hydroelectric development, especially in the *massif central*, the mountainous area in the south central region. In Germany, Italy, and Japan, large hydroelectric developments were pushed as part of the preparation for war. The importance of light metals and of electrochemical and electrometallurgical products in modern warfare greatly favored such a policy. Japan's influence extended also to Korea.

The United States, Canada, the Soviet Union, and Brazil are in a class by themselves. They are countries of continental expanse and hence emphasis must be put on regional aspects. Hydroelectric development in Brazil is virtually confined to the area in which are located the large cities of Rio de Janeiro, São Paulo, and Santos. Development in most of the rest of the country is way behind. In the Soviet Union also development is as yet very spotty and, as is true of Brazil and Canada, only a portion of the country is economically developed. The United States is the only country of continental expanse that is fully developed, in which the ecumene coincides with the total area. Here regional contrasts, such as the one between the fuel-rich East and the fuel-poor Northwest, are the key to understanding the present rate of hydroelectric development.

This analysis of the factors which help to explain the geographical distribution of water-power development would be incomplete without strong emphasis on policy as a highly significant factor. The effect of the New Deal policies on hydroelectric development in the United States has been fully discussed. Whether or not foreign capital will venture into Latin-American water-power development is mainly a question of policies—policies of both the lending and the borrowing countries. Britain's recently adopted policy toward Africa as a raw-material reservoir of the Empire involving vast expenditures of public funds for resource de-

velopment, if sustained, will have a definite bearing on the hydroelectric prospects of that continent. Several large African water-power developments are already in the blueprint stage. As in all improvements calling for heavy investments, the future development of water-power sites will depend largely on the extent to which the present unrest and suspicion yield to tranquillity and confidence.

Potential Water Power

It is most tempting to relate this discussion of developed water power to global statistics of potential water power. Such a correlation, however, is an exceptionally delicate undertaking. One fact is clear from the available evidence. There is relatively little correlation between potential and developed water power. (See Table 36.2.) Many countries with magnificent water-power sites have failed to develop them, while other countries have taken full advantage of the modest endowments provided by nature. There is much "neutral stuff" scattered about the globe, but resources are strictly limited to places where "culture" joins "nature" in an effective partnership.

TABLE 36.2.   Potential and Developed Water Power
by Continents[14]
(million horsepower and percent)

Continent	Potential	Developed	Percent Developed
Africa	274	0.4	0.1
Asia	151	12.1	8.0
North America	84	35.8	42.6
Europe	68	34.9	51.4
South America	67	2.4	3.6
Oceania	20	1.3	6.5
Total	664	86.9	13.1

Calculations of potential water power, as the volume of naturally falling water is often called, are exceedingly difficult. Their proper interpretation by the layman is equally difficult. In the first place, there are the immense difficulties of determining the *technical* feasibility of hydroelectric development. In the second place, there is the additional task of ascertaining the *economic* or *financial* feasibility. Both of these represent clusters of numerous subproblems each of which may present almost unsurmountable difficulties. In the absence of uniform

[14] U.S. Geological Survey, special release, 1948.

standards to which such investigations must conform, it is clear that global estimates of potential water power must be accepted with the utmost caution.

The total flow during the year can be divided into several categories on the basis of the portion of the year during which it is available. Conceivably 10 percent of the total annual water supply available at a given power site flows constantly throughout the year; perhaps 40 percent is available during half the year; and the remaining 50 percent is available only during flood periods.

Very few rivers could be developed for water power if only the all-year-round flow were utilized. Generally, if the natural stream flow is artificially regulated by means of a dam or a system of dams located at selected points on the main stream and its tributaries, the volume of stream flow is regularized considerably. To what extent it pays to regularize the natural flow is a complex engineering and economic question. It must take into account the topography of the river valley and particularly of suitable dam sites. The geology of the terrain must be carefully studied to determine where dam and powerhouse foundations can be properly anchored in bedrock. The extent to which nature permits the development of storage reservoirs must be considered. Besides these engineering problems the vital cost-price question must be faced. What will it cost and what revenue may reasonably be expected? The answers depend on the size of the market, actual and potential; and this, in turn, depends on the distance over which electricity can be transmitted economically and on the price at which power derived from alternative sources can be marketed in the area.

It is clear from the foregoing that the amount of stream flow itself is a mere preliminary in the determination of potential water power. Water that rushes down a river or over a fall is merely "neutral stuff." To refer to the water that thunders down the Victoria Falls of the Zambezi in Africa or the La Guayra Falls on the Paraguay River or the Iguassu Falls in South America as so many million potential kilowatts of electric capacity is only a little better than to refer to the polar icecaps as so many quadrillion potential units of refrigeration. The coal under the Antarctic shelf is "neu-

tral stuff"; so is the bulk of falling water. Only too often the majestic waterfalls in distant lands, while constituting spectacular phenomena of nature, have little connection with hydroelectric development. The prospect of their development is generally too remote to warrant speaking of "potential water power."

The figures for potential water power given in Table 36.2 are at one and the same time very conservative and very liberal. They are liberal because they call any waterfall, no matter where located, "potential" water power. They are conservative because water available 95 percent of the time constitutes only a fraction of the flow subject to water-power development if economic conditions for such development are right. Experience has shown that where electrical installation pays at all, development seldom if ever stops at the limit set by ordinary minimum flow, but generally reaches two to three times that amount. As a rule of thumb, one may say that mean flow or flow available 50 percent of the time is a much more reliable basis upon which to measure potentialities than the ordinary minimum flow. For a few countries figures on potential water power have been computed on the basis not only of "ordinary minimum stream flow" but also of water available 50 percent of the time or, what is very similar, of "mean stream flow." The figures based on "mean stream flow" generally run three times as high as those based on "ordinary minimum stream flow."

A still more meaningful approach to the measurement of potential water power is to study entire river systems with a view to their most effective multiple-purpose use. This has been done by the Federal Power Commission. The introductory statement gives a good idea of the nature of this approach.

The following tabulation shows . . . the amount of available undeveloped water power in the United States as estimated by the Federal Power Commission. The amounts shown are based on estimates made by river basins in accordance with plans which would give the best over-all development of the rivers. The river basin estimates have been apportioned among the states in which the basins lie according to the approximated locations of power sites, and where the power sites are on interstate boundary sections of rivers the available power has been, in general, divided equally between adjoining states. The figures are based upon the best information available to the Commission and are derived from studies by the staff either independently or in conjunction with studies by the Army Engineers, from studies made by the Army Engineers, the Bureau of Reclamation, and other agencies, and from various reports. They are subject to revision either by increase or decrease as additional information becomes available concerning stream flow, reservoir sites and other pertinent matters. The figures represent the rated capacities of generators which would normally be installed at hydroelectric developments, assuming reasonable regulation of flow by storage, depletions due to required consumptive use in different sections of the country, and other factors which are pertinent to the best over-all development of the river for power and multiple-purpose use.

Division	Installation, Kilowatts
Continental U. S.	77,130,000
New England	3,348,000
Middle Atlantic	5,175,000
East North Central	2,574,000
West North Central	4,735,000
South Atlantic	7,462,000
East South Central	4,552,000
West South Central	2,894,000
Mountain	17,755,000
Pacific	28,635,000

But, as was stressed before, mere availability of water is no criterion. A market for the power, capital, skill, military requirements—in other words, cultural considerations—as well as the natural conditions determine the extent to which water-power sites are developed.

Diversity of Water-Power Sites

In appraising the technical difficulties, it is important to be aware of the fact that water-power sites are anything but homogeneous. On the contrary, they are highly individualistic; no two are alike. In the first place, they differ as to the regularity or irregularity of the stream flow. Rivers are a mere fragment of a complex system known as the hydrologic cycle (see Fig. 36.1), the system of water movement from land to sea, from sea to air and back again to land. Whether rivers run clear and regularly depends on a thousand and one factors such as slope, nature of the land surface, forest and other vegetation cover of the headlands of the river system, rainfall, sunshine, etc.

A comparison between Niagara Falls and Muscle Shoals illustrates this point. Niagara Falls furnishes a water supply that is unique

throughout the world for its regularity. The Great Lakes form a natural storage reservoir of exceptional size which absorbs a good share of the seasonal and cyclical variations of rainfall and evaporation due to changing weather conditions. Freezing temperatures may cause some difficulties, but they are not insurmountable. Water power which is available all the time is called primary, or firm, power. Practically all of the water power developed at Niagara Falls is firm power.[15] The situation at Muscle Shoals reveals a surprising contrast. The daily flow of the Tennessee River in 1898, a year of extreme fluctuations, varied from less than 10,000 cubic feet per second during late September and early October, to 481,000 cubic feet per second in the middle of March. Excessive stream flow during flood seasons often reduces the head by causing the water level below the falls to rise. Stream flow varies not only seasonally but also from year to year, for years of drought are often followed by years of excessive rainfall. Thus water power at most sites is quite undependable, a defect which seriously interferes with its full utilization for the generation of electrical energy.

Water-power sites can also be distinguished on the basis of the source of the water, as for example *rain-fed* and *glacier-fed* streams. A good example is found in northern Italy, around Genoa. From the north come the Alpine torrents, carrying most water in the summer when the snow and ice of the Alps melt; from the Apennines come streams dependent mainly on rainfall for their flow. Normally the climatic conditions governing the flow variations in the two types of streams are so timed that they supplement each other during the course of the year. An interconnected system of power plants drawing on both sources is served chiefly from the north in the summer and fall and from the south in the winter and spring. Similar conditions can be found in all regions adjacent to snow mountains, such as the Alps, and to other sections with a high precipitation during the cool season. Because of mixed climatic conditions, the water-power provinces which straddle important watersheds generally furnish more

---

[15] At present, international agreements limit the development of Niagara Falls to 2 million horsepower. The St. Lawrence River project contemplates the ultimate development of 4.5 million.

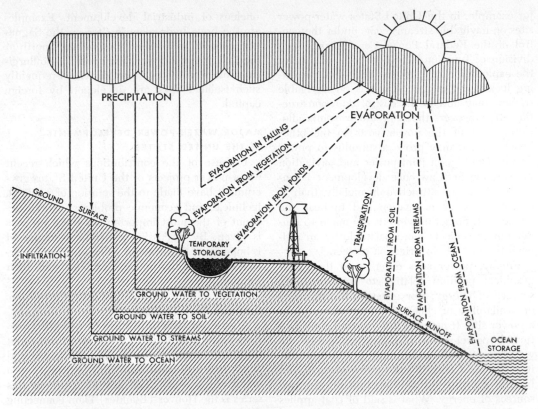

FIG. 36.1. The Hydrologic Cycle. (Figs. 36.1 and 36.2 from U. S. Department of the Interior, Bureau of Reclamation.)

dependable power than those lying entirely in a single climatic zone.

According to the topographical configuration of the power site and its environment, we can differentiate between water-power developments using a *moderate head* (75 to 150 feet) on streams having a *large drainage area*, such as the Tennessee River, and those calling for a *higher head* and a *smaller drainage area*. The first is generally found in the piedmont regions farther downstream; the latter in mountain regions at elevations of 1000 feet or more.[16] Such diverse sites must necessarily be developed in very different ways; as the later discussion will show, their functions in modern power economy likewise vary widely.

According to the manner in which stream flow is utilized, water-power plants may be divided into *run-of-river* plants and plants using *storage*. "The first class takes what water comes to them, and are developed to a capacity to use the flow available from thirty to forty per cent of the time. The second class utilizes water which is stored during floods and sent down stream to supplement dry-weather flow. Such plants are developed to a capacity to use the flow available from fifty to seventy-five per cent of the time. Individual plants may have installed capacities varying widely from these figures, due to special conditions."[17]

Some water-power sites are exploited *solely for the generation of electric power*; others are *multiple-purpose enterprises*, tied up with other functions such as river navigation, irrigation, flood control, etc. This may have a bearing on the legal aspects of water-power utilization;

[16] T. Saville, "The Power Situation in the Southern Power Provinces," *Annals of the American Academy of Political and Social Sciences*, January, 1931, p. 100.

[17] *Ibid.*, p. 101.

for example, in the United States water-power sites on navigable streams come under the control of the Federal Power Commission. Such division of function may both aid and hinder the exploitation of a given site. Thus, providing locks for the use of vessels on navigable streams may add to the cost of dam construction. If, however, the joint use warrants allocating part of the power costs to the other beneficiary, it may prove a stimulus to power development. As a joint power and navigation project, the St. Lawrence development is undoubtedly more attractive financially than if either power or navigation had to bear the whole cost. Sometimes efforts are made to render power projects more palatable by an artificial tie-up with an irrigation project.[18]

Finally, power sites differ as to their geographical position relative to that of other sources of energy. For instance, the presence or availability of cheap coal may kill or make a power site. It may kill it if the coal alone can furnish power more cheaply than either the water power alone or both together; it may help it if the most economical results are achieved by the coördinated development of the two sources of energy. What is said of coal applies also to petroleum, although less generally.

Stationary and Movable Load Centers

In the language of the power industry, markets for power are referred to as "load centers"; they may be "stationary" or "movable." Stationary load centers are urban centers which in the ordinary course of human events stay put. The power must be brought to them. By movable load centers are meant specific industries or industrial plants which consume extraordinary amounts of power and hence may move to the source of it. Among such industries the electrometallurgical and electrochemical are the most important—reduction of alumina to aluminum, electrolytic refining of nonferrous metals, nitrogen fixation by the arc or cyanamide process. Such power sites may spring up in the wilderness, so to speak, and form the

nucleus of industrial development. Examples are the huge hydroelectric sites on the Saguenay, especially Shipshaw in Quebec,[19] north of the St. Lawrence River, and several metallurgical centers on the coast of Norway. Frequently such isolated sites are developed by foreign capital.

MAJOR WATER-POWER DEVELOPMENTS IN THE UNITED STATES

Because of the contributions which recent water-power projects of the United States government have made to the solution of political, technical, and economic problems, a brief account of the most important of these projects is given. By discussing concrete examples, it is hoped that this account will add to the understanding of water-power problems and their solution.

Colorado River Projects

A series of structures have turned the Colorado River (see Fig. 36.2), known throughout the world as the site of the Grand Canyon and once America's most dangerous stream, into a major aid to man. The key structure in this series is the Hoover (Boulder) Dam connecting Arizona and Nevada. This dam, 726.4 feet high, is said to be the tallest dam structure in the world. It required 3¼ million cubic yards of concrete and cost $70.6 million. It furnishes vast amounts of water not only for irrigation and domestic purposes, but also for the generation of electric power. The dam holds back the waters of the Colorado which form Lake Mead, the world's largest reservoir. This lake, 115 miles long and covering 146,500 acres, has a capacity of 30.5 million acre-feet.

The power plant has a capacity of 1,835,000 horsepower and 1,317,500 kilowatts. The falling water is converted into mechanical energy by means of 15 large turbines of 115,000 horsepower each and by two smaller turbines of 55,000 horsepower each. These turbines drive 15 large generators of 82,500 kv-a[20] and two smaller generators of 40,000 kv-a each.

Part of this power is transmitted to Los Angeles by means of a line about 300 miles long. The current is stepped up to 285,000

---

[18] Cf. the statement submitted by Arthur M. Hyde, former Secretary of Agriculture, to the Board of Engineers for Rivers and Harbors, War Department, January 30, 1932 (mimeographed press release).

[19] See chap. 44.

[20] Kilovolt-ampere. (volt × ampere = watt.)

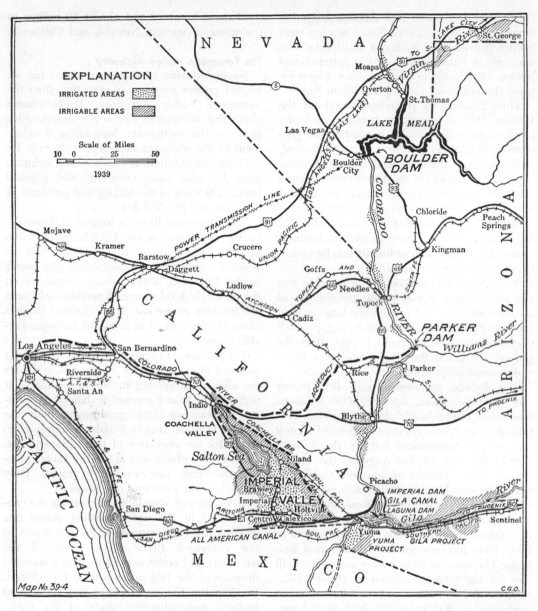

FIG. 36.2. Boulder Dam and Dependent Areas.

volts. This is the longest transmission line in the United States and the voltage is the highest used in this country.

A second dam (Parker Dam; cost, $10,000,-000) about 115 miles downstream from the Hoover Dam serves the Metropolitan Aqueduct, itself a $220,000,000 project, which carries Colorado River water to the Metropolitan Water District of Southern California. This 335-mile aqueduct furnishes about one billion gallons of water a day and has virtually doubled the water supply of the entire coastal basin. The aqueduct climbs to dizzy heights and pierces mountain ranges in long and costly tunnels. The pumping operation consumes large amounts of Hoover Dam power.

Still farther downstream near the Mexican border is the Imperial Dam from which the

Gila Canal leads east into Arizona irrigation areas and the All-American Canal reaches west toward the Imperial Valley of California. The main canal runs parallel to the international border; the Coachilla branch makes a loop toward the northwest around the Salton Sea.[21]

Thus a series of projects pivoted on the Hoover Dam represents a gigantic multiple-purpose river development combining the generation of electric power with flood control, irrigation, and domestic and industrial water supply. It is one of the most ambitious of man's attempts to convert the resistances of nature—a wild and dangerous stream—into resources. It points to the magnitude of tasks that lie beyond the scope usually allotted to private business enterprise, tasks which ordinarily can be undertaken only by governments.

What made this particular feat possible was the coincidence of vast power possibilities at the Hoover Dam and an equally large market for power and water, separated by a gap which engineering ingenuity could bridge. It is the power that made the whole scheme a financially sound proposition.

The federal government sells firm power (see p. 608)—about 4,330,000,000 kilowatt-hours—as "falling water" for 1.63 mills. This falling water is converted into electrical energy not by the government but by the buyers, mainly the City of Los Angeles, the Metropolitan Water District of Southern California, the California-Nevada Power Company, and the Southern California Edison Company.[22] These buyers operate the turbines and generators, which are government property, as well as their own transmission and distribution systems. The receipts from power and water will pay for the total investment of about $152,000,000 for the dam and installation when completed, in fifty years with interest at 3 percent, except for $25 million allocated to flood control. The value of flood control cannot be measured in dollars and cents, but is assumed to exceed the expenditures made therefor. By June 30, 1946, $42 million had been repaid to

the federal Treasury and almost $9 million to the states of Arizona, Nevada, and California.

The Tennessee Valley Authority

No undertaking of any government has attracted greater world-wide attention than the Tennessee Valley Authority. It constitutes man's first attempt to devise a comprehensive plan for the systematic, long-range development of the resources of a region. It calls for bold experimentation, not only along technical lines, but also along economic and political lines. (For some of the history and problems of the TVA, see pp. 572 ff.)

The Tennessee River is formed at Knoxville by the confluence of the Clinch, the Holston, and the French Broad Rivers. These vast arteries of mountain water combine to give power to the Tennessee River, which debouches on the relatively level plains of northern Alabama and western Tennessee. The cities and hamlets along the river lived in dread of its unpredictable temper.

The Army Engineers Corps had long watched this unruly river and had played with the idea of harnessing it. Nothing came of it until World War I created a dangerous nitrogen shortage and the government built the Wilson Dam at Muscle Shoals to supply electricity for the operation of two nitrate plants. One of these plants was to use the Haber process; the other, the cyanamide process. Only the latter ever went into operation.

After the war Muscle Shoals became the center of one of the worst political storms this country has ever witnessed. Serious floods in the Tennessee River valley reminded the wranglers that action was imperative if national disgrace of the first order was to be avoided. In 1928 the Engineers Corps was ordered to make a comprehensive study of the entire watershed. The report, which was completed in 1930, drew attention to the fact that power development could help to defray the expense of flood control and navigation improvements and at the same time help to put to use some of the region's rich mineral deposits and create industrial opportunities. The basis for TVA was thus laid; but it took men like President Franklin Delano Roosevelt, Senator Norris of Nebraska, and David Lilienthal, former chairman of the Atomic Energy Commission, to cre-

---

[21] How even the "best-laid plans of mice and men" may miscarry is shown in Alfred M. Cooper's revealing article, "A Cataclysm Threatens California," *Harper's Magazine,* April, 1950.

[22] Nevada and Arizona are each entitled to 18 percent of the electricity.

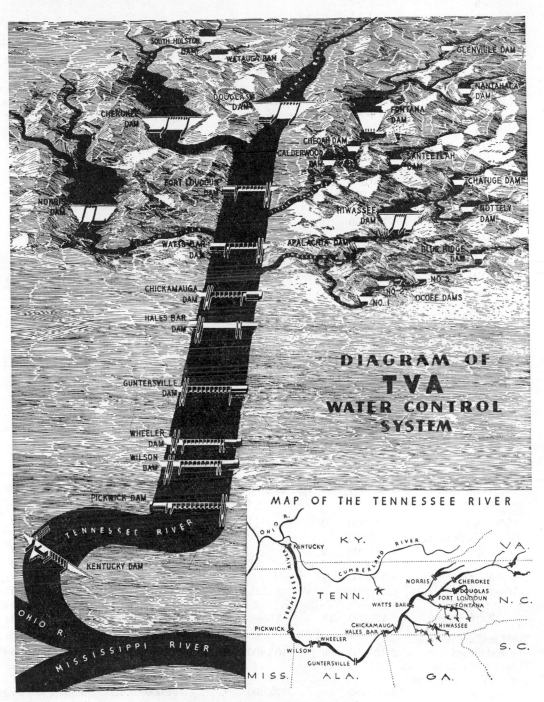

FIG. 36.3. (Tennessee Valley Authority.)

TABLE 36.3.   Capacity at Generating Plants, April 1, 1948

Major Plants	Installed Capacity KW	No. Units	Capacity Under Construction KW	No. Units	Future Capacity KW	No. Units	Total Ultimate Installation KW	No. Units
Hydro								
Apalachia	75,000	2	. . . . .	. .	. . . . .	. .	75,000	2
Blue Ridge	20,000	1	. . . . .	. .	. . . . .	. .	20,000	1
Chatuge	. . . . .	. .	. . . . .	. .	8,000	1	8,000	1
Cherokee	60,000	2	. . . . .	. .	60,000	2	120,000	4
Chickamauga	81,000	3	. . . . .	. .	27,000	1	108,000	4
Douglas	60,000	2	26,000	1	26,000	1	112,000	4
Fontana	135,000	2	. . . . .	. .	67,500	1	202,500	3
Fort Loudoun	64,000	2	64,000	2	. . . . .	. .	128,000	4
Great Falls	31,860	2	. . . . .	. .	. . . . .	. .	31,860	2
Guntersville	72,900	3	. . . . .	. .	24,300	1	97,200	4
Hales Bar	51,100	14	. . . . .	. .	48,600	2	99,700	16
Hiwassee	57,600	1	. . . . .	. .	57,600	1	115,200	2
Kentucky	160,000	5	. . . . .	. .	. . . . .	. .	160,000	5
Nolichucky	10,640	4	. . . . .	. .	. . . . .	. .	10,640	4
Norris	100,800	2	. . . . .	. .	. . . . .	. .	100,800	2
Nottely	. . . . .	. .	. . . . .	. .	10,000	1	10,000	1
Ocoee No. 1	18,000	5	. . . . .	. .	. . . . .	. .	18,000	5
Ocoee No. 2	19,900	2	. . . . .	. .	. . . . .	. .	19,900	2
Ocoee No. 3	27,000	1	. . . . .	. .	. . . . .	. .	27,000	1
Pickwick	144,000	4	. . . . .	. .	72,000	2	216,000	6
South Holston	. . . . .	. .	35,000	1	. . . . .	. .	35,000	1
Watauga	. . . . .	. .	50,000	2	. . . . .	. .	50,000	2
Watts Bar	150,000	5	. . . . .	. .	. . . . .	. .	150,000	5
Wheeler	129,600	4	129,600	4	. . . . .	. .	259,200	8
Wilson	335,200	14	100,800	4	. . . . .	. .	436,000	18
Total hydro	1,803,600	80	405,400	14	401,000	13	2,610,000	107
Steam								
Hales Bar	40,000	2	. . . . .	. .	. . . . .	. .	40,000	2
Memphis (leased)	20,000[a]	. .	. . . . .	. .	. . . . .	. .	20,000	. .
Nashville	48,000	6	. . . . .	. .	. . . . .	. .	48,000	6
Parksville	13,000	2	. . . . .	. .	. . . . .	. .	13,000	2
Watts Bar	240,000	4	. . . . .	. .	. . . . .	. .	240,000	4
Wilson	64,000[b]	5	. . . . .	. .	. . . . .	. .	64,000	5
Total steam	425,000	19					425,000	19
Total major hydro and steam	2,228,600	99	405,400	14	401,000	13	3,035,000	126
Total small plants	31,182	. .	. . . . .	. .	. . . . .	. .	31,182	. .
Total TVA generating capacity	2,259,782	. .	405,400	. .	401,000	. .	3,066,182	. .

[a] TVA may use an additional 15,000 kw in emergencies.
[b] Includes 4000 kw of capacity in station units.

ate the political instruments through which this project could be implemented and to arouse the enthusiasm which alone could bring it to life.

The Tennessee River valley proper comprises approximately 40,000 square miles, but the TVA operates in an area about twice that large (see Fig. 36.3). Its primary tasks are the creation of a 9-foot navigation channel between Knoxville and the mouth of the Tennessee River and the prevention of floods. The generation of power is definitely subordinated to these primary functions; but within the limits of compatibility with these purposes the Authority is charged with developing all the power that can be generated economically. In selling the power preference is given to government agencies (municipalities) and coöperatives; this preference affects not rates, but merely the willingness to sell. Power is also sold to large industries, generally on long-term contracts. Arrangements are made with neighboring utility companies for interchange of power as the need develops.

The most conspicuous features of the TVA are its dams. TVA acquired from the government the Wilson Dam, started in 1918 and completed in 1926. From the Tennessee Electric Power Company were acquired the Hales Bar Dam below Chattanooga, begun in 1905 and completed in 1913, Ocoee No. 1 and No. 2, Blue Ridge, and Great Falls, all but Blue Ridge rather old structures. These five dams together serve an aggregate power installation of 95,570 kilowatts. Later some dams were acquired from the Aluminum Company of America.

All the other dams on both the main stream and the tributaries have been built by TVA itself. The dams on the main river are multiple-purpose, serving navigation as well as flood control, power generation, and other purposes. The dams on the tributaries are multiple-purpose storage dams. On April 1, 1948, TVA had a total installed capacity of 2,259,782 kilowatts; Table 36.3 (from the TVA annual report for 1948) gives data on power-generating capacity by plants.

The Columbia River Basin Project

The Columbia River project is of such colossal proportions that as yet it is almost incomprehensible. The ultimate objective of those who are planning it is the full development of the resources of the portion of the Columbia River drainage basin that lies within the United States, 220,000 square miles out of a total of 259,000 square miles. This area constitutes about 7 percent of the total area of the United States. It is larger than France and about twice the size of the British Isles. The drainage basin includes nearly all of Idaho, most of Washington and Oregon, the western part of Montana, smaller areas of Arizona and Nevada, and the northwestern tip of Utah. In 1940 this enormous basin had a population of 2,191,000 persons—or 1.5 percent of our population on 7 percent of the land.

The Columbia River has its headwaters in a mountain lake in British Columbia and enters the United States near the northeast corner of Washington, after flowing 465 miles through Canada. It is about 1200 miles long and empties into the sea an average of nearly 160,000,-000 acre-feet of water each year, more than any other river in this country except the Mississippi. The most important tributary is the Snake River, itself more than a thousand miles long; it drains almost half the American portion of the basin.

By 1946 about 2.1 million kilowatts of electric generating capacity had been installed in nearly 200 hydroelectric power plants—14.5 percent of all the hydroelectric power of the nation. And this is only about one-fifth of the total potential. Of the total installation, 63 percent was installed in the two largest power sites of the region, Grand Coulee[23] and Bonneville.

The entire plan embraces no less than 238 projects which will provide irrigation water for 5,360,000 acres of land. Because of the uncertainty of cost levels during the time it will take to develop such a vast project, the total cost is more or less unpredictable, but with interest it would probably exceed $10 billion by a wide margin.

Fig. 36.4 shows the 750-mile course of the Columbia River from the Canadian border to the Pacific Ocean. On its way the river drops 1300 feet. It has the distinction of having by far

---

[23] This includes two 75,000-kilowatt generators designed for installation at Shasta Dam, California; they were used at Grand Coulee during the war and subsequently removed.

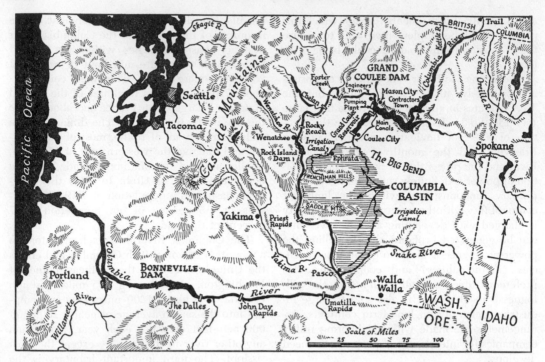

FIG. 36.4.   Grand Coulee and Bonneville, Columbia River Power Sites. (*Fortune*, July, 1937, p. 84; reproduced courtesy of Fortune Magazine.)

the largest water-power potential of any river in the United States. At about 150 river miles (or about 90 miles as the crow flies) the Columbia turns at a right angle, changing its southerly course to a northwesterly one, to form what is known as the Big Bend. In this Big Bend lies the so-called Columbia Basin, a dry flat land of some 2,500,000 acres of rich volcanic-ash soil. About 25 miles on from this northwesterly turn the river passes the Grand Coulee.

The Grand Coulee is a strange geological phenomenon. In the Pleistocene Age glaciers closed the regular channel of the Columbia River about midway on the northwestern stretch that forms the Big Bend. So the dammed waters forced a new passage to the sea in a southwesterly direction. Out of the lava plains they carved a gigantic trough 52 miles long, two to five miles wide, and 600 feet deep. This vast trough surrounded by cliffs of basalt is the Grand Coulee. Later on the glaciers melted and the river returned to its earlier bed.

The Grand Coulee and the Columbia River basin are made for each other. But since the rim of the trough is hundreds of feet above the water level of the river, enormous pumping operations and vast power are required to fill it. A huge dam was built across the Columbia River a short distance downstream from the northern end of the Grand Coulee. Fortunately the river, which in its upper reaches draws water from melting snow and ice, carries most water during the summer growing season and thus fits snugly into the schedule of irrigation water requirements. Moreover, the Columbia's summer floods supply cheap secondary power[24] for pumping operations, leaving the primary (constant, dependable) power for other needs.

The Grand Coulee Dam, built by the Bureau of Reclamation, is the largest of ten planned by the Army Engineers for the flood control and navigation of the Columbia River (see Fig. 36.5). While not as high as either the Hoover or the Shasta, it is the largest concrete dam in the world; it contains almost twice as much concrete as the next largest, the Shasta, and

[24] For a discussion of firm or primary and secondary power, see p. 608.

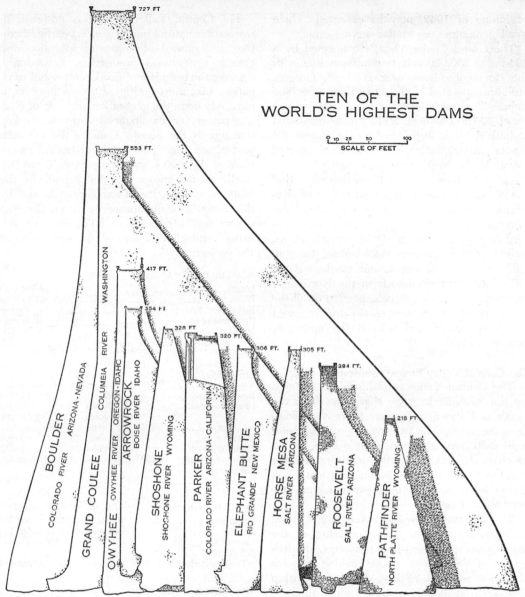

TEN OF THE
WORLD'S HIGHEST DAMS

0 10 25   50   100
SCALE OF FEET

727 FT

553 FT.

417 FT.

354 FT.

328 FT

320 FT.

306 FT.   305 FT.

284 FT.

218 FT

BOULDER
COLORADO RIVER · ARIZONA-NEVADA

GRAND COULEE
COLUMBIA RIVER · WASHINGTON

OWYHEE
OWYHEE RIVER · OREGON-IDAHO

ARROWROCK
BOISE RIVER · IDAHO

SHOSHONE
SHOSHONE RIVER · WYOMING

PARKER
COLORADO RIVER · ARIZONA-CALIFORNIA

ELEPHANT BUTTE
RIO GRANDE · NEW MEXICO

HORSE MESA
SALT RIVER · ARIZONA

ROOSEVELT
SALT RIVER · ARIZONA

PATHFINDER
NORTH PLATTE RIVER · WYOMING

FIG. 36.5. (*The Reclamation Era,* May, 1938.)

over three times as much as the Hoover. The Grand Coulee Dam raises the water level of the Columbia River 355 feet, thereby creating a usable storage capacity of more than 5,000,-000 acre-feet. The power plant is planned to handle an ultimate capacity of 2,742,000 horsepower, or 1,974,000 kilowatts. When completed, it will be equipped with 18 turbines of 150,000 horsepower rated capacity, driving an equal number of 108,000-kilowatt generators— a total rated capacity of 2,742,000 horsepower in turbines and of 1,974,000 kilowatts in generators. In actual service the generator units have proved themselves capable of carrying 125,000 to 130,000 kilowatts, suggesting that a total actual generating capacity of 2,370,000 kilowatts, or almost equal to the 2,570,000-kilowatt capacity of the TVA system at the beginning of 1948, may be expected. Three small generators are station-service units.[25]

The Grand Coulee Dam is connected by a 234-mile, 230,000-volt transmission line with the Bonneville Dam near Portland, Oregon, built and operated by the Army Engineers. The Bonneville power plant has an ultimate capacity of 430,000 kilowatts. The power generated at both dams is distributed by the Bonneville Power Administration, the great wholesaler of power in the Northwest.

Early in the war when it became clear that the Northwest would be a great center of electrometallurgical plants, especially aluminum but also the atom-smashing plant of the Hanford Engineering Works, all the power systems, public and private, in Washington, Oregon, Idaho, western Montana, and northern Utah were intercoördinated to form the Northwestern Power Pool. This interconnection of all the power plants in this vast region greatly raised the load factor[26] and with it the aggregate power available.

The Central Valley Project, California

The Central Valley of California is watered by the Sacramento River that flows from the north and the San Joaquin River that flows from the south. The two rivers meet in a common delta near Stockton, mingle in a myriad of channels, and issue into San Francisco Bay and the Pacific Ocean. The early settlers found the valley region a desolate expanse, part desert and part swamp.

The economic development of the Central Valley rests on the proper ordering of the water supply, draining of the swamps, and irrigation of the deserts. Those seeking to solve this vast problem of land-water relationship long realized that the natural supply situation was out of balance; the northern sector, comprising mainly the Sacramento valley, had about two-thirds of the water supply, and the San Joaquin valley, with most of the land, needed two-thirds of the water supply.

The Central Valley project is designed to correct this natural imbalance. Primarily, therefore, it is aimed at improved irrigation and greater agricultural production. Secondarily, it serves the purposes of flood control and navigation. Like most multiple-purpose projects, it must rely upon the generation and sale of electric power for its financial support. Its key structure is the Shasta Dam in the northern part of the area. This dam will have a power plant of 375,000 kilowatt capacity. There is a smaller dam, known as the Friant, in the southern section. Part of the water stored by this dam will be distributed by means of canals of considerable dimensions.[27] The following statistics[28] will give an idea of the magnitude of the project:

THE GREAT CENTRAL VALLEY:

Length	Almost 500 miles
Width	About 50 miles
Elevation	Sea level to 400 feet
Gross area of basin	58,150 square miles
Irrigable area of project	2,000,000 acres

THE DAMS:	Shasta	Friant
Maximum height..	560 feet	300 feet
Crest length......	3500 feet	3500 feet
Top thickness.....	37 feet	20 feet
Base thickness....	580 feet	250 feet
Concrete content..	5,600,000 cubic yards	1,500,000 cubic yards
Drainage area.....	6665 square miles	1630 square miles
Reservoir area....	30,000 acres	4500 acres
Reservoir length..	35 miles	15 miles
Reservoir capacity	4,500,000 acre-feet	520,000 acre-feet
Power-plant capacity........	375,000 kilowatts	None

THE CANALS:	Length	Diversion Capacity
Friant-Kern......	160 miles	3500 second-feet
Madera..........	40 miles	1000 second-feet
Contra Costa.....	46 miles	350 second-feet
San Joaquin Pumping System	100 miles	3000 second-feet

The Missouri River Plan

The Missouri valley consists of large parts of the states of Missouri, Kansas, Colorado, Minnesota, North and South Dakota, Montana, and Wyoming, all of Nebraska, and a considerable section of western Iowa. This is an area nearly

---

[25] During the war six large generators were installed. As was mentioned before, they were temporarily supplemented by two 75,000-kilowatt generators "borrowed" from the unfinished Shasta Dam in California. Peak loads during the war exceeded 902,000 kw.

[26] See chap. 37, especially p. 607.

[27] Those who wish to learn more about this project are referred to a series of project studies published in 1947 by the Bureau of Reclamation, Department of the Interior, Washington, D.C. They contain a great deal of material of real interest to economists and other social scientists.

[28] Bureau of Reclamation, "Central Valley Project," 1947.

17 percent of the total area of the United States. Its population is about 11 percent of our total population, and is declining. The 2500-mile-long Missouri River, for good reason, is known as the Big Muddy; it does more than its share of carrying the nation's topsoil down toward the ocean. It flows through the region referred to, in years of inadequate rainfall, as the Dust Bowl. The valley is alternately beset by floods and droughts. Property damage from floods in an average year amounts to about $18.5 million and the Dust Bowl in the thirties cost the nation over a billion dollars in relief money. It is calculated that, if properly harnessed to control floods and exploited to supply irrigation water, the river could support a generating capacity of 2.5 million kilowatts which would be able at least to help defray the expense of this vast project.

The need has long been recognized, but only recently have earnest beginnings been made in a comprehensive scheme of remedial action. Flood control and navigation constitute the bailiwick of the Army Engineers Corps, whereas irrigation is the main concern of the Bureau of Reclamation. Seldom are these functions found neatly separated in nature. Hence, there is a conflict of interests, a rivalry which in this area at least has proved a hindrance rather than a help. Only when, encouraged by the success of the TVA, the idea took hold that perhaps a separate Missouri Valley Authority should be set up which would please neither of them, did the two government agencies bury the hatchet and consent to coöperate under the Peck-Sloan or Army-Reclamation plan. Before this was adopted in 1944, the Army Engineers submitted a plan of their own in 1933 and the Reclamation Bureau produced one early in 1944. The present plan has been referred to as a shotgun marriage joining two irreconcilable agencies.

The new plan calls for more than 100 new dams[29] and about 150 irrigation projects. More than 20 power plants are to be built, as well as thousands of miles of transmission lines to make low-cost power available for distribution. The Flood Control Act of 1944 which set the plan in motion authorized appropriations of $200,000,000 for each agency for partial accomplishment of the initial stage. These agencies are to proceed "as speedily as may be consistent with budgetary requirements." The Bureau of Reclamation will work from the headwaters *downstream* to provide for irrigation, hydroelectric power, and the development of land and other resources, and the Army Engineers will work *upstream* from the mouth of the river to provide primarily for flood control and navigation. The Bureau's network of dams and reservoirs upstream will be vital to the Army's flood control and navigation program, and the Army will develop power on its projects which will be marketed by the Bureau along with that generated at its own dams.

TABLE 36.4. The Missouri Valley and TVA Projects

	Missouri Valley		TVA	
	1930	1945	1930	1945
Acre value	$39.17	$25.28	$39.02	$46.30
Value of farm machinery employed per acre	$7.13	$9.34	$7.05	12.72
Index number of hour-rate of electric service	100	200	100	700
Population change	slight loss		...	+12%[a]
Farm tenancy (percent of total farms)	40%	35%	43%	2%

[a] National average, 7 percent.

At least one leading authority on regional resources development[30] is convinced that the plan is inadequate. He reasons that neither the Army Engineers nor the Reclamation Service of the Department of the Interior is permitted under law to do many of the things that are absolutely essential to the success of a plan aimed at control of a vast and unruly river, and that only an authority such as the TVA, endowed with the necessary powers to do *all* that is required, can make a success of such a venture. He argues that, especially in the Missouri valley, soil conservation is vital and that no provision has been made to include it as an organic part of the plan. The striking figures cited by him are given in Table 36.4.

Of course, these figures neither support nor

---

[29] The large Fort Peck Dam in Montana was authorized in 1935 as part of the navigation project. This project, begun in 1912 by the Army Engineers to provide a six-foot navigation channel between Sioux City, Iowa, and the mouth of the Missouri at St. Louis, is practically completed.

[30] Morris Llewellyn Cooke, "Plain Talk About the Missouri Valley Authority," *Congressional Record*, June 10, 1947. Table 36.4 is based on this source.

oppose any of the arguments against the Peck-Sloan plan, for it has not yet had time to prove its worth. But they are a strong argument in favor of the need of the coördinated management which the TVA type of setup makes possible. This coördination need not be identical in all cases; in fact, it probably should not be. The Missouri valley with its over 500,000 square miles is more than twelve times as large as the Tennessee River valley and over six times as large as the area served by TVA. Moreover, while the TVA area is fairly homogeneous, the Missouri drainage basin falls into several distinct segments. But this diversity of subregional characteristics further stresses the necessity for overall coördination beyond that resulting from the coöperation of two agencies inadequately equipped by law with the authority to deal with the totality of problems and difficulties. The democratic process is one of experimentation and free discussion of pros and cons. There is hope that if and as the deficiencies of the present plan manifest themselves, the necessary changes will be forthcoming.

WATER POWER OTHER THAN GRAVITATIONAL
Utilization of Tides for the Generation of Water Power

At present the utilization of water for power-producing purposes is confined to the exploitation of stream flow. In fact, as generally used, the term water power is restricted to the power of falling or rushing water.[31] It is possible that in the future, perhaps even the near future, other forms of water power, if we may use the term in a wider sense, will be used. Some time ago a project for utilizing tidal energy attracted wide attention in this country. At Passamaquoddy Bay, Maine, at the southern end of the Bay of Fundy near the international line, there happens to exist not only such an exceptionally great tidal range, but also such an exceptionally favorable topographical layout of shoreline and islands, that the power engineer may well be tempted to dream of future cities using this vast store of unharnessed energy. The project is so enticing that it has passed the dream stage

---

[31] Water power is commonly defined as "the product of a weight of water multiplied by a fall in feet."

and has repeatedly played a part in Maine politics. In fact, during the early days of the New Deal, when creating employment by public works was a major national policy, considerable preparatory work on this project was undertaken, but it was dropped before real progress had been made. One difficulty is the adverse effect which the power development would have on the rich fishing grounds of the region. Of interest in this connection is the fact that in France, at a favorable point on the Bay of Biscay, an experimental power plant utilizing the tides has been in operation for some time.

The potentialities of this form of energy are almost unlimited. Tidal energy must not be confused with the kinetic energy which the earth possesses by virtue of its diurnal rotation about its own axis. This energy is said to amount to 3.7×10^{28} foot-pounds. It is impossible to make direct use of it; but where the effect of this rotation is combined with the gravitational attraction of the sun and moon so as to produce tides twice a day in the various bodies of water distributed over the surface of the earth, the exploitation of this form of energy becomes possible, at least theoretically. One of its most serious drawbacks is the fact that tidal hours do not coincide with working hours. This necessitates the storage of energy, which, at least under present circumstances, is a serious handicap. Moreover, a favorable combination of tidal range and topography for the development of tidal power is found in relatively few places. Probably the most valuable site is the Bay of Fundy, mentioned above. However, the fiords of Norway and the lochs of Scotland may some day attract the attention of power engineers.

Utilization of Ocean Temperature Differences

Water is indispensable to practically all methods of power generation. As boiler and condensing water it is used in steam-generated power. Internal-combustion engines depend on water to prevent overheating. There is one experiment under way in which water plays an even greater part, although one would hesitate to extend the idea of water power far enough to include the plan. This is the proposal to utilize the difference between the temperatures of the surface waters in tropical seas, which

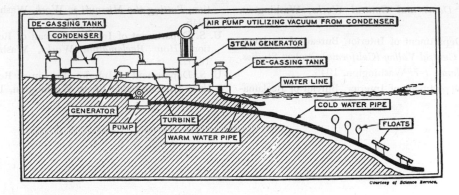

FIG. 36.6. Claude's Plan for Generating Power from Ocean Transportation Differences. (New York *Times*, October 12, 1930.)

range around 80°, and those of the waters 3000 feet below, which average 40°. This plan is associated with the name of Dr. Georges Claude, who is one of the most distinguished physicists and chemists of our time and is well known because of his successful development of a process used in the synthetic production of nitrogen and his discovery of neon light. Although space prevents a full explanation of the technical details, the following quotation and Fig. 36.6 will give some idea of the process.

Water can be made to boil at room temperature by creating a vacuum above it. This fact is practically applied by Dr. Claude. In his power plant warm tropical water is pumped into an evaporator. A vacuum is created in the evaporator, thereby causing the water to boil. The steam given off drives a turbine coupled with an electric generator or dynamo. After it has done its work the steam is exhausted into a condenser. Here icy jets of water pumped up from the bottom of the sea condense it—make it shrink back into water. Thus the vacuum is created which causes the water in the evaporator to boil. To start the plant, a vacuum pump is required, after which the mere act of condensing exhaust steam maintains the vacuum.[32]

Responsible scientists are giving their time and thought to the problem and financiers of note have shown interest in the possibilities of the plan.

[32] New York *Times*, February 6, 1927.
The experimental plant which Dr. Claude built on the coast of Cuba ran into difficulties of a purely technical or structural nature that in no way discredit the principle on which the process is based. Later the French government built a Claude power plant on the coast of French Equatorial Africa; no reports on its success have yet reached the author.

BIBLIOGRAPHY

Allner, F. A., "Economic Aspects of Water Power," Paper presented before American Institute of Electrical Engineers, Baltimore, October, 1932.

Cooke, M. L., "Plain Talk About a Missouri Valley Authority," *Iowa Law Review*, January, 1947.

Edison Electric Institute, *Statistical Bulletin*, New York (annual).

Finer, H., *The T.V.A.: Lessons for International Application*, Montreal, International Labour Office, 1944.

Geological Survey, "Developed and Potential Water Power of the World," Washington, 1948 (multigraphed).

Gilbert, C. G., and Pogue, J. E., *America's Power Resources*, New York, Appleton-Century, 1921.

Huxley, J. S., *T.V.A. Adventure in Planning*, Cheam, Surrey, Architectural Press, 1948.

James, P. E., "Water Power Resources in Brazil," *Economic Geography*, January, 1942.

"T.V.A.," I and II, *Fortune*, May, 1935.

Tennessee Valley Authority, *Annual Reports*, Knoxville.

Tennessee Valley Authority, *The Valley Is Paying Off*, Washington, 1949.

U. S. Department of Interior, Bureau of Reclamation, *Dams and Control Works,* Washington, 1938.

U. S. Department of Interior, Bureau of Reclamation, *Central Valley (California), Project Studies, Problems, 1-7,* Washington, 1945.

U. S. Department of Interior, Bureau of Reclama-

tion, *Putting the Missouri to Work,* Washington, 1945.

U. S. Department of Interior, Bureau of Reclamation, *How Reclamation Works,* Washington, 1947.

U. S. Department of Interior, Bureau of Reclamation, *The Columbia River,* Washington, 1947.

Chapter 37

ELECTRICITY—A MODERN REFINEMENT OF ENERGY USE

For ages men depended mainly on wood as a source of light, heat, and power. Then coal was added, and still later oil and natural gas. Each addition expanded the base of the energy structure. Electricity is not a new source of energy, but a new form into which existing energies can be changed. Although it is not an addition to man's repertoire of energies, it has made tremendous contributions to his available supply of energy.[1]

This has come about in many ways. In the first place, as was shown in the preceding chapter, electricity has emancipated water power from the stranglehold of the power site, the waterfall, and by doing so has awakened water power to new life, adding millions of horsepower to man's robot army. In many cases this water power is available in regions where other energy sources are scarce or nonexistent. In other cases, the competition of water power

has prodded sluggish fuel power to new effort and better performance. In still others, water power, as a coöperating supplement, has raised the efficacy of other energy sources. Without the dynamo and modern transmission systems, this miracle of hydroelectricity would not have been possible.

In the second place, the conversion of steam power and other energy into electricity or the substitution of electricity for them involves a qualitative improvement of the energy supply which has had implications and repercussions without end. The power of steam applied directly to machinery is clumsy; the transmission from engine to machine is cumbersome. There is nothing clumsy about electricity nor can its transmission be called cumbersome. On the contrary, electricity is flexible and divisible to a degree which would be hard to believe were it not demonstrated daily in innumerable ways. The same powerhouse at a moment's notice, at the turn of a switch, will light a 60-watt bulb, heat a toaster or an iron, or turn the fractional motor of a mixer or a giant motor of thousands of watts. Electricity is available on call in almost any quantity desired. This combination

---

[1] According to the *Statistical Abstract of the United States, 1947* (p. 478), 15-20 percent of the coal, over 2 percent of the oil, and 10 percent of the natural gas produced in the United States, as well as virtually all the water used for power purposes, are converted into electricity.

of flexibility and divisibility has created uses for electrical energy in myriads of situations where the older, more clumsy, and more cumbersome forms of energy had failed. Thus, in the refined form of electricity, inanimate energy has reached into every nook and cranny, as it were. Electricity resparked the Industrial Revolution, found new worlds to conquer, and accelerated the process of mechanization not only of manufacture and transport, but of agriculture as well. It set in motion a new wave of inventions which reduced and continues to reduce the cost of inanimate energy and thus encourages the further spread of its use.

In the factory alone it wrought revolutionary changes in machine design, layout, manufacturing processes. Whereas the transmission belt could reach feet, the electric wire and cable can reach miles. This makes possible the complete separation of the power plant from the manufacturing plant. A new electric power and light industry was born that specialized in, and confined its energies to, the generation of electricity. This specialization, in turn, led to advanced research and great technological progress.

By its qualitative superiority, manifest chiefly through this greater flexibility and divisibility, electricity has made it possible to introduce far-reaching innovations, in fact, to create whole industries unthinkable without it. The electric furnace comes to mind. Because of the accuracy with which electrical temperatures and time schedules of electrical operation can be controlled, the electric furnace can produce alloy steels and other alloys of a fineness and complexity possible with no other process and equipment. The creation of such alloys, in turn, has made feasible advances in metallurgy and metal construction unthinkable without them. The host of electric precision instruments, including the electronic microscope and the electronic "brain," opens up a new vista into this vast wonderland that electricity has created. The internal-combustion, gas explosion and Diesel, engines, the jet and rocket, and the gas turbine may be making more spectacular *direct* contributions to transportation by land, water, and air, but where would the motor car be without its spark plugs or the airplane without its instrument panel or the oil-propelled luxury liner without its electric auxiliary engines? New industries resting squarely on electricity come readily to mind: telephone, telegraph, cable, radio, radar, refrigeration, air-conditioning, electronics, television. There seems no end to the miracles which can be traced to this qualitative improvement of ancient energies and the refinement in their use. That all this affects warfare, as well as peacetime endeavor, goes without saying.

So far this appraisal has been limited to electricity used as power and heat. Not a word has yet been said about electric light. Those who lived through the "brownouts" and "blackouts" of World War II have learned the blessings of electric light, or relearned them if they were taken for granted. Those who enjoy, as a matter of course, an average day of 16 or 18 light or lighted hours can hardly imagine the boredom and frustration of earlier times when sunset meant the end of general activity. The increase in the hours spent usefully or pleasantly by millions wherever electricity sheds its light is one of the greatest blessings of mankind. If to this are added the endless hours of drudgery which electrically driven labor-saving devices spare housewives, farm families, and other workers, one gains some idea of the scope of this boon which has come to mankind from a force whose real nature remains a mystery.

With all its strong points, electricity has one serious weakness. It is perishable, in fact highly perishable, perhaps the most perishable "good" on earth. Except in small quantities, it cannot be stored economically. It must be consumed the moment it is produced. It is like a sizzling steak that must be served while it sizzles.

This super-perishability has serious implications. It creates great problems for the electric power and light industry and materially adds to the cost of electricity. How this comes about, what it entails, and what can be done about it will be developed later in this chapter.

THE ELECTRIC POWER INDUSTRY OF THE UNITED STATES

The younger generation who have grown up in electrified homes, who are used to stepping on the electric starter in the family car, who spend their evenings in front of the radio or television, who call up their friends on the telephone, and to whom such names as General Electric, A. T. and T., and Radio Corporation of America are household words, must find it difficult to realize that the first central electric power station was built by Edison in 1882. That date marks the time at which electricity emerged from the laboratory stage and started on a truly meteoric career which lifted the industry into the topmost tier of modern industries.[2]

At present between one-third and one-half of the world's installed electric generating capacity is located in the United States. This country represents by far the most important national segment of the electric power industry. Its industrial progress has not been halted or warped by war as has that of the other countries that led in the production of electric power and of electrical appliances, notably Germany. The growth and present status of the electric power industry in the United States will be discussed first.

---

[2] The electrical industry represents one of the greatest achievements of applied science which man has yet attained. Only the chemical industry among basic industries can be placed on the same level. The electrical industry clearly rests on a series of discoveries and inventions—most of them in the field of pure science—the beginnings of which reach back into antiquity. The etymology of the words *electricity* and its kin, *magnetism*, reveals early Greek contributions, for the first word comes from *electron*, the Greek for amber, and the second, from *Magnesia*, a Greek city in Asia Minor near which lodestone or magnetic iron was found. The mariner's compass is one of the first applications of man's knowledge of magnetic properties. Both Occident and Orient claim this epoch-making invention as their own. So far as is known, little was accomplished for almost two thousand years after the first observations made by Thales. Interest in the mysteries of magnetism awakened anew in the days of Queen Elizabeth and bore fruit in a book on magnetism by Her Majesty's physician, Doctor William Gilbert, which was published in 1600 under the title *De Magnete*. From then on progress continued, first slowly, and later at an accelerated pace, until in our day new discoveries have followed each other with incredible rapidity. It is impossible to review here in detail the gradual exploration and subjugation of that mysterious force, electricity. Suffice it to say that many nations have contributed to it, and that the work in the field of pure science was as indispensable to the final result as its more spectacular commercial application. (From a study of the electric power industry prepared and published by the National Electric Light Association, predecessor of the Edison Electric Institute.)

Generating Capacity and Power Production

Estimates of total electric generating capacity in the United States do not go further back than 1906. In that year, twenty-four years after the opening of the first commercial power plant in this country, total installed capacity is estimated to have amounted to about 6 million kilowatts.[3] Fig. 37.1 shows how this capacity was enlarged without letup, except during the depression of the thirties and World War II, to almost 70 million kilowatts at the end of 1948. For the time being, only the curve indicating total installed capacity is being considered; the ownership aspects will be discussed later.

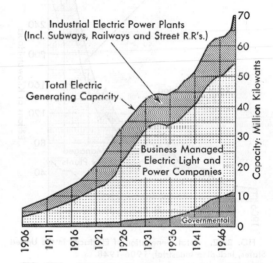

FIG. 37.1. Installed Electric Generating Capacity, United States, 1906-1948. (Figs. 37.1 and 37.2 from Edison Electric Institute.)

Remarkable as the increase in installed capacity is, the increase in production of electricity is even more so. This is shown in Fig. 37.2. A comparison of these two diagrams yields some interesting results. In the first place, the output curve reflects business recessions and depressions more clearly than does the capacity curve. In the second place, the capacity curve comes much closer to conforming to a straight-line trend than does the output curve. The capacity curve has two minor concavities—one for the period 1906 to 1930 and

---

[3] A kilowatt is a unit of capacity; the kilowatt hour measures the electricity actually generated.

the other for the period 1930 to 1947. The output curve is altogether different. Apart from minor irregularities, it resembles a single concave line suggesting a more or less constant acceleration of growth. This, in turn, viewed in relation to the capacity curve, implies a constant trend toward a higher capacity factor. The significance of this trend for costs, rates, demand, etc., will become apparent from the analysis of the economics of the power industry presented later (see p. 604).

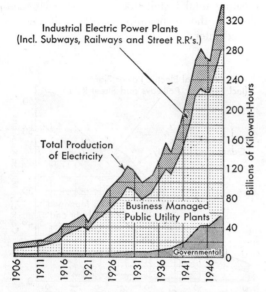

FIG. 37.2. Total Generation of Electricity in the United States, Including Industrial, 1906-1948.

The total generating capacity will now be broken down, first on the basis of service and ownership and then on the basis of kinds of prime movers used to drive the generators. Finally, certain interrelations between these subdivisions will be pointed out.

Public and Private Power Capacity and Output. On the basis of service, the electric power industry is divided into two major sectors—the electric utilities that generate electricity for sale to the public, and the power plants owned by mining, manufacturing, and other companies that generate electricity exclusively or primarily for the owner's use. Of these two, the former is by far the most important. On January 1, 1950, the utilities had an installed capacity of 62.7 million kilowatts, as compared

with approximately 13.4 million of nonutility or industrial capacity.[4] Not only is the public utility section by far the larger, it is also growing faster than the industrial sector. Unfortunately, census data on industrial capacity do not go further back than 1939. In that year there were 10.6 million kilowatts installed in nonutility plants, as compared with 38.9 million in utility plants. Corresponding figures on January 1, 1950, were 13.4 and 62.7 million kilowatts. According to estimates made by the industry, industrial capacity in 1906 was about 3 million kilowatts, the same as the utility capacity. Hence the industrial capacity had expanded slightly more than fourfold by the end of 1948, whereas the utility capacity had increased almost twenty-one times.

The trend in industries seems definitely in the direction of purchasing electricity from public utility systems rather than generating their own current. Only exceptionally large industrial plants or those using exceptionally large amounts of electricity such as electrometallurgical and electrochemical plants still find it economical to generate their own power.[5]

The total power equipment in United States manufacturing industry increased from less than 10 million horsepower[6] in 1899 to more than 50 million (or 37.3 million kilowatts) in 1939. In 1899 electric motors constituted a mere fraction of the total power equipment, about 4.8 percent of installed capacity; in forty years this increased to almost 90 percent of the total power installed, from less than half a million horsepower in 1899 to more than 45 million in 1939. As late as 1914 electric motors driven by purchased power made up less than half—to be exact, 44.2 percent—of the electric

---

[4] For a statistical analysis of nonutility power see Federal Power Commission, *Industrial Electric Power 1939-46*, Washington, 1947.

[5] In some cases even smaller users of power still prefer to generate their own power. This is true particularly where large amounts of live steam are called for in the manufacturing process. Steam and electric power can be generated as joint products by "bleeding" for live steam the turbines that drive the generators. In such instances the combined costs of home-made electricity and steam have proved lower than the combined costs of purchased electricity and home-made steam.

[6] One horsepower is equal to 746 watts. One kilowatt equals 1.34 horsepower.

motors installed, whereas in 1939 they made up almost two-thirds (64.5 percent) of the total.[7]

There are several reasons for this trend from home-made to purchased power or from industrial or nonutility to utility power. In the first place, the electric power and light industry specializes in the generation of electricity. A steelworks specializes in making steel and may incidentally generate power. It is a well-nigh universal experience that specialization promotes efficiency. In the second place, the generation of electric power is peculiarly subject to decreasing costs, meaning that costs tend to decline with increasing size of units installed. A 100,000-kilowatt generator does not cost twice as much as a 50,000-kilowatt generator, far from it; nor does a 100,000-horsepower steam turbine cost twice as much as a 50,000-horsepower turbine. A really large plant can use economically machines which a smaller plant cannot afford to install. These are just random illustrations of a significant trend. In the third place, an industrial power plant normally constitutes and functions as an isolated unit, whereas utility plants can be and nowadays typically are tied into interconnected systems.[8] Finally, utility plants are likely to make better use of the installed capacity and thus to operate at lower cost.[9] Besides supplying manufacturing and other industries with electric current, the public utility industry also serves commercial (stores, offices, etc.) and domestic consumers. The current can be used in the form of light, heat, or power.

Public and Private Ownership of Electric Utilities. The utility sector of the electric power and light industry is further divided on the basis of ownership into privately owned "business-managed" and publicly owned electric utilities. Publicly owned utilities may be federal, state districts, municipal, or coöperative. Table 37.1 shows both production of electric energy and capacity of generating plants by class of ownership, 1920 to 1949. Much of the background for this division by ownership was

given in the preceding chapter in the discussion of why the development of water power came increasingly under government control. Municipal interest in power generation is largely explained by the development of economical Diesel engines which warrant operating small and medium-sized power plants. Cooperatives and state districts function mainly as distributors of publicly generated current.

TABLE 37.1. Production of Electric Energy and Capacity of Generating Plants, by Class of Ownership, 1920-1949[10]

| Year | Electrical Utilities for Public Use | | Industrial Plants | Total |
	Privately Owned	Publicly Owned		
Production in Billion Kilowatt-Hours				
1920	37.7	1.7	....	39.4
1925	58.7	2.8	....	61.5
1930	86.1	5.0	....	91.1
1935	89.3	6.0	....	95.3
1940	125.4	16.4	38.1	179.9
1945	180.9	41.6	48.8	271.3
1946	181.0	42.2	46.4	269.6
1947	208.1	47.6	51.6	307.3
1948	228.2	54.5	54.1	336.8
1949	233.1	57.9	53.5	344.5
Installed Capacity in Million Kilowatts				
1920	12.0	0.7	....	12.7
1925	20.0	1.4	....	21.5
1930	30.3	2.1	....	32.4
1935	31.8	2.6	....	34.4
1940	34.4	5.5	11.0	51.0
1945	40.3	9.8	12.8	62.9
1946	40.3	10.0	12.7	63.0
1947	42.0	10.3	12.8	65.1
1948	45.4	11.2	13.1	69.6
1949	50.1	12.5	13.4	76.1

Kinds of Prime Movers. Another significant division is based on the prime mover used to drive the generator. There is a broad classification into hydro and fuel or thermal electricity. The latter is further subdivided into steam and internal combustion. Steam nowadays means mainly steam turbines, for reciprocating engines are definitely on the way out. Steam is raised by burning coal, oil, or gas. Fig. 37.3 shows installed capacity of utility generating plants (exclusive of "industrial" plants) on the basis of fuel and hydro, 1889 to 1948. Table

[7] J. M. Gould, *Output and Productivity in the Electric and Gas Utilities, 1899-1942,* National Bureau of Economic Research, Inc., New York, 1946, p. 48.

[8] For advantages of interconnection, see p. 607.

[9] For the relation between costs and capacity factor (or load factor) see pp. 604-605.

[10] Edison Electric Institute, *Statistical Bulletin,* No. 17, June, 1950. Tables 37.3 and 37.4 are also from this bulletin.

37.2 shows the distribution of the generating capacity of power plants serving the public on December 31, 1948, and the kilowatt-hours generated during 1948, as reported by the Federal Power Commission.

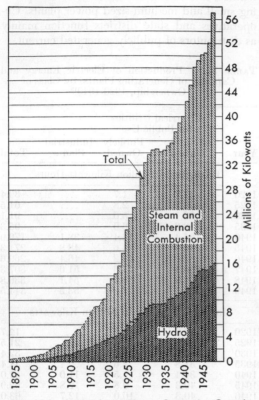

FIG. 37.3. United States Electric Generating Capacity, Fuel and Hydro. (Figs. 37.3 and 37.4 from Federal Power Commission.)

TABLE 37.2. Distribution of Generating Capacity and Kilowatt-Hours Generated, 1949

	Capacity (million kilowatts)		Output (billion kilowatt-hours)	
Steam	44.3	70.7%	197.9	68.0%
Hydroelectric	16.6	26.4%	89.7	30.8%
Internal combustion	1.8	2.9%	3.5	1.2%
Total	62.7	100.0%	291.0	100.0%

Significant Correlations. As can be deduced from the preceding discussion, there is a definite correlation between type of ownership of power plants and type of prime mover used in these plants. Thus industrial power plants are

generally steam plants in the case of ordinary manufacturing concerns, and frequently hydroelectric plants in the case of electrometallurgical and electrochemical concerns. Some interesting facts about the utility sector of the electric power and light industry are revealed in Table 37.3.

TABLE 37.3. Installed Capacity in Electric Generating Plants Serving the Public December 31, 1949 (exclusive of industrial capacity)

	Privately Owned	Publicly Owned	Total	Publicly Owned in Per-cent of Total
	(in million kilowatts)			
Hydroelectric	9.3	7.3	16.6	44.1
Steam	40.2	4.1	44.3	9.2
Internal combustion	0.6	1.2	1.8	66.2
Total	50.1	12.5	62.7	20.0

According to the table, on December 31, 1949, publicly owned installations made up one-fifth of the total utility generating capacity, but this publicly owned fifth was very unevenly distributed among the three types of prime movers—only 9.2 percent of the steam capacity, but 44.1 percent of the hydro and 66.2 percent of the internal-combustion capacity. The explanation is given in the preceding discussion. The larger rivers are navigable and navigable streams come under the jurisdiction of the federal government. Moreover, power plants located on navigable streams are *ipso facto* dual-purpose, and most likely multiple-purpose, plants. Such

TABLE 37.4. Output and Ownership of Capacity

	Installed Capacity December 31, 1949 (million kilowatts)		Output of Electricity During 1949 (billion kilowatt-hours)	
Privately owned utility capacity	50.1	65.8%	233.1	67.7%
Publicly owned utility capacity	12.5	16.5%	57.9	16.7%
Industrial capacity	13.4	17.7%	53.5	15.6%
Total	76.1	100.0%	344.5	100.0%

plants, as was made clear in the preceding chapter, are almost bound to be federally owned and operated. Multiple-purpose power plants are located also on nonnavigable streams. Some of the publicly owned steam plants are

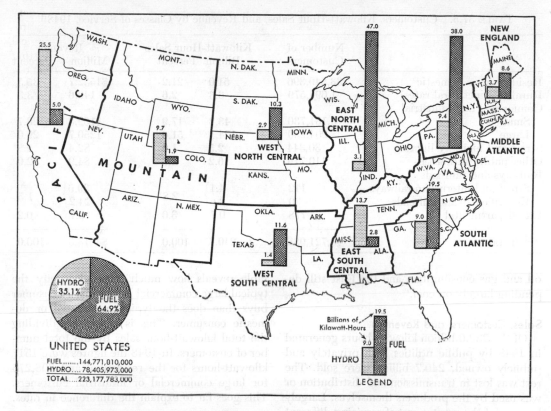

FIG. 37.4. Generation of Electricity by Geographical Divisions, United States, 1946.

stand-by plants operated in conjunction with hydro power plants (see p. 608). Internal combustion refers primarily to Diesel engines. The Diesel engine is a prime mover that is ideally suited to small and medium-sized power plants, such as smaller towns and cities are apt to require.

Another correlation worth comment is that between output and ownership of capacity. Table 37.4 gives the main facts and shows what one would expect to find. The capacity of the private utilities is utilized most fully, that of industrial plants least; publicly owned utility capacity occupies a position in the middle. The reason for this will be brought out in the discussion of power plant economics later in this chapter. The record of the publicly owned utilities is adversely affected by the low capacity factor (see p. 608) of stand-by steam plants and of internal-combustion plants serving smaller communities with insufficient diversity of demand. Publicly owned hydro capacity

generally has a highly satisfactory capacity factor.

Of the 291.0 billion kilowatt-hours generated by utilities in 1949, 89.7 billion, or 30.8 percent, were hydroelectricity. This was unusually low. The average annual percentage for 1920-1946 was 35.7, as reported by the Federal Power Commission.

**Regional Aspects of United States
Power Production**

In a country of continental expanse like our own, it is not surprising to find wide differences in the intensity and nature of electric power development in the different sections of the country. The map prepared by the Federal Power Commission (Fig. 37.4) shows these regional differences so clearly that no comment is needed. The fuel segments, if broken down into coal, oil, and natural gas, would show equally pronounced regional contrasts, with the Southwest and the Pacific coast region leading in

TABLE 37.5.   Customers, Kilowatt-Hour Sales, and Revenue by Classes of Service, 1948[11]

	Number of Customers	Kilowatt-Hour Sales Billion	Kilowatt-Hour Sales Percent	Revenue Million	Revenue Percent
Residential or domestic	33,549,396	51.0	21.2	$1532.7	35.5
Rural (distinct rural rates)	1,694,579	6.3	2.6	140.6	3.3
Commercial and industrial					
Small	5,131,730	43.2	17.9	1152.8	26.7
Large	204,230	124.1	51.6	1250.7	29.0
Street and highway lighting	30,344	2.5	1.0	82.4	1.8
Other public authorities	110,779	6.2	2.6	84.9	2.0
Railways and railroads					
Street and interurban railways	112	4.1 ⎫		39.6 ⎫	
Electrified steam railroads	30	2.6 ⎬ 2.8		24.2 ⎬ 1.5	
Interdepartmental	778	0.7	3.0	5.7	0.2
Total	40,721,988	240.7	100.0	$4313.3	100.0

oil and gas consumption and the East still depending largely on coal.[12]

Sales, Customers, and Revenues

Of the 282.6 billion kilowatt-hours generated in 1948 by public utilities both privately and publicly owned, 240.7 billion were sold. The rest was lost in transmission and distribution or was used by the producers themselves. Largely because of the greater cost of servicing different classes of customers, rates charged for electricity vary widely. Table 37.5 shows the numbers of customers in each class, the amount of electricity sold to each class, and the revenue received from it.

The most striking contrast in this table is that between the 33.5 million residential customers who buy 51.0 billion kilowatt-hours for about $1.5 billion and the less than 200,000 large commercial and industrial customers who buy 124.1 billion kilowatt-hours for less than $1.3 billion. The consumer classes are divided into two groups: those who pay more than the average and those who pay less; a comparison between the two percentage columns easily reveals that division. The difference is based largely on different scales of use. The

table reveals how much more electricity the typical large commercial or industrial consumer buys than does the typical residential or domestic consumer. This is shown by dividing the total kilowatt-hour sales by the total number of customers. In 1948 the figures were 1517 kilowatt-hours for the residential and 608,275 for large commercial or industrial customers. This goes far to explain the difference in rates.

The Post-World War II Expansion Program

During much of World War II and the period immediately following it power and light requirements increased at a rapid pace while expansion of capacity was reduced to a minimum by various scarcities brought on by the war. The result was a dangerous crowding of installed capacity until reserve capacities almost reached the vanishing point. The winters of 1947-1948 and 1948-1949 were months of breath-taking anxiety for power executives, for they were never sure whether "the thin ice would hold."

But in 1947 generators that had been ordered long ago began to leave the plants of the big electric equipment builders like General Electric, Westinghouse, and Allis Chalmers. In that year 2.2 million kilowatts of new generating capacity, almost all steam, was installed. An expansion program of unprecedented dimensions was under way. According to a report submitted by the Electric Power Industry Advisory Committee to the National Security Resources Board on May 11, 1948, total genera-

---

[11] Edison Electric Institute, *Statistical Bulletin, Year 1948*, New York, 1949, pp. 8, 9, 12.

[12] In 1949 electric utilities consumed 84.1 million tons of coal, 66.3 million barrels of fuel oil, and 549.9 million cubic feet of gas, a total of 123.5 million short tons of coal or coal equivalent. (Preliminary figures from Federal Power Commission.)

TABLE 37.6. World Production of Electricity, Selected Years, 1925-1948[13]
(billion kilowatt-hours)

	1925	1929	1937	1940	1944	1948
North America						
United States	73.8	96.9[d]	118.9	179.9[a]	279.5[a]	336.6[a]
Canada	10.5	17.9[d]	27.7	30.1	40.6	44.6
Mexico	0.6	1.8	2.5	2.5	2.7	4.0
South America						
Argentina	...	0.9	2.2	2.5	3.0	3.3[b]
Brazil	...	...	1.0	1.3	1.8	2.4
Chile	...	...	0.5	0.6	0.7	1.2
Europe						
Belgium	3.2	4.3[d]	5.5	4.2	3.7	7.9
Czechoslovakia	...	3.3	4.1	4.9	6.8	7.5
France	9.7	13.0[e]	18.2	17.4	15.4	27.6
Germany	11.5	30.6	24.6[a,c]	...	..	31.3[a,c]
Italy	7.6	12.7	15.4[a]	19.4	13.5	22.7
Netherlands	0.9	1.6	2.2	2.5	2.1	4.1
Norway	4.2	10.5	9.0[a]	8.7	11.1	12.4
Poland	1.3	2.9	3.4[f]	...	...	7.5
Spain	...	2.4	2.5[a]	3.6	4.7	6.1
Sweden	3.5	5.0	8.0[a]	8.6	12.4	14.3
Switzerland	4.2	3.7	5.3	6.3	7.3	8.7
United Kingdom	8.3	10.9[d]	22.9[g]	28.8	38.4	46.5
Asia						
India	...	...	...	2.8	3.8	4.6
Japan	6.4	13.3	27.0[h]	31.0	20.1	33.6
Africa						
Union of South Africa	...	...	5.2	6.9	7.8	9.3
Oceania						
Australia	...	1.9	4.0[i]	5.1	6.7	8.1
New Zealand	...	...	1.2[a,h]	1.8[a,h]	2.3[a,h]	2.6[a,b,h]

[a] Includes industrial plants.
[b] 1947.
[c] Western Germany only.
[d] 1930.
[e] 1928.
[f] Prewar territory.
[g] Excluding Northern Ireland.
[h] Year beginning April 1.
[i] Fiscal year ending June 30.

tion capacity on order and scheduled for shipment between 1948 and 1951 totaled 19,-174,300 kilowatts. The figures ranged from 6,348,750 kilowatts for 1948 to 1,555,500 for 1951. Of the total, over 15 million kilowatts are represented by large steam generators, as compared with only 3 million for water wheels to be installed; the rest are for small steam generators. When one considers that it took the

industry thirty-nine years—from 1882 till 1920—to reach the 20-million-kilowatt capacity level, an expansion in five years amounting to more than 21 million kilowatts is most impressive. Electricity is one of the master keys to high productivity and full employment.

PRODUCTION OF ELECTRICITY IN FOREIGN COUNTRIES

Up to this point the discussion of electric power production has been confined to the United States. While that country's population may constitute less than 6 percent of the population of the earth, their share of the world's electricity output probably exceeds one-half.

[13] Figures for 1925 and 1929 from U.S. Department of Commerce, *Commerce Yearbook, 1931,* vol. 2, p. 701. Figures for 1937-1948 from Statistical Office of the United Nations.

Electricity is that generated by public utilities unless otherwise stated.

In per capita generation of electricity the United States is exceeded by only a few countries exceptionally favored by nature in water-power resources, notably Norway, Canada, and Sweden. Table 37.6 shows the world output of electricity in selected years from 1925 to 1948.

The ten ranking countries are as follows:

		Output of Electricity (billion kilowatts)	Kilowatts per Capita	Per Capita Rank
1.	United States	336.6	2290	3
2.	United Kingdom	46.5	930	5
3.	Canada	44.6	3457	2
4.	Japan	33.6	416	8
5.	Germany	31.3	....	.
6.	France	27.6	674	7
7.	Italy	22.7	297	9
8.	Sweden	14.3	2073	4
9.	Norway	12.4	3875	1
10.	Union of South Africa	9.3	788	6

ECONOMICS OF POWER PLANT OPERATION

Capacity, Plant, and Load Factors

The economic problems of power-plant operation arise primarily from the "perishability" or nonstorability of electricity. If large amounts of electricity could be stored economically, most of the difficulties of power-plant operation would diminish or disappear and the cost of electricity would be greatly reduced. To generate electricity cheaply requires heavy investments in large prime movers and generators, power plants, dams, transmission and distribution systems, etc. This means a large fixed overhead investment. In industries operating with heavy fixed investments the unit cost of production depends largely on the extent to which and the regularity with which the installed capacity is utilized.

Regularity of operation can be achieved without undue difficulty if (1) the product can be stored or (2) the demand for it is not subject to violent daily, weekly, seasonal, or cyclical variations. Electricity cannot be stored and the demand for it is highly variable; moreover, the variations cannot be predicted with accuracy or assurance. The case of hydroelectricity is further complicated by unpredictable variations in stream flow.

It is apparent from the foregoing that a high capacity factor (see below) is at one and the same time the most desirable objective of power-plant operation and the one most difficult of attainment.

The extent to which installed capacity is being utilized is usually measured in terms of three factors: capacity factor, plant factor, and load factor.[14] *Capacity factor* is the ratio of the average load on a machine or equipment for a certain period of time to the rating of the machine or equipment. *Plant factor* is the ratio of the average load on the plant for a certain period of time to the aggregate rating of all the generating equipment installed in the plant. *Load factor* is the ratio of the average load over a designated period to the peak load in that period.

Evidently, capacity factor and plant factor are very similar concepts, the only difference being that capacity factor applies to a *single* machine or equipment, while plant factor applies to the *aggregate* equipment installed in a plant. But the load factor is different. An example will clarify the terms. If a generator with a rated capacity of 10,000 kilowatts generates 43,800,000 kilowatt-hours in the course of a year, it has a capacity factor of 50 percent. The figure is arrived at by the following calculation. There are 8760 hours in a year (365 × 24). A kilowatt is the capacity to generate 8760 kilowatt-hours in a year. A rated capacity of 10,000 kilowatts thus is the capacity to generate 87,600,000 kilowatt-hours in 8760 hours—in other words, full utilization, or a capacity factor of 100 percent. But 43,800,000 kilowatt-hours is exactly 50 percent. Similarly a plant with aggregate equipment of 10,000 kilowatts that generated 43,800,000 kilowatt-hours in a year would have a plant factor of 50 percent.

If it is assumed that the peak or highest load for this plant during the year was reached at 90 percent of the installed capacity—in other words, if at one time during the year 90 percent of the capacity was in use and the other 10 percent remained idle throughout the year —the load factor of this plant is 55.6 percent. This is arrived at as follows: The plant has an aggregate installation of 10,000 kilowatts, but only 9000 are used. The maximum number of kilowatt-hours which 9000 kilowatts can gener-

---

[14] See Federal Power Commission, *Glossary of Important Power and Rate Terms, Abbreviations and Units of Measurement*, Washington, 1936.

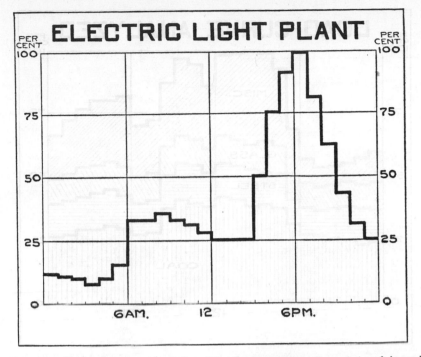

FIG. 37.5. Hourly Load Curve of an Electric Power Plant Selling Light Only. The variation of demand during a twenty-hour period renders a poor load factor (and capacity factor) inevitable. (Figs. 37.5 and 37.6 based on G. M. Gadsby, "Use of Electric Service in Industry.")

ate in the course of a year is 9000 × 8760, or 78,840,000. Actually only 43,800,000 are generated by our imaginary plant. The ratio of the number of kilowatt-hours actually generated to the number which the 9000 kilowatts actually in use could have generated

$$\left(\frac{43,800,000}{78,840,000} = 55.6\right) \text{ is the load factor.}$$

In view of the vital significance of the plant factor for the economics of the electric power industry, the Federal Power Commission compiles annually the plant factors of all generating plants in the United States that serve the public; those for selected years from 1920 to 1948 are given in Table 37.7.

The table brings out several important facts. In the first place, there is the remarkable increase of more than 20 points during the period covered. This is largely explained by the crowding of generating capacity during the war emergency, when, as has been said, many generators were pushed way beyond their rated capacity and reserve capacity dwindled to al-

most zero. In the second place, the table clearly indicates the effects of the business cycle. There was a recession from 1920 to 1921 and another one from 1937 to 1938, both of which

TABLE 37.7. Plant Factors of Generating Plants in the United States, Selected Years, 1920-1948[15]

	All Plants	Hydro	Fuel
1920	35.3	48.4	29.9
1921	32.4	44.1	27.5
1929	36.5	48.0	32.3
1932	26.6	40.8	21.3
1937	38.4	49.7	33.9
1938	35.5	48.5	30.2
1939	38.2	45.9	35.1
1940	41.0	48.5	38.0
1941	45.7	50.4	43.9
1942	48.6	59.1	44.4
1943	53.5	62.9	49.6
1944	53.5	59.1	51.1
1945	51.2	61.9	46.6
1946	50.7	60.2	46.8
1947	56.9	60.0	56.7[a]
1948	59.3	61.4	57.7[a]

[a] Steam only.

[15] Figures for 1920-1946 from Federal Power Commission; 1947 and 1948 figures compiled from data furnished by the Edison Electric Institute.

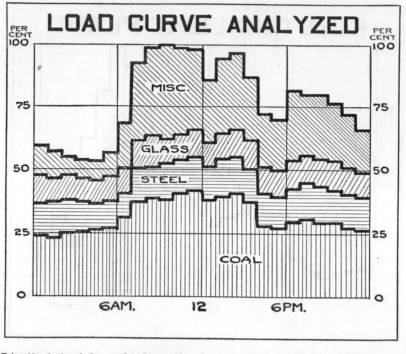

FIG. 37.6. Hourly Load Curve of a Power Plant Serving a Diversified Market. The favorable effect of demand diversification on the load factor is clearly evident.

are reflected in the figures. The fact that 1929 was a boom year and 1932 a depression year is likewise reflected in the dip from 36.5 to 26.6. In the third place, the difference between the plant factors for hydro and fuel equipment is striking. The difference narrowed down toward the end of the period, showing in part the beneficial effects of interconnection (see p. 607) on the plant factor for fuel capacity.

The table does not cover industrial capacity. This plant factor can be calculated from total number of kilowatts installed and total number of kilowatt-hours generated. According to these records, which go back only to 1937, the plant factor was approximately 36 for 1937 and 44 for 1945, showing improvement as industrial activity expanded. That private power plants should have a plant factor lower than utility plants is to be expected. For one thing they are not interconnected and hence must carry proportionately larger reserve capacities. Furthermore, they do not enjoy the benefit of a highly diversified demand.

The load factor, as was shown above, registers the extent to which the *used* portion of

the total capacity is utilized. A power system may have a high load factor and a low capacity factor. The situation in southern California illustrates this. Suppose that the Southern California Edison Company has just completed a vast expansion program, pushing capacity considerably ahead of current needs; for a period of several years the capacity factor is apt to be low. But conditions in California favor a high load factor, because as lighting requirements taper off during the spring the irrigation requirements increase, thus smoothing out the demand curve.

Low load factors may be raised by attracting new customers whose power and light demand schedule is such that it helps to fill the gaps in the load left by present customers' demands. A high load factor depends on the diversity of customers' power needs and on the way in which such diversities dovetail to make a fairly smooth total demand (or load) curve. Figs. 37.5 and 37.6 illustrate this. Fig. 37.5 shows the daily load curve of a small electric light plant. Its poor load factor is manifest. Fig. 37.6 shows how diversity of demand in an interconnected system raises the load factor. The effects of seasonal variation could be shown by similar diagrams.

Interconnection of Power Plants and Power Systems

The interconnection of power plants into coördinated systems and of the systems themselves for purposes of emergency aid is a major element in power plant economics.[16] Just as the interconnection of banks into the Federal Reserve System permits the all-round lowering of bank reserves and thus, by raising the "capacity factor" of banks, tends to lower the cost of banking operations, so the interconnection of power plants and of power systems has similar beneficial effects on their operation. Among these effects are:

1. Lower reserve requirements and, as a result, higher plant factors and lower costs.
2. Higher diversity of demand. An interconnected system operates over a wider area than a single plant. In general, diversity of demand increases with the size of the market area served. As was shown above, higher diversity of demand tends to raise the load factor and thus to lower costs.
3. In the case of hydroelectricity, the evening out of interregional differences in water supply. For example, rainfall frequently varies considerably east and west of the Appalachian Mountains. The Carolinas may suffer from drought while Tennessee may have ample rainfall, and vice versa. By interconnecting plants, or systems, on both sides of the mountains the aggregate power supply can be evened out, with resulting lower reserve requirements and hence lower costs.
4. Better use of the plant itself. As will be shown, there are different types of power plants. The best results can be accomplished by coördinating the various types in

such a way that each can specialize along the lines best suited to it.

Problems of Interconnection. Although there is no doubt that interconnection in the sense of regional integration of power plants is the most efficient way of raising the plant factor and thus lowering the cost of electricity, it does present certain problems. One of the problems stems from the necessity of systematized standardization, without which an interconnected system cannot operate but which renders innovation and experiment exceedingly difficult, thus conceivably slowing up the forward march of technological progress. On the other hand, the greater resources of a larger system may offset this handicap. Another problem has to do with the abuse of interconnection by speculative financial interests that wish to exploit the idea for profit without putting it to the fundamental purpose—better and cheaper service—for which it was conceived. This, however, is a defect which probably adheres to all human effort. With vigilance and resoluteness such abuses can be stopped.

Types of Power Plants

Power plants are classified as to type into two broad categories, hydro and fuel plants; the distinction between them is self-evident. Both of these major divisions, in turn, have subdivisions. Thus, there are two extreme types of hydro sites: the Hoover Dam site, with its high head, in a narrow gorge; and the Conowingo Dam site on the Susquehanna, with its low head spread across a wide river bed. The head itself is indivisible. The enormous head of the Hoover Dam calls for giant turbines and generators, whereas the low spread-out head of the Conowingo favors the installation of a number of smaller generating units. To render the most satisfactory service, large turbogenerators should be operated constantly, supplying what is called the base load, the core of sustained demand. The smaller units such as those installed at Conowingo permit more flexible use; they are well suited to handle peak loads over shorter periods of time. Conowingo is hooked up with giant steam turbogenerator plants in Philadelphia and Baltimore and is drawn upon when these plants cannot meet the peak demands.

Generally speaking, large steam units are

---

[16] Interconnection was formerly referred to as "superpower." When that word became associated with monopolistic abuses, the term "giant power" was suggested to identify interconnection as a means of emphasizing the social benefits of power-plant coördination. See "Giant Power: Large-Scale Electrical Development as a Social Factor," *Annals of the American Academy of Political and Social Science,* March, 1925.

best suited to carry base loads, and smaller units to handle peak loads. Giant turbines are apt to be less flexible. The type of fuel may have some bearing on this. Thus, the steam plant at Long Beach, California, was used as a base-load plant when fuel oil was used to generate steam, but was converted into a peak-load plant when natural gas with higher caloric value was substituted for fuel oil.

Thus, it becomes apparent that there are four types of power plants: hydro base load, hydro peak load, fuel base load, and fuel peak load. The best results can be achieved by the judicious interconnection of different types of plants for the coördinated use of the installed capacity.

Two other types of plants must be mentioned: stand-by plants and pumped storage plants. Stand-by plants are used primarily in connection with hydro plants. It is often desirable to build hydro power-plant capacity in excess of the water power available all through the year. As was mentioned before, power available the year round is called "firm" power; power available only part of the year is called "secondary" power. Unless secondary power can be "firmed up," i.e., made available throughout the year, it is known as "dump power"; this can be sold only on a "when and if available" basis and at a very low rate. Secondary water power can be firmed up by connecting the hydro system with a steam plant which "stands by" for the emergency when the flow of water is inadequate. Obviously, stand-by plants have to operate at a low plant factor and therefore at considerably high cost.[17]

Pumped storage plants are a variety of stand-by plant; but whereas the stand-by plants just discussed firm-up hydro power, the pumped storage plant is designed to raise the efficiency

of steam plants. This idea, which was first developed in 1903, is more commonly applied in Europe than in the United States.

In this type of plant, the off-peak power of a steam turbine is used to pump water into a natural reservoir or, more usually, into one especially built for the purpose. The stored water is released during an extra peak demand. The combined steam turbine-hydro stand-by plant system assures considerable economy. One of the best examples of the pumped storage plant was the one operated in coöperation with the large steam turbines of the Rheinisch-Westfälische Elektrizitätswerke in Essen, Germany. A rather efficient plant is the one on the Rocky River, a small tributary of the Housatonic in Connecticut; its reservoir combines stand-by functions with general storage functions.[18]

Power Plant Location

The question is frequently raised why steam power plants are not located near coal mines to save transportation costs. There are several reasons. In the first place, the relative cost of shipping coal and transmitting electricity must be compared. Where water transportation is available, as on the east coast from Hampton Roads north, hauling coal may be cheaper. Moreover, in the absence of improvements in transmission, coal hauling is constantly gaining on transmission because of the decreasing amount of coal needed to generate a kilowatthour of electricity. Oil and gas are more and more supplanting coal, and that too militates against transmission, because liquids and gases can be transported rather cheaply.

Another weighty reason why large modern steam plants are not likely to be located in coal-mining regions has to do with water supply. The fuel efficiency of the modern steam plant is achieved in part by means of superheated steam that enters the turbines at high temperature and pressure. The efficiency of the steam turbine depends on the spread between the temperature of the steam entering and leaving it. To make this spread as great as possible and also to take advantage of the sup-

---

[17] Such a stand-by plant is the steam plant just below the Watts Bar Dam on the Tennessee River; it is part of the interconnected TVA system. Another stand-by plant is the steam plant at Florence, Alabama, near the Wilson Dam at Muscle Shoals. A third one is planned for New Johnsonville near TVA's Kentucky Dam to firm up power to the western sector of the TVA area.

For a discussion of this third project, see *Hearings Before the Subcommittee of the Committee of Appropriations,* House of Representatives, 80th Congress, 2nd Session, on the Government Corporations Appropriations Bill for 1949.

[18] For further details, see F. A. Allner, "Economic Aspects of Water Power," American Institute of Electrical Engineers, Baltimore meeting, October 10-12, 1932.

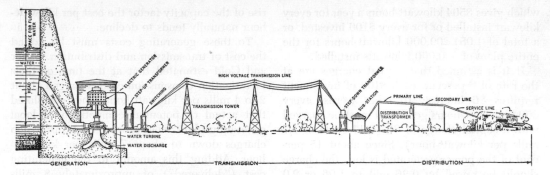

FIG. 37.7.   A Hydroelectric Plant with Distribution. (S. S. Wyer, "Study of Boulder Dam Project," pamphlet issued by the Ohio Chamber of Commerce, Columbus, Ohio, 1928.)

plementary motive force of the turbine, the steam is condensed into water, thus creating a vacuum which "pulls" on the turbine wheels while the superheated steam is pushing from the opposite direction. The amount of condensing water needed to accomplish this is incredible. The Duquesne Power and Light Plant near Pittsburgh is reported to require six times as much water for condensing purposes as the entire city needs for all purposes. The giant power plant on the East River in Brooklyn is said to raise the temperature of the river appreciably for a considerable area.

A body of water large enough to supply this incredible amount of condensing water thus becomes a major factor in determining the location of modern giant steam power plants. The East River is a branch of the Atlantic Ocean, and the Hudson River is an estuary; both are adequate. So also are the Great Lakes, gigantic storage reservoirs, and major rivers. But no region that is not located on such exceptional bodies of water can support a modern giant steam plant.

Cost of Electricity

The cost of generating and distributing electricity fluctuates with technological developments and with general changes in wage and price levels. The objective of the present discussion is not to show current cost but rather to indicate the components which make up the cost of electricity delivered to the consumer. In treating this problem of cost, several points should be made clear. In the first place, the electric power and light industry operates with exceptionally heavy fixed investments. This

means that the rate of utilizing the installed equipment, the plant factor, is by far the most important cost determinant. All cost figures, therefore, have to be given relative to a given plant factor. In the second place, the power and light industry is, generally speaking, one of "increasing returns." Once certain investments have been made, the market tends to grow, thus permitting increasingly full use and consequently lower costs, and, in the absence of neutralizing rate reductions, increasing revenues.

The cost of electricity delivered to the customer is made up of (1) the cost of generating, transmitting, and distributing the electricity (see Fig. 37.7) and (2) general costs of running the business, such as general office expenses and such other expenses as insurance, legal expenses, etc. The costs will be discussed in that order.

Before a plant is built there are expenses for investigation, obtaining the necessary capital, organization, legal fees, etc.[19] Including these preliminary expenses as part of the plant cost, a power plant of 300,000 kilowatts at $100 a kilowatt costs $30,000,000. Theoretically, 300,000 kilowatts in the course of a year can generate 8760 kilowatt-hours per kilowatt installed or a total of 2,628,000,000 kilowatt-hours. Actually, the output will be much less. Here a capacity factor of 40 percent is used,

---

[19] The calculation that follows is based on John Bauer and Nathaniel Gold, *The Electric Power Industry: Development, Organization, Public Policies*, Harper & Brothers, New York, 1939. The figures are representative of the period before World War II.

which gives 3504 kilowatt-hours a year for every kilowatt installed or for every $100 invested, or a total of 1,051,200,000 kilowatt-hours for the entire plant of 300,000 kilowatts installed.

If it is assumed that capital charges are at the rate of 6 percent, each $100 of investment requires $6 interest. In other words, every 3504 kilowatt-hours generated must be charged with a capital charge of $6 (0.17 cents or 1.7 mills per kilowatt-hour). Since about 15 percent of the power generated is lost, the charge should be raised by 0.26 mill to 1.96 or 2.0 mills per kilowatt-hour; this amounts roughly to $1.8 million a year for the 1.05 billion kilowatt-hours generated and the 900,000,000 delivered. Operating and maintenance labor normally comes to about 0.5 mill per kilowatt-hour generated or 0.6 mill delivered to the consumer—roughly $525,000 per year. In fuel plants, the most important material is fuel; its cost depends on price and efficiency of use. If we assume that a ton of bituminous coal of 14,000 B.T.U. per pound costs $5 and that 12,000 B.T.U. are required to generate one kilowatt-hour,[20] the 3504 kilowatt-hours generated per kilowatt installed require about 1.5 tons at a cost of $7.50; the 1,051,200,000 kilowatt-hours generated during the year will require 450,000 tons of coal at a cost of $2,250,000, which amounts to 2.1 mills per kilowatt-hour generated and 2.5 mills per kilowatt-hour delivered. Other materials are estimated at 0.5 mill per kilowatt-hour generated and 0.6 per kilowatt-hour delivered. This leaves depreciation, maintenance, and insurance, which are figured here at the same rate as the interest—6 percent of the entire plant investment, or 1.7 mills per kilowatt-hour generated and 2.0 mills per kilowatt-hour delivered. These costs are summarized in Table 37.8.

Of these expenses, only fuel varies with output but not proportionately since steam must be kept up in readiness for sudden calls.

Any additional power generated has a very low "incremental cost"—at the most 3 mills. This, in turn, warrants granting specially low rates to customers for the purpose of materially raising the capacity factor. With each

rise of the capacity factor the cost per kilowatt-hour naturally tends to decline.

To these generating costs must be added the cost of transmission and distribution. Bauer and Gold estimated that at the time of their investigation transmission costs averaged about 2 to 4 mills per kilowatt-hour. They calculated that actual or potential competition of local generating plants held economical transmission charges down to about 7 mills per kilowatt-hour. Adding this amount to the generating cost ("delivered") of approximately 8 mills gives 1.5 cents per kilowatt-hour as the cost at which any local community is expected to be able to generate its own power.

TABLE 37.8.   Plant Costs

| | Mills per Kilowatt-Hour | | |
	Generated	Delivered to Consumer[a]	Dollars per Year
Capital charge	1.7	2.0	$1,800,000
Labor	0.5	0.6	525,000
Fuel	2.1	2.5	2,250,000
Other materials	0.5	0.6	525,000
Depreciation, maintenance, and insurance	1.7	2.0	1,800,000
Total	6.5	7.7	$6,900,000

[a] Allowing for line losses of 15 percent but not including cost of transmission and distribution.

Distribution costs are very heavy (see Fig. 37.7). They differ widely according to the class of customers served. They are very high for farms, not so high for suburban residential areas, lower for closely settled urban "residential" areas, still lower for commercial customers, and lowest for very large industrials. Distribution costs generally exceed both generation and transmission costs.

In planning transmission installations, it is important to keep in mind that small communities can generate electricity fairly cheaply, generally in Diesel engine plants, and thus save transmission costs; and that larger industrials can build their own power plants.

General costs vary widely with the size and character of the business organization to which the generating unit and transmission and distribution equipment belong. Exclusive of general costs, the cost of electricity delivered to the consumer is made up of the following items:

---

[20] This is better-than-average performance but by no means beyond the capacity of first-rate plants.

Cost of generating	0.77	cents per kilowatt-hour			
Cost of transmission	0.3	"	"	"	"
Cost of distribution	2 to 4.0	"	"	"	"
	3 to 5.07	"	"	"	"

These calculations were made in the late thirties; since then some expenses such as fuel and labor have risen sharply, but overhead and depreciation charges on existing equipment have declined because of the unprecedented rise in the capacity factor. Cost of new construction has risen sharply.

Comparison of Fuel and Hydro Costs

"Which is cheaper, fuel or hydroelectricity?" is a question frequently asked by laymen. They expect a simple answer, but unfortunately there is no such answer. A comparison of fuel and hydro costs is exceedingly complex; it can be tackled only by an operational approach—one applied plant by plant and system by system.

Evidently if hydro plants can do without fuel stand-by plants, they do not have to buy fuel. In the calculation above, fuel cost was set down as 2.5 mills per kilowatt-hour out of a total generating cost of 7.7 mills, or roughly one-third of the generating cost. However, this fuel cost constitutes only a small fraction of the 3 to 5 cents electricity costs delivered at the customer's switch; actually it amounts to one-twelfth (8.3 percent) of the lower figure and one-twentieth (5 percent) of the larger one. Coal can be delivered to a great load center such as New York, Chicago, Detroit, etc.; hence transmission costs are not excessive. The most important water-power sites are so located that transmission costs run considerably higher. Steam turbines operate best at speeds far above those suitable for water turbines. To deliver the same power, therefore, steam turbines can be considerably more compact than water turbines. On the other hand, the steam generators and water-cooling installations may exceed in size and cost the corresponding installations needed to operate a hydro power plant of similar capacity.

On the whole it is true that water-power plants require considerably larger fixed investments (dams, reservoirs, etc.) than do steam plants. Hence, the capital charges are definitely higher. (Average figures do not mean much.) On the other hand, since water-power plants are technically nearer perfection, obsolescence is negligible. Physical depreciation should also be lower because of the absence of high temperatures. But there is the silting-up of dams to be considered.

In the case of multiple-purpose water-power sites the allocation of costs is vital to determining the cost of water-power generation. As was stated before, no definite allocation is possible because many of the corollary functions (recreation, wildlife, protection of life and health, etc.) have no exact pecuniary rating. In the case of such systems as TVA the cost of generating electricity at an individual site does not have much meaning. What counts is the overall cost of maintaining and operating the system. The same holds true, more or less, of any power plant that is part of an interconnected system.

Cost comparisons between hydro and fuel plants should apply not to cost per kilowatt generated but to cost of (1) base-load and (2) peak-load (secondary) power. It is claimed that in general the incremental cost of hydroelectric power is lower than the corresponding cost of fuel power.[21] It will be recalled that the capacity factor of hydro plants is considerably higher than that of fuel plants. Stored water is a good substitute for stored electricity if the equipment is available to convert the water into electricity at a moment's notice. The handicap which water power suffers by virtue of stream-flow variation must not be lost sight of. It can be minimized, especially in interconnected systems such as TVA, but always at a cost. The interruption of the fuel supply by strikes or "Acts of God" possibly corresponds somewhat to the defects of water power. The lack of flexibility of steam-power equipment is also a compensating factor.

In many parts of the world hydro and fuel plants should be considered not as separate entities, but as supplementary units of a system. Steam probably can produce cheaper base-load power where fuel is available at a reasonable cost. Hydro can produce cheaper peak-load power. By building on this basic fact, interconnected systems, drawing on both sources of power, constitute probably the cheapest source of electrical energy that modern science can devise.

---

[21] F. A. Allner, *op. cit.*

BIBLIOGRAPHY

Abrams, E. R., *Power in Transition*, New York, Scribner, 1944.

"American Power Plants—Vital Engineering Data," *Power*, June, 1934.

Bauer, J., and Costello, P., *Public Organization of Electric Power*, New York, Harper, 1949.

Bauer, J., and Gold, N., *The Electric Power Industry*, New York, Harper, 1939.

Bonneville Power Administration, *Report on the Columbia River Power System*, Portland, 1947.

Bonneville Power Administration, *Advance Program of System Development*, Portland, 1948.

Bureau of Reclamation, *The Grand Coulee Dam and the Columbia Basin Reclamation Project*, no date.

Edison Electric Institute, *Statistical Bulletin* (annual).

Federal Power Commission, *Production of Electric Energy and Capacity of Generating Plants*, Washington (annual).

Federal Power Commission, *National Power Survey*, Washington, 1936.

Federal Power Commission, *Electric Rate Survey, Glossary of Important Power and Rate Terms, Abbreviations and Units of Measurement*, Washington, 1936.

Federal Power Commission, *Electric Power Statistics, 1920-1940*, Washington, 1941.

Federal Power Commission, *Consumption of Fuel for Production of Electric Power, 1943*, Washington, 1943.

Federal Power Commission, *Industrial Electric Power, 1939-1946*, Washington, 1947.

Gould, J. M., *Output and Productivity of Electric and Gas Utilities*, New York, National Bureau of Economic Research, 1946.

"Grand Coulee," *Fortune*, January, 1937.

Marlio, L., "Will Electric Power Be a Bottleneck?" Pamphlet No. 40, Washington, Brookings Institution, 1942.

National Security Resources Board, *National Power Supply, 1948-1951*, Washington, May 11, 1948 (mimeographed).

Pritchett, C. H., *The Tennessee Valley Authority*, Chapel Hill, University of North Carolina Press, 1943.

Thomas, P. H., *Electric Power from the Wind, a Survey*, Federal Power Commission, Washington, 1945.

Transactions: First World Power Conference, London, 1924.

Second World Power Conference, Berlin, 1930.

Third World Power Conference, Washington, 1936.

Fourth World Power Conference, London, 1950.

"Washington and Power," *Fortune*, March, 1938.

UNIT 3. THE IRON AND STEEL INDUSTRY

Chapter 38

STEEL—THE BACKBONE OF MODERN INDUSTRY

IMPORTANCE OF IRON AND STEEL

Modern industrial economy rests on regional and international specialization and the exchange of the products of that specialization. Exchange of the products of distant places requires transportation and communication. Today all the parts of the earth which have come under the spell of the mechanical revolution are covered with a network of transportation and communication. That network consists largely of steel, of many millions of tons of steel—steel in the form of rails and bridges, trains and stations, ships, automobiles, trucks, and buses, etc.

Western civilization is an urban civilization with millions of people crowded into cities, many boasting of skyscrapers and other structures that cover many acres. Such giant structures, whether factories, office buildings, apartment houses, are built of steel. Their framework is steel. Steel serves in many ways. The factories house engines of steel, machines of steel, tools of steel. The office buildings are furnished with steel furniture and steel equipment. In the home are found steel refrigerators, washing machines, stoves, and a hundred and one other steel appliances.

Even agriculture is coming to depend more and more on steel and things made of steel. This has long been true with reference to taking crops to market. But now farm production itself is relying more and more on mechanical implements for preparing and conserving the soil, for planting, harvesting, and processing the crops. Modern food-consuming habits are unthinkable without the ubiquitous tin can, which really is a steel can with a thin coating of tin. In short, steel is virtually everywhere. It is the most versatile of all materials known to man.

To say, therefore, that this is the steel age, that steel is *the* most important material in the world does not make much sense. One could with equal justification speak of the electrical age, the chemical age, the atomic age, certainly the coal age or, better, the coal-oil-gas age. The truth is that it is a complex age, an era of a complex civilization. What would steel be without the power to set it in motion? Where would iron and steel come from if not from the coke-using blast furnace, the oxygen-and-gas-quaffing steel furnace, or the electric furnace? Steel cannot exist without carbon, seldom exists without manganese; and the best steels are best because of the presence of one or several of special alloying ingredients. Steel would be lame without electricity and electricity cannot live without either copper or iron. While recognizing this interdependence of scores of materials and energies which renders possible the miracle of modern machine industry, one need not detract one iota from the worth, valor, virtue, and grandeur of steel.

Steel impresses most by its versatility and the bulk of its aggregate supply. Compared with the amount of steel available for use in thousands of forms over the face of the earth, all other metals appear dwarfed. Equally impressive is the annual output of steel, at least in periods of high business activity. In 1947, 150 million tons were produced in a score of countries.[1] Certainly all other metals have an almost picayune output compared with that gigantic total. Only copper, lead, and zinc are in the million-ton group. Copper once passed the 3-million ton mark—the nearest any metal ever approached the steel record. Coal and petroleum are produced in amounts larger than steel; in 1948 the world coal output came close to exceeding that of steel by 10 to 1. But the fuels are raw materials comparable with iron ore rather than with steel.

Size and Scope of the Industry

That the industry which produces and fabricates these vast quantities of iron and steel is one of the leaders of modern industry goes without saying. Viewed geographically it is a far-flung empire, covering a score of countries. In the United States it spreads through twenty-nine of the forty-eight states.

At the end of 1947, the portion of our iron and steel industry which reported to the American Iron and Steel Institute—over 90 percent of the industry—had an investment of $4.7 billion. That year, earnings exceeded $440 million,[2] the 759,534 employees earned over $2.4 billion in wages and salaries, there were 566,258 stockholders who received $183.8 million in cash dividends, and the taxes paid amounted to $428.6 million.[3] The industry produced 59.3

---

[1] American Iron and Steel Institute, *Annual Statistical Report, 1947*, p. 187.

[2] 9.36 percent was earned on investment as compared with 0.47 in 1938.

[3] See American Iron and Steel Institute, *op. cit.*, p. 6.

million net tons of pig iron and ferro-alloys, 84.9 million net tons of steel (ingot and casting), and 66.2 million tons of hot rolled iron and steel products.

To make these products required over 100 million net tons of iron ore, 44.6 million net tons of iron and steel scrap, 94.3 million tons of coal, 2.2 billion gallons of fuel oil, 255 billion cubic feet of natural gas, and 20.7 billion kilowatt-hours of electricity. Besides, huge amounts of lumber, sand, water, and various other materials were required.

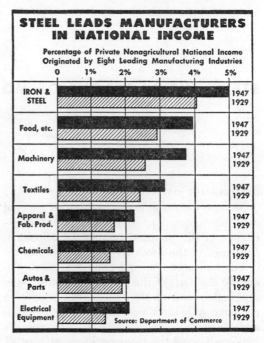

FIG. 38.1. *(Steel Facts, February, 1949, p. 7.)*

As Fig. 38.1 shows, in both 1929 and 1947 steel led all industries of the United States in contributions to the private nonagricultural national income. In this figure, the iron and steel industry *includes* foundries and other closely affiliated activities, but *excludes* mining and certain other operations such as the production of coke and its by-products.

The core of the industry consists of large integrated concerns whose activities include ore mining and beneficiation; coal mining; operation of coke ovens which besides coke yield such by-products as gas, sulfate of ammonia, tar, pitch, etc.; limestone quarrying; operation of iron and steel furnaces, rolling and finishing

TABLE 38.1. Comparison of the Iron and Steel and Related Industries with All Other Manufacturing Industries of the United States, 1939[4]

	Employees		Wages and Salaries		Costs of Material		Value Added by Manufacture	
	Number	Percent	Millions	Percent	Millions	Percent	Millions	Percent
Iron and steel and their products	1,083,487	12.1	$1,611	13.8	$3,636	11.3	$2,956	12.0
Machinery	943,656	10.6	1,482	12.7	2,013	6.3	2,969	12.0
Automobiles and transportation equipment	630,481	7.1	1,065	9.2	3,137	9.8	1,794	7.2
Total iron and steel and related products	2,657,624	29.8	$4,158	35.7	$8,786	27.4	$ 7,719	31.2
All other groups	6,279,086	70.2	7,474	64.2	23,332	72.6	16,992	68.8
Total United States	8,936,710	100.0	$11,632	100.0	$32,118	100.0	$24,711	100.0

mills, and cement mills; shipping operations on rivers, lakes, and oceans; hauling on land by railroad and motor trucks; warehousing, and many other activities. One of the chief by-products of steelmaking is the manufacture of cement, chiefly from furnace slag. Modern steel-making rests on science and the steel industry supports and carries on vast research projects.

Some of the largest steelmaking enterprises constitute parts of other manufacturing industries such as the automobile and agricultural implement industries.

The iron and steel industry as customarily defined does not include the numerous foundries and machine shops scattered throughout the land, or many of the plants that specialize in making alloy steels. It does not embrace the fuel-producing industries which sell to the steel industry, or such chief users of steel as the automobile and machinery industries. If it were possible to cover all the activities associated with and traceable to steel, one would discover that the steel industry, viewed in this wider sense, constitutes a considerable segment of the economy of the United States. Something approaching this is attempted in Table 38.1.

Reasons for the Importance of Iron and Steel

Properties of Steel. The iron and steel industry holds its dominant position among the metals for the simple reason that "it delivers

the goods." It furnishes materials of unsurpassed usefulness at prices which keep competition either out altogether or down to modest proportion. It is true that there is a certain competition between steel and the light metals, but it is only necessary to compare our current steel ingot capacity of over 96 million tons with our current aluminum capacity, which not even on a volume[5] basis is the equivalent of 2 million tons of steel, to realize how limited this competition is.

The dominant position of the industry rests first of all on the properties of steel.

Steel did not become the dominant metal by accident. There is no other metal that has the unique properties which make it so valuable from engineering and constructional standpoints. I will mention only a few. For instance, its high modulus of elasticity, which is much greater than that of any other common metal, allows it to withstand great stresses without appreciable distortion. Another important fact is that steel has a definite proportional strength limit, and if not stressed beyond this limit, it will return to its original form and size. This property is not possessed by other common metals or alloys, but it is of vital importance in all permanent structures and machines.

A third characteristic of steel is its relatively high ductility and toughness compared with other metals. While we can produce aluminum alloys with an ultimate strength approximating that of the mild and common structural steels, it is only possible with a great loss of ductility. From an engi-

[4] Board of Investigation and Research, Transportation Act of 1940, *The Economics of Iron and Steel Transportation*, Senate Document No. 80, 79th Congress, 1st Session, Washington, 1945.

[5] Because of the lightness of aluminum, volume rather than weight favors that metal.

neering viewpoint this is a very great disadvantage.

The ability of steel to be alloyed with other metals imparts to it properties useful in our industries which has widened its field of application and has opened the doors to new industrial developments. Without these alloy steels we could not have air power, we would not be able to produce gasoline in the quantities required for our planes, and we could not carry on many of the processes that are fundamental to our chemical industry. It is only necessary to look back, say 30 years, in any processing industry to realize how the development of steel and its alloys has made possible the tremendous progress that has occurred during that period.

The facility with which steel can be produced in varying degrees of hardness and strength to meet particular needs gives to steel a greater range of ductility and strength and other properties than any other metal or alloy.[6]

Relative Cheapness of Steel. But that is not all. In spite of the current price rise which has lifted the price quotation of a ton of "finished steel composite" to $97.77 (January, 1949) as compared with an average of $56.73 for 1941,[7] iron and steel are still cheap when compared with other metals. A price of $97.77 a ton means 4.89 cents a pound, as compared with 23.5 cents for copper, 22.0 for lead, 17.5 for zinc, $1.03 for tin, 16 cents for aluminum.[8] And finished steel is not strictly comparable with raw unmachined metals. Ingot steel is far cheaper than finished steel, and scrap steel in January, 1949, was selling for about 2.03 cents a pound.

Considering the unique usefulness of iron and steel, such prices are assuring. They are lower than those of other metals for the simple reason that it costs less to produce even finished steel than it does to produce copper, lead, zinc, tin, aluminum, etc. The lower prices are precisely why such enormous amounts of finished iron and steel can be sold not only in the United States but throughout the world. The huge output, in turn, contributes materially to the low costs—a benign circle!

Credit for these low costs and prices goes to the vast number of men in many lands who, in slow painstaking efforts through the centuries, created the miracle of modern iron and steel technology, and to the courageous and keen minds who built up the great empires of iron and steel. But nature too deserves much credit. Of no other metal are there in existence deposits as vast in size or as rich in metal content as there are of iron. As was said in an earlier chapter (p. 441), iron is one of the more common elements in the crust of the earth. But that alone does not mean much. Aluminum is more abundant, yet it sold for 17 cents a pound early in 1949 and for much more only a few years ago. Not only is iron a common constituent of the earth's crust, but there are in practically every continent in the world accumulations of iron ore, so large and so rich that the average metal content of the iron ores used today is probably close to 50 percent. This compares with something like 1 or 1.5 percent for copper. In other words, as regards iron we are still living in the cream-skimming period. This can hardly be said of other metals. The "cream" of our iron wealth may be getting a little thinner, but there are still billions of tons of deposits of rich metallic content.

Because of the richness of the iron ores now in use, the iron and steel industry has thus far avoided the vast expenditures forced on other metal industries by the leanness of their ore. True, a beginning is being made in working leaner ores, and for the first time since the dawn of the modern iron and steel industry iron-masters are getting a foretaste of things to come. But the scales are still heavily tipped in favor of iron. Moreover, the chemical composition of both the ore mineral and gangue[9] is generally such that relatively cheap mass processes can be applied to iron ores, whereas far more complex refining methods, generally involving the use of costly electric current, are necessary with other metals.

Iron ore is relatively cheap also because of the favorable location of important deposits. A favorable location is one that permits the low-cost assembly of raw materials near important

---

[6] Wilford Sykes, "The Future of the Steel Industry," American Iron and Steel Institute, *Yearbook, 1947.*

[7] *Business Week,* January 29, 1949, p. 13.

[8] The prices quoted are those of January, 1949, as listed in the *Journal of Commerce.*

[9] The reader will recall these terms from an earlier discussion (see p. 442). Important ore minerals of iron are magnetite ($FeO \cdot Fe_2O_3$), hematite (Fe_2O_3), and "limonite" ($Fe_2O_3 \cdot H_2O$). Gangue consists of associated impurities mainly of a nonmetallic character.

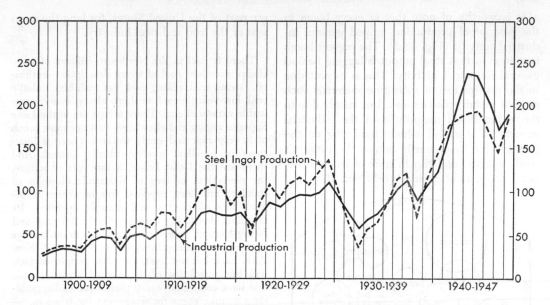

FIG. 38.2. Steel Production, Ingot and Industrial, United States, 1900-1948 (1935-1939 = 100). (Merrill Lynch, Pierce, Fenner & Bean, *Steel*, 1948, p. 9.)

markets. The location of the Minnesota deposits near the head of the Great Lakes, of the Alabama deposits near coal, and of the Swedish, Newfoundland, Chilean, Cuban, and other deposits near tidewater are examples.

Its relative cheapness makes iron the great mass metal of our modern industrial civilization. That, in turn, means production on a larger scale than is possible in any other metal industry. A single steelworks can produce several times the total world output of copper, lead, zinc, or what have you. This gigantic scale of operation, as was mentioned before, contributes to the economy of production. For one thing, the larger aggregate of capital may render feasible research work on a scale greater than is possible in any other metal industry— that is, unless steel is resting on its oars.

Another factor which contributes to the relative cheapness of iron and steel is the availability of vast amounts of scrap. The amount of iron and steel now in use in the United States has been variously estimated at 1.2 to 2 billion tons. Because of physical depreciation as well as obsolescence, this gigantic reservoir is bound to spill millions of tons into the scrap market each year. There have been years when scrap consumption in the steel industry was between 30 and 40 million tons. There simply are

not such amounts of other metals in the world. And, as the ensuing analysis will reveal, scrap is a real cost saver.

The iron and steel industry has an added advantage in the fact that the great concentrations of population, at least in the West, tend to gravitate toward the coal and iron regions. Large portions of the world copper output are produced in distant places, such as the Atacama desert of Chile or the wilds of Rhodesia and the Congo. But the bulk of iron and steel is made at home—because for the millions of industrial workers home is where the steel is!

Implications of the Importance of the Iron and Steel Industry

The Barometer of Business. An industry that reaches into every nook and cranny of modern industrial economy, without which hardly any other *modern* industry is possible, is bound to be an important barometer of business conditions. In business booms, steel requirements are pyramided and its output is pushed to the limits of physical plant capacity. Inversely, in times of depression its magnificent powers are left unused, because steel goes into producers' and durable consumers' goods, neither of which are in heavy demand at a time when people live more or less from hand to mouth.

It is worthy of note that in every boom in the past, steel production topped general industrial activity (Fig. 38.2). The present boom is unique in that steel output is lagging behind general industrial activity. This is in part due to the greater use of substitute materials such as light metals, plastics, etc., but mainly due to the unparalleled magnitude of the industrial activity of a period which, bordering on the freakish, has temporarily outrun the country's steel capacity, and this in spite of its considerable enlargement during World War II.

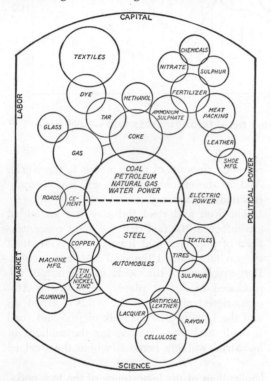

FIG. 38.3. Industrial Agglomeration, Schematic Presentation

The Key to Resource Patterns. Though originally identified with the light textile industry, the Industrial Revolution in the course of the nineteenth century found its outstanding exponents in the heavy industries based on coal and iron. Where coal and iron ore met in economical combination there not only throve the iron and steel industry, its offspring, but many associated and dependent industries likewise sprang up. Coal and iron acted like a powerful magnet forming the center of a huge agglomerative process (Fig. 38.3). One of the best places to observe this process is the northeast-

ern part of the United States, for long the main seat of the iron and steel industry.

There is coal in the Northeast—billions of tons, cheap, excellent coal of every description—anthracite, steam coal, coking coal, gas coal, high volatile coal, low volatile coal, in short, almost every imaginable variety of coal. There is iron ore in the Lake Superior region and elsewhere—vast amounts, much of it very rich and easily worked. There is limestone of excellent quality, ideally located. And there are the Great Lakes, a rare gift of nature, the equivalent of tens of thousands of miles of standard rail lines, supplied free of charge or almost free of charge, and cheaply operated. Its coastline, bordering on the North Atlantic and facing Europe, possesses some of the finest harbors in the world, among them the greatest of all—New York. Last, but not least, there are people—in fact, half the population of the United States, people that have come from every part of the earth, ambitious people, eager for work—and for freedom.

These six items—coal, iron ore, limestone, the Great Lakes, the North Atlantic coast, and people—add up to a marvelous combination of resources out of which has sprung a majestic mass of blast furnaces and steel mills and fabricating plants, turning out more steel than all the rest of the world put together. That steel in turn goes into rails, into structural shapes for factories and skyscrapers, into plates for automobiles and ships, into machines that make a myriad things well and cheaply, and into machines that make machines. Vast amounts of coal go through thousands of by-product coke ovens which, besides coke, yield gas for industrial purposes and household use, coal tar, ammonium sulphate, light oils, and an ever-growing line of other valuable by-products. On these by-products, in turn, are erected ever-larger and higher structures of other industries: chemical industries, including dye and pharmaceuticals, plastics, nylon, the fertilizer industry, etc. Much of the iron ore yields phosphorus, a valuable fertilizing agent, and all the iron ores yield slag, which may go into cement or be used in other ways. The dye industry, in turn, attracts the textile industry, at least the more advanced and more profitable phases of finishing. Thus one industry feeds on another which in turn nurtures a third. Thus the process of industrialization becomes something akin to the process of growth of a living organism.

Industrialization, in turn, leads to urbanization, and urbanization means high population density and the development of more and better cultural and social institutions—schools and churches and colleges, research institutes, etc. It means that the urbanized area is honeycombed with a network of transportation and communication facilities, consisting of pipe lines, railroads, highways, telephone and telegraph lines, power lines, sewer connections, etc. These cultural advantages and improved means of transportation, communication and sanitation in turn attract people into the area and thus contribute to the growth and density of population, setting in motion a further process of organismic growth.

In the cities there develop tertiary activities,[10] meaning innumerable supplementary and auxiliary activities made necessary by the increasing complexity of advanced material civilization. These are the services of trade and of finance, of buying and selling, and advertising, the professions, etc. So important is this development that in time the number of people engaged in these tertiary activities exceeds the number of those engaged in the primary and secondary activities of agriculture, mining, manufacture, construction, and utilities, etc.

Agriculture, too, undergoes changes. It becomes more intensified, more mechanized. It specializes in high-grade products like dairy products, truck products, wrapper tobacco, flower bulbs, seeds, in short, products which yield a high value per acre and find a ready market in the densely populated area of super-industrialization.

The dense, highly urbanized population of this manufacturing belt more and more comes to resemble what may be described as a high-order organism, fully articulated, interrelated and interdependent through regional and occupational specialization. This large and efficient mass of manpower is supported by ever-increasing amounts of inanimate energy, especially of electricity, generated from coal or from water power. Due to this generous support from inanimate energy, the productivity of labor increases by leaps and bounds. Wages rise, purchasing power increases, profits increase, the capital goods industries thrive, and in general the velocity of commercial interchange and the tempo of economic activity are stepped up. Wealth accumulates as nowhere else.

This accumulation of wealth resulting from increased productivity becomes, in turn, one of the

most powerful factors of further material progress. It results in the improvement of schools and other cultural facilities, it makes available larger sums of capital and thus permits further improvements in productivity. In short, it resembles a spiral ever pushing upward. In addition to this contribution to progress, this accumulation of wealth, characteristic of the advanced stage of super-industrialized regions, gives rise to what might be called a quaternary group of economic activities, i.e., economic activities catering to the wants engendered by this increased wealth. These are first of all industries selling luxury goods and deluxe services—mink fur coats, twenty-room apartments in the Waldorf Towers, $30 "permanents" and the like. But even the greater purchasing power of the population in general is capable of engendering such quaternary activities, though on a more modest scale and a somewhat lower level of sophistication.

One more phase of this dynamic process of growth must be mentioned. The improved cultural facilities result in the rising level of labor skills and experience, and in the training of experts capable of achievements unparalleled elsewhere. This unique labor situation becomes one more factor contributing to the almost irresistible drive forward and upward.

Anybody familiar with human affairs knows that such a development of cultural advance cannot occur without its dark sides. So complex is the lofty superstructure of business and social institutions and so intricate becomes the pattern of invisible rights and obligations which develops in the operation of this complex apparatus, that no one seems to be able to comprehend fully the laws which govern its existence and growth. As a result, with increased frequency, this complex machinery gets out of order, causing depression, unemployment, untold misery. Nor is the normal life in such highly artificialized regions altogether ideal, even while the machine is operating in good order. There is vice and degradation, there are slums and ugliness; there is fear that haunts the breadwinner who wonders how long he will keep his job; there is nervous strain, and physical breakdown. But, even after full allowance is made for these structural and functional deficiencies, there is no gainsaying the fact that, in terms of material culture at least, this most highly industrialized region represents the apex of human achievement.

The magnitude of this achievement cannot be measured in terms of what goes on *within* this manufacturing belt itself. Its powerful influence extends far and wide and reaches into the remotest corners of the earth. From all sides there flow into this super-articulated, super-mechanized, and super-productive center, the raw materials from the

---

[10] Economic activities may be divided into:

Primary—agriculture, animal husbandry, lumbering, fishing, etc.

Secondary—manufacture, construction, public utilities, and mining.

Tertiary—wholesaling, retailing, advertising, finance, transportation, communication, personal services, professions (i.e., law, medicine, education, etc.), and government.

Quaternary—luxury industries and services catering to those who possess the power to spend, made possible by the high productivity of the combination of primary, secondary, and tertiary activities.

far corners of the land, and of the earth. And out of it, there flow in an endless stream the mass-production goods of machinafacture as well as the most advanced products of scientific achievement. But more than goods leave this central belt of industrial production. Services are among its most valuable exports. Above all, from its centers of finance surplus capital flows into every part of the globe which needs its stimulus and can afford to pay its price. It is invested in the oil, the sulphur, the gas, and the salt of Texas, in the silver of Nevada, in the oil and gold and mercury of California, in the mines of Mexico, in the oil fields of Venezuela, Arabia, and a score of other countries. These investments are not confined to minerals. They also reach into that "Golden Belt of Plantations" which lies on both sides of the equator—producing rubber, coffee, tea, fibers, and nuts, etc. With these investments generally go the necessary controls, controls over politics and sometimes controls over the entire social and economic life of the regions to which they flow.

The forces which control this flow of goods, services and capital from this super-industrialized area of the United States are focused in a few centers, most of all in New York with its stock exchange, with the head offices of the American Telephone and Telegraph, the Standard Oil Company (N.J.), the United States Steel Corporation, and many other industrial and financial giants.[11]

It is possible that forces are now at work retarding or even terminating this dynamic process of coal-iron-oriented agglomeration. The growth of chemical industries based on oil and gas, instead of on coal as formerly, may be a case in point. The expanding use of hydroelectric power especially in the electrochemical and electrometallurgical industries may be another. The decentralization of industry, prompted by fear of atomic warfare, may be a third.[12] New technologies and shifting population centers may be others. To some extent, the steel indus-

try is able to go along with these developments. The end result, however, may well be a lessening of the hold which the coal-iron complex has had on industrial location in the past. As we shall see later, the older steel centers have tried to fight this centrifugal force by such artificial means as "the Pittsburgh-plus Plan" and multiple basing points. These efforts, too, seem to be weakening.

Steel and World Power. It takes more than steel to make a nation strong in the military sense. But without steel all else is rather meaningless, ineffective, inarticulate. After all, tanks, guns, and battleships are essentially contraptions made of steel. It is also true that steel, the great harnesser of energy, would be worthless without the inanimate power derived from coal, oil, gas, and water power to drive the engines and machines.

Modern military power rests on an all-round industrial basis of which steel is the keystone. Industrial countries can put into the field an armed force far larger in proportion to the size of the population than can agrarian countries that must exhaust themselves in the endless toil involved in producing food by primitive hand methods.

In the Civil War the industrial North defeated the agrarian South. Industrially more advanced Prussia defeated less industrialized France in 1871. The superior industrial strength of the Allies twice defeated the inferior industrial strength of Germany and her partners. Since the mechanical revolution no nation has been able successfully to aspire to the rank of a Great Power that did not possess an iron and steel industry of considerable proportions.

The iron and steel industry is concentrated in the northern hemisphere. No Great Power has yet arisen in the southern hemisphere. England ruled the world when she outranked all the other nations in the manufacture of iron and steel and its products. Germany grew in political stature apace with the growth of her iron and steel industry. So did the United States, only more so. Seeing the causal nexus between world power and steelmaking capacity, Russia and Japan strained every nerve to build up iron and steel industries of their own, the former on a solid foundation of a rich natural endowment, the latter on the shaky basis of borrowed strength.

---

[11] Erich W. Zimmermann, in *Texas Looks Ahead*, vol. 1 of *The Resources of Texas*, University of Texas, Austin, 1944, pp. 359-362.

[12] On January 23, 1949, the New York *Times*, on page F1, reporting on this decentralization movement, reproduced maps prepared by the National Industrial Conference Board showing shifts of industrial capacity by states. As yet, no spectacular results were visible. The text implied that this decentralization movement is in part inspired by the government. It is important that a similar movement is going on in Great Britain; many of her plants are moving to Canada.

As populations and markets grow, as new technologies permit economical operation of moderate-sized steel industries, and especially while economic nationalism is rampant, nation after nation seeks to establish its own steel industry in the hope that its voice, backed by the roar of its iron and steel furnaces, will command a little more respect in the council chambers of the world. Italy, Poland, Czechoslovakia, South Africa, Australia, India, Turkey, Brazil, Chile, Peru, Argentina, and now Colombia and Egypt—to mention but a few outstanding examples—either have acquired a steel industry of their own or are eager to proceed with ambitious plans.[13]

---

[13] There is no desire to associate the steel industry one-sidedly with power politics, for it is, of course, also a powerful leaven of economic progress and peaceful endeavor. Nor is there the least inclination to indulge in silly one-sided determinism, according to which steel is the sole basis of strength, economic, military, or political. Any exposition that singles out one isolated factor is bound to be lopsided and incomplete.

BIBLIOGRAPHY

See the bibliography at the end of Chapter 42.

Chapter 39

RAW MATERIALS AND SERVICE MATERIALS

To understand and appreciate a discussion of the raw materials and service materials of the iron and steel industry one must have at least an elementary knowledge of the nature of iron and steel and the processes by which they are produced and treated.

Iron is an element. It is generally found in nature in chemical combination with oxygen, sometimes with carbon, with water, or with sulfur. By far its most important occurrence is in the iron-oxygen compounds, Fe_2O_3 and Fe_3O_4. These chemical compounds, in turn, are found not by themselves, but in conjunction with earthy materials called gangue. Steel, on the other hand, is an artificial alloy of iron and carbon and usually one or more other ingredients.

The first function of the iron and steel industry is to extract the iron from its chemical compounds and separate it from the gangue. Most of this is done in the so-called blast furnace, by means of the heat generated by the chemical action of coke (carbon) and hot air (oxygen), called combustion, usually aided by limestone used as a flux. But the blast furnace, a gigantic contraption using elementary forces of nature, does not do a thorough job; although it does its work cheaply, it cannot remove all the impurities.[1]

Nor can it perform the steel industry's second task, the making of particular kinds of iron, especially the innumerable kinds of steel which modern industry requires. Particular kinds of iron and steel are made by combining with highly purified iron strictly controlled quantities of other materials, mainly carbon in the case of iron, and carbon and alloying materials in the case of steels. The residual impurities are removed from iron and steel, and the specific properties are imparted, in special furnaces designed for the purpose.

The third basic function of the iron and steel industry is to shape iron and steel to the desired sizes and forms and in general to finish

---

[1] How cheaply the blast furnace works depends, of course, on the quality of construction, the skill of operation, and especially the capacity factor, i.e., the percentage of its lifetime that it is in actual operation. As will be shown further on, efforts are under way to lower blast furnace costs and, if possible, to eliminate the whole blast furnace operation.

TABLE 39.1. Selected Characteristics of Groups of Iron Ores[2]

Type of Iron Ore	Theoretical Percent of Metallic Iron	% Iron in Ore Mined in U.S., 1939	U. S. Production, 1939 (long tons)	% of Total	Average Value per Ton at Mine, 1939	Moisture Content (%)[a]	Color
Hematite	69.94	51.75[b]	47,756,870	92.4	2.89	1.04	Black to brick red
Limonite[c]	59.89	47.00	586,372	1.1	2.12	10.84	Yellowish; red when heated
Magnetite	72.40	61.00	3,377,764	6.5	2.99	0.31	Black
Siderite[d]	48.27	...	463	...	...	0.71[e]	Yellowish or brown

[a] Includes also chemically combined water.
[b] Lake Superior ores.
[c] Also called brown ore and brown hematite.
[d] Also called carbonate.
[e] Also includes organic matter.

its products to the customer's specifications or the requirements of the trade.

From the foregoing it is evident that the basic raw material of the iron and steel industry is iron ore. Today this is heavily supplemented by iron and steel scrap. As was said above, the blast furnace requires coke and limestone. In foundry work sand is needed in large amounts. To make alloy steels, alloying materials are required. Throughout the iron and steelworks heat and energy are called for in large quantities, which means additional requirements of coal and other fuels, such as fuel oil, gas, etc. Electricity, water, and air are used in prodigious amounts, and the construction, maintenance, and operation of iron and steelworks call for many additional materials. All these raw materials and service materials will now be discussed.

IRON ORE[3]

Types of Ores

According to the chemical composition of the iron compound contained in ores, the following types are distinguished:

[2] Board of Investigation and Research, Transportation Act of 1940, *The Economics of Iron and Steel Transportation*, Senate Document No. 80, 79th Congress, 1st Session, Washington, 1945, p. 18.

[3] As has been stressed repeatedly, the concept of ores, like the wider concept of resources, is purely relative. It denotes the portion of mineral deposits that, at given cost-price relationships, pays exploitation. Since these relationships are in constant flux, the amount of ore likewise must fluctuate constantly. Depletion is another dynamic factor that must be taken into account.

1. Iron plus oxygen—"dry" or anhydrous iron oxides (Fe_2O_3 and $FeO \cdot Fe_2O_3$), black, red, or blue iron ores, hematite and magnetite
2. Iron plus oxygen and water—"wet" or hydrous iron oxides ($Fe_2O_3 \cdot H_2O$), brown or yellow iron ores, limonite
3. Iron plus oxygen and carbon—iron carbonates ($FeCO_3$), siderite
4. Iron plus sulfur—iron sulfides, marcasite, pyrite, pyrrhotite
5. Iron plus sulfur and carbon—iron sulfates

Of these the first group, the dry or anhydrous oxides, $FeO \cdot Fe_2O_3$—sometimes written Fe_3O_4 and Fe_2O_3—are by far the most important; they are known as magnetite and hematite respectively. In the absence of gangue, magnetite and hematite contain 72.4 and 69.94 percent iron respectively, and limonite and siderite contain 59.8 and 48.2 percent iron respectively. Hematite makes up the bulk of the iron ore used in the United States, most of the rest consisting of magnetite. All the other iron ores are more or less negligible. Pyrites are exploited for their sulfur content and sometimes compete with sulfur. The only place in this country where limonite and siderite are now used in making iron is at Daingerfield, Texas. In the blast furnaces the oxygen in the iron ore combines with the carbon in the coke and is removed in that manner. Table 39.1 throws further light on types of ore.

Gangue. As was stated before, gangues are the earthy materials which make up the iron ore as mined, other than the ore mineral, the iron compound. Gangue consists of both metallic and nonmetallic materials. Usually silica constitutes the largest part. But alumina in the form of clay, as well as varying amounts of lime, magnesium, sulfur, phosphorus, titanium, arsenic, manganese, and copper may be present. Titanium, arsenic, and copper weaken iron; hence their presence is usually objectionable. Excessive amounts of moisture can be removed at a cost by roasting or similar processes. Ores containing less than 40 percent iron are usually beneficiated, i.e., put through processes designed to raise the iron content to the desired amount. This, too, adds to the expense; but beneficiated ores or concentrates are frequently superior to "direct-shipping ores" as blast furnace charges. They can be used to average up the quality of the charges.

The Mesabi range is the largest source of the current supply of iron ore in the United States; Alabama has the largest reserves. The two ores show significant differences in composition. Because of its comparatively low iron content, the Alabama ore calls for beneficiation; this should bring the Fe content up and the high silica content down to more desirable proportions. The high lime content of this ore makes it self-fluxing, eliminating the necessity and cost of charging limestone into the blast furnace and thus partly compensating for the cost of beneficiation.

Of particular importance is the difference in phosphorus content, 0.84 percent for the Mesabi ore and 0.37 for the Alabama.[4] This difference in phosphorus content materially affects the refining procedure in the steel furnace. The Mesabi ore is highly suitable to the basic open-hearth process,[5] whereas some Birmingham ores require the Duplex process which means that as the iron comes from the blast furnace it goes first to the acid Bessemer converter which removes virtually all impurities except the phosphorus, and then to the basic open hearth which removes the phosphorus.[6]

---

[4] So-called Bessemer ore is ore which in the blast furnace yields pig iron fit for the *acid* Bessemer converter. It must not contain more than 0.05 percent phosphorus; anything over that makes the ore a basic or non-Bessemer ore. Such ore yields pig iron fit for either the basic open hearth, the basic Bessemer converter, or the Duplex process.

[5] See pp. 643-647 for specific processes.

[6] Phosphorus is acid and therefore requires a basic lining for its extraction.

Another ingredient which deserves mention is titanium. This metal had long been a thorn in the side of blast furnace operators. Then it was discovered that it yields a pigment of remarkable whiteness. Makers of paint started research and discovered ways by which titanium could be recovered from iron ore leaving a highly desirable concentrate. According to one report,[7] the titaniferous magnetite ores of the Adirondacks, near Lake Sanford, in the early forties produced about 5500 long tons of ore daily, yielding about 800 long tons of ilmenite (titanium dioxide) concentrates and 1800 long tons of magnetite concentrates, as well as other valuable products. When imported titanium ores became scarce and costly during World War II, the users turned to domestic sources. More recently a successful method of producing metallic titanium has been discovered (see p. 732).

Table 39.2 gives typical analyses of important American and foreign ores. The hematite deposits of Minas Gerais, Brazil, stand out; their iron content, 67.08, is almost as high as that of the highly beneficiated sinter of Lyon Mountain, Adirondacks, New York. The Cornwall crude is processed at the Bethlehem (Pennsylvania) plant of the Bethlehem Steel Corporation; the Chilean Tofo ore and the Cuban Mayari ores move mainly to the same company's plant at Sparrows Point, Maryland. During World War II some of Mexico's Durango hematite went to Houston, Texas, where the Sheffield Steel Company, a subsidiary of Armco (American Rolling Mill Co.), has a small integrated plant. The southern (Birmingham) ores rank highest in phosphorus content.

Physical Characteristics

Besides differing in iron content and the chemical nature of the gangue, iron ores differ widely in physical characteristics. Some are hard rocks; others are fine sand. The blast furnace operators in general prefer a medium material, neither so fine that the force of the blast will blow a considerable portion out of the furnace, nor in solid blocks so large and firm that the chemical force of burning coke

---

[7] See H. F. Otte, *The Expanding Mineral Industry of the Adirondacks*, Albany, 1943, pp. 34 ff.

TABLE 30.2. Typical Analyses of American and Foreign Iron Ores[8]
(in percentages)

Type of Iron Ore	Fe	P	SiO₂	Al₂O₃	CaO	MgO	Mn	S	TiO₂	Cu	Cr	Ni and Co	Loss	Moisture	Combined Water
Lake															
Old Range	51.52	0.052	11.12	2.43	0.78	0.39	0.180	…	…	…	…	…	2.47	8.76	…
Mesabi	48.48	0.070	5.73	3.61	0.25	0.22	0.760	…	…	…	…	…	5.17	14.39	…
Southern															
Red ore	37.10	0.36	13.18	…	…	16.02	0.160	…	…	…	…	…	…	1.00	…
Brown ore (washed)	47.32	0.58	9.85	…	…	…	0.540	…	…	…	…	…	…	…	6.85
Desert Mountain Utah	51.00	0.046	6.30	2.30	2.80	2.20	0.100	0.055	…	…	…	…	…	3.8	…
Adirondack magnetite															
Sanford crude	47.47	0.018	5.18	4.20	0.10	1.48	0.340	0.142	21.02	…	…	…	…	…	…
Sanford concentrate	56.29ᵃ	0.003	2.26	4.52	0.10	1.48	0.270	0.104	12.34	…	1.34	…	…	…	…
Lyon Mountain sinter	68.50	0.003	2.76	1.06	0.54	0.40	0.065	…	…	…	…	…	…	…	…
Cornwall crude	33.24	0.018	22.93	4.61	8.00	10.26	…	1.440	…	0.36	…	…	…	…	…
East Texas brown ore	46.63	0.170	14.46	8.17	0.25	0.01	0.070	0.083	…	…	…	…	…	9.5	…
Cuba, Mayari crude ores	36.50	0.010	3.75	10.00	…	…	0.640	10.180	…	…	1.40	0.72	…	27.50	10.50
Chile, Tofo ore	57.78	0.037	8.60	1.63	1.85	2.55	0.110	…	1.19	…	…	…	…	…	…
Brazil, Minas Gerais:															
Hematite	67.08	0.051	0.54	1.41	0.03	0.01	…	…	…	…	…	…	1.60	1.65	…
Mexico, Durango:															
Hematite	57.80	0.21	13.12	0.99	0.58	0.33	0.050	1.068	0.032	…	…	…	1.08	…	…

ᵃ Contains V, 0.26.

[8] Board of Investigation and Research, *op. cit.*, p. 26.

P = phosphorus, MgO = magnesia, Mn = manganese, S = sulfur, TiO₂ = titanium oxide, Cu = copper, Cr = chromium, N = nickel, Co = cobalt, V = vanadium.

cannot act readily on their content. Some ores have to be nodulized artificially; others have to be broken up in crushers before they are fit for the blast furnace. Needless to say, all these operations involve costs.

Methods of Mining

The bulk of the Mesabi iron ores are mined in open pits with power shovels. If the ore does not actually lie on the surface the overburden has to be removed first. According to a rule of thumb in the Mesabi region, it pays to remove as many feet of overburden as the ore body is deep.[9] This depends, of course, on the quality of the ore and the cost of getting it to market. In lean and inaccessible ores the economic limit of removing overburden is reached much sooner.

There is one drawback to open-pit mining in Minnesota. Because of the inclement weather, open-pit operations are suspended in winter. But since navigation on the Great Lakes is suspended during the winter months, most of the year's supply is shipped during the summer months.[10]

In the southeastern (Birmingham) area shaft mining is the general rule. It is more expensive than open-pit mining, the exact difference in cost depending, of course, on numerous factors.

---

[9] In the Hull-Rust mine in Minnesota the amount of material that has been removed is greatly in excess of the total excavation for the Panama Canal.

[10] The fact that the bulk of the ore supply of the United States is produced by open-pit mining in the Mesabi region has significant strategic implications. Open-pit mining operations are highly flexible; they can be suspended almost at will and expanded with almost equal ease. This is of some advantage in times of business depression but it is of vital importance in time of war. Shaft mining operations can be expanded only slowly, but the output of the Mesabi open pits can be stepped up at a moment's notice. Now that not much of the "direct-shipping" ores from the open pits of the Mesabi is left, it has been suggested that the remaining ores be declared a national emergency reserve and left untouched until another war calls for their operation. In the meantime, the lower-grade ores should be put to work. The idea is sound, but it needs careful working-out so that the transition from one method of ore procurement to the other will be made gradually without upsetting the national economy. One of the best ways to cause war is to upset our economy and bring on another depression.

Some ores are dredged from lakes. This is common practice in central Sweden, where the same area has been mined this way for many centuries.

Beneficiation of Ores

The object of beneficiation is to bring unsatisfactory ores "up to scratch," to remove undesirable ingredients or reduce their presence and thus bring up the iron content of the ore. The beneficiator often succeeds so well that the resultant concentrate is superior in some ways to many "direct-shipping" ores.

There are numerous ways of beneficiating ores: hydraulic, thermal, electric, chemical, and mechanical. As was said before, the two most widely used ores in the United States are hematite and magnetite. Magnetite lends itself to a method of beneficiation not applicable to other ores. This method takes advantage of the magnetic character of the ore. After the ore is reduced to a powder about as fine as cement, the iron particles are removed by magnetic attraction. In some cases froth flotation methods may prove suitable. Finely ground ore is mixed with oil and stirred up while air is admitted. Fine iron particles attach themselves to an oil-air bubble and rush to the surface, forming a froth. The froth is skimmed off and the iron is separated out. Numerous other methods are also available.

At present the problem of beneficiation is attracting much attention. With the bottom of the barrel in sight for the rich Mesabi and other northwestern ores, the problem of developing the poor taconite as the nation's future ore reserves has become very pressing. Taconite is low-grade iron ore, huge deposits of which extend with interruptions from Minnesota to Labrador. Vast sums of money are being appropriated for research. Large-scale expansion and intensification of beneficiating plants are under way. It is hoped that eventually concentrates superior to the present direct-shipping ores will be produced at costs which make the overall cost of operation little if any higher than at present. The alternative is to revamp our entire industrial structure, which is now oriented toward Lake Superior ores. The costs of this are likely to exceed the costs of beneficiating taconite by a wide margin.[11]

In 1947, 26.3 percent of all shipments of

iron ore from Minnesota represented concentrated iron ore. Most of this was "wash concentrates" that had been subjected to hydraulic beneficiation only. Prior to 1907 no Minnesota ores were beneficiated; during 1907-1910, only 16 percent.[12] Since virtually all New York ores, some of Pennsylvania's, most of the southeastern, and the bulk of the western are beneficiated, the national percentage for concentrates must be considerably higher than that for Minnesota alone.

Iron Ore Reserves of the World

A survey of world iron deposits is so great a task that it can be undertaken only once in a great while. In the meantime, the world moves on. Demand expands or contracts, the center of economic gravity shifts, political borders shift and new regimes mean new politics and laws, transportation conditions change, new areas are explored, new processes are invented

---

[11] Under the headline "Big Boom Foreseen in Low-Grade Ores," the New York Times on October 14, 1949, reported on the activities of the Erie Mining Company, operated by several American steel companies, including the Bethlehem Steel Corporation. This company in 1948 put into operation at Aurora, Minnesota, a pilot plant for beneficiating ore. The experiment proved so successful that the company has asked the state of Minnesota to take measures which will assure a water supply sufficient to operate a beneficiation plant with an initial annual capacity of 2,500,000 tons of concentrates; the capacity may be expanded to 10,000,000 tons if the large-scale operation warrants. Metallurgists figure that such a plant would cost from $100,000,000 to $150,000,000.

In the Erie Company's process three tons of taconite are converted into one ton of high-grade iron pellets of 63 to 65 percent iron, superior in some respects to the high-grade ores used at present. The separation process makes use of the magnetic property of the taconite exploited. Reserves of this magnetic taconite may reach as high as 10,000,000,000 tons; deposits exist in various parts of the United States. Their exploitation would make important changes in the geographical pattern of our steel industry and would assure this country's self-sufficiency in iron ore for many decades.

For a discussion of other developments aimed at the exploitation of taconite, see T. W. Lippert, "Cerro Bolivar, Saga of an Iron Ore Crisis Averted," Journal of Metals and Mining Engineering, February, 1950, reprinted by the United States Steel Corporation.

[12] Henry K. Wade, Mining Directory, 1948, Bulletin of the University of Minnesota Institute of Technology, 1948, pp. 222-223.

---

that turn the dirt of yesteryear into the ore of today, and vice versa. The survey of world iron ore most widely referred to is that by Olin R. Kuhn,[13] and it is on this survey that Table 39.3 is based.

TABLE 39.3. Iron Ore Reserves of the World (after Kuhn), and Production of Iron Ore, Pig Iron, and Steel, 1947[14]

Country	Iron Reserves (million long tons)	Production, 1947[a] (million short tons)		
		Iron Ore	Pig Iron	Steel
United States	10,450	104.4	60.1	84.9.
Germany (post-Versailles boundaries)	1,315	4.1[a]	2.5[a]	3.3[a]
Soviet Union	2,057	...	18.0	22.6
United Kingdom	5,970	12.2	8.5	14.3
France	8,165	20.6	5.4	6.3
Japan	85	...	0.4	1.0
Belgium	70	...	3.1	3.2
Italy	18	...	0.4	1.9
Luxemburg	270	2.5[b]	2.0	1.9
Sweden	2,203	4.3[c]	0.8	1.3
India	3,226	...	1.6	1.3
Newfoundland	4,000	0.5[d]	....	....
Brazil	7,000	...	0.0	0.4
Cuba	3,159	...	....	....
Other countries	9,721	...	....	....
	57,812			

[a] American, British, and French zones only.
[b] 1946.
[c] 1945.
[d] 1944.

Iron Ore Reserves of the United States. Kuhn's figures for the United States differ significantly from those of the most recent estimates available, shown in Table 39.4. The total reserves are divided into measured and indicated ores (see p. 444) and potential ores. Measured, indicated, and inferred ores total 5481 million long tons as against 62,915 million long tons of potential ore. The southeastern re-

---

[13] Olin R. Kuhn, "World Iron Ore Reserves," Engineering and Mining Journal, July 17, 1926.

[14] U.S. Tariff Commission, Iron and Steel, 1938, Report No. 128, based on Kuhn's 1926 publication. Kuhn seems to have used the term ore in a sense somewhat different from that in which it is now used. Apparently he recorded deposits that on the basis of geological facts could be ore without raising the question of economic exploitability. In other words, his figures include potential reserves. Moreover, since 1926 some deposits have been depleted, new ones have been discovered, and for others figures have been revised upward or downward.

Figures for iron ore, pig iron, and steel production from American Iron and Steel Institute, Annual Statistical Report, 1947.

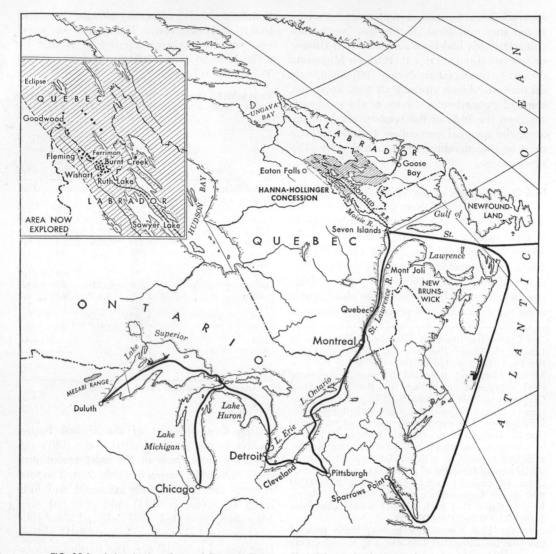

FIG. 39.1.   Labrador Iron Ore and Shipping Routes to United States Steel Centers. (A map by Richard Edes
Harrison in *Fortune*, December, 1948; reproduced by courtesy of *Fortune* Magazine.)

gion is credited with the largest measured and indicated ore, and the Lake Superior region, with slightly smaller measured and indicated ore, is way in the lead with potential reserves, mainly taconite. The Northeast ranks second in potential reserves. The table also indicates the volume of production through 1943—2.1 billion tons for the Lake Superior region as against 0.3 and 0.2 billion for the southeastern and northeastern regions respectively. The northeastern district has only recently come back as a major ore-producing sector of the country;

it produced about 8 million concentrated tons of iron ore in 1943.

Iron Ore Elsewhere in the Western Hemisphere.   Another region which is attracting considerable attention is Labrador (Fig. 39.1), which has been mentioned as a potential successor to the Mesabi range. Large iron deposits have been discovered along its western boundary, straddling both it and the Province of Quebec, and are now being intensively explored. The M. A. Hanna Company of Cleveland and the Hollinger interests of Toronto are engaged in explorative drilling. Operations in winter are handicapped by intense cold. A 300-mile railroad is contemplated from Fort Chimo on Ungava Bay to the port of Seven Islands at the mouth of the Moisie River, which empties into the lower St. Lawrence. If present expectations are borne out by further exploration, this area may come to play an important role in the future development of North America. Incidentally, the argument in favor of the St. Lawrence Waterway may gain strong support.

TABLE 39.4. Reserves of Iron Ore in the United States as of January, 1944, and Production Through 1943[15] (million long tons)

Region	Lowest Grade of Ore Commonly Mined (Percent of Iron, Natural not Dried)	Measured and Indicated Ore[a]	Inferred Ore	Potential Ore	Total Production Through 1943
Lake Superior	51.5	1,306	500	61,000	2,076
Southeastern	35	1,561	560	270	325
Northeastern	25	536	390	1,500	163
Western	50	141	275	140	38
Central and Gulf	50	179	25	5	11
Alaska	....	3	5	......	None
Total	....	3,726	1,755	62,915	2,613

[a] Data insufficient to estimate separately.

Labrador is but one of the areas of the western hemisphere to which this country may look for future supplies of iron ore if domestic supplies prove inadequate. For years the Sparrows Point plant of the Bethlehem Steel Corporation has been drawing on foreign sources, in particular on owned or leased South American properties in Cuba and Chile. Venezuelan ore sources are now being opened up. In 1949 the Bethlehem Steel Corporation released the following statement:

Bethlehem Steel Corporation, through its subsidiary the Iron Mines Company of Venezuela, is presently developing a block of sixteen iron mine concessions in the State of Bolivar, Venezuela, South America. The concessions, which the company is developing at its own expense, are expected to yield up to 2,000,000 tons of iron ore annually at the end of the present construction period. The ore, a hard, high-grade hematite, suitable for use in both blast furnaces and open hearth steel furnaces, will be shipped to the United States for treatment in Bethlehem's eastern steel plants.

The concessions, known as the El Paó mines, are located in an almost entirely undeveloped tropical jungle about 30 miles south of San Felix, a town situated near the confluence of the Orinoco and the Caroni rivers, about 165 miles from the point on the coast where the Orinoco empties into the Atlantic Ocean. [See Fig. 39.2.]

Ore will be shipped from the El Paó mines to a port site named Palua on the Orinoco River, near San Felix. Construction at Palua, now completed, includes ore storage and loading facilities, a diesel-electric power plant, waterworks, shops, warehouses, and a complete village for housing the employees. Regular passenger and mail service is provided twice weekly by the Venezuelan Airlines, using an airport built by the company near Palua.

Because the year is divided into a wet and a dry season, the water level of the Orinoco River has a seasonal variation of 40 feet. For this reason, it will be necessary to load the ore into river boats or barges from a conveyor belt supported on a steel structure overhanging the river. The end of this structure is high enough above the river to allow the boats to moor under it regardless of the height of the water. The ore will drop from the end of the conveyor directly into the hold of the boats. The ore will be taken to Puerto de Hierro, the tidewater port, for unloading into ocean ore carriers. Dredging is now completed at Puerto de Hierro and a camp is under construction.

Work is under way on the construction of a town named El Paó at the mines, with modern houses for about 450 employees and their families, hospital, school, stores, waterworks, telephone system, and facilities for the recreation and health of the employees. The mines are about 2,000 feet above the Orinoco at Palua, and, although the location is in the tropical region, the climate is pleasant and moderate.

An improved highway and a 36-mile, standard-gage railroad connects the port of Palua with the mines. The highway is now completed, while the railroad is expected to be in operation by the end of the year. Telephone lines have been installed between the portside and the mines.

Both open-pit and underground mining will be used in extracting the ore, although initially only the open-pit method will be employed. Electric shovels of 4-cubic-yard capacity will load the ore into 30-ton diesel engine trucks, which will haul it to the crushing plant. Facilities at the mines will include primary and secondary crushers, a diesel-electric power plant, warehouses, air compressors, repair and machine shops, and general offices.

[15] Joint Staffs of Geological Survey and Bureau of Mines, *Mineral Position of the United States*, pp. 251-254.

FIG. 39.2. Venezuela and Labrador, Prospective Sources of United States Iron Ore Supply, and Transportation Routes to Existing and Prospective Steel Centers. (T. W. Lippert, "Cerro Bolivar, Saga of an Iron Ore Crisis Averted," *Journal of Metals and Mining Engineering*, February, 1950.)

At present about 1,250 men are being employed at the various sites, in addition to 350 men employed by contractors.

Even more spectacular and of deeper general significance than Bethlehem Steel's development of El Paó was the United States Steel Corporation's discovery, in April, 1947, at La Parida, of a huge iron mountain fifty miles due south of the town of Ciudad Bolivar on the Orinoco River. This is the most startling of an

entire series of iron ore discoveries in the Venezuelan Guianas. Early in 1949 drilling at Cerro Bolivar, as La Parida was subsequently renamed, had proved over half a billion tons of excellent ore and the new reserves that were blocked out indicated an initial total of over a billion tons. Cerro Bolivar alone is expected to yield more high-grade iron ore than the famous Hull-Rust-Mahoning pit near Hibbing, Minnesota, the largest open-pit mine in the world.

One problem that is still unsolved concerns

TABLE 39.5.   Iron Ore Production in the United States by Districts, 1890-1949
(million long tons)

Year	Lake Superior Production	Lake Superior Percent	Birmingham and Chattanooga	Adirondack	Northern New Jersey and Southeastern New York	Other	Total
1890	8.9	55.8	..	..	..	7.1	16.0
1900	20.6	74.6	..	..	..	7.0	27.6
1910	46.3	81.3	5.0	1.1	0.6	3.9	57.0
1917	63.5	84.3	7.0	1.1	0.6	3.1	75.3
1920	57.9	85.6	5.8	0.8	0.5	2.6	67.6
1929	62.8	86.0	6.4	..	1.1	2.7	73.0
1932	8.1	82.7	1.3	0.03	0.03	0.3	9.8
1937	61.7	85.5	..	..	0.5	..	72.2
1938	21.3	74.9	4.2	2.1[a]	0.2	0.6	28.4
1939	41.7	80.6	5.8	2.7	0.4	1.1	51.7
1940	61.5	83.4	7.1	2.9	0.7	1.5	73.7
1941	78.9	85.3	7.6	3.3	0.6	2.0	92.4
1942	91.0	86.2	8.6	2.5	0.6	2.8	105.5
1943	85.8	84.7	8.0	2.9	0.5	4.0	101.2
1944	79.4	83.9	7.5	3.9	0.5	3.8	94.6
1945	74.8	85.1	6.0	3.2	0.4	3.3	87.9
1946	59.0	83.9	5.9	2.2	0.4	2.8	70.3
1947	76.4	82.6	7.2	3.5	0.5	5.0	92.5
1948	82.6	82.5	7.7	4.0	0.4	6.1	100.5
1949	68.9	81.1	7.3	..	..	8.8	85.0

[a] Figures for 1938-1945 include some other districts, principally Cornwall, Pa.

Source: Bureau of Mines.

the means of transporting the Cerro Bolivar ore to the furnaces in the United States. The first requisite is the building of a railroad from the ore deposits to the Orinoco. There are three possible ways of shipping the ore after it reaches the river. One involves building a railroad to the port of Barcelona on the north coast of Venezuela 274 miles away; another involves dredging the Orinoco up as far as Palua so that it will be deep enough for the 40,000-ton ore boats to load; the third involves using barges as Bethlehem does for its shipments out of El Paó.

The significance of these discoveries, which were made in the course of one of the most thorough and scientific searches for iron ore in human history, extends into the realm of national security and global politics. Together with the beneficiation of taconite and the development of the iron ore deposits in Labrador, Cerro Bolivar will go far to allay, for decades to come, the fear of an iron ore shortage that has plagued steel executives and statesmen alike.[16]

For an idea of the problems involved in ore transportation, see Fig. 39.2.

Production of Iron Ore

Table 39.5 shows the production of iron ore in the United States by districts, 1890-1947. Clearly evident is the preponderance of the Lake Superior district; it would be even more pronounced if iron content rather than ore were the basis of the tabulation. In particular the Birmingham section would lose in relative importance. Another significant aspect shown by the table is the violent fluctuation with which iron ore production responds to business cycles, especially to war demands. The World War I peak of 75.3 million tons in 1917 was not equaled until World War II. The 1929 output of 73.0 million tons towers majestically over the puny 9.8 million tons in 1932. The sharpness of the 1938 recession is clearly brought out by the drop from 72.2 to 28.4 million tons.

[16] T. W. Lippert, op. cit. See also T. C. Campbell, "U.S. Steel's Answer to the Iron Ore Shortage," Iron Age, March 2, 1950.

TABLE 39.6. World Production of Iron Ore by Selected Countries, 1913-1948[17]

(million net tons)

	Approximate Metal Content[a]	1913	1929	1932	1937	1940	1941	1942	1943	1944	1945	1946	1947	1948
United States	50	69.3	81.6	11.0	80.7	82.5	103.5	118.2	113.4	105.4	99.0	79.3	104.4	113.3
Canada	55	..	..	..	..	0.4	0.5	0.5	0.6	0.5	1.1	1.6	1.9	1.3
Newfoundland	..	1.7	1.7	0.2	1.8	1.6	1.1	1.3	0.6	0.5	..	..	..	..
Cuba	..	..	..	0.2	0.5	0.2	0.2	0.1	0.1	..	..	..	..	..
Chile	60	..	1.7	0.2	1.7	1.9	1.9	0.5	0.3	0.7	0.3	1.3	1.9	3.7
United Kingdom	30	17.3	12.5	8.2	15.9	19.8	21.3	22.3	20.7	17.3	15.9	13.6	12.2	14.7
Luxemburg	30	8.0	8.4	3.5	8.6	5.4	7.5	5.6	5.8	3.2	1.5	2.5	2.2	3.7
Belgium	35	..	..	0.1	0.3	0.7	..	..	..	..	..	..	..	..
France	33	24.1	56.1	30.4	41.7	14.0	11.7	14.1	18.6	10.2	8.6	17.9	20.6	25.3
Germany	25	31.5	6.8	1.5	9.4	..	..	..	..	..	..	4.0	4.1	8.0
Austria	35	3.3	2.1	0.3	2.1	3.5	3.2	3.3	3.5	3.3	0.3	0.5	1.0	1.2
Czechoslovakia	30	..	2.0	0.7	2.0	2.3	2.4	2.2	2.1	1.7	0.3	1.2	1.5	1.6
Poland	35	..	..	0.1	0.9	0.3	..	..	..	..	0.5	0.5	0.6	..
Hungary	35	..	..	0.1	0.3	0.3	0.3	0.4	0.4	..	0.1	0.1	0.3	..
Yugoslavia	..	..	..	..	0.7	0.7	0.6	..	..	..	..	..	..	..
Rumania	..	..	..	..	0.1	0.2	0.2	0.2	..	..	..	..	..	..
U.S.S.R.	..	10.5	7.8	13.4	30.9	30.3	25.1	..	..	..	..	..	..	..
Greece	..	..	..	..	0.3	..	..	..	..	..	..	..	..	..
Italy	50	..	..	0.5	1.1	1.4	..	..	..	..	..	0.1	0.2	0.2
Spain	51	10.9	7.2	1.9	1.4	2.5	1.9	1.8	1.7	1.7	2.1	2.6	1.7	1.8
Norway	..	..	..	0.4	1.1	0.7	..	..	..	..	..	..	..	..
Sweden	60	8.3	12.6	3.6	16.5	12.4	11.6	10.7	11.9	8.0	4.3	7.6	9.7	12.1
Algeria	55	1.3	2.4	0.5	2.6	1.1	0.4	0.3	0.2	0.9	1.3	1.8	..	..
Tunis	55	..	..	0.2	1.1	0.4	..	..	..	0.1	0.1	0.2	0.4	0.8
(British) India	..	0.4	2.8	..	..	..	..	..	..	..	..	..	..	..
Japan	50	..	..	..	0.7	1.2	1.5	2.4	2.9	3.9	1.3	0.6	0.5	0.6
Union of South Africa	60-65	..	..	..	0.5	0.7	0.9	0.8	0.8	0.9	1.0	1.0	1.3	1.3
China	..	8.1	1.9	..	..	..	..	..	..	..	..	..	..	..

[a] As listed in Statistical Office of the United Nations, Monthly Bulletin of Statistics.

[17] Figures for 1913 and 1929 from U.S. Department of Commerce, Commerce Yearbook, 1931, vol. 2, p. 696; 1932-1946 figures from American Iron and Steel Institute, op. cit., pp. 180-182; 1947 and 1948 figures from Statistical Office of the United Nations, Monthly Bulletin of Statistics, August, 1949, pp. 50-51. This source was also used to fill in some gaps in the Iron and Steel Institute records. The two sources do not agree on all countries.

In interpreting the figures, changes in political boundaries must be kept in mind.

The magnificent response to wartime emergency needs made by the Lake Superior region, especially the Mesabi field, is indicated by the jump from 61.5 million tons in 1940 to 91.0 million tons in 1942.

World ore production is shown in Table 39.6. The bulk of the iron ore produced in the world originates in a relatively small group of countries. The United States, France, the Soviet Union, the United Kingdom, and Sweden usually account for three-fourths to four-fifths of the world output. Germany, Luxemburg, Spain, North Africa, Chile, and others constitute a secondary group of minor producers. The balance is scattered among still less important contributors.

FERRO-ALLOYS

Iron ore is the basic raw material of the iron and steel industry. But besides iron, steels also contain carbon and various other ingredients that are added to impart particular properties. The carbon can be added in various ways, in the form of charcoal or graphite or in conjunction with scrap. This will be discussed further in the description of steelmaking processes.

Here attention is turned to the so-called ferro-alloys. All the basic facts about ferro-alloys one needs to know are contained in Table 39.7. It lists reasons for the use of ferro-alloys, typical applications, the position of the United States as producer and consumer of these materials both before and during World War II, and the sources from which she procured them both before and during World War II.

Although the table lists metals, actually most of the ingredients are added to iron not as pure elements but in chemical compounds such as spiegeleisen (a grade of ferromanganese), ferrochromium, ferrotungsten, ferromolybdenum, etc. Some of these ingredients are used in practically all modern steels; others, especially combinations of others, are used only in making special alloy steels. Alloy steels are steels which owe their characteristics or special properties to the presence of an element or a combination of elements other than carbon. Carbon steels are tonnage steels, i.e., mass-produced steels. Alloy steels are quality steels. But there are some quality steels which do not rate as alloy steels, for the classification of alloy

steels is very rigid. It includes stainless steels and all other steels containing the following elements in the designated amounts:

Manganese in excess of 1.65 percent
Silicon " " " 0.60 "
Copper " " " 0.60 "

or such amounts of other elements as are known to produce certain specific alloying effects. Among these elements are aluminum, chromium, cobalt, columbium, magnesium, molybdenum, nickel, titanium, tungsten, vanadium, and zirconium.

Ferro-alloys are extracted from their ores by melting them either in open-hearth or electric furnaces in the presence of iron and steel scrap added in proper proportions to obtain the desired results. The simpler ferro-alloys are produced by the steel companies themselves; the more complex ones are produced by specialists. Steel companies generally prepare their own ferrosilicon and ferromanganese, the two most widely used ferro-alloys. Their main use is in the preparation of tonnage steels, not alloy steels.[18]

As Table 39.7 shows, the United States is dependent on foreign countries for most of her ferro-alloy supplies. Molybdenum is the only alloying metal of which she produces an exportable excess; in fact, she produces 90 percent of the total world output. We break even with aluminum, but most of it is made from imported bauxite. On all the other elements we are short, 25 percent in some cases and almost 100 percent in others.

A comparison of the two columns showing our chief sources of supply, prewar and wartime, shows the disappearance of the Soviet Union and the Far East and our dependence on the western hemisphere in wartime.

Of all the ferro-alloys, only manganese involves large-scale material handling. World production of manganese ore (generally 35 percent Mn and over) during the early forties ran somewhat above 5 million tons, which would indicate that about 1.5 to 2 million tons of manganese were produced. Most of the other alloying materials are produced in smaller

---

[18] For a list of producers of ferro-alloys in the United States, see *Minerals Yearbook, 1945*, p. 584.

TABLE 39.7. Principal Nonferrous Metals Used by the Steel Industry[19]

Metal	Reason for Use	Typical Applications	Prewar Average			Wartime Average		
			% of World Production Produced in U.S.	% of World Production Consumed in U.S.	Chief Sources of U.S. Supply	% of World Production Produced in U.S.	% of World Production Consumed in U.S.	Chief Sources of U.S. Supply
Aluminum	Removes gases and impurities; aids surface hardness	Seldom more than a trace remains, except in nitrided steel	30	40	United States	35	35	United States
Chromium	Small amounts improve hardening qualities; more than 10% prevents rust	Tools; machinery parts; stainless and heat- and acid-resisting steels	Insignificant	35	Africa, Cuba, Greece, New Caledonia, Oceania	5	50	Africa, Cuba, Greece, New Caledonia, Oceania
Cobalt	Holds cutting edge at high temperatures. Improves electrical qualities	High-speed cutting tools; permanent magnet steel	None	10	Canada, Belgian Africa, Australia	Insignificant	50	Canada, Belgian Africa, French Morocco
Copper	Retards rust	Roofing and siding sheets, plates	40	35	United States	40	60	United States, Chile
Lead	When mixed with tin, forms a rust-resisting coating for steel. Small amounts alloyed with steel improve machinability	Sheet steel for roofing, auto gasoline tanks, etc.; machinery parts	30	35	United States	27	50	United States, Mexico, Australia, Canada, Peru

	Effect on steel	Uses						
Manganese	Small amounts remove gases from steel; 1 to 2% increases strength and toughness; 12% imparts great toughness and resistance to abrasion	Small amounts present in all steels; 1 to 2% used in rails; 12% or more for frogs and dredge switches and bucket teeth	Insignificant	20	Russia, Gold Coast, Brazil, India	5	30	Gold Coast, Brazil, India, Cuba
Molybdenum	Increases strength, ductility, and resistance to shock	Tools; machinery parts; tubing for airplane fuselage	80	40	United States	90	75	United States
Nickel	Increases toughness, stiffness, strength, and ductility. In large amounts resists heat and acids	Tools; machinery parts; stainless steels; heat- and acid-resisting steels	Insignificant	50	Canada, Norway, New Caledonia	Insignificant	75	Canada, Cuba, New Caledonia
Tin	Forms corrosion-resisting coating on steel	Sanitary cans; kitchenware	Insignificant	45	British Malaya, United Kingdom, Netherlands, India	Insignificant	45	Bolivia, Belgian Congo
Tungsten	Retains hardness and toughness at high temperature	High-speed cutting tools; magnets	10	20	China, British Malaya, United States	25	40	United States, Bolivia, China, Argentina, Brazil
Vanadium	Increases strength, ductility, and resiliency	Tools; springs; machinery parts	15	25	United States, Peru, Rhodesia	50	75	United States, Peru, South West Africa
Zinc	Forms corrosion-resisting coating on steel	Galvanized roofing and siding sheets; wire fence; pails, etc.	35	35	United States	40	50	United States, Mexico, Canada, Peru, Australia

[19] American Iron and Steel Institute, *Steel Facts*, February, 1947, p. 4.

TABLE 39.8. Consumption and Exports of Iron and Steel Scrap by Districts, Compared with Population Distribution by Districts, 1939[20]
(long tons)

District	Home Scrap		Purchased Scrap		Export Scrap				Percent of U.S. Total Population, 1939[b]
	Quantity	Percent of U.S. Total	Quantity	Percent of U.S. Total	Quantity	Percent of U.S. Total	Total Quantity	Percent of U.S. Total	
New England	215,117	1.3	344,469	2.3	378,898	10.7	938,784	2.6	6.40
Middle Atlantic	5,214,809	29.8	4,161,527	27.9	1,096,811	31.0	10,473,147	29.1	21.10
Southeastern	2,315,569	13.2	1,803,232	12.1	668,563	18.9	4,787,364	13.3	21.50
Southwestern	35,954	0.2	112,471	0.7	703,334	19.8	851,759	2.4	9.90
North Central	9,254,712	52.8	7,561,185	50.7	153,668	4.3	16,969,565	47.2	30.50
Rocky Mountain	200,006	1.1	250,882	1.7	73	...	450,961	1.2	3.20
Pacific coast	283,743	1.6	681,091	4.6	542,632	15.3	1,507,466	4.2	7.40
Total	17,519,550	100.0	14,914,857	100.0	3,543,979	100.0	35,978,386	100.0	100.00

[a] Compiled from data published in U.S. Bureau of Mines Report of Investigation, 3329.
[b] U.S. Bureau of the Census.

amounts. Considerable amounts of them are recovered from scrap. Thus, during the war scrap yielded as much as 95 percent of all the nickel needed for alloying purposes.

During World War II when alloy metals in general were very scarce, the so-called NE (National Emergency) alloys were introduced. The chief objective was to economize in the use of alloying ingredients. The effort was encouraging and contributed measurably to our knowledge of alloys.

IRON AND STEEL SCRAP

Next to iron ore the most important raw material is scrap, both iron and steel scrap. In the United States about 90 percent of all steel produced is open-hearth steel. Furnace operators look upon a 50-50 charge—half pig iron or hot metal from the blast furnace and half scrap—as highly desirable. In 1947 our steel furnaces turned out 87 million tons of steel; they used 50.5 million tons of pig iron or hot metal from the blast furnace and 49.2 million tons of scrap.[21] Of these 49.2 million tons of scrap, 24.5 million were so-called run-around or home scrap and 24.7 million were market scrap, i.e., scrap purchased in the open market.

Market scrap is subdivided into industrial scrap, or scrap discarded by industries, railroads, etc.; and country scrap, or scrap collected by junk dealers, either in the open country or in cities. Industrial scrap makes up about 80 percent of the market scrap. Home scrap results from operations of iron and steelworks especially in the rolling and finishing departments where products are cut to the desired size, holes punched, etc. This home scrap goes far to explain the significant difference between ingot steel production and finished steel production; more will be said about this later.

Scrap can be used readily in open-hearth and electric furnaces, but only under special conditions in the Bessemer converter. This difference has greatly contributed to the ease with which the open-hearth furnace has outstripped and virtually displaced the Bessemer converter. The use of scrap is highly economical. It saves the costly blast furnace operation, which may use as much as four tons of raw material to turn out one ton of pig iron or hot metal. Naturally, using cold scrap instead of liquid iron increases fuel consumption in the open hearth and the current required in the electric furnace. But this does not begin to wipe out the savings its use makes possible.

Scrap is most plentiful and most easily collected and therefore cheapest in densely populated, highly industrialized areas. Hence its use has contributed much toward strengthening the

[20] Board of Investigation and Research, *op. cit.*, p. 29.
[21] The difference between 99.7 (50.5 plus 49.2) and 87 is accounted for by losses and by a year-end surplus of run-around or home scrap.

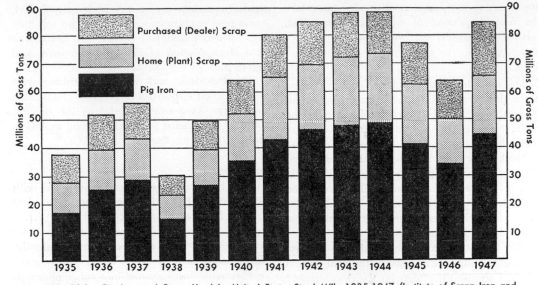

FIG. 39.3.   Pig Iron and Scrap Used by United States Steel Mills, 1935-1947. (Institute of Scrap Iron and Steel, *Yearbook,* 1948, p. 6.)

position of iron and steel centers located within the older, densely populated and highly industrialized areas of this country and of other countries as well. Table 39.8 shows how widely scrap consumption varies in different regions of the United States.

Some steel centers in the world rely almost exclusively on scrap, domestic and imported. A country possessing adequate coking coal but lacking both home ore supplies and easy access to foreign ore sources may yet build up a steel industry by relying on scrap. In rare instances (Italy, Argentina) countries try to build up steel industries by relying on imports of both fuel and scrap. Before World War II large amounts of scrap were shipped to Japan, especially from the United States. Some of this was exported in the form of old ships ready for the scrap torch.

Scrap is used not only by steel furnaces, which normally take about 75 percent, but also by foundries, which take about 20 percent, and blast furnaces, which use the remainder.

Fig. 39.3 shows the consumption of pig iron (hot metal) and scrap in the United States for the period 1935-1947. The proportions used vary with the business cycle and the size of the total demand. Market scrap is a rather erratic speculative commodity. When business is on the upgrade scrap dealers tend to hold

out for higher prices, and in times of depression the tendency is to unload at greatly reduced prices. Thus, in boom periods and when the demand is abnormally expanded, as in war, in the absence of price control the price of scrap is likely to be high relative to the cost of ore and pig iron; the opposite holds true in depression periods. Since open-pit mine operations are quite flexible it is easy to shift during a depression from ore-pig iron operations to greatly enhanced reliance on scrap. When, in wartime, total steel output rises to unprecedented heights, it may well happen that even government-sponsored scrap drives will not result in enough scrap being gathered to meet requirements based on normal furnace practices. It is then that the unparalleled demands on the nation's ore mines develop.

SERVICE MATERIALS

Besides these three raw materials—ore, ferroalloys, and scrap—which actually enter into the products of the iron and steel industry,[22] there

---

[22] Strictly speaking, the part of coke that contributes carbon to steel is also an alloy material. This alloying function, however, is inseparable from the far more important function as an agent of combustion. Moreover, vast amounts of fuels are used in processing operations. Hence, the fuels, including coke, are here treated as service materials.

are needed vast amounts of service materials, the most important of which are fuels, flux, refractories, water, air, and sand.

Fuels

The most important fuels are coal and coke. Since these were discussed in an earlier chapter, only facts that contribute further to the understanding of their use and importance are given here.

Most modern blast furnaces use coke. Some still use charcoal either to produce quality pig iron or because coke is not available or is too costly to compete with charcoal. In the interior of Brazil, for instance, charcoal is the only blast furnace fuel available.

The transition from the beehive to the by-product coke oven discussed in the coal section has had significant effects on the development of the steel industry largely because some coals not suitable for the beehive oven can be converted into acceptable metallurgical coke in the by-product coke oven. This has contributed to the geographical spread of the industry. In particular, Pittsburgh lost some of its early hold that rested on the fact that Connellsville coals were eminently suited for use in beehive coke ovens. By-product coke ovens yield not only more coke per ton of coal charged, but also valuable by-products and large amounts of hot gas. Whereas beehive ovens were located near the coal mines, by-product coke ovens generally are an integral part of the modern steelworks. Their introduction may have lowered the cost of steelmaking and thus encouraged their wider use. Of 76.4 million tons of coal used to make coke in 1946, 18.6 million were charged in Pennsylvania, 11.9 in Ohio, 9.2 in Indiana, 7.1 in New York, 6.5 in Alabama, 4.5 in Illinois, 3.5 in Michigan, and 3.1 in Utah; the rest were scattered.[23]

Flux

Flux is used in the blast furnace to draw a portion of the impurities (except phosphorus) out of the melting ore. Flux consists of limestone or dolomite (limestone that contains a certain percentage of magnesium). Both materials are common, though sources of high-grade materials are not widely distributed. Some ores contain enough lime to be self-fluxing. As was mentioned earlier, this holds true of a large portion of the Alabama ores, and also of most of the Lorraine ores.

The limestone and dolomite combine with the extracted impurities to form slag. The slag may serve as a raw material in the cement industry or be used for road-building materials and for other purposes.

Refractories

Both blast and steel furnaces are lined with refractories. Ordinarily the lining of a blast furnace is expected to last about three years, but the lining of open hearths and Bessemer converters has to be replaced more frequently. Refractories may be clay brick, silica brick, or chromium brick. Sometimes other materials are preferred. Steel companies may own the source from which these materials are obtained and make their own firebrick, or they may purchase them.

Water

The iron and steel industry of the United States consumes daily about 4 billon gallons, or 1,460,000,000,000 quarts, of water, a truly fantastic quantity.[24] Its use is distributed about as follows: to quench coke, 7 percent; to cool blast furnaces, 20 percent; to make steam, 40 percent; to cool furnace doors and rolls in steelworks, to operate hydraulic machinery and rolling mills, 30 percent; sewage disposal, less than 1 percent.[25]

Air

About 4 tons of air are required to make a ton of steel. A blast furnace alone may call for 50,000 cubic feet per minute. A Bessemer converter of 25-ton capacity needs 30,000 cubic feet per minute.

Because of the ubiquity of air and the quasi-ubiquity of water, these raw materials add little to cost except to the extent that their manipulation involves expense. Naturally, a blast that has a high pressure per square inch and is at

---

[23] *Minerals Yearbook,* 1946.

[24] Board of Investigation and Research, *op. cit.*
[25] C. F. Jones, *Economic Geography,* The Macmillan Company, New York, 1941, p. 483, quoted in Senate Doc. No. 80.

1500° F. is not obtainable free of charge, but the air itself is. Water is beginning to cause worry, for water tables are sinking. Densely industrialized areas and locations near large bodies of water may yet become as advantageous to steelworks as they have long been to large power houses.

BIBLIOGRAPHY

See the bibliography at the end of Chapter 42.

Sand

Sand is used chiefly in foundries. In 1936 the iron and steel industry of the United States used 3.7 million tons of sand for molding.

How these materials are used in the iron and steel industry will be explained in the following chapter.

Chapter 40

EQUIPMENT, PROCESSES, AND PRODUCTS

HISTORICAL DEVELOPMENT

Some historians place the time when man first consciously made iron at about 1350 B.C. Ore was placed close to burning fuel (charcoal), air was induced, and the resultant heat removed impurities from parts of the ore. The pieces of iron so produced were picked by hand from the cooling heap.

By a strange coincidence, another significant date in iron history happens to be 1350 A.D., twenty-seven centuries later. At that time, after long, patient effort and experimentation, man finally succeeded in building a furnace strong and large enough and in developing a temperature high enough to cause the iron in the ore to melt. This was the birth of the blast furnace. In Spain the Catalan forge had been slowly perfected. When the Moors pressed north, some of the Spanish ironmakers who fled reached the Meuse valley near the present Marche Les Dames in Belgium, long a center of metal production. Some believe that it was here that the Catalan forge became a full-fledged blast furnace.

In those days charcoal served as fuel. Centuries of charcoal making inevitably resulted in the depletion of forests; hence a substitute fuel became urgent. Coke was first made in England in the seventeenth century and applied in the blast furnace in the eighteenth. Ores suitable to these primitive processing methods abounded in many parts of the earth. A small furnace can make good use of small ore bodies, but our modern giant plants have no use for them; they must look to the rarer mass accumulations.

Another milestone on the highway of human progress was the year 1855, when Sir Henry Bessemer patented his fuelless pneumatic converter which turned iron into cheap steel, the first cheap mass steel known to man. Until then both iron and steel were made by processes involving the direct contact of ore and metal with fuels and calling for considerable muscular labor. The Bessemer invention opened a new chapter in metal history—the chapter of indirect steelmaking; for the ore is first converted in the blast furnace to pig iron, and the pig iron is then converted to steel in separate steel furnaces.

No sooner had Bessemer taken out his patent than Sir William Siemens a year later patented his open hearth, which applies the so-called regenerative furnace principle to steelmaking. This principle also helped to raise the blast furnace to its present level of efficiency. Two other revolutionary inventions followed in 1878, when Sir William developed an electric furnace for steelmaking and the Welshmen, Thomas and Gilchrist, gave the world the basic process. A few years later the Martin brothers of France modified the Siemens open hearth to make it suitable for the use of scrap.

By that time the roster of essential modern steelmaking facilities was complete: the blast furnace with its regenerative stoves, the Bessemer converter, the open-hearth and the electric furnace, all with either acid or basic lining. There followed in the nineties several versions of by-product coke ovens and the stage was set for the great expansion of iron and steel production in the twentieth century. The facilities will be discussed more fully later.

The following data throw light on the role of the United States in iron and steel history. In 1834, for the first time in this country, the blast for the blast furnace was heated. In 1837 coke was used for the first time. In 1864 the first acid Bessemer converter was put in operation, and in 1868 the first acid open hearth. In 1880 the basic open hearth was introduced. The first Koppers oven was built in 1898. The electric furnace came into use around 1900.

The shift in production from iron to steel was rapid. In 1870, the United States produced 1 million long tons of wrought iron, and 100,000 long tons of steel; wrought iron production was up to 3 million long tons in 1890, but steel output had increased to 10.2 million; by 1929, wrought iron had dropped to 0.5 million long tons, whereas steel had soared to 56 million.

EQUIPMENT AND PROCESSES

The Blast Furnace

The first step in the conversion of iron ore into iron and steel is to free the iron from impurities. This is done in the blast furnace. Ore, coke, and generally limestone or dolomite are charged into the furnace at the top and a hot blast is introduced near the bottom. The gases formed by the burning coke remove the oxygen from the ore and the flux helps to fluidize the gangue into slag. The slag, being

lighter, settles on top of the molten iron. The iron is drawn off every five or six hours; the slag is removed more frequently.

A modern blast furnace (Fig. 40.1) is a circular brick-lined steel shell, sometimes over 100 feet tall and with a hearth diameter as large as 27 feet. The hearth, the lowest and

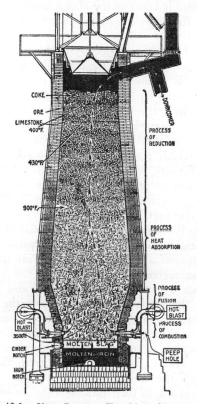

FIG. 40.1. Blast Furnace. The blast furnace proper shown here is only part of a complex structure which includes (1) charging apparatus, (2) stoves in which exhaust gases from the furnace heat the blast, (3) dust catcher which cleans the exhaust gases, (4) blowing engine which puts air under pressure, (5) cooling devices and other equipment. The largest blast furnaces turn out 1500 tons of pig iron a day. The furnace temperatures reach as high as 3500° F. (American Steel and Wire Company.)

widest part of the furnace, is about 10 to 12 feet deep. Above it is the bosh, about 9 to 12 feet in depth, from which rises the stack, about 70 feet high. The furnace is capped by the top, which carries the charging mechanism. The waste gases are fed into the regenerative furnace plant which supplies the hot blast.

The blast furnace proper is but a unit in the complex setup that is needed to make the blast furnace work. There is the loading apparatus which feeds the raw materials into the furnace. Back of that apparatus is the transportation setup, which brings the raw materials from the outside, and the storage pile, which assures a more even supply. There are the facilities for tapping both the pig iron, or "hot metal" as the product of the blast furnace is called, and the slag. The balance is the elaborate contrivance which furnishes the blast, hot air under pressure.

The blast is provided by a blowing engine which sucks air from the atmosphere, cleanses and chills it, and subjects it to a pressure of 2 or 3 pounds p.s.i. At this pressure the air is forced down through one of three or four blast-heating stoves located between the blowing engine and the blast furnace, into the bustle pipe, which runs around the hearth of the blast furnace, and through tuyeres into the blast furnace proper. The three or four cylindrical preheating stoves are usually 100 or more feet high and about 22 feet in diameter.

It is through these stoves that the Siemens regenerative furnace principle is applied to the operation of a blast furnace. They are devices for the regeneration of heat, for the chilled blast air is heated to between 1000 and 1700° F. by the waste gases coming from the blast furnace. The hot blast helps to produce the exceedingly high temperatures in the blast furnace which, in turn, account for the great heat of the waste gases that escape from the top through the downcomer. It is these waste gases which, in their turn, heat the air blast as it enters the furnace. A complete circle—regeneration in the full sense of the word.

The stoves are heat traps. Their interior is filled with layer upon layer of heat-absorbing brick, each layer arranged like a checkerboard, each successive layer slightly turned from the one beneath so as to expose the maximum surface to the hot waste gases rushing up through the stoves. When the brick in the stoves is saturated with heat, a valve at the bottom shuts off the gas and a valve at the top allows access to the chilled forced blast coming from the blowing engine which then absorbs the accumulated heat in the tower. Only one stove heats the blast at any one time; the others are being heated. Since it takes several times as long to heat a stove as it takes for the blast to absorb

the heat, three or four stoves are needed for this regenerative operation. Formerly five or even more were required, but as the process becomes more efficient fewer are needed.

The regenerative system of heating the blast is a great coke saver and renders the entire operation of the blast furnace more efficient, and therefore cheaper.

As was stated before, iron ore, coke, and limestone are charged into the top of the furnace. This is done by means of skip cars that run on individual tracks set at steep angles. The cars are loaded, preferably by gravity, either from stock piles or from railroad hopper cars. The material enters the top of the furnace through a double bell hopper which prevents the escape of dust or gases from the furnace. (See Fig. 40.1.)

The largest blast furnace in operation at present yields 1500 tons of iron a day; it also produces about 750 tons of slag and 9000 tons of gas. At a daily output of 1500 tons of iron such a "monster stack" produces close to 550,-000 tons of iron a year. If two of them (combined output 1,100,000 tons) are fed iron ore with an iron content of 50 percent, they will consume in one year 2,200,000 tons of iron ore. Assuming a lifetime of thirty years, the two furnaces will consume a total of 60 to 70 million tons of ore. This almost incredible amount must be visualized if the modern ironmaker's disdain for small and modest ore pockets is to be understood. It does not pay to erect such blast furnaces in places to which these vast amounts of ore cannot be delivered economically.

Blast furnace practice varies with many factors; but for every ton of pig iron a typical blast furnace in the United States consumes about 2 tons of ore, 1 ton of coke, and 0.4 ton of limestone. Applying these proportions to the 1500 "tonner," one gets a daily charge of 3000 tons of ore, 1500 tons of coke, and 600 tons of limestone, a total of over 5000 tons, exclusive of air. If that charge were moved in 50-ton railroad cars, over 100 would be required for one day's operation of one furnace.

On the average, blast furnaces in the United States are larger than in most countries. The average annual output for the blast furnaces of several countries during the thirties was estimated as follows: United States, 210,000 tons; Germany, 125,000; Belgium, 85,000; France, 70,000; United Kingdom, 65,000; Scotland (included in the United Kingdom figure), 35,000.[1] Charcoal furnaces cannot exceed a modest size because charcoal is easily crushed by heavy burdens. Furnaces using lean ores in general must be smaller than those charged with rich ores. The difference in size therefore reflects different conditions rather than merely technical proficiency. Labor productivity tends to rise with increased size of the furnace.

In 1947 blast furnaces in the United States produced 58.5 million tons of iron. Of this, 50.5 million tons went into steel furnaces where the iron was mixed with iron and steel scrap. Of the remaining 8 million, 6 million went into foundry iron or directly into castings. Foundry iron goes through various processes which impart to it the desired properties.

Formerly the iron drawn from the blast furnace was run into sand forms which by their arrangement, resembling suckling pigs, gave the iron its name, pig iron. Today the bulk of the iron is rushed in molten form ("hot metal") to the steel furnace to be converted into steel. If pigs are to be made for storage and shipment, they are now frequently made in special machines.

During World War II the demand for steel for war purposes was so great that every effort was made to increase the industry's productivity at every point possible. The pressure was particularly great on blast furnaces because of the impossibility of procuring amounts of scrap adequate to maintain the traditional ratio of pig iron and scrap in making steel. As a result, two significant innovations in blast furnace practice were introduced, both of them still in the experimental stage. One of them sounds very simple. The idea is to throttle the escape of the gases from the top of the blast furnace in such a way that the pressure of the blast within the furnace is materially increased. While the pressure increases, the velocity of the gases is slowed down, reducing the loss of iron dust at the top. By thus throttling the blast furnace and operating it at higher vacuums, the blast was increased from 75,000 to 120,000 cubic feet per minute in one big furnace in Cleveland. This made it possible to raise the output of iron for a given charge by 20 percent and reduce coke consumption by 12 percent.[2]

The other innovation is the feeding of oxygen or oxygenated air into the blast furnace, instead of ordinary air. The idea is to reduce or eliminate the nitrogen content and thus render the blast more potent. The prospect of a larger supply of cheap tonnage oxygen produced by an improved Linde-Fraenkl process (see p. 494) holds out considerable promise. This innovation can be applied not only to the blast furnace but also to the open hearth and the Bessemer converter.[3]

The Bessemer Converter[4]

In 1856 Henry Bessemer, an Englishman of French descent, read before the British Association for the Advancement of Science a scientific paper entitled "Manufacture of Malleable Iron and Steel Without Fuel." The process described therein was destined to revolutionize industry and to usher in an era of unparalleled expansion, for it assured cheap steel produced *en masse,* and this meant millions of tons of machinery, of rails, of ship plates. Until then steel had been an expensive rarity; now it became a cheap commonalty. Moreover, with cheap steel the steel industry could lift itself by its own bootstrap, as it were, for its own steel requirements could be met with increasing ease and at progressively lower costs.

The Bessemer converter is a pear-shaped steel vessel varying in size and capacity. The older converters are cylindrical, but the more

[1] U.S. Tariff Commission, *Report on Iron and Steel,* 1938, p. 42.

[2] For a full description of this innovation, see J. H. Slater, *American Iron and Steel Institute Yearbook, 1947,* pp. 125-198; also B. S. Old, A. R. Almeida, R. W. Hyde, and S. L. Pepper, "Economics of the Blast Furnace," *Iron Age,* September 18, 1941; J. Revie, "High Top Pressure Operation," *Iron and Steel* (British), February, 1948; also "A Spark in Steel," *Fortune,* December, 1948, pp. 75 ff.

[3] For a full discussion, see J. H. Strassburger, "Tonnage Oxygen for Increased Iron and Steel Production," paper read before the general meeting of the American Iron and Steel Institute, May 26-27, 1948.

[4] For a brief account of the parallel invention of the tilting converter by William Kelly, an American of Irish descent, in Kentucky, see *Steel Facts,* February, 1945.

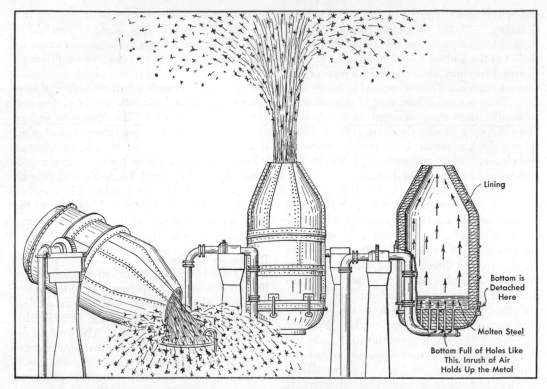

FIG. 40.2. Bessemer Converter. The lining consists of acid material if the charge contains no phosphorus, or only a little. Otherwise the lining must consist of basic materials such as dolomite or magnesite. (American Steel and Wire Company.)

modern ones are spherical. The converter is lined with refractory material and mounted on trunnions so that it can be tilted one way to receive the charge of molten iron—15 to 60 tons according to its size—a different way to "blow," and a third way to pour out its contents into a ladle. The bottom is detachable and perforated with many small openings called tuyères through which air is forced into the charge.

In burning the silicon, the oxygen of the air produces great heat, and in burning the manganese, carbon, etc., it produces more heat until the entire content of the converter is in a wild state of combustion which burns out all the impurities and leaves a characterless iron. This is usually turned into steel by treatment with ferromanganese, which reimparts the elements carbon, manganese, and silicon in the desired proportions ranging from a mere trace to about 1 percent of carbon, from 0.3 to 1 percent of manganese, and from 0.05 to about 0.3 percent of silicon. Fig. 40.2 shows the Bessemer converter in various positions.

If the refractory material with which the Bessemer converter is lined is acid it can remove basic impurities; if it is basic it can remove acid impurities, especially phosphorus. In the United States only the acid Bessemer process is in use, whereas in Europe the basic or Thomas process is widely used.

The product of the Bessemer converter satisfies all requirements for ordinary pipe and ordinary steel wire, and for some so-called free-cutting steels. But for many other requirements Bessemer steel is no longer considered adequate. The process is too quick to permit careful testing, too brutal to allow accurate control.[5] Moreover, for best results the Besse-

[5] Some years ago experiments were made in controlling the Bessemer process by means of the electric eye. The objective was to fix the exact time schedule of the process in terms of split seconds. Knowing beforehand what would happen next, the operator could be forewarned and prepared to interfere. Since then, however, the Bessemer converter has lost further ground, indicating that this control still leaves much to be desired.

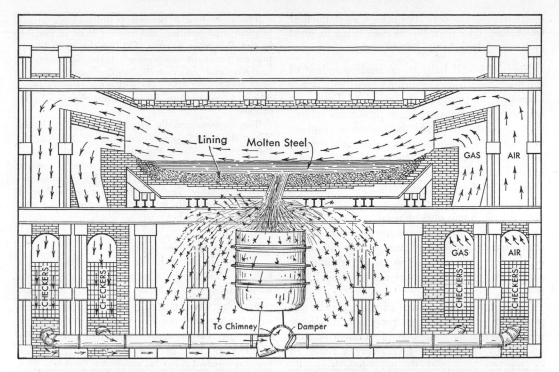

FIG. 40.3. Open Hearth. On the sides are checker brick chambers that heat the mixture of gas and air forced into the reverberatory furnace in which pig iron and iron and steel scrap are turned into refined steel. The direction of the heat charge alternates at regular intervals from right to left (as shown in the figure) to left to right. The lining, as in the Bessemer converter, is either acid or basic depending on the phosphorus content of the charge. The supply of gas is usually obtained from nearby by-product coke oven plants. This process of making steel in the open hearth is much slower than the Bessemer process and hence permits frequent checking and more careful production. (American Steel and Wire Company.)

mer converter requires pig iron made from a rather narrow range of ores, which means that without alternative processes the supply of commercial ores would soon have been reduced. Finally, the Bessemer converter does not lend itself to the conversion of scrap into steel. For all these reasons, other processes have come to the fore.

The Open Hearth

Among these, the open-hearth process, introduced soon after Bessemer's epoch-making announcement, is the most important when appraised in terms of quantity of output. The open hearth is generally credited to Sir William (Karl Wilhelm) Siemens, a British inventer of German birth. However, as is true of most inventions, credit cannot be allotted accurately to any one person; some believe that the so-called regenerative principle was an idea of Sir

William's brother Friedrich.[6] The regenerative principle which underlies the open-hearth process, as well as blast furnace operation, is described as follows:

In an ordinary furnace a very large part of the heat of combustion is lost by being carried off in the hot gases which pass up the chimney. In the regenerative furnace the hot gases pass through a regenerator, or chamber, stacked with loose bricks which absorb the heat. When the bricks are well heated the hot gases are diverted so as to pass through another similar chamber, while the air necessary for combustion, before it enters the furnace, is made to traverse the heated chamber, taking up as it goes the heat which has been stored in the bricks. After a suitable interval the air currents are again reversed. The process is repeated periodically, with the result that the products of

[6] For some details, see entry for Sir William Siemens, *Encyclopædia Britannica*, 11th ed.

combustion escape only after being cooled, the heat which they take from the furnace being in great part carried back in the heated air.[7]

Fig. 40.3 will help to an understanding of the open-hearth process. In Siemens' day it was necessary to produce the required hot gases in specially constructed gas producers which, through distillation and the complete combustion of coal, furnished the necessary gas supply. Nowadays, open-hearth furnaces are generally located in close proximity to by-product coke ovens, blast furnaces, and other sources of hot gases, on which they can draw. Natural gas, oil, tar, and pitch can also be used.

Moreover, the economic significance of the open-hearth furnace has been greatly enhanced by the fact that some scrap as well as iron ore can be charged, besides the molten iron drawn from the blast furnace.

The greatest advantage of the open-hearth process over the Bessemer process is its slower tempo. Whereas the Bessemer converter may take 9 to 15 minutes to convert a batch of molten iron into steel, the open hearth usually takes about 12 hours. For one thing, the charge of an open hearth is larger—100 to 175 tons of "hot metal," scrap, and ore, as against 15 to 60 tons of "hot metal" for the Bessemer. Furthermore, the Bessemer converter can produce only "tonnage steel," whereas the open hearth can produce quality steels, i.e., the simpler alloy steels. In the United States the basic open-hearth process is by far the most important one used.

The basic open-hearth furnace, which is the furnace most widely used, is charged with cold scrap comprising about half the metallic charge. Limestone, about 10 per cent of the weight of the metallic charge, is charged prior to the scrap, to build up slag. After the scrap has melted down pig iron is added, usually in molten form. If cold pig iron is used it is added as soon as the scrap has melted down sufficiently to provide space. If alloy steel is being made the alloys are added at the proper time.

There are two phases of the operation—first, the melting-down period, then the refining period. During the latter period the operator must exercise especially good judgment, which is gained by long experience and assisted by the latest metallurgical and scientific apparatus and devices.

[7] *Ibid.*, vol. 25, p. 48.

The open-hearth process permits closer metallurgical manipulation and control than is possible in the Bessemer process. During the open-hearth process frequent samples are taken for chemical analysis and other tests, and extensive use of instruments and scientific apparatus permits regulation of temperature, furnace atmosphere and conditions.

The process usually requires about 12 hours. When the steel is properly refined and has reached the desired analysis, the furnace is ready to tap. The tap hole at the rear of the furnace is opened and the content is drained into a large refractory-lined steel ladle. The slag flows out last and spills over the filled ladle into an adjacent slag pot, also known as a thimble.[8]

The Electric Furnace

As has been said, the open-hearth furnace has, at least in the United States, come close to replacing the cheaper and faster Bessemer converter. One reason is the superior control over the product possible with the open hearth. Although this control is sufficient for a large number of low or simple alloy steels, even greater control must be assured in making high alloy steels, stainless steels, and certain tool steels. This is achieved in the electric furnace.

Two types of electric furnaces are in use in the steel industry—the arc and the inductive. Arc furnaces are all of the tilting type. Tilting permits easy and frequent removal of slag, and this in turn creates a "neutral atmosphere" in which close metallurgical control is possible. Arc furnaces vary in capacity from a few hundred pounds to 75 tons and over. The electric current is fed to the bath through carbon or graphite electrodes which pass through the roof. Electric arcs between the electrodes and the bath furnish the heat.

In the inductive furnace the heating current is induced into the metallic charge itself. As the result of the action of the current the metal bath is in constant circulation and the swirling motion assists in removing undesirable non-metallic particles. Induction furnaces are considerably smaller than arc furnaces.

Acid and Basic Processes of Steelmaking

The distinction between acid and basic processes of steelmaking was mentioned but its im-

[8] *Steel in the Making*, Bethlehem Steel Company, 1942, pp. 18-19.

portance warrants additional remarks. Both the Bessemer converter and the Siemens open hearth were originally fitted with acid lining materials capable of absorbing basic impurities. This acid lining of the acid Bessemer converter and the acid open hearth could not cope with phosphorus in amounts greater than 0.05 percent of the ore. But ores containing so little phosphorus are rare; furthermore, the English ores of that type and the north Spanish ores which England acquired for use in acid Bessemer converters were beginning to run out.

Just as the threatening exhaustion of charcoal drove the iron and steel industry to use coal and later coke, so the fear of exhausting the limited deposits of ores suitable for acid Bessemer converters and acid open hearths encouraged the search for new processes that would permit a wider choice of iron ores. The solution of the problem is one of the romances in the history of inventions. Although the question had long occupied the best minds of the industry, the answer was provided by Thomas and Gilchrist, two young Welshmen who were little more than amateurs in the field. They reasoned in simple logic: if an acid lining does not remove phosphorus, a basic lining will. So they substituted basic lining materials —limestone and dolomite—in the Bessemer converter and their idea worked. But the experts did not trust this simple answer; hence the scientific papers which Thomas and Gilchrist were to have read in Paris in 1878 were allowed to remain unread for a whole year, withholding from humanity one of the greatest inventions of all time.

Duplex and Triplex Processes

As was mentioned earlier, under special circumstances not one steelmaking process is used to produce steel, but two or three are combined. One speaks of the Duplex and the Triplex process. Thus, in the Birmingham area high-phosphorus pig iron is sometimes first routed through acid Bessemer converters and then through the basic open hearth. The Triplex process, involving the additional use of the electric furnace, is said to be in use in India.

Direct Reduction Process

Until about 1350 A.D., as we have seen, the heat developed in the iron furnace was in-sufficient to melt the iron. The pre-melting processes are referred to as direct reduction processes. Modern melting requires metallurgical coke; but where that is scarce, direct reduction methods may be resorted to. Thus Sweden, which lacks coal but produces ample and cheap hydroelectricity, has developed processes for making sponge iron, as the unmelted, directly reduced product is called.[9]

IRON AND STEEL TECHNOLOGY
Economic and Political Implications

It is important to know what improvements in iron and steel technology have been made. It is even more important to understand their effects and to appreciate their implications, for their epochal importance for the course of human history cannot be questioned.

The objective of this technological evolution is larger amounts of iron and steel at lower costs, a result achieved by fuller and better use of what nature offers and by man's greater application of capital, including both technical and managerial science, to the making of iron and steel, thus raising labor productivity. In increasing the production of steel from a few hundred thousand tons in the middle of the nineteenth century to a hundred million or more, the steel industry encountered one bottleneck after another—ore, fuel, labor, etc. Today we are again face to face with such a bottleneck—high-grade ore. And again as always the industry is joining forces in the effort to eliminate it.

Both the Bessemer converter and the open hearth are masterpieces of fuel economy. Air is cheaper than coal and coke; the regenerative furnace is the acme of fuel economy. The Martin modification of the Siemens open hearth which permits the use of scrap is a great ore saver directly and a great all-round saver of everything—ore, coke, labor, capital, etc.—indirectly. The basic process rendered possible the wholesale transformation of dirt into a valuable raw material—perhaps the largest single transformation of neutral stuff into valuable resources.

---

[9] See C. F. Ramseyer, "The Manufacture of Sponge Iron," *Blast Furnace and Steel Plant*, May and June, 1943, and also "Sponge Iron—Its Possibilities and Limitations," *Iron and Steel Engineer*, July, 1944.

The economic significance of alloy steels cannot be exaggerated. Not only can they perform tasks far beyond those possible with ordinary steels, but they are great material savers. If a pound of alloy steel can do the work of five or ten pounds of ordinary steel the direct or indirect savings in raw materials are phenomenal. The implications of alloy steels are manifold. If a freight car or an automobile or a ship is built in part out of alloy steel, its capacity to do useful work and earn revenue is greatly enhanced. Boilers with greater resistance to steam pressure can be built from a smaller quantity of metal. The weight of metal required to harness a horsepower is being constantly reduced, with remarkable effects on engine performance and untold savings in metal.[10]

One of the most significant features of iron and steel technology is the trend toward increased size. This is especially noticeable in the case of the blast furnace, and it has political significance. As was said earlier, the largest blast furnaces turn out more than half a million tons of "hot metal" a year. This is a great deal more than many nations with small local markets can afford to produce in a year. If they want a blast furnace it must be more modest in size and perhaps less economical than those in the large steel-producing nations. Protection may be needed to assure the survival and growth of iron and steel production in smaller countries.

Of particular political importance was the invention of the basic process. This became generally known seven or eight years after the newborn Germany, victorious in the Franco-Prussian War, had occupied Alsace-Lorraine. The ore in Lorraine had long been known as "minette," a term expressing contempt and implying the worthlessness of the "dirt." Because of its effect on this "minette," the discovery made by Thomas and Gilchrist is one of the most important and, perhaps, most fatal discoveries in history, for it led inevitably to Germany's industrial hegemony on the continent and it made the industrial position of the United Kingdom, the home of the inventors, increasingly more vulnerable. It had a bearish effect on the value of Bessemer ores, especially those of England and Spain. In Thomas meal[11] it gave a valuable by-product to the steelmakers using phosphorus ore, thus enabling them to obtain a powerful weapon in the competitive struggle. Through its application to the open-hearth process, the basic process vitally affected the steel industry of the United States and the value of the Lake Superior ores and those of northern Sweden. It remade the industrial map and, perhaps more than any other single event, is tied in fateful causality to wars.

THE MODERN STEELWORKS

This discussion of the technological evolution of the iron and steel industry would be incomplete without reference to the changing interrelations of the various processes which thus far have been considered singly. Originally the different processes involved in making iron and steel and the auxiliary functions such as the preparation of metallurgical coke were carried on independently, as a rule in different locations. A blast furnace could produce pig iron, i.e., cold iron in the shape of "pigs," and sell it in the open market to a Bessemer converter or open-hearth steel plant, which in turn would sell the steel to a rail mill or a wire manufacturer. The blast furnace would buy its coke from a beehive coke oven, etc.

This physical separation of functions resulted in much waste, especially of heat. The fact that cold pig iron was charged into the steel furnace and cold steel was supplied for the rolling mill meant either a loss of efficiency for the furnace or mill operation or the necessity of costly heating operations in so-called soaking pits. Moreover, the beehive oven wasted not only the by-products obtained in

---

[10] That changing technology will affect the locational aspects of the iron and steel industry is obvious. This will be discussed more fully later.

[11] In Europe the basic Bessemer process is known as the Thomas process. Steel made by it is known as Thomas steel. When saturated with phosphorus, the basic lining of the Bessemer converter is ground and sold as Thomas meal, a valuable fertilizer material. Lake Superior ore contains considerably less phosphorus than the Briey and Lorraine ores of France. The pig iron they make is most suitable for the open hearth. The basic open hearth is as characteristic of the United States as the basic Bessemer converter is of Europe.

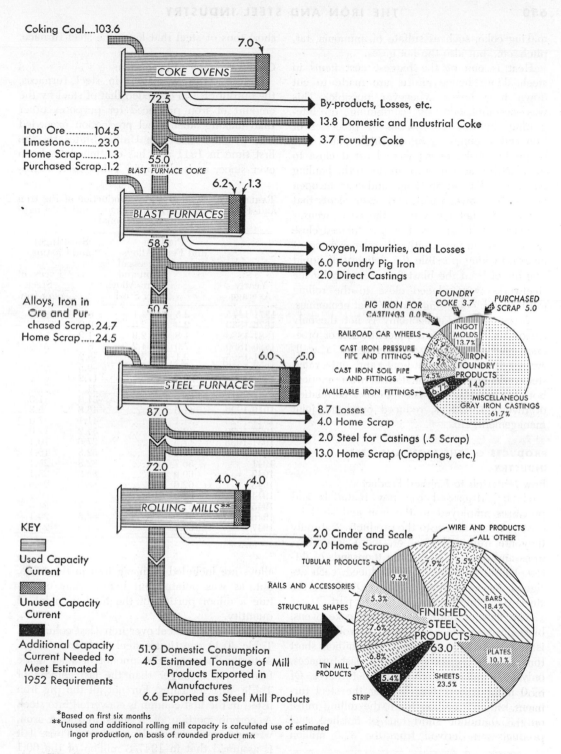

Coking Coal....103.6

7.0

COKE OVENS

72.5

→ By-products, Losses, etc.
→ 13.8 Domestic and Industrial Coke
→ 3.7 Foundry Coke

Iron Ore..........104.5
Limestone.........23.0
Home Scrap.........1.3
Purchased Scrap..1.2

55.0
BLAST FURNACE COKE

6.2   1.3

BLAST FURNACES

58.5

→ Oxygen, Impurities, and Losses
→ 6.0 Foundry Pig Iron
  2.0 Direct Castings

Alloys, Iron in
Ore and Pur
chased Scrap.24.7
Home Scrap.....24.5

50.5

6.0   5.0

FOUNDRY
COKE 3.7   PURCHASED
                   SCRAP 5.0

PIG IRON FOR
CASTINGS 6.0

RAILROAD CAR WHEELS   INGOT
                             MOLDS
CAST IRON PRESSURE   13.7%
PIPE AND FITTINGS
CAST IRON SOIL PIPE   IRON
AND FITTINGS   FOUNDRY
                             PRODUCTS
MALLEABLE IRON FITTINGS   14.0

                             MISCELLANEOUS
                             GRAY IRON CASTINGS
                             61.7%

STEEL FURNACES

87.0

→ 8.7 Losses
  4.0 Home Scrap
→ 2.0 Steel for Castings (.5 Scrap)
→ 13.0 Home Scrap (Croppings, etc.)

72.0

4.0   4.0

ROLLING MILLS**

→ 2.0 Cinder and Scale
  7.0 Home Scrap

KEY

[light hatch] Used Capacity
Current

[dark hatch] Unused Capacity
Current

[black] Additional Capacity
Current Needed to
Meet Estimated
1952 Requirements

WIRE AND PRODUCTS
ALL OTHER
TUBULAR PRODUCTS   7.9%   5.5%
                    9.5%
RAILS AND ACCESSORIES
                    5.3%   BARS
STRUCTURAL SHAPES   18.4%
                    7.6%   FINISHED
                          STEEL
                          PRODUCTS
                          63.0   PLATES
                    6.8%   10.1%
TIN MILL
PRODUCTS   5.4%   SHEETS
                          23.5%
STRIP

51.9 Domestic Consumption
4.5 Estimated Tonnage of Mill
Products Exported in
Manufactures
6.6 Exported as Steel Mill Products

*Based on first six months
**Unused and additional rolling mill capacity is calculated use of estimated
ingot production, on basis of rounded product mix

FIG. 40.4.   Flow from Raw Materials to Finished Products, United States Iron and Steel Industry, 1947.
(Department of the Interior, *Krug Report*, 1948, p. 52.)

making coke, such as sulfate of ammonia, tar, pitch, etc., but also the hot gases.

Heat is one of the biggest cost items in steelmaking; hence efforts are made to cut down heat losses whenever possible. This was accomplished by combining or integrating the different phases or processes of iron and steelmaking into a single plant. The by-product coke ovens were located close to the blast furnace so as to cut down the hauling distance and avoid breakage, and near the open hearth, the power plant, and other plants that can use the hot gases from the coke ovens.[12] Similarly the blast furnaces were placed close to the steel furnaces, either Bessemer or open-hearth, making possible the delivery of liquid iron direct from the blast furnaces. Finally the steelworks were placed close to the rolling mills, thereby enabling further heat economies.

To be sure, heat economy is not the only reason for this physical concentration of processes. Other advantages offered by a well-arranged, carefully laid-out and integrated steelworks are the elimination of waste motion, both transporting and lifting, closer correlation of diverse functions, reduced overhead, joint management, etc.

PRODUCTS OF THE IRON AND STEEL INDUSTRY

Raw Materials to Finished Product

Having discussed the raw materials and processes employed in the iron and steel industry, we now turn to the products. Naturally they are iron and steel or, more accurately, irons and steels. For literally thousands of different irons and steels are produced, each designed for a specific purpose. Of these, the steels constitute by far the greater part.

The flow of materials through coke ovens, blast furnaces, steel furnaces, and rolling mills is shown in Fig. 40.4. Of 58.5 million short tons of pig iron coming from the blast furnaces, only 50.5 million reach the steel furnaces. Of 87.0 million short tons leaving the steel furnaces, only 72 million reach the rolling mills; only 63.0 million short tons of finished steel products are derived from the 87.0 million

[12] Coke oven gas has about 540 B.T.U. per cubic foot as compared with over 1100 for natural gas, 145 for producer gas, and 90 for blast furnace gas.

short tons of steel that leave the steel furnace.

General Survey of Production

Before scrap was used in steel furnaces, the output of iron exceeded that of steel by the amount of iron produced for purposes other than making steel. Steel production exceeded iron production in the United States for the first time in 1911 and has continued to do so ever since, as is shown in Table 40.1. Ferro-

TABLE 40.1. United States Production of Pig Iron and Ferro-Alloys, and Steel Ingots and Castings[13] (million short tons)

Yearly Average	Pig Iron and Ferro-Alloys	Excess of Iron and Ferro-Alloys over Steel	Steel Ingots and Castings	Excess of Steel over Iron
1871-1875	2.5	2.1	0.4[a]	....
1876-1880	2.9	2.0	0.9	....
1881-1885	4.8	2.9	1.9	....
1886-1890	7.9	4.2	3.7	....
1891-1895	9.1	3.9	5.2	....
1896-1900	12.9	3.4	9.5	....
1901-1905	20.4	3.2	17.2	....
1906-1910	26.9	2.1	24.8	....
1911-1915	30.8	...	31.8	1.0
1916-1920	41.5	...	46.8	5.3
1921-1925	34.1	...	41.1	7.0
1926-1930	42.2	...	54.2	12.0
1931-1935	17.5	...	27.6	10.1
1936-1940	36.2	...	52.3	16.1
1941	56.7	...	82.8	26.1
1942	60.9	...	86.0	25.1
1943	62.8	...	88.8	26.0
1944	62.9	...	89.6	26.7
1945	54.9	...	78.7	24.8
1946	46.5	...	66.6	20.1
1947	60.1	...	84.9	24.8

[a] 1875 only.

alloys are included with pig iron in the table, but, as was pointed out before, they constitute a minor portion of the total in point of quantity.

The excess of steel over iron (last column of Table 40.1) constitutes steel made from scrap. Actually, however, the amount of steel made from scrap is larger than the last column of Table 40.1 indicates. For not all the pig iron listed in the first column is converted into steel. A certain portion of it goes into cast iron, wrought iron, and similar products. Thus, if it is assumed that in 1947 3 million of the 60.1

[13] American Iron and Steel Institute, *Annual Statistical Report*, 1947.

million tons of pig iron and ferro-alloys went into iron production, not 24.8 million tons, but 27.8 million, of the 84.9 million tons of steel made were derived from scrap.

Table 40.2 shows the disposition of our production of pig iron and ferro-alloys in million short tons.

TABLE 40.2.   United States Production of Pig Iron and Ferro-Alloys[14]
(million short tons)

Year	For Sale	Percent	For Maker's Use	Total
1915	9.6	28.7	23.9	33.5
1920	12.0	29.0	29.3	41.4
1925	10.1	24.5	31.0	41.1
1930	7.9	22.3	27.6	35.6
1935	4.5	18.9	19.4	23.9
1940	6.8	14.4	40.6	47.4
1944	9.5	15.1	53.4	62.9
1945	8.4	15.2	46.6	54.9
1946	7.6	16.0	38.9	46.5
1947	9.1	15.0	51.0	60.1

Aside from the tremendous increase in steel production from less than half a million tons in 1875 to close to 90 million at the peak of the war effort in 1944, and close to 100 million tons during the postwar boom, the remarkable feature is the shift in manufacturing process,

TABLE 40.3.   United States Steel Production of Ingots and Steel for Castings, 1890-1947
(million short tons)

Year	Total, Including Crucible and Other Minor Processes	Open Hearth Total	Basic	Acid	Bessemer	Electric
1890	4.8	0.6	....	...	4.1	....
1900	11.4	3.8	2.8	1.0	7.5	....
1910	29.2	18.5	17.1	1.4	10.5	0.06
1920	47.2	36.6	35.1	1.5	9.9	0.68
1930	45.6	39.3	38.4	0.9	5.6	0.7
1940	67.0	61.6	60.9	0.7	3.7	1.7
1944	89.6	80.4	79.2	1.2	5.0	4.2
1945	79.7	71.9	71.1	0.9	4.3	3.5
1946	66.6	60.7	60.1	0.6	3.3	2.6
1947	84.9	76.9	76.2	0.7	4.2	3.8

from the Bessemer to the open-hearth and more recently to the electric furnace. This trend is shown in Table 40.3. In 1890 the Bessemer converter overshadowed the open hearth, producing almost seven times as much steel, but by 1910 the open hearth was ahead. In 1944 the production of open-hearth steel was more than sixteen times that of Bessemer steel. The electric furnace is coming up from behind, its output recently almost approaching that of the Bessemer converter. The steel industry is clearly becoming more and more a quality industry, making steels of sufficiently high quality to meet the increasingly exacting demands of modern manufacturing and other industries.

Chemically the products of the iron and steel industry differ in the percentage of carbon and other ingredients they contain. Pig iron or cast iron usually contains about 3.5 percent carbon, whereas wrought iron contains almost no carbon. Steel usually contains from 0.1 to 0.15 percent carbon. Table 40.4 shows representative analyses of iron and steel.

TABLE 40.4.   Representative Analyses of Iron and Steel[15]
(percent)

	Carbon	Manganese	Phosphorus	Sulfur	Silicon	Slag
Pig iron	3.50	2.00	0.04	0.30	1.25	...
Wrought iron	0.02	0.03	0.12	0.02	0.15	3.00
Bessemer steel (basic)	0.10	0.50	0.07	0.07	0.01	...
Open-hearth steel (basic)	0.15	0.50	0.02	0.025	0.15	...
Electric furnace steel	0.15	0.50	0.002	0.003	0.15	...

Steels are generally divided into tonnage or low-grade carbon steels, high-grade carbon steels, low-grade alloy steels, and high-grade alloy steels. High-grade carbon steels differ from tonnage steels chiefly in the care and amount of labor spent on making them. Heat treatment, forging, and the mixture of metals are all important in the development of special properties of alloy steels.

Low-grade alloy steels are used largely by the automobile industry. They usually contain slight admixtures of nickel, chromium, and molybdenum. A widely used steel of this type contains 1.5 percent chromium and 0.75 percent nickel.

In contrast, a high-grade alloy steel may

---

[14] Tables 40.2 and 40.3 from *ibid.*

[15] H. K. Ihrig, *Outline of the Metallurgy of Iron and Steel*, Globe Steel Tubes Co., 1941, pp. 11, 15, 17, 18, 20.

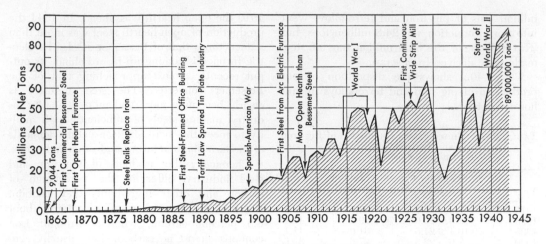

FIG. 40.5. Eighty Years of United States Steel Production, 1863-1943. (Figs. 40.5, 40.6, and 40.7 from *Steel Facts.*)

contain as much as 18 percent tungsten, 32 percent chromium, and 45 percent cobalt. This steel is used in high-speed cutting steels and is one of the hardest and most heat-resistant steels known. It is so hard that it must be cast; it cannot be forged. Such a steel sold for about $16,000 a ton in the late thirties.[16] A commonly used high-speed tool steel contains 18 percent tungsten, 4 percent chromium, and 1 percent vanadium. There are several types of stainless steels. That from which streamlined trains are made contains 18 percent chromium and 8 percent nickel.

The output of alloy steels in the United States increased from 4.4 million tons in 1929 to 13.1 million in 1943. There was a sharp rise in production after 1940, reflecting the importance of alloy steels for the war effort. From 65 to 80 percent of alloy steel is made with the open-hearth process,[17] the rest in electric furnaces.

As was mentioned before, during the war many national emergency (NE) alloy steels were developed in which low percentages of alloy materials were used and, when possible, more common materials were substituted for rarer ones.[18]

Another important trend in steelmaking is

---

[16] "Crucible Steel," *Fortune*, November, 1940.
[17] See U.S. Tariff Commission, *Iron and Steel,* War Changes in Industry Series Report No. 15, 1946, p. 113.
[18] *Steel Facts*, November, 1943, p. 1.

from heavy to lighter products. This is epitomized by the shift from rails and structural shapes to automobile "strip" and thin plate for the container industry.

Fig. 40.5 shows the growth of steel production in the United States from 1863-1943. Important events affecting that growth are indicated on the figure.

Rolling Mill Products

When the steel leaves the furnaces—Bessemer converters, open hearths, electric furnaces—it is poured into ingot molds so tapered that they can be lifted up after the ingots shrink by cooling. Capacity figures of the steel industry are usually given in terms of ingots. But, as was shown in Fig. 40.4, only about three-fourths of the ingot output appears as marketable products, as finished steel. Most of the balance is lost as home or run-around scrap, which is fed back into the furnaces.

Finishing in steelmaking means largely rolling, mostly hot rolling. Two sets of mills are used for finishing—the roughing mills, which change the shape of the ingots as required for processing in the second group of mills, the so-called finishing mills. Some ingots go directly to plate mills or forges; the practice varies widely from one steelworks to another.

Sheet steel rolling was revolutionized when, in 1926, the American Rolling Mill Company (Armco) built the first continuous rolling mill. Since then other steel companies, mainly in

CONTINUOUS MILL METHOD

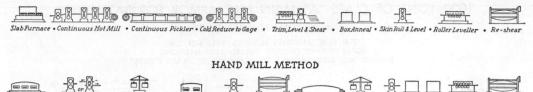

Slab Furnace • Continuous Hot Mill • Continuous Pickler • Cold Reduce to Gage • Trim, Level & Shear • Box Anneal • Skin Roll & Level • Roller Leveller • Re-shear

HAND MILL METHOD

Bar Furnace • Breakdown Sheet Bar • Pickler • Pack Furnace • Hot Sheet Mill • Shear • Normalizer • Pickler • Cold Roll • Box Anneal • Roller Leveller • Re-shear

FIG. 40.6. Typical Procedure for Producing Full Finished Sheet Steel.

the United States but also here and there in foreign countries, have been granted licenses to build continuous rolling mills under the Armco patents. How this invention has revolutionized the rolling industry is shown in Fig. 40.6.

The continuous strip mill, which operates with amazing speed, processes huge quantities of steel with great rapidity. A hot slab of steel is discharged from the heating furnace, passes through a train of roughing mills, gathers speed as it travels through the finishing mills, and, about two minutes later, ends up in the form of cold strip, nearly 1000 feet from the starting point.[19]

Tin-plating underwent a revolutionary change during World War II, when improved methods of electroplating made it possible to produce satisfactory tin plate with a fraction of the tin formerly required.

Another revolutionary invention in finishing steel, though much older than the one just mentioned, is the making of seamless tubing by the Mannesmann process.

In the commonly used Mannesmann process (or modifications of that method), the piercing is accomplished by passing the thoroughly heated round billet between two conical-shaped rolls revolving in the same direction. As the billet is pulled slowly through the rolls it is squeezed from opposite sides, causing the other two sides to bulge. The alternate squeezing and bulging of the revolving billet draws the metal away from the center of the billet, forming a hole at that point.

This action is enhanced and the hole is further enlarged by means of a plug or mandrel, known as the piercer, which is inserted between the rolls and centered on the billet. The piercer is held in place by a bar, the length of which exceeds that of the finished tube. Although the piercer assists to some extent in the piercing action, its principal function is to guide the billet and make the hole of fairly uniform dimension. Thus a rough tube with heavy walls is produced, which requires further processing.[20]

An idea of the complexity involved in finishing special products can be gained from Fig. 40.7 which names the various steps and gives the time schedule.

Product Improvement and the Economy

The continuous strip mill constitutes such a revolutionary improvement in steel finishing that it offers a unique demonstration of the effects of technological change not only on the industry involved but also on the economy at large.

Although the continuous strip mill is one of the costliest investments in all industry—a single mill may cost as much as $60 million—it reduces the cost of operation and makes possible lower prices. A company making steel sheets by the hand-mill method had been getting $100 a ton for its product; ten years later it was receiving $46 a ton for similar products made by the continuous strip mill.[21] Between 1923 and 1937 automobile fender steel was reduced over $50 a ton—from $135 a ton to $68—and quality was improved. The unit price of an electric refrigerator dropped from $390 in 1926 to $173 in 1937, partly at least because of the lower price of the sheet steel (about 190 pounds) which goes into the making of refrigerators.

---

[19] *Steel in the Making*, Bethlehem Steel Company, 1940, p. 31. For illustrations, see *ibid.*, pp. 31 ff.

[20] *Ibid.*, 1942, p. 58.

[21] The depression had something, possibly a great deal, to do with this drop in price; but, on the whole, steel prices stood up pretty well, the prices of some products hardly changing.

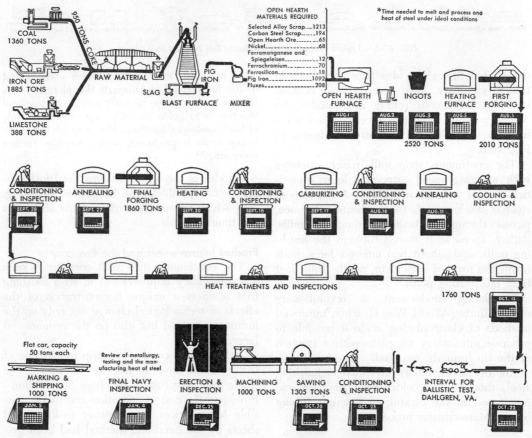

PRINCIPAL OPERATIONS IN PRODUCTION OF

1000 TONS OF CLASS "A" MAIN BELT ARMOR FOR BATTLESHIPS

APPROXIMATELY 12" THICK

TOTAL RAW MATERIALS REQUIRED - 5481 NET TONS
TOTAL FINISHED PRODUCT YIELDED - 1000 NET TONS
ELAPSED TIME, STEEL FURNACE TO SHIPPING DEPT. 5 MO. 6 DAYS*

OPEN HEARTH MATERIALS REQUIRED

Selected Alloy Scrap	1213
Carbon Steel Scrap	194
Open Hearth Ore	65
Nickel	68
Ferromanganese and Spiegeleisen	12
Ferrochromium	70
Ferrosilicon	18
Pig Iron	1092
Fluxes	208

*Time needed to melt and process one heat of steel under ideal conditions

FIG. 40.7. Time Schedule and Material Requirements of Quality Steel Production.

Lower prices encourage the use of steel; the more steel there is in the finished product, the more the demand for steel increases. The result is that such labor-saving devices as the continuous strip mill cause a shift of labor rather than a net reduction of total employment. That such a shift, especially from a highly skilled position to one less skilled, can be painful to the workmen it affects, goes without saying.

BIBLIOGRAPHY

See the bibliography at the end of Chapter 42.

Chapter 41

IRON AND STEEL INDUSTRIES OF THE WORLD

GENERAL SURVEY

The world iron and steel situation is closely tied up with the history of wars. This holds true especially since 1913, a period of bloody wars separated by an uneasy armistice. Even today the world steel situation is still under the shadow of World War II and the cloud of postwar hatred and suspicion, the United Nations notwithstanding.

In trying to understand steel history of the past thirty-five years one must visualize the map of the world and the changed frontiers that two World Wars have left. Germany, her wings clipped at Versailles in 1919, nevertheless became Greater Germany, with almost the whole European continent and even some of Russia at her feet, only to be again shattered into fragments by World War II. In 1913 and 1937 Germany as a steel producer ranked second only to the United States. In 1947 she ranked fifth—after the United States, the Soviet Union, the United Kingdom, and France. The old Austro-Hungarian monarchy was blasted into bits, the splinters forming a truncated Austria, Czechoslovakia, Hungary and parts of Italy, Poland, Rumania, and Yugoslavia. Poland

gained at the expense not only of Austria but also of Germany and Russia. Czarist Russia disappeared, to be replaced by the far more dynamic Soviet Union, whose expansionist ambitions recall the days of Ivan and Peter and Catherine. Japan gained much from World War I but lost everything except her bare existence in World War II. Burma broke away from India. India, throwing off British rule, became a Dominion in the British Commonwealth of Nations, and herself split up into two parts. Turkey, having lost all but the last remnant of the old Ottoman Empire in Europe, shrank to a mere nation but gained in national vigor. As an outpost against the Soviet Union she holds a dangerous position but has a good bargaining position. After World War II the Soviet Union moved the Iron Curtain westward to the Elbe, thus hiding from view not only all of Panslavia including Poland, Czechoslovakia, Yugoslavia, and Bulgaria, but also the activities of such alien racial groups as the Magyar Hungarians and the Latin Rumanians, the Baltic nations—Latvia, Lithuania, and Esthonia—and parts of Finland, and Germany. Trieste has been internationalized. A new nation, Israel, has been born, and the fate of the Italian colonies in Africa hangs in the balance. As an oil producer the United States has become more than a distant spectator in the Near and Middle East; her influence is felt strongly in Turkey and Greece and in fact throughout Europe this side of the Iron Curtain.

Behind these changes in boundaries there are also changes in ideology. It looks as if mankind were drifting or driving toward a great global struggle—East versus West, democracy versus communism, free institutions versus tyranny.

In this global split-up the preponderance of steel thus far is heavily in western hands: the United States, the United Kingdom, France, the Benelux countries (Belgium, Netherlands, and Luxemburg), probably most of Scandinavia, Italy, the British Empire, and an internationalized Ruhr, with Japan a mere pawn on the chessboard—a formidable line-up. But western Europe is facing tremendous internal conflicts and readjustments which the Marshall Plan is expected to help solve. In particular the Ruhr,

the industrial heart of Europe, is still hitting on only one or two cylinders, slowing up the rest of the convoy, as it were. Whatever one writes about the world outside the United States is bound to be hopelessly dated; cataclysmic changes may occur before the manuscript reaches the printer or before the printer's ink is dry.

RAW-MATERIAL POSITION

Before beginning a regional survey of the steel industry of the world, a brief summary of the raw-material situation, based on 1947 production, may help in general orientation. Only the most important iron- and steel-producing countries are included. Since limestone is a commonalty, water a quasi-ubiquity, air a ubiquity, and ferro-alloys, and also scrap within limits, are normally circulated through international trade, the summary below is confined to ore and fuel.

Adequacy of reserves, as was pointed out earlier, is a strictly relative term. Adequacy depends on the rate of use. If a country like

Country	Ore	Fuel
United States	Deterioration through depletion of largest, richest, and most easily worked deposits offset by encouraging progress in the beneficiation of vast low-grade deposits and spectacular discoveries in nearby countries, especially Canada (Labrador) and Venezuela (Cerro Bolivar), calling for partial change in industrial pattern but averting national iron ore crisis.	Very large reserves of coal, but metallurgical grade of coking coal limited and regionally restricted. Use of natural gas expanding, but reserves limited.
Soviet Union	Young expanding industry tapping many newly discovered or opened-up reserves. Long-run ability to maintain ore output commensurate with size of country and population is problematic.	Large coal reserves, but first-rate metallurgical coking coal not widely or easily accessible.
United Kingdom	Large deposits of medium and low-grade ores, usable after beneficiation. High-grade ores imported.	Large coal reserves, including coking grades.
France	Abundant ore; large exports.	Inadequate coal supply, slightly enlarged by acquisition of Saar. Little metallurgical coke available.
Germany (western)	Poor ores; heavy imports, especially high-grade ores.	Considerable coal reserves, including excellent coking grade.
Belgium	Little ore reserves; heavy imports.	Adequate coal reserves except coking coal.

An overall view of the charging side of the open-hearth shop at the Geneva Steel Works. (U.S. Steel Corporation.)

Finishing stand of the 80-inch hot strip mill of the Irvin Works, Dravosburg, Pa. (U.S. Steel Corporation.)

Geneva Steel Works, Geneva, Utah. (U.S. Steel Corporation.)

An electric furnace. (Courtesy of Bethlehem Steel.)

Open-pit copper mining in the Atacoma Desert, Chile, at an altitude of 10,000 feet. (Anaconda Copper Mining Company.)

Leaching vats, Chuquicamata, Chile. Leaching extracts the copper from oxide ores. (American Brass Company.)

Flotation machines used to concentrate low-grade copper at the Morenci concentrator in Arizona. (Phelps Dodge Corporation.)

Cross section of flotation machine. (Western Machinery Company, San Francisco.)

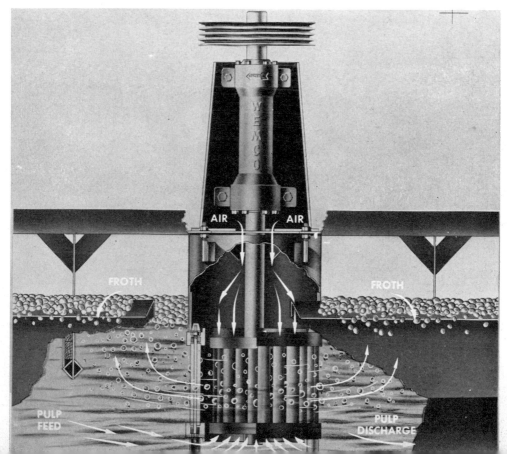

General view of the copper smelter at Anaconda, Montana. The chimney is the tallest in the world. (Anaconda Copper Mining Company.)

Copper smelter at Cananea, Sonora, Mexico. (Cananea Consolidated Copper Company.)

Interior of Russian copper works. (Sovfoto.)

Removing 99.9 percent copper cathodes from electrolytic cell at the International Smelting and Refining Company in Perth Amboy, New Jersey. (American Brass Company.)

Interior of copper works in the Belgian Congo. (*Engineering and Mining Journal.*)

Electrolytic refinery in Chuquicamata, Chile. (American Brass Company.)

Alumina works in Mobile, Ala. (Jack Ammann.)

Aluminum reduction works at Alcoa, Tenn. (Jack Ammann.)

Mining bauxite in Surinam, Dutch Guiana. (Aluminum Company of America.)

Kelly filter presses in the Mobile, Ala., plant of the Aluminum Ore Company. (Aluminum Company of America.)

Fabricating plants in New Kensington, Pa. (Aluminum Company of America.)

Zinc mine in New York state. (St. Joseph Lead Company.)

Electrolytic cells at Alcoa, Tenn. (Aluminum Company of America.)

Lead mine in southeastern Missouri. (St. Joseph Lead Company.)

Du Pont works on the Kanawha River for the high-pressure synthesis of nitrogen products. (E. I. du Pont de Nemours & Company.)

The bewildering multitude of finished products made from a few raw materials. (E. I. du Pont de Nemours & Company.)

Du Pont neoprene plant. (Photograph for E. I. du Pont de Nemours & Company by Robert Y. Richie.)

Turning out 500 sheets of cellophane at a time. (E. I. du Pont de Nemours & Company.)

China were to produce steel on a per capita basis comparable to production in such countries as the United States or the United Kingdom, reserves would be hopelessly inadequate. Adequacy is relative to the length of time during which reserves are expected to last.

WORLD PRODUCTION OF PIG IRON AND STEEL

In a world of war and strife the iron and steel industry plays a major role. A healthy iron and steel industry is the core of industrialization, and industrialization is the hallmark of a Great Power.

Tables 41.1 and 41.2 trace the growth of the iron and steel industries as they spread from their birthplace in the Black Country of England to the five continents of the earth. These are perhaps the most significant tables in this entire book. Together with the coal and petroleum tables, they constitute the statistical core of modern industrialism and hence deserve careful study.

In the table showing world pig iron production one is struck by the increased output, from less than 5 million tons in 1850 to over 113 million in 1937. Even this was exceeded in 1943, when close to 127 million tons were produced. Of particular interest is the sharp drop from 106 million tons in 1929 to 42.1 million in 1932—one of the best barometric readings of the violence of the Great Depression that followed the wild speculative boom of the twenties. The drop was sharpest in the United States—from 46.5 million to 9.8 million. During the same period the output of the Soviet Union, unaffected as she was by capitalist market gyrations, actually advanced from 4.3 million to 7 million tons.

The increase in world pig iron production was accompanied by a considerable increase in the number of countries that produce iron and steel. The modern phase of iron and steel manufacture began in the United Kingdom and then spread to the United States and Germany, both of which soon surpassed the United Kingdom—the United States around 1890 and Germany around 1910. While the United States was forging ahead to a position of unchallenged leadership, the industry spread to other European countries, as well as to Asia, Africa, Australia, and South America. From four countries listed as producers in 1850, the number increased until in 1947 no less than twenty-two were important enough to deserve enumeration.

The record of world steel production shown in Table 41.2 is even more impressive. The modern phase of steelmaking began with the invention of the Bessemer process in the late 1850's. By 1870 output had passed half a million tons and it continued to rise until 1929, when it reached 128.3 million tons. During the depression it fell sharply, to little over 40 percent of the 1929 figure. However, by 1937, stimulated by preparation for war, production reached 148.2 million tons and almost touched 175 million during the war itself. It dropped back to 126.7 in 1946, a period of postwar readjustments, but resumed its climb the next year.

Comparing the two tables, one notices that while in 1870 pig iron output amounted to 13 million tons as compared with only 560,000 tons for steel, steel output was 22.3 million tons ahead of pig iron in 1929, and approximately 42 million tons ahead in 1947. This increasing spread clearly indicates the growing importance of scrap as a raw material of the steel industry.

This increased use of scrap is not characteristic of all countries. Thus India regularly produces more pig iron than steel, the Netherlands produces pig iron but not steel, and Luxemburg frequently produces slightly more pig iron than steel. Italy, Japan, and Mexico, on the other hand, rely heavily on imported scrap and therefore produce considerably more steel than pig iron, as do the heavily industrialized countries where considerable amounts of scrap have been accumulated.

Table 41.3 shows, in percentages, the position of the leading iron- and steel-producing countries in the world from 1871 to 1945. During these seventy-five years there have been radical shifts in position. Thus the United Kingdom in 1871-1875 produced 47.0 and 42.9 percent of the world output of iron and steel respectively; but by 1941-1945 her output had fallen to 6.9 and 8.8 percent of the world total respectively. For the United States the shift took the reverse direction; her production of iron and steel increased from 16.3 and 14.5 per-

TABLE 41.1. World Pig Iron Production, 1850-1948[1]

(million net tons)

	1850	1860	1870	1880	1890	1900	1910	1920	1929	1932	1937	1940	1945	1946	1947	1948
United States	0.6	0.9	1.8	4.2	10.1	15.2	30.0	40.0	46.5	9.8	41.6	47.4	54.9	46.5	60.1	61.0
Canada										0.2	1.1	1.4	2.0	1.5	2.2	2.4
Brazil											0.1	0.2	0.3	0.4	0.6	0.6
United Kingdom	2.5	4.3	6.6	8.5	8.7	9.9	11.1	7.6	8.4	4.0	9.5	9.2	8.0	8.7	8.5	10.3
France	0.4			2.1		3.0	4.4	3.7	11.2	6.1	8.7	4.1	1.3	3.8	5.4	7.2
Belgium								1.2	4.4	3.0	4.2	2.0	0.8	2.4	3.1	4.3
Luxembourg								0.8	3.2	2.2	2.8	1.2	0.3	1.5	2.0	2.8
Netherlands										0.3	0.3	0.3		0.1	0.2	0.5
Germany	0.4	0.6	1.4	2.7	4.4	8.2	14.2	8.8	14.5	4.3	15.1	15.4	1.6	2.4	2.5[a]	6.4
Saar								1.1	2.3	1.5	2.4	2.0		0.3	0.7	1.3
Austria										0.1	0.4			0.1	0.3	0.7
Hungary										0.1	0.4	0.5		0.2	0.3	0.3
Russia									4.3	7.0	16.0	16.5	18.8	16.8	18.0	18.5
Czechoslovakia								0.8	1.8	0.5	1.8	1.8	0.6	1.1	1.6	1.8
Poland										0.2	0.8	0.1	0.3	0.8	0.9	1.2
Italy										0.5	1.0	1.2	0.1	0.2	0.4	0.6
Spain										0.3	0.2	0.6	0.5	0.5	0.6	0.6
Sweden										0.3	0.8	0.9	0.8	0.8	0.8	0.9
Japan								0.8	1.8	1.7	3.1	4.4	0.6	0.2	0.4	0.9
India								0.3	1.5		1.9	2.3	1.5	1.7	1.6	1.6
Union of South Africa											0.3	0.3	0.7	0.7	0.7	0.7
Australia											1.0	1.3	1.2	1.0	1.3	1.3
Total	4.9	8.0	13.0	20.0	29.4	43.8	71.2	67.5	106.0	42.1	113.5	113.1	94.3	91.7	112.2	125.9

[a] Western zones only.

[1] Figures for 1850-1910 from Horace B. Davis, "Iron and Steel Industry," *Encyclopaedia of the Social Sciences*, vol. 8, p. 301, and O. R. Kuhn, *The Iron Age*, February 18, 1926. Figures for 1920-1932 from U. S. Department of Commerce, *Commerce Yearbook, 1931*, vol. 2, p. 697. Figures for 1937-1946 from American Iron and Steel Institute, *Annual Statistical Report, 1947*, pp. 183-185. Figures for 1947 and 1948 from Statistical Office of the United Nations, *Monthly Bulletin of Statistics*; this source was used to supplement the records of the American Iron and Steel Institute.

In interpreting this table, changes in political boundaries must be kept in mind.

TABLE 41.2. World Steel Production, 1870-1948[a]

(million short tons)

	1870	1880	1890	1900	1910	1913	1920	1929	1932	1937	1940	1945	1946	1947	1948
United States	0.04	1.4	4.7	11.2	28.1	34.4	46.3	61.3	15.3	56.6	67.0	79.7	66.6	85.0	88.4
Canada	...	...	...	...	0.8	1.1	1.2	1.5	0.4	1.5	2.2	2.8	2.3	2.9	3.2
Mexico	...	...	...	...	...	...	...	...	...	...	...	0.2	0.3	0.4	0.3
Brazil	...	...	...	...	...	...	...	...	...	...	0.2	0.2	0.4	0.4	0.5
United Kingdom	0.24	1.4	3.9	5.4	7.0	8.5	10.0	10.7	5.9	14.5	14.5	13.2	14.2	14.2	16.4
France	0.09	0.4	0.8	1.7	3.7	5.1	3.3	10.5	6.2	8.7	4.9	1.8	4.9	6.3	8.0
Belgium	...	0.1	0.2	0.7	1.1	2.6	1.3	4.5	3.1	4.3	2.1	0.8	2.5	3.2	4.3
Luxemburg	...	...	...	0.2	0.7	1.4	0.7	3.0	2.2	2.8	1.1	0.3	1.4	1.9	2.7
Germany	0.14	0.8	2.3	7.1	14.2	20.5	10.0	17.6	6.4	19.3	21.1	0.3	3.0	3.3	6.0
Saar	...	...	...	...	...	...	0.8	2.4	1.5	2.6	1.2	...	0.3	0.8	1.3
Austria	0.02	0.1	0.5	1.1	2.3	2.9	0.2	0.6	0.2	0.7	...	0.2	0.2	0.4	0.7
Hungary	...	...	...	...	...	...	...	...	0.2	0.7	0.8	0.1	0.4	0.7	0.8
Russia	0.01	0.2	0.6	2.4	3.8	4.6	0.2	5.3	6.4	19.6	20.1	19.8	20.0	22.0	22.2
Czechoslovakia	...	...	...	...	...	...	1.1	2.3	0.3	2.6	2.6	1.0	1.8	2.5	2.9
Poland	...	...	...	...	...	...	...	1.5	0.6	1.6	1.6	0.5	1.3	1.7	2.1
Italy	...	...	0.3	0.3	1.1	1.0	0.9	2.3	1.5	2.3	2.5	0.4	1.3	1.9	2.3
Spain	...	...	...	0.1	0.3	0.2	0.2	1.1	0.6	0.2	0.8	0.6	0.7	0.6	0.6
Sweden	0.01	0.03	0.2	0.3	0.5	0.6	0.4	0.7	0.6	1.2	1.3	1.3	1.3	1.3	1.4
Japan	...	...	...	...	...	0.3	1.0	2.3	2.6	6.4	8.3	1.2	0.6	1.0	2.0
India	...	...	...	...	...	...	0.2	0.7	0.7	1.0	1.4	1.4	1.4	1.3	1.3[a]
Union of South Africa	...	...	...	...	...	...	...	...	...	0.3	0.4	0.6	0.6	0.7	0.7
Australia	...	...	...	...	...	...	...	...	...	1.3	1.4	1.4	1.2	1.4	1.4
Total[b]	0.56	4.6	13.5	30.6	65.3	83.2	77.8	128.3	55.2	148.2	155.5	127.8	126.7	153.9	169.5

[a] Estimated on basis of first eight months.

[b] Totals for 1870 to 1910 include estimates for scattered production. Totals for 1913-1948 are approximations, scattered production being omitted.

[2] Figures for 1870-1910 from Ervin Hexner, *The International Steel Cartel*, University of North Carolina Press, Chapel Hill, 1943, pp. 324-325. Figures for 1913-1929 from U. S. Department of Commerce, *op. cit.*, vol. 2, p. 150. Figures for 1922-1947 from American Iron and Steel Institute, *op. cit.*, pp. 186-187. Figures for 1948 from Statistical Office of the United Nations, *op. cit.*; this source was used to supplement the records of the American Iron and Steel Institute.

TABLE 41.3.   Relative Share of Leading Producing Countries in World
Output of Iron and Steel, 1871-1945[3]
(in percentages)

	Pig Iron				Steel			
	United States	United Kingdom	Central Europe[a]	All Others	United States	United Kingdom	Central Europe[a]	All Others
1871-1875	16.3	47.0	27.6	9.1	14.5	42.9	34.4	8.2
1876-1880	17.4	45.1	28.5	9.0	27.7	34.0	29.8	8.5
1881-1885	20.3	40.0	29.2	10.5	28.1	32.5	29.3	10.1
1886-1890	21.6	32.9	28.0	17.5	32.8	31.3	25.8	10.1
1891-1895	31.4	28.0	29.8	10.8	34.2	22.6	31.6	11.6
1896-1900	32.4	25.1	30.5	12.0	35.5	19.3	31.7	13.5
1901-1905	40.2	19.3	28.9	11.6	42.7	14.3	30.4	12.6
1906-1910	41.5	16.9	30.5	11.1	43.3	11.9	31.5	13.3
1911-1915	41.4	13.9	31.2	13.5	42.7	11.3	31.2	14.8
1916-1920	57.4	13.3	20.1	9.2	57.6	12.5	21.4	8.5
1921-1925	50.1	9.4	30.8	9.7	51.9	9.5	27.6	11.0
1926-1930	44.3	7.1	34.1	14.5	47.2	7.5	30.3	15.0
1931-1935	28.5	8.6	37.4	25.5	34.0	9.8	30.7	25.5
1936-1940	34.2	8.3	30.0	27.5	40.9	9.6	25.5	24.0
1941-1945	51.0	6.9	18.6	23.5	53.9	8.8	16.6	20.7

[a] Germany, Saar, France, Luxemburg, Belgium.

cent respectively in 1871-1875 to 51.0 and 53.9 percent respectively in 1941-1945. Her lead was even more pronounced during World War I, when her production of iron and steel for the four-year period 1916-1920 amounted respectively to 57.4 and 57.6 percent of the world total. On the other hand, she was hit harder by the Great Depression than were other producing countries, her production of iron and steel dropping to 28.5 percent and 34.0 percent respectively during 1931-1935.

THE IRON AND STEEL INDUSTRY OF THE UNITED STATES

The most striking fact concerning the location of the iron and steel industry of the United States is its concentration in the Northeast. It is true that recently, especially since Pearl Harbor, some outlying areas have gained in importance, but even so the Northeast still maintains the lead. Table 41.4 shows production, by regions, from 1904 to 1936.

Eastern district includes New England, New York, New Jersey, Maryland, Virginia, and all of

Pennsylvania except the region west of Johnstown.

Pittsburgh district includes (1) Pittsburgh and its satellite cities: Homestead, Braddock, McKeesport, Donora; (2) the valleys district made up of the Youngstown cluster of mills in the Mahoning valley and the Sharon district in the Shenango valley; (3) the Wheeling district to the southwest of Pittsburgh, and scattered plants in the area.

TABLE 41.4.   Iron and Steel Production by Major Districts[4]
(percentage of total)

District	Pig Iron			Steel		
	1904	1929	1936	1904	1929	1936
Eastern	13.8	12.2	18.4	25.7	17.0	17.3
Pittsburgh	63.8	56.4	42.8	53.5	52.5	44.7
Great Lakes	11.4	22.6	30.7	16.1	23.2	32.0
Total Northeast	89.0	91.2	91.9	95.3	92.7	94.0
Southern	8.8	6.5	6.8	2.9	4.7	3.4
Western	2.2	2.3	1.3	1.8	2.6	2.6

Great Lakes district centers on the Great Lakes and stretches from west of Buffalo in the east to Chicago and Duluth-Superior in the west.

[3] Figures for 1871-1930 from Horace B. Davis, *op. cit.*, p. 313. Figures for 1931-1945 computed by the author from American Iron and Steel Institute, *Annual Statistical Reports,* and Statistical Office of the United Nations, *Monthly Bulletins of Statistics.*

[4] E. B. Alderfer and H. E. Michl, *Economics of American Industry,* McGraw-Hill Book Company, Inc., 1942, p. 59.

Southern district includes Alabama, Kentucky, Tennessee, Georgia, Virginia, and Texas.

Western district includes Colorado, Utah, and the west coast.

The distribution of steel ingot capacity and production in 1947 is shown in Table 41.5. A

TABLE 41.5. Steel Ingot Capacity and Production[5]

States	Capacity, January 1, 1947 (million net tons)	Production, 1947 (million net tons)	Production as Percent of Capacity
Massachusetts, Rhode Island, Connecticut	0.5	0.4	86.0
New York, New Jersey	4.6	4.3	94.4
Delaware, Maryland, Virginia	4.6	4.4	96.1
Pennsylvania	26.6	25.1	94.2
Ohio	18.6	17.3	92.9
Indiana	11.1	10.4	93.8
Illinois	8.2	7.1	86.6
Michigan, Minnesota, Missouri	4.2	4.2	100.4
Northeast	78.4	73.2 (86.5%)	93.4
West Virginia, Kentucky	3.4	3.1	90.5
Georgia, Alabama, Texas	4.3	3.9	92.2
Oklahoma, Colorado, Utah, Washington	3.0	2.6	85.9
California	1.8	1.8	95.8
South and West	12.5	11.4 (13.5%)	91.2
Total	90.9	84.6	93.1

comparison of the two tables reveals a considerable percentage increase in southern and western steel production from 0 percent in 1936 (3.4 percent southern and 2.6 western) to 13.5 percent in 1947. The completion of two integrated steel plants during World War II—one in Fontana, east of Los Angeles, and the other, the Geneva plant in Utah—has contributed much to this development.

Except for the Kaiser plant at Fontana which is "fully integrated," all the steel produced on the west coast and much of that produced in Texas is made from scrap or from pig iron brought in from the outside. Texas has limited blast furnace capacity attached to a steel plant at Houston and at Daingerfield.

By July, 1950, United States steel-making capacity passed the 100-million-ton mark. Additional expansion, definitely scheduled and

publicly announced by steel companies, was expected to bring this total up to 105,750,000 tons by the end of 1952. There were those who considered even this remarkable expansion insufficient in the light of the world political situation as it developed at the mid-century mark.

The Northeast

The Northeast is a term applied rather loosely to the region east of the Mississippi and north of the Ohio and Potomac. This area is shown in Fig. 41.1, as are also ore movements within and into the region. Within this region, as already mentioned, there are three subregions of iron and steel production: the eastern district, the Pittsburgh district, and the Great Lakes district.

The Eastern District. The core of the eastern district is the eastern Pennsylvania and Maryland district shown on the map. But it also includes New England, New York around Buffalo, Johnstown, Pennsylvania, and Virginia. The Bethlehem Steel Corporation, by far the most important unit in this district, relies largely on eastern scrap and on imported ores. These, however, are supplemented by the Cornwall ores near Harrisburg and by Lake Superior ores. The latter move cheaply to the Lackawanna plant in Buffalo but less cheaply to the other western mills of the eastern district. The advantages offered by this district are cheap scrap, cheap imported ore, and access to coastal and foreign markets. Its disadvantage is fairly high assembly costs.

The Pittsburgh District. The Pittsburgh district came to be the chief steel center of the nation largely because of the proximity of the Connellsville coking coal, unexcelled for metallurgical purposes, and the general accessibility of cheap coal based on excellent river transport facilities. Lake Superior ore, made available through low-cost Lake-rail transportation, took the place of local ores. Rail transportation between the "lower Lake ports," i.e., those along the south shore of Lake Erie, and the Pittsburgh district is perhaps the lowest-cost rail transportation anywhere. Coal, coke, and finished steel products moving north toward the Lake furnish return shipments for the ore that moves south, thus

[5] American Iron and Steel Institute, *op. cit.*, 1947, p. 31.

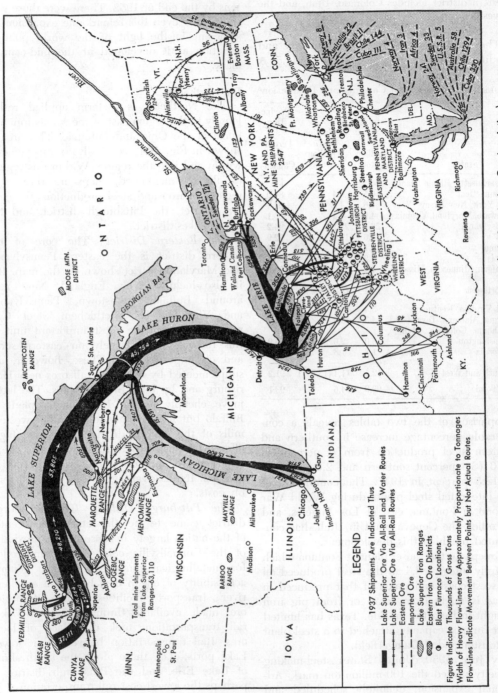

FIG. 41.1. Movement of Iron Ore to Steelworks in the United States, 1937. (Lake Superior Iron Ore Association.)

LEGEND

1937 Shipments Are Indicated Thus

Lake Superior Ore Via All-Rail and Water Routes
Lake Superior Ore Via All-Rail Routes
Eastern Ore
Imported Ore
Lake Superior Iron Ranges
Eastern Iron Ore Districts
Blast Furnace Locations

Figures Indicate Thousands of Gross Tons
Width of Heavy Flow-Lines are Approximately Proportionate to Tonnages
Flow-Lines Indicate Movement Between Points but Not Actual Routes

Total mine shipments
from Lake Superior
Ranges—63,110

assuring an almost perfect load coefficient[6] and a capacity factor close to 100. Moreover the topography favors convergence on Pittsburgh. Although still a good location, the Pittsburgh district no longer enjoys the almost unique advantages it once possessed. It was favored by policies of the United States Steel Corporation, especially the basing-point pricing system, aimed at protecting its large investments in the area.

The Great Lakes District. The Great Lakes district also falls naturally into several subdivisions. By far the most important is the Chicago-Gary region which includes Chicago, Indiana Harbor, Gary, and Joliet, a short distance west. This district produces about half the steel made in the Great Lakes area and about one-sixth of all the steel produced in the nation. Its northwestern outpost is Duluth and it extends as far east as Erie, Pennsylvania.[7] The lower Lake ports from Toledo to Erie are "natural" "secondary" steel centers, natural because they are meeting points of coal, coke, and iron ore, and secondary because the presence of steel is in part a reflection or secondary effect of primary forces operating in the Pittsburgh district. Detroit, the automobile capital of the nation, is becoming increasingly important as a steel center.

The Southeast

The great steel-producing center of the Southeast is Birmingham, Alabama, "the masterpiece of the steel God," the perfect natural assembly place of raw materials, coking coal and iron ore. The city itself is built on a huge ore bed in a valley at the foot of Red Mountain. On the western side of the valley are vast coal deposits that contain excellent coking coal. Raw-material assembly costs are perhaps lower in Birmingham than anywhere else, but these costs constitute only part of the total cost. The ore is reached by shafts of considerable depth, which makes the extraction costs fairly high, certainly when compared with those of the Mesabi open-pit mining. Moreover, the ore is not as high grade as that of the Lake Superior region. It is true that much of it is self-fluxing because of its high lime content; but, as was stated before, some of it is so high in phosphorus that it requires the Duplex process (see p. 647) with its high investment cost.

Birmingham lies in a region which, in spite of the remarkable boost southern industry received during World War II, is still not highly industrialized or densely populated. This has two implications. (1) Unlike Pittsburgh and Chicago, Birmingham has no large local market surrounding it or accessible to it. (2) The accumulation of market scrap per square mile is less rapid in an agricultural region than in a highly industrialized area, and scrap collection is more expensive. So long as Birmingham stays within the rather modest limits of its present steel production (3.6 million tons, or 4.2 percent of the total output of the United States in 1947), these handicaps are not burdensome; but if it ever rose to the heights of Pittsburgh or Chicago, scrap costs might rise rather sharply, causing greater reliance on expensive ore and thus raising production costs. Marketing costs would likewise increase as large amounts of finished products had to be sent to distant markets.

Birmingham has probably been held back by the pricing policy of the absentee owners. Some critics, speaking of "colonialism," suggest that, like England in colonial times, the North regards the South as a source of raw materials but does not care to foster the region's industrial growth.[8]

The West

As the statistical records show, the West experienced a remarkable expansion of steel capacity during World War II. Before Pearl Harbor the Colorado Fuel and Iron Company had a "fully integrated" iron and steel works at Pueblo, Colorado, drawing on ores from nearby Wyoming and using local coals. It specialized in railroad materials and wire, especially barbed wire. In 1930, the United States Steel Corporation purchased the Columbia Steel Cor-

---

[6] Ratio of load going in one direction to load going in opposite direction.

[7] Geographically speaking, it includes Buffalo; but because of its affiliation with Bethlehem, Buffalo is included in the eastern district.

[8] For a development of this theme, see W. Prescott Webb, *Divided We Stand*, Adams Publications, Austin, Texas, 1948.

poration which as the Columbia Steel Company became a member of the U. S. Steel family. It owned a blast furnace at Provo, Utah, and steel furnaces at Pittsburg (near San Francisco), California, and at Towanee (near Los Angeles), California. The Provo blast furnace, which began operation in 1924, has a capacity of 450 tons of iron a day and is supplied with coke from nearby by-product coke ovens using Utah coals and with ore from nearby mines. In 1930 Bethlehem Steel bought the Pacific Coast Steel Company and the Southern California Iron and Steel Company with small plants in Los Angeles, San Francisco, and Seattle. Bethlehem has no blast furnaces in the West, but, economically speaking, its blast furnace at Sparrows Point may be as close to the "coast" as is the blast furnace at Provo.

World War II brought a number of important developments in the West. Apart from enlargements and additions made by U. S. Steel and Bethlehem, iron and steel capacity was greatly expanded by the creation of wholly new producing units. In this the federal government, concerned over the steel supply for its vast shipbuilding program on the Pacific coast, played an important role. The largest addition was the Geneva plant on Utah Lake (the lake location suggests the importance of an adequate supply of fresh water), forty miles south of Salt Lake City. Here a wholly integrated steelworks—by-product coke ovens, blast furnaces, steel furnaces, and rolling mills—was erected. Three blast furnaces with a daily capacity of 1100 tons of pig iron each can deliver about 1,200,000 tons of pig iron a year, from which can be made about 1,300,000 tons of ingot steel or about 950,000 tons of finished steel. The plant depends for raw materials on Utah and other nearby sources.

Having withdrawn an earlier offer for the Geneva plant, U.S. Steel, at the suggestion of the federal government, renewed its bid. This was accepted by the War Assets Administration in May, 1947, and approved by the Attorney General in June. On June 19, peacetime operation started. U.S. Steel paid $47.5 million for the plant and inventories (the plant had cost about $200 million). The corporation

also obligated itself to add facilities which would convert the plant from wartime to peacetime needs and correlate it with its other Pacific coast properties.

Henry Kaiser's plant at Fontana is also fully integrated, but considerably smaller. The ingot capacity is about 700,000 tons; the blast furnace produces about 400,000 tons of iron. The plant depends on coal shipped in from Utah, a long and costly haul, but obtains ore by truck from the Vulcan mine about 175 miles inland. The Fontana plant is close to its market and therefore has a great advantage over the eastern mills which try to supply the west coast.

Besides the Utah and California plants, an integrated iron and steelworks was also built at Houston, Texas, by the Sheffield Steel Company, a subsidiary of Armco, formerly the American Rolling Mill Company. So far as can be ascertained, the plant obtains coking coal from Oklahoma and ore from local sources; the latter was supplemented during the war by small imports from Durango, Mexico. The plant has access on favorable terms to scrap and natural gas and has the advantage of being located in a regional market of growing importance. Both the Fontana and the Houston plants were financed by the Reconstruction Finance Corporation.

A blast furnace of about 400,000 tons' capacity has been built in Daingerfield, in northeast Texas. Limonite and siderite ores are found nearby and coking coal is brought in from Oklahoma. At first the ores gave considerable difficulty, but, according to the latest reports, this seems to have been overcome by novel methods of beneficiation. Although beneficiation is costly, even considerable costs do not deter the bold so long as pig iron sells for as much as $75 a ton. The blast furnace, coke ovens, ore properties, and beneficiation plant belong to the Lone Star Steel Company. The pig iron is sold almost exclusively to foundries.

As natural gas—and to a lesser extent oil—come into greater use in making iron and steel, the Southwest may have an advantage over older locations where those fuels are available only at high prices.

The West's greatest handicap as a producer

of iron is the relative scarcity of iron ore. In spite of renewed search during World War II, only three major deposits have thus far been located—the Sunrise mine in Wyoming, supplying the Colorado Fuel and Iron Company's plant at Pueblo, Colorado; the Iron Mountain mine in southwestern Utah; and the Eagle Mountain mine in southern California. Other mining districts, such as the Orient mine in Colorado, the Fierro mines in New Mexico, and the Vulcan mines in California, which are now supplying Fontana, must be considered as supplementary sources, since, by themselves, they cannot supply a fully integrated modern iron and steelworks with ore through and beyond the period of amortization. Still other districts, e.g., in Nevada, Oregon, and Washington, may in the future become supplementary sources. Except for the Sunrise mine in Wyoming in which underground operation was recently resorted to, all the western ores are produced by open-pit methods. While the West has enormous coal deposits, the supply of coals suitable for the production of metallurgical coke is very limited.

Another handicap of the West is its vast size relative to its population and capital assets. Except in certain areas—among them California, the Puget Sound region, and the Texas gulf coast—both population and industry are spread very thin.

LOCATION OF THE IRON AND STEEL INDUSTRY

The iron and steel industry handles enormous masses of cheap raw materials and distributes vast quantities of bulky and relatively cheap products. Under such conditions an ideal plant location is primarily one in which the cost of hauling raw materials to the plant and finished products to the market is minimized. Actual production costs, as was pointed out earlier, are primarily a function of the capacity factor. Production costs vary with capacity far more than with differences in location. In other words, plants that are equally modern and are operating at the same capacity may be assumed to have very similar production costs, apart from assembly and delivery costs.

As is true of most modern industrial costs, the costs of making iron and steel are not static but dynamic. The dynamics stem from several sources. There is, first of all, the structure of the industry. In the old days when blast furnaces, coke ovens, steelworks, rolling mills, etc., were isolated in different places, the problem of plant location naturally involved only a proper location for each separate unit. But today it involves the location of an integrated iron and steelworks, or even perhaps an iron and steel empire made up of several mutually balanced plants including mines, limestone quarries, blast furnaces, steelworks, etc. The problem of location is no longer simple but has become tremendously complex and comprehensive.

In the second place, there is the dynamic technology of the industry. Progressive mechanization gives new meaning to the labor factor. The number of laborers and a low wage scale become less important; skill and experience gain in importance. By raising scrap to the rank of a major raw material, the Siemens-Martin furnace has revised the locational importance of ore deposits. The invention of the basic process remade the iron ore map of the world. Improved techniques of beneficiation have definite effects on location. The introduction of the by-product coke oven has revised the importance of coal as a locational factor. The increased use of oil and gas and the possible elimination of coke by the introduction of "direct" methods of making steel may have revolutionary effects in the future.

In the third place, a shifting market contributes to the dynamics of location. The population of the United States is in constant flux. Some regions stand still, others advance, and still others fall behind or actually lose. Moreover, the needs for steel products change continuously as new industries arise and others lose in importance or actually pass from the scene. This, too, has locational implications.

The problem of location is basically an economic problem. Its chief objective is to minimize costs and maximize profits. In theory this economic calculus is strictly rational. Actually however, in the course of history, it involved a compromise between the preservation of the status quo—i.e., of the vested rights of older firms established in older regions—and the urge for change, the quest for a chance to break into the game, the demand for a new deal on the part of younger elements.

For long we in the United States believed that the location of business and industry was solely an economic problem, that only benighted foreigners were stupid enough to let political considerations enter into the conduct of business. Two World Wars have taught us differently. The problem of locating basic industries on which our nation depends in peace and war alike has become definitely and inevitably charged with political considerations. Should this integrated industry be dispersed? Should this one go underground to be safe from atomic attacks? What should be done to assure the availability of foreign goods? What about stock-piling strategic materials? All these questions suggest problems whose solution, at least in part, is beyond the competence and the financial ability of private enterprise.

As between iron ore and coal, coal has been found more important in the location of the iron and steel industry. This may seem surprising in view of the fact that the average blast furnace uses about twice as much ore as coke; but the following facts must be kept in mind:

1. Coke represents 70 to 75 percent of the weight of the coking coal.
2. The blast furnace is only one piece of coal-using equipment. Coal is used to raise heat and supply power at many points of the steelmaking process.
3. Ore is more transportable. It stows better and is not damaged by transport and handling, whereas coal and coke are subject to serious damage and loss.
4. Railroad rates in the United States favor ore over coal.
5. Much ore is mined in rather desolate regions. The coal-mining regions tend to overlap with centers of population and industrialization.
6. Beneficiation, in raising the iron content, renders ore more shippable because it reduces the amount of dirt and inert rock in the ore.

When poor ores are used without beneficiation, as in Lorraine, the coke is apt to move to the ore, the pig iron being shipped for further fabrication as return cargo against the coke to the coal field whence the coke came.

The ore vs. coal question is complicated by other factors. Of course, when coal and ore are found together as in Birmingham, there is no problem. Utah coal is used at Geneva and Provo, but it also moves to Fontana to be used with ore near the market. Oklahoma coal moves to Texas ore and a nearby market.

The manner in which the industry will react to the threatened exhaustion of the ore supplies in the Lake Superior region, especially the Mesabi, depends mainly on private cost and profit calculations, but also on considerations of wartime security and operation. One writer[9] suggests that no one region can assume the burden so long carried by the Lake Superior area. According to him, the answer is manifold. Taconite must do its share but it alone cannot replace the ore of the Mesabi and its satellites. If at all possible, Labrador will have to be brought into the picture. Foreign ores, especially the nearby Latin-American ores, will have to be imported in ever-larger amounts. From his speculation on future ore supplies Barloon concludes that the center of gravity of our iron and steel industry will shift toward the Atlantic and gulf coasts, more particularly the Chesapeake Bay and Mobile areas.

The point of this discussion is not so much the problem of future location as to show the extent to which, even in the western hemisphere, political considerations have come to affect industrial location. At last history seems to have caught up with us. The Atlantic and Pacific have ceased to be moats behind which the people of the United States could imagine themselves isolated from global strain and stress and in their isolation pursue their own private game undisturbed by outsiders.

THE IRON AND STEEL INDUSTRY ELSEWHERE IN THE WESTERN HEMISPHERE
Canada

Canada's steel production passed the million-ton mark during World War I. The industry owes its beginnings to liberal bounties paid by the Dominion government, and its continued existence largely to tariff protection,

---

[9] Marvin Barloon, "Steel: the Great Retreat," *Harper's Magazine*, August, 1947.

imperial preference, and war. Although Canada has some of the largest iron deposits in the world, the bulk of the industry relies on imported materials including ore, limestone, and coke.

The most important iron deposits are the so-called Wabana ore of Newfoundland[10] which, according to Kuhn, amount to 4 billion tons, the Labrador ores discussed above (see p. 628), and a rich deposit of premium-grade Bessemer lump ore at Steep Rock Lake in northwestern Ontario, which was opened up during World War II. To permit large-scale open-pit mining operations, a river had to be diverted and the lake drained, power lines had to be brought in from Port Arthur, a distance of 142 miles, a spur line and docks had to be built.

Canada is a good example of the importance of comparative cost and availability. With 4 billion tons of rich iron deposits at Newfoundland she still imports iron ore from the United States.

World War II led to considerable expansion of the Canadian iron and steel industry as shown by the following production figures (ingot steel and steel castings): in 1913, 1.0 million tons; 1937, 1.4 million tons; 1947, 2.7 million tons.

Latin America

As a producer of iron and steel, Latin America suffers from several serious handicaps:

1. Scarcity of coal in general and almost complete lack of good coking coal.

2. Low average purchasing power of her population.

3. The cutting up of her market into national compartments, most of which are far too small to support a modern iron and steel industry.

4. Low labor skills and general inexperience with the tasks and problems of a modern industrial civilization.[11]

Whatever iron and steel industries Latin America has can exist only behind high tariff walls buttressed by stiff transport charges. Most enterprises either enjoy government backing or are actually owned, in part or wholly, by the government.

Mexico. In 1947 Mexico produced about 300,000 tons of steel, which put her in second place, after Brazil. Compared with the steel production figures of the United States, the Soviet Union, or the United Kingdom, such an output is almost negligible. But in the quasi-colonial semifeudal economy of Latin America it looms large.

Mexico has two fully integrated iron and steelworks, one at Monterrey, and the other at Monclova, northwest of Monterrey. The Monterrey plant, privately owned, has been in operation for decades. The Monclova plant is new, having been erected during World War II by Armco for Altos Hornos de Mexico, a company financed by the Mexican government with the aid of the Export-Import Bank.

Coal, including good coking coal, is produced in the state of Coahuila, north of Monterrey. Most of the ore consumed by the Mexican iron industry comes from the Cerro del Mercado outside of the city of Durango. There are other important iron deposits besides Cerro del Mercado, among them Las Truchas and El Mamey on the Pacific coast.

Mexico uses some scrap, most of it imported from the United States. The two steelworks in Mexico City use scrap exclusively. One of them, La Consolidada,[12] owns open-hearth steel furnaces at Piedras Negras near the Texas border. This plant operates on imports of both scrap and natural gas. Natural gas is also piped from Texas into Monterrey.

Brazil. Brazil is the classical land of rich iron deposits and poor coal supply. Compared with the vastness of her iron deposits, her iron and steel industry is pitifully small, in spite of the fact that much of it depends on charcoal for fuel and all of it depends on government aid in the form of subsidies, high import duties, etc.

Brazil is credited with 7 billion tons of iron deposits ("ore"),[13] half of which are in the state of Minas Gerais, the rest in Bahia, Matto

---

[10] Newfoundland and Labrador joined the Dominion in 1948.

[11] See G. Wythe, *Industry in Latin America*, Columbia University Press, New York, 1945.

[12] "Mexican Steel," *Fortune*, October, 1941.

[13] O. R. Kuhn, *op. cit.* Other estimates run up to 8 and even 13 billion tons for Minas Gerais alone.

Grosso, and Maranhão. Some of the deposits are incredibly rich in iron and remarkably free of harmful impurities. But coal mining is largely confined to the southern states of Santa Catarina and Rio Grande do Sul, a long way from the iron. And it is poor coal at that; some of it yields as little as one-third usable material. So the raw-material situation is bad. But in spite of everything, the government is bent on having a national steel industry.[14]

In 1939 the Brazilian government considered forming a "mixed company" to be owned and operated jointly by itself and the United States Steel Corporation, but in view of the world situation and for other reasons the latter decided to stay out of the deal. In January, 1941, the National Steel Company (Companhia Siderurgica Nacional) was created. For about $100 million (of which the Export-Import Bank lent $45 million) it built a fully integrated iron and steel plant at Volta Redonda in the Paraiba valley on the main line from Rio to Minas Gerais. The capacity of the Volta Redonda plant is given as 425,000 tons of iron, of which 375,000 tons go to the steel furnace; 375,000 tons of ingot steel, and about 275,000 tons of finished steel.

Coking coal comes from Santa Catarina by coastal steamer and is delivered at an outport south of Rio; here it is transferred to the railroad and hauled into the Paraiba valley. Ore comes down from Minas Gerais.

A long-range program ties up the Volta Redonda plant with the iron mountain of Itabira, reported to be the richest iron deposit in the world. The plan is to export Itabira iron ore through the port of Vitoria in Espirito Santo and have the returning ore boats bring in metallurgical coke for use at Volta Redonda and other steel centers. Private companies held concessions for the explcitation of this fabulous iron hoard. A railroad connects Itabira with the coast by way of the Rio Doce valley but the terrain is exceedingly difficult and the railroad was incapable of handling heavy traffic. So the private companies were taken over by

---

[14] Since 1927 a Belgian company has been making iron in the state of Minas Gerais, first only at Siderurgica, but later also at Montevada. All the blast furnaces use charcoal. Their aggregate capacity is about 200,000 tons of pig iron.

the government and large sums appropriated (about $19 million were lent by the Export-Import Bank) to modernize the railroad. In March, 1947, this bank made a further loan of $7.5 million for modern machinery and equipment to operate the Itabira deposit. The idea of the iron ore-coke exchange seems sound; the problem is to find the other party into whose scheme of operation such an exchange happens to fit.

Argentina. Argentina is worse off than Brazil, for she is poorer in iron ore and has virtually no coal. However, the present regime seems determined to develop a national iron and steel industry. Some blast furnaces, probably using charcoal, are said to be in operation at the northernmost tip of Argentina, at Palpala in the province of Jujuy. A scrap-using steel plant is being operated in Buenos Aires by the Directorate of Military Industries. An ambitious integrated plant, embracing blast furnaces, steel furnaces, and rolling mills and depending on imported ore and coke, was to be erected at San Nicolas on the Paraná River between Rosario and Buenos Aires. Armco is reported to have drawn up plans for the works, but there are rumors that the scheme has been given up, at least for the time being.

Chile. At present there are only small plants in Chile that are making iron and steel. The most important is in Valdivia in the south. However, the government-sponsored Corporación de Fomento de la Producción (Corporation for the Promotion of Production) financed the construction of a steelworks at Talcahuano, the port of Concepción, which will have a yearly ingot capacity of 180,000 tons; this will be doubled if the demand warrants. The plant cost $88 million, of which the Export-Import Bank has supplied $48 million, and the equipment suppliers in the United States have advanced another $5 million. This plant, known as the Huachipato steel mill, obtains its iron ore from the coastal region north of Valparaiso and most of its coal from the Loto mines on the Lebú peninsula to the south. The mill is located on San Vicente Bay, with dock facilities for incoming raw materials and outgoing products. The plant was built and is now being managed by the Koppers Company. By-product coke ovens started operation in April, 1950, the blast furnace was blown in in June, and the blooming mill started production sometime thereafter.

Peru. For some time the government of Peru has been considering the erection of a steel plant at Chimbote, a port in the northern part of the country. Chimbote is at the mouth of the Santa River, which flows through the Cañon del Pato and furnishes considerable water power. An electric power plant with an ultimate capacity of 125,000 kilowatts is being constructed at Hidroelectra; part of it is reported to be in operation. The Santa River valley is also rich in coal. Coal and hydro-electric power were to be delivered to Chimbote where iron ore, coming from the Marcona region about 500 miles south near the coast, would meet the coal. According to latest reports only coal-loading docks have been com-pleted at Chimbote from which it is planned to export coal to Argentina.

If the world were being run according to the old rules of classical economics, probably no iron and steel industry would exist or could survive in Latin America. But we are no longer living in a world of laissez faire and "comparative costs." Too many people have suffered too much from war-caused interruptions of international trade; furthermore, the memory of the Great Depression is still fresh. Perhaps the best one can say about these uneconomic ventures into the field of heavy industry is that they may have a certain insurance or risk-bearing value. Beyond that, they may be the entering wedge and training ground of the Industrial Revolution.

BIBLIOGRAPHY

See the bibliography at the end of Chapter 42.

Chapter 42

IRON AND STEEL INDUSTRIES OF THE WORLD (CONT.)

THE IRON AND STEEL INDUSTRY OF EUROPE WEST OF THE IRON CURTAIN

Not only was the modern iron and steel industry born in Europe, but until she became the central arena of global wars Europe led the world in the production of iron and steel. A peaceful and preferably united Europe could again surpass the western hemisphere in this respect. As it is, she is split in the middle geographically, racially, ideologically, strategically; she is still groggy from the horrors of war and she is staggering under the difficulties of a peace that is no peace. Such conditions make it impossible to say anything about her capacity to regain her strength.

Great Britain

British production of iron rose from 17,000 tons in 1740 to 1 million tons in 1835. In the early eighties the output of wrought iron exceeded 2.5 million tons, but declined to about 1 million tons in 1913 and to 330,000 tons in 1929. Steel was replacing iron. From 330,000 tons of steel (ingot and castings), the output rose to 7.7 million tons in 1913 and, after fluctuating, rose to 13 million tons in 1937,

which is approximately the present production for Great Britain by herself. Although a splendid record, it does not compare with the expansion of the steel industry of the United States, and of Germany up to her collapse in 1945. Whereas the United Kingdom accounted for nearly one-half of the world output of steel from 1870 to 1874, her share during 1909-1937 was about 10 percent, as it is now.

The British industry originally was based on local charcoal and domestic ores. Later domestic coke was substituted for charcoal and high-grade foreign ores supplemented domestic supplies. Because of this partial dependence on foreign ores and for other reasons such as favorable location for exports, proximity to shipyards, etc., many British steelworks moved to the coast. Recently, however, new ways of utilizing low-grade ores have favored inland locations.

More than any other single factor, the discovery of the basic process by Thomas and Gilchrist accounts for the relative decline of Britain's position, not so much because it hurt her as because it helped other producers, notably the United States and Germany. When once rivals get a foothold in a field formerly held by a single country, that country sees the advantages of an early start become handicaps—obsolete equipment, a false sense of security, faith in miracles, etc.

Even at her height Britain was not so much an industrial country as a processing middleman and a specialist in invisible services. Her domestic market was relatively small compared with the world market and her domestic raw-material supplies were puny in terms of those of the whole globe. Even in iron and steel Britain was a trader as well as a producer. In view of her privileged position as head of the empire, the little kingdom could at times profit more by importing the iron and steel dumped by continental producers and reëxporting them to empire markets, with or without additional processing such as rerolling, than by producing the goods from start to finish. Largely because of her geographical location, Britain was peculiarly suited to this middleman's game. Furthermore, cheap imports of semifinished iron and steel products helped the finishing industries, especially shipbuilding and machine construction.

Another factor which affected Britain's position unfavorably was the shift from coal to oil. Coal exports, as we saw earlier (see p. 456), were once the backbone of British shipping and went far to account for the low cost of imported raw materials. With the loss of coal exports the tramp ship, once a peculiar forte of British shipping, also lost ground.

How Britain suffered in World War II and how this helped to bring the socialist labor government into power is too well known to need recounting. This is not the place to join the heated controversy over the relative merits of private enterprise and state control. But it is essential to know that in Britain at present the area of truly free enterprise is exceedingly limited. Coal mining and the power industry are state-owned and state-controlled. The iron and steel industry may be next. Much will depend on political developments. Freedom of enterprise and rugged individualism thrive in an atmosphere of security. Fear elicits state control and encourages collective action.

In 1926, according to Kuhn,[1] Britain had

close to 6 billion tons of iron ores, most of them low grade (about 30 percent).[2] For long the practice was to mix the low-grade domestic ore with imported ores, mainly Swedish, Spanish, and North African. More recently highly efficient beneficiation processes have been introduced which enable low-cost production from domestic ores. This, in turn, has affected the location of the industry, making possible its return to inland locations. Fig. 42.1 shows the geographical distribution of the British steel industry. Of the nine districts shown, the northeast coast and South Wales are the most important.

During the thirties the British iron and steel industry spent large sums remodeling its plants, especially the steelworks and rolling mills in Lancashire, South Wales, the Cleveland District, Lincolnshire, and Scotland. Several new continuous strip mills were built, one at Ebbw Vale, South Wales, and another at Shotten, near Liverpool. A completely new iron and steel plant was built at Corby in Northamptonshire. This plant is of particular interest because it uses the basic Bessemer or Thomas process as well as the Duplex process. The Corby plant is based on 100 percent local ores and, as soon as it got into full production, it made the cheapest steel in Europe.[3] The remodeled Ebbw Vale works in South Wales also uses the basic Bessemer and Duplex process. The arrangement is flexible, allowing the production of straight basic Bessemer (Thomas) steel, straight open hearth steel, and Duplex steel. The Corby and Ebbw Vale works have a raw steel capacity of 600,000 tons each.

The Corby works are situated about 90 miles north of London in the middle of the vast Northampton ore beds. These beds, esti-

[1] O. R. Kuhn, *The Iron Age*, February 18, 1926.

[2] "The British domestic ores are mostly low-grade carbonates, averaging between 22 and 32 percent Fe, the Lincolnshire and Oxfordshire ores being limier are self-fluxing, whereas the Northamptonshire ores need an addition of lime to produce a normal slag. These deposits are estimated to still contain some 3 billion tons of ore. There is also some ore on the South Coast near Dover." H. A. Brassert, "Some Recent Developments in the Iron and Steel Industries of the European Continent," *Blast Furnace and Steel Plant*, January, February, March, and April, 1940.

[3] *Ibid.*

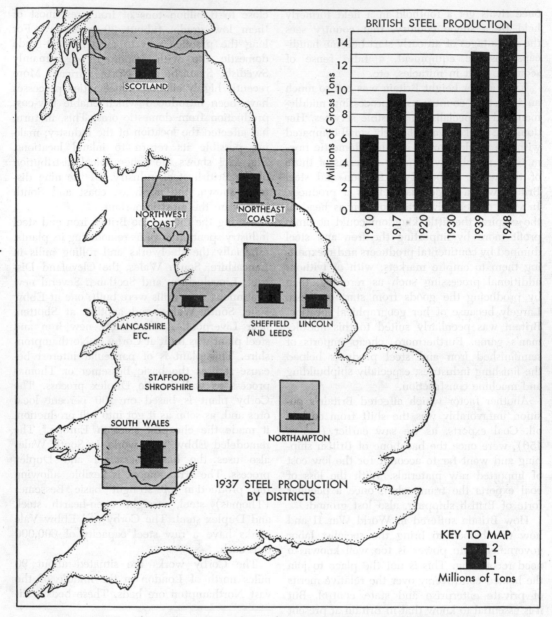

FIG. 42.1. Steel Industry of Great Britain. (Figs. 42.1, 42.2, and 42.3, from *Steel Facts.*)

mated at about 1.2 billion tons, are near enough to the surface to permit strip mining. The ores are heterogeneous and have to be carefully mined and sorted to provide a uniform charge for the blast furnace. In spite of considerable preparation and beneficiation of the ores, pig iron costs are remarkably low.

On June 18, 1949, the New York *Times* reported that the biggest steel plant in Europe,

the Abbey Works, was under construction at Port Talbot, Wales. Its owner, the Steel Company of Wales, is reported to be spending between $200 and $240 million, but details as to ore supply and type of processes are not available.

One implication of the age of the British iron and steel industry is the survival of old family firms. This tends to hold down the size

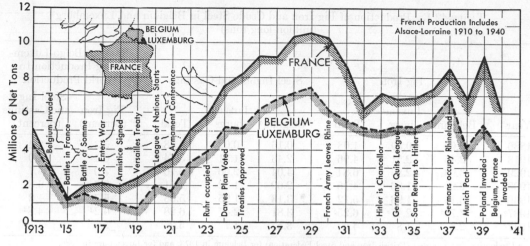

FIG. 42.2. Steel Production of France and Belgium-Luxemburg, 1913-1940.

of the typical steel company and leads to greater decentralization of ownership than is found in either the United States or Germany. That, in turn, leads to considerable coöperation or cartelization. The British iron and steel cartel collaborated with the international steel cartel which at times embraced the steel industry of practically the entire world with few exceptions, especially the Japanese and Soviet Union industries.[4] Early in 1945 the British Iron and Steel Federation was reorganized to provide for a strong central governing body. Iron and steel manufacturers are much concerned with rising costs of labor and coal and with the threat of industrial nationalization.

France

France is one of the greatest producers of iron ore in the world. In 1937 she produced 37.2 million long tons of iron ore, of which about half was consumed within the country. The ore runs about 30 percent Fe. Pig iron production in 1937 was 7.6 million long tons, considerably less than the peak of 12.0 million tons produced in 1929. The decline is partly explained by France's loss of the Saar in 1935 and also by the fact that

social and political difficulties retarded her recovery from the depression.

The steel production of France, together with that of Belgium and Luxemburg, is shown in Fig. 42.2. France's output more than doubled between 1913 and 1929, rising from 5 to 10.7 million net tons. This is largely explained by her acquisition of Alsace-Lorraine under the Treaty of Versailles. When the Saar was included in the French customs area, its iron and steel output was reported separately. In 1934, the last year before its return to Germany, the Saar produced 1.8 million tons of pig iron, nearly 2 million tons of steel, 11 million tons of coal, and almost 2 million tons of coke. After World War II the Saar was ceded to France.

Isolated iron and steelworks are scattered widely throughout France, but the industry is heavily concentrated in the east and north, which is responsible for about 90 percent of the output. The eastern sector is located over the large ore deposits of the Briey Basin and Lorraine, and depends to a considerable extent on coal or coke imported from the Ruhr because the Lorraine coal does not possess good coking qualities. The northern sector is located near the coal deposits of the Departements du Pas de Calais and du Nord. The North is heavily industrialized and yields considerable scrap. Whereas in the eastern area the basic Bessemer (Thomas) process is widely used, the North relies more heavily on the open hearth.

---

[4] See Ervin Hexner, *The International Steel Cartel*, University of North Carolina Press, Chapel Hill, 1943; George W. Stocking and Myron W. Watkins, *Cartels in Action*, Twentieth Century Fund, New York, 1946; Ervin Hexner, *International Cartels*, University of North Carolina Press, Chapel Hill, 1945.

TABLE 42.1. Production of Pig Iron and Crude Steel in Belgium and Luxemburg[5]
(million long tons)

Year	Pig Iron			Steel Ingots and Castings			Ratio of Belgo-Luxemburg Production to World Production	
	Belgium	Luxemburg	Total	Belgium[a]	Luxemburg[a]	Total	Pig Iron (percent)	Steel Ingots and Castings (percent)
1886	0.69	0.39	1.08	0.16	0.02	0.18	5.3	2.4
1913	2.45	2.51	4.96	2.43	1.31	3.74	6.4	5.0
1929	3.98	2.86	6.84	4.04	2.66	6.70	7.0	5.7
1933	2.29	1.86	4.15	2.69	1.82	4.51	8.6	6.8
1936[b]	3.16	1.96	5.12	3.13	1.95	5.08	5.7	4.2
1937[b]	3.78[c]	2.47[c]	6.25[c]	3.81	2.47	6.28	6.2[d]	4.8[d]
1947[e]	2.8	1.8	4.6	3.5	1.7	5.2	...	...

[a] Production first reported (British Iron and Steel Federation) for Belgium in 1873, and for Luxemburg in 1886.
[b] Preliminary.
[c] Includes ferro-alloys.
[d] Based on estimated world production as published in *The Iron Age*, January 6, 1938.
[e] Metric tons.

The French iron and steel industry is made up of a number of medium-sized firms organized into various cartels and trade associations. The highest capitalization of any such firm in 1937 was 180 million francs. The record output for a single firm is probably about 1.5 million tons of pig iron and over 2 million tons of steel in 1930.

French colonies in North Africa—Algeria, Tunis, and Morocco—have rich iron deposits, and France herself is supposed to have 8 billion tons of iron ore and 4 billion tons of potential ore. She is thus one of the best-endowed countries in the world in terms of quantity. However, the ore is rather lean, around 30 percent iron, and the large eastern deposits contain much phosphorus. Furthermore, the deficiency of coking coal is a serious handicap.

In 1936 the plant of the famous munitions maker Schneider of Le Creusot came under state control, and general large-scale nationalization of the industry took place after World War II. The future of France's iron and steel industry depends primarily on political developments both within her own borders and in western Europe, as well as in the world at large.

The Belgium-Luxemburg Customs Union

Before World War I Luxemburg was included in a customs union with Germany, but in 1922 she entered into such a union with Belgium.[6] The Belgium-Luxemburg union is one of the largest iron and steel producers in the world and its products play an extraordinarily important role in international trade. Like all western European centers, Belgium and Luxemburg benefited a great deal from the invention of the basic steelmaking process, especially the Thomas (basic Bessemer) process, for it turned the dirt of Lorraine and parts of Luxemburg into valuable ore.

During World War I much of the Belgian industry was destroyed but was rebuilt later with modern equipment. Both Belgium and Luxemburg must look to export markets as their normal outlet, for domestic markets are relatively small, especially in Luxemburg. Table 42.1 shows iron and steel production in these two countries.

Belgium and Luxemburg depend largely on imported ores, mainly French, and supplement their coal production with coal and coke im-

---

[5] Figures for 1886-1936 from British Iron and Steel Federation, *Statistics of the Iron and Steel Industries*, 1937, pp. 167, 169; 1937 figures from British Iron and Steel Federation, *Statistical Bulletin*, January, 1938; figures for 1947 from Statistical Office of the United Nations, *Monthly Bulletin of Statistics*.

[6] The Netherlands recently joined the Belgium-Luxemburg union in the so-called Benelux (Be = Belgium, Ne = Netherlands, Lux = Luxemburg) agreement.

ported from Germany, the United Kingdom, and the Netherlands. In 1937 Belgium produced about 29.2 million tons of coal and 5.8 million tons of coke. Her imports of coal amounted to 6.1 million tons and her exports to 4.2 million tons. Imports of coke that year were 3.1 million tons as against exports of 1.2 million tons.

The Netherlands[7]

The iron and steel industry of the Netherlands consists primarily of one producer of pig iron and of numerous steel-fabricating concerns and iron foundries. The industry is in a unique position because of its dependence on foreign countries for both raw materials and markets. Having no large deposits of iron ore, the Netherlands must import it for the manufacture of pig iron; and since she produces practically no steel, she must sell the bulk of her output of pig iron in foreign markets. The steel-fabricating concerns must likewise depend largely upon imports for their requirements for rolled and finished steel products. Although her total production of pig iron is comparatively small, the Netherlands ranks high among exporters of it. Between 1932 and 1936 she was the principal foreign supplier of pig iron to the United States.

During the nineteenth century, limited quantities of pig iron were produced in the Netherlands in a few small furnaces. The last of these furnaces, however, ceased operations in 1884, and for forty years thereafter no pig iron was produced. Notwithstanding the lack of facilities for producing either pig iron or steel, fabricating industries gradually developed. The outbreak of World War I made it impossible for these industries and the country's iron foundries to obtain the necessary materials. In an effort to avoid a repetition of such conditions, the Koninklijke Nederlandsche Hoogovens en Staalfabrieken (Royal Dutch Blast Furnaces and Steel Works) was organized in 1918 for the production of pig iron and steel. Its original capital was subscribed partly by the Netherlands government, partly by the city of Amsterdam on condition that the enterprise

be located near the city, and partly by private individuals and corporations. According to trade reports, the government has no control over it other than as an ordinary stockholder.[8]

In 1924 the company's first blast furnace went into operation, but no steelworks have been built because potential competition with nearby low-cost steel-producing countries is considered too severe to justify the manufacture of steel on a large scale. Thus the original intention in establishing the company has not been accomplished.

Germany

By the Treaty of Frankfurt which ended the Franco-Prussian War, Germany acquired Alsace-Lorraine and with it huge reserves of iron ore mixed with much phosphorus and lime. In the Ruhr, Germany possesses the most productive single coal field in the world; from it large amounts of excellent metallurgical coking coke are made. Political control over the ore of Lorraine and the coal of the Ruhr gave Germany a basis for heavy industry, especially iron and steel, that was second only to that of the United States and was unsurpassed in Europe. Blast furnaces were erected on the low-grade ore deposits of Lorraine and fed with coke brought from the Ruhr in trains. These trains took ore and pig iron back to the Ruhr, where more blast furnaces were constructed near the coal. Thus a vast steel industry sprang up, and one of the largest and most efficient industrial structures was erected. The Ruhr became the industrial heart of Germany and, to a lesser extent, of Europe. In 1913 Germany produced 17.3 million long tons of steel, or 23 percent of the world total, compared with 31.3 million or 41.6 percent, for the United States.

In addition to the Ruhr coal field, Germany also owned the rich coal fields of Silesia in the southeastern corner of the Reich. These reserves are enormous, but the coking coal is neither as abundant nor as good as that in the Ruhr. Besides this, she possessed large lignite deposits, the two most important fields lying north of Leipzig and east of Aachen (Aix-la-Chapelle). Germany's coal production

---

[7] This discussion of the iron and steel industry of the Netherlands is based on U.S. Tariff Commission, *Iron and Steel, 1938,* pp. 190-191.

[8] *Iron and Coal Trades Review,* November 6, 1936, p. 824.

reached an all-time high in 1943, with 158.6 million metric tons, almost four-fifths of which came from the Ruhr. Lignite production in the same year amounted to 254.5 million metric tons. If a ton of lignite is rated at one-fifth a ton of coal, Germany in 1943 produced over 200 million tons of coal and lignite expressed in its coal equivalent.[9]

In 1919, under the Treaty of Versailles, Germany lost Alsace-Lorraine with its coal and iron mines, its iron and steelworks and many other industries. At the same time she lost control over the Saar, a small region adjoining France that was rich in coal and had powerful iron and steel and other industries. She lost to Poland and Czechoslovakia the bulk of the Upper Silesian coal fields and the industries that had been built there, and to Poland she lost large zinc mines and smelters.

Germany rebuilt on the Ruhr coal and the lignite deposits in the central and western part of the country. Although she continued to buy ore from France, she relied more heavily on Swedish ore; in summer this was brought in through the Swedish port of Lulea on the Bay of Bothnia and the Baltic, and through the Norwegian port of Narvik in winter when the Gulf Stream keeps the coast of Norway free of ice. Germany drew also on Spain and North Africa and other regions from which suitable ores could be bought. Because of its ports on the Rhine and the system of canals and canalized rivers, the Ruhr region enjoys virtually a tidewater location and is thus in a favorable position to import foreign ores. Its location in the heart of Europe gives it an unexcelled market position for both domestic sales and exports.

Domestic ores, especially from the Siegerland southeast of Cologne and from small deposits in the Lahn, Harz, and Thuringia regions, played a merely supplementary role. However, in 1936 the Nazi government, determining to reduce drastically Germany's dependence on imported ore, decided to exploit the large Salzgitter deposits (1.5 billion tons) near Braunschweig in central Germany. These ores are low-grade, containing about 30 percent iron and 24 percent or more silica. All but a small portion of them have to be produced by underground mining.[10]

To exploit these ores, the Hermann Goering Company was formed in 1937 under the four-year plan of industrial expansion. The company planned a gigantic iron and steelworks at Watenstedt, south of Braunschweig and a short distance both from the mines and from the Mittelland Canal, a vital east-west waterway connecting the Rhine and the Elbe Rivers. This canal provides easy and cheap access to imported ores, especially Swedish, and to Ruhr coke and coal. As return cargo, the coke and coal boats were to take back high-grade concentrates of iron ore for use in the blast furnaces of the Ruhr.

The Watenstedt works were planned for a total ingot capacity of 4 to 5 million tons. There were to be four units, each unit with eight blast furnaces and the corresponding number of ore beneficiation plants, coal treating plants, by-product coke ovens, steel furnaces, rolling mills, etc. They were to produce basic (Thomas), Duplex, and straight open-hearth steels. The first unit, of an ingot capacity of 1 million tons, was completed and the second unit of 1.5 million tons was under construction when World War II broke out. Germany's conquest of France and her acquisition of the Lorraine and Briey ores rendered the Watenstedt plant unnecessary; consequently it was never completed.

When Germany annexed Austria the Hermann Goering Company undertook the construction of a plant, with an ingot capacity of over a million tons, at Linz on the Danube. For its ore, the plant depended on the famous Erzberg (Ore Mountain) in Styria, a deposit that ranges from almost barren rock to ores with as high as 50 percent iron. The ore was graded at the mines, formerly to about 34 percent, but 28 percent was considered more economical for the Linz plant. The ore moved by rail about eighty miles; the coal was to be brought in from Silesia or the Ruhr by water and possibly by rail as well. Fig. 42.3

---

[9] By January, 1948, lignite was being produced at two-thirds the peak rate, and coal at half the peak rate.

[10] Twenty-four double-compartment shafts were sunk to a level of 3000 feet. The acid ores from the Salzgitter were to be mixed with limestone ores from the nearby Peine-Ilsede district.

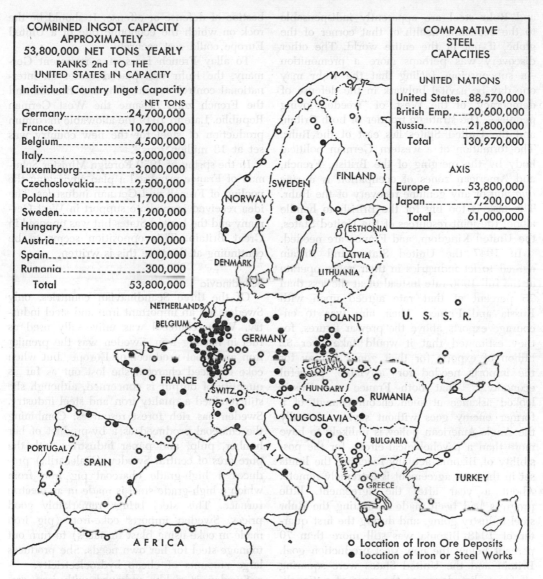

COMBINED INGOT CAPACITY APPROXIMATELY 53,800,000 NET TONS YEARLY RANKS 2nd TO THE UNITED STATES IN CAPACITY	
Individual Country Ingot Capacity	NET TONS
Germany	24,700,000
France	10,700,000
Belgium	4,500,000
Italy	3,000,000
Luxembourg	3,000,000
Czechoslovakia	2,500,000
Poland	1,700,000
Sweden	1,200,000
Hungary	800,000
Austria	700,000
Spain	700,000
Rumania	300,000
Total	53,800,000

COMPARATIVE STEEL CAPACITIES	
UNITED NATIONS	
United States	88,570,000
British Emp.	20,600,000
Russia	21,800,000
Total	130,970,000
AXIS	
Europe	53,800,000
Japan	7,200,000
Total	61,000,000

○ Location of Iron Ore Deposits
● Location of Iron or Steel Works

FIG. 42.3. Steel Capacity of Axis Europe and the Rest of the World, 1942.

shows the steel industry of Axis Europe at the height of its power.

While these war-born plants, at least at present, have no economic significance—the Watenstedt plant was largely destroyed; what was left was "cannibalized" by the victors—they are important as a suggestion of things to come, of what may be done when the techniques of ore beneficiation and iron recovery have made still more progress. Any revival in the future will depend largely on political

developments in Europe and the outcome of the tension between East and West.

For the time being it seems as if Germany's fate as a steel producer hinges mainly on the Ruhr. Even though the Morgenthau Plan envisaged virtual destruction of that strategic zone, its industrial future brightened considerably as the result of two discoveries. One was the growing realization that western European recovery is more or less impossible unless the Ruhr also recovers, for Ruhr coal and Ruhr steel are apparently indispensable to the economic health of that corner of the globe, if not of the entire world. The other discovery was perhaps more a premonition —a subconscious feeling that the Ruhr may one day be a vital bulwark in the defense of democracy, of the West, of "freedom-loving peoples." The strategic frontier of both Britain and the United States lies east of the Ruhr. The formation of a western German political body by the merging of the British, French, and American zones of occupation is a *sine qua non* of any genuine recovery of the Ruhr. The task is too big for the British to handle alone; the joint resources of the United States, the United Kingdom, and France are needed.

In 1947 the United States and Britain agreed to let industries in their zones operate at the full 1936 rate instead of at the less than 75 percent of that rate agreed upon with Russia and France. Their aim was to encourage exports above the prewar figures, for they estimated that it would take over $2 billion of exports for their zones to pay for the imports needed for "a viable, peaceful economy."[11] That both France and Russia looked askance at such encouragement of a former enemy goes without saying. Actually the Anglo-American policy is unlikely to have more than a psychological effect, for the possibility of Bizonia actually reaching the limits set in the new agreement is extremely remote. About a year after the agreement, little progress had been made in getting the Ruhr steel industry going, and during the first quarter of 1948 Bizonia was still more than 70 percent below the new steel production goal. Britain and the United States were squaring off for a showdown on the issue of nationalization, the American authorities accusing the British of promoting nationalization rather than decartelization.

One of the underlying causes of the East-West tension is the Ruhr. With the Ruhr under eastern influence the West lacks a vital defensive bastion; with the Ruhr in the hands of the West, the tables are turned and an offensive against western Europe is extremely risky. Even in an atomic age, warfare depends on industry. The Ruhr should be no one's

[11] *Business Week*, September 16, 1947, p. 101.

bastion of defense or offense. It should be the rock on which the economic fate of a United Europe could rest securely.

To allay French fears of a renascent Germany, the Ruhr was placed under an international control commission, and Bizonia and the French zone became the West German Republic. Late in 1949 the allowable maximum production of steel for the new country was set at 13 million tons.

In the spring of 1950 Foreign Minister Schuman of France proposed a plan envisaging the pooling of French and German industries. The idea received immediate support in West Germany and the United States but was opposed in Great Britain. This opposition seems to be continuing at the time this is written.

Scandinavia

Of the three Scandinavian countries, only Sweden has an important iron and steel industry. When charcoal was universally used as fuel in making iron, Sweden was the premier iron and steel producer of Europe; but when coke replaced charcoal she lost out as far as quantity of output is concerned, although she still retained a quality iron and steel industry. Sweden has rich forest resources. Combining the charcoal produced as a by-product of her lumber, pulp, and paper industries with the pure ores of central Sweden (Dalecarlia) produces a high-grade charcoal pig iron from which a high-grade steel is made in an electric furnace. This steel brings remarkably good prices. Sweden imports coke-iron (pig iron made in coke-using blast furnaces) to turn out tonnage steel for her own needs. She produces large amounts of cheap hydroelectricity.

Sweden is richly endowed with iron ore. Her ore deposits, estimated at 2.2 billion tons actual, and an additional 700 million potential, are concentrated in two widely separated sections: the central region, Dalecarlia, and the northern region, Lappland. The bulk of the deposits—about 1.5 billion tons of actual ore —is found in the northern area. This ore is a hematite with 60 to 65 percent iron and a varying phosphorus content. Much of the iron ore contains so much phosphorus that it could not be exploited until the basic process was introduced in 1878.

While the Dalecarlia mines serve mainly the domestic industry, the Lappland ores are exported via Lulea, Sweden, in summer and via Narvik, Norway, in winter (see p. 676). A large part of the deposits in both sections belongs to the Trafik A.B. Grangesberg-Oxelösund.[12] The Lappland ores are exploited by a subsidiary in which the government has a 50 percent interest. The Grangesberg company owns steam and motor ships, railroads, and explosive factories, and controls A.B. Hematite which is interested in North African iron ore mines.

Italy

Italy shares with Sweden the advantages of cheap hydroelectricity but lacks Sweden's wealth of iron ore and forests. Like Sweden, Italy is dependent on imported coal and coke.[13] Italy has a large population and hence a large labor force and a not inconsiderable domestic market. Her climate is milder and therefore less coal per capita is required for space heating than is the case in Sweden. A large proportion of the imported coal can go into industrial production.

Before World War II, Italy produced a little over 2 million tons of steel a year, mainly from imported scrap. Her steel industry was carefully nurtured by the fascist regime, which lost no opportunity to promote its expansion. Italy's meager domestic ore deposits were exploited as never before until they supplied about one-fourth of the country's needs. Another 10 percent was obtained by treating pyrites electrolytically to economize on the iron content; the rest was obtained from scrap, most of it imported. Most of Italy's iron ore —about 600,000 metric tons—came from the island of Elba; another 350,000 tons came from the Val d'Aosta, and about 250,000 from northern Sardinia. The Elba deposits are government property.

Early in 1948 Italy was producing steel at about the same rate as in 1937-1938. War is a great source of scrap, and the coal was supplied by the United States. Italy had to be saved from communism.

---

[12] A.B. = Aktiebolaget (Swedish for corporation).

[13] In 1938 Italy produced 2.3 million tons of coal and imported 12 million.

Spain

Spain is still largely an agricultural country; most of it lies in "Europe B" (see p. 130). Her steel output runs about 400,000 tons a year and is protected by a high tariff. Spain has considerable iron ore—most of it pure Bessemer (acid) grade—both in the extreme north in the Basque country along the Bay of Biscay and in the southeast. Bilboa is a great ore-shipping port.

THE IRON AND STEEL INDUSTRY OF THE SOVIET UNION AND HER SATELLITES

Today the Soviet Union is the second largest iron and steel producer in the world. In 1947 she is reported to have produced 14 million metric tons of steel[14] or as much as 10 percent of the world output. If to this is added the output of the satellite countries—Czechoslovakia (2.3), Poland (1.6), and Hungary (0.6)—the total output of steel "behind the iron curtain" in 1947 amounted to 18.5 million metric tons, or 13.7 percent of the world total. On this depend over 300 million people inhabiting something like one-fifth of the land area of the globe. Since the industry of this part of the world suffered severely in World War II, it is reasonable to expect that in a few years the steel output will be considerably higher. The last Gosplan (State Plan of Production) called for the production of 19.5 million tons of iron and 25.4 million tons of steel in the Soviet Union alone by 1950. These goals do not seem to have been reached.

Czarist Russia in 1913 produced 9 million long tons of iron ore, 4.1 million long tons of pig iron, and 4.4 million tons of ingot steel and castings. The new Russia that emerged after the Bolshevist Revolution of 1917 was bent on industrial expansion on a scale never contemplated in Czarist times. Not only was industrial output to be increased, but industries were to be modernized, and industrialization to be extended into new branches of manufacture and new regions hitherto untouched. Instead of being merely a colonial appendage to European Russia, Siberia is now being converted into the industrial heart of the Soviet Union.

---

[14] Business Week, June 5, 1948, p. 109. Other estimates run considerably higher.

Czarist Russia was predominantly agricultural. The inefficiency of a peasant economy under which possibly as many as 80 percent of the people were bound to the land and had to support both themselves and the other 20 percent of the people set a definite limit on industrial production. Lenin changed all that, for he saw clearly the connection between inefficient agriculture and backward industry. Hence the mechanization and socialization of agriculture, under which the productivity of the farmer would be raised and rural peoples thus be freed to migrate or be moved to the industrial urban centers, became the heart of the revolutionary scheme. Instead of 20 percent of the people in industry, government, trade, transportation, etc., and 80 percent on the land, the ratio had to be changed drastically to something like 30 percent in mining and manufacturing, 15 percent in services (government, professions, transportation, etc.), and 55 percent in agriculture. But the mechanization of agriculture, in turn, depends on industries which can mechanize the farm and supply the farmer with the goods for which he is willing to toil and sell his surplus. A stupendous transformation had to take place, involving a veritable migration of the peoples and a wholesale creation of resources such as the world had never seen before. As a means of achieving this transformation, a series of four "Five-Year Plans" was undertaken, beginning in 1922; the sequence was interrupted during World War II. Table 42.2 gives a general picture of their plans and achievements, in so far as they are known.

Compared with the United States, the Soviet Union has many handicaps. Whereas the United States represents virtually a solid block of "ecumene," or effective territory, the effective territory of the Soviet Union represents only a modest portion of her whole area. Starting with a wide base stretching from the Baltic to the Black and Caspian Seas, the ecumene of the Soviet Union tapers off as one moves east. Even in the west considerable parts of European Russia consist of swamps and wooded areas of low productivity. Farther east taiga and tundra make up the bulk of the land. Industrial areas stand out from the barren land like economic oases, and agriculture itself becomes increasingly extensive and less productive the farther east one goes.

Under such conditions space is a costly luxury that puts a tremendous burden on those who would make the whole land area into a single organically related economy. Aware of this problem, the Soviet government is striving toward regional autonomy, so far as conditions permit, and at considerable cost.

TABLE 42.2. The Four Five-Year Plans of the U.S.S.R.[15]
Actual or Target Production in the Final Year of the Plan as a Percentage of Actual or Target Production in the Final Year of the Preceding Plan[a]

	First 5-Year Plan 1932 (1928=100)	Second 5-Year Plan 1937 (1932=100)	Third 5-Year Plan 1942T (1937=100)	Fourth 5-Year Plan 1950T (1940=100)
Gross production	247	220	188	148
Fuel and power				
Coal	183	198	181	151
Oil	194	136	176	114
Electric power	270	270	206	170
Iron and steel				
Pig iron	188	234	152	130
Steel	140	300	155	139
Rolled steel	126	302	162	136
Machinery and engineering				
Freight cars	237	273	153	...
Automobiles	105	840	200	236
Metal-cutting lathes	833	240	194	218
Locomotives	173	191	132	167
Light industry				
Cotton textiles	97	128	142	135
Woolen textiles	95	118	167	140
Leather shoes	294	189	143	113

[a] Figures refer to actual output unless marked "T," in which case they refer to production targets.

The United States economy is built upon the principle of regional specialization, with each region serving the whole economy. This entails tremendous transportation services and costs,[16]

[15] United Nations, A Survey of the Economic Situation and Prospects of Europe, Geneva, 1948, p. 152.
Data based on absolute figures given in final Report on the Fulfillment of the First and Second Five-Year Plans, official statistical handbooks, and the Law on the Fourth Five-Year Plan.

[16] Estimated at $40 billion in 1948, or 20 percent of our national income. See C. L. Dearing and W. Owen, National Transportation Policy, The Brookings Institution, Washington, 1949.

but it means that production costs are lowered by regional specialization along the line of greatest aptitude. To avoid the heavy transportation charges which might easily wreck the whole system, the Soviet government is foregoing a large part of the benefit of regional specialization and is building up a series of partially autonomous regional industrial centers stretching from the Ukraine in the southern part of European Russia to the area along the Pacific coast.

The Soviet Union

Peter the Great strove valiantly to raise the industrial efficiency of Russia. The iron industry was by no means overlooked. An industry based on charcoal was developed in the Ural region, and such small-scale production became widespread.

A modern private iron and steel industry that used coke developed in the southern Ukraine after 1870, partly with the aid of foreign capital, especially Belgian and French. This industry was based on two foundation pillars: the coal of the Donets region in the eastern Ukraine and the iron ore of Krivoi Rog west of the Dnieper River. This private industry competed successfully with plants in other parts of the country operated by the czarist government. Russia's total pig iron production increased from 350,000 metric tons in 1870 to 2.9 million in 1900. The production in the southern Ukraine went from 6000 to 1,525,000 tons during the same period. This is the foundation on which the Soviet regime based its modernization and expansion program begun in 1928.

Before discussing that program, we shall briefly survey the raw material situation of the Soviet iron and steel industry. In 1933 iron reserves were estimated at 16.4 billion metric tons, of which 9.2 billion were earmarked as actual reserves.[17] Of the actual reserves, 5.5 billion tons are classified as brown limonite, 2.4 as magnetite, and 1.6 as red hematite ores.

In addition to these iron deposits, the Soviet Union possesses rich manganese deposits. Reserves were estimated in 1936 at 700 million tons, the largest known in the world. The largest deposit is at Nikopol in the southern Ukraine. A smaller deposit at Chiatury in Georgia, south of the Caucasus Mountains, is of higher grade. Other deposits are in the Urals, in Kazakhstan, and west of Krasnoyarsk. Much of the manganese is exported.

A remarkable feature of the ore situation in the Soviet Union is the relative newness of some of the most important discoveries. The Soviet government is most energetic in mineral exploitation and has had a number of remarkable successes since 1930. Even now hardly a year passes without the announcement of some new important find.

At the beginning of its great industrialization scheme in 1928, the Soviet government decided to shift the center of industrial gravity eastward into Siberia, for the German invasion during World War I had demonstrated European Russia's vulnerability. If excessive space and vast distances are a great drain on the resources of a country in peacetime, they are also a great asset in time of war. On them is based the master strategy of defense in depth, of bartering space for time, of retreating until the enemy has been weakened by overextended lines of communication and by an excessive strain on his logistics. To carry out this strategy, the Soviet industry east of the Urals must be large enough to support the counterattack when the time is ripe.[18]

As a result of this decision to expand eastward, the older centers of heavy industry, especially the Donbas,[19] have lost in relative importance although their actual output has greatly expanded. The Donbas is still one of the truly great centers of industry. Its natural setting is exceptional. Vast reserves of various coals, including good coking coals and anthra-

---

[17] G. B. Cressey, *Asia's Lands and Peoples, a Geography of One-Third the Earth and Two-Thirds Its People*, McGraw-Hill Book Company, New York, 1944, p. 292.

[18] There can be no doubt that Russian strategy will be vitally affected by the development of atomic warfare, but it is believed that the old tactics, first applied with excellent results against Napoleon, is still considered the sound basis of strategy in case of prolonged war. See Carl Spaatz, "On Atomic Warfare," *Life*, August 11 and 18, 1948.
[19] Donbas is an abbreviation for Donets basin; the Donets River is a tributary of the Don.

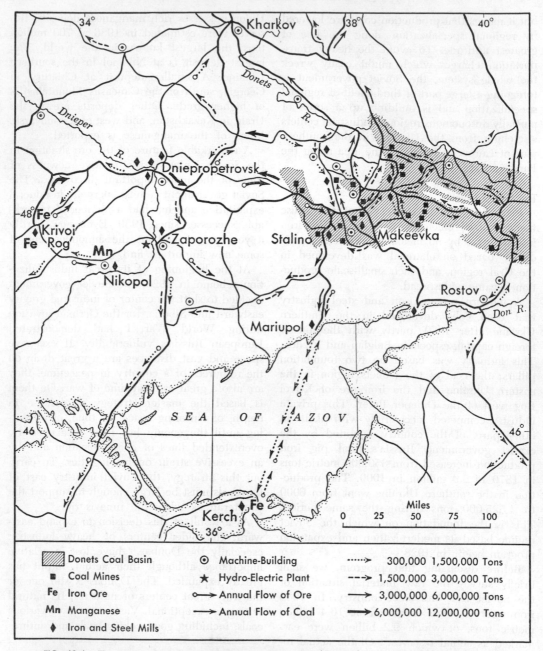

FIG. 42.4. The Donets Coal Basin with Sources of Iron Ore (Krivoi Rog and Kerch) and of Manganese (Nikopol). (From *Asia's Lands and Peoples*, by George B. Cressey, 1944. McGraw-Hill Book Co.)

cite, lie only 200 miles east of the great Krivoi Rog iron ore deposits and a similar distance north of the Kerch deposits. Blast furnaces and steelworks are centered in the Donbas at Makeevka and Stalino (see Fig. 42.4).

The Donbas, nearly 10,000 square miles in area, stretches from Stalino to Rostov-on-Don. The coal fields underlie an area of about 250 miles by 100 miles and yield from 60 to 90 million tons of coal.[20] From this center, coal

[20] E. C. Robes, "The Donets Basin," *Foreign Commerce Weekly*, October 30, 1943, p. 3.

moves in all directions to the outposts of the Russian "Ruhr"—west to Krivoi Rog and the intermediary points of Zaporozhe, Dnepro-Dzerzhinsk (steel plant) and Dnepropetrovsk (blast furnaces and steelworks); north to the great machine industry center of Kharkov; east to Rostov (a great oil-refining and general industrial center) and on to Stalingrad with its steel mills and tractor plant; south to Mariupol where Donbas coal meets Kerch ore brought across the Sea of Azov; finally to Kerch itself where blast furnaces are located near the ore.

The layout in part resembles the Pittsburgh-Youngstown area, with its northern satellites strung out along the south shore of Lake Erie and the Duluth region. Just as the trains that haul ore to Pittsburgh and Youngstown take back coal and coke, and the ships that bring ore to the lower Lake ports take back coal to the mills of Duluth, so the trains that bring coal to Mariupol bring back ore from the Kerch peninsula, and the ships that carry the ore across the Sea of Azov take back coal to the ore region. Mariupol corresponds to Conneaut or Ashtabula or Cleveland, and Kerch to Duluth, though the distances are not comparable.

The Donbas is unique in the completeness of its natural endowment. Coal on the spot, iron ore nearby, manganese at Nikopol, oil from the fields north of the Caucasus, and hydroelectricity from the Dneprostroi—the largest water-power plant in the world at the time of its completion but now surpassed by the Hoover and Grand Coulee Dams. The Donbas lies in the midst of the richest agricultural area in the Soviet Union. Three mighty rivers —the Dnieper, the Don, and the Volga—connect it with the vast lands to the north, and easy access is had to the Black Sea to the south. Thus, there is little wonder that this area remains the premier industrial center of the Soviet Union. In 1940 it produced 11.3 million tons of steel out of a total of 18.7, or 61.5 percent. Its partial destruction during World War II was a body blow that sent the entire Soviet economy reeling. The current Five-Year Plan calls for only partial restoration of the Donbas but for considerable expansion of Siberian industries.[21]

The only other center of heavy iron and steel industry in European Russia is in the central part, east and south of Moscow in the Tula and Voronezh districts (oblasts). There are blast furnaces at Novo-Tula and Kosnyo-Gora in the Tula district and at Lipetsk and Svobodny-Sokol in the Voronezh district. Steelworks and machine industries are scattered throughout the area, including Moscow itself. The natural endowment of this region is far less satisfactory than that of the southern Ukraine. Moreover, the area is somewhat overcrowded; as a result there are bottlenecks in transportation which interfere with the prompt delivery of raw materials, especially coal.

There are other sections of concentrated industrialization, notably Leningrad, but there are no blast furnaces—in other words, no fully integrated iron and steelworks in European Russia outside of the two areas just discussed.

In Siberia the two outstanding centers of integrated iron and steel production are the Urals and the region around Stalinsk, formerly Kuznets. In the Urals, the center of the charcoal iron production of earlier centuries, there are said to be no less than thirty-nine different localities where iron and steel are produced.[22] The two main production centers in that region are Magnitogorsk and Nizhni Tagil; the works at Magnitogorsk are larger and newer than those at Nizhni Tagil.

Under the first Five-Year Plan the Soviet Union engaged two American firms in the early thirties to build a large modern iron and steelworks simultaneously at Kuznets and Magnitogorsk. The two plants were to be the eastern and western anchors respectively of the so-called Magnitogorsk-Kuznets Kombinat. Magnitogorsk was to supply the ore from the great Magnet Mountain (Magnitnaya), and Kuznets, 1417 miles to the east by the Trans-Siberian Railroad, was to supply the coal—a fantastic industrial project not based on the tenets of Adam Smith or David Ricardo. The train that hauled the coal west was to bring ore and pig iron east and integrated iron and steelworks were to be located at both ends.

[21] See L. M. Herman, "Soviet Iron and Steel Industry," U.S. Department of Commerce, *International Reference Series,* July, 1947, p. 7.

[22] G. B. Cressey, *op. cit.,* p. 298.

Soon after the steelworks in Kuznets and Magnitogorsk had been built, ore deposits were discovered south of Kuznets in the Gornaya Shoria and coal was rediscovered[23] at Karaganda in Kazakhstan; the latter cut the coal haul down to about 600 miles. Moreover, the Kizel coal of the Urals can be used when mixed with Karaganda coal. Both centers are now based on a firmer and more favorable natural foundation, and the Soviet economy must function more smoothly as a result of these lucky discoveries.[24]

Besides the five blast furnaces at Magnitogorsk—each has a daily capacity of about 1400 tons of pig iron (an aggregate yearly capacity of over 2.5 million tons)—there are blast furnaces at Nizhni Tagil, Sverdlovsk, Chelyabinsk, Khalilovo, and Bakal. The Stalinsk works (formerly Kuznets) are smaller than the Magnitogorsk plant and in general the region is less important than the Urals. During World War II the Urals became the heart of Soviet industry. There are also steel plants at Petrovsk-Zabaikal east of Lake Baikal and at Komosomolsk on the lower Amur near the Pacific.

In addition to expanding the Soviet Union's steel capacity from 18.3 million tons in 1940 to 25.4 million by 1950, the current Five-Year Plan provides for technological improvements at many points. The "other regions" that produced 6.5 percent of the output in 1940 are expected to supply 14 percent by 1950. To make this possible, six new steelworks are planned, five of them under construction by 1947:

1. A fully integrated iron and steel plant near Tbilisi (Tiflis), the capital of Georgia.

2. A new steel center, known as the Orsk-Khakilovo combine, now being erected near Orsk at the southern end of the Urals.

3. Expansion of a wartime steel mill near Karaganda in Kazakhstan.

4. A war plant at Begovat in the Uzbek Republic now being expanded into a fully integrated iron and steelworks.

5. A new iron and steel center now under construction in the northern Urals.

6. A fully integrated iron and steel plant to be erected at Cherepovets, 210 miles east of Leningrad on the railroad to Vologda.

In addition to these six new centers, the plants at Novo Tagil, Chelyabinsk, and Magnitogorsk are to be expanded.

Looking beyond 1950, Stalin in his speech of February 9, 1947, called for 50 million tons of pig iron and 60 million tons of steel. In other words, the fourth Five-Year Plan is to be not the end but instead more of a midpoint in the industrialization of a nation which not so long ago was generally considered to be constitutionally destined to remain agrarian, "a hewer of wood and a drawer of water." There is no better proof of the theory that resourceship evolves out of the interaction of human will and ability, cultural achievement and natural endowment, than Soviet Russia.

Czechoslovakia, Poland, and Hungary

The most famous steelworks in Czechoslovakia is the Skoda works near Pilsen. The plant makes and finishes steel and also manufactures automobiles, machinery, etc. For some time before Munich it was under the control of the French munitions firm, Schneider of Le Creusot.

Under the Treaty of Versailles, Germany lost the bulk of her Silesian metal industries and coal mines to Poland and Czechoslovakia. The steel industry of Silesia had long been dependent on scrap. The loss of much of the German scrap supply rendered difficult the restoration of the transferred industry to its former production level. However, as a result of World War II, the entire Silesian industrial complex is now in Polish and Czechoslovakian hands.

In February, 1948, the government of Czechoslovakia became communistic, as the Polish government had been for some time; hence closer political and economic collaboration between the two countries became possible, as well as closer coöperation with the Soviet Union. On August 9, 1948, the New York *Times* reported that Poland and Czecho-

---

[23] Its existence had been known for almost a hundred years, but it seems to have been overlooked by the Gosplan.

[24] However, according to the New York *Times* (October 16, 1949), Mr. G. Nosov, the director of the Magnitogorsk iron and steel combine, wrote in *Pravda* about the rapid depletion of high-grade iron ores in the Urals and the pressing need for a speedy solution of the problem of enriching leaner ores.

slovakia were planning the joint development of the area between Katowice in Poland and Ostrava in Czechoslovakia, in the hope of bringing its steel-producing capacity up to 10 million tons. This area is connected with the Baltic by the canalized Oder River, which is to be developed as a major traffic artery; Szczecin (the former Stettin) at the mouth of the Oder used to be a secondary steel center under the German regime. Whether Swedish ore is to be brought up the Oder is not known. Poland used to export a great deal of coal through Gdynia near Danzig, and she could exchange coal for Swedish ore. Sweden needs coal badly, and the market for her ore must have suffered severely as a result of the collapse of the Ruhr, formerly her best customer.

THE IRON AND STEEL INDUSTRY OF ASIA (EXCEPT THE U.S.S.R.)

The part of Asia that lies south of the Soviet Union has about two-thirds of the world's population but very little modern industry. There is coal and iron, some of good quality and plentiful; but on the whole the region is not well endowed with what it takes to make modern industry run. At one extreme are deserts and mountains inhabited by too few people; at the other, the monsoon lands (see p. 134) with too many people to make easy or even possible the transition from a vegetable to a machine civilization. It is a region of unspeakable poverty, of famine, of strain and stress, of internal strife. Moreover, on the whole, strong central governments are lacking.

The only country in the area that achieved a degree of industrialization somewhat comparable to that of the West was Japan, and Hiroshima put an end to that. In 1947 all of Asia, exclusive of the U.S.S.R., produced no more than 2 million tons of steel—2 million tons for about a billion people, as against the over 80 million tons for about 145 million people produced in the United States.

The only fully integrated steelworks in India, a country whose population is approaching the 400-million mark, are those of the Tata Iron and Steel Company (Tisco) at Jamshedpur, 115 miles west of Calcutta. The works are owned by a Parsee family, and only Indian capital is involved. In 1948 the output per month was 80,000 long tons of pig iron, 75,000 long tons of steel ingots, and 60,000 tons of finished steel. The rest of India's steel output is negligible. There are several other plants that make iron for foundries, forges, etc.

The Tata works are among the lowest-cost producers of iron in the world. Raw materials of good quality are accessible nearby—60 percent iron ore comes from mines forty-five miles away, coal from mines 115 miles away, and flux has only forty miles to travel.

The Tata Company does not confine its activities to making iron and steel; it is the largest industrial concern in India, owning textile mills and mills that make railroad wheels, locomotive boilers, picks, shovels, etc. Work has begun on a $22-million locomotive plant, and in 1948 the company considered borrowing $60 million from the Indian government to finance an expansion which would add another 600,000 tons to its ingot capacity.[25]

Throughout its history, Japan's steel industry was tied up closely with preparation for war. It was controlled by the zaibatsu, the powerful industrial families of the country; it was Big Business which could exist only by accommodating itself to the military. Japan in 1943 produced about 7.8 million metric tons of steel. That was the peak of her production effort. It was a miracle, a magician's trick that shows what a patient long-suffering people can be made to do by unrelenting taskmasters and what industry can achieve when backed to the limit by aggressive military power. Such an output of steel was possible only in a country in which everything was sacrificed on the altar of Mars. Machinery that should have turned out consumers' goods was scrapped and melted. Metal household goods went on the scrap pile whether they were needed or not. Iron for war machines was brought in from Korea and China, from Malaya, Australia, and the Philippines— wherever it was available. By 1944 the strain was beginning to tell, and steel production dropped to 5.9 million tons. In 1945, the year

---

[25] See *Business Week*, July 17, 1948, p. 112.

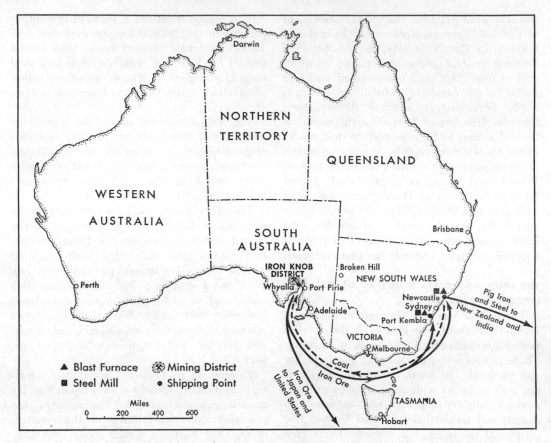

FIG. 42.5. The Geographical Pattern of Raw-Material Movements of Australia's Iron and Steel Industry. (U. S. Department of State, Division of Geography and Cartography, 1945.)

of Japan's downfall, production was a mere 1.1 million tons, and this was cut in half in 1946. In 1947, however, under the benevolent tutelage of the victor, production was again up to 1.7 million tons.

The iron and steelworks of Manchuria constituted a vital part of the Japanese steel industry during the fifteen years before Hiroshima; Korea's iron and steel industry had a minor part. Today Manchuria, stripped by the Russians, is part of communist China, and Russian influence is stronger than it was before the Russo-Japanese War. Korea has been proclaimed an independent nation.[26]

Turkey is a country in which the West is keenly interested because it joins the Soviet Union and controls the Bosporus and the Dardanelles. When Kemal Atatürk modernized Turkey he did not overlook the building of an iron and steelworks. The plant, built by an English firm, has a capacity of 150,000 metric tons of finished steel a year. It is located in Karabük, which is on the railroad leading north from Ankara to the Black Sea. There is coal a short distance to the west at Zonguladk, and the source of ore is only 600 miles away. According to Max Weston Thornburg, the state-owned and state-operated industry is more or less a failure.[27] Perhaps private enterprise will be given a chance to show what it can do.

---

[26] New York Times, August 17, 1948. In June, 1950, communist northern Koreans invaded South Korea, a republic set up under the auspices of the United Nations.

[27] Max Weston Thornburg, Turkey—An Economic Appraisal, Twentieth Century Fund, New York, 1949.

THE IRON AND STEEL INDUSTRY OF AUSTRALIA

The iron and steel industry and the other heavy industry of Australia are controlled by one company, the Broken Hill Proprietary Company, Ltd. (BHP). This is by far the largest business concern on the continent; its capitalization is about five times as large as that of its nearest competitor. Not only does it control the entire iron and steel industry of Australia, it also controls the country's supply of copper and all other nonferrous metals, and, by association with Imperial Chemical Industries, the country's chemical production. It controls outright the Commonwealth Aircraft Corporation, which produces all Australian planes, and it owns a fleet of ocean-going ships used mainly to haul ores, pig iron, and coal.

The company was organized in 1885 for the purpose of mining the rich lead carbonate and sodium chloride ores exposed at the surface at Broken Hill, a mining region in New South Wales near the border of South Australia (see Fig. 42.5). Subsequently, the company erected at Port Pirie, South Australia, what is reported to be the largest lead smelter in the world. Because iron ore was used as a flux in treating the lead ore, BHP became interested in the Iron Knob deposits in South Australia. Eventually BHP became a fully integrated iron and steel company, one of the largest in the British Empire and the leading producer of iron and steel in the southern hemisphere.

In 1915 an iron and steel plant was completed at Port Waratah near Newcastle, N.S.W. In 1935 BHP obtained control of Australian Iron and Steel, Ltd., a company which continued to produce iron and steel under its own name near Port Kembla, N.S.W. Port Kembla is south and Newcastle is north of Sydney. In 1938 when the government agreed to extend the iron ore lease for another fifty years, BHP contracted to build a blast furnace at Whyalla,[28] the ore shipping point opposite

Port Pirie about twenty miles distant from the ore mines, Iron Knob, Iron Monarch, and others. The relative importance of the company's three plants is shown in Table 42.3.

BHP also has developed and equipped an iron ore mine in the Yampi Sound district on the northwest coast of the continent. It was from this district that ore was shipped to Japan and other countries before forbidden by an embargo in 1938. Late in 1949 it was reported that a large expansion of Australia's iron and steel industry was to be based on

TABLE 42.3. Pig Iron and Ingot Steel Production in Australia, by Plants, 1942[29]
(thousand long tons)

	Pig Iron	Ingot Steel
Newcastle, N.S.W. (Port Waratah)	682.3	780.0
Port Kemble, N.S.W.	593.4	504.0
Whyalla, S.A.	188.3	...
	1464.0	1284.0

the iron ore deposits of Koolan Island in Yampi Sound. The new development, which includes a considerable expansion of the tin-plate mills at Broken Hill, was to cost in the neighborhood of $80 million and was to be in charge of a New York City firm.[30]

A small charcoal iron industry, based on local ores and timber resources, exists near Perth in western Australia.

THE IRON AND STEEL INDUSTRY OF THE UNION OF SOUTH AFRICA

The iron and steel industry of the Union of South Africa produced about 600,000 metric tons of ingot steel and steel castings in 1947; this was exactly double the 1938 output. She possesses large and high-grade deposits of ore and limestone, also various ferro-alloys. Her

---

[28] This is another example of a secondary iron center being established to take advantage of return cargo. With coal moving from New South Wales to South Australia, the ore movement in the reverse direction constitutes an economical use of ship tonnage. Other examples are Mariupol in the southern Ukraine, Kerch in the Crimea, and

Duluth, Minnesota. Iron and steelworks in the lower Lake ports are based on the same principle, but railroad cars rather than ships are involved.

[29] *Foreign Minerals Survey*, Vol. 2, *The Mineral Industry of Australia*, March, 1945, p. 48. (The same figures are given on the same page for 1943, so there may be an error in the year. The figures were estimated by the United States Foreign Economic Administration.)

[30] New York *Times*, November 20, 1949.

present output represents but a small portion of what the raw-material equipment could support. Being a mining country, the Union also produces considerable amounts of market scrap. The limiting factor is the market and the modest scale of production which that market can consume. In 1936 the International Steel Cartel allotted the Union a production quota of 350,000 tons of iron and steel products for the home market; this was equal to about 500,000 tons of raw steel.

Steel had been made from scrap in South Africa for many years. But not until 1928 did a blast furnace go into operation, for not until that year was a company able to comply with the conditions of the Iron and Steel Industry Encouragement Act, passed in 1922. This act set 50,000 tons of iron or steel as the annual minimum for which subsidies would be paid. The blast furnace was shut down in 1933 during the depression.

In 1928 the government organized the South African Iron and Steel Industrial Corporation, Ltd. It is largely financed with government funds and serves certain markets, especially railroads and ports. Its plant is located near Pretoria in the Transvaal near coal and ore deposits. The Union Steel Corporation of South Africa, Ltd., has a plant at Newcastle in Natal. Another company makes steel from scrap.

BIBLIOGRAPHY

"A Spark in Steel," *Fortune*, December, 1948.

Adams, W. (ed), *The Structure of American Industry*, New York, Macmillan, 1950, chap. 5.

"Adirondack Iron Mining," *Mining and Metallurgy*, November, 1943.

Alderfer, E. B., and Michl, H. E., *The Economics of American Industry*, New York, McGraw-Hill, 1942, chaps. 2-4.

American Iron and Steel Institute, *Directory of Iron and Steel Works of the United States and Canada*, New York, 25th ed., 1948.

American Iron and Steel Institute, *Yearbook of the American Iron and Steel Institute* (annual).

American Iron and Steel Institute, *Steel Facts* (7 issues a year).

American Iron and Steel Institute, *Annual Statistical Report*.

Anstey, V., *The Economic Development of India*, New York, Longmans, Green, 1942.

"Armco and Argentina," *Fortune*, May, 1945.

"Australia, Its Resources and Strategic Position," *The Index*, New York, New York Trust Co., summer, 1942.

Bain, H. F., *Ores and Industry in the Far East*, New York, Council on Foreign Relations, 1933.

Bain, H. F., *Pattern for Western Steel Production*, Information Circular No. 7315, U. S. Department of Interior, Bureau of Mines, 1945.

Bain, H. F., and Read, T. T., *Ores and Industries of South America*, New York, Council on Foreign Relations, and Harper, 1934.

Barloon, M., "Steel, the Great Retreat," *Harper's Magazine*, August, 1947.

"Basing Points in the Middle," *Fortune*, September, 1948.

Baum, A. W., "Utah's Big Baby," *Saturday Evening Post*, May 15, 1948.

Baykov, A., *The Location of Heavy Industry in the U.S.S.R.*, Institute of Statistics, Oxford, Bulletin No. 3, August 9, 1941.

Behre, C. H., Jr., "India's Mineral Wealth and Political Future," *Foreign Affairs*, October, 1943.

Bergson, A., Blackman, J. H., and Erlich, A., "Postwar Reconstruction and Development in the U.S.S.R.," *Annals of the American Academy of Political and Social Science*, May, 1949.

"Bethlehem Steel," *Fortune*, April, 1941.

Brassert, H. A., "Some Recent Developments in the Iron and Steel Industry of European Countries," *Blast Furnace and Steel Plant*, January, February, March, April, 1940.

Brassert, H. A., and Co., Inc., "A Blueprint for the Iron and Steel Industries," New York, 1948 (brochure).

"British Steel," *Fortune*, October, 1945.

Burn, D. L., *The Economic History of Steelmaking, 1867-1939*, Cambridge, Cambridge University Press, 1940.

Burns, A. R., *The Decline of Competition*, New York, McGraw-Hill, 1936.

Camp, J. M., and Francis, C. B., *Making, Shaping, and Treating of Steel*, Pittsburgh, Carnegie Steel Co., 4th ed., 1925.

Campbell, T. C., "U.S. Steel's Answer to the Iron Ore Shortage," *Iron Age*, March 2, 1950.

Carus, C. D., *Japan: Its Resources and Industries*, New York, Harper, 1944.

Clark, J. M., *The Economics of Overhead Costs*, Chicago, University of Chicago Press, 1923.

Clark, J. M., "Imperfect Competition Theory and the Basing-Point Problem," *American Economic Review*, June, 1943.

Clark, J. M., "Law and Economics of Basing-

Points," *American Economic Review*, March, 1949.

Cooke, M. L., "Some Observations on World Industrialization," *Mechanical Engineering*, May, 1946.

Cressey, G. B., *China's Geographic Foundations*, New York, McGraw-Hill, 1934.

Daugherty, C. M., de Chazeau, M. C., and Stratton, S. S., *The Economics of the Iron and Steel Industry*, New York, McGraw-Hill, 2 vols., 1937.

Davis, E. W., "Iron Ore Reserves of the Lake Superior District," *Mining and Metallurgy*, January, 1944.

Dennison, S. R., *The Location of Industry and the Depressed Areas*, Oxford, Oxford University Press, 1939.

Doble, M., *Soviet Economic Development Since 1917*, New York, International Publishers, 1948.

Edwards, C. D., "Basing Point Decisions and Business Practices," *American Economic Review*, December, 1948.

Ellsworth, P. T., *Chile: An Economy in Transition*, New York, Macmillan, 1945.

Feller, F. A., *The Masquerade of Monopoly*, New York, Harcourt, Brace, 1931.

Fisher, D., *Steel Making in America*, New York, U.S. Steel Corporation, 1949.

Givens, M., "Iron and Steel Industry," *Encyclopædia of the Social Sciences*, New York, Macmillan, 1932.

Greer, G., *The Ruhr and Lorraine Industrial Problem*, Washington, Brookings Institution, 1925.

Gubkin, I. M., *The Natural Wealth of the Soviet Union and Its Exploitation*, Moscow, Cooperative Publishing Society of Foreign Workers in the U.S.S.R., 1932.

Harris, C. D., "The Ruhr Coal Mining District," *Geographical Review*, April, 1940.

Harris, C. D. (ed.), *Economic Geography of the U.S.S.R.*, New York, Macmillan, Amer. ed., 1949.

Hasenack, W., *Wirtschaftsgefahren an der Ruhr durch Demontagen*, Köln, Westdeutscher Verlag, 1948.

Hatcher, H., *A Century of Iron and Men*, Indianapolis, Bobbs-Merrill, 1950.

Herman, L. M., "Soviet Iron and Steel Industry," U. S. Department of Commerce, Office of International Trade, *International Reference Service*, July, 1947.

Hexner, E., *The International Steel Cartel*, Chapel Hill, University of North Carolina Press, 1943.

Hoover, E. M., *The Location of Economic Activity*, New York, McGraw-Hill, 1948.

Hotchkiss, W. O., "Iron Ore Supply for the Future," *Economic Geology*, July, 1947.

"Inland Steel Co.," *Fortune*, October, 1938.

Institute of Scrap Iron and Steel, *Yearbook*, 1948.

"Iron Ore Dilemma: Foreign Ores or Mesabi," *Fortune*, December, 1945.

Isard, W., "Some Locational Factors in the Iron and Steel Industry Since the Early Nineteenth Century," *Journal of Political Economy*, June, 1948.

Isard, W., and Capron, W. M., "The Future Locational Pattern of Iron and Steel Production in the United States," *Journal of Political Economy*, April, 1949.

Julihn, C. E., and Moon, L. B., *Summary of Bureau of Mines Exploration Projects on Deposits of Raw Material Resources for Steel Production*, Report of Investigations 3801, Bureau of Mines, Washington, 1945.

King, C. D., "Seventy-five Years of Progress in Iron and Steel," in Parsons, A. B. (ed.), *Seventy-five Years of Progress in the Mineral Industry, 1871-1946*, New York, American Institute of Mining and Metallurgical Engineers, 1947.

Kostov, I., "The World's Manganese Ore," *Mining Magazine*, 1945.

Lie, K. C., and Wang, C. Y., *Tungsten*, New York, Reinhold, 1943.

Lloyd, W. A., "Iron Ore Research," *Iron Age*, January 6, 1949.

Löwegren, G., *Swedish Iron and Steel: A Historical Survey*, Stockholm, Svenska Handelsbanken, 1948.

Lynch, D., *The Concentration of Economic Power*, New York, Columbia University Press, 1946.

MacCallum, E. D., *The Iron and Steel Industry in the United States*, London, King, 1931.

McLaughlin, G. E., "Industrial Expansion and Location," *Annals of the American Academy of Political and Social Science*, November, 1945.

"Mexican Steel," *Fortune*, October, 1940.

Mikami, H. M., "World Iron Ore Map," *Economic Geology*, January, 1944, pp. 1-25.

Mitchell, K. L., *Japan's Industrial Strength*, New York, Knopf, 1942.

Moulton, H. G., and Junichi, Ko, *Japan: An Economic and Financial Appraisal*, Washington, Brookings Institution, 1931.

National Bureau of Economic Research, *Price Research in the Steel and Petroleum Industries*, New York, 1939.

National Resources Planning Board, *Industrial Location and National Resources*, Washington, 1943.

Old, B. S., Almeida, A. R., Hyde, R. W., and Pepper, E. L., "Economics of the Blast Furnace," *Iron Age*, September 18, 1947.

Orchard, J. E., *Japan's Economic Position*, New York, Whittlesey House, 1930.

"Ore, Ships, and Gentlemen," *Fortune*, June, 1940.

Otte, H. F., *The Expanding Mineral Economy of the Adirondacks,* State of New York, Executive Department, Division of Commerce, Albany, 1943.

Park, C. F., Jr., "What to Do About Our Iron Ore Reserves," *Mining and Metallurgy,* April, 1947.

Ramseyer, C. F., "The Manufacture of Sponge Iron," *Blast Furnace and Steel Plant,* May and June, 1943.

Ramseyer, C. F., "Sponge Iron—Its Possibilities and Limitations," *Iron and Steel Engineer,* July, 1944.

"Republic Steel Corporation," *Fortune,* September, 1933, and December, 1935.

"Russian Industry," *Fortune,* June, 1941.

Schumacher, H., "Location of Industry," *Encyclopædia of the Social Sciences,* New York, Macmillan, 1933, vol. 9.

Schumpeter, E. B. (ed.), *The Industrialization of Japan and Manchukuo, 1930-1940,* New York, Macmillan, 1940.

Scott, J., *Behind the Urals,* Boston, Houghton Mifflin, 1942.

"Scrap Iron and Steel," *Fortune,* May, 1937.

Smithies, A., "Aspects of the Basing Point System," *American Economic Review,* December, 1942.

"Steel and the West," *Fortune,* February, 1944.

Temporary National Economic Committee, *Hearings,* vols. 19-21, November 1939-June, 1940 (on the iron and steel industry).

Temporary National Economic Committee, *Price Discrimination on Steel,* Monograph 41, 1941.

Temporary National Economic Committee, *The Basing Point System,* Monograph 42, 1941.

Tennessee Coal, Iron and Railroad Co., *Steel Making at Birmingham,* 1940.

"The Earth Movers III," *Fortune,* October, 1943 (Fontana Steel Works).

"The Great Labrador Venture," *Fortune,* December, 1948.

"The House of Tata," *Fortune,* January, 1944.

"The New Canada," *Fortune,* July, 1943 (Steep Rock).

"The Ruhr," *Fortune,* December, 1946.

United Nations, Department of Economic Affairs, *European Steel Trends in the Setting of the World Market,* Geneva, 1949.

U. S. Department of Interior, Bureau of Mines, *Foreign Minerals Quarterly.*

U. S. Department of State, *Report of the Joint Brazil-United States Technical Commission,* Rio de Janeiro, February 7, 1949.

U. S. Department of State, Division of Geography and Cartography, *Mineral Industry of Australia,* 1945 (unclassified, 1947).

U. S. House of Representatives, 80th Congress, *Manganese,* Hearings Before Subcommittee on Mines and Mining, February 12-27, 1948.

U. S. Senate Document No. 80, 79th Congress, 1st session, Board of Investigation and Research (Transportation Act, 1940), *The Economics of Iron and Steel Transportation,* 1945.

U. S. Steel Corporation, *TNEC Papers,* especially Ynteman, T., *A Statistical Analysis of the Demand for Steel, 1919-1938,* New York, 1939.

U. S. Tariff Commission, *Iron and Steel,* Report No. 128, second series, 1938.

U. S. Tariff Commission, *Latin America as a Source of Strategic and Other Essential Materials,* Report No. 144, second series, 1941.

U. S. Tariff Commission, *Iron and Steel,* War Changes in Industry Series, Report No. 15, 1946.

Von Eckardt, Hans, *Russland,* Leipzig, Bibliographisches Institut Ag., 1930.

Weber, A., *Reine Theorie des Standortes,* Tübingen, 1909.

White, C. M., "Iron Ore and the Steel Industry," in Parsons, A. B. (ed.), *Seventy-five Years of Progress in the Mineral Industry, 1871-1946,* New York, American Institute of Mining and Metallurgical Engineers, 1947.

Wright, C. W., *The Iron and Steel Industries of Europe,* U. S. Department of Interior, Bureau of Mines, Economic Paper No. 19, 1939.

Wright, C. W., "Germany's Drive for Mineral Self-Sufficiency," *Mining and Metallurgy,* May, 1939.

Wythe, G., *Industry in Latin America,* New York, Columbia University Press, 1945.

Wythe, G., Wright, R. A., and Midkiff, H. M., *Brazil: An Expanding Economy,* New York, Twentieth Century Fund, 1949.

UNIT 4. OTHER METALS AND METAL INDUSTRIES

Chapter 43

COPPER AND THE COPPER INDUSTRY

Because of their striking appearance, it is likely that gold and silver impressed themselves upon man earlier than did copper; nevertheless, copper is one of the oldest metals known to man. It is also one of the most useful, for it can be hardened easily by hammering, and it retains a sharp edge. It alloys readily with other metals, especially tin, to form bronze, and with zinc, to form brass. Like the precious metals, gold in particular, it is easily worked. It does not rust; in fact, it is known as "the everlasting metal." Thus, copper was used for thousands of years to make tools, utensils, and weapons; only gradually did it yield part of this field to other metals, particularly iron.

But these older uses of copper did not take advantage of one of its properties that is of the utmost importance today, its ability to conduct electricity. Today the major uses of this metal are tied up, directly or indirectly, with electricity. Although copper pots and pans yielded to aluminum kitchen utensils and steel replaced bronze and brass in the making of guns, in the electrical field copper is still indispensable. Only silver has greater electrical conductivity than copper, but its price makes this use of the metal uneconomical.

In 1880, about the time the electrical industry came into existence, the world output of copper was less than 200,000 short tons. In 1943, at the peak of the war effort, production passed 3 million tons, a fifteenfold increase. Of the metals, copper today ranks second only to iron in quantity produced. However, many times more iron and steel are produced than of all the other metals put together. In 1940, the world production of steel amounted to 155.5 million net tons, as against less than 2.5 million for copper; the corresponding figures for the United States that year were 67.0 million net tons of steel, as against 0.9 million of copper.

In terms of value the gap is not as wide as it is in terms of quantity, for copper sells for a multiple of the price of iron and steel. In mid-1950 electrolytic copper was selling at Connecticut valley points for 22.5 cents a pound, as compared with 3.837 cents for a pound of "finished steel composite."[1]

---

[1] *Business Week,* July 1, 1950, p. 13.

This comparison of steel and copper prices brings out a significant difference between steel and copper. As we saw in the discussion of iron and steel, there are hundreds and thousands of

COPPER ORES

Types of Ore

Copper occurs in the native state and also is found in a variety of ores. The names and formulas of some copper ore minerals are as follows:

Cuprite	Cu_2O
Malachite	$CuCO_3 \cdot Cu(OH)_2$
Chalcocite	Cu_2S
Covellite	CuS
Brochantite	$CuSO_4 \cdot 3 Cu(OH)_2$
Chalcopyrite	$CuFeS_2$
Bornite	$CuFeS_4$

Three main classes of copper ores may be distinguished: (1) ores containing pure or native copper, (2) ores containing copper oxides, and (3) ores containing copper sulfides. The first category yields pure copper without requiring either chemical manipulation such as leaching or heat treatment such as smelting. In the United States the ores containing pure copper, the so-called Lake ores, were found in the upper Michigan peninsula and were the first to be exploited on a large scale. They dominated this country's production from 1845 until about 1885. From then until about 1910, oxidized ores, generally mined in vein deposits, provided the bulk of the copper; since 1910 sulfides occurring as vast "porphyries"[2] have been the main source of the metal.

Generally speaking, copper oxide ores are of high grades, as that term is used in the copper industry, as to both copper and other metal values; but, as a rule, the deposits are rather small. Exceptions are the huge deposits at Chuquicamata and those in the Upper Katanga region of the Belgian Congo. Frequently oxide ores are underlain with sulfide ores.[3]

The Porphyries and the Shift to Mass Mining. Typical sulfide ores are low grade, averaging around 1 percent copper or even less. The largest bodies of the sulfide ores are the so-called porphyries, in which minute particles of copper are disseminated in vast masses of earth or rock. It was not until about 1910 that these ores came to the fore. The shift was accompanied by a change from shaft to open-pit mining in which power shovels and modern earth-moving and -handling machines were used. Another significant change also occurred, the shift from selective to nonselective and, later, to mass mining. When high-grade ores are worked, it is very important to avoid contaminating the ore mineral with gangue; hence the individual miner must exercise keen judgment and great care. This selective mining was the method generally used throughout the ages. As methods of exploration grew more scientific and efficient, it became possible, on the basis of drilling records and geological studies, to block out bodies of ore which the miner was to take out. Although this is sometimes referred to as nonselective mining, actually, of course, there is selection. Responsibility for selection has shifted from the individual

---

steels; the goal is a multiplicity of types, a diversity adapted to an endless variety of needs and uses. Electrical conductivity, on the other hand, calls for copper as pure as human ingenuity can make it, because even a trace of impurity impairs the metal's ability to conduct electricity. The price of steel therefore constitutes an average of the price of different iron alloys, whereas the price of copper measures the value of as homogeneous a commodity as is known to trade. The bulk of the iron enters industry in the form of steel, but only a minor portion of the copper is converted into alloys such as brass and bronze. Copper alloys are probably more comparable to alloy steels than to common steels, which are also alloys.

[2] The dictionary defines porphyry as (a) originally a rock consisting of feldspar crystals embedded in a compact dark-red or purple groundmass; (b) now, commonly, any igneous rock of similar (porphyritic) texture, regardless of its mineral composition; sometimes, loosely, any of the various igneous rocks without this texture, especially when occurring in connection with ores. According to Parsons: "The essential characteristics of the de-

posits that are universally, if not quite precisely, designated as porphyry coppers are: their huge size, particularly with respect to horizontal dimensions; the relative uniformity with which the copper minerals are disseminated throughout the mass; and the low average per-ton copper content of the exploitable ore." A. B. Parsons, *The Porphyry Coppers*, American Institute of Mining and Metallurgical Engineers, New York, 1933, p. 26.

For a complete list of copper ore minerals, see A. M. Bateman, *Economic Mineral Deposits*, John Wiley & Sons, Inc., New York, 2nd ed., 1950, p. 483.

[3] In 1948 it was reported that the Chile Copper Company, exploiting the Chuquicamata deposits, was preparing to open up huge sulfide deposits underlying the oxide ores. The recovery of copper from sulfide ores requires smelting.

miner to the engineers, geologists, etc., super-
vising the operations.

The discovery of the vast bodies of porphyry
in which minute particles of copper are diffused led to an entirely new method of mining.
Up to that time, ore constituted a small portion of the mineralized area in which mining
operations were carried on. Now an entire
mountain may be declared ore, perhaps after
the barren overburden is stripped off. The
whole mountain—tens of millions of tons—is
shoveled up and put through the mill. It is
the enormous scale and high efficiency of
operation which makes low-grade ores pay.

Mass mining of copper ores began in the
boundary district of British Columbia, when
American engineers exploited copper ore containing only 1.35 percent copper with no regard to selection other than endeavoring to
stay within the margins of mineralization.[4]
Mass mining was introduced in the United
States by Jocklin, at Bingham, Utah. When he
first started, many experts were scornful and
predicted his early doom. Instead, his operations netted fantastic profits.[5] By about 1940,
300 million tons of ore containing 4.5 billion
pounds of copper had been mined. At 10 cents
a pound this amounts to $450 million.

Special Copper Ores. In a class by themselves are the ores in which copper is a valuable
by-product rather than the main product. The
best example of these ores are the nickel-
copper ores of Sudbury, Ontario, Canada, the
center of world nickel production. Along with
other metals, especially platinum, these ores
contain typically 1.5 pounds of copper for every
pound of nickel. But since nickel generally sells
for two or three times as high a price as copper,
the nickel market determines the output of
nickel-copper ores and copper is a by-product.[6]

Copper ores differ widely in the extent to
which metals other than copper contribute
to the profitableness of operation. The copper
ores now worked in the Cerro de Pasco mines
in Peru also yield lead, silver, gold, and bismuth. At the Flin Flon mines of the Hudson
Bay Mining and Smelting Company in Manitoba, Canada, zinc, silver, and gold are the main
by-products.[7] In the Rio Tinto mines in Spain
the sulfur content of the copper ore is so high
that sulfur constitute the main by-product. At
present the bulk of the world copper output,
probably two-thirds, is derived from large low-
grade ore bodies that have only minor by-
product values.

A distinction is made between leaching and
smelting ores. Leaching ores contain impurities
which can be removed most economically by
leaching, i.e., by chemical action, especially of
acids. Smelting ores are treated by fire or heat
methods. Chuquicamata until recently had no
smelter but prepared the ores for the refinery
by treatment with sulfuric acid and subsequent
leaching. Leaching is used also at Rio Tinto in
Spain, and at certain copper mines in Utah,
Arizona, and other places.

Reserves

As has already been made clear (see pp. 441
ff.), the analysis of reserves is a highly precarious undertaking, and figures given for a
particular date only apply to that date. Thus,
in the reserve figures in Table 43.1 a price of
less than 15 cents a pound is assumed. But the
price hit a high of 23.5 cents a pound early
in 1949. If, in this interval, costs did not rise
pari passu with the market price—and it is
unlikely that they did—it is safe to assume that
a current survey of reserves would show larger
totals than those listed in the table.

Not only must known reserves be marked up
as price-cost ratios improve, but depletion as
well as new discoveries must be taken into account. Two important discoveries have recently
been made. One is at San Manuel, about 45
miles north of Tucson, Arizona, where the
Magma Copper Company is developing about
half a billion tons of 0.8 percent copper ore.[8]

---

[4] See C. E. Julihn, in F. G. Tryon and E. C.
Eckel (eds.), *Mineral Economics*, McGraw-Hill
Book Company, Inc., New York, 1932, chap. 6.
This chapter is an excellent analysis of metallurgi-
cal technology as applied to copper.

[5] Mass mining demands mass concentration. This
became possible when the flotation process was
introduced. See p. 700.

[6] For this reason the owners of the nickel mines
did not join the international copper cartels, al-

though they favored their main objective, copper
price stabilization at a higher level.

[7] See "Hudson Bay Mining and Smelting Company," *Fortune*, June, 1938.

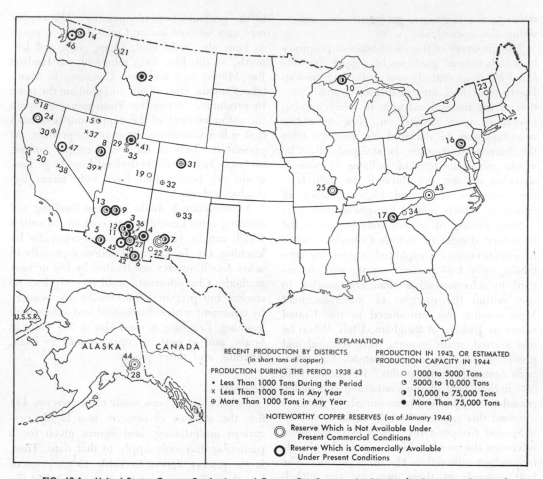

FIG. 43.1. United States Copper Production and Copper Ore Reserves by Districts (in short tons of copper). Production in 1943, or estimated production capacity in 1944. (U. S. Department of the Interior, Geological Survey and Bureau of Mines, *Mineral Position of the United States*, 1947, opposite p. 240.)

More than 75,000 tons: (1) Bingham, Utah, (2) Butte, Montana, (3) Globe-Miami, Arizona, (4) Morenci, Arizona. 10,000 to 75,000 tons: (5) Ajo, Arizona, (6) Bisbee, Arizona, (7) Central, New Mexico, (8) Ely, Nevada, (9) Jerome, Arizona, (10) Lake Superior, Michigan, (11) Ray, Arizona, (12) Superior, Arizona.

5,000 to 10,000 tons: (13) Eureka (Bagdad), Arizona, (14) Chelan, Washington, (15) Cope, Nevada, (16) Cornwall, Pennsylvania, (17) Ducktown, Tennessee, (18) Siskiyou County, California. 1,000 to 5000 tons: (19) La Sal (Big Indian), Utah, (20) Calaveras County, California, (21) Coeur d'Alene, Idaho, (22) Lordsburg, New Mexico, (23) Orange County, Vermont, (24) Shasta County, California, (25) southeastern Missouri, (26) Tyrone, New Mexico. Production from other districts during the period 1938-1943: More than 1000 tons in any year: (27) Bunker Hill, Arizona, (28) Copper River, Alaska, (29) Ophir, Utah, (30) Plumas County, California, (31) Red Cliff, Colorado, (32) San Juan Mountains, Colorado, (33) San Pedro, New Mexico, (34) Swain County, North Carolina, (35) Tintic, Utah. Less than 1000 tons in any year: (36) Banner, Arizona, (37) Battle Mountain, Nevada, (38) Bishop Creek, California, (39) Jack Rabbit, Nevada, (40) Old Hat, Arizona, (41) Park City, Utah, (42) Patagonia, Arizona. Less than 1000 tons during the period: (43) Gossan Lead, Virginia, (44) Orange Hill, Alaska, (45) Silver Bell, Arizona, (46) Snohomish County, Washington, (47) Yerington, Nevada.

The second is known as The Greater Butte Project; according to engineers of the Anaconda Copper Mining Company, it will make available about 130 million tons of low-grade ore of 1.37 percent copper down to a level of 3500 feet, with more below that level. "Recovery of the ores known to be available above 3500 feet will take at least 35 years. After that the same method can be applied to deeper levels in this area or to the many other sections in the Butte district whose low grade ore reserves have not yet been fully investigated."[9]

TABLE 43.1.　Summary of World Copper Reserves[10]

Country	Metal Content (1000 short tons)	Percent of World Total
United States	29,220	26.4
Canada (including Newfoundland)	7,734	7.0
Mexico	600	0.5
Total, North America	37,559	33.9
Bolivia	40	0.04
Chile	25,900	23.38
Peru	2,526	2.28
Total, South America	28,466	25.70
Africa	28,648	25.9
Asia	1,880	1.7
U.S.S.R.	9,000	8.1
Australia	419	0.4
Europe	4,860	4.3
World total	110,800	100.0

According to a compilation made from published estimates by the Federal Trade Commission, the metal content of the world copper reserves on January 1, 1945, amounted to 110.8 million short tons. This was distributed as shown in Table 43.1. The amount of ore in which these reserves are contained is not known. If a world average content of 1.5 percent copper is arbitrarily assumed, the ore pile would weigh 7386.7 million tons. At the rate of 3 million tons

[8] Ira B. Joralemon, "Geology and the New Mines," *Mining and Metallurgy*, April, 1948.
[9] Joseph Kinsey Howard, "What Happened in Butte," *Harper's Magazine*, August, 1948, p. 93. It should not be assumed that all the ore made available in this expansion program necessarily constitutes additions to previous reserve listings.
[10] Federal Trade Commission, *Report on the Copper Industry*, Washington, 1947, p. 34.

of copper a year, it would take less than thirty-seven years to consume this amount. The annual average output of ore would run to about 200 million tons, which would look highly respectable in relation to the annual output of iron ore. But the dynamics of reserves make such calculations highly speculative at best and misleading at worst.

Fig. 43.1 shows the most important copper properties in the United States.

Control of Ore Reserves. One of the peculiarities of the copper situation is the extent to which a few corporations, representing even fewer nations, have gained ownership and control over the world's copper reserves. This is explained partly by the geographical distribution of copper deposits, partly by historical developments. If central Europe had large copper reserves, Germany might be an important factor. As it is, the bulk of the reserves are found in the western hemisphere and in Africa, which means that the great sea powers are the logical nations to control both their own and foreign deposits. Only Britain and the United States possessed sufficient sea power to assure access to South American and African deposits in wartime. Most of the African deposits are located in British possessions, and this tends to favor British capital investments (see p. 696). Table 43.2 shows the ownership of almost 83 percent of the world's known copper reserves.

COPPER PROBLEMS
Vanishing Reserves

The steel problem, if there is one, is primarily one of providing adequate producing capacity to meet at reasonable prices the peak needs of an industrial society in peace and war. There is no fear that we shall run out of iron in the predictable future. It is premium iron ore that is getting scarce, not iron ore as such.

In the case of copper the situation is far graver, for the world ran out of premium copper ore a long time ago. By and large, the new phase of copper history, the electrical phase, was made possible only by the perfection of old processes and the discovery and development of new ones which so far have provided adequate supplies of copper. The modest needs of the pre-electrical age could be met by the relatively simple processing of the rich copper ores then being exploited.[11]

In other words, the threat to iron and steel is higher cost, but the threat to copper is absolute exhaustion. The fabulous progress made in the use of inanimate energy is encouraging modern man to aspire to lofty goals

TABLE 43.2. Ownership of World Copper Reserves[12]

Ownership by Nationality	Metal Content (1000 short tons)	Percent of World Total
By United States owners in:		
United States	29,220	26.37
Mexico	300	0.27
Bolivia	18	0.01
Peru	2,000	1.81
Chile	23,630	21.33
Total United States	55,168	49.79
By British owners in:		
Canada[a]	7,739	6.98
Australia	419	0.38
Africa[a]	21,182	19.12
Total British	29,340	26.48
Total United States and British	84,508	76.27
By Belgian owners in Africa[b]	7,400	6.68
	91,908	82.95

[a] United States nationals own a large share.
[b] British nationals own a large share.

of full employment and global industrialization. With the further liberation from power limitations implied in the use of nuclear energy, his hopes for a better world through industrialization are rising high. Will these hopes be dashed by the early exhaustion of indispensable earth materials such as copper?

[11] According to Robert Hunt (British Mining and Metalliferous Ores, London, 1844, pp. 891-892), English copper ores of the late eighteenth century contained as much as 13 percent copper. By 1800 this had dropped to about 9 percent and to 8 percent forty years later. This source is quoted by C. E. Julihn, op. cit.

[12] Federal Trade Commission, op. cit., p. 37. Ownership today is typically lodged in corporations whose stock is held by individuals. Some stockholders may reside outside the country in which the corporation is domiciled. The table shows corporate rather than individual ownership, except as noted.

No definitive answer can be given to such a question. But relevant facts can be cited which may help in making a reasonable appraisal of the situation. In the first place, some encouragement may be found in the fact that the copper reserves in the earth constitute a pyramid, the tip of which represents native copper, i.e., pure copper found in the earth's crust. Each widening layer below contains progressively poorer copper deposits. Roughly speaking, the amount of these poorer grades of copper ore exceeds the amount of the better grades by so wide a margin that the copper content of the poorer grades exceeds that of the richer grades. The low-grade ores processed today may yield as much new copper in a single year as the high-grade ores of earlier times yielded in decades and even centuries.

Advancing technology has pushed world copper production upward, from 200,000 short tons in 1880 to over 3 million during the peak of World War II. The question today is: How long can this technological miracle continue? How near the bottom of the barrel are we?

This question breaks down into several others. For example, it took a series of revolutionary technological improvements and innovations to make possible the downward revision of the required copper content of copper ore from 13 percent in the eighteenth century to 0.7 percent in 1948. Will another series of such advances push the limit of profitable copper ore down to 0.3 or 0.1 or even 0.07 percent? Much will depend on what effect the use of nuclear energy has on mining and metallurgy. That such developments will be greatly affected by price movements—in particular, the copper price in relation to the price of other metals as well as the general price level—goes without saying. Moreover, the possibility of important new discoveries of copper ore should not be entirely ruled out.

In the second place, copper has unusually high lasting qualities. Moreover, only little of the metal goes into dissipative products such as copper sulfate. Most of it, perhaps 85 to 90 percent, goes into durable producers' and consumers' goods such as electrical equipment, automobiles, etc. As a result of its durability, copper can be reused more freely and more often than most metals. Secondary supplies, or copper scrap, constitute a vital source of supply.

Few problems in statistics are more controversial than those arising from the attempt to present a true picture of secondary copper supplies. Methods of presentation vary widely and statistics must be used with great caution. The Federal Trade Commission has this to say:

In terms of total copper added to supply in the United States, including freshly mined American copper, imports and old scrap, the last named source has come to represent increasing proportions of the total. At intervals of approximately 5 years from 1910 to 1944, scrap copper has represented the following percentages of the total:

Year	Reclaimed in Percent of Total	Year	Reclaimed in Percent of Total
1910	8.4	1930	23.6
1915	12.4	1935	36.2
1920	16.6	1939	21.5
1925	20.0	1944	20.4

According to the British Nonferrous Metals Federation, about one-third of Great Britain's copper supply early in 1936 was reclaimed copper. It seems possible that as the machinery and equipment in which greatly increased quantities of copper have been embodied in past years are finally junked and their copper content reclaimed, old scrap may come to represent around one-third of the copper consumed in the United States as well as in other countries.[13]

The importance of secondary copper in the United States becomes even clearer when it is related to consumption rather than to total supply. This is shown in Table 43.3.

The future recovery rate for secondary copper is of course unknown; but it will depend partly on the rate of obsolescence, which itself is hardly predictable, and partly on the technology of copper recovery, which is highly dynamic, but mainly on the price situation. This is the powerful factor which will largely govern the situation. It seems safe to predict that to an increasing extent the copper mines of the future will be found above ground in the form of worn-out and obsolete copper objects.

In the third place, as in the case of steel, the usefulness of copper can be stretched. A

[13] Federal Trade Commission, *op. cit.*, pp. 6-7.

pound of copper can be made to do double duty or even better as the result of the new and more efficient copper alloys now available. Beryllium in particular is proving highly effective as an alloy element with copper. As we approach the point of absolute exhaustion of the metal, surprising economies in its use will be made, and substitutes will be discovered and used more generally.

TABLE 43.3. Total Copper Consumption and Secondary Copper Production, 1919-1937

Year	Copper Consumed[a] (short tons)	Secondary Copper Produced[b] (short tons)	Secondary Copper Production as Percent of Total Consumption
1919	621,375	152,600	24.6
1920	684,035	168,960	24.7
1921	459,865	131,990	28.7
1922	539,113	202,800	37.6
1923	737,700	270,900	36.7
1924	765,950	266,200	34.8
1925	836,000	291,010	34.8
1926	909,900	337,300	37.1
1927	862,450	339,400	39.4
1928	990,700	365,500	38.9
1929	1,159,800	404,350	34.9
1930	956,150	342,200	35.8
1931	650,000	261,300	40.2
1932	368,000	180,980	49.2
1933	415,000	260,300	62.7
1934	463,000	310,900	67.1
1935	574,000	361,700	63.0
1936	749,000	382,700	51.1
1937	860,000	408,900	47.5

[a] From issues of *Year Book of the American Bureau of Metal Statistics*.
[b] From issues of *Mineral Resources of the United States* (U.S. Dept. Int., Geol. Survey and U.S. Dept. Com., Bur. Mines) and *Minerals Yearbook* (U.S. Depts. Com. and Int., Bur. Mines). These figures represent the copper recovered from old scrap, including the copper content of old brass scrap.

In summary, it is safe to say that continuance of anything like the recent peak output of primary copper will prove difficult, and maintenance of the rate of increase of the past half century or so will hardly be possible. Adjustments to a sharply reduced global reserve of copper ores are definitely called for.

Maldistribution of Copper Reserves

In the past, the major industrial clusters on the earth developed in the neighborhood of coal and iron. Since there is no reason to assume that the geographical occurrence of copper neatly coincides with the geographical distribution of coal and iron, it follows that industrial development does not depend on

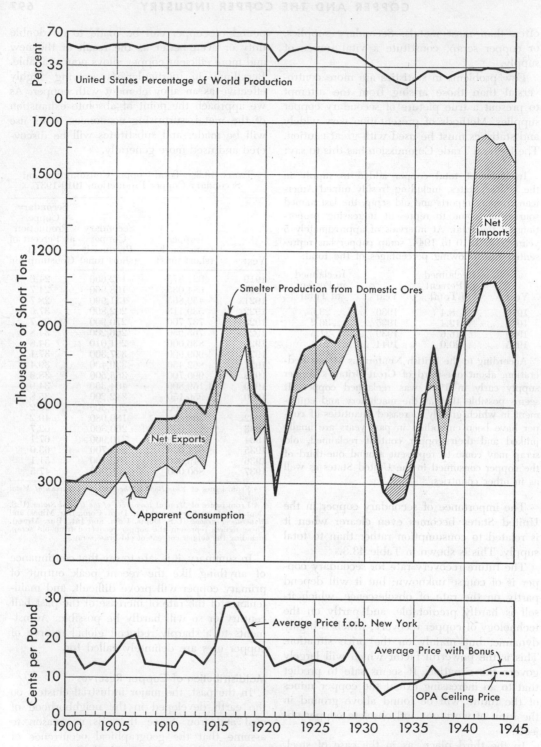

FIG. 43.2. Trends of Production, Consumption, and Price of Copper in the United States, 1900-1945. (U. S. Department of the Interior, Geological Survey and Bureau of Mines, *Mineral Position of the United States,* 1947, p. 238.)

proximity of copper reserves. Great Britain continues to be a leading industrial nation even though the copper ores in Cornwall have long since been used up. Europe normally is a beehive of industry but is virtually without copper ores. Almost the only important copper ores left there are in Spain, especially the Rio Tinto deposits, long controlled by British capital, and in Yugoslavia, the Bor mines, until recently controlled by French capital but now nationalized. The copper mines of Sweden and Germany, long famous in history, have more or less played out.

In fact, the only industrial nation which has a copper industry more or less commensurate with its industrial position is the United States. This country is a continental economy which combines within its borders a large share of all branches of production—agricultural, mineral, and industrial. Until 1920 the United States was the leading producer of copper in the world and until World War II she exported the metal. But as her industrial economy expanded and her copper reserves shrank, she inevitably had to shift from an export to an import basis. (See Fig. 43.2.)

Not enough is known about the copper reserves of Soviet Russia to permit any definitive statement. Moreover, the question of degree of industrialization enters. The Soviet Union may have enough copper to maintain for some time her current level of general industrialization, but will she have enough to support a level comparable to that of the United States? Canada is another industrial nation which produces considerable amounts of copper, but her industrial economy is not as highly developed as our own and does not support a superstructure of copper-using industries comparable to ours.

As has been shown, the bulk of the copper reserves lie in nonindustrialized countries. The known reserves are divided roughly as follows: one-third in North America, one-fourth each in South America and Africa, and the remaining 16 or 17 percent scattered over the remaining parts of the earth including all of Eurasia and Australia.

But in a world of colonies and economic exclaves mere geographical distribution does not give a clear picture of the situation. As we have seen, virtually all the copper reserves of the entire western hemisphere are owned by corporations in whose ownership and management United States capitalists are dominant. Moreover, American capital participates with British capital in controlling the African reserves that lie in British territories. The reserves in the southern part of the Congo, the Upper Katanga, are controlled by the Belgian government. Thus, almost 83 percent of all the known reserves are controlled by nationals of three countries—the United States, Great Britain, and Belgium.

This situation is not much different from the situation with regard to petroleum; substitute France and the Netherlands for Belgium, and the situation is very similar. In fact, *mutatis mutandis*, the same situation holds true in the case of many minerals. This condition reflects the overwhelming effect of naval supremacy. Only countries whose navies control the sea lanes of the world can consider their overseas investments secure and accessible through peace and war. The Anglo-American naval bloc has long ruled the sea, and this explains the investments made by nations politically allied to or affiliated with that bloc. The concept of "have" and "have-not" powers has real meaning only against the background of naval supremacy and global alliances.[14]

This tremendous economic and/or political control exercised by a few nations over the mineral sinews of industrial strength is one of the great challenges of our age which the Atlantic Charter recognized in lofty phrases but which the political developments of recent times have aggravated but not met. To point out that in peacetime private owners of copper reserves are anxious to sell to all who wish to buy and can afford to pay, does not meet the issue. Fair-weather free trade leaves unsolved a tremendous number of problems regarding equal opportunity for all. Real equality of opportunity cannot exist in a world

---

[14] The author is, of course, fully aware of the fact that sea power is not constant and that alliances are not permanent. What is said here applies to the global situation as it evolved over the past century or so; which coincides with the period during which modern industry matured and most overseas investments in minerals were made.

in which the basic problem of peaceful and equitable collaboration of all nations is still not solved.

Concentrated Control

Not only are the copper reserves, like other mineral reserves, held by corporations dominated by a few nations, but the control is concentrated in remarkably few hands. This, too, constitutes part of the copper problem. It involves the question of equitable price and of safeguards against abuse, if not extortion. As the record will show, the temptation implicit in this tremendous power over one of the basic raw materials has at times proved too great for mere man.[15]

COPPER TECHNOLOGY

Copper technology differs from iron and steel technology in at least two significant respects. The first stems from the typically low content of 0.5 to 6.0 percent copper in copper ores as against 25 to 60 percent iron in iron ores. This necessitates vast preliminary steps designed to bring copper ores up to a level of concentration comparable to that of iron ores. While it is true that, because of the gradual exhaustion of the best iron ore bodies, beneficiation is coming into wider use, most iron ores can still be fed directly into the blast furnace. The situation in copper is wholly different. Some copper ores are prepared for refining by leaching. Most copper ores must first be converted into "concentrates" by means of mechanical processes or by flotation, or both, and then smelted. Since most concentrates are finely ground, the blast furnace is being progressively replaced by a reverberatory furnace[16] in copper smelting. Copper at this stage is known as matte. It is then "bessemerized"

just as iron is in the steel industry. However, the Bessemer converters used in the copper industry are constructed somewhat differently from those used in the steel industry. The product of the Bessemer converter is known as "blister copper." It goes to the refinery.

The second major difference between iron and steel technology and copper technology is that the chief aim of the latter is to produce pure metal, whereas the steel industry produces many different steels and pure iron is a laboratory curiosity. Consequently, the final stage of copper processing is refining, generally electrolytic. Refining is carried on for two reasons. In the first place, if the copper is to be used in the electrical industry it must be as pure as possible. In the second place, the "impurities" removed may be valuable, such as other metals whose value exceeds the cost of extracting them.

Two major methods of ore concentration must be distinguished—the physical method, employing mainly gravity and water, and the flotation method.

The process of separating the valuable mineral from waste material by gravity concentration is based upon the principle that when two particles of different specific gravity are allowed to fall through a resisting fluid the metallic particles, having a higher specific gravity, develop a faster falling rate than those containing primarily waste material, of relatively low specific gravity. Numerous devices are employed in gravity concentration. With water as a resistive medium the machines employed most commonly are mechanical and hydraulic classifiers, jigs, shaking tables, vanners, and slime tables. The last two, however, are used much less since the development of the flotation process.[17]

Physical methods were highly perfected during the nineteenth century. In particular there was developed a very efficient ore classifier which went far in making useful highly complex deposits that formerly defied the efforts of the metallurgist. But the most revolutionary improvement in ore concentration was the invention of the flotation process early in the twentieth century.[18]

---

[15] This ties up with a basic problem not confined to copper, the concentration of economic power. No one can be certain that a different system would have worked better. No one can know whether the progress in technology would have been as rapid had keener competition among producers held copper prices at lower levels, which in turn would have meant smaller surpluses to the producers.

[16] In the reverberatory furnace the flames strike from above; no powerful blast is forced through the charge.

[17] Works Projects Administration, *Copper Mining*, National Research Project, Philadelphia, 1940, p. 170.

TABLE 43.4. World Total Primary Copper Production and Percentage of Total by Continents, 1801-1939[19]

Period	Total World Production (short tons)	Percentage of Total				
		North America	South America	Europe	Asia	Africa
1801-1850	1,502,256	5.16	17.34	63.21	13.12	. . . . .
1851-1900	9,970,111	37.29	21.04	29.70	4.89	2.01
1901-1925	25,726,406	65.77	11.07	10.33	5.78	3.03
1926-1939	12,276,040	49.49	19.15	11.26	5.78	13.46

As was explained before, in this process, which has revolutionized virtually all nonferrous metal industries, finely crushed ore is mixed with water to form a slime. To this slime are added air and chemicals, mainly oils. Fine particles of metal attach themselves to a particle of oil and to a bubble of air and are thus carried to the surface, forming a froth out of which the metal is separated. By changing the chemical, different metals can be removed successively. This process made possible far higher rates of recovery than were obtainable with earlier methods and thus permitted the exploitation of leaner ores and even tailings, i.e., waste heaps left from earlier operations. It also rendered profitable the working of complex ores.

WORLD COPPER PRODUCTION

Some of the implications of these technological developments are obvious, others not so obvious. Among the obvious implications is the increased production of copper as it became feasible to turn from rare high-grade to abundant low-grade ores. The rate at which the world output of copper has risen is astounding. According to calculations made by the United States Bureau of Mines, world production amounted to 1.5 million short tons during

the first half of the nineteenth century and to 10 million during the second.[20] During the first quarter of the twentieth century, it rose to 25.7 million tons and output during the second quarter promises to reach about 42 million, a total of 67.7 million tons for the first half of the present century. From 1.5 to 67.7—an amazing record. Reducing these totals to average annual output gives the following figures: 1800-1850, 30,000 tons; 1851-1900, 200,000 tons; 1901-1950, 1,400,000 tons. The figures for the first and second quarters of the present century are 1 and 1.7 million tons respectively, a sevenfold increase in the output from 1800-1850 to 1851-1900, and about the same from 1851-1900 to 1901-1950 annual average.

Geography of Production

An obvious implication of this tremendous increase in production is the accelerated exhaustion of copper deposits throughout the world, more rapid in the older copper-producing areas than in the newer. This differential rate of exhaustion, together with the differential "marking up" of reserves and the discovery of new ores, leads to the geographical shifts of production shown in Table 43.4. The rise of the United States to her position as premier copper producer (she took the lead in 1883) is indicated by the rapid increase in the percentages for North America in the first three periods. During the last period the shift toward South America and Africa is noticeable.

It is not possible at the present time to bring this table down to date. In particular, figures for the Soviet Union and Yugoslavia are not available. Furthermore, the events of

---

[18] A mining engineer observed that soapsuds running into a creek carrying waste water from a nearby copper works turned red, suggesting the presence of copper particles in the creek and the capacity of soapsuds to absorb them. That observation is said to have led to one of the most important innovations in mineral exploitation.

A good description of the flotation process is contained in Works Progress Administration, *op. cit.*, pp. 171-178.

[19] U.S. Department of Commerce, Bureau of Mines, *op. cit.; Year Books of the American Bureau of Metal Statistics*, 1934, 1940.

---

[20] U.S. Department of Commerce, Bureau of Mines, *Summarized Data of Copper Production*, Economic Paper No. 1, 1928.

TABLE 43.5.   World Copper Production, According to Origin of Ore[21]
(thousand short tons)

Country	1917	1921	1929	1932	1937	1939	1940	1943	1944	1945	1946	1947
United States	961	238	1026	256	835	735	892	1114	1007	805	604	874
Canada[a]	56	23	121	125	262	320	337	294	280	242	191	231
Mexico	52	14	87	38	52	54	45	51	48	68	65	73
Cuba	11	9	16	6	14	11	11	8	6	9	12	15
Peru	50	37	60	24	39	39	48	39	36	35	26	28
Chile	113	143	349	114	456	376	400	548	550	518	399	470
Bolivia	7	11	8	3	4	4	7	7	7	7	7	8
Ecuador	...	...	...	...	...	...	2	3	4	4	3	...
Belgian Congo	...	...	...	59	166	135	164	173	182	177	158	166
Rhodesia	47	43	173	80	234	238	293	277	246	216	205	218
Other Africa	...	...	...	15	16	20	21	29	26	27	30	37
Finland	...	...	...	7	14	15	20	17	17	17	19	19
Germany[b]	32	21	32	34	32	33	40	26	23	...	17	10
Italy	...	...	...	...	...	4	5	2	...	...	...	...
Norway	2	6	16	17	22	21	17	18	16	6	14	15
Spain	45	37	54	33	35	28	15	12	12	9	10	13
Sweden	5	1	4	4	8	11	10	20	18	16		17
Yugoslavia	12	4	23	33	43	46	47	c	c	c	c	c
India (incl. Burma)	...	...	7	10	11	11	12	7	6	7	7	7
Japan	119	61	83	79	84	c	c	c	...	...	...	c
Philippine Islands	...	...	...	...	...	4	10	...	...	...	...	...
Turkey	...	...	...	...	7	3	10	11	12	11	11	11
Cypress	...	...	...	...	...	30	11	...	...	...	3	17

a Including Newfoundland.
b Figures conjectural.
c Not available.

World War II do not throw much light on secular trends, for wartime is a period of emergencies, and copper statistics must be treated with perhaps even more caution than most statistics.

There are two sources of difficulty in dealing with copper production statistics. The first involves the basis used for the figures, whether mine, smelter, or refinery; for, depending on the basis, considerable discrepancy may result. Theoretically, a producer may (1) mine ore, concentrate, smelt, and refine in one country; or (2) mine ore, concentrate, and smelt in one country, and refine in another; or (3) mine ore and concentrate in one country, and smelt and refine in another; or (4) mine ore and concentrate in one country, smelt in a second, and refine in a third. There is considerable international trade in copper concentrates, as from Africa to Great Britain and from South America to the United States. The trend is toward refining near the point of ore production; this trend is particularly pronounced in Rhodesia.

The second source of difficulty is secondary copper, especially reused market scrap. It is not easy to avoid duplication here. This is one of the main reasons for the sometimes very considerable discrepancies in copper figures compiled by different statistical agencies.

Table 43.5 shows copper production for selected years, on the basis of origin of ore. Particularly noteworthy are the following facts: The United States production (ore basis), although responding vigorously to the business cycle and the exigencies of war, seems unable to reach levels materially higher than those attained in World War I. On the other hand, production figures for Canada, Chile, and Africa are considerably higher; the increase

[21] Federal Trade Commission, op. cit., pp. 69-72, for figures through 1939. Also Year Books of the American Bureau of Metal Statistics for figures from 1940 to 1947.
Data for the U.S.S.R. not available.

TABLE 43.6. End Uses of Copper in the United States, in Percent[22]

Year	Electrical	Automobile	Industry Building	Marine	Miscellaneous	Export[a]
1920	44.8	8.9	5.1	5.6	19.9	15.7
1925	56.5	12.8	5.6	0.4	17.8	6.9
1930	62.7	9.1	5.5	0.5	14.8	7.4
1935	49.9	16.5	9.5	0.2	18.7	5.1
1940	50.6	9.6	10.4	0.8	14.7	13.9

a Copper content of manufactured goods.

in Africa's output, from 47,000 tons in 1917 to 421,000 in 1947, is particularly astounding. Even so, Chile can still outproduce Africa. Recent developments in Peru point to a considerable expansion of production there. Spain's decline is in sharp contrast to the increased production in the Scandinavian countries.

Certain basic trends are clearly revealed by this table. They are the continental shifts discussed earlier in this chapter—Canada, Africa, and Chile up, the United States and some other countries down, still others stationary. Underlying these shifts are the fundamental forces of the depletion of old sources, the discovery of new sources, technological trends, shifts in cost-price relationships, etc. But when one tries to interpret the more detailed changes he is baffled by the bewildering array of incidental and fortuitous factors which transform history into a veritable mosaic. There are wars with their boom periods, armistice and peace treaties with their depression periods, and international cartels, with their frantic efforts to "stabilize" prices at high levels, thus stimulating output and bringing on the inevitable aftermath of price collapse and slump in output. There are the sometimes startling decisions of corporate management and their financial backers to go easy here and to throw vast sums into the fray there. Not the least important factor is the artificial interference with the free flow of international trade, especially by tariffs. All these and more examples of economic dynamics are hidden in these figures.

Geographical shifts similar to those in the world at large occurred within the United States. In 1850 the Michigan mines took the

lead with their famous Lake ores containing native copper. In 1875 rich copper deposits were discovered in Arizona and Montana. In 1911 the large-scale development of Utah and Arizona porphyries started a new era in copper mining and metallurgy. In 1943 the copper-mining regions ranked as follows in the production of copper:

Southwest (mainly porphyries)

	(short tons)
Arizona	397,434
Utah	325,961
New Mexico	78,804
Nevada	71,553
	873,752 = 80 percent

Northwest

	(short tons)
Montana	138,295
Idaho	2,330
	140,625 = 13 percent
Michigan	45,498 = 4 percent
Scattered	33,064 = 3 percent

The preponderance of the Southwest is remarkable.

COPPER CONSUMPTION

As was said at the beginning of this chapter, the new era of copper began around 1880 with the birth of the electrical industry.[23] At that time, when electric lamps were first used and the first central stations were being built, the production and use of copper in the United States started to move up sharply. Its production increased 300 percent in the five years 1880-1884. From then on electrical uses multiplied and the electrical industry absorbed roughly 50 percent of the peacetime produc-

22 Federal Trade Commission, *op. cit.*, p. 61.

23 The term electrical industry as used here includes the makers of electrical appliances and equipment and the electrical light and power industry.

tion. Electrical developments are responsible for part of the demand for copper in industries other than electrical. Thus the automobile industry uses copper mainly for the electrical equipment installed in automobiles, and the building industry uses large amounts of copper in "wiring" buildings for electricity. Although satisfactory statistical records are lacking, it is safe to assume that the situation in other leading industrial countries resembles that in the United States.

The American Bureau of Metal Statistics compiled detailed estimates of the end uses of copper from 1920 through 1940. Its findings are summarized in Table 43.6.

COSTS AND PRICES

Another important implication of the technological revolution is a progressive decrease in the cost of producing copper. Although this cost reduction is not easily traced—in fact it probably cannot be revealed fully—the fact that the United States government was able to procure the bulk of its copper requirements during World War II for 12 cents a pound as against about double that price during World War I, would seem to establish a strong presumption in favor of lower costs. The revolutionary shift from selective to nonselective and especially to mass mining is part of the same fundamental evolution that underlies the great cost-reducing processes of modern industry: the substitution of objective science for the art of the individual craftsman and for rule of thumb, and the supplementation of man's feeble energy with nature's vast energies harnessed by engines and machines. According to the Bureau of the Census, horsepower per man employed in copper mining in the United States increased from 1.18 in 1870 to 7.63 in 1912 and to 15.8 in 1929.[24]

Of course, the output of ore per capita increases much faster than the output of copper because the copper content of ore tends to decline. Thus, the WPA found that output measured in tons of ore produced per labor hour amounted to an average of 0.36 ton during the decade 1912-1921.[25] Later studies conducted by other branches of the government

put production during 1936-1945 at 1.12 tons.[26] This increase in labor output was bought at vastly increased capital expenditure. Naturally the concentration and smelting of 1 percent ore are bound to cost more than the processing of ore with a much higher copper content. But here, too, revolutionary changes occurred.

Table 43.7 lists (1) average annual copper prices (weighted annual prices of primary copper as reported to the U.S. Bureau of Mines); (2) the index of wholesale commodity prices (1926 equals 100), Department of Labor; (3) the amount of smelter production of primary copper from domestic ores and (4) the value of copper produced in millions of dollars by selected years 1860-1945.

TABLE 43.7. Copper Prices and Production for Selected Years, 1860-1945[27]

	Average Annual Copper Prices[a] (cents per pound)	Wholesale Commodity Price Index[b]	Smelter Production of Primary Copper from Domestic Ores (thousand short tons)	Value of Copper Produced (in millions)
1860	22.9	61.0	8.1	$ 3.7
1870	21.2	87.0	14.1	6.0
1880	21.4	65.0	30.2	12.9
1890	15.6	56.2	129.9	40.5
1900	16.5	56.1	303.1	100.6
1910	12.9	70.4	540.1	137.2
1917	29.2	117.5	943.1	514.9
1920	17.5	154.4	604.5	222.5
1929	18.2	95.3	1001.5	352.5
1935	8.8	80.6	381.5	63.5
1937	13.3	86.3	834.5	202.0
1939	11.1	77.1	712.5	148.2
1940	11.4	78.6	909.0	205.5
1941	11.9	78.3	966.0	228.0[c]
1942	11.9	98.8	1088.6	256.8[c]
1943	11.9	103.2	1093.5	257.9[c]
1944	11.9	104.7	1003.0	236.8[c]
1947	21.0	151.8	874.1	367.1

[a] Weighted annual prices of primary copper as reported to the Bureau of Mines.
[b] 1926 = 100.
[c] Exclusive of premium payment.

The price of 22.9 cents a pound in 1860, when the general price level stood at 61, corresponds to 37.5 cents a pound at the 1926 price level of 100 and to 57 cents at the 1947 level. The actual prices in 1926 and 1947 were 13.8 and 21 cents a pound respectively. This calculation suggests a very considerable drop in copper costs during the 87-year period. According to

---

[24] See C. E. Julihn, *op. cit.*, p. 134.
[25] Works Progress Administration, *op. cit.*

[26] See Federal Trade Commission, *op. cit.*, p. 115.
[27] *Ibid.*, pp. 30-31; *Year Book of the American Bureau of Metal Statistics*, 1947, p. 9.

the Tariff Commission, the weighted average price at which domestic copper was sold by American producers was 14.252 cents a pound for the period 1850-1899 and 13.548 cents for the 91-year period 1850-1940.[28]

Another way to bring out the decrease in copper cost and prices is to contrast the two World Wars, even though our national price policy had much to do with the difference in relative costs and prices. In 1917, at the height of World War I, the price of copper in the United States averaged 27.2 cents a pound; that is, producers received that much for electrolytic copper in New York, regardless of cost of production. During World War II another policy was pursued. The "Big Three" —Anaconda, Kennecott, and Phelps-Dodge— who produce the bulk of our copper received 12 cents a pound for most of their output. The smaller high-cost producers were paid whatever was necessary to put them on a profit basis comparable to that of the "Big Three." Some of them received as much as 37 cents a pound. The value of our smelter copper production in 1917 was almost $515 million, almost exactly double the 1944 figure of $258 million. These two years represent the respective heights of the two World Wars. But this comparison between the two wars should be taken as only a suggestion of these cost differences. To trace them accurately would require a far more subtle analysis including taxing policy, profit rates, etc.

Mechanization has progressed rapidly, more scientific methods are in use, far larger amounts of capital per man and per pound of copper produced are used today than was the case ten or twenty years ago. All these advances have helped to raise labor productivity and have, thus far, lowered costs even in the face of great obstacles in the form of poorer grades of ore. But how long this trend will continue is not known.

WORLD REFINING CAPACITY[29]

The total refining capacity of the world, according to estimates of the American Bureau

of Metal Statistics, was about 3,241,000 short tons in 1940. Of this, about 1,549,000 tons, or around 48 percent of the total, was attributed to the electrolytic refineries of the United States. The capacity of these refineries has been increased by about 76,000 tons since 1940, which, together with our furnace refining capacity, gives us a total refining capacity of about 1,720,000 tons. There are no data on capacity increases in other parts of the world since 1940, but it is thought that they have been small. At present, therefore, the total capacity of the United States is probably about 52 percent of the world total.

World consumption of new copper in 1937, the last peacetime year for which reasonably reliable data are available, was 2,408,000 short tons, or about 74 percent of the capacity of the primary refineries. Even the unusual war demands for copper apparently created no serious difficulty as far as any overall shortage of refinery capacity was concerned. The main problem with respect to refineries is that the greater part of the capacity is located in the United States, whereas the increase in mine production and in consumption has occurred in other countries.[30] Table 43.8 shows the world situation.

Smelters are located at points accessible to ores and concentrates and where fuel, power, and flux are available at reasonable cost. By the time copper leaves the smelter, generally as blister copper, it has a high degree of purity and can therefore stand considerable shipping. Thus the ores from the Potrerillos mines of the Andes Copper Mining Company of Chile are concentrated and smelted nearby but, at least in part, refined in the Raritan Copper Works of Anaconda in Perth Amboy, New Jersey. The copper of the Cerro de Pasco Copper Corporation is smelted in Oroya, Peru, near the mines, but refined in the American Metal Company refinery in Carteret, New Jersey. Much Canadian copper is refined in Canada, but some is shipped to the Tacoma, Washington, refinery of the American Smelting and Refining Company. Much African copper is shipped as blister copper to British or Belgian refineries. The Rhokana Corporation does a good deal of refining in Africa. The Union Minière du

---

[28] U.S. Tariff Commission, *op. cit.*, p. 114.

[29] For information regarding the location of copper smelters and refineries, see Federal Trade Commission, *op. cit.*

[30] *Ibid.*, p. 50.

TABLE 43.8. World Distribution of Refining Capacity, Production, and Consumption of Copper[31]

Area	Refining Capacity, 1940[a] Quantity[b]	% of Total	Copper Production, 1937 Quantity[b]	% of Total	Copper Consumption, 1937 Quantity[b]	% of Total
British Empire group						
Canada, Newfoundland	238	7.21	269	10.78	62	2.57
United Kingdom	231	7.00	...	...	335	13.91
Northern Rhodesia	37	1.12	234	9.38	c	c
Union of South Africa	14	0.42	16	0.64	4	0.17
British India, Burma	7	0.21	11	0.44	10	0.42
Australia	41	1.24	22	0.88	15	0.62
Total British Empire	568	17.22	552	22.12	426	17.69
Europe (excluding U.S.S.R.)						
Sweden	12	0.36	8	0.32	56	2.33
Norway	5	0.15	22	0.88	c	c
Belgium-Luxemburg	160	4.85	...	...	36	1.50
Belgian Congo	50	1.52	166	6.65	c	c
France	28	0.85	1	0.04	132	5.48
Yugoslavia	12	0.36	43	1.72	4	0.17
Germany, Austria	245	7.42	34	1.36	273	11.34
Finland	15	0.45	14	0.56	c	c
Other Europe	...	...	38	1.52	227	9.43
Total Europe	527	15.98	326	13.06	712	29.57
U.S.S.R.	265	8.04	99	3.97	173	7.18
Asia (excluding Russian, British) and Japanese Empire (includes Manchuria)	111	3.37	118	4.73	210	8.72
World (excluding Pan America)	1471	44.60	1079	43.24	1521	63.16
Pan America						
United States	1446[d]	43.84	835	33.47	878	36.46
Chile	381	11.55	456	18.28	9	0.37
Other Pan America	...	...	109	4.37		
Total Pan America	1827	55.40	1400	56.11	887	36.84
Total World	3298	100.00	2495	100.00	2408	100.00

[a] Refining capacity includes both electrolytic and furnace refining; the latter is a minor factor (about 10 percent) in the United States. Statistics on capacity of foreign refineries are incomplete, and vary with different authorities. Capacity figures as of the end of 1940.
[b] Thousands of tons.
[c] Negligible.
[d] Capacity given by American Bureau of Metal Statistics is 1,549,000 tons electrolytic and perhaps 80,000 tons furnace-refined at Lake Superior mines.

Haut Katanga of the Belgian Congo refines part of their own smelter output in Katanga. Chuquicamata has a large refinery as has

[31] C. K. Leith, J. W. Furness, and C. Lewis, *World Minerals and World Peace*, Brookings Institution, Washington, 1943.

the Braden Copper Company. There is no hard and fast rule. Conditions change, affiliations shift, and changing market conditions and tariffs play their part. The only rule that holds is that shipments of useless dirt are avoided whenever possible. Low-grade ore is concen-

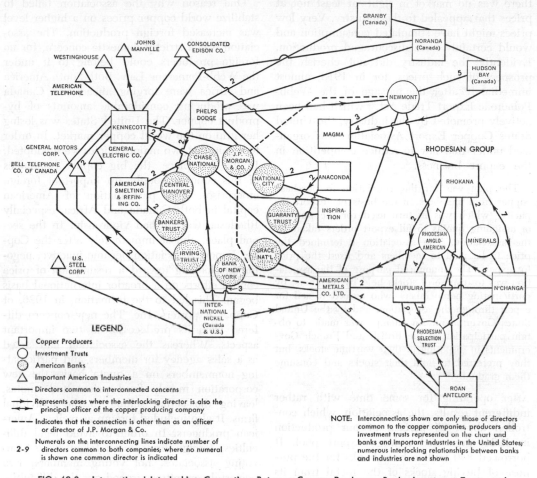

FIG. 43.3. International Interlocking Connections Between Copper Producers, Banks, Investment Trusts, and Important American Industries. (Federal Trade Commission, *Report on the Copper Industry,* 1947, opposite p. 175.)

trated as near the point of origin as possible. High-grade concentrates can stand considerable shipment to the smelter, and blister copper is virtually footloose. There are far fewer smelters than concentrating plants and still fewer refineries than smelters.

INTERCORPORATE RELATIONS AND INTERNATIONAL CARTELS

The copper industry of the United States and the other leading copper-producing countries is dominated by a few large corporations. There is also a certain degree of intercorporate collaboration through interlocking directorates involving leading banks, copper-consuming industries, etc. Fig. 43.3, prepared for the Fed-

eral Trade Commission, shows such interconnections.

Besides forming these more or less permanent interconnections, the leading copper producers of the world have from time to time entered into cartels for the alleged purpose of stabilizing the price of copper. Although such attempts have been made during various periods of history, only the more recent cartels will be discussed here.

World War I greatly stimulated copper production. In the United States alone production increased from 575,000 tons in 1914 to 943,000 in 1916 and to 954,000 in 1917. When the armistice suddenly cut off the war demand, huge supplies accumulated for which there was no market in sight—at least not at prices that appealed to the industry. Very low prices might have stimulated consumption and would certainly have discouraged production. Evidently the industry did not cherish the prospect of such prices, for in 1918, almost immediately after the passage of the Webb-Pomerene Export Trade Act,[32] which had been actively promoted by the industry, the United States Copper Export Association was organized under that law to reduce competition in the export business.

The plan was for the association to purchase copper from members on the basis of "export capacity" which was in turn used for the purpose of assigning quotas to fill export orders taken by the association. The association determined the price to be paid to members and fixed the price for export. The announced purpose of the association was to dispose of stocks held by members, by participating nonmembers, who agreed to sell for export through the association, and by the United States Government. An attempt was made to obtain participation of the British and French Governments in disposing of their wartime stocks, but they preferred to hold their stocks and consume them gradually.[33]

After operating for some time with rather indifferent results, the association, which controlled about 85 percent of our production in 1921, organized a large export pool. It borrowed $40 million from banks for the purpose of buying stocks of the metal from its members and selling them abroad at higher prices, the members sharing in the profits on a pro rata basis. Production was drastically curtailed and surplus stocks were disposed of abroad at some profit to the members. However, this profit was costly, for it was bought at the expense of output and of reduced control over the export trade. Outside interests managed to raise their share of exports to almost half the total. The last copper was sold by the pool in 1923 and soon thereafter the association became inactive, though it was not formally dissolved until 1933.

[32] This act exempted the export activities of United States business interests from certain limitations of the antitrust laws provided that their activities abroad did not *artificially or willfully* enhance or depress domestic (United States) prices.
[33] Federal Trade Commission, *op. cit.*, p. 12.

One reason why the association failed to stabilize world copper prices on a higher level was increased foreign production. The association was a strictly domestic concern, for no foreign producers could belong to it under the Webb-Pomerene Law. Both South America and Africa were forging ahead and Canada was producing considerable amounts of by-product copper. The United States was losing her grip on the world copper market. In order to regain this two major policies were adopted. In the first place, the big copper companies of this country bought up important foreign enterprises, and participation of American capital in both Canada and Africa, especially Rhodesia, was pushed vigorously. In the second place, almost immediately after the Copper Export Association became inactive, negotiations looking toward a resumption of price control efforts on a broader international basis began. This led to the formation, in 1926, of Copper Exporters, Inc. The new concern differed from its predecessor in two important aspects. Whereas the association had acted as a sales agency for members and participating nonmembers on a quota basis, the new corporation merely fixed prices and quotas, leaving the actual selling to the individual firms. It also included foreign as well as American producers. In order to avoid legal difficulties, foreign firms were taken in as nonvoting associates, not voting members; two powerful committees ironed out the difficulties which were bound to arise from this discriminatory treatment. The inclusion of foreign interests raised the amount of world copper controlled by the cartel from 68 percent under the old association to 86 percent under the new. Thus a Webb-Pomerene association was elevated to the rank of a first-class international cartel. The price rose rapidly during the business boom, and the cartel continued to maintain it at an artificial level after the crash of 1929. Again American producers were left holding the bag, for they had to curtail production while both foreign associate producers and domestic nonmember producers reaped a golden harvest from their larger output at pegged prices.

The Federal Trade Commission investigated the activities of the cartel and of the Copper

Institute, Inc., a trade association and statistical clearing house, to determine whether the cartel had "artificially or willfully" affected the domestic copper market. Before the formal recommendation was handed down, the depression brought on a collapse of the copper market and the disintegration of the cartel. Furthermore, an excise tax of 4 cents a pound (in lieu of an import duty) became effective in 1932,[34] and this more or less isolated the American market from the rest of the world.

In 1936 foreign producers, seeing that their output tended to exceed demand outside the American market, entered into another international cartel agreement. Foreign subsidiaries of the American copper industry's "Big Three" participated. Thus, although United States firms were not direct participants, a definite *esprit de corps* bound most of the copper producers of the world. Again artificially stimulated prices encouraged production in excess of the natural market situation and tended to accentuate the boom-and-bust nature of the industry. Then came World War II, with its gigantic production program under government control. The postwar situation was marked by an unexpectedly high demand which quickly cleared away the war surpluses and led to sharp price rises once government controls were ended in 1946; this in turn stimulated vast expansion programs.

While this account has stressed the centripetal forces in the copper industry which caused the leaders to search for a common policy for their mutual benefit, there are some very real conflicts in the industry which render difficult complete harmony and coöperation. These conflicts can be discussed most clearly country by country.[35]

Canada

Copper in Canada is largely a by-product of more valuable minerals. Hence the price can be whatever is necessary to sell it. Canada's output is as great as that of Rhodesia. The home market being small, most of the copper must be exported. The export volume may closely match the United States deficit. Wall Street bankers have heavy interests in Canadian mines; they are also interested in properties in the United States. Canadian mines have not been members of cartels. The United States is a natural market. The marginal mines problem is relatively unimportant.

The United States

The output of all our mines cannot meet our postwar requirements. The probable deficit is about equal to Canada's export surplus or about one-half of Chile's wartime production. The maximum output from our mines will require subsidies for marginal copper, or a price level of about 20 cents. Two companies, Anaconda and Kennecott, who produce over 60 percent of the domestic supply, control 90 percent of Chile's copper. They have no apparent direct interest in Canadian or in African copper. They have no domestic market problem, but they must find a world market for their Chilean and Mexican copper. Opening the United States market to Chilean copper by trade pacts also opens it to Canada and to any other country enjoying "most-favored-nation" treatment. American Metal Company and related financial groups are interested in Canadian and Rhodesian copper. Under the present duty and the costs in Chile, including taxes, a price level of about 16 cents in the United States is required for the profitable entry of Chilean copper, and not over 14 cents for Canadian copper. In 1946, Kennecott protested the 14-cent level as too low.

Under a free market and with a reasonable balance between production and consumption, actual production costs in most of the world would justify a world copper price of about 15 cents per pound. Supply and demand relationships during the reconversion period have already pushed the price far above this level.

Chile

High revenue from copper companies is needed to support Chile's economy. The present revenue from taxes, between 3 and 4 cents per pound of copper, destroys the competitive advantage of low-cost production. Chile's former large market in the United Kingdom may be lost to Rhodesia and Canada because of Empire preferences and price competition; her

---

[34] As was mentioned before, this excise tax was suspended in April, 1947, for a two-year period.

[35] Federal Trade Commission, *op. cit.*, pp. 177-179.

European market is impoverished or lost to the Belgian Congo for the time being; her Japanese market is also lost. The political problems inherent in a possible commercial union between Argentina and Chile impel the United States to be interested in the international situation in South America. Higher production costs are ahead as the result of the depletion of some of the richer deposits and the necessity for the Chile Copper Company to alter treatment methods and change from surface to deep mining in a few years. The Chilean government has a big stake in maintaining high prices for copper; so have the producers, especially in view of increasing costs.

Rhodesia

Great Britain has a definite interest in maintaining production and employment at a high level in Rhodesia, and so is likely to be a preferred market for Rhodesia's copper. Northern Rhodesian production will almost take care of United Kingdom requirements at peacetime levels. British capitalists are the principal owners of Rhodesian mines. They have relatively small interest in Canadian operations. American Metal Company, Ltd., has an important stake in Rhodesia; other American investors (J. P. Morgan, for example) are likewise interested. American Metals also is heavily interested in Canadian copper. Rhodesia is not the world's cheapest copper producer, according to her governor.[36] Rhodesian producers have been cartel-minded, but they may be inhibited somewhat by Britain's policy—and need—of keeping prices low enough to maintain a competitive position for English copper manufacturers.

---

[36] *Minerals Yearbook, 1944*, p. 31, copper preprint.

Other Countries

Belgium probably can absorb all of Katanga's production (Belgian Congo) for redistribution in Europe. France's needs probably can be met from Belgian and other sources, with Chile and Canada as leading competitors for the business. Soviet Russia may be an important market, though she is not now so regarded. Finland, Norway, Sweden, Portugal, Germany, Spain, Cyprus, and Yugoslavia can probably supply copper to Europe at the prewar level of around 175,000 tons. Battlefield and other scrap supplies may be an important factor. Conflict arises in the need of the producing nations to secure maximum foreign exchange through high prices, and of the impoverished consuming nations to secure a maximum supply at minimum prices.

The Atlantic Charter

In the Atlantic Charter, the United States and Great Britain, whose nationals control the bulk of the world's copper resources, pledged themselves to endeavor, with due respect for their existing obligations, to further the enjoyment by all states, great or small, victor or vanquished, of access, on equal terms, to the trade and raw materials of the world which are needed for their economic prosperity.

An attempt was made at Havana, Cuba, during the winter of 1947-1948 to work this idea of fair trade into the charter of the International Trade Organization, but fair trade has limited meaning and potency in a world torn into hostile political camps. War and the fear of war are the greatest enemies of an orderly economy. When the cry of *Sauve qui peut* is heard, people are too preoccupied to worry much about the fairness of trade.

BIBLIOGRAPHY

"African Copper," *Fortune*, September, 1931.

American Institute of Mining and Metallurgical Engineers, *Modern Uses of Non-ferrous Metals*, New York, 1935.

"Anaconda, I," *Fortune*, December, 1936.

"Anaconda, II," *Fortune*, January, 1937.

Birchard, R. E., "Copper in the Katanga Region of the Belgian Congo," *Economic Geography*, October, 1940.

Crane, C. H., "Copper, Lead, and Zinc Mining in the Future," in Parsons, A. B. (ed.), *Seventy-five Years of Progress in the Mineral Industry, 1871-1946*, New York, American Institute of Mining and Metallurgical Engineers, 1947.

Davis, W., *The Story of Copper*, New York, Appleton-Century, 1924.

Elliot, W. Y., May, E. S., Rowe, J. W. F., Skelton, A., and Wallace, D. W., *International Control of Non-ferrous Metals*, New York, Macmillan, 1937.

Federal Trade Commission, *The Copper Industry*, Parts I and II, Washington, 1947.

"Hudson Bay Mining and Smelting Company," *Fortune*, June, 1938.

Joralemon, I. B., *Romantic Copper, Its Lure and Lore*, New York, Appleton-Century, 1934.

Julihn, C. E., "Copper, an Example of Advancing Technology and the Utilization of Low-Grade Ores," in Tryon, F. G., and Eckel, E. C. (eds.), *Mineral Economics*, New York, McGraw-Hill, 1932, chap. 5.

Laist, F., "Seventy-five Years of Progress in Smelting Copper and Lead," in Parsons, A. B. (ed.), *Seventy-five Years of Progress in the Mineral Industry, 1871-1946,* New York, American Institute of Mining and Metallurgical Engineers, 1947.

Marcosson, I. F., *Metal Magic*, New York, Farrar, Strauss, 1949.

"Nababeep and O'okiep," *Fortune*, July, 1947 (South African Copper Mines).

"Nababeep and O'okiep," *Mining and Metallurgy*, September, 1947.

Parsons, A. B., *The Porphyry Coppers*, New York, American Institute of Mining and Metallurgical Engineers, 1933.

Parsons, A. B., "Greater Butte Project," *Mining and Metallurgy*, November, 1947.

Peirce, W. M., "Seventy-five Years of Progress in Non-ferrous Metallurgy," in Parsons, A. B. (ed.), *Seventy-five Years of Progress in the Mineral Industry, 1871-1946*, New York, American Institute of Mining and Metallurgical Engineers, 1947.

"Presbyterian Copper," *Fortune*, July, 1932 (Phelps Dodge).

Shea, W. P., "Foreign Ore Reserves of Copper, Lead, and Zinc," *Engineering and Mining Journal*, January, 1947.

Taggart, A. F., "Seventy-five Years of Progress in Ore Dressing," in Parsons, A. B. (ed.), *Seventy-five Years of Progress in the Mineral Industry, 1871-1946*, New York, American Institute of Mining and Metallurgical Engineers, 1947.

Turnbull, C. C., *A Century of Copper*, London, Wilson, 2 vols., 1900-1906.

Chapter 44

THE LIGHT METALS

ALUMINUM

Aluminum is the most abundant metallic element in the crust of the earth. But, as is so often the case, the gap between physical occurrence and economic availability is very wide. For aluminum does not occur in the native state as pure metal; it is securely locked up in complex minerals, especially clays. So difficult is it to extract aluminum from its ores and ore minerals and so exacting are the specifications of aluminum ores that even now this abundant constituent of the earth's crust is selling for a price about five times that of steel.

Aluminum and Technological Progress

Aluminum was first isolated in 1825 by the Danish chemist Hans Christian Oersted. Later improvements made in the chemical procedure by the German scientist, Frederick Wöhler, and the French chemist, Henri Saint-Claire Deville, resulted in additional production of the light metal in very small quantities. In 1852 the price stood at $545.00 a pound. Soon thereafter small-scale commercial production began and the price fell rapidly, to $34.00 a pound in 1856 and to $17.00 in 1859.

In the nineties it dropped to $1.50 and reached a low of 14 cents a pound for aluminum pig during the 1940's. Ingot at that time sold for 15 cents a pound.

In the eighties several important inventions materially reduced the cost of producing the new metal. The idea of using an electric current for the reduction of aluminum oxide, known as alumina (Al_2O_3), and thus producing pure aluminum electrolytically had long interested scientists. Traditionally two men, the American Charles Martin Hall and the Frenchman Paul Louis Toussaint Héroult, are credited with the invention of the process currently in use. Hall made his invention in 1886 and received a patent in 1889. However, three others—the Cowles brothers and Charles S. Bradley—came close enough to solving the problem so that their names deserve mention in this connection.

At about the same time, 1889, the German chemist Karl Josef Bayer greatly simplified the process of extracting pure alumina from aluminum ore, bauxite. This process, in turn, benefited considerably from earlier inventions, especially those of Solvay which greatly reduced the price of caustic soda. Together these men—Cowles, Bradley, Hall, Héroult, Bayer, Solvay, etc.—succeeded in laying the foundation for a commercial aluminum industry which in the course of half a century lifted this metal out of the class of curiosities and laboratory specimens into the class of industrial metals to which copper, lead, and zinc had long belonged. In the late forties aluminum was selling in the United States for less than either of these three other metals. At the peak of the war effort probably more aluminum was produced than either lead or zinc.

What put aluminum on the map in a really big way was the airplane, especially the fantastic expansion of aviation during World War II. The large-scale use of aluminum in planes became possible when aluminum alloys, such as duralumin, were developed which combined exceptional lightness with great strength.

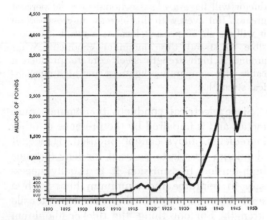

FIG. 44.1. World Production of Aluminum, 1850-1947. (Figs. 44.1, 44.2, and 44.3 from Aluminum Company of America, *An Outline of Aluminum,* 1949.)

World Production

World aluminum production increased from approximately 2 metric tons (worth about $38,000) in 1859 to 12 metric tons in 1886 and to 1240 in 1894. By the time World War I broke out, production stood at less than 70,000 metric tons; planes in that war were made of wood and "doped" canvas. In 1929 world production of aluminum rose to 276,800 metric tons worth about $150 million. The depression brought considerable curtailment, but by 1939 the output had risen to 720,000 metric tons worth about $300 million. The

peak was reached in 1943, with over 1.9 million metric tons which sold for about $600 million. In 1946 world production fell back to the 1939 level but thereafter recovered considerable ground.

Aluminum production in the United States, which amounted to 148.6 thousand metric tons in 1939, reached its wartime peak of over 820 thousand in 1943. After a postwar low of 372 thousand in 1946, production recovered considerably.

Expanding Markets and Growth

In terms of main uses, the history of commercial aluminum production can be divided into several phases. At first kitchen utensils were the chief outlet. Here the excellent heat conductivity of aluminum as well as its non-toxic and rust-resisting properties stood in good stead. Lightness was an added attraction. Then aluminum began to invade other markets—it was used for parts of motors and automobile bodies, construction materials, doors, sashes, electric transmission wire, etc. As was mentioned before, it finally came into its own when aviation put a premium on lightness and thereby rendered large-scale use of the light metals inevitable.[1]

In each new field aluminum had numerous and sometimes great obstacles to overcome. Scientists had to establish accurately what it could and could not do; new techniques of machining, welding, extrusion, etc., had to be worked out; new aluminum alloys and new ways of making alloys had to be found; and, what is more, this knowledge had to be taught to the trade. Handbooks had to be prepared that fitted aluminum into the tables with which engineers are accustomed to work. There is no cozy niche all ready to receive a new metal. On the contrary, it must fight its way into the market over the barriers of ignorance, tradition, lethargy, and competition.

To appreciate the extent and force of this competition, one must keep in mind that there are two basic ways of achieving the combination of strength and lightness so desirable in

[1] There was a similar development in the case of copper which, after long serving various uses, came into its own when the electrical industry put a premium on the ability to conduct electricity.

many material uses. Either a light but relatively weak metal like aluminum or magnesium is made strong by being alloyed with certain strengthening ingredients, or the strength of a strong but heavy metal like iron or copper is multiplied by means of alloys, thus reducing the amount and weight of metal required for a given purpose. Germany built her pocket battleships not from aluminum or magnesium but from alloy steels. Thus there is a definite and considerable field of commodity competition, i.e., competition from substitute materials, with which aluminum has to reckon—pyrex glass and stainless steel in kitchen utensils, beryllium-copper alloys, stainless and rustless superstrong alloy steels, etc. These substitute materials are particularly dangerous rivals if they are produced more competitively than aluminum is.

One factor that proved a particular difficulty was the fact that until about 1941 the Aluminum Company of America was the sole producer of new pig aluminum in the United States.[2] In Europe a German government-controlled firm played a similar role. In other words, various industries in the United States were virtually dependent on one source for aluminum. This was a great handicap for the newcomer among the metals, for industries dread to be dependent on one source; they will do without something rather than submit to monopolistic control.

On the other hand, the strong position of the Aluminum Company of America may have had advantages. Unless squandered in bloated dividends, profits provide the funds for undertaking costly research and experimentation, for assuming risks which a more precariously situated firm may refuse to take, for defraying the vast expenses involved in introducing a new material into the market.

PROPERTIES AND MAIN USES OF ALUMINUM
Specific Gravity and Strength

The outstanding characteristic of aluminum is its lightness. Its specific gravity is 2.7, as compared with 7.8 for mild steel and 8.9 for copper. Magnesium, with a specific gravity of only 1.74, is even lighter than aluminum. A cubic foot of mild steel weighs almost three times as much as a cubic foot of aluminum, and a cubic foot of copper about 3.3 times as much. The figures for weight per cubic foot are 165 pounds for aluminum, 487 pounds for mild steel, and 556 pounds for copper.

But pure aluminum has only one-fourth the tensile strength of ordinary steel. Hence, before alloys were developed, aluminum was limited to such uses as kitchen utensils, in which strength was a negligible requirement, but nontoxicity, good heat conductivity, noncorrosiveness, and lightness were great advantages.

The lightness and high conductivity of aluminum make it possible to produce electrical conductors from the metal. Aluminum possesses 61 percent of the electrical conductivity of copper, and for equal resistance in unit length, the aluminum conductor will have a cross-sectional area 59 percent greater. But even with this increase in cross section it will weigh 52 percent less. As a result it is possible to strand the aluminum conductor wires around a high-strength steel core to produce a cable with comparative lightness and high mechanical strength.[3]

Since electrical conductivity demands pure metals and is impaired by the presence of other ingredients, alloys cannot be used. Hence, if aluminum wire is to be used for long-distance high-tension transmission it is usually necessary to reinforce the aluminum lines with a steel core to impart the necessary tensile strength. For one thing, the thicker aluminum lines must sustain a greater load from ice and wind.[4]

Properties, Prices, and Uses

The future use of aluminum depends on two main factors: (1) further improvements of the metal and its alloys and of processing techniques and (2) price. Since aluminum competes with steel, especially stainless steel, and with glass, plastic, magnesium, zinc, and copper, a comparison of the prices of these various

---

[2] In 1941 the Reynolds Metals Company began operating an aluminum plant at Listerhill, Alabama, and soon extended its activities to Longview, Washington.

[3] Aluminum Company of America, *An Outline of Aluminum*, New York, 1949, p. 40.

[4] See U.S. Tariff Commission, *Aluminum*, War Changes in Industry Series, Report No. 14, Washington, 1946, p. 28.

products is significant. This is given in Table 44.1 on both a per pound and a per cubic foot basis.

The price relationship changed materially after war price controls were terminated; for, although the price of aluminum ingot rose to only 17 cents a pound, the price of most other commodities increased rather sharply. Thus the price of copper shot up from 12 to 23.5 cents. Steel, too, is selling at materially advanced prices. This should be a good opportunity for aluminum to fight its way into new

TABLE 44.1. Prices of Aluminum and Competitive Materials, by Weight and Volume, 1944[5]

Material	Weight per Cubic Foot (pounds)	Average Quoted or Ceiling Price, 1944 Per Pound (cents)	Per Cubic Foot	Ratio of Price to That of Steel Ingot as 1.0 Per Pound	Per Cubic Foot
Carbon steel ingot	490	1⅓	$ 6.52	1.0	1.0
Stainless steel sheet	490	35	171.50	26.3	26.3
Glass	157	5[a]	7.85	3.8	1.2
Secondary aluminum ingot	170	11	18.70	8.3	2.9
Plastics	87	25[b]	21.75	18.9	3.3
Magnesium ingot	112	20½	22.96	15.4	3.5
Primary aluminum ingot	170	15	25.50	11.3	3.9
Slab zinc	440	8¼	36.30	6.4	5.6
Copper ingot	556	12	66.72	9.0	10.2

[a] Price on rolled glass. For many types of glass the price on a weight basis is higher.
[b] For many varieties of plastics the price is considerably higher.

segments of the metal market, now that aluminum alloys are available that are six times as strong as pure aluminum. Aluminum should have an excellent fighting chance, especially since the menace of monopoly control seems removed for the time being. Even though during the past two years the building industry has been the No. 1 consumer of aluminum, in the long run the greatest future use of the metal on a volume basis should be in the transportation field where lightness is a major asset. The possibilities of using it in transportation equipment, other than airplanes—for example, in railroad equipment including dry freight cars, tank cars such as those used by the rayon, dairy, sugar, explosives, rubber, and brewing industries (where resistance to the cor-

[5] *Ibid.*, p. 35.

rosive action of chemicals is important) and in buses, trucks, and passenger cars—are considerable.[6]

It is not the price of the raw metal but the overall cost of attaining a desired objective in terms of weight, strength, appearance, durability, installation charges, etc., that counts. So long as the techniques of using aluminum were inadequately developed its uses were limited beyond mere cost calculation. But phenomenal progress has been made along that line, and it is continuing. To cite one example, the improvements made in the finishes for aluminum—the surface can be made highly reflective, frosted, or colored—opened up entirely new fields of use, especially for ornamental purposes and for packaging.

Aluminum is also used for chemical purposes, including metallurgy. It is a deoxidizer in the steel industry, about one pound going into each ton of steel produced in the United States. There are also the aluminum paint conspicuous on radiators, highway posts, and water tanks, and ink in magazine advertisements.

Industrial Uses

Table 44.2 shows the industrial uses of aluminum by major industrial groups. In 1940, the largest item was transportation, which means mainly airplanes and railway equipment. The second most important item was miscellaneous foundry and metalworking, which includes builders' hardware, window sashes, trim for buildings, etc. Cooking utensils made up a modest though not insignificant part of the total.

At the peak of the war effort airplane construction naturally took the lead in aluminum consumption, but after World War II the building industry became the leading consumer. The shifts from prewar to postwar consumption are shown in Table 44.3. The situation, however, is far from static. Thus during the first six months of 1949 transportation called for as much aluminum as did building construction.

[6] Five million passenger cars each using 75 pounds of aluminum—a rather modest amount—would require 375 million pounds or almost half this country's entire output of the metal in 1946.

TABLE 44.2. Industrial Uses of Aluminum in the United States, by Major Industrial Groups, Average, 1933-1938, and Annual, 1930 and 1940[7]

(short tons)

Industrial Group	1930 Quantity	% of Total	1933-1938, Average Quantity	% of Total	Increase or Decrease over 1930 (percent)	1940 Quantity	% of Total	Increase or Decrease over Average, 1933-1938 (percent)
Transportation (land, air, and water)	59,730	38	42,470	29	−28.9	110,754	40	+160.8
Electrical conductors	25,149	16	14,645	10	−41.8	13,844	5	−5.5
Cooking utensils	22,006	14	20,503	14	−6.8	16,613	6	−19.0
Machinery and electrical appliances	14,146	9	21,967	15	+55.3	24,920	9	+13.4
Ferrous and nonferrous metallurgy	12,575	8	7,322	5	−41.8	11,075	4	+51.2
Building construction	6,287	4	11,716	8	+86.4	13,844	5	+18.2
Miscellaneous foundry and metalworking	6,287	4	5,858	4	−6.8	63,684	23	+987.1
Chemical	3,144	2	7,322	5	+132.9	13,844	5	+89.1
Food and beverage	1,572	1	8,787	6	+459.0	5,538	2	−37.0
Miscellaneous	6,287	4	5,858	4	−6.8	2,769	1	−52.7
Total	157,183	100	146,448	100	−6.8	276,885	100	+89.1

ROLE OF ALUMINUM IN METAL CONSUMPTION

The consumption of nonferrous metals including aluminum is modest indeed, compared with steel consumption. Thus, in 1929, of the total steel, aluminum, copper, lead, zinc, and tin consumed in the United States, steel accounted for 94.6 percent and nonferrous metals for 5.4 percent; aluminum represented a mere 0.3 percent. The corresponding figures for Germany were 91.5, 8.5, and 0.4; for Great Britain, 89.2, 10.8, and 0.5; and Japan, 93.2, 6.8, and 0.4. These figures are on a weight basis. Naturally aluminum would show up better on a volume basis, but even then it could not claim more than about 1.5 or 2 percent at best. Consumption of all metals expanded during World War II, though aluminum undoubtedly registered some gain in its percentage position.

When steel is left out and only the nonferrous metals listed above are considered, aluminum makes a better showing. Thus, in 1942 it

constituted 15 percent of our consumption of nonferrous metals, as against 41.9 for copper, 23.5 for lead, 18.3 for zinc, and 1.2 for tin. In Germany in 1938 aluminum was credited with 16.2 percent as compared with 38.5 for

TABLE 44.3. Shifts in Aluminum Consumption, Prewar and Postwar, in Percentages
(Source: Bureau of Mines)

	Prewar	1946
Transportation	29	9
Machinery and electrical appliances	15	10
Cooking utensils	14	13
Electrical conductors	10	8
Building construction	8	29
Food and beverages	6	3
Chemical	5	2
Ferrous and nonferrous metallurgy	5	3
Foundry and metalworking	4	19
Miscellaneous	4	4
	100	100

copper, 23.9 for lead, 24.6 for zinc, and 2.3 for tin; that 16.2 was almost four times the corresponding figure for 1929. Great Britain and Japan did not push their aluminum production to the same point as did Germany during the late thirties and both Germany and the United States during the early forties.

---

[7] Bureau of Mines, *Minerals Yearbook;* U.S. Department of Commerce, *Commerce and Navigation;* U.S. Tariff Commission, *op. cit.,* p. 31.

Germany found it more difficult to step up her imports of copper, lead, zinc, and tin than her aluminum output. Japan placed greater reliance on her domestic copper reserves. Britain had exceptionally good access to overseas sources of almost all the metals. The increased production of aluminum between 1935 and 1944 is largely traceable to military preparation and production in general and to the increased output of military aircraft in particular.

ALUMINUM ORES

Natural Aluminum Compounds

Aluminum, as was stated before, is not found in the native state as a pure metal. It generally occurs as an ingredient of chemical compounds in highly complex minerals. There are four natural compounds of aluminum:

1. Corundum, a native alumina.[8] Because of its hardness it is highly valued as an abrasive; hence it is not used for aluminum extraction.
2. Cryolite, a double fluoride of aluminum and soda ($AlF_3 \cdot 3\ NaF$). It was first used as an ore, and later as a solvent in the electrolysis of alumina (Hall-Héroult process). Almost the only place where cryolite is found in commercial quantities is on the west coast of Greenland, near Ivigtut. It can now be produced synthetically.
3. Kaolin, or china clay ($Al_2O_3 \cdot 2\ SiO_2 \cdot 2\ H_2O$), essentially a pure disilicate. Kaolin is ruled out as a source of aluminum for two main reasons: its alumina content as a rule is too low and its silicate content is too high.
4. Bauxite.

Bauxite

Because of certain requirements of the metallurgical processes in use today, almost the only ore from which aluminum is extracted commercially is bauxite.[9] Bauxite is the name given an ore containing hydrated aluminum oxide as its important mineral.

Commercial bauxites are of two types: the

---

[8] Alumina is aluminum oxide, Al_2O_3.

[9] Named after the city of Le Baux in southern France, where some of the largest deposits of this ore are found.

Mediterranean or monohydrate ($Al_2O_3 \cdot H_2O$), also known as boehmite, and the Caribbean or trihydrate ($Al_2O_3 \cdot 3\ H_2O$), also called gibbsite. Commercial bauxite should contain at least 50 percent alumina (Al_2O_3) and less than 7 percent silica. The metal content of a good aluminum ore ranges from 25 to 32 percent, as against 40 to 60 percent in iron and 0.7 to 6 percent in copper. In other words, aluminum ores stand halfway between iron and copper ores in terms of metal content. A typical bauxite contains 55 to 65 percent alumina, 2 to 10 percent SiO_2, 2 to 20 percent Fe_2O_3, 1 to 3 percent TiO_2, and 10 to 30 percent chemically combined water. As is true with all other ores, the limits of tolerance in aluminum ores are determined by known practical processes of purification and reduction, their costs plus the other costs incidental to preparing the product for the market and delivering it, and the prices the product will command. Thus certain minima of aluminum content are laid down, as well as maxima of certain impurities. For long the Bayer process was the main determinant of what constitutes commercial bauxite and it is still very important, although the considerable advance in aluminum technology during World War II (see p. 721) has resulted in less exacting specifications for aluminum ore.

By no means is all the bauxite used to make aluminum. In 1939, the last year of peace before World War II, only 46 percent—180,329 short tons out of a total of 391,256—of the bauxite consumed by United States industries went into the making of aluminum. The rest was used in abrasives (24 percent), chemicals (23 percent), and miscellaneous uses (7 percent), the last category including cement, absorption media, refractories, insulating materials, and flux in alloy steel. Naturally, during the war a far greater proportion of bauxite went into aluminum.

Geography of Bauxite Deposits. Bauxite is found chiefly in the tropics or in regions where a tropical climate prevailed when bauxite was formed. Tropical climates with their higher temperatures and alternate wet and dry seasons favor the chemical reactions which lead to the formation of bauxite.

In Table 44.4 are listed the estimated

TABLE 44.4. Reserves of Bauxite, and Nationality of Capital Control, 1945[10]
(millions of metric tons)

Area	Quantity	Reserves Percent of Total	Percent of Al_2O_3	Nationality of Capital Control
Western hemisphere[a]				
United States	35	3.3	48–52	U.S., 100%
British Guiana	65	6.1	50–61	U.S., 15%; Canadian 85%
Surinam	54	5.1	50–58	U.S., 85%; Netherlands 15%
Jamaica	70[b]	6.6	45–50	U.S., 15%; Canadian 85%
Brazil	40	3.8	50–60	Brazilian, 100%
Haiti	8	0.8	45–50	U.S., 100%
Dominican Republic	2	0.2	45–50	Unknown
Total	274	25.9	...	
Europe (excluding U.S.S.R.)				
France	50[c]	4.7	50–58	French, 40%; Swiss, 20%; British 20%; Canadian, 20%
British Isles	d	...	e	British, 100%
Italy	16.5	1.6	48–58	Canadian, 35%; Italian, 25%; Swiss, German, and Hungarian-Swiss, 40%
Hungary	150[f]	14.2	50–57	German, 80%; Hungarian-Swiss, 20%
Spain	0.5	...	52–58	Spanish, 100%
Yugoslavia	15[g]	1.4	48–55	Canadian, 20%; German, 20%; Yugoslav, 60%
Rumania	20	1.9	53–58	German-Hungarian-Swiss
Greece	25	2.4	52–57	Canadian, 35%; Greek, 65%
Total	277	26.2	...	
Africa				
Gold Coast	80[i]	7.6	48–55	British, 100%
Mozambique	10	0.9	48–52	British, 100%
French West Africa	100	9.5	52–60	Canadian, 20%; French, 80%
Nyasaland	60	5.7	45–55	British, 100%
Total	250	23.7	...	
Soviet Union	26[i]	2.5	38–60	Russian, 100%
Far East				
India	19	1.8	50–58	British, 35%; British-Canadian, 35%; Indian, 30%
Netherland Indies	25	2.3	53–56	Netherlands, 100%
British Malaya	5	0.5	54–60	Mixed Malayan-Canadian-Chinese-Japanese
Japanese mandated islands	5	0.5	52–56	Unknown
Australia	25	2.4	35–50	Australian, 100%
China	150	14.2	45–55	Chinese, 100%
Total	229	21.7	...	
Total, world	1056	100.0	...	

[a] In addition to the countries listed, bauxite is reported to have been found in French Guiana, Venezuela, Colombia, Mexico, Nicaragua, El Salvador, and Cuba.
[b] Some estimates are as high as 100 million tons.
[c] Readily available; 200 million tons geologically possible.
[d] Not available.
[e] Low grade.
[f] German-dominated; 100 to 150 million additional tons geologically possible.
[g] German-dominated; an additional 50 million tons geologically possible.
[h] Some estimates are as high as 225 million tons.
[i] Approximately 5 million tons of passable grade; the rest high in silica.

[10] U.S. Tariff Commission, op. cit., p. 51.

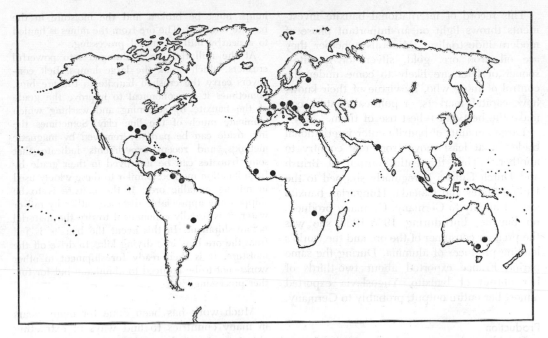

FIG. 44.2. World Bauxite Deposits.

bauxite reserves by countries, and also the nationality of capital control.

According to this table, Hungary and China rank first, with 150 million tons each, followed by French West Africa and probably Jamaica, with about 100 million tons each. Jointly the Guianas, Demarara and Surinam, outrank these latter two regions, with an aggregate of about 120 million. The Gold Coast is down for 80 million, France for 50, Brazil for 40, and the United States for 35 million. The rest is scattered.[11]

The United States has probably eaten more deeply into her bauxite reserves than has any other country. World War II was especially hard on her reserves, for enemy submarines cut imports down sharply for a time, and consumption of domestic reserves was stepped up tremendously by her military aviation program. Between 1930 and 1934 the United States ranked second to France as the world's lead-

ing producer, 90 percent of her bauxite coming from two counties in Arkansas, Salinas and Pulaski. During that time around 54 million tons were produced, about 10 million between 1940 and 1944. About 35 million tons were left in 1945.

Political Aspects of Bauxite Geography. Evidently the estimates are rather rough; moreover, as was stressed before, the definition of ore varies with each technological improvement and with changes in the price-cost ratio. The Hungarian, Rumanian, and Yugoslavian deposits, now behind the Iron Curtain, are presumably under Russian or at least eastern control. The frequency with which Canadian control is mentioned in Table 44.4 is readily explained by the important position held by Aluminum, Ltd., or Alted, as it is often called. Most of the deposits formerly owned by subsidiaries of Alcoa, as the Aluminum Company of America is usually called, were turned over to Alted in 1928. On the basis of political, not capital, control, the British Empire has almost one-third of all the bauxite deposits. The U.S.S.R. ranks second, if the deposits of Hungary, Rumania, and Yugoslavia are included with hers; and France ranks third.

---

[11] In 1948 O. C. Schmedeman, chief geologist of the Reynolds Mining Company, claimed that between 1942 and 1948 alone over 350 million tons of bauxite had been discovered in Jamaica, Haiti, and the Dominican Republic. See *Mining and Metallurgy*, July, 1948.

This record of international bauxite investments throws light on an important phase of modern industrialism. Minerals—whether they are oil, iron ore, gold, silver, or bauxite—sooner or later are likely to come under the control of those who, by virtue of their know-how, capital, markets, or political control, can make the best and fullest use of them.

Large amounts of bauxite enter international trade, or at least move from one country to another.[12] Thus the entire output of British and Dutch Guiana is regularly shipped to the United States and Canada. Hungarian bauxite moved mainly to Germany. Germany produces no bauxite, but during 1935-1938 she was the premier consumer of the ore and the world's leading producer of alumina. During the same period France exported about two-thirds of her output of bauxite. Yugoslavia exported almost her entire output, probably to Germany.

Production

World production reached a peak of over 14 million metric tons in 1943. This exceeds by almost 10 million tons the amount produced in the years immediately preceding and following World War II. In 1943, the United States produced 6.3 million tons; British Guiana and Dutch Guiana (Surinam) ranked next, with 1.9 and 1.7 million tons respectively. Hungary led European production with an output of 1 million tons, and France came close to that figure. Other important producers were the Netherlands Indies, which supplied Japan, and the Soviet Union.

Treatment of Ores

Before the bauxite can be converted into alumina, it is subjected to various treatments. Alcoa describes its ore-treating activities in the Guianas as follows:

The bauxite coming from the mines is a mixture of lumps and fine material. In it there is also a variable amount of clay in which is present a high percentage of silicon oxide, or silica. The large lumps must be broken and the moisture in the bauxite removed. The ore from the mines is hauled to a nearby mill for initial processing.

At the mill the ore is dumped into powerful crushers which break the large lumps. Belt conveyors carry the crushed bauxite to the ore bins. Sometimes it is economical to improve the grade of the bauxite by screening and washing which eliminate much of the fine clay. Sometimes the iron oxide can be partially removed by magnetic methods, and recent experiments indicate that some bauxites can be improved in their grade by froth flotation methods similar to those widely used in milling metallic ores. If the bauxite is to be shipped any appreciable distance, either by rail or water, it is usually economical to dry the material before shipment. In this event the bauxite is fed from the ore bins into drying kilns to drive off the moisture. It is then ready for shipment to other works—not to be reduced to aluminum but for further processing.[13]

Much work has been done for many years in many countries to find ways of extracting aluminum from aluminous materials other than bauxite, such as alunite, leucite, anorthosite, andalusite, nephelite, labradorite, etc. This became especially important in World War II, when scanty bauxite reserves created a dangerous bottleneck in aircraft production. But apparently no real substitute for the Bayer process, and therefore for bauxite, has as yet been found. The war did, however, lead to one extremely valuable technical triumph, the Alcoa Combination process which supplements the Bayer equipment, permits the use of lower-grade bauxite than was formerly possible, and in particular raises the permissible silica content.[14] It is reported that this enabled the production of aluminum from lower-grade ores "at prices no higher than before the war."[15] The most important plant using this process is the Hurricane Creek Plant in Arkansas which will be mentioned later. However, in wartime when cost is of secondary consideration, it is feasible to extract aluminum from minerals other than bauxite. The reserves of these other

---

[12] Since the chief bauxite producer in Surinam (Dutch Guiana) is a subsidiary of the Aluminum Company of America, it may perhaps be questioned whether the movement of bauxite from Surinam to the United States is international *trade* in the full and true sense of the word.

[13] Aluminum Company of America, *op. cit.*, 1949 ed., p. 14.

[14] See J. D. Edwards, *The Combination Process for Alumina*, American Institute of Mining and Metallurgical Engineers, Technical Publication No. 1833, April, 1945.

[15] U.S. Tariff Commission, *op. cit.*, p. 45.

materials in the United States are ample; for example, there are almost unlimited quantities of anorthosite in Wyoming.

PRODUCTION OF ALUMINA AND ALUMINUM

Iron, Copper, and Aluminum Technologies Compared

As was said in an earlier chapter, iron is extracted from its ore in a blast furnace and then converted into steel by various processes. Nowadays iron and steel are produced in one integrated works; i.e., blast furnaces and their coke ovens, and steel furnaces—Bessemer converters, open hearths, or electric furnaces—are physically interlocked in interrelated processes. Copper, on the other hand, is converted to blister copper in a smelter and then shipped to an electrolytic refinery where the last traces of impurities are removed. Smelter and refinery generally are situated in different localities. Aluminum production resembles copper production in that it, too, generally involves two separate processes, the production of alumina and the making of pure aluminum. Both copper and aluminum use electricity in the final stages, but there is an important difference. In a copper refinery blister copper is purified, whereas in an aluminum reduction works alumina is converted to aluminum. Since alumina is aluminum oxide, containing about half its weight in oxygen, an entirely different operation is involved.

The Bayer Process and Recent Improvements

The process by which bauxite is refined to produce pure alumina was developed in 1889 by the German chemist Karl Josef Bayer.

In this process the crushed, washed, and dried bauxite from the mines is further reduced in size in crushers and hammer mills. Finally, it is ground into a powder, mixed with a hot solution of sodium hydroxide, or caustic soda, and pumped into large pressure tanks, or digesters. In these digesters, the caustic soda dissolves the aluminum hydroxide out of the bauxite to form a sodium aluminate solution:

$$Al(OH)_3 + NaOH = NaAlO_2 + 2 H_2O$$

The impurities in the ore, not affected by the caustic, remain in solid form and are removed from the sodium aluminate solution when it is pumped from the digesters into filter presses. The solution, being liquid, passes through the filters, while the impurities remain behind as a residue. This residue is commonly called "red mud."[16]

The Bayer process, as we saw above, puts very definite limitations on the range of admissible ores; in particular it precludes the use of much silica-bearing clay.

The reason for this is apparent when it is realized that the clay is attacked by the caustic soda solution, forming sodium silicate, which in turn reacts with the sodium aluminate to produce an insoluble sodium aluminum silicate. Thus, the silica in the clay not only decreases the amount of alumina recovered from the bauxite but robs the purifying solution of caustic soda, thereby increasing the cost of purification.

After passing through the filter presses, the sodium aluminate solution is pumped into precipitating tanks as high as a five- or six-story building. As the solution slowly cools in these tanks, fine crystals of aluminum hydroxide begin to settle out of the solution; thus the term *precipitating tanks*:

$$NaAlO_2 + 2 H_2O \longrightarrow Al(OH)_3 + NaOH$$

The solution is allowed to remain in the precipitating tanks until the precipitation process has been completed, after which the aluminum hydroxide (alumina hydrate) is transferred to other tanks in which it is washed to remove the caustic. The caustic-soda solution is then pumped back into the digesters to treat a new batch of bauxite; while the aluminum hydroxide, which is nothing more than aluminum oxide chemically combined with water, is heated white-hot in large rotating kilns to drive off the chemically combined water and change the character of the material so it will not reabsorb moisture from the air.[17]

As was mentioned above, the Bayer process was supplemented during the war by the Combination process to permit the use of low-grade bauxitic ores with substandard aluminum content and excessive silica content. In this process the "red mud" is calcified with limestone and soda ash. This process was installed in the Alcoa plant at East St. Louis, Illinois, and at Hurricane Creek, Arkansas.

Reduction of Alumina to Aluminum

To change the powder alumina into the metal aluminum, electricity is required. The reduction is accomplished in rectangular elec-

---

[16] Aluminum Company of America, *op. cit.*, pp. 15 ff.

[17] *Ibid.*, pp. 18 ff.

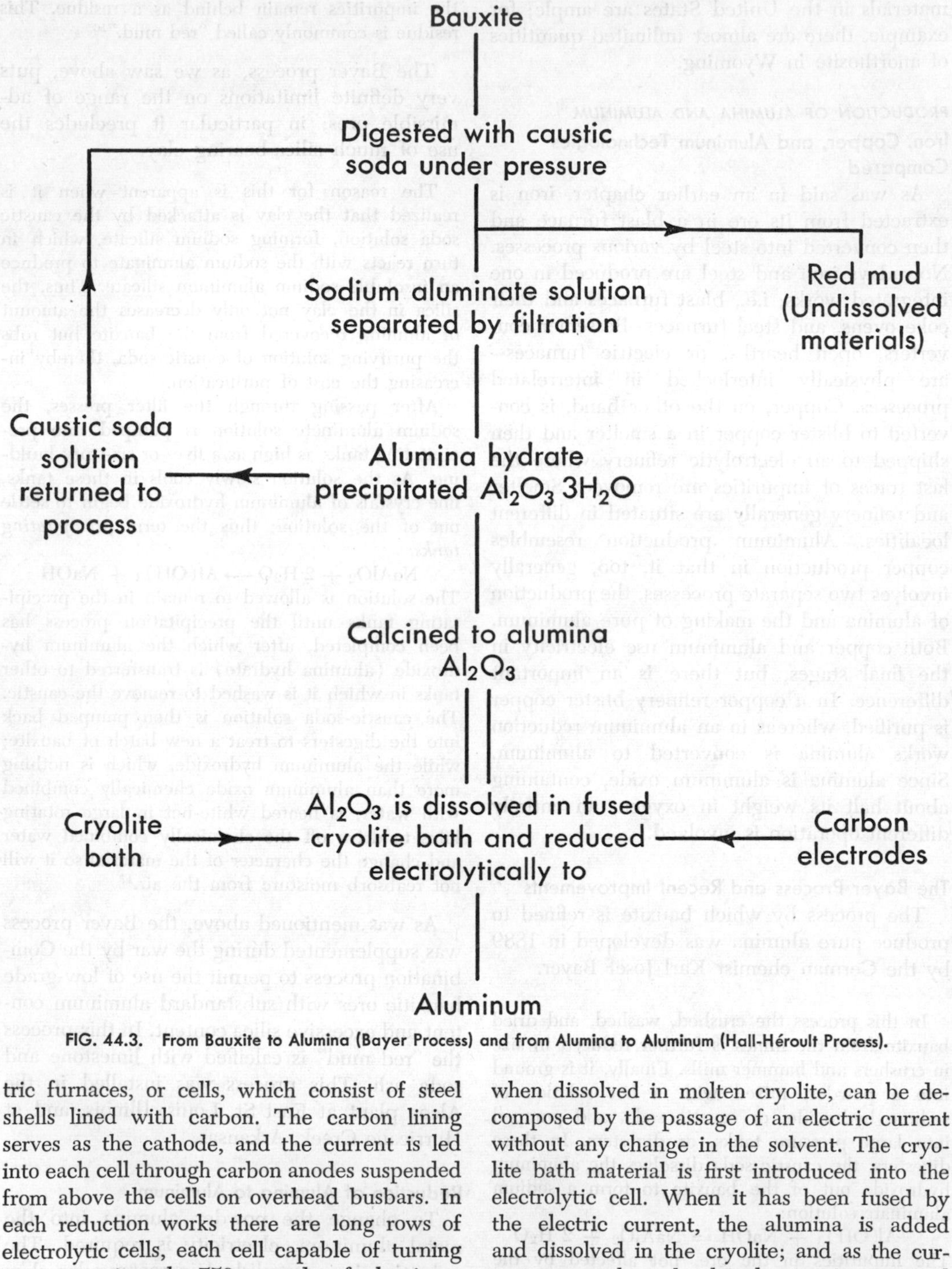

Bauxite

Digested with caustic
soda under pressure

Sodium aluminate solution
separated by filtration

Red mud
(Undissolved
materials)

Caustic soda
solution
returned to
process

Alumina hydrate
precipitated Al$_2$O$_3$ 3H$_2$O

Calcined to alumina
Al$_2$O$_3$

Cryolite
bath

Al$_2$O$_3$ is dissolved in fused
cryolite bath and reduced
electrolytically to

Carbon
electrodes

Aluminum

FIG. 44.3. From Bauxite to Alumina (Bayer Process) and from Alumina to Aluminum (Hall-Héroult Process).

tric furnaces, or cells, which consist of steel shells lined with carbon. The carbon lining serves as the cathode, and the current is led into each cell through carbon anodes suspended from above the cells on overhead busbars. In each reduction works there are long rows of electrolytic cells, each cell capable of turning out approximately 750 pounds of aluminum a day.

The successful operation of the Hall-Héroult process is based on the fact that alumina, when dissolved in molten cryolite, can be decomposed by the passage of an electric current without any change in the solvent. The cryolite bath material is first introduced into the electrolytic cell. When it has been fused by the electric current, the alumina is added and dissolved in the cryolite; and as the current passes through, the alumina is separated into its component parts of aluminum and oxygen. The oxygen, liberated at the anodes, combines with the carbon and escapes through the crust of the bath. The aluminum is deposited on the bottom of the cell (the cathode) where it remains as a molten layer. It is tapped from the cell into large mixing ladles and cast into pigs, each of which weighs approximately 50 pounds. The cryolite bath material is not affected by the decomposition of the alumina; hence the process is continuous, alumina being added to the bath from time to time.

When the metal comes from the electrolytic cells it contains some dross and bath material. For this reason, pig aluminum should first undergo a remelting operation to remove these nonmetallic impurities. If alloys rather than commercially pure aluminum are desired, the alloying can take place during this remelting. The principal alloying elements are copper, silicon, magnesium, manganese, zinc, nickel, iron, and more recently chromium. After remelting, the metal is cast into ingots for use by industry.[18]

RAW MATERIALS AND SERVICE MATERIALS

To make a ton of steel ordinarily takes about two tons of ore and maybe two tons of other materials besides air, water, sand, etc. But to make a ton of aluminum in the United States or Canada takes from 4 to 6 tons of bauxite alone.[19] This quantity of bauxite yields about 2 tons of alumina, which in turn yields about 1 ton of aluminum. It should be remembered that before shipment the bauxite is processed or beneficiated by removing moisture and impurities. Considerably more than 4 to 6 tons of raw bauxite would be needed to produce a ton of aluminum.

In addition to the bauxite, considerable amounts of fuel, chemicals, and other service materials are required. In the United States natural gas is progressively supplementing and in some cases supplanting coal as the source of heat in the Bayer process of alumina production. Besides fuel, this process calls for caustic soda and the Combination process calls for limestone and soda ash. The Hall-Héroult process requires 10 kilowatt-hours of electricity for each pound of aluminum, or 20,000 kw.-h.

per short ton, about 1200 pounds of carbon electrodes, about 200 pounds of cryolite, and 100 pounds of aluminum fluoride for each ton of aluminum made. All in all, the raw and service materials required for one ton of aluminum amount to about 8 or 9 tons in the United States and Canada; they may run double this in Germany where lignite is used instead of coal and no natural gas is available.

These figures do not remain constant. For example, when Alcoa opened its large alumina plant in Mobile, Alabama, in 1938, it could make fuller use of natural gas, thus cutting down on coal consumption. So far all the electricity used in private aluminum plants has been hydroelectric, but in a new aluminum reduction plant (capacity, 114,000,000 pounds per year) at Point Comfort across the bay from Port Lavaca, Texas, Alcoa is using electric power generated with natural gas.

Secondary Aluminum

As is the case with most secondary metals, two sources of secondary aluminum must be distinguished: old market scrap and new home or plant scrap. In the fabrication of aluminum about one-fourth of the weight of the raw material is "lost" and reappears as new scrap. As was pointed out in connection with new steel and copper scrap, such scrap is merely part of the flow of material in process, "runaround" as it is sometimes called, and does not constitute a net addition to the supply of primary aluminum. On the other hand, the old scrap collected by junk dealers that is made up of discarded utensils, machine parts, building material, etc., is a definite addition to the market supply, although it cannot now be used for many of the purposes to which virgin aluminum is put. However, its usefulness and competitive strength are increasing because the technique of preparing aluminum scrap for fabrication is constantly improving. In particular the use of secondary aluminum alloys is increasing.

Normally, old scrap constitutes an addition to the supply equal to about 20 or 25 percent of the output of primary aluminum, but the ratio varies with the business cycle and other forces that influence the respective cost-price ratios. During World War II, when aluminum

---

[18] *Ibid.*, pp. 19-22.
[19] The amount varies, depending on the grade of the ore. High-grade bauxite, i.e., ore with a low silica content, is preferred.

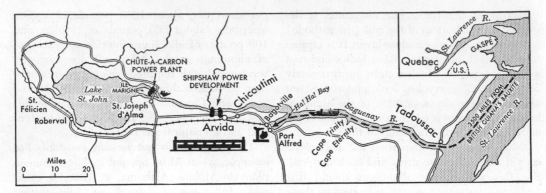

FIG. 44.4.   The Saguenay Valley. (*Time*, map by R. M. Chapin, Jr., courtesy of *Time*, copyright Time Inc., 1948.)

fabrication reached fantastic heights, the new scrap amounted to hundreds of thousands of tons, while the collection of old aluminum, accelerated at first by national scrap drives, lagged because of increasing costs of collection and the gradual drying up of sources of scrap.

OWNERSHIP AND LOCATION OF PLANTS
Plant Expansion of Alcoa

Before 1902, when the company opened its own alumina plant, Alcoa bought alumina first from Germany and later from the Pennsylvania Salt Manufacturing Company which processed Alcoa bauxite. From 1902 until 1938 there was only one alumina plant in the United States. It is owned and operated by Alcoa and located at East St. Louis, Illinois. This location possesses the following advantages: easy access to Arkansas bauxite, proximity to coal mines, availability of chemicals, especially caustic soda, access to industrial markets that need bauxite for other purposes than aluminum production, favorable location for distributing alumina to aluminum plants in eastern Canada and the United States. Even bauxite imported from Alcoa's mining properties in Surinam (Dutch Guiana) can be brought up the Mississippi to East St. Louis at reasonable cost. Besides alumina, the East St. Louis plant also makes synthetic cryolite and has access to fluorspar mines controlled by Alcoa.

In 1938 Alcoa opened its large plant at Mobile, Alabama; this is favorably located to receive Guiana bauxite and to deliver alumina to aluminum plants farther north at Badin, North Carolina, and Alcoa, Tennessee, and in

the Northwest. The use of natural gas instead of coal may favorably affect production costs at the Mobile plant. Until 1948, aluminum plants in the United States and Canada were invariably located at hydroelectric sites. The following plants, all belonging to Alcoa or its affiliated companies, were built prior to the large expansion program of the late thirties:

1895   Niagara Falls, Niagara River (closed in 1949).
1901   Shawinigan Falls, St. Maurice River, Canada.
1903   Massena, N. Y., St. Lawrence River.
1914   Alcoa, Tennessee, the Little Tennessee River System.
1916   Badin, North Carolina, the Yadkin River.

In 1926 Alcoa began to manufacture aluminum at Arvida on the Saguenay River in eastern Quebec, Canada, and in 1928 alumina works were added; hence Arvida became the first integrated plant in North America. It converts mainly British Guiana bauxite first into alumina then into aluminum. There are separate plants for the production of synthetic cryolite, aluminum fluoride, and electrodes. The bauxite, coal, coke, pitch, fluorspar, and other raw materials are brought up to Port Alfred on the Saguenay from where they move by railroad about twenty miles to Arvida (see Fig. 44.4). During World War II the ingot capacity of Arvida was stepped up to 1.1 billion pounds (550,000 tons), which means about 1.1 million tons of alumina produced and about 2.2 million tons of bauxite consumed.

In order to produce this vast amount of aluminum, 550,000 tons at one place, a stupendous amount of electric power must be available. Figuring only 10 kilowatt-hours per pound gives a total of 11 billion kilowatt-hours for the reduction itself. The actual installation has a capacity of 1.3 million kilowatts.

This enormous power is provided at Shipshaw, which experts have called the finest power site in the world. Alcoa interests had their eye on it as early as 1925, but the site was not developed until during World War II. The cost, $62.5 million (estimated peacetime cost $39 million), was provided by Allied governments who were in desperate need of more aluminum to support the air war against the Axis. Previously Chûte-à-Carron, another site farther up the Saguenay, had provided power for Arvida.[20] The following gives an idea of the size of the Shipshaw project:

Five great dams were built, directing the entire flow of the Saguenay River into a new channel hewn out of solid rock. Concrete-lined tunnels of thirty foot diameter were cut through rock to carry water down a two-hundred foot drop to the turbines. Storage dams were built on tributaries of the Saguenay, to stabilize the water flow throughout the year. Planes flew men and materials to Lake Manouan, wilderness storage reservoir of the Shipshaw power plant. Temperatures often dropped to 25-35° below zero. Sixty-two lives were lost in the course of two winters' work. But the work proceeded to completion in the fall of 1943.

Besides the plants at Arvida and Shawinigan Falls there are two other reduction plants in Canada, one at Beauharnais and the other at La Tuque.

But things did not stand still in the United States while these developments were going on in Canada. Beginning in about 1939 Alcoa

---

[20] The Saguenay forms a large lake, Lake St. John, and on emerging from the lake is divided by the Isle Maligne into two turbulent channels, each an excellent water-power site. The western one was developed in 1924 by the Duke (tobacco)-Price (paper) interests. The other channel was developed by the aluminum interests and provides power for Arvida. Shipshaw is farther down the river and has a far greater head, about 200 feet, than the old sites. The total drop from Lake St. John to sea level is about 300 feet. When Shipshaw was built, the older site was given a stand-by status.

invested large sums to step up production of both alumina and aluminum. The opening of its Mobile alumina plant in 1938 has been mentioned. In addition, an aluminum reduction plant was opened in Vancouver, Washington, in 1940.

Government-Sponsored Expansion and Competition

In the summer of 1940 the United States government, long eager to break the Alcoa monopoly, assisted the Reynolds Metals Company,[21] by means of substantial loans, to build a reduction plant at Longview, Washington, and a combined alumina-aluminum plant at Listerhill, Alabama. Reynolds also entered the bauxite mining business in the United States and later acquired bauxite reserves in the Caribbean, especially Haiti, the Dominican Republic, and Jamaica. In 1941 there were three alumina and seven aluminum plants in operation in the United States:

Alumina:	East St. Louis, Ill	} Alcoa
	Mobile, Alabama	
	Listerhill, Alabama	Reynolds
Aluminum:	Niagara Falls, New York	} Alcoa
	Massena, New York	
	Alcoa, Tennessee	
	Badin, North Carolina	
	Vancouver, Washington	
	Listerhill, Alabama	} Reynolds
	Longview, Washington	

Their aggregate capacity exclusive of Canadian capacity was 426,000 tons, of which Alcoa controlled 345,000 and Reynolds 81,000. This was wholly inadequate as the basis of the tremendous aircraft program imposed on this country by World War II. This raised the same question that many other of our industries were facing: Should private enterprise take upon itself the enormous task of wartime expansion, knowing that peace most likely would bring with it a sharp curtailment of aluminum requirements? As in many other cases, it was decided to have the government underwrite the risks of ownership and to rely on experienced private entrepreneurs to build and op-

---

[21] Long known as a producer of aluminum foil used in the cigarette industry, especially by the Reynolds Tobacco Company.

erate the plants. But there was only one experienced private entrepreneur—Alcoa. Consequently, except for a small plant at Tacoma, Washington, which was operated by the Olin Corporation, all the government-owned reduction plants were operated by Alcoa. Table 44.5

TABLE 44.5. United States Aluminum-Reduction Plants, Operator and Capacity, 1944[22]

Ownership and Location of Plant	Operator	Capacity (short tons)
Alcoa-owned		
Niagara Falls, N. Y.	Alcoa[a]	21,000
Massena, N. Y.	"	82,000
Alcoa, Tenn.	"	170,500
Badin, N. C.	"	55,500
Vancouver, Wash.	"	86,000
Total, Alcoa-owned		415,000
Reynolds-owned:		
Longview, Wash.	Reynolds	31,000
Listerhill, Ala.	"	50,000
Total, Reynolds-owned		81,000
Government-owned		
Jones Mill, Ark.	Alcoa[a]	70,500
Los Angeles, Calif.	"	89,000
Modesto (Riverbank), Calif.[b]	"	54,000
Troutdale, Ore.	"	70,500
Burlington, N. J.	"	53,000
Maspeth (Queens, L.I.), N.Y.[c]	"	149,500
Massena (St. Lawrence), N.Y.	"	52,500
Meade (Spokane, Wash.)	"	108,000
Total, government-owned, Alcoa-operated		647,000
Tacoma, Wash.	Olin Corp.	20,500
Total, government-owned		667,500
Grand total		1,163,500

[a] The lease on which Alcoa's operation of these seven government-owned plants was based was canceled August 30, 1945, effective October 31, 1945.
[b] Closed.
[c] Partly dismantled.

lists these plants. But not all these plants are equally efficient. The two plants in the Greater New York area—Maspeth, one of the largest ever constructed, and Burlington—hardly went into production. Their power rates are excessive. To some extent that applies also to the Los Angeles and Modesto plants.

The Struggle to End a Monopoly

When peace brought with it the problem of disposing of these plants, their relative effi-

[22] U.S. Tariff Commission, op. cit., p. 76. The last two figures are corrected to agree with the rest of the table.

ciency was kept in mind. But one other problem was dominant in the minds of the policymakers: how to break the monopoly of Alcoa. For years the government had tried to prove that Alcoa was a monopoly but had been woefully unsuccessful in the lower courts. Finally, when the case was ready to go before the Supreme Court, no disinterested quorum of its members was available. So Congress, in June, 1944, passed a law providing that the Supreme Court certify the case to the three senior judges of the appropriate Circuit Court of Appeals. The court chosen was that of the Second District (New York), Judges Learned Hand, Swan, and Augustus Hand. Although this court upheld the lower courts on virtually all the 140 counts of the indictment, it reversed the lower courts on one important count, i.e., the question of monopoly. It found that Alcoa had a monopoly of the aluminum ingot market in 1940. Moreover, the opinion stressed the fact that Alcoa was not a passive beneficiary of conditions that inevitably pointed to monopoly but an active aggressive seeker after monopoly power. Recognizing that Alcoa's position after the war depended to a large extent on the disposal of the government plants, the court refused to take any action against the company but reserved that right for a later date.

This court decision gave the government a strong leverage in its plant disposal policy. Alcoa held an ace card in the patents on the Combination process without which the giant Hurricane Creek plant in Arkansas was more or less a white elephant because there was not enough high-grade bauxite in the neighborhood to warrant anything like full-scale operation. On the other hand, a dissolution suit was hanging over the heads of Alcoa executives like the sword of Damocles. So the government held a strong hand too, in fact so strong that it succeeded in inducing Alcoa to license its patents covering the Combination process to the government free of charge and unencumbered. These patents, in turn, were the key to the postwar situation, for they made it possible to work the Hurricane Creek alumina plant on a scale large enough to keep unit costs on a competitive level. With this plant as a core around which to build a competitive national aluminum industry, the government leased Hurricane Creek, the aluminum plants at nearby Jones Mills, Arkansas, and the one at Troutdale, Oregon, to Reynolds on terms supposedly assuring a competitive set-up. In addition, it disposed of the plants at Meade (Spokane) and Tacoma, Washington, and at Baton Rouge, Louisiana, to the Henry Kaiser interests.[23] Aluminum plant capacity was thus distributed as follows: Alcoa, 325,000 tons; Reynolds, 188,865 tons; Kaiser, 128,750 tons. The closing of the old Niagara works in October, 1949, reduced Alcoa's capacity to 294,000 tons. Reynolds' capacity was slightly increased to 196,865 tons by the addition of a third potline at Jones Mills. The Kaiser capacity remained the same as in 1946.

In judging the postwar competitive situation one must not lose sight of the potentialities of Shipshaw. Its natural and acquired advantages are such that Reynolds and Kaiser would be uneasy did not the tariff keep foreign aluminum at arm's length. Strange to say, in this case the removal of the tariff might result in lessening rather than strengthening the power of competition. One should also keep in mind that both Reynolds and Kaiser own manufacturing plants that require considerable portions of the aluminum they produce. In other words, it would be an error to put too much faith in the advent of two additional producers of aluminum, for their capacity to serve the general market is limited by their own needs.

There is talk of putting one or more alumina plants in the Pacific Northwest. Such plants might conceivably draw on the reserves of bauxite in Indonesia and some islands of the South Pacific. There is also talk of using the large laterite deposits in British Columbia; they are being explored to determine the possibility of extracting both iron and aluminum. The Port Lavaca aluminum plant of Alcoa, which has been mentioned, illustrates the point that the situation is constantly changing. Its future development will depend much on the outcome of the East-West struggle that casts its shadow on all economic speculations of our day.

Besides alumina and aluminum plants, nu-

merous fabricating plants are scattered over a considerable area, mostly in the industrial Northeast but also in California, near the huge airplane factories. These fabricating plants represent a very large investment.

THE ALUMINUM INDUSTRY OUTSIDE OF THE UNITED STATES AND CANADA

Before the collapse of the Axis there existed on the European continent a large aluminum industry built chiefly around the bauxite deposits of Hungary and France. The alumina plants were concentrated in Germany; they used German lignite as fuel and in reduction made use of the hydroelectric power of the Alps, including Bavarian, Austrian, Swiss, French, and Italian sectors. Table 44.6 gives a bird's-eye view of the world situation.

The countries in Group I are the great industrial centers, and also the chief military powers, where most of the aluminum was produced—about 80 percent—and even more—about 92 percent—was consumed before World War II. Group II includes the hydroelectric export group, countries which because of their cheap power sites are logical places for aluminum plants but whose markets cannot absorb the output. These centers—Switzerland, Norway, and Canada—contributed almost three-fourths of prewar aluminum exports. Most of their production capacity was foreign-controlled. The countries in Group III have a small domestic market and small aluminum plants designed to serve these markets. Sweden, Hungary, Brazil, and India have considerable bauxite deposits.

Before World War II Germany was the world's leading producer and consumer of aluminum. The industry was born during World War I and was strictly government-owned and -controlled. As was mentioned before, Germany found it easier to make aluminum than to import other nonferrous metals. Furthermore, at this time she was far advanced in aluminum technology, especially that pertaining to aluminum alloys.

The last two columns of the table show how World War II completely altered the aluminum map of the world. The combined United States-Canadian capacity jumped to 61.4 percent of the world total, leaving 38.6 percent for the

---

[23] Kaiser at first leased Spokane and Baton Rouge, and bought Tacoma; but in July, 1949, he bought both Spokane and Baton Rouge.

TABLE 44.6. Production, Imports, Exports, and Estimated Consumption of Aluminum, by Producing Countries, Annual Average, 1935-1938, and Capacity, 1944[24]

Country	Rank as Consumer	1935-1938 Average				Apparent Excess of Production over Consumption		1944 Estimated Smelting Capacity at End of Year	
		Primary Production	Imports	Exports	Estimated Consumption[a]	Quantity (1000 short tons)	Percent	Quantity (1000 short tons)	Percent of World Capacity
Group I									
Germany	1	125.7	13.9	9.0	130.7	-5.0	-4	254	9.7
United States	2	115.5	13.7	2.9	126.2	-10.7	-8	1086	41.6
United Kingdom	3	20.4	38.7	8.8[b]	50.3	-29.9	-60	56	2.2
Soviet Union	4	37.8[b]	2.6		40.4	-2.6	-6	76	2.9
France	5	36.2	1.3	8.3	29.2	7.0	+24	115	4.4
Italy	6	21.6	1.5	1.9	21.2	0.4	+1	65	2.5
Japanese Empire	7	10.6	10.4	1.1	20.0	-9.4	-47	195	7.5
Group II									
Switzerland	13	21.3	3.7	23.8	1.2	20.1	+1,709	38	1.5
Canada	17	42.8	1.6	44.2	c	42.8	+21,300	515	19.8
Norway	15	22.7	c	23.3	0.5	22.2	+4,441	37	1.4
Group III									
Sweden	8	2.2	3.4	c	5.4	-3.2	-60	5	0.2
Hungary	11	1.0	0.6	c	1.5	-0.5	-34	19	0.7
Austria	10	4.1	0.5	2.5	2.0	2.1	+100	106	4.1
Spain	14	0.7	c	b	0.8	-0.1	-12	17	0.7
Yugoslavia	16	c	c	c	c	0.2	+47	5	0.2
Brazil	12	d	1.5		1.5	0.0	...	6	0.3
India	9	d	2.9		2.9	0.0	...	9	0.3
Total, world		462.9		126.2	454.2	...	...	2604	100.0

a Nearly all these figures are understated because they do not include domestic secondary aluminum.
b Not available.
c Less than 500 tons.
d Not in production during this period.

24 U.S. Tariff Commission, op. cit., p. 94.

rest of the world. To be sure, that 61.4 percent included some government-sponsored plants which later proved uneconomical to operate. A more striking illustration of the meaning of "military potential," and especially the problem of predicting it, would be hard to find.

The United Kingdom depends largely on imported aluminum to supply her considerable fabrication industry. Much of the Russian aluminum capacity was destroyed during the war, but a new industry is rising with an expected capacity of about 75,000 tons, about 3 percent of the world total. Italy has good bauxite in Istria. Japan managed to push her aluminum output, including that of plants in Manchuria and Korea, to nearly 200,000 tons during the war.

INTERNATIONAL CARTELS

Like most metal industries, the aluminum industry was subject to international cartel control. So long as the basic patents were valid, they constituted the controlling influence. But when their expiration threatened to bring competition into the field, international cartels were organized. Because of the anti-trust laws, the Aluminum Company of America, as such, never joined such cartels. Aluminum Limited was organized in 1928 to take over all of Alcoa's foreign holdings except bauxite deposits and mining properties in Surinam. These holdings included (1) bauxite deposits in France, Istria, Yugoslavia, Rumania, and other parts of Europe; the holdings were later expanded to include Africa, India, the West Indies; and (2) stock interests in such producing companies as Norway Aluminum Company (Norske Aluminium Akskelschap) and Norwegian Nitrit Company. The Canadian holdings were placed under a single subsidiary of Alted, called Alcan (Aluminum Company of Canada). Outside of Russia and Japan the world aluminum industry was largely controlled by Alcoa, Alted, and Germany's government-controlled aluminum industry whose influence was strongly felt in the international cartel. The cartel influenced prices and other interests by allocating markets and controlling output.[25]

[25] For a full discussion, see Ervin Hexner, *International Cartels*, University of North Carolina

MAGNESIUM

Sources

Even lighter than aluminum is magnesium. Magnesium-bearing minerals are very abundant. In fact, magnesium is the third most common metallic element in the crust of the earth. But like aluminum it does not occur in the native state but only as part of chemical compounds in complex minerals, such as:

Carnallite (a potash-magnesium salt,
$KC \cdot MgC_2 \cdot 6 H_2O$)
Dolomite ($MgCO_3CaCO_3$)
Magnesite ($MgCO_3$)
Brucite ($Mg(OH)_2$)

The magnesium content of these minerals varies from 13.8 percent in dolomite to 41.6 percent in brucite.

Magnesium is found not only in solid minerals but also in liquids such as ocean water, subsurface brines, and stagnant lakes like the Great Salt Lake in Utah and the Dead Sea in Israel. Ocean water contains 0.48 percent magnesium chloride, or 0.13 percent magnesium. It has been calculated that a cubic mile of this water contains 4 million tons of magnesium, but sucking up a cubic mile is no little task. In the Great Salt Lake the magnesium content ranges from 0.6 to 3.2 percent. The famous brines of Michigan vary considerably. During World War II new reservoirs were tapped which proved much richer than older ones.

Main Products and By-Products

According to the source from which it is obtained, magnesium may be produced as a by-product, a co-product, or the main or sole product. In the latter case, its production is likely to be correlated with other chemical operations. When magnesium is obtained from carnallite it is generally a by-product of potash production and chemical operations centering around potassium; this is the case with most German magnesium production. The Michigan brines yield numerous basic chemicals, such as caustic soda, chlorine, etc.; the prewar mag-

Press, Chapel Hill, 1946, pp. 216-221; G. W. Stocking and M. W. Watkins, *Cartels in Action*, Twentieth Century Fund, New York, 1947, pp. 216-303; Donald H. Wallace, *Market Control in the Aluminum Industry*, Harvard University Press, Cambridge, 1937.

nesium output constituted a by-product operation.[26]

History

Magnesium was first produced in France in 1830 but remained a laboratory curiosity until 1886, the year the Hall-Héroult process was invented. In that year the electrolytic recovery of magnesium from carnallite was put on a commercial basis in Germany, first in a small plant near Bremen and later on a larger scale in Bitterfeld. The firm, Chemische Fabrik Griesheim Elektron, in 1916 joined four other chemical concerns to form a chemical trust which in 1925 became known as IG Farbenindustrie AG.[27]

Magnesium production in the United States began in 1915, when the Dow Chemical Company of Midland, Michigan, obtained magnesium electrolytically from brines. Later a second company, the American Magnesium Company, entered the field; it became a subsidiary of the Aluminum Company of America in 1919. Magnesium is needed in the manufacture of certain aluminum alloys.

The extreme lightness of magnesium—two-thirds the weight of aluminum[28] and one-fifth

---

[26] Which products are main products and which by-products is largely a matter of relative demand and prices. When the demand for caustic soda provides the backlog of earnings it is the main product, and the magnesium output is determined by the caustic soda operation. If, on the other hand, the government offers to pay a multiple of the market price for all the magnesium it can put its hands on, magnesium may conceivably become the main product, pulling the other products obtained from the brine along with it. During the war, the bulk of the magnesium output in the United States was produced as the main product.

An interesting example of a by-product of magnesium output is styrene, an important constituent of synthetic rubber, which is produced from the natural gas that generates the electricity required to electrolyze magnesium. Another example is the so-called "magnesium black" produced at the Kaiser-controlled plant of the Permanente Metals Corporation of Manteca, California, and used by the synthetic rubber, rayon, and refractory industries.

[27] IG means Interessengemeinschaft, or community of interest; AG means Aktiengesellschaft, and corresponds to Ltd. in Britain and Inc. in the United States.

[28] The specific gravity of magnesium is 1.74; of aluminum, 2.7; and of copper, 8.92.

---

that of copper—made it a top strategic material during World War II. When the Allies shot down German planes over Britain and discovered that numerous parts, weighing hundreds of pounds in the aggregate, were made of magnesium, there was nothing to do but create an *ad hoc* magnesium industry—the synthetic rubber industry all over again—for the industry that had supplied the modest peacetime demand was totally inadequate to meet the competitive challenge of Germany's wartime aircraft industry. The response was magnificent. In the United States alone, magnesium output rose from 6.7 million pounds in 1939 to 367.2 million in 1943; aluminum, from 163,545 tons in 1939 to 920,179 in 1943. This record wartime expansion in the production of both metals is a valuable lesson. It shows what science and technics can achieve when life and death are involved and cost counts little or nothing at all. Conversely, it goes to show to what extent economic considerations may disregard technical possibilities in peacetime.

Properties and Uses

In addition to its lightness, magnesium has other properties of great practical importance. When alloyed with such elements as aluminum, zinc, and manganese, it attains increased strength and can be used widely for structural purposes. In fact, it is only when, through alloying, strength is added to lightness that magnesium reaches its full economic significance.

Magnesium also is a glutton for oxygen. In powdered form it is used for fireworks, flares, tracer bullets, flash bulbs, and incendiary bombs. During the war about half Germany's output is believed to have been used for such purposes. Magnesium is also used in metallurgy as a deoxidizer. As magnesium chloride it goes into the making of quick-setting cement and stucco. As milk of magnesia it has long been a household stand-by.

Technology

When the Allies were suddenly faced with the necessity of producing magnesium in amounts never before envisaged, there was no time to decide beforehand on the most efficient process. Practically every known process and every plausible raw material was pressed into service. Previous experience was no prerequisite for obtaining government backing, financial and otherwise, for a magnesium plant. As a result our war effort represents virtually a complete survey of magnesium technology. Incidentally, in our building program we overshot magnesium requirements by a wide margin.

The production methods used in the United States during the war fall into two main groups: (1) the electrolysis of magnesium chloride and (2) the thermal reduction of magnesium oxide. The electrolytic method was represented by the Dow process, which was the only one used in the United States from 1928 to 1942; and by the German Griesheim Elektron process, developed by British Magnesium Electron, Ltd., which was licensed by Griesheim in 1937, and which later incorporated some improvements made in the United States. The thermal method was represented by the Carbothermal process invented by Dr. Hansgirg of Vienna (also known as the Radentheim process, so called after the town in Austria where Hansgirg's first plant, later destroyed by an explosion,[29] was built) and by the ferrosilicon or Pidgeon process.

These various processes have diverse advantages and drawbacks. Thus the Dow electrolytic process has the advantages of long experience and of applicability to both subsurface brine and sea water, and the drawback of high electric power consumption, 10 to 14 kilowatt-hours per pound of metal produced. At a time when aluminum producers were taking close to 10 percent of all the electricity available in the United States, the prospect of adding another industry, if anything even hungrier for electric power, was none too pleasing. The Pidgeon process, developed in Canada, requires less than half as much electric power per pound of magnesium produced; hence it was warmly recommended by the Academy of Science in spite of the fact that ferrosilicon is a costly material. The Carbothermal process (Hansgirg) looked good from

the raw-material angle, but proved the most difficult from an engineering standpoint. Experts apparently still consider that it and the Dow sea-water process are probably the cheapest large-scale processes. The Dow process applied to brines is really a by-product proposition.

The largest single magnesium plant built in the United States during World War II is the Las Vegas, Nevada, plant of the Basic Magnesium Company. Its capacity equals the combined total of the three sea-water plants on the Texas coast at Freeport and Velasco. It was first operated under British supervision but did not hit its stride until its management was turned over to Anaconda, whose personnel evidently have had more experience with the large-scale operation of intricate processes.

In many respects the most interesting magnesium-producing plants in this country are the three built and operated by Dow at Freeport and Velasco, Texas. The first was built privately by Dow at Freeport; it had a capacity of 10,000 tons a year. As soon as this plant proved its feasibility the government ordered two similar plants, one at Freeport and the other at Velasco. What makes these plants so interesting is the remarkable combination of conditions that favor their location. A sea-water plant first of all must be topographically suited to the handling, drawing in, and emitting of large amounts of water.[30] The process used in the Texas plants calls for lime, caustic soda, and electricity. The lime can be obtained from oyster shells, large accumulations of which are found on the nearby coast. Caustic soda is a derivative of salt; the coast is studded with salt domes. Cheap electricity can be made with natural gas, especially when, as was mentioned before, the gas yields styrene as a by-product.

Production

It soon developed that the United States government had overshot the mark in planning

---

[29] After the explosion the equipment was transferred to an IG plant in Germany. In the meantime Hansgirg process pilot plants were established in Britain and, of all places, in Korea.

[30] Dow had previous experience with the selection of such sites. When tetraethyl lead was introduced as an antiknock ingredient in gasoline, back in the early thirties, Dow built a large sea-water plant on the coast of North Carolina to extract bromine for making ethylene dibromide, a solvent to keep the lead in tetraethyl lead from depositing on the spark plugs.

TABLE 44.7.   Production of Magnesium by Important Countries[31]
(tons of 2000 lbs.)

Year	United States	Canada	France	Germany	Italy	United Kingdom
1938	3,216	...	2,000	14,661	80	2,450[a]
1939	3,350	...	4,318	20,172	237	5,600[a]
1940	6,260	...	2,824	22,156	483	6,700[a]
1941	16,295	5	2,192	26,786	2,209	10,340
1942	48,963	404	1,470	29,762	2,749	16,386
1943	183,584	3,575	1,700	33,069	2,223	21,049
1944	157,100	5,290	930	34,171	3,300	14,433
1945	32,792	3,679	305	...	450	7,661[a]
1946	5,317	160	779	...	1,108	1,885[a]
1947	12,314	...	841	...	...	2,778[a]
1948	10,000	...	716	...	...	3,909[a]

[a] Includes secondary.

for magnesium production. The full capacity of 295,000 tons was never utilized; top production was reached in 1943, with 183,584 short tons. Cutbacks became the order of the day and by 1946 production was down to 5317 tons. Table 44.7 shows magnesium production in important countries, 1938-1946.

Stocks on hand more or less necessitated suspension of production once the war needs had been met.

Price

The story of magnesium prices is that of aluminum prices compressed into a shorter period. In the nineties aluminum was still selling at about $5 a pound; during World War II it came down to 15 cents a pound. During World War I magnesium was selling in the United States at about $5 a pound; during World War II it came down to 20.5 cents a pound. Since magnesium is about one-third lighter than aluminum, magnesium at 20.5 cents and aluminum at 15 cents sell at about comparable prices

[31] *American Bureau of Metal Statistics Yearbook, 1948*, p. 93.

per cubic foot. The future of magnesium is tied up with the world political situation. Heavy rearmament may well call for the recommissioning of wartime capacity. But now, as before the war, Dow is the sole producer of magnesium in the United States.

TITANIUM

Titanium, a newcomer in the light metal field, is at present attracting wide attention (see p. 624). Like aluminum and magnesium, titanium is a common ingredient in the crust of the earth and does not occur in the native state. Titanium compounds have been used for some time, especially by the paint industry, but metallic titanium was unknown until very recently, when the Bureau of Mines announced that it had succeeded in producing small amounts of it. In 1948 Du Pont announced that they had succeeded in developing a process for producing the metal commercially. The available light metals seem to be increasing in number. And still there remain some people who claim that resources are fixed and static!

BIBLIOGRAPHY

"Aluminum and the Emergency," *Fortune*, May, 1941.

Aluminum Company of America, *An Outline of Aluminum*, New York, 1949 (pamphlet).

Barksdale, J., *Titanium, Its Occurrence, Chemistry, and Technology*, New York, Ronald, 1949.

Dow Chemical Co., *Dow and Magnesium*, Midland, Mich., 1944.

Edwards, J. D., and others, *The Aluminum Industry*, New York, McGraw-Hill, 2 vols., 1930.

Engle, N. H., Gregory, H. E., and Mosse, R.,

Aluminum: An Industrial Marketing Appraisal, Chicago, Irwin, 1945.

Herres, O., "Titanium—A Growing Industry," *Mining and Metallurgy,* April, 1946.

"Magnesium by the Ton," *Fortune,* March, 1944.

Muller, C. F., *Light Metals Monopoly,* New York, Columbia University Press, 1946.

U. S. Tariff Commission, *Magnesium,* War Changes in Industry Series, Report No. 10, March, 1945.

U. S. Tariff Commission, *Aluminum,* War Changes in Industry Series, Report No. 14, 1946.

Wallace, D. H., *Market Control in the Aluminum Industry,* Cambridge, Harvard University Press, 1937.

Chapter 45

BASE METALS

Some years ago the Western Electric Company published a fascinating booklet entitled *From the Far Corners of the Earth* which contained an account of the materials that go into a modern telephone and the places they come from. It fell only little short of a catalogue of industrial materials and of a world economic geography. Its story of the raw materials that go into one end product of modern industry must have been a revelation to most readers who otherwise could never have imagined the global ramifications of modern industrial procurement. Later on the automobile industry released a similar story about its raw materials and their sources.

Both these publications drove home a fundamental fact about modern industry: its dependence on many parts of the earth for its raw materials, most of them minerals, many of them metals. Some of them are as old as history; others are newcomers or recent arrivals. Some are abundant and cheap; others rare and expensive. Some are produced in many parts of the earth and are competitive commodities as metals go; others are subject to rigid monopoly control. Some are largely dissipated in use; a considerable portion of others is reused as scrap. Some are produced in the industrial countries which consume them; others are produced in one corner of the earth and consumed in another. Each metal fills a niche of its own, each has its own story to tell. Here we are concerned only with the five most widely used of those not already discussed.

LEAD

Lead is one of the oldest metals known to man. It was used for money by the Chinese before 2000 B.C., and the famous silver-lead deposits at Laurion near Athens were worked as early as 1200 B.C. The lead pipes which provided the citizens of Pompeii with drinking water are as well known as are the lead roofs of the Venetian jails. Lead was used by the ancients for ornaments, coins, solder, bronzes, vases, and pipes.[1] In the course of history both its uses and its usefulness increased.

---

[1] Alan M. Bateman, *Economic Mineral Deposits,* John Wiley & Sons, Inc., New York, 1942, p. 525.

Properties

Pure lead is a soft, heavy metal which melts at 327° C. Because of its softness it is easily worked. The addition of a small amount of antimony imparts great strength and hardness. Lead is remarkably resistant to the action of many chemicals. Paints made from lead, especially white lead and red lead, possess excellent coloring power and resist weathering.[2] Lead is marketed in four principal grades—corroding, chemical, common, and antimonal or hard.

Until recently, lead was a cheap metal that sold for a fraction of the price of copper, aluminum, etc. At present, however, because of an acute shortage, lead is bringing prices higher than ever before.[3] During World War II premiums were paid to high-cost producers, but the base price was around 6 cents a pound. The present high price is bound to encourage a thorough search for substitutes. Like most commodities, lead has marginal uses from which it is easily displaced by competitive materials when its price is excessive.[4]

Uses

The properties of lead determine its uses. Its resistance to acids adapts it to use in storage batteries. Its resistance to weather and to the action of sea water makes it suitable for cable covering. Its resistance to the action of the chemicals in water accounts to a great extent for its use in construction work. Its capacity to harden when alloyed with antimony and other elements renders it suitable as a bearing and type metal. Table 45.1 shows the uses of lead in the United States.

Unlike copper and aluminum which have been lifted up to a new level of significance by new industries—electricity and aviation—

that depend on them, lead continues to serve many more or less old uses. It is true that lead has gained new importance in the automobile industry in two ways—in storage batteries and as tetraethyl lead in antiknock gasoline. On the other hand, it has lost part of the paint market to titanium and to lacquers. Lead consumption, therefore, has not risen as fast as has that of copper and aluminum. Thus in 1900 per capita consumption of lead in the United States was 7 pounds as against 4.6

TABLE 45.1.   Uses of Lead in the United States in Selected Years[5]
(thousand short tons)

Use	1939	1943	1947
Storage batteries	198.0	257.0	380.0
Pigment	132.3	129.6	120.6
Cable covering	74.4	141.0	158.7
Building	50.0	62.0	78.0
Tetraethyl	30.0	60.3	66.6
Automobiles	8.9	1.0	1.0
Ammunition	42.3	178.0	40.0
Terne plate	6.0	5.0	. . .
Foil	21.8	13.0	3.6
Bearing metal	12.8	35.0	40.1
Solder	20.0	38.0	59.6
Type metal	14.0	17.0	25.0
Calking	16.0	30.0	49.9
Other uses	40.6	133.7	148.9
Total	667.0	1100.0	1172.0

pounds for copper. In 1936 the corresponding figures were 5.6 and 9.8. The difference was less pronounced in 1947, with about 16 pounds for lead and 18 pounds for copper.[6]

A significant distinction in the use of lead is that between dissipative and nondissipative uses, for this determines the amount of lead that is recovered and reused as secondary lead. Lead used in storage batteries, cable covering, and in type and bearing metal can be recovered, but most of that used for other purposes is dissipated. In 1947 nondissipative uses constituted over half the total, which means that probably between 55 and 60 percent of the lead consumed in the United States that year can be classified as recoverable.

---

[2] The danger of lead poisoning has led to the use of lead paints being prohibited in some countries. Because of its purer whiteness, titanium is beginning to replace lead in white paint.

[3] The average price in New York was 14.673 cents a pound in 1947, 18.043 cents in 1948, and 21.5 cents in February, 1949. Previous highs were 9.02 in 1925 and 8.787 in 1917. The usual range was from 3 to 6 cents.

[4] In this connection the replacing of the more perishable lead batteries by durable cadmium batteries takes on particular significance. See *Reader's Digest*, September, 1948, pp. 79 ff.

---

[5] Tables 45.1 and 45.2 from U.S. Department of the Interior, Bureau of Mines.

[6] Battery output in 1947 was exceptionally large, consequently lead consumption was pushed somewhat out of line.

Secondary Lead

In 1946 the secondary lead industry approached the volume of its peak year, 1941, the year of the great wartime scrap drives. In 1946 close to 400,000 tons of lead worth almost $66 million were recovered from over 500,000 tons of lead scrap. The average price of scrap was 8.4 cents a pound, considerably more than the price of primary lead throughout most of its history. The 1946 figures were surpassed in 1947, with a record total production of 511,970 short tons of secondary lead, of which 444,578 tons came from old scrap.

As in all scrap recovery operations, a sharp distinction must be made between old or market scrap and new or home scrap. In the case of lead, new scrap constitutes a minor element —in the United States, about a sixth of the total in 1946. This means that most secondary lead is a net addition to the year's lead supply. Ordinarily secondary lead recovered from old scrap makes up 36 percent of the supply.

In 1946, for the first time on record, the production of primary lead smelter in the United States was exceeded by our smelter output of secondary lead, the figures being 293,309 and 392,787 tons respectively. This strange development was the result of an abnormally low output of primary lead caused by strikes and other disturbances and uncertainties, and of an output of secondary lead considerably in excess of the average. In 1947, the production of secondary lead exceeded the lead smelter output from both domestic and foreign ores by over 16,000 tons.

Lead Ores

By far the most important lead minerals are lead sulfide (PbS), known as galena, lead carbonate ($PbCO_3$), known as cerrusite, and lead sulfate ($PbSO_4$), known as anglesite. The lead content of these minerals is 86.6, 77.5, and 68.3 percent respectively. Lead ores are ores containing enough lead, along with other recoverable metals, to pay for their operation. Many lead ores are argentiferous. If there is enough silver, a lead content of even 2 percent may justify exploitation; but in the absence of silver the lead content must be 3 to 4 percent higher. Many lead ores are much richer; in some the lead content runs as high as 20 percent or more.

Galena is generally associated with zinc blende, the sulfide of zinc and its commonest ore mineral. One of the great exceptions is the famous lead belt of southeastern Missouri, "the greatest lead district in the world." Here lead is virtually the sole metal product, although a little silver is produced with it. Lead and zinc frequently occur in complex minerals that also contain copper, silver, tungsten, and antimony. It is these complex ores which benefited most from the flotation process—especially its more advanced development, selective or differential flotation. As was explained before (see p. 700), this process turned unmanageable complexity, a liability, into a multiple source of profit.

TABLE 45.2.   Lead Production in the United States by Leading Districts
(thousand short tons)

	1939		1943		1946	
Southeastern Missouri	153.6		197.3		135.8	
Coeur d'Alene region	81.7	76.7%	89.8	78.6%	56.5	61%
Joplin region	44.2		34.7		23.4	
Bingham, Utah	36.8		35.4		12.3	
Others	97.7	23.3%	96.1	21.4%	147.3	39%
Total United States	414.0		453.3		375.3	

Lead deposits are widely scattered, but at present the bulk of the world output comes from relatively few regions. Thus about three-fourths of the lead produced in the United States comes from three mining areas: (1) the lead belt of southeastern Missouri, which usually produces about one-third of our output; (2) the Coeur d'Alene district of Idaho, near the Montana border, which, one of the richest mineral areas in the world, "normally" contributes over one-fifth; (3) the so-called Joplin or tri-state district, Missouri-Oklahoma-Kansas, which yields over 10 percent of our national lead output and almost 40 percent of our national zinc output. The production of lead and zinc at Bingham, Utah, is overshadowed by the tremendous copper output of the nearby copper mines. The rest of our output of lead is scattered over the west from Montana down to Colorado and Utah.

Similarly in the rest of the world, a few regions supply the bulk of the lead output.

In Canada the Sullivan mine of the Consolidated Mining and Smelting Company of Kimberly, British Columbia, generally produces 98 percent of the lead and, incidentally, three-quarters of the zinc produced in that country. The ore averages 10 percent lead and 4.5 percent zinc and is rich in silver. There is also some copper and gold. If central Mexico and the northern extension into Coahuila are considered one region, there is considerable concentration. As a lead-producing country, Mexico ranks second after the United States. The ores generally contain zinc and silver as well as lead. About 80 percent of Mexico's production is controlled by four companies: American Metal, Howe Sound, Fresnillo (Zacatecas), and San Francisco (Chihuahua). South America is poorly endowed with lead. The Cerro de Pasco Company, which operates in Peru, is the largest producer. Argentina, with the Aguilar mine controlled by the St. Joseph Lead Company, is the second important lead producer, and Bolivia is third.

In Australia the Broken Hill area of New South Wales, where German capital was once active, yields about 80 percent of the lead and 77 percent of the zinc supply of that continent. The chief zinc-lead district of Europe was in the German province of Silesia which was lost to Poland after World War I and now lies behind the Iron Curtain. Yugoslavia, also in the eastern bloc, though not as docile as Moscow might wish, is also a leading lead-producing country. Russia is the only important lead-producing center of Asia; however, no reliable information has been available since 1937, when 60,000 tons of lead were produced mainly in Kazakstan with its famous Ridderski mines. Manchuria is another country concerning which no reliable data are available. Considerable lead deposits are scattered over Europe, but few countries are self-sufficient. Spain used to be the leading lead producer of Europe. Many of the lead deposits of the Mediterranean world were worked in ancient times, those of Sardinia by the Phoenicians, those of Laurion by the ancient Athenians, those of Spain by the Romans, etc.

Recovery of Lead from Lead Ores

The method of recovering lead from lead ores depends partly on the character of the ore.

If it contains sulfur the ore is roasted to remove most of the sulfur. The resultant concentrate is put through a blast furnace which produces base bullion, the lead counterpart of pig iron. This base bullion is generally further refined before it reaches the market; silver in particular, commonly present in it, is removed by one of several methods. Relatively little lead is purified by electrolysis. This sharp difference between copper and lead technology is due to the difference in uses to which the two metals are put. Lead is not used as an electrical conductor; hence there is no need for the extreme purity required in the case of copper.

TABLE 45.3. Lead Production of the World (exclusive of U.S.S.R.), Selected Years[7] (thousand short tons)

	1939	1943	1947	1948
United States	414.0	453.3	384.2	386.9
Canada	194.3	222.0	161.7	164.3
Newfoundland	26.8	32.9	23.3	22.1
Mexico	242.0	209.3	216.6	217.7
Total North America	877.0	917.6	785.8	791.0
Argentina	32.7	20.5	23.0	24.0
Bolivia	15.6	12.6	12.5	28.2
Peru	51.0	52.7	60.4	53.5
Total South America	99.3	85.8	95.9	105.7
Germany	100.4	115.3	16.3	24.6
Italy	48.6	14.2[a]	26.2	33.1
Spain	25.7	36.3	33.6	…
Yugoslavia	76.1	…	…	…
Burma	86.7	…	…	…
Japan	16.3	23.4	6.4	7.4
Korea	8.8	20.4	…	…
Australia	313.6	211.6	209.7	229.0
French Morocco	23.6	7.6	23.6	31.1
Rhodesia	0.3	1.4	17.5	14.6
Southwest Africa	16.2	…	14.4	28.0
Tunisia	20.0	2.6	13.7	14.7

[a] January-June only.

As was said earlier, the recovery of lead from complex ores is greatly facilitated by selective flotation, an ingenious process which removed many of the obstacles that confronted earlier lead smelters. Selective flotation not only has made available many additional ore bodies but has lowered production costs by distribut-

[7] *Yearbook of the American Bureau of Metal Statistics*, 1948, p. 33. The figures indicate the lead content of the lead ores mined.

ing them over the several metals that are extracted from complex ores.

Because some lead-mining regions lack fuel for smelting and refining and are handicapped by a lack of capital in setting up expensive equipment, a considerable amount of lead, generally in the form of concentrates, enters international trade. Thus in 1947 the total lead supply of the United States was made up of three almost equal parts: (1) ores from domestic mines, (2) ores and concentrates from foreign mines, and (3) scrap. Domestic mines supplied almost exactly one-third, foreign sources a little less than a third, and scrap a little more than a third. Total lead consumption amounted to about 1.2 million tons.

Lead Production and Consumption

Because of the considerable movement of ores and concentrates across international borders, there is considerable divergence in lead production recorded on a "mine basis" and on a "smelter basis." Belgium is not listed among the countries that mine lead ore but is credited with 105,500 tons of lead smelted in 1939, for several large smelting and refining works owned by international capital interests are located in Belgium.[8] Germany produced 214,949 tons of lead (smelter basis) in 1939, but her production that year on a mine basis showed only 100,406 tons. For France the corresponding figures for 1939 were 46,300 tons smelter basis and 5963 mine basis. On the other hand, the situation in such countries as Yugoslavia, Morocco, Spain, Argentina, Bolivia, and Peru is reversed, for these countries lack adequate smelting facilities and export considerable amounts of lead as concentrates.

Some countries consume more lead than they produce. The outstanding example is Great Britain. In 1938 she produced 12,125 tons (smelter basis) and consumed 428,200

tons. Evidently British capital was invested in other parts of the Empire and found more suitable locations for lead smelters outside the kingdom. Belgium, on the other hand, produced 99,758 tons (smelter basis) in 1938 but consumed only 38,600. France consumed 94,900 tons as against an output (smelter basis) of 46,300 tons. Large quantities of the mine output of Asia, Africa, and Australia are exported.

The United States and the World Lead Situation

During the period 1909 to 1939 inclusive, the United States produced about 35 percent of the total lead output of the world. However, the trend was downward after 1916, from a peak of 49 percent that year to a low of 20 percent in 1938. Until the end of World War I the United States was a net exporter of lead; but thereafter, with the exception of a few depression years, she became a net importer, her imports assuming large proportions after 1938. (See Fig. 45.1.)

Consumption of primary and secondary lead in the United States jumped from 546,000 tons in 1938 to over a million in 1941 and has remained around this figure except during 1946, when it dropped to 925,000. In 1947 it rose to 1,172,000 tons. The domestic mines were pushed to the utmost during World War II, in part by the stimulus of premium prices, but they are proving utterly incapable of satisfying our expanding demand; hence imports almost equaling our domestic mine output have to be resorted to. It must be recognized that while production of metals was pushed vigorously during the war, the development of new capacity lagged; and it will be some time before it can recover from the setback.

Reserves

No accurate estimates of lead reserves are available. Those in the best position to make them—the owners of the mineral properties—are not so much concerned with determining the grand total of recoverable metal as in blocking out their working reserves for from one to five years ahead; furthermore, they are usually not anxious to reveal their reserve position. Also there are many areas where modern scientific methods may reveal ore bodies not

---

[8] One reason why such plants are built in Belgium is the presence of a large desert area where poisonous fumes from the chimneys can do little harm. Most of Europe is too crowded to permit fume-spreading smelters. At least at first, the works now belonging to the Compagnie des Métaux d'Overpelt-Lommel et de Corphalie owed their location in the province of Limburg to that consideration.

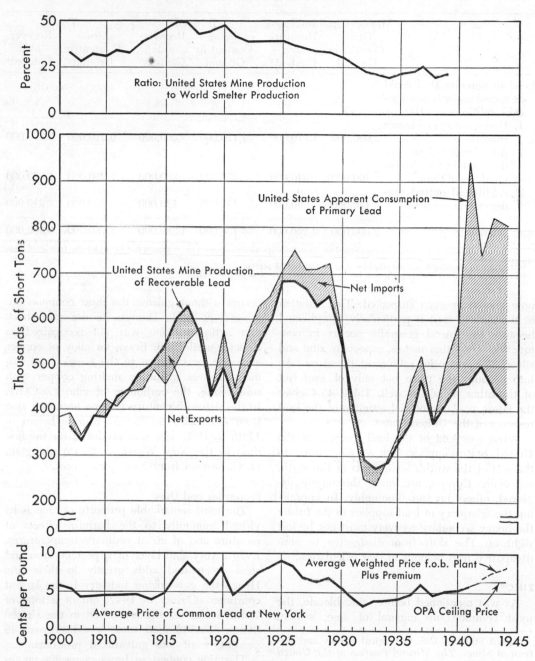

FIG. 45.1. Trends in Production, Consumption, and Price of Lead in the United States, 1906-1945. (U. S. Department of the Interior, Geological Survey and Bureau of Mines, *Mineral Position of the United States*, 1947, p. 255.)

TABLE 45.4. Estimated Lead Reserves of the United States, January, 1944[9]
(short tons of metallic lead)

	Measured and Indicated[a]		Inferred		Total	
	Gross Content in Ground	Recoverable Content[b]	Gross Content in Ground	Recoverable Content[b]	Gross Content in Ground	Recoverable Content[b]
Lead in deposits that could be mined under technological conditions in 1944:						
1. Under normal economic conditions	2,090,000	1,770,000	4,120,000	3,500,000	6,210,000	5,270,000
2. Additional output, under more favorable economic conditions	400,000	340,000	890,000	760,000	1,290,000	1,100,000
3. Additional output, under emergency prices	110,000	90,000	140,000	120,000	250,000	210,000
Total	2,600,000	2,200,000	5,150,000	4,380,000	7,750,000	6,580,000

[a] Includes estimates of measured and indicated ore in some properties where such ore is known but for which the tonnage figures are unavailable.
[b] Milling and smelting losses are considered to be roughly 15 percent.
[c] Price equivalent to 6 cents per pound for both lead and zinc, and prewar costs.

now known or even suspected. The situation in the case of lead is particularly complicated because this metal generally occurs in conjunction with other metals, especially zinc and silver. The cost-price ratio must therefore take into account the price not only of lead but of the other metals as well. Table 45.4 gives the latest available official estimate of the lead reserves of the United States.

What was said of the lead reserves of the United States applies with varying force to the rest of the world. Some parts of the earth, especially Europe, are more thoroughly explored, others far less thoroughly. In appraising the adequacy of lead supplies in the future the heavy secondary recovery must not be lost sight of. The shift from dissipative to nondissipative uses belongs in that calculation.

ZINC[10]

As was mentioned before, zinc blende, the most common ore mineral of zinc, seldom

[9] Joint Staffs of U.S. Geological Survey and Bureau of Mines, *The Mineral Position of the United States*, p. 257.
No figures available for lead in deposits whose exploitation depends on future technological advances.
[10] Most commercial zinc is known in the trade as spelter. Literally spelter is an alloy of zinc containing small amounts of lead and/or cadmium.

occurs without galena, the most common ore mineral of lead. Though its use goes back into antiquity, zinc was not recognized as a metal until 1520. Brass, an alloy of copper and zinc, was known to the Greeks and Romans. It was made by melting copper with smithsonite, the carbonate of zinc ($ZnCO_3$). In the sixteenth century Europe imported zinc from Asia. Zinc mining in Europe began in 1740. In 1838, zinc was produced for the first time in the New World at the Washington, D. C., arsenal from New Jersey ores.[11]

Properties and Uses

The most remarkable property of zinc is its virtual immunity to the harmful effects of moisture and of air at ordinary temperatures. Even a very thin layer of it protects iron and steel sheets and adds greatly to their life. Hence the galvanizing industry is the largest consumer of zinc. In 1947, out of a total of 780,675 tons of zinc consumed in the United States, 359,583 short tons, or a little over 46 percent, went into galvanized products.

The zinc content in brass generally ranges from 15 to 30 percent but may run as high as 50 percent. During the war brass constituted the largest outlet for zinc. Thus, in 1943,

[11] A. M. Bateman, *op. cit.*, pp. 525-526.

419,100 tons of zinc were used for brass, as compared with 253,200 for galvanized products. In 1948 brass requirements were low; consequently considerably less zinc went into brass than into zinc-base alloys—107,400 tons as against 232,500. A further use is rolled zinc products such as plates for battery cans, glass-jar tops, photoengraving sheets, etc. Zinc sulfide and zinc oxide are important raw materials in the paint industry. Zinc also has pharmaceutical uses. Table 45.5 shows zinc consumption in the United States in selected years.

TABLE 45.5. Slab Zinc Consumption in the United States, by Major Uses[12]
(thousand tons)

	1939	1943	1948
Galvanizing	275.0	253.2	366.0
Brass and bronze	175.0	419.1	107.4
Rolled zinc	62.0	48.5	76.7
Zinc-base alloys	84.0	76.3	232.5
Other purposes	30.0	19.7	24.2
	626.0	816.3	806.8

In Great Britain more zinc is used for brass than for any other product. About 60 percent of all the zinc consumed there in 1943, and over a third of the 1947 consumption, went into brass.

Secondary Zinc

Comparison of the uses of zinc and of lead indicates that secondary zinc recovered from old scrap is far less important than secondary lead. The scrap recovery of the leading nonferrous metals is compared in Table 45.6. The salient figure is the 91,300 tons of secondary zinc derived from old, or market, scrap, as compared with 309,800 tons for lead and 497,100 tons for copper. Old scrap is an important source of lead, six times as important in point of quantity as new or home scrap. In the case of zinc, new scrap furnishes three times as much secondary metal as does old scrap. In the case of copper the two sources are about equal. However, it should be remembered that the table covers only one year, a year that was far from "normal."

Although no revolutionary new use has developed for zinc, the production of the metal

has increased at an amazing rate. About 55 percent of the total output since 1800 was produced during the past twenty-five years; 78 percent was produced since 1900. Zinc definitely is a beneficiary of the mechanical revolution. Its use is swept along with the steel plate and iron pipe and copper that are used in a thousand mechanical devices.

Zinc Ores

The most common zinc ore minerals are zinc blende or sphalerite, the sulfide of zinc (ZnS), which contains 60 percent zinc; smithsonite, the carbonate of zinc ($ZnCO_3$), which contains 52 percent zinc; and calamine, the silicate of zinc ($ZnOH_2)SiO_3$. However, the second important zinc-producing center of the United States, Franklin Furnace, N. J., is a unique mineral area where more than 100 minerals have been identified, among them many occurring nowhere else.[13] Zinc is recovered from quite different ores, such as zincite (ZnO), containing 80.4 percent zinc, and willemite and franklinite. The latter also contains iron and manganese. The zinc makes up 15 to 20 percent of the ore mineral and is recovered as a by-product. Franklinite yields a zinc oxide used for paints; zincite also produces zinc white. Only willemite (Zn_2SiO_4) is a source of metallic zinc produced at Franklin Furnace.

The greatest center of zinc production in the world is the tri-state district of the United States, mentioned above as a source of lead. This is part of the great lead-zinc ore region which centers around the Joplin area and reaches as far north as Wisconsin. A parallel belt lies to the east in the lower Appalachians and embraces mines in both Tennessee and Virginia, and a western belt stretches from Colorado to New Mexico. The area covers a total of over 2000 square miles and has yielded metals worth about $900 million. While the tri-state district is the greatest zinc district in the world, it also has the distinction of having the lowest-grade ores.

The Sullivan mine in Kimberly, British Columbia, mentioned in connection with lead, yields about 75 percent of all the zinc produced in Canada. Her second largest zinc

[12] *Yearbook of the American Bureau of Metal Statistics,* 1948, p. 64.

[13] See A. M. Bateman, *op. cit.,* p. 535.

TABLE 45.6.   Recovery of Nonferrous Metals in the United States, 1945[14]

	From New Scrap		From Old Scrap		Total	
	000 Short Tons	Value, Million $	000 Short Tons	Value, Million $	000 Short Tons	Value, Million $
Aluminum	271.1	77.5	27.3	7.8	298.4	85.3
Antimony	2.1	0.7	15.1	4.8	17.1	5.4
Copper	509.4	120.2	497.1	117.3	1006.5	237.5
Lead	53.2	6.8	309.8	39.7	363.6	46.5
Magnesium	8.4	3.5	0.8	0.7	9.2	3.4
Nickel	4.3	3.0	2.2	1.6	6.5	4.5
Tin	11.2	11.6	24.0	24.9	35.1	36.5
Zinc	269.2	46.3	91.3	15.7	360.4	62.0
		269.5		212.1		481.6

producer is the Flin Flon mine of the Hudson Bay Mining and Smelting Company in Manitoba, 450 miles north of Winnipeg. This is primarily a copper mine but yields large returns of zinc along with cadmium, gold and silver, selenium and tellurium. The assay shows about 2.10 percent copper, 3.86 percent zinc, 0.08 ounce of gold, and 1.28 ounces of silver per ton.[15] But present methods do not permit the recovery of all this return. Table 45.7 lists import lead and zinc ore reserves.

Technology of Zinc Recovery

Most zinc and zinc-bearing ores must be concentrated by gravity mills[16] or by flotation before they can be smelted.

The recovery of zinc is complicated by several facts. In the first place, as was pointed out above, simple zinc ores are rare, most zinc being derived from lead-zinc, zinc-lead, or copper-lead-zinc ores, or from even more complex ores. In the second place, most zinc is recovered from sulfide ores, which means that there is the problem of removing the sulfur. In the third place, by-products must be dealt with, cadmium with zinc, antimony with lead, silver and gold with both, and so forth. In the fourth place, its relatively low boiling point causes zinc to vaporize at the tempera-

tures commonly used in nonferrous metallurgy. Finally, by no means all zinc is recovered as metal; much of it is recovered as oxide.

Metallic zinc is made by two main methods: electrolysis and distillation. If the zinc is combined with sulfur, the sulfur is first removed by roasting; this generally yields by-product sulfuric acid. The roast is then leached by acid solutions and either electrolyzed into very pure zinc sheets or distilled in retorts and condensers by means of heat. This retort-condenser process was introduced in Belgium in the eighteenth century and has remained virtually unchanged; hence there is much room for improvement.

Whether electrolysis or distillation is used depends partly on the nature of the raw material, partly on the relative accessibility of fuel or electricity. For a long time, about the only source of cheap electricity for electro-metallurgical purposes was hydroelectricity. Hence zinc refineries began to move to Norway, Canada, Tasmania, Rhodesia, Montana, and other sources of cheap hydroelectricity. But more recently natural gas has been coming to the fore as a source of cheap electricity, and the Texas coast is therefore being considered as a logical location for metal smelters. The new aluminum plant at Lavaca Bay has been mentioned. Other examples are the tin smelter at Texas City and the American Smelting and Refining Company's zinc smelter at Corpus Christi. Zinc concentrates are shipped by rail to the Corpus Christi refinery

[14] Bureau of Mines, "Secondary Metals—Non-Ferrous," *Minerals Yearbook, 1946,* p. 1065.
[15] See *Fortune,* June, 1938, p. 56.
[16] See discussion of gravity methods of copper ore concentration, p. 700.

TABLE 45.7.   Lead and Zinc Ore Reserves[17]

Company or Mine	Location	Year	Tonnage of Ore	Zinc %	Lead %	Copper %	Silver (oz. per ton)
					Average Grade of Ore		
Canada							
Amulet Dufault	Quebec	1947	1,997,739	4.2	...	5.7	1.51
Hudson Bay	Manitoba	1948	22,700,000	4.3	...	3.0	1.20
Normetal	Quebec	1947	1,760,000	7.6	...	3.6	2.66
Quemont	Quebec	1947	9,431,000	2.7	...	1.5	0.94
Mexico							
Fresnillo Co.	Zacatecas	1947	3,536,993	5.5	4.9	0.6	11.10
San Francisco Mines	Chihuahua	1947	3,865,290	9.2	6.6	0.7	5.11
South America							
Matilde Mine	Bolivia	1944	4,100,000	18.7	2.5	0.7	1.75
Europe							
Rammelsberg	Germany	....	6,000,000	19.0	10.0	...	.....
Royale Asturienne (Reocin)	Spain	1946	11,900,000	14.0	2.5		.....
Trepca Mines Stantrg Mine	Yugoslavia	1940	4,848,000	5.6	9.2	...	3.90
Africa							
Rhodesia, Broken Hill	Rhodesia	1945	3,774,000	28.8	13.9	...	.....
Asia							
Burma Corp.	Burma	1941	3,130,199	12.1	19.5	0.8	15.10
Australia							
Broken Hill South	New South Wales	1947	1,915,000	11.1	13.8	...	5.10
Lake George Mining Corp.	New South Wales	1947	1,654,578	12.0	6.7	0.7	1.46
North Broken Hill	New South Wales	1947	5,174,000	10.0	14.0	...	8.00
Zinc Corp.	New South Wales	1946	4,682,000	11.4	14.5	...	3.24
Electrolytic Zinc Co.	Tasmania	1947	1,500,000	22.5	6.0	...	6.90
Mount Isa	Queensland	1947	9,697,819[a]	7.5	8.6	...	6.30

[a] Of which 5,662,070 tons are prospective ore; in addition, there are 300,143 tons of carbonate ore (9.4 percent Pb).

from both New Mexico and Mexico.[18] The zinc is present in the form of sulfide; hence it is subjected to the roasting and leaching processes described above and is then converted by electrolysis into sheets of very pure zinc. Cadmium is removed and cast in the form of balls. The slush from the leaching plant is dried and sent to another plant of the American Smelting and Refining Company at El Paso for the recovery of whatever metals it still contains. One problem at the Corpus Christi refinery is the dwindling water supply. It is now planned to use sewage water purchased from the city and purified.

[17] *Yearbook of the American Bureau of Metal Statistics*, 1947, p. 75.

[18] The Mexican concentrate is shipped by the Mexican Zinc Company of Rosita, Coahuila, a subsidiary of the American Smelting and Refining Company.

The Corpus Christi refinery has a capacity of 32,000 short tons of cathode zinc. Late in 1948 it was producing close to capacity. It is dwarfed by the refining capacity of the Anaconda Copper Mining Company—175,000 tons at Great Falls and 80,000 tons at Anaconda, Montana, a total of 255,000 tons. Other electrolytic zinc refining plants in the United States are those of the American Zinc Company of Illinois at Monsanto, Ill. (capacity, 36,000 tons), and the Sullivan Mining Company at Silver King in the Coeur d'Alene region of Idaho (capacity, 44,700 tons). The largest foreign electrolytic zinc plants are those of the Consolidated Mining and Smelting Company (Sullivan mine), whose refinery at Trail, British Columbia, has a capacity of 173,000 tons. The refinery of the Electrolytic Zinc Company of Australia at Risdon, Tasmania, has a capacity of 100,000 tons. Flin Flon (Hudson

Bay Mining Company) has a zinc refining capacity of 56,000 tons. Other zinc refineries are in Belgium, France, Germany, Italy, Norway, Poland, and northern Rhodesia.[19]

Zinc contained in lead-zinc ores, i.e., ores which pay working chiefly because of their lead content, may be recovered in the following fashion. The zinc is combined with a flux to form a slag, which is then treated in so-called fuming plants. The zincky slag derived from the lead blast furnace is put through a special blast furnace which operates at higher temperatures than the lead furnace and in addition uses a blast consisting of a mixture of air and powdered coal. The powdered coal reduces the zinc in the slag to a metallic state. The metallic zinc is volatilized in the intense heat and then cooled in a series of condensers. These impure fumes can then be further refined by distilling.[20]

Structure of the Zinc Industry

The fact that much zinc is obtained in combination with other metals and is in part a by-product of copper, lead, and other nonferrous metals precludes the development of a simple industry specializing in the production of zinc. Several companies concentrate on producing it, notably the New Jersey Zinc Company, which owns the famous Franklin and Sterling mine at Franklin Furnace, mentioned earlier. But most zinc is produced by companies whose major interest lies in other fields. Thus much zinc is produced by lead companies.[21] Zinc is also produced by the custom smelters of copper companies, such as the American Smelting and Refining Company. Even the United States Steel Corporation is represented by one of its subsidiaries, the American Steel and Wire Company, whose zinc refinery at Donora, Pennsylvania, attracted some attention in connection with the poisonous

"smog" which caused several deaths in the fall of 1948.

Production and Consumption of Zinc

International statistics on zinc ore production and consumption are quite satisfactory. However, data on zinc production are not kept uniformly—some countries include secondary zinc, whereas others do not—hence an accurate statistical tabulation is difficult. Moreover, relatively little is known about developments in Europe and Asia during World War II.

The complexity of zinc production is suggested by the following figures showing total production in the United States for the peak year of 1941. A total of 881,503 tons of slab zinc (spelter) were produced, of which 652,-600 tons came from domestic ores, 169,400 from foreign ores, and 59,503 from secondary material. Of the 24,429 tons of zinc dust produced, 2900 tons came from ore and 21,529 from secondary material.[22]

In addition to the 652,600 tons of slab zinc and the 2900 tons of zinc dust extracted from domestic ores, the following amounts of zinc compounds (zinc content only) were also obtained from domestic ores: 121,000 tons of zinc oxide; 20,000 tons of lithopone (a compound of barium sulfate and zinc sulfate), and 1600 tons of zinc sulfate. If statistical records of this nature were available for all the countries that produce zinc, a comprehensive tabulation would be possible; but that is not the case.

Table 45.8 shows zinc ore production in thousand short tons of zinc content, either by assay or estimated as recoverable.

NICKEL

The province of Yünnan in the southwest of China is important not only as the source of important rivers—the Brahmaputra, Irrawaddy, and Yangtze, which flow to the west, south, and east respectively—but also as a rich mineralized mountain area. Here centuries ago were found copper, zinc, and nickel in proximity, the joint occurrence suggesting an alloy of these metals widely used in the East for gongs and musical instruments.[23] It became

---

[19] For further details, see *Yearbook of the American Bureau of Metal Statistics*, 1948, p. 67.

[20] "Fuming" is a fairly new process. Zinc can be "fumed" out of low-grade ores, smelter slag, brass junk, etc.—sources formerly ignored because no practical process of utilizing them was known.

[21] The St. Joseph Lead Company, which happens to exploit domestic zinc-less lead ores, is an exception to this rule, although its Aguilar mine in northern Argentina produces some zinc.

[22] *Yearbook of the American Bureau of Metal Statistics*, 1947, pp. 59 ff.

TABLE 45.8. Zinc Ore Production by Assay or Estimated as Recoverable[24]

	1939	1943	1948
North America			
United States	583.8	744.2	621.5
Canada	197.3	305.4	236.8
Newfoundland	54.6	66.4	43.3
Mexico	146.9	227.9	189.1
Total	982.6	1343.8	1090.7
South America			
Argentina	24.0	21.2	13.4
Bolivia	8.9	19.5	19.6
Peru	23.4	37.8	64.9
Total	56.3	78.4	97.9
Europe[a]			
France	0.6	2.9	13.5
Germany	174.7	263.0	31.9
Italy	104.9	32.3	87.9
Norway	6.4	5.4	6.6
Spain	52.1	45.4	51.9
Sweden	37.5	34.6	40.0
Australia	203.9	158.9	167.2
Asia			
Burma	38.4	. . .	. . .
Indo-China	6.5	5.4	
Japan	64.4	100.0	36.9
Africa			
Algeria	4.4	3.3	6.8
Belgian Congo	7.6	22.5	51.3
French Equatorial Africa	1.4	0.7	. . .
French Morocco	3.2	0.6	2.6
Rhodesia	14.2	15.0	24.8
Tunis	0.5	0.2	2.7

[a] Excludes the U.S.S.R., Poland, Finland, and Yugoslavia.

known in Europe as the so-called "nickel silver," a substitute of silver.[25] The element nickel was isolated by Cronstedt in 1750 and produced in its present form by Richter in 1801. It was

[23] It is reported that in the eighteenth century Connecticut copper-nickel ores were shipped to Yünnan via Canton to supplement the dwindling ore supplies. For this and other historical items, see A. Skelton's chapter on nickel in W. Y. Elliott, E. S. May, J. W. F. Rowe, A. Skelton, and D. W. Wallace, *International Control of Non-ferrous Metals*, The Macmillan Company, New York, 1937, pp. 109-209.

[24] *Ibid.*, p. 54. The original table has numerous footnotes indicating bases of calculation, geographic boundaries, etc.

[25] The word nickel is traced back to the nickel-bearing copper ore deposits of Saxony that were opened up in the eighteenth century but found unconvertible because of the presence of nickel. In the miners' jargon, the word nickel denoted a gremlin, a personified cause of trouble not scientifically understood.

not until the middle of the nineteenth century that Europeans learned to imitate the Chinese *paktong*, or nickel silver. This discovery, together with the discovery of nickel-plating based on alloying nickel with magnesium, and the use of nickel for coinage, stimulated the use of the metal and justified the search for, and exploitation of, nickel ore deposits.

Until about a century ago, the nickel that was produced came from small isolated pockets. However, in 1854 a large concentration was discovered in New Caledonia, a French-held island in the Pacific; the Paris Rothschilds became interested in this development. New Caledonia remained the chief source of nickel until the twentieth century, when Canada became the largest source of the metal in the world. She has supplied over 85 percent of the world supply, with New Caledonia forced into third place by the recent rise of Cuba.

The development of the Canadian deposits was largely the result of the growing realization, on the part of American and other naval authorities, of the value of nickel as an alloy in armor plate; H.M.S. *Dreadnaught* was just ushering in the age of heavy "battle wagons." Impressed by the excellence of the nickel steel obtained from the French armament-maker Schneider of Le Creusot, the United States navy ordered one million pounds of nickel. Later on, an American company, the Orford Copper Company, became interested in nickel. This company owned nickel-bearing copper ores in Canada, near Sudbury, Ontario, about 250 miles east of Sault Ste. Marie. An accident led to the discovery that the addition of niter cake, a by-product of the manufacture of nitric acid, made it possible to separate the nickel sulfide from the copper, iron, and other ingredients in the ore. Here is another striking example of the "creation" of resources. Demand leads to search for technological innovations which in turn convert "neutral stuff" in the earth's crust into valuable resources.

In the meantime, Dr. Ludwig Mond, a native of Cassel, Germany, had become a leader in Imperial Chemicals, Ltd., and developed a chemical process for extracting nickel from ore. This process was the chief asset of the Mond Nickel Company, which acquired deposits in the Sudbury region. In 1929 the

American-controlled International Nickel Company merged with the Mond Nickel Company to form the International Nickel Company of Canada, a company in which American and British holdings are fairly well balanced and Canadian shareholders constitute an important minority group. In the same year, however, a newcomer arrived on the scene—Falconbridge Nickel Union, Ltd. This company uses a third process of nickel production, electrolysis, and also owns an electrolytic refinery in Christiansand, Norway. Electrolysis is successful where cheap water power is available; both Canada and Norway are richly blessed with that resource. International Nickel later built an electrolytic refinery at Port Colborne, Ontario, on Lake Erie near the southern terminus of the Welland Canal. This proved more economical than a nickel refinery which was built at Bayonne, New Jersey, during World War I. The Bayonne refinery subsequently was dismantled.

During World War II the United States government financed the opening up of the nickel-bearing ore deposits near the northeastern shore of Cuba. The particular deposits chosen for the operation belong to the Nicaro Nickel Company, a subsidiary of the Freeport Sulphur Company, which produces sulfur at Freeport, Texas. Through various government agencies such as the Reconstruction Finance Corporation, the Defense Plant Corporation, and the Metals Reserve Corporation and through the Cuban Nickel Company, a special company organized to handle this particular project, the necessary capital was provided and placed at the disposal of the Freeport Sulphur Company.[26]

By 1945 the Cuban output exceeded that of New Caledonia and thus ranked second in the world. However, the Nicaro Company does not produce metallic nickel but nickel oxide which can be used for alloying purposes in the steel industry; it is thrown right into the steel melt. The Nicaro works has a capacity of about 16,000 tons of nickel. Approximately 40 million tons of 1.45 percent nickel ore have been blocked out.

---

[26] This company also owns manganese mines on the southern shore of Cuba, near Cristo, and produces about half of Cuba's manganese ore output.

Properties and Uses

Nowadays by far the greatest use of nickel is as an alloying metal. It imparts to its alloys toughness, strength, lightness, and anticorrosiveness, as well as valuable electrical and thermal properties. Nickel ranks second only to manganese as a ferro-alloy. Its chief use is in nickel steel and nickel cast iron, but nickel brasses and bronzes are also important. A nickel-copper alloy, called Monel metal after Dr. Mond, is widely used in kitchens and hospitals, especially for sinks and table covers; it is easy to keep clean and shiny. A recent distribution of nickel among the different uses was as follows:[27]

	Percent
Nickel steel	60
Nickel cast iron	3
Nickel-copper alloys ("nickel silver," Monel metal, and similar products)	23
Nickel brasses and bronzes	2
Heat- and electrical-resistant alloys	3
Nickel-plating	6
Miscellaneous	3
	100

Nickel Ores

The nickel ores of New Caledonia are nickel silicates that run about 4 to 6 percent nickel. Most of the other nickel ores such as the Sudbury ores of Ontario, Canada, and the Petsamo ores—formerly Finnish but now U.S.S.R.—are nickel-copper sulfide deposits.

By far the largest concentration of nickel ores are those at Sudbury; in recent years they have yielded annually about 125,000 tons of nickel, 150,000 tons of copper, 250,000 ounces of platinum, 80,000 ounces of gold, 2.5 million ounces of silver, 100,000 pounds of selenium, and 4000 pounds of tellurium. The ore reserves run over 200 million tons, averaging about 1.5 percent nickel and 2 percent copper. The copper-nickel content is estimated at about 6.7 million tons.

The Petsamo ores are similar to the Sudbury but much smaller—about 4 million tons of ore, 1.6 percent nickel and 1.3 percent copper. The Soviet Union has nickel deposits in the Ural region and most likely others in other parts not yet adequately explored. The

---

[27] U.S. Department of the Interior, Bureau of Mines.

Cuban ores have been mentioned. Rich ore bodies have recently been opened up on the island of Celebes in Indonesia. Minor nickel deposits have been worked from time to time in the United States. This country also produces moderate amounts of secondary nickel.

Production of Nickel

Quantitatively speaking, nickel is relatively unimportant compared with copper, production of which has reached as high as 3 million tons, and with lead and zinc which have reached the 2-million-ton level. The world's peak production of nickel was reached in 1943, with 169,600 tons. From the very modest levels of the nineteenth century, production rose to 52,000 tons in 1918, the World War I peak, and reached 63,000 tons in 1920, only to drop back to 23,000 tons in 1932. This was followed by an upward pull which lifted nickel into the 100,000-ton class for the first time in history.

TIN

Tin is one of the oldest metals known to man. Highly purified tin foil has been found on Egyptian mummies that date from thousands of years before Christ. Bronze, an alloy of copper and tin, possesses properties superior to those of copper; its use reaches back into the dimly recorded past. The Phoenician tin monopoly was mentioned in another chapter (see p. 423). Until the Industrial Revolution gave new meaning to minerals and altered their roles in civilization, tin ranked fourth among the metals in amount used, being surpassed only by iron, copper, and lead. One reason for the early importance of tin is the relative ease with which it can be mined in certain regions and smelted to a usable state.

Tin Among the Metals

At present the quantity of tin produced annually is similar to the current nickel output. Tin has been surpassed and in fact left way behind by zinc and aluminum. Because of its high price tin ranks higher among the metals in terms of value than it does in quantity. The following list of metal prices tells why.

	Price in Cents per Pound	
	1937-1938 average	1947
Tin (Straits tin in New York)	48.25	77.95
Aluminum (No. 1 virgin ingot 99+ percent in New York)	20.04	15.00
Copper (electrolytic copper in New York)	11.81	20.96
Zinc (prime western slab zinc in New York)	5.93	10.50
Lead (soft Missouri lead in St. Louis)	5.23	14.47

Tin is almost unique in the extent to which the areas in which it is produced are geographically separated from the areas in which it is consumed. For reasons to be explained later, tin is largely a product of the tropics.[28] Tin consumption is highly concentrated in about half a dozen industrialized countries; the United States, the leading consumer, uses almost half the world output. As a result, tin has an extraordinary part in international trade and is the object of keen conflicts of interest between producing and consuming groups. The United States, virtually devoid of domestic tin ores, pays for imported tin more than she pays for any other imported industrial metal. Tin constitutes a major export item in several countries, notably Bolivia, whose government derives most of its revenues from this metal.

Properties and Uses

Until recently tin was used chiefly in the making of bronze, an alloy of copper. Tin is highly malleable and nontoxic. Moreover, even a thin coating provides reliable protection against almost all acids, atmospheric effects, corrosion, influence of water, etc. This property coupled with its malleability has given rise to the modern tin-plate industry which manufactures a large proportion of all our food containers. This industry is the greatest consumer of tin in the modern world. Through the ubiquitous tin can, which is made of steel covered with a very thin tin coating, it has revolutionized the food habits and indeed the general living conditions of a considerable portion of mankind.

In addition to extraordinary malleability, corrosion resistance, and nontoxicity, tin also

---

[28] The Cornish mine led world output for a long time but it never produced quantities comparable to the present output in other parts of the world.

possesses the useful properties of a low melting point and easy fusibility, softness, lightness, and attractive appearance. These properties explain the uses to which tin is put, and Table 45.9 lists some of them.

TABLE 45.9.   Consumption of Primary and Secondary Tin in the United States, Average, 1935-1939[29]

Uses	Consumption	
	Tons	Percent
Metallurgical	73,964	95.7
Tin plate	32,089	41.5
Solder	17,066	22.1
Babbitt	5,642	7.3
Bronze and brass[a]	5,577	7.2
Collapsible tubes	3,522	4.6
Tinning	2,247	2.9
Foil	1,812	2.3
Terneplate	1,247	1.6
Type metal	1,161	1.5
Pipe and tubing	1,058	1.4
Galvanizing	891	1.2
Bar tin	794	1.0
Miscellaneous alloys	435	0.6
White metal	423	0.5
Chemical	2,729	3.5
Tin oxide	1,157	1.5
Other chemicals	1,572	2.0
All others	620	0.8
Total	77,313	100.0

[a] In 1935-1936, bronze only.

Because of its high price tin is constantly subjected to attacks from would-be substitutes. Tin foil has been largely replaced by such new products as aluminum foil and cellophane; tin vessels, by aluminum vessels; and tin tubes, by aluminum tubes. For the same reason, constant efforts are also made to cut down the amount of tin used for specific purposes. These efforts are greatest when tin is scarce, as during wars. Thus consumption of tin in the form of solder was sharply reduced in the United States during World War II, one automobile manufacturer reporting a reduction from an average of 5 pounds to 2 pounds of tin per car.[30] The greatest saving, however,

was made by the tin-plate industry, when it introduced the electroplating of tin plate to replace or at least supplement the older hot-dipping methods. In 1946 a ton of electroplated tin plate contained an average of 11.9 pounds of tin, as against 27.1 pounds per ton of hot-dipped plate. It has been reliably estimated that this process enabled the saving of over 60,000 tons of tin in one year in this country. Although electroplated tin plate is not suitable for all the purposes to which tin plate is put, it is thoroughly satisfactory in enough uses to assure its lasting success.[31] Finally, the high price of tin encourages the use of secondary tin even when its recovery is difficult and costly. Between 24 and 30 thousand tons of secondary tin, ranging in value from 30 to 40 million dollars, was recovered annually during the period 1925 to 1946.

Tin Ores

There are several tin provinces. By far the largest is the belt of placers[32] which lies in an area extending for 1000 miles from Yünnan province in China through Thailand, the Malay Peninsula, and into Indonesia. It is about 120 miles wide and reaches into Burma on the west. This region is estimated to have supplied close to 70 percent of all the tin produced to date. There are other provinces in Africa, especially in Nigeria, the Belgian Congo, and South Africa; in South America, Bolivia; in Europe, Cornwall (now virtually exhausted), and small deposits in Germany (Erzgebirge) and Portugal; and in Australasia. North America is conspicuous for her virtual lack of tin.

Most of the tin produced in Asia comes

[29] E. W. Pehrson and J. B. Umhau, "Tin," in *Minerals Yearbook, 1939,* p. 691; *ibid., 1940,* p. 685; *ibid., 1941,* p. 713.

[30] It is claimed that 80 percent of the tin now used in solder could be replaced by cadmium if enough of this by-product of zinc refining were available. See Josef Wollnik, *Zinn; Wandlungen in der Erzeugung und Verwendung des Zinns nach dem Weltkrieg,* vol. 6 of *Wandlungen in der*

Weltwirtschaft, edited by Hermann Schumacher, Bibliographisches Institut, Leipzig, 1936, p. 24.

[31] This wartime experience once more illustrates the important fact that many technical innovations that are feasible are not introduced because change is costly. In wartime when cost is a minor consideration technological improvements often are given "the green light."

[32] A placer deposit differs from a lode deposit in that a lode is a concentrated, usually vein-like deposit embedded in rock. A placer deposit, on the other hand, is a superficial gravel or similar deposit; it often results from the action of erosion on the lode, as when a mineral deposit is washed down from its original location.

from placers, although in Yünnan, China, tin is produced by shaft mining. As a rule, placers are soft materials, such as gravels, that are easily worked by hydraulic methods and by dredges. They encourage exploitation by individual miners and frequently give satisfactory returns even under primitive methods.

However, the increased demand for tin and the consequent rising prices encouraged gradual mechanization under the control of European capital. While mechanization is more efficient, it involves the use of heavy fixed investments and thus sacrifices flexibility of operation. Supply loses its price elasticity and is likely to expand in the face of falling prices, the entrepreneur seeking lower unit costs through fuller use of equipment in place. It was this mechanization which, face to face with violent cyclical disturbances in industrial markets, led to price and production control schemes; these will be discussed later.

After the placers are exhausted a search for the mother lode frequently takes place. Little is yet known of the extent and nature of these mother lodes. The Federated Malay States contain the greatest number of placers; they consistently supply over one-third of all the tin produced in the world. Here the miner is likely to come into conflict with the peasant, who resents the presence of mines and tailings on his farm and the diversion of water to nonagricultural uses.

Malay tin stone, as the ore is called, is easily smelted. There are three smelting centers in this part of the world: at Singapore, Penang, and Selangor. These smelters also treat ores brought in from Thailand, Burma, and other neighboring parts. French Indo-China has a smelter operated by French interests.

Next to the Malay Peninsula, Indonesia is the leading Asiatic tin producer. The operations are confined to the islands of Banka, Billiton, and Singkep, Banka producing almost two-thirds, Billiton one-third, and Singkep minor amounts. Giant sea dredges are used near the river deltas. There are smelters on Banka and Billiton, and in Batavia. Some of the ores go to the Dutch smelter at Arnheim, Netherlands, and some of the tin stone goes to Singapore.

Outside of Asia the most famous tin district

is in Cornwall, England, from which the Phoenicians supplied the Mediterranean market. It is estimated that from 550 B.C. until recently, when it was exhausted, this district produced about 3.3 million tons, an annual average of about 1350 tons for about 2450 years. It was first produced from placers, but by 1600 lode mining began on a large scale, reaching its peak during the middle of the nineteenth century.[33]

In Bolivia tin ore is mined by shaft mining, frequently at great depths; there are altogether ten tin mining centers. The average tin content of the ore runs about 3.5 percent, with some silver; some ores also contain bismuth. The most prolific district is at Llallagua-Uncia, the chief domain of the Patiño interests (see p. 750). Others are at Oruro and Potosi, both famous earlier for silver.

Tin production in Africa did not begin until about 1909, when first Nigeria, later the Belgian Congo, and still later South Africa increased the world's supply of this metal. Nigerian production was greatly aided by the discovery of coal there and the construction of railroads to tidewater. Being British, Nigeria enjoyed the benefit of imperial preference; a discriminatory export duty levied after 1916 directed her concentrates exclusively to British smelters.

Smelters

The entirely different character of the Bolivian and African ores created a smelter situation different from that in Asia. Bolivia exports not tin, but a concentrate known as *barilla;* this is shipped from Pacific ports nearest to her mines, mainly from the Chilean port of Arica where Bolivia enjoys certain rights as an exporter. The *barilla* is prepared by treating ores partly by gravity methods, partly by flotation. The latter process in particular had much to do with making profitable the exploitation of low-grade, hard-to-work ores. Because their exploitation called for the services of highly trained European metallurgi-

---

[33] See A. M. Bateman, *op. cit.*, p. 551. Bateman points out that Cornwall is one of the most striking examples of mineral zoning, silver-lead veins at the surface pushing downward into copper veins and copper veins yielding to tin veins at great depths.

cal experts, the ores began to move to smelters in England, Germany, the Netherlands (Arnheim), and Belgium (Hoboken). England's early knowledge of tin through her Cornwall deposits, her position in the Empire, and her early leadership in machine industry and metallurgy in general gave her several great advantages.

Early in the present century when Standard Oil was fighting Shell for the privilege of supplying "oil for the lamps of China," Standard Oil planned to build a tin smelter first in Malaya, then in New Jersey. Both efforts failed because of Britain's imperial prerogatives of directing to the motherland the flow of products of the lands under her political control. During World War I several moderate-sized tin smelters were built in the New York area, only to succumb to renewed British competition once the war was over. It is claimed that besides these imperial prerogatives Britain enjoys the added advantage gained from handling diverse ores. Some concentrates, especially Bolivian, are extremely balky when treated by themselves but become more tractable when mixed with higher-grade materials from other regions, e.g., Malaya.

During World War II when the Asiatic tin provinces were overrun by Japan and Germany held the smelters at Arnheim in the Netherlands and at Hoboken in Belgium, a tin shortage ensued. The United States government accordingly decided to build the largest tin smelter in the world in Texas City, near Houston. Almost the only raw material which this smelter could attract was the low-grade balky *barilla* from Bolivia. The better-grade ores and concentrates went to the English smelters with which the Patiño and other Bolivian interests had long-term contracts. Manned by Dutch experts from Arnheim, the Texas City smelter, known as the Longhorn smelter, by the end of 1946 had turned out no less than 151,000 tons of tin, the greater part of it grade A. The bulk of this metal was extracted from substandard Bolivian *barilla*.[34]

The fate of the Longhorn smelter is as yet undecided. It depends largely on political decisions. In a world sunny with peace prospects it may not survive, but in a cold war as in a shooting war it may prove essential to security.

Organization of the Industry

The tin industry is an old industry that is scattered over widely separated parts of the earth. This condition makes for diversity. The old and primitive survives alongside the new and modern; small establishments relying mainly on hand labor exist side by side with highly mechanized, heavily capitalized corporate enterprises. Difficult shaft mining competes with the easy exploitation of placers and dredgings.

This diversity of conditions is reflected in a similar diversity of industrial organization. Small native mining companies employing a few coolies are found beside gigantic holding companies that control many mines and own completely integrated setups, from mines to smelters. In the British possessions the industry is mainly private but cartelized. The Dutch government owns the lion's share of the industry in Indonesia. In the Belgian Congo the industry is in the hands of the Union Minière du Haut Katanga (see p. 710), a corporate enterprise owned jointly by the government and private interests.

The situation in Bolivia is of particular interest. Here the Patiño interests control the largest single block of tin mines. Simon Patiño, "tin's fantastic hero,"[35] is credited with having carved a two-hundred-million-dollar fortune out of the cassiterites of Bolivia. Besides his tin mines and beneficiating plants, Patiño at one time or another controlled important banks and railroads as well as the alcohol monopoly of Bolivia; entered into a close financial rela-

---

[34] Much of this *barilla* came from the mines of Mauricio Hochschild, a relative newcomer in the Bolivian tin world who got a foothold in Bolivia as a *rescatador*, i.e., a man who grubstakes small

mining enterprises in return for part of the yield. When government banks threatened to cut the ground from under him he bought and reorganized mines, especially the Oruro and Potosi properties. Coming onto the scene long after Patiño, Hochschild had to be content with the culls as it were. It was he who urged the erection of the Longhorn smelter and undertook to deliver *barilla* up to certain amounts from both his own mines and those of small independents. See *Fortune*, July, 1947.

[35] See *Fortune*, July, 1947, pp. 76 ff.

tionship with the National Lead Company, one of the largest tin consumers in the world;[36] gained control over Nigerian and Malayan tin mining and smelting enterprises, and, jointly with the National Lead Company, over Williams Harvey and Company, the largest tin smelters in the world, with plants at Bootle, near Liverpool. This brings the largest seller of tin ore, Patiño, one of the largest buyers of tin, the National Lead Company, and the largest smelters of tin into close coöperation. Prior to World War II, Patiño had been sending his concentrates to Essen, to Goldschmidt of "thermit" fame.

Besides the Patiño group there are the Hochschilds and the Aramayo group; the latter have a long-time working agreement with the Guggenheim interests. There are also the *medianos* or middle-sized mines and a large number of small ones.

Overexpansion

An industry which, like tin, tolerates the existence side by side of small primitive producers and giant mechanized and integrated corporations, is likely to be marked by a wide spread of unit costs among its members. This competition between small handicraft and giant corporate enterprises creates peculiar problems. When demand is brisk and the large enterprise with its heavy overhead is operating at full capacity, the low-cost producer is likely to be making the largest profit. But when demand slackens and only part of the capacity is utilized, the unit costs of concerns with heavy overhead rise rapidly, and the greater flexibility of the small establishment proves of great advantage. At such times the roles may well be reversed, the giant being relegated temporarily to the position of marginal producer. In such cases the price inelasticity of the demand for tin is keenly felt; even generous price concessions do not stimulate demand. The main reason for this inelasticity is the fact that tin constitutes only a minute part of the final product in which it is used —a motor car, a refrigerator, or even a can of tomatoes. A tin can sells for about 1.5 cents,

but the cost of the tin is only a small fraction of the total cost of the can.

This situation at times tempts highly mechanized, heavily capitalized producers to expand their output in the face of shrinking demand. They hope to reduce their unit cost by fuller utilization of capacity and thus conquer a larger share of the market for themselves. Unfortunately, however, many of their competitors are applying the identical logic and what may make sense when applied to an individual firm becomes nonsense when applied collectively to the entire industry or a large segment of it.

The Great Depression created a situation in tin which demonstrated clearly the disastrous working of these subtle forces. During the twenties high profits derived from mechanization and modernization, from the introduction of new processes such as flotation into Bolivia, encouraged wholesale expansion. New countries joined the ranks of tin producers. This explosive supply situation was hit by the world's worst collapse in demand. Industry in general reacted by cutting output to the bone. For example, the steel industry of the United States reduced output to below 20 percent. But the steel industry is organized wholly differently from the tin mining industry. Because of its peculiar setup, the latter seemed unable to throttle production in response to the collapsing demand. Artificial measures were necessary to bring the many diverse producing units into line. Finally, in 1931, after several false tries, the International Tin Control Scheme was organized with the support of several governments and was renewed repeatedly until December 31, 1946. Because of World War II, the cartel became inoperative not only in the Far East but also in the tin-mining countries of the West. Efforts are under way to set it up again.

The United States produces virtually no virgin tin and consumes about half the world output. Any artificial concerted action to raise the price of tin above the level of a free competitive market price is bound to be at the expense of the consumer, i.e., largely the American consumer. It is not surprising, therefore, to see this cartel and many others attacked as clumsy and even vicious attempts

---

[36] Certain important metal alloys contain both lead and tin; tin and lead are used in solder.

to solve producers' problems at the expense of consumers.[37] The most controversial issue is the elimination of inefficient capacity. There is no gainsaying that any attempt to solve problems of overcapacity without regard to the relative efficiency of different producers is bound to result in excessive charges to consumers.

The problem of tin price stabilization is further complicated by political considerations. The government of Bolivia is dependent on the revenues collected from tin mines. Large numbers of Indians are employed in the tin industry. Both these facts prevent ready shut-

TABLE 45.10. World Production of Tin and Annual Averages, 1801-1948[38] (thousand long tons)

	Amount	Annual Average
1801-1810	88.9	8.9
1811-1820	102.6	10.3
1821-1830	122.8	12.3
1831-1840	144.2	14.4
1841-1850	166.1	16.6
1851-1860	189.3	18.9
1861-1870	249.5	24.9
1871-1880	387.3	38.7
1881-1890	573.9	57.4
1891-1900	794.3	79.4
1901-1910	1019.0	101.9
1911-1920	1258.7	125.9
1921-1930	1485.6	148.6
1931-1940	1551.4	155.1
1941-1948	1046.0	130.8
Total	9182.6	

downs in response to market developments. Similarly, in Malaya the problems of native producers cannot easily be brushed aside. The prolonged discussions of such problems in connection with the ITO Conference in Havana in 1947-1948 seem to point to a saner and fairer way of solving such problems than has yet been found.

---

[37] See especially K. E. Knorr, *Tin Under Control*, Food Research Institute, Stanford University, 1945; also G. W. Stocking and M. W. Watkins, *Cartels in Action, Case Studies in International Business Diplomacy*, Twentieth Century Fund, New York, 1947.

[38] Figures for 1801 to 1930 from J. B. Umhau, *Summarized Data of Tin Production*, Bureau of Mines Economic Paper No. 13, Washington, 1932; 1931-1940 figures from Bureau of Mines, *Minerals Yearbook*; 1941-1948 figures from *Yearbook of the American Bureau of Metal Statistics*, 1948, p. 99.

World Production

Table 45.10 shows world tin production and annual averages, in thousand long tons, 1801-1948. According to the table, 6.8 percent of the tin output from 1800-1948 was produced during the first half of the nineteenth century, 23.9 percent during the second half, and 69.3 percent during the past forty-eight years. Although World War II stimulated the output of most metals, tin production declined for reasons which it does not take too much imagination to fathom. Thus Malayan output[39] fell from 85,342 long tons in 1940 to 15,748 in 1942 and to 3152 in 1945.

TABLE 45.11. World Production of Tin Ore in Terms of Metal[40] (thousand long tons)

	1939	1943	1948
United States	0.1	. . .	. . .
Canada	. . .	0.3	0.3
Mexico	0.3	0.4	0.2
Argentina	1.8	0.6	0.3
Bolivia	25.4	41.5	37.3
Portugal	1.0	2.5	0.4
Spain	0.1	0.2	. . .
United Kingdom	2.0	1.4	1.3
China	11.0	4.4	4.8
Japan	2.3	1.1	0.6
Burma	5.0	1.0	1.3
Indo-China	0.5	0.7	. . .
Malayan Union	43.2	26.0	44.8
Thailand	13.5	5.8	4.2
Indonesia	21.0	17.6	30.6
Australia	3.3	2.6	1.9
Nigeria	7.3	12.8	9.2
Union of South Africa	0.6	0.5	0.5
Belgian Congo	7.3	17.5	14.1
Uganda	0.4	0.3	0.2
All others	1.5	1.9	1.0
Total	148.6	139.3	152.9

During the period covered by Table 45.10, the geographical distribution of tin production underwent drastic changes. During the first half of the nineteenth century Europe, i.e., mainly Cornwall, supplied over one-third the output, and Asia the rest. Between 1850 and 1948 Europe practically dropped out of the picture, first Australia for a short while, Bolivia (after 1890), and later Africa (around 1910) entering the scene. The recent distribution of production by countries is shown in Table 45.11.

---

[39] Malaya was politically reorganized into the Malayan Union.

[40] *Yearbook of the American Bureau of Metal Statistics*, 1948, p. 99.

BIBLIOGRAPHY

"Bolivia," *Fortune,* June, 1942 (tin).

Campbell, R. F., and Maury, J. L., *The Premium Price Plan for Copper, Lead and Zinc,* Office of Price Administration, Metal Mining Analysis Office, December, 1945.

Cunningham, G. H., and Jephson, A. C., "Electrolytic Zinc at Corpus Christi, Texas," *Transactions,* American Institute of Mining and Metallurgical Engineers, New York, 1944, vol. 159.

"Eagle Picher," *Fortune,* September, 1947 (lead and zinc house).

Henderson, C. B., "The Longhorn Tin Smelter," *Mining and Metallurgy,* April, 1943.

"Hudson Bay Mining and Smelting Company," *Fortune,* June, 1938.

Ingalls, W. R., *World Survey of the Zinc Industry,* Mining and Metallurgical Society of America, 1931.

Ingalls, W. R., "The Great Lead and Zinc Mines," *Mining and Metallurgy,* September, 1946.

International Nickel Co., *The Romance of Nickel,* Copper Cliff, Ontario, Canada, no date.

Knorr, K. E., *Tin Under Control,* Stanford University, Food Research Institute, 1945.

Li, K. C., and Wang, C Y., *Tungsten,* American Chemical Society Monograph No. 94, New York, Reinhold, 2nd ed., 1949.

McGilvra, D. B., "Compania Minera Aguilar, S.A.," *Mining and Metallurgy,* April, 1947.

McLaren, D. C., "Vanadium," *Mining Magazine,* 1944.

Mantel, C. L., *Tin,* American Chemical Society Monograph No. 51, New York, Reinhold, 2nd ed., 1949.

Marcosson, I., *Metal Magic,* New York, Farrar, Strauss, 1949.

Merrill, C. W., *World Reserves and Resources of Tin,* U. S. Bureau of Mines, Information Circular 624g, 1928.

"St. Joseph Lead Company," *Fortune,* June, 1937.

"The International Nickel Company," *Fortune,* August, 1934.

"The Lives of Mauricio Rochschild, Bolivia's Tin Magnate," *Fortune,* July, 1947.

"Tin," *Fortune,* May, 1932.

Tin, New York, Pardners Mines Corporation, 1935.

Tyler, P. M., "Economics of Tungsten," *Metals and Alloys,* February, 1931.

Wollnik, J., *Zinn,* vol. 6 of Schumacher, H. (ed.), *Wandlungen in der Weltwirtschaft,* Leipzig, Bibliographisches Institut, 1936.

Young, R. S., *Cobalt,* American Chemical Society Monograph No. 108, New York, Reinhold, 1948.

Chapter 46

PRECIOUS METALS

Traditionally gold and silver are known as the precious metals. For ages they have been eagerly sought and highly prized by many peoples and their rulers. More recently there has been added a group of rare metals, known as the platinum group, which besides platinum includes osmium (the heaviest metal), iridium (the hardest metal), palladium, rhodium, and ruthenium.[1]

Viewed in some ways, the precious metals constitute a rather motley group. The main property they all share is a high price, for all of them cost considerably more than the base metals. They are usually handled in small quantities, not in tons like coal and iron, and seldom in pounds like copper, lead, zinc, and other common metals. In fact so small are these quantities that a special system of weights peculiarly adapted to them has been devised and is used in the English-speaking world today. Named after the city of Troyes in France, it is known as the troy system as distinguished

from the avoirdupois system used for coarser goods.[2]

Furthermore, gold and silver have long been used for coinage and for monetary purposes in general. For a short period platinum too was so used in Russia until the increased demand for the metal raised its price above its monetary value.

While they share these characteristics and undoubtedly others, the precious metals differ greatly in other respects. In the first place, they vary widely in price. In 1948 the average silver price in New York was 74.361 cents a fine ounce as compared with $86.25 a fine ounce for platinum and $35.00 a fine ounce for gold. Silver is cheap compared with the

---

[1] These metals are not only mineralogically related to and associated with platinum but generally alloyed with it.

[2] The basis of both systems is the grain, which originally meant just that, a kernel of wheat. The weight of the grain was later standardized at 0.064 gram. While the pound avoirdupois is made up of 7000 grains, the pound troy equals only 5760 grains, or 82 percent of 7000. This figure is arrived at as follows:

24 grains = 1 pennyweight (dwt.)
20 pennyweight = 1 ounce fine
12 ounces fine = 1 pound troy
(24 × 20 × 12 = 5760)

other two metals. Indeed, in the fairly recent past it has sold for even less, the average New York price in 1932 being 27.892 cents a fine ounce.[3]

In the second place, the world output of precious metals varies widely in both quantity and value. In 1946 the output of platinum was 245,265 troy (or fine) ounces. Figured at $57.20 a fine ounce, the average New York price that year, the value of the world output was worth a little over $14 million. The output of silver that year was estimated by the Bureau of Mines at 129 million fine ounces. At that year's average New York price, 80.151 cents, the 1946 world output was worth about $103.4 million. Gold production that year amounted to 21,471,793 fine ounces and was worth about $751.5 million. These differences are striking whether measured in terms of weight or value. In the third place, while platinum is a commercial commodity like wheat or tin and silver nowadays comes close to being one, gold derives its value mainly from the fact that it serves as the foundation of the world's monetary systems. Its price is regulated by law. Supply and demand, which govern the prices of silver and platinum, affect the price of gold only indirectly, through a possible impact on monetary laws. The implications of this difference will be developed more fully later. Finally, although most silver and platinum are at present produced as by-products of base metals, the bulk of the gold supply is derived from gold ores, i.e., ores valued predominantly if not exclusively for their gold content. Here again the significance of this fact will be left for later discussion.

GOLD AND SILVER
History

Both silver and gold were known to man before the dawn of history. A significant difference in the geological occurrence of the two metals accounts for the fact that in early times considerably more gold was obtained than silver. Native gold occurs both in lodes and in placers from which it can be won by primitive methods. Gold ores are classified as "free milling" or "refractory" according to the ease with which the gold can be extracted.[4] On the other hand, silver is not found in placers and seldom occurs in the native state. Its production requires mining, smelting, and possibly refining.

The greatest silver mining enterprise of early times was probably that of the Athenians at Laurion. From the size of the slag dumps and the average tenor of the ores in the district, it has been estimated that during the producing period from 600-300 b.c., 900,000 ounces a year, or an aggregate of about 270,-000,000 ounces, were produced.[5] This figure was exceeded by the world production of a single year, 1940, when 275.7 million ounces were produced. Comparing Laurion with the Cobalt district in Canada, a modern producer, we find that the Canadian district, in twenty-three years' production, surpassed the 300-year performance of its ancient counterpart by more than 100,000,000 ounces. In other words, the rate of annual yield from the Cobalt district under modern methods of exploitation is about eighteen times as great as that at Laurion.

The relative ease with which gold could be obtained from innumerable streams, in sharp contrast to the difficulties involved in silver production, resulted in a value ratio of gold to silver quite different from that in modern times. It is believed that during much of Roman history silver exceeded gold in value at the rate of 10 to 1 and over. Silver rather than gold played the major role in the vast commerce and tax and tribute-levying system of the Roman Empire. Not infrequently in modern times gold has been valued as high as seventy times the value of silver, and even

---

[3] Compared with prices of the base metals, which range from 5 to 30 cents a pound avoirdupois for copper, 50 to 90 cents for tin, 5 to 23 cents for lead, 5 to 18 cents for zinc, and 1 to 4 cents for iron, even 27.892 cents a fine ounce ($3.36 a pound troy and $4.09 a pound avoirdupois) appears rather high. Yet silver is closer to the base metals than to platinum.

[4] See Alan M. Bateman, *Economic Mineral Deposits*, John Wiley & Sons, Inc., New York, 1942, p. 419.

[5] C. W. Merrill, and staff, *Summarized Data of Silver Production*, Bureau of Mines Economic Paper No. 8, 1930. In *Silber*, vol. 5 of *Wandlungen in der Weltwirtschaft* (edited by H. Schumacher, Bibliographisches Institut, Leipzig, 1936, p. 6), H. Wegner gives 900 million ounces as the probable output during the period.

more—a truly surprising reversal of the relative value of the two metals. In the Dark Ages that followed the collapse of the Roman Empire a large part of the precious metals accumulated in antiquity was dissipated.

With the discovery of America, world gold and silver production entered an entirely new phase. By far the largest portion of the silver known to have been produced in the world up to now—probably between 85 and 90 percent—has come from the New World. While the New World's share of the total gold production is not quite so large it is nevertheless very impressive. Table 46.1 shows the phe-

TABLE 46.1.   World Gold and Silver Production
Since 1493[6]
(million fine ounces)

	Gold		Silver	
	Total	Annual	Total	Annual
1493-1600	23.0	0.2	746.9	7.0
1601-1700	28.8	0.3	1271.9	12.7
1701-1800	61.2	0.6	1832.8	18.3
1801-1900	374.3	3.7	5698.6	57.0
1801-1850	38.0	0.8	1064.3	21.2
1851-1900	336.2	6.7	4034.3	80.6
1901-1946	1106.2	24.0	9899.0	215.2
1901-1925	477.5	19.1	4901.3	196.0
1926-1946	628.7[a]	29.8	4997.7	238.0

[a] Partly estimated.

nomenal increase in world gold and silver production since 1493. The annual rate of gold output during 1925-1946 was about 150 times as large as during the period 1493-1600. Silver output increased thirty-four times. In terms of value, gold shows an even greater lead over silver, for the phenomenal increase in gold production eventually proved to be the undoing of silver.

The period of growth falls clearly into two phases. The earlier period, which ended about 1850 and saw a fourfold increase in the annual output of gold, was a time of the fortuitous discovery of bonanza mines, fabulously rich finds which kept the tide of precious metals rising at a moderate rate. During the later period some of the largest discoveries of history were made, but the accumulation of past

[6] Figures through 1927 from C. W. Merrill and staff, *op. cit.*, and from their *Summarized Data of Gold Production*, Bureau of Mines Economic Paper No. 6. Figures after 1927 from *Yearbooks of the American Bureau of Metal Statistics*, and from Bureau of Mines, *Minerals Yearbooks*.

successes progressively and inevitably reduced the residual number of new finds to something approaching the vanishing point.

The Ascendancy of Gold

But in the meantime two other factors had become active—modern machine technology and science. Together they achieved the momentous change from selective to mass mining, previously discussed (see p. 692), which altered the economics of mining almost completely and changed the gold and silver mining industry almost beyond recognition. It is the set of forces released by this new development that accounts for the increase in average annual gold production from about 800,000 ounces during the first half of the nineteenth century to almost 30 million during 1926-1946 and in average annual silver production from about 21.2 million ounces to 238 million during the same two periods. Again it is important to note that the rate of expansion of world gold production is far greater than that of silver production.

The importance of that fact lies in the gradual demonetization of silver, which not only sharply cut the demand for this metal but resulted in inordinate additions to the nonmonetary supply whenever larger amounts of demonetized silver were thrown on the market. The situation became particularly desperate when even the Orient, especially India and China, long the proverbial "sink" into which vast sums of precious metals used to disappear, reversed their position and began to add to, rather than subtract from, the world's supply of nonmonetary silver. Under these conditions, it may be surprising that much silver is still being produced; this is largely because most of the silver produced now is a by-product of other metals sorely needed for industrial purposes. This will be developed more fully later (see pp. 758-759).

Geographical Shifts in Production

The phenomenal increase in world gold and silver production was accompanied by spectacular shifts in the sources of supply. Latin America at first was the chief source of supply of silver, as Table 46.2 makes clear. She dominated the world silver situation from the time of Columbus until the middle of the nineteenth century. From 73 percent of the world total during 1493-1600 her share rose to 87 percent during the seventeenth and to 89 percent during the eighteenth century. It held up well during the first half of the nineteenth century, with 85 percent. But there was a shift within Latin America—from South America, whose share dropped from about 61 to 29 percent, to Mexico, whose share rose from 12 to about 57 percent of world output. Mexico has maintained her position as a leading silver producer; indeed, she is the only country that still exploits on a large scale silver ores, i.e., ores depending on silver for profitable operation.

TABLE 46.2. Silver Production by Regions, in Percentage of World Total[7]

	Mexico	South America	United States	Canada
1493-1600	12.10	60.76	...	...
1601-1700	24.11	62.94	...	...
1701-1800	57.00	32.07	...	...
1801-1850	56.85	28.63	0.04	...
1851-1900	31.21	17.16	33.15	0.75
1901-1925	32.94	8.48	31.31	9.47

After the conquest of the Inca Empire Bolivia became the leading source of silver in South America, the Cerro Rico of Potosí being the chief center of production. But Bolivia's share dropped from about 48 percent during 1493-1600 to about 36 percent during the seventeenth century and to 11.7 during the eighteenth. It was down to 9.5 percent during the first half of the nineteenth and to 2.2 percent during the first quarter of the present century. The corresponding figures for Peru are 12.6, 26.1, 19.7, 2.11, and 4.9. The only other South American country which made considerable contributions to the world supply was Chile. The decline in South American production was particularly pronounced during the period following the wars of independence which led to a considerable reorganization of the economies of that continent. The situation in the United States will be discussed more fully later.

It is estimated that between 1493 and 1927 there were produced in the world 14.4 billion

fine ounces of silver. This was divided among the producing countries as shown in Table 46.3. The dominant role of the New World is clearly revealed. Mexico, Bolivia, Peru, and Chile together have produced 8.3 billion ounces, or 58.05 percent of a total of 14.36 billion. Adding to that the share of the United States and Canada—3.54 billion ounces or 24.63 percent—gives a total of 82.68 percent for the western hemisphere. Even that does not do full justice to the preponderance of the New World because such countries as Colombia, Nicaragua, Honduras, Argentina, and Brazil are hidden in the "all others" category.

TABLE 46.3. World Silver Production, 1493-1927, by Countries[8]

	Billion Ounces	Percent
Mexico	5.1	35.60
United States	3.0	20.87
Bolivia	1.6	10.92
Peru	1.3	9.1
Canada	0.54	3.76
Germany	0.50	3.46
Australia	0.46	3.19
Austria	0.33	2.26
Chile	0.30	2.05
Japan	0.24	1.69
Spain	0.20	1.40
All others	0.76	5.32
Total	14.36	100.00

In gold production also the Americas played an important role during the first centuries after their discovery, but the strange concentration of silver deposits in the Americas is not paralleled in the case of gold. Workable gold deposits are more widely diffused throughout the entire world. Moreover, after the discovery of the Witwatersrand in the Transvaal, the Americas definitely had to yield world leadership to Africa, though they are still an important source of gold.

During the sixteenth century South America and Mexico contributed close to 40 percent of the world output of gold; Africa is credited with about 35 percent and Europe (mainly the area which later became known as Austria-Hungary) with about 21 percent. During the seventeenth century Latin America contributed over two-thirds of the world total, with Colombia the ranking gold-producing country

[7] C. W. Merrill and staff, *Summarized Data of Silver Production.*

[8] *Ibid.*

in the world. In the eighteenth century Latin America's share increased to more than four-fifths, with Brazil taking the lead from Colombia. Latin America held her lead until about 1820 when the wars of independence interfered with mining operations. In 1820, as a result of discoveries in Siberia, Russia took the lead, holding it until 1849, when the United States took over. The outbreak of our Civil War and the remarkable discoveries in Australia put the antipodes in the lead. However, the United States resumed it again in 1863 and held it until 1905,[9] when South Africa assumed it. The 1946 discovery in the Orange Free State may sustain South Africa's leadership for some time unless the Soviet Union pushes ahead to first place.

This checkered history of world gold production is suggestive of several facts. In view of the wide diffusion of gold throughout most of the world it seems logical that the New World should make major contributions during the first century after its discovery. The sequence of regional developments follows more or less the course of exploration, colonization, and settlement. To appreciate the speed with which one area after another snatches the glory of being premier gold producer from its predecessor, it is necessary only to recall the fury of the typical gold rush, the frenzy of hasty exploration, and the rather primitive methods applied for centuries. Nor is it surprising that Africa should be the last on the list. For there are no readily found and easily worked placers in Africa. The ore is mined, much of it under great difficulties, much of it not too rich. The Transvaal gold mining industry is definitely a product of modern science and highly capitalized advanced industrialization, not a simple adventure of pioneers penetrating the wilderness and stumbling on a lucky strike.

Technological Innovations

While gold mining, like the rest of metal mining that underwent the shift from selective to mass mining, came under the spell of ma-

chine production, the technology peculiar to mining and recovering precious metals underwent only three major changes. These changes, however, were of great significance. The first was the introduction of the amalgamation process, also known as the patio process, during the sixteenth century. This process, which easily superseded the older fire-using techniques, can be applied only to placer gold and to so-called free-milling native gold and silver ores, i.e., ores in which the gold and silver occur free, not in chemical combination with other elements, and from which the gold and silver can be freed by grinding. The ground ore is brought into contact with mercury, which absorbs the precious metal and forms an amalgam. The process was aided by the discovery of mercury deposits in areas close to gold mining operations. The best known in the New World are those in Huancavelica, Peru, and New Almaden, California.

The second great technological advance affecting gold and silver production was the introduction of the cyanidation process in 1887. This process is applicable to a wider range of silver and gold ores, its main innovation being the dissolution of finely ground silver and gold by means of a solution of potassium cyanide. This process is responsible for much of the increase in production during the quarter century preceding the outbreak of World War I. A third invention which has greatly influenced recent developments in the silver and gold mining and producing industry is the flotation process, already discussed (see pp. 700-701).

SILVER AND SILVER-BEARING ORES

A sharp distinction must be made between true silver ores, i.e., ores which "pay" because of their silver content, and argentiferous or silver-bearing ores, i.e., ores exploited for some other metal or metals which incidentally also yield silver. Formerly silver ores were the main source of the metal. But as the richest silver ore deposits became exhausted, as progress in the art of metal recovery made it possible to recover even minute traces of precious metals, and as the production of base metals expanded, more and more silver was recovered from argentiferous ores. Silver became largely a by-

---

[9] Except for a short period during 1898-1899, when South Africa led in gold production. But it reverted to the United States again when the Boer War interrupted mining operations.

product, a momentous fact that has fundamentally affected the economics of silver; it will be discussed more fully later.

Repeatedly it was found that silver mines were merely the top layers of mixed areas of mineralization. As the silver ore became exhausted, or at least when the cream was skimmed off, rich copper ores or highly complex ores were frequently found below it. Thus the famous Cerro Rico at Potosí in Bolivia shifted from silver to tin, the Cerro de Pasco in Peru from silver to copper, Cornwall from silver to copper and then to tin, etc. Usually, however, the deeper base metal ores contained some silver. The Cerro de Pasco Copper Company is today one of the largest producers of silver, but the silver is a by-product of copper.

As was mentioned before, the ores of silver and gold are either *free milling* or *refractory*. Free-milling ores yield the native metal after grinding; refractory ores are treated much like base metal ores, i.e., subjected to concentration and smelted and then perhaps refined. The methods of extracting the precious metals vary with the accompanying ore metal. Free-milling ores are also known as *dry and siliceous ores*.

The tenor of silver ores, i.e., the amount of silver they must contain to pay their exploitation, varies of course with the price of silver, the costs of mining, and the nature of the ore. In general, at recent prices, straight silver ores must assay about 15 fine ounces to the ton.

Most silver, as was stated before, comes from the western hemisphere. The most prolific silver district extends from Utah south through Nevada and Mexico down to Honduras (Rosario mine). In it are located some of the most famous mining centers: Tintic, Utah; Comstock and Tonopah, Nevada; and, in Mexico, Guanajuato, Pachuca, Real del Monte, San Luis Potosí, Zacatecas, Fresnillo, Mapimi, Parral, Sierra Mojada, and Santa Eulalia. In addition there are three silver mining districts in North America—one in Colorado; another in Idaho, the Coeur d'Alene district with extensions into southern British Columbia; and the Cobalt district in Ontario, Canada. Besides these there is also the Andean district in South America which extends from Colombia to Argentina. But most silver districts have more

or less played out. Today the Cerro de Pasco Copper Company is the most important silver producer in South America.

Mexico, the leading silver producer in the world, is the only country where true silver ores are still of real importance. Pachuca, Fresnillo, and El Oro are famous for their silver ore; and Santa Eulalia and San Francisco del Oro, both in Chihuahua, for their silver-lead-zinc ores. About the only true silver ore of major importance left in the United States is the Sunshine mine in the Coeur d'Alene district. The Cobalt district of Canada was rich in native silver, but that is now exhausted. The Sullivan mine of British Columbia, long the largest silver producer in the British Empire (see p. 743), is also the largest single producer of lead and zinc in the world.

So tremendous was the flow of silver from the New World to the Old that silver mining outside of America was bound to suffer. Germany was the leading European producer. When Spain lost her American empire, mining in Spain was revived. Considerable amounts of silver were produced at the Broken Hill mine in Australia. But in comparison with the output in the New World all the rest appears small.

GOLD ORES

A fundamental difference in the occurrence of gold and silver is the vital role of placer deposits in the history of gold production. Even today when lode mining has come to dominate production, close to one fourth of all the gold produced in the United States is found in placers. The modern method of placer mining employs giant dredges. Another difference is the fact that relatively little gold is obtained as a by-product—only about one-eighth of the annual output in the United States. Most gold is derived from free-milling ore which can be treated by cyanidation or amalgamation or both.

The tenor of gold ores varies widely. Probably the lowest-grade ores that are successfully exploited are those of the Alaska Juneau mine.[10] These ores average 0.04 fine ounce (0.8 pennyweight, or \$1.40)[11] a ton. The South

---

[10] *Ibid.*, p. 420.
[11] Since 1934 the mint price of a fine ounce of gold has been \$35. 0.04 × \$35 = \$1.40.

African mines from which about half the world's current output of gold is obtained average 0.3 ounce (6 pennyweight, or $10.50 a ton). In the old bonanza days ores as rich as 20 ounces a ton (which at the old price of about $20 an ounce brought $400 a ton) were not unknown.[12]

When in 1934 the United States government raised the price of gold from a little more than $20 an ounce to $35, it not only vitally affected economic conditions and trade relations throughout the world but it provided one of the grandest examples of the "creation" of resources. The stroke of a pen lifted submarginal gold-bearing deposits into the ore category and gave great encouragement to exploration for gold. The creative spell will last until prices and costs have adjusted themselves upward to gold's new price level.

The leading gold producer in the western hemisphere is the Homestake mine at Lead, South Dakota. Since 1879, when it was opened up, it has produced about 400 million dollars' worth of gold, and it is still going strong; it is reported to have greater ore reserves than any other gold mine in the world.

Another important gold-producing center is Mother Lode, a cluster of mines scattered throughout a 120-mile belt in the western foothills of the Sierra Nevada of California. It has produced about 300 million dollars' worth of gold in a little less than a century. Mining operations have been pushed to a vertical depth of 6000 feet. A less important district is the Grass Valley-Nevada City district in California, which is credited with about $140 million.

So far only lode areas have been mentioned. In earlier times placer deposits were the chief source of gold. It is estimated that around two-thirds of the gold produced on the Pacific coast has been obtained from gravel deposits, about 150 miles long and 50 miles wide,[13] along the middle and lower reaches of the western slopes of the Sierra Nevada. These deposits are said to have yielded gold to the value of about $1.3 billion since their opening in 1848.

Another placer area is located around Cripple Creek, Colorado; it is credited with over 360 million dollars' worth of gold. The Alaska Juneau mine, already mentioned, can boast of two records: it has produced more ore than any other single gold mine and it has the lowest-grade ore on record in the gold mining industry. As was said above, the ore brings $1.40 a ton; what was not mentioned there was the cost—72 cents.[14]

Canada is generally ranked third among gold-producing countries, after South Africa and the Soviet Union, Ontario being her leading province. Most of the gold is produced by lode mining. The premier gold district is the Porcupine region in which is located the Hollinger mine; for a number of years this mine was the leading producer.

The world gold situation was radically altered by the discovery in 1886 of the Witwatersrand, the gold mining district around Johannesburg, the capital of the Transvaal, then an independent Boer Republic. By the end of 1948, this district, about 50 by 20 miles, with workings reaching a depth of about 9000 feet, had produced about 15 billion dollars' worth of gold.[15] In 1941 the output was valued at $504.3 million.[16] Since then, however, it has been dropping; in 1948 it amounted to about $400 million. The decline probably is due to the rise in the general price level which may cause marginal producers to close down. The average cost-price ratio in the Witwatersrand, according to Bateman, is extremely favorable; the average recovery of gold is 0.33 ounce (about eight times the Alaska Juneau figure) which at $35 an ounce means a return of about $11.65 a ton.[17] The average working cost is said to be $4.50 a ton. No wonder Johannesburg is one of the greatest centers of mining stock speculation in the world. It is through the sale of such stock that the owners of a bonanza seek to anticipate future earnings.[18]

The amount of ores handled in the Rand

---

[12] A. M. Bateman, *op. cit.*, p. 429. Bateman cites Goldfield, Nevada, as an example.

[13] *Ibid.*, p. 427.

[14] *Ibid.*, p. 433.

[15] *Fortune*, October, 1946, p. 109. Later years added by the author.

[16] International Monetary Fund, *International Financial Statistics*, September, 1948, p. 11.

[17] A. M. Bateman, *op. cit.*, p. 441.

[18] "Gold," *Fortune*, October, 1946; "Seven Gold Houses," *ibid.*, November, 1946.

mines is surprisingly large. To produce 425 tons of gold, approximately 67 million short tons of ore are raised to the surface in the average year, a figure comparable to the amount of iron ore handled in a typical year in the Lake Superior region of the United States.

In 1946 the world was startled by news of a rich strike at Odendalsrust in the Orange Free State about 150 miles south of Johannesburg. The find was made by Sir Ernest Oppenheimer, one of the leading mining men of South Africa. Thirty-four boreholes proved the presence of a payable "reef" extending over an area of approximately 150 square miles at a depth about half that of the deepest Rand mines. Because it takes years to develop gold mines in that part of the world, the full meaning of the new strike will not be known for some time. In the meantime, however, speculators have reaped great wealth out of their own optimism and their ability to talk other people into it. Later reports have thrown some doubt on earlier claims.

Information about the gold deposits of the Soviet Union is very meager. From time to time there emanate from behind the Iron Curtain fantastic stories about equally fantastic outputs of gold, gold to be used in the gigantic struggle between East and West, gold produced by prison labor under inhuman conditions. Exact knowledge about all this is a secret carefully guarded by the Kremlin. According to Bateman, the Soviet Union possesses both lode and placer deposits.[19] The most important lode deposits are in the trans-Baikal region, the region east of Lake Baikal. Smaller lodes are believed to be scattered throughout Siberia in the drainage basins of most of the larger rivers. The most important placer deposits are in the Lena section of Siberia. This district was worked for a long time by a British mining company but was taken over by the Soviet Union after the Revolution. The placer deposits of the Ural region are thought to be low grade and costly to work. The Soviet Union is believed to rank second as a producer of gold, after the Union of South Africa; Canada and the United States rank third and fourth.

Australia became famous as a gold producer

in the 1850's when she temporarily took the lead in world gold production. Probably the best-known mining region is the famous "Golden Mile" at Kalgoorlie in west Australia, although there are other lode deposits of similar importance. The placer deposits of Victoria are comparable to those of California; they have yielded over 700 million dollars' worth of gold. Queensland is credited with $450 million, mainly from lodes; New South Wales with $300 million, and New Zealand with about $470 million.[20]

In Asia the gold mines of Japan and Korea and the famous Kolar gold field of Mysore in southern India deserve mention.

USES OF GOLD AND SILVER

Both gold and silver have played great roles in the monetary history of the world. They have been coined, been used as security for note issues, and have functioned as standards of monetary value. They were chosen for these parts largely because of their high value, their ease of identification, their resistance to corrosion, and their divisibility. Their high value, in turn, is based on the universal appeal to man's acquisitive instinct which derives from their luster and beauty on the one hand and their relative scarcity on the other.

As was said before, in ancient times silver was valued more highly than gold because of the greater difficulty of obtaining it and its consequent greater scarcity. As mining and recovery techniques were perfected, and especially after the discovery of the great deposits of the New World, silver became increasingly more plentiful and dropped progressively in value, particularly after 1871, when one country after another adopted some form of gold standard and demonetized silver, retaining it only for debased fractional coins.

Gold and the General Price Level

The supply of newly mined gold is ordinarily affected by the general commodity price level, a low one encouraging mining operations and a high one discouraging them. It is also affected by changes in the laws affecting the mint price and the monetary status of gold. Thus the increase in the mint price of gold in 1934 in

---

[19] A. M. Bateman, *op. cit.,* p. 445.

[20] *Ibid.,* p. 449.

the United States from $20.67 to $35 an ounce was a great stimulus to gold mining. The rising price level during the twenties put a brake on gold mining. During the depression some submarginal properties were opened up and gold operations in general expanded. The inflationary price trends during and especially after World War II discouraged gold mining. The agreements formulated at Bretton Woods, New Hampshire, in July, 1944, and culminating in 1945 in the creation of the International Monetary Fund and the International Bank for Reconstruction and Development, may have had a bullish effect on gold mining prospects because they reinforced the position of gold in international finance which had been badly shaken during the past thirty years. Moreover, like all mining, gold mining is affected by the exhaustion of working deposits and the discovery of new ones.

Not only is gold mining affected by the general price level, but the value of the gold produced theoretically can, and in practice generally does, affect the general price level. This was particularly true after 1872 when Germany, taking advantage of the gold she received as part of the French indemnity payment, adopted the gold standard and when her example was followed by one European nation after another. It happened that this period of increased demand for gold as a basis of national currency systems and credit structures was also a period of stationary production of the metal. It is widely believed that the inadequate supply of new gold was largely responsible for the decline in the general price level which lasted until about 1893.

The Gold Standard

The gold standard—i.e., the system under which gold, *to any amount*, is freely accepted for coinage and circulates freely both internally and in international exchange at a *fixed* mint price—was mainly a nineteenth-century phenomenon, associated with the period of British global dominion. The gold standard could function satisfactorily only so long as all the conditions peculiar to that period were met. It was part of something much bigger than a mere monetary system. That bigger thing gradually collapsed and disintegration brought on the World Wars of the twentieth century. The collapse dragged the gold standard down with it.

Today the old-fashioned Victorian gold standard is gone. Nowhere in the world does gold circulate freely. Almost everywhere it has been nationalized; i.e., private property in monetary gold is forbidden or sharply circumscribed. The monetary stocks are the property of the government. Gold still moves in international trade as a means of stabilizing exchange rates, but international trade itself has been so warped by the effects and after-effects of two World Wars that monetary measures may prove impotent. How successful the International Monetary Fund and the Bank for Reconstruction and Development will be in reviving the balancing power of gold remains to be seen.

The fundamental fact in the world economic situation today is the tremendous economic power of the United States. This country has become the chief source of food and of almost all the products of industry; as a result, so large a portion of the world's total gold stock has found its way into her coffers that gold can hardly play the role of a global balance wheel. Table 46.4 shows gold holdings of central banks, treasuries, etc., both before and after World War II.

The developments during these ten years are remarkable: Central gold reserves have risen almost $10 billion, reflecting the greater concentration of gold holdings and in part the effects of the high price paid for gold. The share of the United States has increased from about 55 to 66 percent. The Old World has lost much, the New World has gained more. Evidently it pays to have oil and wheat and wool to sell in time of war, or chromite and manganese.

What is left of the gold standard is in reality a gold exchange standard, which means that gold is made freely available for the settlement of international balances but not for internal use.

Demonetization of Silver and Price Control

What virtually drove silver out of the monetary system was first of all the instability inherent in bimetallism. If the respective value

TABLE 46.4. Gold Holdings of Central Banks, Treasuries, etc., Before and After World War II[21]
(in million dollars)

December, 1938		June, 1948	
United States	14,592	International Monetary Fund	1,363
United Kingdom	3,449[a]	Bank of International Settlements	30
France	2,761	United States	23,740
Netherlands	998	United Kingdom	1,906[d]
Belgium	773	Switzerland	1,345
Switzerland	701	Belgium	622
Spain	525[b]	France	548[e]
Argentina	469[c]	Union of South Africa	370
Sweden	321	Brazil	354
India	274	Cuba	289
Union of South Africa	220	India	274
Italy	193	Venezuela	264
Canada	· 192	Rumania	217
Rumania	133	Uruguay	203
All others	965	Argentina	201
		Netherlands	184
Total	26,566	Iran	172
		Turkey	164
		All others (est.)	3,784[f]
		Total (est.)	36,000

[a] September, 1930.
[b] April, 1930.
[c] 1939.
[d] Gross official gold and United States dollar holdings only.
[e] Central bank holdings only.
[f] Most of this is Soviet Union.

of gold and silver remained at a fixed ratio, bimetallism might work; but each of the two metals has its own market and the two markets are subject to diverse forces on both the supply and the demand side which cause their prices to move continuously either closer together or farther apart but hardly ever along parallel lines. For one thing, the relative amounts of gold and silver produced in a period of time vary greatly. In the seventeenth century 44.1 times as much silver as gold was produced. In 1851-1875 the ratio was only 6.7 to 1. During the sixteenth century gold was valued 11.3 times as high as silver; in 1906-1910 the ratio was 36.8 to 1; in 1940 it was over 100 to 1.

Because the silver-producing states of the Union have great political influence, especially in the Senate, and are supported in their fight for the valorization of silver by powerful corporations that control silver properties in Mexico and elsewhere, and also because of

our government's desire to maintain economic stability in Mexico, the greatest silver-producing country in the world, our Congress has from time to time passed laws designed to maintain the price of silver at an artificial level. One of the most important of these laws is the Silver Purchase Act of 1934, which directs the Treasury to purchase silver in amounts sufficient to bring the value of silver reserves up to one-third the value of gold reserves. In view of the fact that the value of our gold reserves is now over $24 billion, one can readily imagine how such a law, if persistently carried out, could drastically affect the silver situation throughout the world.[22]

[21] Based on International Monetary Fund, *op. cit.*, September, 1948, pp. 14-15.

[22] Actually, our net acquisitions of silver from 1931 to 1947 inclusive amounted to 2237 million ounces—2820 million ounces gross less 583 million sold. International Monetary Fund, *Information on Silver as Submitted by Member Countries*, p. 4.

The only other countries which show net acquisitions of major proportions are Mexico, which acquired 135 million ounces (1937-1947), and the United Kingdom, with 106 million ounces (1932-1947). India sold a net of 54 million ounces.

Even at the high price of one dollar a fine ounce, something of the magnitude of 8 billion fine ounces would be involved, a truly fantastic amount. Whether rigidly enforced or not, it is clear that laws such as the Silver Purchase Act of 1934 cannot really stabilize the world silver situation.

Another factor that renders silver unsatisfactory for monetary purposes is its by-product character, mentioned earlier. Because of this, the bulk of the silver supply loses its economic autonomy; it responds not to its own price but to the price of the metal or metals of which it is a by-product. When high industrial activity steps up the production of lead and zinc and copper, the output of silver automatically rises also, regardless of whether this metal is needed or not. Under these conditions, in the absence of artificial valorization the price of silver can almost disappear. It is precisely to avoid such drops in price which would prove catastrophic to the free mining of silver that laws such as the Silver Purchase Act of 1934 come into being.

Precious Metals and the Orient

Of particular importance to an understanding of the world gold and silver situation and of the problems affecting the precious metals are India and China. As was said above, for centuries the Orient was the great "sink" into which unknown amounts of gold and silver were drained. The West had good use for many products of the East and was able to pay for them, but the East had no comparable need for western products so the balance was traditionally settled by shipping gold and silver. In India a large portion of these precious metals was "hoarded," i.e., converted into ornaments to be worn on the body, for this seemed to be the only safe way to accumulate savings for a "rainy" day. Immensely wealthy potentates hoarded bullion. China was for long the only large country on a silver standard. There too a certain amount of hoarding probably was common, but she had an old-established exchange economy with highly developed banking institutions in which silver served as the basis of credit. One of the by-products of the recent silver policy of the United States was to drive China off the silver

standard. An attempt in October, 1948, to establish a gold *yuan* as the basis of currency failed.[23] But until peace comes to China, an orderly monetary system seems an impossibility.

Industrial Uses of Gold

It has been estimated that of a total world gold stock worth about $42 billion in 1935, approximately one-fourth was used for nonmonetary purposes. By far the greatest user of nonmonetary gold is the jewelry industry; it is followed by the dental industry. Beside these two major uses there are innumerable minor ones. Among these is the manufacture of gold leaf. Gold is the most malleable of all metals. A single gram can be reduced to a series of leaves 1/300,000 inch thick and aggregating 6 square feet. It is claimed that one gram of gold can be drawn into a wire 1.5 miles long. The telephone uses gold in its contact points. Some rayon spinnerets are made of alloyed gold. Gold is used in making glass, porcelain, medicine, dyes, etc. Some industries absorb chiefly scrap gold; in fact, in some years practically all the gold used for industrial purposes has been scrap gold.

Industrial Uses of Silver

Silver has far more uses in the industrial arts than has gold. The principal properties upon which much of its usefulness is based are its resistance to a wide variety of corrosive agents; its strong bonding power; its electrical and thermal conductivity; its remarkable optical reflectivity; and its ability to form salts and compounds with valuable photosensitive and bactericidal properties.

Silver is in the same class with gold and platinum as regards corrosion resistance. It is not subject to atmospheric corrosion[24] and is exceptionally resistant to weak acids and organic compounds, including those in food products. Because of its resistance to alkalis,

---

[23] In July, 1949, newspapers reported talk of China's "going back to silver."

[24] Except for tarnishing, which is the formation of a thin coating of silver sulfide caused by the presence of minute amounts of hydrogen sulfide in the atmosphere. The results of tarnishing, however, are not of the type usually implied by the term "corrosion."

organic acids, and certain mineral acids (including many products which attack tin), silver is widely used in the chemical industry as a lining for such equipment as stills, condensers, autoclaves, tanks, piping, heating coils, and reaction vessels, even when tin is readily available. Silver is resistant to acetic, lactic, formic, and carbolic acids; acetate rayon; dyestuffs; sodium and potassium hydroxide; ink; tanning chemicals; essential oils; and perfume essences.

The fact that joints made of silver are strong, leak-proof, and corrosion-resistant has led to its wide use in marine and navy piping, high-pressure boilers, transformers, bus-bar assemblies, and oil floats. For ordinary soldering purposes it is used in a variety of products; welding rods containing even as little as 1 percent silver are favored by coppersmiths.

The superiority of silver for electrical purposes has long been recognized. It is a better conductor of electricity than copper, the relative conductivity being 100 to 92.7; furthermore, it is free from oxides which resist the passage of the current.

Silver is the whitest of all metals, its reflectivity being of the order of 95 percent in the most sensitive region of the human eye; in the infra-red section, the metal may reflect as much as 98 percent.

The photosensitivity of silver salts—for example, the halides—is the basis upon which the photographic industry has been built. Aerial photography has increased the demand for silver in this field.

Price and Utilization. The only deterrent to the use of silver for many purposes is its price. In some cases, such as photographic film, there are no acceptable substitutes. In many of its other uses, including aviation engine and other bearings, electrical contacts, brazing alloys, solders, surgical plates, and chemical equipment, performance rather than price has been the determining factor. However, its price has restricted its use for many purposes for which silver is eminently fitted, such as container lining. Recently the scarcity of nickel, tin, copper, and other metals, resulting from the war, has lessened the importance of the price factor.

The recent prices of silver—foreign, 45 cents per troy ounce or $6.56 per avoirdupois pound; domestic, 71.11 cents per troy ounce or $10.37 per avoirdupois pound—would prohibit many of its present uses were it not for the effectiveness of the metal even in small quantities. Faced with shortages of other less expensive metals, manufacturers have found additional opportunities for using silver by coating with it electrolytically, by alloying it with other metals, by sintering or mixing it with other metals in a powdered form, and by limiting its application to specific parts of products.

Certain silver-plated steel products can at present compete successfully in price with products made entirely or partly of tin, nickel, aluminum, or stainless steel. The feasibility of its commercial application depends in many instances upon how much surface is to be covered per unit of weight. The silver in coatings less than 0.0001 inch thick costs less than 3 cents per square foot and can be used on nonreturnable containers; coatings over 0.0001 inch thick are economically feasible for returnable shipping containers (drums, barrels, and pails for certain beverages, foodstuffs, pharmaceuticals, and chemicals). It is estimated that silver of this thickness for lining a 12-ounce can for foodstuffs costs 1 cent.

The silver used in lining a steel-backed aircraft bearing 2.625 inches in diameter, 3.25 inches long, and 0.02 inch thick is worth about $1.50; that in an automotive bearing 2 inches in diameter, 0.5 inch long, and 0.01 inch thick costs about 10 cents. Cost is a secondary consideration in the manufacture of aircraft bearings and bearings for Diesel engines, tractors, trucks, and buses, where performance is the primary objective, particularly in wartime. Continued use of the metal in peacetime in some of these bearings will doubtless be justified by their longer life.

At prevailing market prices, soft solders containing silver, such as the lead-silver solder containing 2.5 percent silver, cost less than lead-tin solders containing 25 percent or more of tin.

Copper sheet or tubing can be clad (a bonding process) with silver, thus obtaining the benefit of a silver surface, at comparatively low cost; the silver is often 10 percent or less of the total thickness; it seldom exceeds 20

TABLE 46.5. Industrial Consumption of Silver by Selected Countries, 1931-1946
(thousand fine ounces)

Year	United States[a]	Great Britain	Canada	Mexico	Peru	France	Sweden	Switzerland
1931	24,336	8,500	...	259	...	...	...	450
1932	14,461	7,500	...	48	...	...	...	158
1933	10,811	8,000	674[b]	48	...	2,047	611	158
1934	11,492	8,000	877[b]	48	...	4,822	495	158
1935	5,289	7,500	462	48	...	5,921	482	734
1936	19,139	8,000	1,275	48	...	5,723	437	158
1937	27,727	8,500	668	48	...	1,470	571	257
1938	20,182	12,000	1,096	...	...	...	604	...
1939	44,613	7,000	2,096	677	...	...	694	96
1940	44,499	...	1,555	...	482	...	429	...
1941	72,432	...	2,000	651	707	...	...	783
1942	101,399	...	4,000	1,457	1,336[c]	...	...	...
1943	118,000	...	4,500	5,545	1,511	...	...	...
1944	120,100	16,000	4,971	6,740[d]	1,720	...	...	...
1945	126,300	14,000	4,685	10,935	2,144	...	...	1,125
1946	87,000	15,800	6,500	5,000	...	...	...	...

[a] Net figures; excludes silver returned from industrial use.
[b] Reported to the Director of the Mint in value only; converted to fine ounces on basis of legal silver content of the coin and at the average price of silver in New York.
[c] For June, 1942, to May, 1943.
[d] Represents amount sold by Bank of Mexico.

percent. This is true also of silver-clad steel sheets.

In the electrical industry, silver is used for contacts in layers, inserts, and buttons; only the contact areas consist of silver. For example, grooves in copper plates are filled with silver in portions of the surface selected for contacts. Electrical contacts are also sometimes made of alloyed and powdered silver mixed with other elements. In telephone apparatus, contacts on relays are in the form of silver buttons welded on contact springs. Thus only a few grains of silver are used in each of the millions of contacts required in making telephone connections.

Electric bus bars containing tons of silver would not be economically feasible at prevailing prices if the silver had to be purchased outright. As an emergency measure to conserve copper, the government has lent silver for this purpose. Because it later can be replaced by copper with no loss of material, government-loaned silver is being used for bus bars in new plants producing aluminum, magnesium, and chlorine.

During World War II silver was in great demand for certain war purposes and large amounts were released from monetary stocks.

The price paid by the government for newly mined domestic silver is regulated by presidential proclamation. It was set at about 35 cents during 1939-1942, but in August, 1942, it was raised to 45 cents. Some of the silver held by the Treasury serves as 100 percent backing for silver certificates. This amounted to about 2 billion ounces in 1943, leaving about 1250 million ounces of so-called free silver. Of this, 1 billion ounces were allocated to the Defense Plant Corporation for recoverable uses in war industry, especially for bus bars used in the reduction of aluminum and magnesium. Copper and other nonferrous metals were very scarce, whereas silver was lying idle in the vaults of the government; and silver excels all metals in electrical conductivity. For once price was no consideration.

Tables 46.5 and 46.6 show respectively the industrial uses of silver by selected countries, 1931-1946, and its principal industrial uses in the United States, 1936-1946.[25]

[25] Both tables are from the International Monetary Fund, *The Industrial Demand for Silver*, Washington, September, 1947. Most of the preceding discussion of the industrial uses of silver was based on this publication.

TABLE 46.6. Principal Industrial Uses of Silver in the United States, 1936-1946 (million fine ounces)

Year	Sterling Ware	Plated Ware	Nitrate	Unclassified	Total
1936	8.7	3.9	...	...	...
1937	10.8	4.4	12.5	...	27.7
1938	9.1	3.7	11.9	2.3	27.0
1939	11.2	4.2	12.8	5.8	34.0
1940	14.4	3.9	12.0	10.7	41.0
1941	30.0	5.0	18.0	27.0	80.0
1942	29.0	3.5	21.0	61.5	115.0
1943	16.5	4.3	20.5	78.7	120.0
1944	18.0	2.2	24.5	80.3	125.0
1945	27.0	2.3	26.8	83.9	140.0
1946	50.0	6.8	22.5	25.7	105.0

RECENT SILVER AND GOLD PRODUCTION

Table 46.7 shows world silver production in million fine ounces by countries, 1939, 1943, and 1946-1948. Note that the western hemisphere produces about four-fifths of the world total.

TABLE 46.7. World Silver Production[76] (million fine ounces)

	1939	1943	1946	1947	1948
Western hemisphere					
United States	57.8	44.8	21.4	36.1	36.1
Canada	23.2	17.3	12.5	11.5	14.6
Mexico	75.9	11.2	48.3	49.2	45.8
Newfoundland	1.4	1.3	1.1	1.0	0.9
Central America and West Indies	4.8	3.6	3.6	3.1	3.7
Argentina	3.9	2.2	3.1	2.4	1.2
Bolivia	7.2	7.3	6.1	6.2	7.6
Chile	1.2	1.0	0.6	0.8	0.0
Colombia	0.2	0.2	0.2	0.1	0.1
Ecuador	0.1	0.3	0.2	0.2	0.2
Peru	18.8	14.9	12.3	10.3	9.3
Others	0.05	0.1	0.05	0.05	0.05
Total	197.55	164.0	109.45	120.95	120.30
Europe	21.7	...	...	...	...
Australasia	14.6	10.6	9.3	9.5	9.4
Asia	22.4	...	...	...	...
Africa	4.6	4.8	...	...	...
Total world	257.9	195.0	131.1	...	...

Normally Germany and Russia are leading silver producers in Europe, with Yugoslavia third. In Asia, Japan, India, and Korea rank in that order. In Africa the Belgian Congo leads.

[26] *Yearbook of the American Bureau of Metal Statistics,* 1948, p. 78.

Table 46.8 shows the world gold production by countries for the same years.

Table 46.8. World Gold Production by Countries[27] (million fine ounces)

	1939	1943	1946	1947	1948
Western hemisphere					
United States	5.6	1.4	1.6	2.3	2.1
Canada	5.1	3.7	2.8	3.1	3.5
Mexico	0.8	0.6	0.4	0.5	0.3
Newfoundland	0.02	0.02	0.02	0.01	0.01
Central America and West Indies	0.2	0.3	0.3	0.3	0.3
Brazil	0.2	0.3	0.1	0.1	0.1
Chile	0.3	0.2	0.2	0.2	0.2
Colombia	0.6	0.6	0.4	0.4	0.3
Peru	0.3	0.2	0.2	0.1	0.1
Venezuela	0.1	0.1	...	...	...
Other South American	0.2	0.1	0.2	0.2	0.2
Total	13.5	7.4	5.3	7.1	7.2
Europe (excluding U.S.S.R.)	0.6	0.5	0.5	0.4	0.4
Soviet Union (including Asiatic)[a]	5.0	4.0	6.0	...	...
Total	5.6	4.5	6.5	...	...
Oceania	2.2	1.0	1.0	1.2	1.2
Asia	2.7	1.6	0.5	0.4	...
Africa					
Transvaal, Cape Colony, and Natal	12.8	12.8	11.9	11.2	11.6
Rhodesia	0.8	0.7	0.5	0.5	0.5
British West Africa	0.8	0.6	0.6	0.6	0.7
Other Africa	1.1	0.9	0.7	0.5	...
Total	15.5	15.0	13.7	12.8	...
Total world	39.5	29.5	27.8	...	...

[a] Estimated.

THE PLATINUM METALS

The platinum metals are discussed separately because, unlike silver and gold whose past and present use for monetary purposes affects if not dominates their market position, platinum has not been used for monetary purposes except for a short period in Russia.

As was mentioned above, the platinum metals constitute a closely related group made up of platinum, iridium, palladium, osmium, rhodium, and ruthenium. Of these, platinum is quantitatively the most important. In 1945 refineries in the United States recorded the following amounts of the platinum metals in thousands of troy ounces:

[27] *Ibid.,* p. 77.

	Platinum	Iridium	Palladium	Others	Total
New	162.0	5.8	28.6	8.0	204.5
Secondary	58.9	0.8	33.0	3.4	96.1
Total	220.9	6.6	61.1	11.4	300.6

In 1925 the average annual price for platinum in New York was $119.09 a troy ounce. In 1946 it was $57.20. At this price, the world output of new platinum in 1946 (exclusive of the Soviet Union) was worth $14.1 million.

In the United States about half the platinum is used for jewelry. The rest is used for miscellaneous purposes such as electrical, dental, and chemical. Platinum is also used as a catalyst.

Platinum deposits were discovered in the Ural Mountains in 1819, and Russia was for long the sole producer. Later the Chocó district of Colombia contributed considerably to the supply. In this area about equal amounts of platinum and gold are found in the placer gravels. However, the Chocó seems to be playing out. Now Canada ranks ahead of Russia as the premier platinum producer. In the lower levels of the Frood mines, one of the chief sources of copper-nickel ore, an unusual concentration of platinum metal is found. The ore runs about 0.05 ounce of platinum per ton, in addition to 0.0375 ounce of allied platinum metals, chiefly palladium, as well as considerable amounts of gold and silver.

In addition to the Soviet Union, Colombia, and Canada, the Union of South Africa and the United States produce considerable quantities of the platinum metals. South Africa is the only country where straight platinum ores are mined; there are about sixty known deposits. The United States produces platinum in placers in Alaska near Goodness Bay; it is also a by-product of gold and silver refining.

In recent years the different platinum-producing centers have ranked about as follows: No. 1, Canada, whose output fluctuates between 100,000 and 250,000 ounces. No. 2, the Soviet Union, whose prewar output ranged around 100,000 ounces but for recent years is estimated at 150,000. No. 3 and No. 4, Colombia and South Africa, which produce similar amounts when longer periods are considered; but Colombia's output is erratic and evidently declining, whereas South Africa's is fairly steady and is increasing. No. 5, the United States.

BIBLIOGRAPHY

Anderson, P. M., "The Future of Gold in the World Economy," in Parsons, A. B. (ed.), *Seventy-five Years of Progess in the Mineral Industry, 1871-1946,* New York, American Institute of Mining and Metallurgical Engineers, 1947.

Bratter, H. M., "Silver, Some Fundamentals," *Journal of Political Economy,* June, 1931.

Bratter, H. M., "Silver," *Encyclopædia of the Social Sciences,* New York, Macmillan, 1934.

Brown, W. A., *The International Gold Standard Reinterpreted 1914-1934,* New York, National Bureau of Economic Research, 1940.

Busschau, W. J., *The Theory of Gold Supply,* Oxford, Oxford University Press, 1936.

Dallin, D. Y., and Nicolaevsky, B. I., *Forced Labor in Soviet Russia,* New Haven, Yale University Press, 1947.

Einzig, P., *The Future of Gold,* New York, Macmillan, 1935.

Emmons, W. H., *Gold Deposits in the World,* New York, McGraw-Hill, 1937.

"Gold! South African Boom," *Fortune,* October, 1946.

Graham, Frank D., "The Silver Question Once More," in *Explorations in Economics, Essays in Honor of F. W. Taussig,* New York, McGraw-Hill, 1936.

Hansen, A. H., *Full Recovery or Stagnation,* New York, Norton, 1938.

Hawtrey, R. G., *The Gold Standard in Theory and Practice,* New York, Longmans Green, 1937.

Kitchen, J., "Gold," *Encyclopædia of the Social Sciences,* New York, Macmillan, 1931.

Leavens, D. H., *Silver Money,* Bloomington, Principia Press, 1939.

Leong, Y. S., *Silver: An Analysis of Factors Affecting Its Price,* Washington, Brookings Institution, 1934.

Nikolaevsky, B. I., "Stalin's Eldorado: the Kolyma Goldfields," *Fortune,* August, 1947.

Prince, C., "Golden Bullets in the Cold War," *United Nations World,* December, 1947.

"Russian Gold," *Federal Reserve Bulletin*, April, 1948.

"Seven Gold Houses," *Fortune*, October, 1946.

U. S. Bureau of Mines, *Minerals Yearbook*, chapters on "Gold" and "Silver."

Wegner, H., *Silber*, vol. 5 of Schumacher, H. (ed.), *Wandlungen in der Weltwirtschaft*, Leipzig, Bibliographisches Institut A.G., 1936.

Williams, J. H., *Postwar Monetary Plans and Other Essays*, New York, Knopf, 1944.

UNIT 5. NONMETALLIC MINERALS

Chapter 47

NONMETALLIC MINERALS OTHER THAN FUELS

Minerals are divided into two groups: the metallic and the nonmetallic. The nonmetallic, in turn, are subdivided into fuels and nonfuels. Both the metals and the fuels—coal, oil, and natural gas—have already been discussed in earlier chapters. This leaves the nonmetallic minerals other than fuels, and they will be treated in a rather cursory fashion for several reasons. While nonmetallic minerals such as sand, gravel, limestone, gypsum, salt, etc., are needed in large amounts, they are so abundant that they do not rate anywhere near as high in value as they do in quantity. Moreover, because of their abundance and wide distribution they are not likely to constitute major national or global resource problems. As a rule, the technological problems involved in the extraction and preparation of metals are more or less absent. However, hauling costs run so high that the nonmetallic minerals are often consumed near the point of production. An increasing number of them serve as raw materials of the chemical industry and hence will be discussed in Chapter 48.

While most nonmetallic minerals are cheap, their aggregate value is rather large in the United States. In fact, if the fuels are included, the nonmetallic minerals make up about 75 percent of the total value of our mineral products. Thus in 1948 our mineral products had a total value of $15,670,000,000, of which the metallic minerals accounted for $3,510,000,000 and the nonmetallic for $12,160,000,000. Of the total for the nonmetallic minerals, fuels amounted to $10,266,000,000 and nonfuels to $1,894,000,000.

The ratios of these values have shifted from time to time. Thus, in 1880 the metals exceeded the nonmetals in value—$190.9 million for metals as against $176.6 million for nonmetals ($120.2 million for fuels, $56.3 million for nonfuels). In 1927 the nonmetallic minerals other than fuels were valued at $1249.3 million and exceeded the metals by almost $30 million, and fuels were valued at more than $3 billion. From 1880 to 1948 the value of metals produced in the United States increased more than 18 times, that of fuels more than 85 times, and that of nonmetallic minerals about 34 times.

In this study of world resources it is not necessary to give a full account of the occurrence of the nonmetallic minerals. Little more

TABLE 47.1. Classification of Major Nonmetallic Minerals by Major Uses[1]

Uses	Nonmetallic Minerals
Ceramic	Clays, feldspar, bauxite, sillimanite minerals, borax, magnesite, and others.
Structural and building	Building, roofing, crushed stone, hydraulic cements, building sands and gravels, gypsum, lime, magnesite, mineral pigments, heat and sound insulators (mineral wool), asphalt and other native bitumen, clay and clay products, miscellaneous.
Industrial and manufacturing	Asbestos, mica, talc, barite, glass sand, mineral filters, optical crystals, lime, miscellaneous materials.
Abrasive	Diamonds, corundum, emory, garnet, miscellaneous materials.
Chemical	Salt and salt brines, borax and borates, sodium compounds, calcium and magnesium chloride, bromine and iodine, potash, sulfur, lithium, miscellaneous.
Fertilizer	Potash, nitrates and nitrogen phosphates, agricultural limestone and lime, sulfur.

seems called for than a survey showing the main uses to which they are put, such as that in Table 47.1. While many of these minerals are used for several purposes, most of them are more closely identified with a particular industry or group of industries.[2]

CERAMIC MATERIALS

The ceramic industry produces a wide variety of products ranging from common brick to the most delicate china, and including terra cotta, tile, and vitreous ware. Its chief raw material is clay. Clay is a composite of earthy substances which generally become plastic when wet, and like stone under fire. The layman to whom clay is a simple lowly substance may be surprised to learn that clay minerals include such compounds as kaolinite $(A_2O_3 \cdot 2\ SiO_2 \cdot 2\ H_2O)$ and montmorillonite $(A_2O_3(MgCa)_6 \cdot 5\ SiO_2 \cdot NH_2O)$. Hydrous aluminum silicates apparently are a sort of common denominator of clay around which are grouped various colloidal materials and which themselves are interspersed with specks of rock.

There are various types of clays and they have different uses. Some are high-grade fine-grained white-burning kaolin, like the china clay and paper clay used in making whiteware and paper. Ball clays may be added to assure high plasticity and bonding qualities. On the basis of the temperature at which clay becomes fusible, there are common brick clays, which become fusible around 1000° C., and refractory brick, which does not fuse below temperatures of 1300-1400° C. Some clays, such as butonite or fuller's earth, are valued for their absorptive qualities and are used as industrial filters. About 90 percent of the clays produced are common brick clays. It is estimated that in the United States in a single year the output runs as high as 35 million tons.

On the other hand, the United States is short of high-grade kaolin and ball clay, much of which must be imported. The highest-grade kaolins are found in England, Czechosiovakia, Germany, France, and China. Famous porcelain or chinaware industries have sprung up near both the market centers and the chief deposits, as in Limoges and Sèvres, France; Dresden, Germany; and Kingteh, in Kiangsi province, China. There are minor kaolin deposits in the United States, chiefly in North Carolina and Delaware. Paper clays are produced in the same countries in which kaolins are produced. In the United States, Georgia and South Carolina produce some. Ball clays come mainly from Germany and England; Kentucky and Tennessee are the chief producers in the United States. Fine clays are produced in England, Germany, and Belgium; in the United States their production is widely

[1] Based on *Economic Mineral Deposits*, 1st ed., by A. M. Bateman, published by John Wiley & Sons, Inc., 1942. A revised and enlarged edition was published in 1950.

[2] In general this survey is based on data in *ibid.*, Part 3.

scattered from New Jersey to California.

Feldspar is used in making pottery, both in the body and in the glaze, and also in enamels for household utensils, in tile, porcelain, and sanitary ware, and for some minor purposes. There are several types, each with its own special properties and uses. World production of feldspar is estimated at about half a million tons, of which approximately two-thirds is produced in the United States. Over half our output goes to the glass industry.

Special types of porcelain require special ingredients. Thus bauxite imparts strength, and resistance to heat, corrosion, and abrasion. Spark plug porcelain is likely to contain mullite derived from sillimanite minerals. Porcelain used to coat iron and steel household goods may contain borax. Borax also facilitates the use of pigment on porcelain, and gives brilliance to glazes and glass. This list of ingredients could be continued all the way to zirconium, which is added if the porcelain is to go into high-temperature crucibles. But enough examples have been given to illustrate the basic fact that the attainment of specific properties requires specific materials with specific characteristics. It is one of the triumphs of modern science that it has discovered and examined these specific materials on a scale never before approached.

STRUCTURAL AND BUILDING MATERIALS

The surface of the earth consists largely of rock. From rocks selected for strength, durability, and ease of quarrying and processing, stones are broken loose which can be cut and dressed to the dimensions wanted, or crushed for road-building material or cement making. The most important rocks used for commercial stone are granite, limestone, marble, slate, and soapstone.

The use of stone is as old as history. The chief difference between the modern and ancient use is the shift from solid stone structures like the pyramids and ancient temples to buildings with a steel skeleton on which stone is used like skin on the body, often in the form of cement, concrete, etc.

Building stone varies widely in durability. In New York coarse limestone lasts for five to ten years and granite may last for cen-turies. Some building stones—among them Vermont and Carrara (Italy) marbles, Mexican onyx marble, Indiana limestone, Minnesota granite, Virginia soapstone—have acquired national and even international fame. They may be called for even when haulage costs are staggering and when local products could be substituted with great saving and little impairment in quality and final effect.[3] Similarly it used to be common practice to haul cement halfway around the world to places which abounded in the raw materials needed to make cement of like quality.[4] Nevertheless, even today Carrara marble and other special quality stones may be specified to assure the desired artistic effects.

In both tonnage and value, crushed stone production now exceeds building stone output by a wide margin. The raw materials are generally local products prepared mechanically for road construction, concrete making, and similar purposes. Crushed stone is one of the cheapest products of industry; it sells for about $1 a ton.

The cement industry has become one of the leading mineral industries of the United States. Cement is a mixture of about 75 to 80 percent limestone, or its equivalents, and 20 to 25 percent clay or shale, calcined in rotary kilns to near fusion and then ground to a powder. When mixed with water it "sets," i.e., hardens. Nowadays most cement is the so-called Portland cement, first discovered in England in 1824 by Aspdin and named after the Portland stone used in making it. Its peculiar properties derive from the character of the clayey material that is used. To prevent too rapid setting some gypsum is added before the final grinding. The raw material may be blast furnace slag, oyster shells, rocks, or mixtures—in short, whatever meets the requirements of the formula. World production is estimated at 80 to 90

---

[3] A striking example is Duke University at Durham, North Carolina, in whose construction a special limestone hauled from a considerable distance was at first contemplated but which actually was constructed of stone from a nearby quarry that was opened up for that purpose and connected with the site by a spur line. The savings are reported to have been enormous.

[4] Rio de Janeiro used to depend on imported cement but now obtains it from a local plant at Niteroi, across Guanabara Bay.

million tons, about one-fourth of which is produced in the United States.[5] Cement production is spreading to the far corners of the earth.

Sand and gravel are among the most widely used building materials. Literally speaking, sand is any mineral material reduced to a certain form of comminuted rock. But technically the term is confined to particular minerals, especially quartz. There are also special sands such as coral sand, gypsum sand, black (magnetite) sand.

Gypsum, or hydrous calcium sulfite, is one of the most important nonmetallic minerals. It occurs in various forms, from the well-known white solid to the translucent alabaster and the transparent selenite. Its chief commercial use is based on the fact that, after calcining, merely adding water transforms it into plaster of Paris and other quick-setting plasters. (Gypsum occurs extensively in the Paris basin; hence the name "plaster of Paris.") The bulk is used for building purposes in the form of plaster, cement, plasterboard, etc. World production is estimated at from 8 to 10 million tons distributed about as follows: United States, 32 percent; France, 15; Canada, 13; United Kingdom, 12; all others, 27 percent.

When limestone is heated in kilns to 903° C., carbon dioxide is driven off and quicklime (CaO) results; 100 pounds of pure limestone yields 56 pounds of quicklime. Slaked with water and mixed with sand, quicklime makes mortar or plastic. Dolomite is a substitute for limestone.

Magnesite has already been mentioned in this book twice—once as a source of metallic magnesium, and once in connection with the iron and steel industry where it and dolomite serve as a basic lining in the Bessemer converter or open hearth. Magnesite can also be converted into special cements that have superior weathering properties and hence are used for stucco. In addition to these few, there are numerous other uses for the almost 2 million tons of magnesite produced in the world. The Soviet Union and Austria each produce about 25 percent; Manchuria produces about 18 percent, the United States 10, Greece 8.5, Czechoslovakia 2.2, Korea 2, and all the others 3.3. Manchuria is supposed to possess the largest deposits of magnesite in the world.

Mineral pigments are obtained from natural mineral deposits, chiefly iron-ore-bearing minerals so constituted as to provide brilliant and dependable colors. Red generally comes from some variety of hematite (hema = blood), and brown and yellow from limonite (see p. 623). These minerals are known as ochers. If they contain various percentages of manganese, upon roasting they become burnt umber, a rich brown, or burnt sienna, a yellowish brown. The presence of chlorite is likely to produce green effects.

Besides these natural pigments, many other pigments are obtained by subjecting minerals to a manufacturing process. The use of lead, zinc, and titanium in paint manufacturing has already been discussed. Barium (lithopone), copper, iron ores, carbon black (see p. 565), chrome, mercury, cadmium, and cobalt are among the other minerals used for this purpose.

In modern building much use is made of heat and sound insulators. They can be either natural or manufactured products. Vermiculite and diatomite[6] are natural products; rock wool and glass wool are manufactured products. In both the presence of innumerable air pockets provides insulation. Some mineral wool is made from blast furnace slag but most is made from molten silicate.

Asphalt is useful because of its semisolid nature. About two-thirds of the asphalt consumed in the United States is used for street paving. One of the most famous sources of asphalt is a lake on the island of Trinidad; another but less well-known source is a similar lake in Venezuela. Asphalt is also a residual product of refining asphalt-base crude oils.

INDUSTRIAL AND MANUFACTURING MATERIALS

Asbestos is the only mineral that consists of fine spinnable fibers. It resists fire and acid

---

[5] In 1948 our cement industry attracted much attention by the decision of the Federal Trade Commission regarding the legality and social desirability of the basing-point system of pricing.

[6] Vermiculite is a type of mica which under heat "exfoliates" into thin sheets. Diatomite consists of innumerable microscopic shells and hence is very porous. Pumice is a good insulator because of the porous spaces traceable to its volcanic origin.

and is a good nonconductor of heat and electricity. Its modern use dates from 1878, when large deposits were discovered in Quebec, Canada. The Canadian deposits lie in a belt about seventy miles long and six miles wide which projects into Vermont. Today asbestos is an important mineral raw material with a thousand uses. World production amounts to almost half a million tons and is distributed as follows: Canada, 60 percent; South America, 20; southern Rhodesia, 8.5; Union of South Africa, 4.2; the rest is scattered. The United States is by far the largest consumer of spinnable asbestos.

There are several types of mica. The more valuable types are those that split into fine sheets about 1/1000 of an inch thick. Mica is flexible, tough, and resilient; it is a poor conductor of heat and electricity and hence makes an ideal electrical insulator. Nonsplitting mica is usually ground and used as a lustrous sprinkle on wallpaper, for roofing, stucco finishes, lubrication, and other purposes. The mica deposits in Bihar and Madras, India, supply most of the sheet mica for electrical uses. The 30 to 50 thousand tons of mica (all grades) produced annually are distributed as follows: United States, 51 percent (mostly scrap-ground mica); India, 23; Soviet Union, 14; all others, 12.

Talc, the softest of all minerals, is widely used in the manufacture of face powder. Soapstone consists chiefly of talc. Only 3 percent of the talc consumed in the United States goes into toilet articles. Industrial uses (ceramics, paints, roofing, paper, etc.) account for the rest. The United States produces about half the world output of talc. Other important producers are Manchuria, France, and Italy.

Barite is valued because of its weight and chemically inert and stable behavior, properties which make it an ideal filler. But, as was said before, most of the barite in this country goes into the manufacture of paint. The world output is about one million tons, of which Germany normally produces close to one-half, the United States one-third, the rest being scattered.

Glass consists mainly of silica sand but also contains soda and lime as well as various ingredients added to produce desired colors, special properties, etc. For some glass the sand must be very pure (99.8 percent silica); for others it can contain various degrees and kinds of impurities. Optical glass is made from very pure sand whose ingredients are carefully controlled. Thus for this glass the alumina content may not exceed 0.1 percent, whereas for ordinary glass it may run as high as 4 percent. All common glass contains lime, magnesia, and alkalis.

Glass sand production in the United States normally ranges from 2 to 3 million tons. Three-fourths of it comes from West Virginia, Pennsylvania, Illinois, and Missouri. Some sands are so fine that they can be pumped out.

Color effects are produced mainly by the presence of metals. Thus iron oxides impart green and yellow tints. Amber glass may contain as much as 1 percent manganese. After long exposure to the sun, manganese gives glass delicate amethystine or lavender colors. Metallic gold makes ruby glass, selenium turns glass red, chromium and copper make green glass, cobalt makes blue glass, calcium fluoride and tin oxide make opal glass.

Many industrial products—textiles, linoleum, cements, roofing, fertilizers, paints, paper, plastics, and rubber—contain fillers, inert materials which add to the bulk and weight without ordinarily impairing desirable properties. Thus "2-8-2 fertilizer" contains 2 percent nitrogen, 8 percent phosphorus, 2 percent potassium, and 88 percent filler. The materials used as fillers are legion; they may be either natural or processed.

For reasons not yet completely understood, some minerals are used as filters in the purification of oils, sugar, water, chemicals, etc. Among these, diatomaceous earth and fuller's earth are particularly important. Certain types of bentonite after activation[7] have replaced fuller's earth as bleaching clays. Activated bauxite is also used as a substitute for fuller's earth. It is cheap but cannot be revivified indefinitely.

Optical instruments require crystals of special quality and purity. Iceland spar not only is unusually transparent and pure but is crys-

---

[7] "Activation consists in the removal of ions loosely held at the surface." A. M. Bateman, *op. cit.*, p. 757. Activation can be repeated indefinitely, thus paying for the higher costs by longer use.

tallized in such a way as to be "doubly refracting"; i.e., a single dot appears as two dots. This peculiar property is exploited in the polarizing microscope and other scientific instruments. Most of this rare mineral comes from Iceland but some of it comes from near the Cape of Good Hope. Quartz crystals of fine quality and having some optical characteristics are used in making radio instruments,

telephones, etc. Brazil has long been a chief source; but, according to recent reports, such crystals can now be "grown" artificially.

Tourmaline is used in studying polarized light. More recently, it has also been used "for 'crystals' in radio transmitters to give a definite frequency of sending waves."[8]

---

[8] A. M. Bateman, op. cit., p. 760.

BIBLIOGRAPHY

Bateman, A. M., Economic Mineral Deposits, New York, Wiley, 2nd ed., 1950.

Backman, J., The Economics of the Potash Industry, Washington, American Potash Institute, 1946.

Bowles, O., "Non-metallic Minerals," Mining and Metallurgy, February, 1945.

Bowles, O., "Seventy-five Years of Progress in the Nonmetallics," in Parsons, A. B. (ed.), Seventy-five Years of Progress in the Mineral Industry, 1871-1946, New York, American Institute of Mining and Metallurgical Engineers, 1947.

Dolbear, S. H., Potash Reserves of the United States, Washington, American Potash Institute, 1946.

Eckel, E. C., "Cement," Encyclopædia of the Social Sciences, New York, Macmillan, 1930.

Industrial Minerals Division, Industrial Minerals (Non-metallics), New York, American Institute of Mining and Metallurgical Engineers, 1947.

Josephson, G. W., "Nonmetallic Industrial Minerals," Mining and Metallurgy, February, 1947.

Ladoo, R. B., Non-metallic Minerals, New York, McGraw-Hill, 1925.

Turrentine, J. W., Potash, American Chemical Society Monograph No. 91, 1943.

U. S. Tariff Commission, Mercury, War Changes in Industry Series Report No. 4, June, 1944.

U. S. Tariff Commission, Refractory Magnesia (Magnesite), War Changes in Industry Series Report No. 12, 1945.

U. S. Tariff Commission, Mica, War Changes in Industry Series Report No. 21, 1947.

Chapter 48

THE CHEMICAL INDUSTRY

THE CHEMICAL REVOLUTION

The chemical revolution is one of the joint achievements of modern science and industry. The ancients used chemical processes when they made glass, dyed cloth, brewed beer and made wine, tanned leather and made soap. But their proficiency as chemical processors was limited by the shortcomings of their understanding of chemical processes. Scientific chemistry, as we understand it today, was unknown. There was no periodic table of the elements, no theory of valences, no real understanding of chemical change. What knowledge there was, was purely pragmatic, based on trial and error and rule of thumb. Slowly throughout the centuries observation was added to observation, experiment to experiment, until, with the aid of modern laboratory techniques, instruments, and scientific methods, the fundamental laws of matter were gradually deduced from the observed facts. Thus modern scientific chemistry was born and with it the chemical industry as it is known today.

There were encouraging beginnings of scientific advance toward the end of the eighteenth century, especially when Scheele in Sweden, Lavoisier in France, and Priestley in England discovered oxygen and established the nature of combustion as a chemical reaction. When Le Blanc in France discovered a process which permitted the cheap production of alkalis[1] from common salt he broke the monopoly of the vegetable soda industry and laid the foundation of the early English chemical industry. One does not go far wrong in dating the beginning of the modern chemical industry around 1800. A milestone in its early history was passed when Wöhler in Germany discovered that ammonia, an organic compound, could be synthesized from inorganic elements. Another milestone was passed when Mendeleev in Russia and Lothar Meyer in Germany formulated the periodic law based on atomic weights showing the orderly relationships of the chemical elements to each other.

---

[1] Soluble bases, chiefly those of sodium, potassium, and calcium, are known as alkalis. The word alkali is of Arabic origin and refers to the ashes of the saltwort, a plant, known in commerce as soda.

This chemical revolution, now in full swing, will, in the opinion of some observers, in the course of time prove as far reaching in its effect on economic life and human existence in general as did the mechanical revolution. The mechanical revolution resulted from a fuller and better utilization of energy; the chemical revolution is based on a fuller and deeper understanding of the structure of matter, of the changes it may undergo, and of the energy factor involved. Needless to say, the mechanical revolution and the chemical revolution have to some extent progressed hand in hand. Without chemistry, it would have been impossible to manufacture large engines and generators; and without engines and generators, many of our large-scale chemical processes would be impossible. The mechanical revolution in its earlier phases is often identified with the textile industry, especially cotton textiles. That industry in turn could not have progressed as it did without the chemist Le Blanc, the founder of the chemical bleaching industry and the father of the alkali industry.[2]

Chemical changes are constantly occurring around and within us. The growing leaf builds sugars and starches from the carbon dioxide of the air and the water from the earth, under the influence of radiation from the sun; iron rusts under the attack of air and moisture; coal burns; bread rises because of the action of yeast. All these, and many others, are chemical phenomena within our everyday experience. Chemical processes are essential to the technology of a number of important industries.

There is hardly a mineral industry in which a chemical process does not play a major role. The conversion of bauxite to alumina—the Bayer process—is a chemical process. Magnesium is obtained from the sea by chemical processes.

Dynamics of Chemical Development

The commutation and permutation of combinations of more than 100 elements[3] is the field of scientific chemistry. It comes close to infinity; for, once man starts out on this venture of limitless discovery, there is no stopping. One step leads to another, to still another, and so on, *ad infinitum*.

The Du Pont Company illustrates this mushrooming, pyramiding, recompounding nature of chemistry.[4] Eleuthère Irénée Du Pont, a refugee from dictatorship, who in his native France had learned how to make black powder, started to manufacture it on a modest scale in Delaware in 1802. For decades he and his co-workers clung to their specialty with almost fanatic tenacity, but the pressure to branch out proved irresistible. To black powder was added smokeless powder, nitroglycerin, dynamite, and other high explosives. Here the true nature of chemistry reveals itself. Nitrocellulose is the basic material not only for smokeless powder but also for celluloid, photographic, including moving-picture, films, lacquers, automobile finishes, and artificial leather. The momentum developed and the research, engineering and distributive facilities and abilities set up to meet the needs in one field drive on to other fields with almost elemental force. Thus the Du Pont interests expanded to include the manufacture of dyes and pigments, synthetic resins, ammonia, methanol, neoprene, rayon, nylon, and cellophane. And the end is not in sight. On the contrary, perhaps this is only the beginning; for if pure research, deliberately aimed at definite goals, enables a Carothers to conjure up nylon, what is to stop his confreres and

---

[2] Until about the middle of the eighteenth century bleaching brown linens was a slow process. In northern Europe, it lasted from about March to October—at least that was the time that textile goods were either in process or in transit and out of the hands of the merchants. The cloth was steeped in lye, washed, and spread on the grass for weeks. This process was repeated five or six times. The cloth was then steeped in sour milk, washed, and bleached again. Holland with her herds of dairy cattle and large areas in grass did considerable bleaching for other countries, especially for rainy Britain.

The discovery that sulfuric acid could take over for sour milk and that chlorine could substitute for the actinic rays of the sun put the modern textile finishing industry on its feet and enabled it to do in hours what used to take months.

[3] Recently the figure has been raised to 104. See *Life*, May 16, 1949.

[4] W. S. Dutton, *Du Pont, One Hundred and Forty Years*, Charles Scribner, 1942. See also Arthur D. Little, "The Chemical Revolution," an unpublished lecture delivered before the Examiner's Club, May 7, 1934.

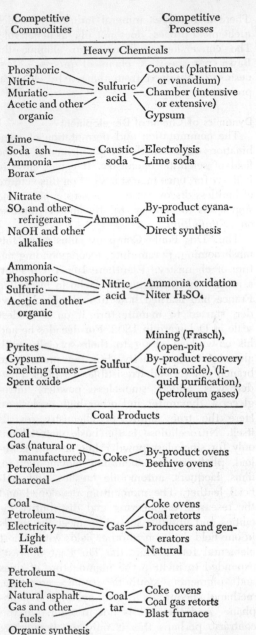

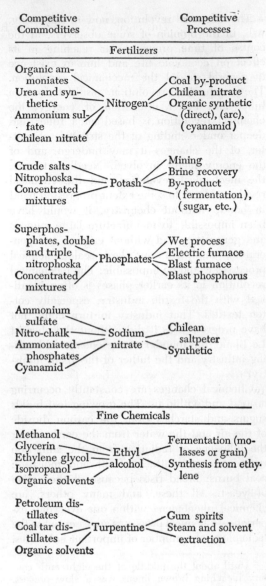

FIG. 48.1. Commodity and Process Competition in the Chemical Industry. (*Chemical and Metallurgical Engineering,* January, 1931.)

successors from bringing forth new surprises, new gifts of science for mankind?

The story of Du Pont is a theme with many variations. If one substitutes carbon and air for cellulose he will have the story of Union Carbide and Carbon. Coal-tar dyes bring to mind the fantastic story of the German chemical trust, the famous and notorious IG (see p. 793), with its seemingly endless ramifications into synthetic gasoline, synthetic rubber, synthetic camphor, and a thousand other wonders.

ACHIEVEMENTS OF THE CHEMICAL INDUSTRY
Raw-Material Options

What the chemical industry has done and is doing for mankind has far-reaching effects. The most obvious effect is what Arthur D. Little aptly refers to as increased raw-material options, or a tremendously increased commodity competition. New metals are made available at lower costs by means of chemical innovations such as the Bayer process of alumina production, and the amalgamation, cyanidation, and flotation processes. Plastics compete with both metals and wood. Alloy metals replace base metals. Nylon competes with silk, and rayon with cotton and wool. Hydrogenated oils become fats which compete with natural fats. Synthetic rubber competes with natural rubber, synthetic methanol with natural wood alcohol, synthetic ammonia with Chilean nitrate and by-product sulfate of ammonia. Paper made from southern pine by new chemical processes competes with paper made by older processes from northern pine. Countless other examples could be listed.

Frequently this competition works along two lines. Not only is one source pitted against another—coal, yielding sulfate of ammonia, against caliche, yielding nitrate—but process is pitted against process. Thus coke made by the Koppers process may compete with coke from the beehive oven; sulfuric acid made by the chamber process may compete with sulfuric acid made by the contact process.

In Fig. 48.1, no less than fourteen examples of both commodity and process competition are listed from four different fields of chemical production, and it would be easy to add to these examples.

Price Reduction and the Breakdown of Monopolies

In many instances this process competition has reduced prices greatly; in others it has broken powerful monopolies. A classical example of price reduction resulted from the introduction of the Le Blanc and later the Solvay process of producing alkalis, in which common salt was substituted for a relatively scarce plant, the saltwort, as the source of soda and soda products. Price drops also followed the use of coal tar for dyes, instead of the old sources of coloring matter such as Brazil wood, the "purple snail," cochineal, madder root, anil (the indigo plant), and so forth. It is true that the introduction of coal-tar dyes did some harm to established agricultural and commercial interests; the virtual destruction of indigo farming in India brought great hardship. But the final result strongly favors science, for coal tar has given mankind far more and far better dyes at a fraction of the former cost.

Another striking example is furnished by nitrogen, for here too a powerful monopoly fell before the blowtorch of scientific inquiry. For almost three hundred years India had had a virtual monopoly in saltpeter, or potassium nitrate, but toward the middle of the nineteenth century her deposits of it were approaching exhaustion. In 1809, vast deposits of sodium nitrate were discovered in Peru,[5] and had attracted wide attention. In 1840 a new school of agricultural chemists headed by Justus von Liebig[6] demonstrated the possibilities of increasing agricultural production by enriching the soil with chemicals, especially potash, phosphorus, nitrogen, and lime. Thereupon the Peruvian sodium nitrate deposits were exploited for commercial nitrogenous fertilizer as a possible substitute for India's rapidly waning deposits of potassium nitrate. But attempts to make gunpowder with the Chilean raw material were unsuccessful until 1857, when Lammot Du Pont found a formula which yielded an excellent "soda powder," i.e., a powder made from sodium nitrate instead of from potassium nitrate. This is said to have been the first real improvement in gunpowder in six hundred years.[7]

Thus two bold strokes by chemists gave the desert shores of what today is northern Chile unheard-of resource value, gave them magic power to raise the earth's agricultural potential and to increase man's rock-splitting, projectile-propelling power. Peruvian nitrate became one of the most coveted com-

---

[5] These deposits were transferred to Chile after the War of the Pacific.

[6] Samuel W. Johnson, the father of agricultural chemistry in the United States, entered Liebig's laboratory as a student in 1854.

[7] W. S. Dutton, *op. cit.*, pp. 81 ff.

modities of world trade and the Pacific coast of South America became one of the busiest sections of ocean front anywhere on earth. After conquering the Peruvian coastal strip in the War of the Pacific, Chile profited vastly from the monopoly position into which foreign scientists had thrust her. Again scientific chemistry broke the monopoly, this time a monopoly that chemistry itself had created. This time it was a double-barreled gun that was leveled at the monopolists; for, like the nitrate mined in Chile, ammonia has become the source of both explosives and of fertilizer. The by-product coke oven perfected by Koppers in the nineties (see p. 491) became the backbone of the coal-tar industry and the source of sulfate of ammonia, a nitrogenous compound; and in 1913 Fritz Haber succeeded in making synthetic ammonia from nitrogen extracted from the air. The powerful part explosives play in war makes us realize the momentous impact of this revolutionary invention on the course of history and the political map of the world. But the full significance of cheap and reliable high explosives is not so readily apparent. For example, the cement industry rests squarely on the use of high explosives to obtain the vast amounts of its raw materials. Similarly, modern dam construction and most modern mass mining are unthinkable without an abundant supply of cheap explosives.

Creation of New Industries

The penetrating power of chemical invention is further seen in Goodyear's discovery of vulcanized rubber, as a result of which a natural curiosity of uncertain disposition became a dependable raw material of modern industry. It has made possible modern highway transport and it is indispensable to air transport and tractors alike; through these improvements it has literally remade the map of the earth. But that was not good enough. Probing into the mysteries of natural rubber, and finding that it is composed of giant polymers, man has learned to synthesize them from coal and petroleum and natural gas and to create not imitation rubber but an almost endless variety of rubbers, each with its special properties.

War and Peace and Chemistry

Perhaps no example of chemical achievement better illustrates the political implications of the chemical revolution than the basic process of steelmaking. The story has been told elsewhere (see pp. 648 ff.). Here it is sufficient to recall how Germany rode to power on the tidal wave released by this momentous invention, how the center of industry shifted to the New World partly because of its impact. It is most unlikely that Germany's military might would ever have reached the heights it did had it not been for the two Welsh boys who by a simple chemical trick transformed the dirt of Lorraine into the largest iron ore deposit of Europe. The question has often been raised whether Germany would have dared start World War I if Fritz Haber had not succeeded in extracting nitrogen from the air in 1913. Would Hitler have dared fight the world without knowing what German chemists could do?

These political calculations are highly speculative. But no "if" is attached to another claim that chemistry can justifiably make. It has created the modern pharmacopoeia and with it has given medicine new weapons with which to fight the enemies of mankind.

The totality of these achievements of the chemical revolution is too vast for the human mind to encompass in one sweep. They constitute almost perfect proof of the thesis underlying this book—that resources *are not*, but *become*. The chemist is indeed a creator of resources.

SCOPE OF THE INDUSTRY

So pervasive is the influence of chemistry on modern industry that it is difficult to determine satisfactorily the scope of the chemical industry. To meet this difficulty a distinction has developed between chemical manufacturing industries and chemical process industries. The manufacturing industries are a fairly definite group engaged in the manufacture of chemicals. The process industries are more or less arbitrarily selected industries in which the use of chemical processes is so dominant that they deserve separate classification as chemical process industries. The Bayer process of alumina production is definitely a chemical

TABLE 48.1. Basic Data for Chemical Manufacturing and Chemical Process Industries[8]

	Chemical Manufacturing Industries[a]			Chemical Process Industries[b]		
	1929	1937	1947	1929	1937	1947
No. of establishments	2,393	2,787	2,728	15,846	14,133	18,153
No. of salaried employees	29,212	24,035	[d]	173,246	159,281	[d]
Salaries paid ($1000)	75,279	58,031	[d]	458,556	382,883	[d]
No. of wage earners	81,634	119,779	238,324[c]	1,025,311	1,056,209	1,912,315[c]
Wages paid ($1000)	118,031	141,125	[d]	1,363,669	1,329,724	[d]
Cost of materials, containers, fuel and power ($1000)	492,095	569,222	1,993,620	7,156,447	6,930,593	21,607,417
Value of product ($1000)	988,103	1,183,931	3,855,146	...	...	...
Chemical process industries	...	...	...	11,966,714	11,228,433	35,411,130
All manufacturing industries	...	...	...	70,434,863	60,712,872	[d]
Percent of total	...	...	...	17.4	18.5	...

[a] Includes U.S. Census classifications for chemicals, not elsewhere classified (such as general inorganic compounds including acids, alkalis, and salts; general organic compounds including coal-tar products, dyes, synthetic organic chemicals, and plastics); compressed and liquefied gases; insecticides and fungicides; salt; tanning materials; natural dyestuffs; mordants, assistants, and sizes; turpentine and rosin; wood distillation products.

[b] Includes U.S. Census classifications for chemicals (see note a); coke oven products; drugs and medicines; perfumes, cosmetics, and toilet preparations; distilled liquors; explosives and fireworks; fertilizers; glass, clay products and refractories, pottery, porcelain, and sand-lime brick; leather tanning; lime and cement; oils and fats (cottonseed, linseed, and essential oils and greases); paints, pigments, varnishes, and lacquers; paper and pulp; petroleum products; rayon and allied products; rubber goods (tires, tubes, boots, shoes, etc.); soap and cleaning and polishing compounds; beet and cane sugar refining; and miscellaneous products as follows: coated fabrics; blacking, stains, and dressings; blueing; bone black, carbon black, and lamp black; candles; manufactured fuels; glue and gelatine; graphite; gypsum; printing and writing inks; linoleum and asphalt-felt base floor coverings; matches; ground and treated minerals and earths; mucilage, paste, and other adhesives; photographic materials; paving materials (other than brick and stone); prepared roofing; wallboard and building insulation; wood preserving.

[c] Includes all employees. The 1947 Census does not give a comparable breakdown of salaried employees and wage earners.

[d] Not available.

process, but the aluminum industry is not listed as a chemical process industry. Similarly the cyanidation process of recovering gold is a chemical process, but gold does not appear on the list of chemical process industries. Evidently the chemical processes are not considered dominant. The chemical process industries are the best customers of the chemical manufacturing industries. Table 48.1 furnishes basic statistics for the two groups of chemical industries and lists in footnotes the main categories included.

In further comment on the difficulty inherent in this classification, it may be mentioned that frequently the same corporate organization is engaged in both branches. Thus Du Pont manufactures dyes and acids and is engaged in such "process" activities as the making of rayon, nylon, fertilizers, rubbers, insecticides, explosives, etc. It is true that these activities are generally carried on by separate subsidiaries. Vice versa, the petroleum industry to an increasing degree is extending its activities into strictly chemical fields such as the manufacture of TNT, synthetic rubber, candles, pharmaceuticals, insecticides, and so forth. The steel industry is not considered a chemical industry but it makes sulfate of ammonia, a heavy chemical, and coal tar, a fine chemical, to mention but two of its chemical products.[9] Moreover, the boundaries of the fields are fluid, reflecting the dynamics of modern chemical technology. Increased reliance on natural gas and on petroleum-refining vapors as sources of chemical products increases the shifting of the boundaries. Incidentally, it also affects the location of chemical industries, not necessarily away from coal but definitely toward the sources of petroleum vapors and natural gas, especially the gulf coast of Louisiana and Texas.

The chemical manufacturing industry of the United States has grown rapidly in recent decades. In 1899 the total value of the chem-

[8] Data supplied by the editors of *Chemical Engineering*, published by McGraw-Hill.

[9] Actually the list is much larger; it includes creosote, naphthalene, phenol, cresylic acid, benzol, toluol, xylol, etc. For various reasons, the biggest steel companies, especially U.S. Steel, feel compelled to plunge deeper and deeper into the chemical field. See *Business Week*, April 10, 1948, pp. 30 ff.

ical industry's production was reported as $99.5 million; this constituted only 0.86 percent of the total value of all manufactures. By 1937 it had increased to $1.2 billion, or almost 2 percent of the total value of all manufactures. Between 1914 and 1937 the annual value of the chemical industry's output increased by almost a billion. To a large degree this was due to deliberate efforts on the part of industry and government to create a large national chemical industry, efforts activated by our bitter experience in World War I when the extent of our dependence on Germany for vital and strategic chemicals became painfully apparent. Two methods were applied to accomplish this goal of greater self-sufficiency in chemicals. In the first place, a high tariff, virtually prohibitive in the case of competing German imports, was imposed on imported chemicals, assuring our own nascent industry high prices for its output. In the second place, through the Chemical Foundation the government placed at the disposal of American chemical producers thousands of German patents which had been confiscated during World War I. (It is true that in the period between the two wars Germany to some extent regained control over important chemical production in this country, notably dyestuffs production.[10]) Although these artificial stimulants, tariff protection and the free use of patents, accelerated the growth of our chemical industry, it must also be recognized that many branches of chemical manufacturing are "naturals" in a country which not only possesses perhaps the largest array of chemical raw materials but offers by far the largest market for chemical products.

The value of the output of the chemical process industries behaved rather erratically. From $2.1 billion in 1899 it shot up to $12.2 billion in 1919 (much of this increase reflecting the war-inflated price level), and then dropped back to $8.5 billion in 1921 (reflecting the postwar depression). Not until World War II did it manage to pass the $12-billion peak of 1919. It hit a low of $6.6 billion in 1933 and rose to $11.2 billion in 1937. After 1939 the value rose as the rest of our economy

expanded to unprecedented size. The value of the chemical process industry's output in 1937 constituted almost one-fifth of the total value of goods produced by all manufacturing industry. The chemical process industry consumes about four-fifths of all chemicals sold in the United States.

RAW MATERIALS OF THE CHEMICAL INDUSTRY

In their investigations of the nature of matter, chemists and physicists have found that all complex materials are built from a little over 100 fundamental substances, known as elements. They cannot be transformed one into the other at will, but are fixed and stable. By combining these elements in various ways and in various proportions, chemists have made hundreds of thousands of different compounds in the laboratory. Nature also performs similar building operations, but her syntheses are frequently so complex that man cannot duplicate them. Since elements cannot be created at will, when industry demands a certain element it must be sought in nature—on land, in the sea, or in the air.

The raw materials of the chemical industry come in part from matter that once had life. The element carbon is peculiarly associated with life, and most carbon-containing substances can be traced to living things. Coal, for example, had its origin in living trees. Lard, a complex mixture of carbon-containing compounds, originated in living animals. Smokeless powder, moving-picture film, and cottonseed oil can be traced to the cotton plant. Such materials as wood, coal, tanbark, petroleum, natural gas, and cotton are the basic raw materials for the organic chemical industries.

The gases of the air, the minerals of the earth, and the dissolved salts of the sea are also sources of much-needed elements. Pyrites supply iron and sulfur, and perhaps copper as well. From the air is obtained neon, the rare gas which provides the red-colored light in electrical signs. Phosphate rock is a source of phosphorus; common clay is a potential source of aluminum, and rock salt is a source of chlorine gas. These are the raw materials of the inorganic chemical industries.

---

[10] See G. W. Stocking and M. W. Watkins, *Cartels in Action*, Twentieth Century Fund, New York, 1947, p. 471.

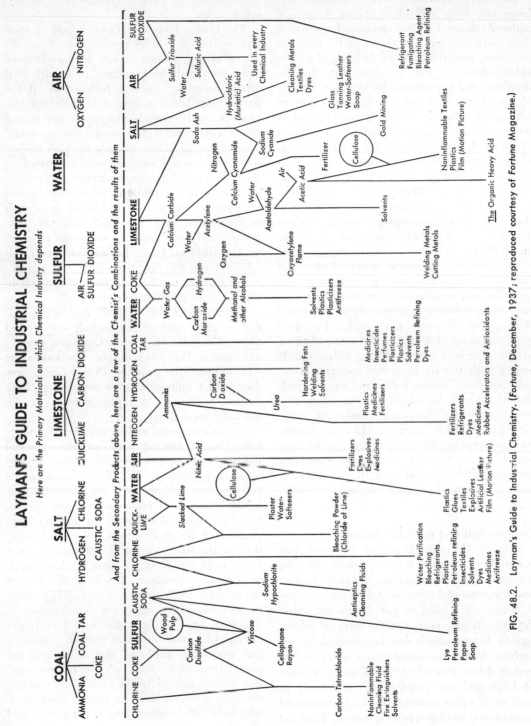

FIG. 48.2. Layman's Guide to Industrial Chemistry. (Fortune, December, 1937; reproduced courtesy of Fortune Magazine.)

In general, however, it is unnecessary and frequently very difficult to break these raw materials down into the elements from which they were derived, for they can be made to form new materials without isolating the individual elements. For the most part, the desired material is produced by means of a series of operations of varying complexity, starting with some naturally occurring raw material or some substance that was originally a product of living things. It is through the interaction of these fundamental raw materials, often with the aid of heat or electricity, that new materials are formed. These in turn may be subject to further processing, until eventually there has been produced a complex product like a dye, a fertilizer, alloy steel, or a synthetic fiber.

To attempt a complete survey of chemical raw materials at this point is both out of the question and unnecessary, for these materials have been referred to frequently in this book. Here a few comments must suffice. Fig. 48.2 gives a general idea of the chief materials used in the chemical manufacturing industries. It begins with the six basic raw materials—coal, salt, limestone, sulfur, water, and air, to which should perhaps be added cellulose or wood—from which are derived a number of intermediary products such as chlorine, caustic soda, ammonia, nitrogen, oxygen, quicklime, etc. Most of the end products of chemistry are produced by combining these intermediaries in unlimited permutations and commutations.

Common Salt and the Alkali Industry

One of the most important chemical raw materials is common salt, or sodium chloride, a compound of two elements, the metal sodium and the nonmetal chlorine. Salt is mined when it occurs as a solid in salt domes and other deposits. It also occurs in the form of subterranean brines which can be pumped to the surface. Salt is contained in sea water and in certain lakes (notably in the Great Salt Lake of Utah and the Dead Sea in Palestine) as well as in saline marshes. It can be recovered from oceans and lakes by evaporation. The total amount of salt in the world is estimated at astronomical figures; that in the ocean alone is estimated to have a volume of 4,500,000 cubic miles.

The human body tends to maintain an even balance of about 0.88 percent salt. Normally about twelve pounds of salt a year obtained from food and drink suffices to furnish that vitally necessary amount. Incidentally, if the earth's population is figured at 2,250,000,000 persons, at 12 pounds per capita the annual direct consumption by human beings would amount to 27 billion pounds or 13.5 million tons. Since world production is estimated at 30 million tons,[11] apparently about 16.5 million tons are used for purposes other than human consumption, especially industrial uses. Salt is distributed over the land area very unevenly, and accessibility to salt water depends on the distance from the sea and from salt lakes. Hence the procurement of salt can become a major problem, as Gandhi's march to the sea demonstrated so dramatically.

The countries that normally produce a million or more tons of salt include the United States, Great Britain, China, Germany, France, and India. The 1945 output was valued at $46 million. That year the United States produced 15.4 million tons, or double her 1935 output, suggesting a rapid increase in the chemical uses of salt.

As was mentioned earlier, salt played a major role at the beginning of the modern chemical industry when, toward the close of the eighteenth century, Le Blanc developed a process for making soda ash (sodium carbonate) from such common materials as salt, limestone, and sulfuric acid. An unwanted by-product of his process was chlorine. France, then in the throes of the Revolution, was not ready to benefit from Le Blanc's achievement. In England, however, it led to the rise of the modern alkali industry (see p. 777) which in turn materially aided the development of the soap and textile industries. The brines around Liverpool furnished the salt, limestone and coal were available, and sulfur was imported from Sicily. Soda ash can be converted into caustic soda or lye by chemically reacting the soda ash with lime. Le Blanc's main product, soda ash, was used in making soap and

[11] Alan M. Bateman, *Economic Mineral Deposits,* John Wiley & Sons, Inc., New York, 1942, p. 764.

glass; and chlorine, the formerly unwanted by-product, was made into bleaching powder. This early development of an alkali industry gave England a head start in the modern chemical industry which she held until the early 1870's when Germany wrested supremacy away from her.

In 1863 another process of making soda ash was perfected commercially; this was the Solvay or ammonia-soda process named after its Belgian inventor, Ernest Solvay. In this process, ammonia is used again and again as a service material, and soda ash is obtained from salt at costs considerably lower than those prevailing in the Le Blanc process; hence the Solvay process soon replaced the Le Blanc process.[12] Solvay plants sprang up in the leading industrial countries. In the United States one was built near Syracuse in the early eighties; in 1892 the Michigan alkali works built a plant at Wyandoth, Michigan; and in 1893 the Mathies alkali works were established in Saltville, Virginia.[13]

Toward the close of the nineteenth century developments occurred which had powerful repercussions on the alkali industry. The newly created electrical industry made electric current available for electrolysis.[14] When the rapidly growing paper and pulp industry demanded ever larger amounts of chlorine, a new phase of the alkali industry began—the electrolytic production of chlorine and caustic soda (sodium hydroxide) from brine, in roughly equal amounts.

Before long the paper, pulp, and textile mills, all of them heavy consumers of chlorine for bleaching purposes, began to manufacture their own chlorine electrolytically, with caustic soda as a by-product. This by-product was thrown on the market and of course seriously affected the Solvay plants. These plants, in turn, reacted by building their own electrolytic plants and producing cheap by-product chlorine and caustic soda with "soda ash-subsidized power."[15] By the end of 1942 all but two Solvay plants—those at Saltville, Virginia, and at Detroit—were equipped to produce chlorine and caustic soda electrolytically.

Besides needing cheap salt and limestone, all alkali plants require cheap fuel. Therefore, they are located on the northeastern brines within reach of the coal fields of Ohio, West Virginia, and Pennsylvania, and over the salt domes of the gulf coast in Louisiana (Lake Charles) and Texas where natural gas supplies cheap fuel for the generation of electricity. The shift to the Southwest was further encouraged by the growing market that developed among petroleum refineries, Kraft pulp and paper mills, viscose rayon mills, and alumina plants. Tidewater transportation is another factor.

The production of alkalis runs into millions of tons. The glass industry is the heaviest consumer of soda ash, with the soap industry second. The alkali industry is typical of the heavy chemical branch of the chemical industry.

Other important products obtained chemically from salt are bicarbonate of soda or baking soda, and salt cake, which is obtained in preparing hydrochloric acid from salt. The alkali industry is an excellent illustration of the dynamics of an industry based, as no other industry is, on science which is forever looking for new worlds to conquer. That these dynamics have repercussions on the industry's economic problems goes without saying; that phase will be discussed later.

---

[12] The shift from the Le Blanc to the Solvay process eliminated the chief market for sulfuric acid, thus releasing sulfuric acid for other industries, and created a great demand for ammonia. This encouraged the shift from beehive to by-product coke ovens. The latter yields sulfate of ammonia as the primary by-product.

[13] See Elmer H. Johnson, in *Texas Business Review*, April, 1943, p. 7.

[14] In 1800 Alessandro Volta invented the electric battery. Soon thereafter it was discovered that the electric current has a chemical effect. Thus, it will decompose water into hydrogen and oxygen. This electrically induced chemical process is known as electrolysis. One of the first practical applications of electrolysis was made by Hall in the early eighties, in reducing alumina to aluminum.

[15] This term needs explanation. The manufacture of soda ash by the Solvay or ammonia-soda process calls for large amounts of low-pressure steam. If high-pressure steam is first fed into turbines to generate electric power and the low-pressure exhaust steam is then used in the production of soda ash, the soda ash might be said to be "subsidizing" or sharing the cost of the electricity.

Sulfur and the Sulfuric Acid Industry

Another important raw material of the chemical industry is sulfur. On it is based an important branch of the heavy chemical industry. Its main product, sulfuric acid, is used so universally by major industries that it has been recommended as one of the best barometers of industrial activity.[16]

Salt is found in many parts of the earth, but the occurrence of sulfur is highly concentrated in a few spots. Whereas sodium is supposed to make up 2.85 percent of the earth's solid crust (to a depth of ten miles), sulfur constitutes only 0.05 percent. Sulfur occurs in its native state around volcanoes (Japan, Mexico, Chile), in salt-dome cap rocks (gulf coast of the United States), and as sedimentary beds (Sicily and the Soviet Union). Sulfur ores are known as pyrites, sometimes called fool's gold. The sulfur may be associated with iron, copper (cupreous pyrite), or other metals. Important deposits of pyrites are found in Spain (Rio Tinto region), Portugal, Cyprus, Norway, Soviet Russia (Urals), Canada (especially the Noranda mines in Quebec), and the United States (especially Ducktown, Tennessee,[17] but also in Pulaski, Virginia, and other areas). Most pyrites are roasted to extract the sulfur. In some cases sulfur is obtained as a by-product of the flotation of sulfur-bearing ores. It is also extracted from the fumes created in roasting such ores. Some sulfur is extracted from coals.

Until about the middle of the nineteenth century Sicily supplied most of the sulfur, her mines giving her a virtual monopoly which she exploited lustily. This monopoly was first dented when pyrites became a source of sulfur, Spain being the leading exporter of pyrites. The real collapse came when Herman Frasch, a petroleum engineer familiar with the geology of the gulf coast of the United States, invented an ingenious, simple, and cheap process for recovering sulfur from the salt-dome cap rocks of the coast of Texas and Louisiana. A well not unlike an oil well is driven down to the sulfur-bearing formation (the depth of the formation makes the use of ordinary methods impossible). The well has a 10-inch casing, inside of which is an 8-inch hot-water pipe that delivers water at 330° F.[18] to dissolve the sulfur. The liquid sulfur is then forced to the surface by air that descends through a third connecting pipe (1¼ inches). The liquid solidifies to pure yellow sulfur in wooden stock bins, from which it is loaded by power shovels into railroad cars and boats.

So cheap is the Frasch process that the United States rapidly became the world's leading producer of sulfur; sulfur from her gulf coast has come to dominate the market not only here but also abroad.[19] As late as 1902 she was still on an import basis, but production climbed to over 2.5 million tons in 1930. In 1945 about 3.8 million long tons were produced here, 3 million in Texas and the rest in Louisiana. In addition, over 700,000 tons were extracted from about 7.5 million long tons of pyrites. Over 1 million short tons of sulfuric acid (60°) were recovered as a by-product of metal mining, chiefly copper and zinc—the equivalent of about 275,000 long tons of sulfur. According to recent estimates, the United States produces about 90 percent of the world output of crude sulfur (exclusive of U.S.S.R.; Russian figures are not available). Italy produced about 400,000 tons in 1938; she has not yet recovered from the effects of the war. The world output of pyrites in 1938 was around 10 million metric tons, of which Spain produced about 2.7 million, Norway 1.0, Italy 0.9, Russia, the United States, and Portugal 0.6

---

[16] For uses, see page 783.

[17] The Ducktown pyrites were first worked as copper ores, the sulfurous fumes destroying the landscape (for a vivid description, see Stuart Chase's *Rich Land—Poor Land*, Whittlesey House, New York, 1936, pp. 49-53.

[18] The water is kept from vaporizing by a pressure of 110 psi.

[19] Those who assume that the competition between Sicilian and United States sulfur, between sulfur and pyrites, between sulfuric acid obtained from sulfur, pyrites, and smelter fumes led to a material reduction in price, overlook the fact that the production and sale of sulfur and sulfur products, as is true of most mineral products, are ordinarily regulated by international cartels. For an account of the sulfur cartel, see Ervin Hexner, *International Cartels,* University of North Carolina Press, Chapel Hill, 1946, pp. 270-273. Sulfur price quotations are among the most inflexible of all quotations. However, as is often the case with quotations, they do not always accurately reflect the price actually realized.

each, Cyprus and Germany about 0.5 each, the rest being scattered.

In the United States the chief uses of sulfur are in heavy chemicals, fertilizer, and pulp and paper; explosives and rubber are important among its minor uses. In 1945, 9.1 million short tons of sulfuric acid were consumed in this country, of which 2.8 million went into fertilizer, 2.2 into chemicals and defense,[20] 1.1 into petroleum refining, 0.6 into coal products and iron and steel casts, 0.5 into paints and pigments, and 0.5 each into rayon and cellulose fibers. One of the major uses of sulfuric acid is in the preparation of commercial fertilizer, more particularly in the treatment of phosphate rock. That same year she exported close to a million tons of crude sulfur worth about $16.6 million and over 26,000 tons of refined and otherwise treated sulfur worth $1.6 million.

Since transportation charges on sulfur, and especially on sulfuric acid, are high, regions not easily accessible from the production centers on the gulf coast continue to depend on pyrites and by-product sulfur.

The Fertilizer Industry and Its Raw Materials

The three basic raw materials of the commercial fertilizer industry are potassium, phosphorus, and nitrogen. They will be discussed in that order.

The first country to exploit its potash[21] deposits systematically was Germany, whose famous Stassfurt deposits, discovered in 1861, enjoyed a virtual world monopoly before World War I. Less important deposits were discovered later in Alsace. When Alsace was

returned to France after that war, the French government readily collaborated with Germany's government-sponsored potash syndicate. But potash production soon became more widely distributed as the various nations, remembering their experiences when the war cut them off from German sources, strove to become self-sufficient as regards potash. In particular, the brines of Searles Lake in California were exploited, and large deposits of potassium salts were discovered in New Mexico, near Carlsbad. In 1938 the United States output of potassium salts amounted to 287,500 tons (K_2O content); it rose to almost 800,000 in 1948, under pressure of World War II and the postwar economic expansion. Germany's output in 1938 was 2.2 million tons and it has stayed around the 2 million level. Alsace produces about 600,000 tons in typical years. Poland and Russia both produced about 100,000 tons each, and Spain recently has come up to that level. The Dead Sea in Palestine is being exploited. The 1938 output was distributed as follows, in percentages: Germany, about 60; France, about 17; the United States and the Soviet Union, about 9 each; other producers, 5 percent.

Here again a geographical spread in production did not lead to increased competition. The chief American producers of potash seem to have been controlled by British, Dutch, and German interests. Thus, in 1942, 90 percent of the capital stock of one American potash company was confiscated as disguised enemy alien property. It is believed that until World War II, more or less all the important potash producers, with the possible exception of the Soviet Union, conformed to the control exercised by the international potash cartel.[22]

The second important fertilizer mineral is phosphorus. Its main source is phosphate rock, including apatite. Phosphate deposits are largely fossil remains. A large share of the world's phosphate rock comes from North Africa in the area from Egypt to Morocco. In 1939 it produced almost 4 million metric tons, distributed as follows: Egypt, 178,000; Tunisia, 1,628,000; Algeria, 500,000; Morocco, 1,703,-000. The United States output that year was 3.8 million tons, but it soared during and after

---

[20] Combined so as not to reveal military secrets.

[21] Potash gets its name from the ash made in pots when iron pots were used to evaporate the leachings of wood ashes in soap making. The product was mostly potassium carbonate, but the term was later applied to the caustic potash obtained from treating pot ashes with lime. Commercially, potash is a general term for potassium compounds; but true potash is K_2O, a compound that is neither a natural mineral nor a manufactured product but a term used to denote, for comparative purposes, the potassium content of different compounds. A. N. Bateman, *op. cit.*, p. 787.

Although used mainly for fertilizers, potash also plays important roles in other branches of chemistry.

[22] See Ervin Hexner, *op. cit.*, pp. 267-270.

World War II to unprecedented heights of almost 6 million tons (1945). Russia ranks third, with about 2 million tons. Another important source is the Pacific island of Nauru, which produced about 1.25 million tons in 1939.

Florida is the chief producer and exporter of phosphate rock in the United States. She increased her output from 2.6 million long tons in 1935 to 3.8 million in 1948. During the same period Tennessee, the second leading state, expanded production from 0.5 million long tons in 1935 to 1.3 in 1945; and the western states—especially Idaho, Montana, and Utah—increased production from 87,000 tons in 1935 to 324,000 in 1945.

Phosphorus is also contained in iron ores. In particular the French, Swedish, and Lake Superior and Alabama ores yield considerable amounts of phosphatic slag from which superphosphate may be prepared. In Europe the ground phosphate slag is known as Thomas meal (see p. 648).

The third basic raw material of commercial fertilizer is nitrogen. Nitrogen in the form of the element comprises by volume four-fifths of the air that surrounds us. Plants and animals need nitrogen for growth, but it must be fixed, that is, combined with some other element. In its free state it is simply inhaled and exhaled by man. A few plants can make use of it, because they have the power of nitrogen fixation; but in general the enormous mass of nitrogen in the air behaves as though it were inert and nonreactive.

To make life possible, nitrogen must be supplied in fixed form. For centuries refuse was saved and used to fertilize the fields; the few plants capable of fixing nitrogen were plowed under to enrich the soil. In the nineteenth century it was found that certain mineral deposits in various parts of the world, notably those in the northern part of Peru, later taken over by Chile, contained material which was beneficial to soil fertility. Commercial exploitation of these deposits proceeded slowly until about 1880, from which time rapid progress was made. Because of inefficient processes, only the better-grade material was treated. The product recovered is known as nitrate of soda, or saltpeter.

The development of the by-product coke oven made possible the recovery of ammonia gas which was formerly wasted. This was converted into sulfate of ammonia by the action of sulfuric acid, so that two major sources of fixed nitrogen became available. Several minor sources were also tapped, especially cottonseed meal, packing-house tankage, fish scrap, Peru guano, etc.

It became evident by the end of the nineteenth century that the Chilean nitrate deposits were not inexhaustible and, furthermore, that there was a very definite limit to the amount of fixed nitrogen that could be expected from the by-product coking of coal. In addition, Chile was a long way from Europe and America, and in the event of war the long water trip would subject the valuable material to naval attack, or perhaps the Chilean coast would be blockaded, thus completely cutting off the supply.

It is a paradox of nature that fixed nitrogen, so necessary to life and happiness, should also be essential to all explosives. During the latter part of the nineteenth century, the governments of the world were probably less concerned over the possible loss of fertilizer than over the loss of raw material essential to warfare. For a period of one hundred years or more, chemists had been attempting, with occasional success, to fix nitrogen. Further diligent investigation during the first years of the twentieth century developed three major commercial processes for fixing the recalcitrant atmospheric nitrogen. The first, the arc process, caused nitrogen to combine with the oxygen of the air. It required large amounts of power and hence was economically feasible only where abundant cheap power was available. The second was the cyanamide process developed by the German chemists Frank and Caro; it required roughly only one-fourth as much power as the arc process and was the only widely used nitrogen-fixing process when World War I broke out. The investigations resulting in the arc and cyanamide processes from the nitrogen of the air by the Haber and his co-workers on the direct synthesis of ammonia from nitrogen and hydrogen. In 1913, after years of patient labor, the first commercial plant using the Haber process was put in operation. Since that time, this process,

TABLE 48.2. World Production of Chemical Nitrogen by Process, and World Capacity, Selected Years, 1900-1937[23]
(in thousand short tons)

Year	Chilean Nitrate	By-product Nitrogen	Cyanamide Nitrogen	Synthetic Nitrogen[a]	Total Production	World Capacity
1900	220.0	110.0	. . .	. . .	330.0	379.5
1910	420.3	226.6	4.5	5.1	656.5	896.5
1920	430.2	318.3	103.5	141.8	993.8	1551.0
1930	419.7	476.5	255.6	1019.0	2170.8	3917.0
1935	205.0	434.3	275.6	1545.4	2460.3	. . .
1936	219.4	498.2	308.6	1779.1	2805.3	. . .
1937	237.0	519.2	328.5	1988.5	3073.2	. . .

[a] Includes output of arc process and synthetic ammonia plants.

in one of its numerous modifications, has crowded the arc process from the scene, and the cyanamide process also is rapidly losing ground. As technical advance succeeds technical advance, the price of ammonia drops lower and lower. The power requirements of the direct synthetic ammonia process are low, and each improvement results in a lowered cost.

During World War I, fixed nitrogen was in great demand. Germany, cut off from the Chilean deposits, was able to make explosives from the nitrogen of the air by the Haber and cyanamide processes. The Allies of necessity relied on Chilean nitrate to a large extent. After the war, when technical knowledge again began to flow from nation to nation, arrangements were made to erect in the United States nitrogen-fixation plants like the Haber plants in Germany. The goal was nitrate independence for America; and plant after plant, each better than its predecessor, was erected. As each new plant took up its share of the market, less and less nitrate was purchased from Chile. Inasmuch as other countries were likewise seeking to increase their nitrogen-fixing capacity, the price of Chilean nitrate declined.

At one time Chile had a practical monopoly on nitrate of soda, and her government imposed heavy export taxes on it. But as the demand for it fell off, it became necessary to lower the export tax, and then to lower it again. Meanwhile, the Chilean nitrate industry was rationalized by the introduction of the

[23] U.S. Tariff Commission, *Chemical Nitrogen*, Report No. 114, Washington, 1937, p. 60; G. W. Stocking and M. W. Watkins, *op. cit.*, p. 126.

Guggenheim process, and a few of the largest operators modernized their recovery plants and processes in order to lower costs. But even with greatly increased efficiency (the Guggenheim process is reported to raise the recovery average from 50 to 90 percent), the process cannot compete with synthetic and by-product nitrates.

Table 48.2 shows world production of chemical nitrogen for selected years, 1900-1937, and the world capacity.

Under the impact of World War II nitrogen capacity increased greatly. The United States is reported to have expanded her capacity from 600,000 tons in 1939 to 1,451,000 in 1945, thus taking the lead from Germany. The bulk of the war-born increment is government-owned. The effect of the war on European nitrogen capacity is not definitely known. The period after World War II was one of great food scarcity and of unprecedented demand for fertilizer to raise agricultural yields to the utmost. Consequently, immediately after the war there was a shortage rather than an oversupply of fertilizer chemicals. In the long run, the atomic bomb will materially alter the position of nitrogen as a strategic material. This will remove one of the most disturbing elements in the situation, i.e., the wartime expansion of nitrogen capacity to meet military needs for explosives, which, if not restricted, is likely to upset the market equilibrium.

When the extraordinary postwar demand for fertilizer has subsided, when more and more food deficits once more become surpluses, the real test of the position of nitrogen will come. In the scramble for survival by-product nitrogen will be strong and Chilean nitrates weak. As after World War I, efforts will be made to solve the problem of surplus capacity by means of international cartels.[24]

Other Raw Materials

The list of chemicals used as raw materials by the chemical industry could be considerably lengthened. The lithium minerals could be added, as well as borax[25] and borates, iodine,[26] calcium and magnesium, and many others. Of increasing importance are oil-refining vapors and natural gas from which such products as nylon salts, TNT, synthetic rubber, alcohol, acetate, calcium carbide, etc., can be obtained.

Beside mineral raw materials the chemical industry also draws heavily on vegetable and animal products. Thus the packing industry produces pharmaceutical and other chemical preparations from various parts of slaughtered animals. Glues and Jello alike are animal products. Casein derived from milk is the source of plastics. Of particular importance is cellulose in the form of both cotton linters and wood.

ORGANIZATION OF THE CHEMICAL INDUSTRY

The chemical industry is not a homogeneous group of industries but is made up of units engaged in widely differing activities. Generalizations regarding the organization of this heterogeneous industry must be made and accepted with utmost caution. In the United States there are literally thousands of chemical companies. Some of them are young and small, and make a specialty of only minor importance.[27] Others are old-timers, giant con-

cerns that supply vital materials and extend over a considerable segment of the entire field of chemical industry. The presence of many small and medium-sized firms side by side with a few giants is not peculiar to the chemical industry, but is rather a characteristic feature of modern industry, the inevitable corollary of dynamic evolution and of product diversity.

Trend Toward Concentration

This observation, however, cannot obscure a powerful and almost universal trend toward combinations, giantism, intercompany understandings, and cartelization. This trend, which is frequently accompanied by a desire to tamper with competition, is not entirely different from that appearing in most modern industries that operate under "overhead economy." If it is more pronounced in the chemical industry, it may be because of the superbly scientific character of the industry which puts a premium on technological changes in both products and processes. It employs whole armies of researchers who, while seeking to improve processes and products, cannot help but undermine the existing technological bases and create uncertainty stemming from unpredictable innovations.

Concentration in the chemical field proceeds along three lines—horizontal, vertical, and circular.[28] Horizontal combination joins two or more firms engaged in producing the same products. Vertical combination brings successive steps of manufacture under one management and ownership. Circular combination refers to the absorption of cognate or allied lines of production. Such concentration may assure greater control over the market and over sources of supply and it tends to spread the risks.[29]

Table 48.3 lists eleven companies in the United States that are engaged in the manu-

---

[24] For a diagram of the international nitrogen cartel in 1939, see G. W. Stocking and M. W. Watkins, *op. cit.*, p. 145.

[25] Death Valley, California, was made famous by the "Twenty Mule Team" trade-mark and the radio advertising of this brand of borax.

[26] A by-product of the Chilean sodium nitrate industry, recovered from *caliche* and also from kelp and from petroleum refinery vapor.

[27] Of the 9203 separate plants in the field of chemical and allied products reported by the Census of Manufactures in 1939, such groups as drugs, medicines, toilet preparations, insecticides, paints, varnishes and colors, hardwood distillation and naval stores, fertilizers, animal and vegetable

oils, cleaning and polishing preparations, and soap and glycerin, together accounted for some 6800.

[28] See G. W. Stocking and M. W. Watkins, *op. cit.*, p. 378 note.

[29] How far chemical companies will go in their desire to spread risks is illustrated by Du Pont's heavy investments in the stock of General Motors and other nonchemical corporations. It is not suggested that these investments were made solely for the purpose of reducing risks.

facture of chemicals and whose net sales in 1946 were in excess of $100 million. Their net sales in 1936-1939 (average), 1944, and 1946 are also given. A comparison of the earliest and the 1946 figures shows the tremendous increase in chemical production in this country during and after World War II. (Increased prices, however, must also be taken into account.) The increase in Celanese Corporation sales from $32.3 million in 1936-1939 to $135.2 million in 1946 is particularly noteworthy. This company increased its sales over one-third from 1944 to 1946 while other companies had to curtail production. However, Celanese is principally engaged in rayon manufacture, whereas the other companies specialize in products more directly affected by war.

TABLE 48.3. Net Sales and Other Revenues of Eleven American Manufacturers of Chemicals[30] (million dollars)

	1936-1939 (average)	1944	1946
1. E. I. du Pont de Nemours & Co.	270.2	646.2	661.8
2. Union Carbide & Carbon Co.	155.5	490.4	415.0
3. Allied Chemical & Dye Corp.	163.5	294.7	280.5
4. Eastman Kodak Co.	132.3	303.7	274.7
5. American Cyanamid Co.	....	165.5	170.0
6. Pittsburgh Plate Glass Co.	81.7	142.8	184.7
7. Celanese Corp. of America	32.3	101.7	135.2
8. Koppers Co., Inc.	53.3	132.2	115.1
9. Dow Chemical Co.	23.9	123.1	103.3
10. Hercules Powder Co.	38.8	105.7	100.7
11. Monsanto Chemical Co.	34.2	88.4	100.0

This list of companies shows the difficulty of classifying chemical concerns. Thus Du Pont makes mainly chemicals but also produces rayon. Celanese makes rayon primarily, but also makes chemicals both for its own use and for sale to others. Eastman Kodak is the leading manufacturer of photographic apparatus and supplies but is also heavily involved in the manufacture of chemicals for its own needs and for sale in the market. The Pittsburgh Plate Glass Company is first of all a glass manufacturer but is also strongly represented in paints and chemicals. Union Carbide is a leader in electrometallurgy but is also powerful in the field of chemicals. This evident tendency to cover several fields including the

chemical may again point to the desire to reduce the peculiar risks inherent in the chemical field, but it may also reflect the versatility of the chemist and the basic homogeneity of chemical processes.

Intercorporate Relationships

A casual glance at the diverse activities of different chemical companies may give the impression that the chemical field is something of a "free-for-all." Actually further scrutiny reveals careful observation, on the companies' part, of fields of special interest. When several companies are engaged in directly competitive lines of production they frequently consult and collaborate to avoid head-on collisions. In some cases competitive firms join in owning the property that makes the competitive product. Thus, in 1931 Pittsburgh Plate Glass, which made caustic soda in competition with American Cyanamid, joined with the latter company to organize the Southern Alkali Company.[31] When Standard Oil (New Jersey) in collaboration with IG Farbenindustrie entered the chemical field on a scale until then not associated with petroleum companies, consultations were held with Du Pont to forestall competitive clashes which, though welcomed by consumers, might have proved unfortunate to producing interests. In short, the chemical industry is, by and large, what may be called an "orderly" industry.

. . . the chemical industry, despite its slowly lowering curve of real prices, is an "orderly" industry. It was practicing "cooperation" long before General Johnson invented it in 1933. It has seldom been bedeviled by overproduction, has had no private depressions of its own, and has not often involved itself in long or bloody price wars. The alcohol sector of the industry has frequently been guilty of disorderly conduct, and alkali made by the Solvay process has got into some nasty brawls with electrolytic alkali. But by and large the chemical industry has regulated itself in a manner that would please even a Soviet Commissar. . . . Its gentlemanly instincts are all against pushing and crowding. . . . The industry . . . is . . . the practitioner of one definite sort of planned economy. . . .

[30] Merrill Lynch, Pierce, Fenner and Bean, *Chemicals,* 1947.

[31] G. W. Stocking and M. W. Watkins, *op. cit.,* p. 351.

Today the whole chemical picture has an air of financial stability that is unusual in so new an industry. There is no evidence of fighting among its companies for position: price structures are steady. . . . This is the unique industry that knows its costs and refuses to sacrifice profits for the sake of volume. Competition is chemical . . . but the surface, the financial surface, is serene. And it will probably continue to be: new developments seek outlets through established chemical industrial channels, for there lie the talent and the money for development, one as vital as the other for any new process.[32]

Chemical Prices

This "orderliness" is reflected in the price behavior of chemical commodities. Although there is noticeable a secular trend toward lower prices reflecting the reduction of costs as the result of new inventions, it is not disorderly competitive jostling which passes on to the consumer prematurely the fruits of costly research and implementation, but careful price management which uses lower prices as an incentive for sales promotion without unduly impairing profit margins. On the whole, chemical prices are administered prices.[33]

Only occasionally do matters get out of hand. A classical example is caustic soda (see p. 784), which, for a short time at least, represented an extreme case of process competition, some companies making it by electrolysis as a by-product in competition with the established alkali producers who used regular chemical processes.

Another example of extreme commodity competition is furnished by industrial alcohol. Alcohol can be made from molasses, a by-product of sugar manufacture, from grain, coal, petroleum, natural gas, wood—in short, from so many substances that producers drawing on different segments of the far-flung raw-material range occasionally run into serious competitive snags. Industrial alcohol production is not controlled by the major chemical companies but is a specialty of medium-sized companies.[34]

In appraising the price behavior of chemicals and the price policies of chemical manufacturers certain aspects of demand and of costs must also be considered. Typically industrial chemicals constitute a minor cost factor in the consuming industry (e.g., sulfuric acid in petroleum refining). At the same time, the chemical is vitally needed and in many instances substitutes are not available. Under such circumstances economists speak of a low price elasticity of demand, meaning thereby that demand does not respond readily to price fluctuations—it does not readily expand when prices drop or readily decline when they rise.

In the long run prices in general tend to reflect costs of production. This response to costs can be traced fairly easily in the case of simple single products such as roasted peanuts or popcorn; but finding the true costs of single chemicals in the welter of interrelated products, co-products, by-products, and joint products is beyond the cost accountant. If to this is added the effect of volume of output on costs, it is readily apparent why the prices of chemicals do not and cannot always exactly reflect costs.

The situation is further complicated by the diversity of uses to which chemicals are put. The same chemical product may satisfy an elite demand which can afford to pay high prices and at the same time be used for lowly purposes for which the price cannot be high. A plastic that sells to dental laboratories for several dollars a pound may have to be available to other buyers at a much lower price.[35] In such cases the separation and insulation of separate segments of the market may present considerable difficulties.[36]

Sometimes a chemical is sold to a large customer at a price considerably below average

---

[32] "Chemical Industry: I," *Fortune*, December, 1937, pp. 157 ff.

[33] See Claire Wilcox, *Competition and Monopoly in American Industry*, TNEC Monograph No. 21, p. 202.

[34] How dynamic the field of industrial alcohol production can be is dramatically described in *Fortune* in an article entitled "Commercial Solvents" (October, 1949, pp. 134 ff.). Fiction is rarely more exciting than this true story of the tribulations and triumphs of a chemical company.

[35] See G. W. Stocking and M. W. Watkins, *op. cit.*, p. 402.

[36] It is hardly necessary to add that such "price discrimination" is not confined to chemicals. In one form or another it is found throughout the economy. Railroad and steamship rates adjusted to the value of the goods carried are as good examples as any.

market levels to discourage him from starting to produce it himself. An illustration is the sale of synthetic methanol by Du Pont to Standard Oil (New Jersey).

Integration and Cartelization of Foreign Chemical Industries[37]

In comparing the organization and structure of any industry in the United States with its counterpart in Europe, it is well to remember that all Europe represents a productive capacity and market potential comparable to those of the United States and that the European market is cut up into a number of national segments. Even if each nation had a chemical monopoly, the overall European situation would still resemble an oligopolistic setup unless it could be shown that the different national chemical monopolies, in combination, constitute a joint monopoly as well.

The I.C.I. During the nineteenth century there developed in England a strong alkali industry that made caustic soda, chlorine, etc.; it was based first on the Le Blanc and later the Solvay process. The cheaper Solvay process, which was introduced in England in 1873 by Brunner, Mond and Company,[38] threatened the existence of the older alkali manufacturers who used the Le Blanc process. To ward off disaster, about fifty Le Blanc soda ash makers merged and formed United Alkali. United marketed its exports through Brunner, Mond.

In 1918 the Nobel Dynamite Trust joined with other leading explosives manufacturers to form Explosives Trades, Ltd. Its monopoly extended throughout the British Empire. Nobel, like Du Pont, considered the explosives field too narrow a base for a strong chemical enterprise; consequently he diversified the company's activities to include artificial leather, paints, lacquer, ammunition, and nonferrous metals.

British Dyestuffs, like Explosives Trades, was organized in 1918, during World War I. It was sponsored by the government and was built around Levinstein, Ltd., long the leading dyestuff manufacturer in Great Britain.

---

[37] The discussion of European chemical industries is based on G. W. Stocking and M. W. Watkins, *op. cit.,* pp. 406 ff.

[38] Ludwig Mond was a native of Kassel, Germany, where he had studied under Bunsen.

In 1926 these four concerns, themselves mergers of former independents, merged under the leadership of Sir Alfred Mond to form Imperial Chemical Industries, Ltd., known as I.C.I. Although enhanced technical efficiency was given as the major objective of the nationwide organization, in reality the commercial advantages of superior market control and an improved position vis-à-vis rival national trusts probably weighed more heavily in the balance. The founders of I.C.I. looked beyond the creation of an empire-wide chemical structure to an international setup that would embrace Germany's IG and our own Du Pont and Allied Chemical and Dye and would substitute the "civilized" rule of negotiations, conferences, and arguments for the chaos of market competition. How Adam Smith and the old masters of the laissez-faire school must have groaned in their graves!

Since its creation in 1926 I.C.I. has absorbed more than forty additional companies and has reached agreements with Lever Brothers, Ltd., and Courtaulds, Ltd., leaders in soap and rayon respectively.

Germany's I.G. For various reasons Germany by 1914 had become the leader in the field of coal-tar chemistry. The core of the industry was the manufacture of coal-tar dyes but it extended into other fields, especially pharmaceuticals. As early as 1904 the leading dye manufacturers, the "Big Six," began to gravitate toward each other. In that year two groups were formed, one embracing the Höchst Dye Works, Leopold Casella of Frankfurt, and Kalle of Bieberich, the other made up of the Badische Anilin und Soda Fabriken of Ludwigshafen (opposite Mannheim), the Bayer plants at Elberfeld and Leverkusen (near Deutz, across the Rhine from Cologne), and Agfa, Aktiengesellschaft für Anilinfabrikation (corporation for the manufacture of anilin). In 1916 these two groups joined in a fifty-year agreement and took in two additional concerns, Weiler-ter-Meer and Griesheim Elektron. In 1925 the group was incorporated in the IC (Interessengemeinschaft Community of interests) Farbenindustrie (dye industry) AG (equivalent to Inc.).

IG Farben, as the combination came to be called, at first produced a full line of organic chemicals including dyes, pharmaceuticals, and photographic supplies as well as a number of electrochemical products such as light metals. But since its foundation it has expanded greatly. It began to manufacture rayon and other artificial fibers, synthetic nitrogen, fertilizers, alloys, industrial gases, synthetic gasoline, synthetic rubber, and plastics. It expanded its output of heavy chemicals and basic organic chemicals. It gained control of sources of raw materials and power. One important acquisition was that of 45 percent of the share capital of the Rheinische Stahlwerke (Rhenish Steelworks), a large producer of coal and coke. "In 1930, I.G. controlled the entire German production of dyes, nearly all the explosives, 90 percent of chemical acids, 65-85 percent of synthetic nitrogen, 40 percent of pharmaceutical, 30 percent of rayon. At the outbreak of World War II it controlled some 40 percent of total German chemical output."[39]

In addition IG owned considerable blocks of stock in other chemical concerns in Germany and had close working agreements with still others. In 1943 General Eisenhower reported as follows:

I.G. Farben produced in 1943 100% of synthetic rubber, methanol, sera, and lubricating oil; 95% of poisonous gases, and nickel; 92% of plasticizers; 90% of organic intermediates; 90% of plastics; 88% of magnesium; 84% of explosives; 75% of nitrogen; solvents, 75%; gunpowder, 70%; calcium carbide, 61%; x-ray film, 50-60%; pharmaceuticals, 55%; insecticides and fungicides, 55%; synthetic resins, 53%; chlorine, 46%; high octane gasoline, 46%; compressed gases, 45%; sulphuric acid, 35%; synthetic gasoline, 33%; spun rayon (1939), 28%; artificial silk (1938), 24%; gasoline total, 23%; aluminum, 8%.[40]

The report adds that IG had stock interests in 613 corporations, including 173 in foreign countries, piled up assets of 6 billion Reichsmarks, and "operated, with varying degrees of power, in more than 2000 cartels."[41]

Because of its dependence on coal tar and for other reasons, IG was one of the largest producers of coal in Germany. All in all, before the collapse of Germany, it was one of the most powerful producing units in the world. At the time of this writing its future is still uncertain.

Chemical Industries in Other Countries

Although Frenchmen like Lavoisier and Le Blanc had an important part in the early stages of chemical development, France herself did not attain a role of great prominence in the field of chemical industry. By far the most important French chemical manufacturer is the Etablissements Kuhlmann, which up to World War I confined its activities to the manufacture of heavy chemicals. After that war the French government took over certain plants formerly belonging to German nationals. The bulk of these were sold to Kuhlmann, who thus jumped with both feet, as it were, into the field of coal-tar products. Kuhlmann also participated in the development of synthetic nitrogen. A considerable number of smaller French chemical manufacturers specialize in specific products. In Italy Montecatini has a role similar to that of Kuhlmann in France. The pattern seems more or less world-wide. It is found in Japan almost exactly the same as in Europe and America. Everywhere there is a tendency for large concerns to enter agreements, national as well as international, among themselves to reduce the rigor of competition and decrease the risks. Here is what Stocking and Watkins have to say on this point:

When a few large, fully integrated concerns produce a myriad of joint products, utilize complicated and rapidly changing techniques, and employ capital on a vast scale, market behavior is inevitably unlike that when the number of sellers is large, the product homogeneous, the processes simple, and the capital investment of any single producer relatively small. The size, financial strength, and technical resources of such companies as du Pont and ICI make them unwilling to engage in a real competitive struggle. None is likely seriously to consider trying to supplant the others in world markets, even though at the moment it may have a specific or general competitive advantage.[42]

[39] G. W. Stocking and M. W. Watkins, *op. cit.*, p. 413.

[40] New York *Times*, October 21, 1945, pp. 1, 12 (section 1).

[41] G. W. Stocking and M. W. Watkins, *op. cit.*, p. 413.

[42] *Ibid.*, p. 425.

The international situation is complicated by the fact that many chemical industries are, or can be converted into, war industries of strategic importance. Even a nation as well endowed as the United States would have been sorely handicapped without a synthetic rubber industry.

The problem of concentration and cartelization of chemical industries extends over into the field of international politics.[43] Moreover, the survival of a minimum of competition is held by many leading thinkers to be the *sine qua non* of free enterprise itself and, with it, of true democracy.

[43] See R. A. Brady, *Business as a System of Power*, Columbia University Press, New York, 1943.

World War II has lifted the United States to a position of global leadership. Leadership means responsibility and no responsibility is felt more keenly by the citizens of the United States than that of keeping democracy alive, of keeping the fires of western civilization alight wherever live embers have survived the ravages of war, and shutting out the cold blasts blowing in from the icy wastes of totalitarianism.

When the structure of an industry takes on such transcending significance that it becomes intimately connected with the preservation of peace and the survival of democracy, it ceases to be a matter of mere economics.

BIBLIOGRAPHY

"A 1950 Guide to the Plastics," *Fortune*, May, 1950.

"Allied Chemical and Dye Corporation," *Fortune*, October, 1939.

"American Cyanamide," *Fortune*, September, 1940.

Borth, C., *Modern Chemists and Their Work*, New York, New Home Library, new ed., 1943.

"Carbide and Carbon Chemicals," *Fortune*, September, 1941.

Chemical Engineering (monthly).

"Chemical Industry, I," *Fortune*, December, 1937.

"Commercial Solvents: Not the Biggest Chemical Company, But the Most Exciting," *Fortune*, October, 1944.

"D.D.T.: Just Begun to Fight," *Fortune*, January, 1946.

Deming, H. G., *In the Realm of Carbon*, New York, Wiley, 1930.

Dutton, W. S., *DuPont, One Hundred and Forty Years*, New York, Scribner, 1942.

Greiling, W., *Chemie Erobert Die Welt*, Berlin, Wilhelm Limpert Verlag, 1938.

Hale, W. J., *Farmward March, Chemurgy Takes Command*, New York, Coward-McCann, 1939.

Haynes, W., *Chemical Economics*, New York, Van Nostrand, 1933.

Haynes, W., *Money and Molecules*, Garden City, Doubleday, Doran, 1936.

Haynes, W., *The Chemical Age*, New York, Knopf, 1942.

Haynes, W., *The Stone That Burns*, New York, Van Nostrand, 1942.

Hempel, E. H., *The Economics of Chemical Industries*, New York, Wiley, 1939.

Hexner, E., *International Cartels*, Chapel Hill, University of North Carolina Press, 1945.

"Industry's Chemicals, II," *Fortune*, December, 1937.

Kahn, A. E., "The Chemical Industry," in Adams, W. (ed.), *The Structure of American Industry. Some Case Studies*, New York, Macmillan, 1950, chap. 6.

Kreps, T. J., "Chemical Industries," *Encyclopædia of the Social Sciences*, New York, Macmillan, 1930.

Kreps, T. J., "Modern Dyestuffs," *Encyclopædia of the Social Sciences*, New York, Macmillan, 1931.

Kreps, T. J., *The Economics of the Sulphuric Acid Industry*, Stanford University, Stanford University Press, 1938.

Little, A. D., "The Chemical Revolution," talk delivered before Examiner's Club, May 7, 1934.

"Merck," *Fortune*, July, 1947.

Montgomery, R. H., *The Brimstone Game*, New York, Vanguard, 1940.

Morrison, A. C., *Man in a Chemical World*, New York, Scribner, 1937.

National Industrial Conference Board, *Chemicals I-IX Basic Industrial Data for Investment Analysis*, New York, 1947.

"Nitrogen: Competition or Not," *Fortune*, 1944.

Slosson, E. E., *Creative Chemistry*, New York, Appleton-Century, 1930.

Stocking, G. W., and Watkins, M. W., *Cartels in Action*, New York, Twentieth Century Fund, 1946.

Stocking, G. W., and Watkins, M. W., *Cartels or*

Competition, New York, Twentieth Century Fund, 1948.

"The Chemical Century," *Fortune,* March, 1950.

"The Silicones: High-temperature Resistant Synthesis Made from Sand," *Fortune,* May, 1947.

"Union Carbide I: The Corporation," *Fortune,* June, 1941.

"Union Carbide II: Alloys, Gases and Carbon," *Fortune,* July, 1941.

"U.S. Gypsum Company," *Fortune,* February, 1936.

U.S. Tariff Commission, *Chemical Nitrogen,* Report 114, Washington, 1937.

U.S. Tariff Commission, *Industrial Alcohol,* War Changes in Industry Series Report No. 2, Washington, 1944.

U.S. Tariff Commission, *Dyes,* War Changes in Industry Series Report No. 19, Washington, 1946.

U.S. Tariff Commission, *Plastic Products,* War Changes in Industry Series Report No. 28, Washington, 1948.

Wilcox, C., *Competition and Monopoly in American Industry,* T.N.E.C. Monograph No. 21, Washington, 1940.

Yarsley, V. E., and Couzens, E. G., *Plastics,* New York, Penguin Books, 1941.

Zischka, A., *Wissenschaft Bricht Monopole,* Leipzig, Wilhelm Goldmann Verlag, 1936.

PART FOUR

RESOURCE PROBLEMS

Chapter 49

CONSERVATION

A book dealing with resources and their utilization cannot avoid the delicate and complex problem of conservation, for the fundamental issue of conservation is the proper rate of exploitation and utilization of resources. In the problem of conservation, the conflict between group and individual, between social and private interests, finds its most poignant expression.

A detailed analysis of the problem, as generally understood, presupposes a knowledge of economic theory, especially of value and interest; it is connected with innumerable issues, and touches on some of the most difficult and complex questions in economics. Moreover, attitudes toward conservation are radically affected by one's faith or lack of faith in economic doctrine, by his general outlook on life, by his social philosophy, and in particular by his reliance on laissez faire or on social control. Finally, conservation is a moral issue that gives rise to claims and counterclaims not subject to verification or proof.

In view of these difficulties, it would be unwise to attempt a brief for or against conservation in a single chapter, but the issue is too important in its bearing upon the utilization of resources to be ignored.

HISTORY OF CONSERVATION

Before 1900 there was little time and less inclination to consider conservation in the United States. As the new century revealed with increasing clarity the implications of the "passing of the frontier" in this country, it was more or less inevitable that the realization that there was no more new land to settle should come with a shock and cause thoughtful leaders to take an inventory of the nation's wealth-creating assets and to consider the new course called for by the changed prospects ahead. Thus the first stage in the conservation movement was reached, a stage closely identified with the name of Theodore Roosevelt.

The second stage was reached under Coolidge and continued under Hoover. Interest in conservation was sharply focused on oil, though not confined to it. Oil's vital significance in both peace and war was fully appreciated for the first time during the twenties. Memories of a World War in which the Allies had rolled to victory on oil, as it were, were still fresh;

furthermore, the automobile was hitting its stride and was becoming a major factor in the nation's life, social as well as economic.

The third stage is associated with Franklin Delano Roosevelt and the New Deal. Again the nation was shocked into stock taking, this time by the Great Depression. Whereas only a few thinking people had grasped the full significance of the "passing of the frontier," hardly anyone escaped the impact of the Great Depression. This time interest was centered in the nation's soil, but for the first time a more comprehensive view of the issues involved in conservation developed. What is more, thought and talk ripened into action—something was actually done.

Whether the situation after World War II should be recognized as the fourth stage in the conservation movement is uncertain at this time. There is no doubt of the widespread interest in conservation that followed the vast wartime destruction and accelerated exploitation of irreplaceable stocks of earth materials. Books by conservationists are best sellers, and conservation conferences are the vogue.[1]

A survey of this movement as it passes from stage to stage reveals steady progress, on the whole, in understanding the issues involved. As will be brought out later, this does not apply to the Coolidge era—at any rate, that period definitely falls out of line in what appears a logical evolutionary trend. The four stages will now be discussed in some detail.

Conservation and Theodore Roosevelt

When in 1908 Theodore Roosevelt launched his ambitious campaign advocating the conservation of "natural resources," he was fully aware that success meant the virtual reversal of the popular attitude which more than a century of national tradition had firmly established in the minds of the American people. Throughout the nineteenth century national interest had been absorbed in the winning of the West. Every energy had been bent on con-

quering space, on overcoming an almost insuperable handicap of labor shortage, on making available to a widely scattered population a supply of earth materials which could better and more easily have served the needs of a much larger population. To put it bluntly, the problem had been one of too much space, of too much land, of too much timber. "Land" had been superabundant, but there had been a scarcity of man power and capital. Under such circumstances, there could be no place in the American dictionary for the word *conservation*.

With the close of the century the conquest of the continent was virtually complete. "Transcontinentals" and trunk lines spanned the huge expanse of land from the Atlantic to the Pacific; the frontier had passed. What remained of the public domain was land of doubtful value, submarginal land. The time had gone by when the farmer who had exhausted one farm by heedless "robber" methods could move farther west and start anew on another farm. Forests, once liabilities and impediments to economic progress to be removed by fire, had begun to be viewed as valuable assets, sorely needed in the promotion of economic progress. Even the coal and oil in the ground no longer looked quite as inexhaustible as they had when the population was smaller, and when knowledge of the geographical distribution of minerals and of the properties of these minerals was not yet as complete, and the requirements of industry were not yet as exacting as regards amounts and quality of raw materials, as they are now.

Not only did our natural endowment appear less inexhaustible than it had a century or even fifty years before, but our cultural resources, especially scientific knowledge and capital equipment, were being developed rapidly. Moreover, the population was growing rapidly, immigration was at its height, and a relationship between "land," labor, and capital was evolving which was altogether different from that which had existed during the pioneering stage. The United States was entering the early phases of the maturity stage. We could no longer afford to live like a heedless youth, from hand to mouth; we had to think of the tomorrow. In order to solidify our gains, our

---

[1] During the summer of 1948 a conference devoted to the conservation of renewable resources met in Colorado. A second conference was held in Washington, D. C., in May, 1949, and in the fall of 1949 the United Nations sponsored an international conference on the technical aspects of conservation at Lake Success, N. Y.

institutions and our economic and social life had to be put on a more permanent basis.

It was here that Theodore Roosevelt stepped in. In his characteristic manner, he managed to arouse great enthusiasm for the new cause. Governors met with him to discuss gravely what should be done to put the national train of thought into reverse. Large volumes were written by experts and published at government expense. A university president devoted his time and energy to a book called *The Conservation of Natural Resources*. But just as all the excitement about "trust busting" left few visible scars on the physiognomy of big business, so it is difficult to discover any tangible and far-reaching effects of the enthusiasm for conservation which Roosevelt managed to arouse.

After all, the reversal of a national attitude is a task which perhaps can be better achieved by the slow process of education functioning through carefully directed publicity in the daily press and in periodical literature, and by enlightened teaching in public schools and colleges, than by the more dramatic methods of a whirlwind political campaign. This is apt to be the case, particularly in a country where the very fundamentals of jurisprudence seem to resist every effort to make conservation effective. American law stresses the inviolability of private property and the right to free contract. Behind these basic ideas, and largely determining their interpretation, lurks a surviving philosophy which owes more to Bentham than to Blackstone, and which has successfully resisted the effects of decades of economic, social, and technical change. This is the old laissez-faire doctrine, according to which private initiative and unrestrained pursuit of self-interest may be depended upon to reward individual enterprise and to serve the public need at one and the same time. One corollary of this doctrine is the belief that that government governs best which governs least; another is its blind faith in competition as the life of trade. In Europe, on the other hand— at least in those parts where jurisprudence was not affected by Anglo-Saxon thought, and especially where social, economic, and political conditions compelled a much greater willingness on the part of the individual to subordi-

nate his immediate private interest to the wider and more lasting interest of the group organized as the state—conservation has long been accepted as current ware.

Conservation Under Coolidge and Hoover

In the twenties the word conservation again blazed forth in the headlines, flaunted itself immodestly in the economic literature of the day, and engaged the attention not only of politicians but also—and this was the novel feature of the situation—of big business. When a corporation president waxes enthusiastic over conservation, either something has happened to Benthamite traditions or the denotative and connotative meanings of the word conservation as used by its advocates must be carefully scrutinized.

The curtain had risen on the second act of the American conservation drama, and the center of the stage was occupied by the oil industry. A Federal Oil Conservation Board was sitting in Washington. Prominent leaders of the petroleum industry had become ardent believers in what they chose to call conservation. The leading oil-producing states were passing conservation laws, and prominent lawyers were trying to disentangle the legal knots in oil conservation. This second phase, however, was not identified exclusively with oil conservation. Reforestation; the protection of the existing forest resources—a Timber Conservation Board had also been appointed— control over power, especially water-power resources; waterway developments; rationalization of the national irrigation program; soil erosion and the conservation of soil fertility in general, and other similar problems were attracting renewed interest.

Conservation and Franklin Delano Roosevelt

The New Deal came into power when the people, or a considerable majority of them, had lost confidence in the old laissez-faire business leadership. The New Deal put the seal of political approval on the shift in economic ideology discussed earlier in this volume (see pp. 4-6) and recognized the need for stronger government controls. The Great Depression had been a hard taskmaster but it had driven home its lessons with force and clarity. It was now clear that the long-run interests of the public welfare cannot be safe-guarded so long as that welfare is assumed to be the inevitable automatic by-product of the individual's pursuit of his own selfish interests. True conservation must rest on strong government control.

The New Deal was also on the side of the underdog. The farmer had been a notorious underdog since World War I, so it took him under its wing. Most soil is owned by farmers. Soil had to be conserved. Farmers were underdogs. Adding these facts together gives the New Deal soil conservation policy, which holds the government responsible for the achievement made by soil conservation not only in the long run in safeguarding the continuity of group life but also in the present in dollars and cents paid to the farmer who does the actual conserving.

The two things that stand out as probably the chief contributions to conservation made by Franklin D. Roosevelt's administration are (1) the emphasis on stronger government control, and (2) the idea that if the social group wants individuals to conserve privately owned assets of great social significance, especially for the future, the government must devise a scheme by which conservation will pay these individuals. The government may pay for this conservation either by using tax money for subsidies or by allowing an increase in the price of the goods sold by the conservationists, in which case the burden is shifted to the consumer.

A possible third contribution of the New Deal is its broad and comprehensive approach to conservation. The conservationist's effort and interest are not confined to "natural resources" such as wildlife, soil, water, and forests, but are extended to other resources as well, especially human resources. Recognition that public health is a conservational measure of the first magnitude, that research which enables man to stamp out such scourges as tuberculosis, cancer, arthritis, venereal diseases, may be the highest possible aim of conservation, is an achievement of the New Deal.

Conservation After World War II

Little more need be said about present-day conservation than has already been said.

The idea of compensating the individual who makes a sacrifice to conserve socially vital assets seems to be gaining. Is not that the chief idea behind the Raushenbush plan (see p. 816) so widely discussed as a major contribution to the cause of conservation? Apart from this, there is evident a strong interest in conservation problems, especially when they are presented in clear, eloquent language. People are willing to listen; but they want to know a great deal more about the issues before they make up their minds and give Congress a clear-cut mandate, thus indicating unequivocally that they are ready for the sacrifice which conservation sooner or later demands.

CRITICAL INTERPRETATION

On the whole the conservation movement is based on rather simple reasoning. People come to realize that if past and present practices are allowed to continue unrestrained, their children and grandchildren will suffer for the heedlessness of their ancestors. The social conscience is aware of certain moral obligations to generations yet unborn. This was the background of all the stages of the conservation movement with the exception of the Coolidge-Hoover stage, which for various reasons deviated from the norm.

The contrast between conservation under Theodore Roosevelt and under Coolidge and Hoover is particularly sharp. Commenting on the spirit of the movement under Theodore Roosevelt, Garet Garrett had this to say: "Twenty years ago [i.e., about 1910] conservation was a word that thrust itself between good and evil. On one side the idea of stewardship and forethought for posterity; on the other side, the forest killers, the soil wasters, those who disembowelled the earth of its mineral sources in a spirit of greed."[2] We stood before the world as the champion of unbridled profligacy and unprecedented prodigality. Roosevelt's magnetic personality and oratorical power, supported by a group of national leaders such as Andrew Carnegie and James J. Hill, succeeded in firing the imagination of governors and political leaders in general, no

[2] Garet Garrett, "Faith in Bonanza," *Saturday Evening Post*, May 25, 1929, p. 8.

less than of the masses. A spirit of moral crusading was aroused.

In the twenties conservation, no longer viewed as a political issue, had become a business proposition. The movement was led by sober businessmen and was based on the cold calculations of the engineers. It appeared in the form of the standardization and simplified practice championed by the Department of Commerce, in the tenets of the Taylor Society advocating scientific management, in the efforts of the oil man to harness the flood tides of "black gold," and in the achievements of the reclamation engineer in turning waste products into basic resources. The old school looked on conservation as a governmental function; the new school believed in entrusting it to businessmen and engineers.

There are several reasons why the early conservation movement, which began with such bold trumpet blasts, petered out. Little actual conservation, in the Rooseveltian sense, was achieved. The menace of soil erosion continued until another Roosevelt took over. The depletion of our forest resources goes on almost unabated. What was behind this apparent failure of the early movement, and what were the driving forces behind the new?

The early movement died out partly because of the weakness of its own foundations. The crusader is likely to be carried away by his enthusiasm and to distort the facts by a mistaken emphasis. For example, it does not take one hundred years to replenish our timber supply as the crusaders under Theodore Roosevelt maintained, and the economic value of spontaneous second growth is greater than we were led to believe. Soil erosion does not necessarily mean food famine; estimates of our mineral reserves have been marked up again and again since the Cassandra cries of the Theodore Roosevelt period were heard. Above all, the pessimistic appraisers of our resources underrated the power of technological progress. We may still leave too much coal in the ground, but we make the coal that is mined go thrice as far, and sometimes even further. In their enthusiasm, the early conservationists laid too much emphasis on hoarding and too little on intensive utilization. It was only natural that the pendulum should swing back.

The greatest weakness of this early conservation campaign lay in the unwillingness or the inability to draw the logical conclusions from their own proposals. It was recognized that cheapness was the primary cause of waste. Because of their stimulating effect on demand, the low prices at which irreplaceable national resources were offered in the market were seen as the greatest obstacle to conservation. The connection between overproduction and low prices was likewise recognized. But there the line of thought seemed to stop. It was evident that overproduction was due to unbridled competition. Unfortunately, however, the philosophy of the day believed as strongly in competition as it tried to make itself believe in the virtues of conservation. The trust-buster and the conservationist are strange bedfellows. One cannot at one and the same time hold prices down to a competitive level for the sake of the living consumer and keep them up at a level high enough to assure conservation for the sake of the consumer yet to be born. When Theodore Roosevelt addressed the conference of governors which he called to the White House in 1908, he said: "In the past we have admitted the right of the individual to injure the future of the Republic for his own present profit. In fact, there has been a good deal of demand for unrestricted individualism, for the right of the individual to injure the future of us all for his own temporary and immediate profit. The time has come for a change." Commenting on this momentous statement, Garrett aptly remarks:

All he could have meant was that it was time that time had come. Twenty years have passed and it has not yet come. Holding to the American tradition of the pioneer's right to possess what he finds and to exploit it as he privately pleases, wastefully or efficiently, the individual is still a powerful political influence. It is not only that he has the sympathy of Congress. Some of that is fictitious. Behind him is the will of states and communities to exploit the land and all natural resources within their reach. It is their shortest way to self-aggrandizement.

Land, forests and minerals are national assets, but farming, lumbering and mining are regional activities on which to build vital statistics, taxable wealth, concrete roads, cities, commerce, banking, state power. The nation's agriculture may be already overexpanded; for that reason a state will not forbear to water a desert if it has one, and plant irrigated farming upon it. The lumber industry at large may be suffering from overproduction; a state will not for that reason prefer the soughing of the wind in a primeval forest to the sound of a band saw. If the lumber has no market within the country, it may be exported, and that means ships in the harbor, port development, benefit of foreign commerce.[3]

The East has always been willing to support conservation at the expense of the West, but thus far the West has successfully resisted it. East and West are living in different stages of social and economic evolution; their philosophies, therefore, cannot be the same. The way in which a million-dollar corporation, expecting to stay in business for decades or longer, views oil conservation is entirely different from that in which a small producer or a western community which is still in the exploitive stage sees it.

The conservation movement, therefore, lost out partly because of its own misinterpretation of the resource situation, and partly because of the fact that the time had not come for the kind of conservation which the moral crusader was advocating when the century was young. It may not be too much to say that the time has not yet come, even today.

So much for the failure of the first movement. What were the forces behind the second? As was said above, the petroleum industry occupied the center of the stage, and the Federal Oil Conservation Board was the chief spokesman of the new movement. The greatest change was the enthusiastic support which big business was giving the new movement. If we can explain this support, we shall discover the force behind this revival of interest.

There was a time—soon after World War I—when a few oil experts, most of them associated with our national government, were alone advocating oil conservation. The petroleum industry overlooked and even ridiculed the warnings of these prophets crying in the wilderness, these pessimists who did not realize the possibilities of future discoveries and inventions whereby today's apparent scarcity might—and, touched by the magic wand of

rising prices, undoubtedly would—be turned into tomorrow's plethora. It happened that the industry was right.

But, strange to say, in the later twenties it was the industry, at least the most powerful elements in it, which was not merely advocating but clamoring for conservation and imploring the government to take steps which would make it a reality. It is difficult to realize the remarkable reversal of attitude behind this new viewpoint of the petroleum industry. When the available data indicated an apparent scarcity, the private interests associated with the production and sale of petroleum and its products were indifferent, if not averse, to conservation. But when ample reserves were in sight, the industry—at least the strongest elements in it—clamored for conservation. To understand this drastic change of attitude, one must look behind the scenes and keep in mind the stages through which the petroleum industry had passed recently.[4] If one questions the authenticity of this phase of the conservation movement, he engages mainly in a debate on semantics, i.e., the meaning of words. Only those not familiar with developments in the petroleum industry will question the social values inherent in actual performance, whether this is called conservation, "conservation," or economy.

Next to the petroleum industry, the power industry claimed much credit for large-scale practical conservation. With justifiable pride it pointed to the fact that a kilowatt-hour is now produced with much less coal than was necessary even ten or fifteen years ago (see p. 483). Other industries appear as champions of conservation on the ground that they reclaim old rubber tires, make paper out of rags, use copper and steel and other metals over and over again, and salvage hundreds of millions of dollars' worth of materials from the junk pile.

THE MEANING OF CONSERVATION

Evidently the two movements for conservation briefly outlined in the preceding paragraphs do not see eye to eye as to the deeper meaning of the term. The word *conservation* seems impossible of final definition, for its meaning changes with time and place. It

---

[3] *Ibid.*, p. 212.

[4] For this, see chaps. 30–34.

means one thing to the statesman who has the security and prosperity of unborn generations at heart, and another thing to the chairman of the board of a giant corporation who must skillfully divide his loyalties among many interests, among which a multitude of stockholders clamoring for dividends are the most vociferous.

The underlying cause for so much misunderstanding of the question of conservation may be seen in the multiplicity of its aspects. According to his background and special interests, a writer will stress certain aspects at the expense of others. Conservation can be approached from two angles: first, from that of the natural sciences, in which case engineers, geologists, agronomists, chemists, etc., are the most active agents in the movement; and second, from the angle of the social sciences, with economists, historians, and sociologists being the logical spokesmen for the movement. According to which group is discussing conservation, one of the following two aspects will receive a more or less one-sided emphasis: the excessive drain on our wasting and irreplaceable assets which are of vital importance to society, or the physical waste characteristic of our present production and consumption practices. The social scientists stress the exhaustibility, and the natural scientists emphasize the physical waste.

But this is only one of the difficulties. There is another very serious obstacle to proper understanding. The natural scientist, who thinks first of all in terms of physical waste, does not adequately consider the implications of pecuniary economics. He apparently is not fully aware of the dynamic processes of modern economy. Above all, he does not seem to be conscious of the close organic relationship between the elimination of physical waste and the effect of that elimination on cost, price, rate of consumption, and rate of exhaustion —in the absence of conscious restraint. Is it not true that, generally speaking, the elimination of waste—or, to put the same idea positively, the increase in productive efficiency— tends to lower the cost, that the lower cost tends to reduce the price, and that a reduced price tends to stimulate demand? Stimulated demand may and usually does mean an accel-

erated rate of exploitation of natural resources. The elimination of needless waste is laudable economy; that is self-evident. But an accelerated rate of exploitation is not conservation; that is equally self-evident. We cannot escape the fact that we are living under a price economy and that therefore the rate of exploitation of natural resources is generally determined by the price which can be obtained for the product in the market and the profit which can be made. This causal relationship between waste elimination and rate of exploitation is vital; a disregard of the pertinent facts of price dynamics precludes a sound understanding of the conservation of natural resources.

The economist who realizes this organic interaction has always stressed the element of sacrifice involved in conservation. According to Ely, an authority on the subject: "Conservation means a sacrifice of the present generation to future generations, whenever it is carried far; this conflict beginning far before the ideal is reached which conservationists are inclined to advocate." L. C. Gray, another economist and an authority on the subject of conservation, likewise finds "the real heart of the conservation problem" in "the conflict between the present and future . . . . The primary problem of conservation, expressed in economic language," he asserts, "is the determination of the proper rate of discount on the future with respect to the utilization of our natural resources." We can hardly expect to make much progress in this field unless we bring about closer coöperation and understanding between all the various agencies that are legitimately interested in the problem.

Many interpretations of the meaning of conservation are too vague to be useful. If conservation is defined as wise use, the question is immediately raised, what is wise? Is conservation wise? In other words, the argument goes in a circle. Likewise, its definition as "the elimination of needless waste," the elimination of waste "so far as possible" or "consistent with reasonable economic use,"[5] does not promote clarity. What is "possible"? What is "reason-

---

[5] L. Havemeyer (ed.), *Conservation of Our Natural Resources*, The Macmillan Company, New York, 1930, p. 19.

able"? What is "economic"? One cannot solve equations by substituting one unknown for another.

Economy and Conservation Contrasted

If, as most contemporary writers suggest, conservation is to mean economical use, intensive utilization, waste elimination or reduction of waste, standardization, scientific management, "wise utilization," etc., one wonders how it differs from economy. If to conserve means nothing more than to economize, why burden our vocabulary with this synonym and blur the issues? Little can be gained by the adulteration of a word which, prior to this sophisticated interpretation associated with the present-day conservation movement, quite generally conveyed the idea of a reduced rate of consumption. If a person continues to spend his money as rapidly as before, or even more rapidly, but makes better use of it and spends it more wisely, he may be said to economize but not to save or to conserve. Conservation involves a reduction of the rate of disappearance or consumption, and a corresponding increase in the unused surplus left at the end of a given period. Economizing, on the other hand, does not necessarily affect the rate of consumption but expresses the ratio of input to output or of sacrifice to benefit. Economy may, and often does, result in conservation; but to conclude from this that economy is therefore conservation seems hardly justified.

Whether economy results in conservation depends primarily on two conditions, namely, the nature of the industry and the elasticity of demand. It makes a great deal of difference whether an industry is operating under competitive or monopolistic market conditions. If a commodity whose demand is elastic—that is, its demand responds readily to price changes—is produced under highly competitive conditions, more economical methods of production will tend to lower the cost, reduce the price, and bring about increased consumption. If, because of production economies, competition forces the price of gasoline down from thirty to twenty cents a gallon, with the result that twice as many gallons are sold, the crude oil reserves above or below ground may, as a result of this improved economy, be subjected

to a more rapid exhaustion than they were before. In this case the industry may be justly proud of the greater *economy* of production, but it can hardly claim credit for *conservation*. If scientific improvements, such as the cracking and hydrogenation processes, result in lower prices, and if these lower prices stimulate the demand for petroleum products to such an extent that the rate of the depletion of oil resources is accelerated, economy does not lead to conservation. As long as conservation is inseparably linked up with a reduced rate of output or of consumption, economies which stimulate output or consumption cannot be conservation.

If an industry which enjoys monopolistic control over the supply of a commodity, the demand for which is inelastic, chooses to retard the rate of production, the relationship between economy and conservation may be altogether different; for, under such circumstances, economic action may result in conservation. This type of conservation may involve a sacrifice on the part of the present consuming generation.

Economization, Conservation, Economancy, and Conservancy

There are evidently two different ways of slowing up the exploitation of natural resources. One involves conscious interference with the free play of economic forces, with the avowed purpose of helping posterity even at the expense of the present generation of producers and consumers. The other is merely an incidental effect of the free play of economic forces in a competitive price economy, especially an overhead economy, or of private monopolistic control over resources. Both competitive and monopolistic price economies seek their reward in the present, but they differ as to the manner in which that reward is distributed among producers and consumers. To distinguish this by-product conservation from conservation for its own sake, it may be called conservancy. The word as generally used may not now possess this particular connotation. In the interest of clarifying this discussion, this innovation seems justified.

There is a counterpart to conservancy which may be called economancy. Just as conservancy is by-product conservation resulting incidentally from the pursuit of economic ends, so by-product economy, or economancy, may result as an incidental effect, or by-product, of conservation. When a copper company is ordered by a government agency to discontinue emitting vegetation-killing poisonous fumes into the atmosphere and in the course of time discovers ways of converting these fumes into valuable products, such as sulfuric acid, which yield large profits, the result achieved as a by-product of conservation is incidental economy or economancy.

Since the suffix -ancy is here reserved to express incidental or by-product effects and the suffix -ation is given the meaning of willful action or intent, it may be legitimate to form the word economization as the counterpart to conservation.

Thus, in the analysis of conservation as contrasted with economy, one comes face to face with four concepts. Two of them—economization and conservation—express willful action or intent, one to serve the present and the other to serve the future; the other two—economancy and conservancy — express incidental or by-product effects of the others. Economization may result in conservancy and conservation may result in economancy.

To sum up, there are four distinct ideas which shade imperceptibly into one another but must nevertheless be clearly distinguished if hopeless confusion is to be avoided.

1. *Economization* in a price economic system covers all the efforts to improve the economic ratio of production, the ratio of output to input, or, expressed socially, the ratio of benefit to sacrifice, of utilities produced to labor expended.

2. *Conservation* is any act reducing the rate of consumption or exhaustion for the avowed purpose of benefiting posterity. If this objective is gained by economies, conservation and conservancy become identical in effect, though not in intent. If the objective cannot be gained by economy in harmony with the free play of economic forces, conservation must be imposed on private economy by means of social control through the exercise of the police power or through taxation.

3. *Conservancy* means reduction in the rate of exhaustion of a natural resource which is not sought for its own sake but is incidental to the exercise of economy.

4. *Economancy* is the by-product economy that results incidentally from conservation.

WIDER IMPLICATIONS OF CONSERVATION
Resource Strategy

Thus far we have discussed conservation largely in terms of a reduced rate of consumption of tangible goods, and most of the illustrations given were chosen from the petroleum industry. But conservation means more than simply putting on the brakes on the production of minerals and other material objects. In so far as conservation is tied up with economy, it can result from economy of use as much as from economy of output. Economy of use again is not merely a matter of curtailment but a question of judicious choices. The strategy of judicious use recognizes two general principles. In the first place, resources should be devoted primarily, if not exclusively, to those uses for which they possess peculiar or particular qualifications. Crude oil can either be burned under a boiler in competition with coal or, when refined into gasoline, be used in ways with which coal cannot compete. The strategy of resource utilization decrees a preference for those uses which take advantage of the peculiar fitness of particular commodities.

In the second place, strategy of resource utilization decrees a preference for flow resources—vegetation, water, sunshine, etc.—over fund resources. Whether or not this priority should be pushed to the point where flow resources are used in preference to fund resources, even at the expense of economic value, calling for the sacrifice of the present generation on the altar of posterity, is again a moral question which the moralist is better prepared to answer than the economist. The priority system can be elaborated by differentiating fund resources on the basis of absolute scarcity, possibilities of recovery, rate of exhaustion, etc.

To come back to the petroleum industry. Oil conservation lies in the hands not only of petroleum engineers and economists but also of the automotive engineer. The introduction of a motor which pulls a serviceable car at a satisfactory speed forty or fifty miles on a gallon of gasoline would be a revolutionary step in the direction of real conservancy. The cost of motor construction depends on labor costs and the cost of material. A more efficient motor is likely to require more labor, more expensive materials, and perhaps more capital equipment and would therefore be more expensive than the typical motor marketed today. Where gasoline is cheap, the automobile owner prefers a cheap but relatively wasteful engine to a more expensive one which economizes on gas. It is evident that economy is largely a question of factoral proportions, i.e., of the proper apportionment of "land" (natural resources), capital, and labor, and that by shifting the emphasis from "land" to labor and/or capital, conservancy may be achieved. This point is discussed more fully later on.

One could extend this broader interpretation further and mention the waste of resources which results from the "malformation of industrial growth due to faulty railroad rate structure."[6] A leading authority on conservation calls this "one of the most outstanding evidences of present-day economic waste," and he adds, "The reformation of railway rate structure affords a most fertile field for conservation activities."[7] Thus, the Interstate Commerce Commission, as well as the Department of the Interior[8] with its interest in national parks, public lands, irrigation, watershed protection, etc., or the Department of Commerce which for years has carried on a campaign in favor of standardization and simplified practice, might be an important agency of conservancy and perhaps even of conservation in this country.

Above all, conservation does not pertain merely to natural resources, to what the economist calls "land"; it must take into account the other agents of production—labor, and capital which, within reasonable limits, can be substituted for "land." All the factors of production, to some extent, are mutually compensatory. Up to a certain point, each production agent can perform the functions of any of the others. However, this does not mean that capital can be substituted for "land" or labor for "land," or capital for labor. It does mean that man can produce a given amount of goods either with the aid of "land," little capital, and little labor (this combination is characteristic of the pioneer stage), or with much capital, considerable "land," and little labor (this is the recipe used in modern machine civilization), or with much labor, considerable capital (rice terraces), and little "land" (the factoral proportion characteristic of Monsoonia). Needless to say, many other combinations producing numerous gradations and nuances are possible.

The law of supply and demand applies to production agents no less than to commodities. If conservation results in an artificial scarcity of "land," it may lead to the ruthless exploitation of labor and/or capital. This is no argument against conservation, but merely an exposition of its possible economic effects. Any act which artificially restricts or dilutes the supply of either labor or capital—immigration laws, legal restrictions on interest, blue-sky laws, etc.—will be found upon closer scrutiny to have an indirect but potentially important bearing on conservation.

Conservation of Specific Resources

Even if conservation is applied solely to natural resources such as water, soil, minerals, etc., it does not call for a single set of rules but for several, carefully adapted to the peculiar nature and requirements of the different types of resources. Evidently the conservationist has a much keener interest in scarce, irreplaceable, nonrenewable fund resources than in the opposite type. In an article called "Economic Possibilities of Conservation" which, although written several decades ago, remains one of the most valuable contributions to the literature on the subject, Gray gives a valuable classification of natural resources.[9]

---

[6] See R. T. Ely, R. H. Hess, C. K. Leith, and T. N. Carver, *The Foundations of National Prosperity,* The Macmillan Company, New York, 1923, p. 112.

[7] *Ibid.*

[8] This Department in 1931 published a most interesting and attractive volume, *Conservation in the Department of the Interior.*

[9] L. C. Gray, in *Quarterly Journal of Economics,* May 19, 1913.

In a footnote he says, "In terminology the . . . classification resembles one proposed some years ago by B. E. Fernow."

Recognizing the differences in the nature of natural resources, Havemeyer suggests different rules of behavior toward power, machine, and agricultural resources. As to power resources he says: "When they are extracted from the earth they are used within a short time, and when they have been used they are gone forever." Therefore he suggests that the conservation of coal must consist of the reduction of waste in mining and in use. The smoke nuisance should be abolished; gas engines should be substituted for steam engines; water power and substitute minerals should replace coal "so far as practicable."[10] Oil should be reserved for those higher uses for which there are no adequate substitutes. We might add that cracking and hydrogenation should be encouraged; and the best way to encourage these technical improvements, as we have seen, is to curtail the output. This curtailment in turn calls for a reorientation of our legal philosophy in keeping with economic and social changes. The Diesel engine is making great contributions to oil economy. As was pointed out before, Diesel oil is a by-product of gasoline production. A judicious balance between gasoline motors and Diesel engines may form an important part of the oil conservation strategy.

A similar classification is suggested by Hess in R. T. Ely, R. H. Hess, C. K. Leith, and T. N. Carver, *op. cit.*, p. 117, quoted by permission of The Macmillan Company:
"Considered from the point of view of relative present and future scarcity and value, natural resources fall within the four fairly distinct groups indicated below.
"I. Resources which are so abundant as to have negligible present values, but bear promise of future scarcity and value.
"II. Resources which have present value and are subject to increasing scarcity or demand:
  "a. Not exhaustible by use.
  "b. Exhaustible in use but subject to maintenance and restoration.
  "c. Exhaustible in use and not restorable.
"III. Resources which have present value, but are subject to deterioration or loss of value through non-use.
"IV. Resources which have no present value, but are subject to 'reclamation' and development to a condition of usefulness and value."
Notes: "Value is here used in a commercial sense and should be distinguished from social value. Social value would include both present and future usefulness."
[10] L. Havemeyer (ed.), *op. cit.*, p. 509.

In the meantime, further research in the hydrogenation of coal, in the production of alcohol with the aid of cheap tropical sunshine, and other similar measures looking toward the replacement of oil after it is gone, should be encouraged.

In the case of metals, a sharp distinction must be made between those which are destroyed in use and those which can be used again and again. The possibilities of transferring metals from one category to the other should be studied and put into practice.

In the interest of conservation, forests should be "cropped" and not "mined." Much soil erosion is due to ignorance and carelessness. To the extent that it arises from these causes, little doubt need be entertained as to the economic justification of corrective measures.

Conservation and Technological Progress

By injecting a highly dynamic element into the problem of conservation, changes in the arts render the formulation of hard and fast rules difficult. Who dares to predict the future needs for forest products when the technique of scrap recovery is rapidly advancing, when science is delving deeper and deeper into the study of possible uses of such agricultural products as wheat straw, cornstalks, and other sources of cellulose; when the possibility of turning common clay into aluminum looms on the horizon, and innumerable other improvements promise to throw an entirely new light upon the need and availability of basic resources?

Nothing has gone further in calming the fears which Theodore Roosevelt's dramatic "menetekel" aroused than the recent improvements of technology along almost the entire battlefront between man and nature. Garrett appropriately closes his discussion of conservation with this paragraph:

Twenty years ago the power of science and technology to effect higher utilization of natural products and so reduce waste at the point of use was underestimated. The case today is that we take this power to be a source of magic. Ask a man joy-riding in his motor car or one plowing his field with a tractor what will happen when the oil gives out. He answers: "Oh, by that time we can turn a switch and get our juice from the radio, or something else."

Faith in bonanza still, though it may be bonanza of science. Luck so far. Conservation at the source foolishly bankrupt, and nobody to blame.[11]

The relationship between improvement of the arts and the problem of conservation will now be briefly examined, and we shall begin with a question. Which is better, a primeval forest of well-nigh unlimited timber stands, without steam engines and circular saws and high-speed tools and mechanical logging devices; or a forest half the size, plus a highly developed knowledge of how best to use and exploit the supply of timber, and a highly advanced stage of the arts through which this knowledge can be applied? If the second alternative is chosen, then every advance in science and arts compensates to some extent for the loss of physical reserves which use may entail.

Since scientific knowledge and the arts are included in our resource concept, we could express this process of substituting better knowledge for tangible natural resources as a gradual shift from one type of resources—tangible natural resources—to another—intangible, institutional, or cultural resources.

However, a difficulty presents itself. Thus far, increased knowledge and improved arts have usually resulted in a large absolute increase in population. As long as the benefits derived from the increased knowledge and improved arts are absorbed by increasing numbers of consumers who draw on a reduced supply with redoubled vigor, this cultural progress cannot be counted upon as a substitute for conservation. If, on the other hand, birth control or other forces hold population growth in check, improved arts and increased knowledge may actually compensate posterity for its reduced supply of material resources.

The conservation problem was formerly considered most acute with regard to "fund resources with present or future scarcity," especially metals. The fuller utilization of scrap metals, however, is reducing the drain on the waning supply of virgin metals. As the saturation point is reached in railroad demand, automobile demand, and other demands for metallic devices, and as the new population trends

become operative, the demand for new metals may actually decrease, and the possibility of solving the problem of the future metal supply through increased knowledge and improved arts may assume real significance. As yet, that point seems rather remote.

One of the most effective conservation measures that man can apply is to avoid the catastrophe which, more than anything else, helps to drain the supply of resources without correspondingly advancing the compensatory arts and sciences—war, war on the scale which the political condition on the earth today makes not only possible but probable.

Conservation, Laissez Faire, and Social Control

If conservation were identical with economy, we could safely rely on private initiative and the other moving forces of the economic price system. But if, on the other hand, the essence of conservation is the sacrifice of present economic interests on behalf of posterity, the profit motive cannot be relied upon to assure conservation, and social controls must be resorted to. Conservation is sometimes considered an investment proposition pure and simple, the assumption being that the same psychological forces which cause people to save automatically and adequately, take care of conservation through the investment of savings in natural resources. Unfortunately, four obstacles stand in the way of individuals' investing in natural resources as freely as they would in marketable securities and similar liquid values. These obstacles are: (1) imperative present personal needs; (2) lack of foresight; (3) limited expectation of life; and (4) perfunctory interest in social and national welfare.[12]

Those advocates of laissez faire who are willing to concede the existence of these obstacles rightly emphasize the fact that corporations are in a better position to conserve natural resources than are individuals and partnerships.

There can be no doubt that the growth of the corporation as an institution, and the ascendancy of such giant corporations as the American Telephone and Telegraph Company, the United States Steel Corporation, General

---

[11] G. Garrett, *op. cit.*, p. 215.

[12] See R. T. Ely, R. H. Hess, C. K. Leith, and T. N. Carver, *op. cit.*, p. 130.

Motors, etc., have materially enhanced the possibilities of conservancy. As long, however, as corporate management considers public interests as merely incidental to private interests, we can hardly expect the final solution of the conservation problem from voluntary decisions of directors of corporations.[13] It is true that the corporation aspires to the longevity of the social group and that, to that extent, corpora-

tion and group interests tend toward fuller harmony. But as long as the maximation of profit remains the cornerstone of acquisitive society and capitalistic economy, corporations will retain their interest in scarcity as a creator of economic value. Social welfare demands abundance, distributed justly and spread out over a longer time than even the most progressive and liberal corporation executive at present dares consider. Van Hise said, "Conservation is the greatest good to the greatest number—and that for the longest time."

---

[13] See A. A. Berle, Jr., and G. C. Means, *The Modern Corporation and Private Property*, The Macmillan Company, New York, 1933.

BIBLIOGRAPHY

Baer, M. E., *Pandora's Box*, New York, Farrar and Rinehart, 1939.

Bennett, H. H., *Soil Conservation*, New York, McGraw-Hill, 1939.

Bennett, H. H., *Our American Land*, Washington, Soil Conservation Service, 1946 (pamphlet).

Chase, S., *Rich Land, Poor Land*, New York, Whittlesey House, 1936.

Cheyney, E. G., and Schantz-Hansen, T., *This Is Our Land*, St. Paul, Itasca Press, Webb, 1946.

Elliott, C. N., *Conservation of American Resources*, Atlanta, T. F. Smith, 1940.

Flynn, H. E., and Perkins, F. E., *Conservation of the Nation's Resources*, New York, Macmillan, 1941.

Frank, B., and Netboy, A., "Water Water Everywhere but . . . ," *Scientific Monthly*, June, 1949.

Garrett, G., "Faith in Bonanza," *Saturday Evening Post*, May 25, 1929.

Graham, E. H., *Natural Principles of Land Use*, New York, Oxford University Press, 1944.

Kellogg, C. E., *The Soils that Support Us*, New York, Macmillan, 1941.

Lieber, R., *America's Natural Wealth*, New York, Harper, 1942.

Mather, K., *Enough and to Spare*, New York, Harper, 1944.

Mitchell, W. C., and others, *The Foundations of Conservation Education*, New York, National Wildlife Federation, 1941.

Osborn, F., *Our Plundered Planet*, Boston, Little, Brown, 1948.

Parkins, A. E., and Whitaker, J. R., *Our Natural Resources and Their Conservation*, New York, Wiley, 2nd ed., 1939.

Pearson, F. A., and Harper, F. G., *The World's Hunger*, Ithaca, Cornell University Press, 1945.

Raushenbush, S., *Our Conservation Job*, Public Affairs Institute, Report No. 4, Washington, 1949.

Sears, P. B., *Deserts on the March*, Norman, University of Oklahoma Press, 1935.

Smith, G.-H. (ed.), *Conservation of Natural Resources*, New York, Wiley, 1950.

Standard Oil Company (New Jersey), "Conservation" (pamphlet), New York, no date.

Tryon, F. G., "Conservation," *Encyclopædia of the Social Sciences*, New York, Macmillan, 1931.

United Nations, *Scientific Conference on the Conservation and Utilization of Resources*, Lake Success, 1949.

Valie, L., "Are We Short of Water?" *Collier's*, May 15, 1948.

Vogt, W., *Road to Survival*, New York, William Sloane Associates, 1948.

Whitaker, J. R., *The Life and Death of the Land*, Nashville, Peabody Press, 1946.

Whyte, R. O., and Jacks, G. V., *Vanishing Lands*, New York, Doubleday, 1939.

Chapter 50

RESOURCE ADEQUACY

WHITHER MANKIND

Few individuals concern themselves with problems of the future or ultimate adequacy of world resources. In many countries the masses live from hand to mouth, the helpless victims of every caprice of weather and every catastrophe of nature. Perhaps they too pray, "Give us this day our daily bread." But they have neither the inclination to worry about the future, nor the requisite knowledge to warrant their doing so. Famines, like plagues, are taken as supernatural phenomena about which man can do little, if anything.

Even in more advanced countries individuals do not ordinarily and of their own accord concern themselves with matters beyond the range of their own or their dependents' interests. Intelligent and provident people take out insurance and seek, through education and otherwise, to safeguard the future earning power of their families. But beyond that, they are not likely to give much if any thought to the future.

It is different with leaders of men and of thought. The story of Joseph of Egypt comes to mind. But his was a hard-headed policy, based to be sure on the interpretation of a dream which extended a mere seven years into the future, a short period in the life of a great kingdom. Kings and high priests strove to provide for themselves even in the hereafter; their monuments survive thousands of years. They did more; they promoted vast public works—irrigation canals, drainage systems, terracing, etc.—designed to enlarge and assure food supplies and to safeguard the food-supplying assets of their realms.

As the earth shrinks and human knowledge of mankind solidifies, as historical records become available which permit projections of past trends into the future, it is natural for thinkers to speculate on the future of the race. The question "Whither mankind?" is as fascinating as it is baffling.

As man's powers to shape his destiny grow with wider knowledge and deeper understanding of the resources on which he depends and with increasing control over the race's procreative tendencies, there awakens in him the desire to better, if possible, the fate that lies ahead, and to avoid, if feasible, the blind rushing toward abyss or catastrophe that was the lot of many before him. History records the tragic death of many civilizations. Can we who pride ourselves on our achievements learn from their mistakes and avoid a like fate?

THE PESSIMISTS' ANSWER
The Dismal "Scientist"

We of today refuse the simple answer of a Malthus who, on the basis of a strange mixture of logic and mere assumptions, answered the question "Whither mankind?" with a resounding "Nowhere." According to Malthus, man's own nature and that of his environment condemn him to live forever in misery. Nature holds him in perpetual bondage and the Four Horsemen are her henchmen. Malthus thought he knew that man's resources could expand only at a rate far slower than that at which nature compels man to increase his numbers.[1] There was no problem of future adequacy, for nature solved it by preventing human numbers and human needs from outstripping the adequacy of resources. There was enough for a limited number to live in misery, but certainly not "enough and to spare."

Malthus could not foresee what we now know. He could not foresee either man's capacity to cause fantastic spurts of resource availability or that strange phenomenon which we have called the negative phase of the mechanical revolution, voluntary curtailment of offspring, a curtailment so drastic that whole nations may be facing an actual decline of numbers, not because of lack of means of subsistence, but because men consciously and deliberately prefer to have their children live in dignity.

Malthus was a product of a period before the mechanical revolution, a product of an age that knew no other demographic pattern than high birth rates kept in check by high death rates or, vice versa, high birth rates trying to keep up with high death rates. He was a product of the eighteenth century, a century that made a fetish of *natural law.*

Neither he nor his age dreamed of what had already been conceived but was not yet born —man's control over vast new supplies of inanimate energy, and, above all, over mankind's own numbers.

The New Cassandras

We today know what Malthus could not know. We know that we have steam power and that steam power made "the earth become pregnant with new earths." We have the power of gasoline and Diesel oil explosion, electricity, nuclear energy, science, and—birth control. As these great new powers gradually unfolded, Malthus became obsolete. People shifted from his extreme pessimism to the opposite: a faith in bonanza, in unlimited resources provided by science and technology.

And yet every so often writers warn us that mankind is headed for a new catastrophe, a globe so crowded with starving billions that the highest values of our civilization will be crushed to death in the world struggle for a bare existence. Such writers appeared during the twenties.[2] In the thirties several valuable books on soils and land use were published, among them some that will live as classics in their respective fields.[3] The story was continued in the forties.[4] Finally in 1948 the crest of the wave seemed to be reached with the appearance of two best sellers in rapid succession.[5] These books are reaching literally millions and

---

[1] In the first edition of *An Essay on the Principle of Population*, published anonymously in 1798, Malthus spoke of the arithmetic ratio at which the means of subsistence increased and the geometric ratio at which the human population increases. This mathematical expression was dropped in later editions.

[2] E. M. East, *Mankind at the Crossroads,* Charles Scribner's Sons, New York, 1923; E. A. Ross, *Standing Room Only,* The Century Company, New York, 1927.

[3] Paul B. Sears, *Deserts on the March,* University of Oklahoma Press, Norman, 1935; H. H. Bennett, *Soil Conservation,* McGraw-Hill Book Company, Inc., New York, 1939; R. O. Whyte and G. V. Jacks, *Vanishing Lands,* Doubleday and Company, New York, 1939.

[4] Charles E. Kellogg, *The Soils That Support Us,* The Macmillan Company, New York, 1941; Edward H. Graham, *Natural Principles of Land Use,* Oxford University Press, New York, 1944; Frank A. Pearson and Floyd G. Harper, *The World's Hunger,* Cornell University Press, Ithaca, 1945; Theodore W. Schultz (ed.), *Food for the World,* University of Chicago Press, Chicago, 1945.

[5] Fairfield Osborn, *Our Plundered Planet,* Little, Brown & Company, Boston, 1948; William Vogt, *Road to Survival,* William Sloane Associates, New York, 1948. For a fuller discussion of the recent literature in this field, see Wilma Belden Fair-

are leaving their mark on the minds of many throughout the world.[6]

Whence does this new wave of pessimism come? On what facts do these new Cassandras base their predictions of dire calamities ahead unless men mend their ways and heed the warnings?

Both Vogt and Osborn are natural scientists—zoölogists, in fact. Vogt, now head of the conservation division of the Pan-American Union, long specialized in ornithology, the science of birds. Osborn is president of the New York Zoological Society. As natural scientists these authors are concerned less with the cultural superstructure of contemporary civilizations than with the natural underpinning. Their chief concern is the food supply for the vast hordes of people yet unborn but expected to arrive. Surveying the earth through the eyes of ecologists, they find that modern man, more particularly western man, has broken the laws of ecology and in doing so has ruined much land and is ruining still more. Thus the resources of the earth seem to be shrinking while large segments of mankind are on a rampage of unprecedented increase of numbers. To Vogt and Osborn, man is "the only creature that lives by destroying the basis on which life depends." They advocate a program of conservation and reclamation of basic earth resources, backed by research and education. Both of them know that none of these positive measures can stave off disaster unless birth control spreads over the earth like wildfire. How to set and feed that wildfire neither they nor anyone knows.

Probably neither of these two books contains much that some expert has not already said. What is new is, first, a certain holistic all-embracing, all-coördinating approach that reveals the woods where other experts pointed to single trees, and second, an eloquence born of evangelistic zeal that few experts can muster.

Regardless of what one thinks of specific statements and claims, there can be no question as to the tremendous propaganda value of these two books. They are stirring up thought on resource problems as it has never been stirred up before. They point out serious evils in the current uses of land and water which must be stopped. They stress the grave truth, brought out repeatedly in the present book,[7] that, in the relentless pursuit of his own selfish interests, individual man tends to sacrifice the long-range interests of the group and to impair the basic assets on which group continuity depends, that at no time have individuals been allowed to indulge in this dangerous game of license more freely than under the ideology of laissez faire, and that at no time have they been able to do more harm to basic assets than since the mechanical revolution armed them with superhuman powers. It is to be hoped that the clarion calls to research and education aimed at ecological sanity will not go unheeded and that men of courage and wisdom will find remedies for the grave ills that threaten the future peace and welfare of mankind because of rugged individualism run ragged.

RESTATEMENT OF FUNDAMENTALS

If in this section questions are raised as to the dependability of some of the conclusions reached by the modern pessimists, it is done in a spirit of humility. The author lays no claim to superior knowledge. Like other scientists, he is groping for truth. In some respects, the approach in the preceding analysis points to other, less fearful prospects. It may be worth while examining them.

The preceding analysis is predicated on the following beliefs: Resources are highly dynamic functional concepts; they *are not, they become,* they evolve out of the triune interaction of nature, man, and culture, in which nature sets outer limits, but man and culture are largely responsible for the portion of physical

child, "Renewable Resources: A World Dilemma. Recent Publications on Conservation," *Geographical Review,* January, 1949, pp. 86-98.

[6] It is strange that only four years before Vogt and Osborn released their messages of gloom another natural scientist, Kirtley F. Mather, Professor of Geology at Harvard University, wrote a book, *Enough and to Spare* (Harper & Brothers, New York, 1944), which has the following message: "There is enough for all. The earth is a generous mother; she will provide plentiful abundance for all her children if they will but cultivate her soil in justice and peace." The layman, bewildered by such contradictory statements, wonders whether they can be reconciled and, if so, how.

[7] Especially in chap. 2.

totality that is made available for human use. The command over energy, especially inanimate energy, is the key to resource availability. And, finally, the world is not "a bundle of hay" but a living, growing complex of matter and energy, *a process rather than a thing*.

In Defense of Industrial Man

In a condensation of Vogt's book, this paragraph occurs: "Every grain of wheat and rye, every sugar beet, every egg, and piece of wheat, every spoonful of olive oil, every glass of wine, depends on an irreducible minimum of earth to produce it. The earth is not made of rubber; it cannot be stretched. *As the number of human beings increases, the relative amount of productive earth decreases by that amount.*"[8]

Is it realistic to state that the earth cannot be stretched? We are talking of the earth as the source of human food, as the basis of man's existence. Has "industrial man," the villain in Vogt's dramatic story, done nothing else but destroy? Has he not added materially to the food-yielding capacity of the earth? Has he not bred drought- and frost-resistant varieties of wheat that grow in regions which before this achievement were virtually barren so far as man was concerned? Has he not brought varieties of plants from desolate parts of the earth into the orbit of his activity and thus added greatly to the food-bearing capacity of the earth? Has he not transformed the pampas of Argentina so that they bear rich food instead of scanty feed for scrawny cattle? Has he not covered the pampas with railroads and linked them with markets, thus providing the means of defraying the cost of this face lifting of the pampas? Has he not stopped the waste involved when cattle were slaughtered merely for their hides? Has he not, by refrigeration, reduced the loss from spoilage? If today cattle are fattened on ground corncobs that formerly were wasted, plus supplements with a high protein and vitamin content, is it realistic to say that the earth cannot be stretched? It may still be true that every piece of meat "depends on an irreducible minimum of earth to produce it," but it makes a great deal of dif-

ference how closely man can creep up to that irreducible minimum.

Have not tractors replaced horses and mules, thus setting free for food production millions of good acres formerly needed to produce feed for work animals? The loss of manure must not be overlooked, but it is compensated, at least partially, by commercial fertilizers. Do not the fossil fuels provide heat as well as power, and thus cut down the need for food? If China could mine and distribute coal to heat her homes during the winter, the pressure on the land might well be reduced in three ways: (1) by substituting space-heating coal for part of the warmth now derived from food, (2) by liberating for food production acreage now used to grow vegetable fuel, and (3) by making available for fertilizer the animal dung now burned for fuel.

All the food that man eats is derived from the earth, to be sure; but there is a vast difference in the degree of dependence on the earth. Sugar is made up of hydrogen, carbon, and oxygen derived from air and water. If the rest of the sugar beet or sugar cane is returned to the soil, man can produce trillions of calories in the form of sugar without having to drain the earth of its strength. Does not the synthesis of vitamins in diets vastly improve the economy of our diets? And does not the use of "trace minerals" in certain soils greatly improve their productivity? After all, science does create resources!

Is it not true that without the individualism which Vogt maligns so unmercifully and without the science that industrialization has nourished, all these possibilities of improving and enlarging man's capacity to raise food would be impossible? The very knowledge of ecology on which Vogt and Osborn base their attack against modern methods of production is a gift of industrial civilization. The remedies of reclamation, research, and education depend on the surplus and leisure that industry and the use of inanimate energy give us. If industrial man has raped the earth and wantonly impaired its productive powers, he also has furnished the wisdom to recognize his folly and may yet supply the means to make amends.

Now and then one reads in current newspapers and periodicals of the miraculous trans-

[8] *Reader's Digest*, January, 1949, p. 141; italics the present author's.

formation of run-down farms into veritable gardens of Eden. What all such stories have in common is a congregation of experts—soil experts, plant and animal experts, chemists, engineers—and a vast assemblage of machinery—bulldozers, terracers, harrows, and what have you. The experts were trained in institutions supported largely by the wealth created by modern machine industry. The machines and the fuels that power them are the direct products of that industry.

If the people of the West are able to solve the problems their past mistakes have created, it will be precisely because the same ideologies and drives that are responsible for their errors have generated their own antidotes and furnished the means needed to carry through the remedial programs.

Industrial civilization has done more. If there is any hope that the vast problems so clearly depicted by Vogt and Osborn will be solved, it will be by industry not only supplying the means, especially the vast amounts of energy needed, but also generating the psychological forces which alone can call a halt to the "torrent of babies." People have been willing to practice birth control when their own appraisal of values showed them that it was to their advantage to curtail the size of their family.

Conservation and the Individual

Theoretically great reforms can be achieved either by forcing measures down people's throats or by creating incentives which make voluntary reforms appear desirable. In practice, the first method has invariably failed. If conservation is to succeed, conditions must be created which will make it pay those who are to practice it. If the vast soil conservation program under way in this country has been successful, it is because of its superb scientific management and because it made soil conservation profitable. Certainly in a democratic society individuals cannot be compelled to act against their own interest for the sake of creating values which will accrue too late for them to enjoy. Therein lies the chief value of a recent proposal now widely discussed in this country.[9] Commenting editorially on this plan,

[9] Stephen Raushenbush, *Our Conservation Job*, Report No. 4 Public Affairs Institute, Washington, 1949.

the New York *Times* on June 26, 1949, had this to say:

Exhaustion of the soil and forest resources of this country is one of the truly serious problems facing the people of the United States. The facts of the case are slowly but surely forcing attention to this situation, which has far more direct bearing on the welfare of the nation than much of the more exciting news that properly makes the headlines.

Recently an ingenious and carefully worked out plan to save some of the threatened natural resources of the country was put forward by Stephen Raushenbush, under the auspices of the Public Affairs Institute in Washington. We are not here endorsing the plan; but we are suggesting that the scope of the proposal is such that it merits study and discussion.

In essence, Mr. Raushenbush proposes to establish a Government credit agency, called the National Resources Corporation, which would finance private owners of soil and forest resources in carrying out conservation practices on a long-term, self-liquidating basis, at no cost to the taxpayer. The thesis is that now, no matter how much one talks conservation, it is too expensive for the individual owner or it pays off after a longer time than he can afford to wait. The cost of restoring soil to full productivity, of protecting farms from erosion, of turning worn-out crop land to other uses, of reforestation and woodland management often cannot be met by the average landowner under present conditions. Good conservation practices do pay in the long run; but they yield their benefits too slowly, it is felt, to make private bank loans on an adequate scale practicable. Furthermore, the task is so gigantic that it could not be met by annual government appropriations, even if that method were desirable.

The problem is urgent. It is estimated that 115 million acres—one-fourth of the potential good crop land—are now being damaged by erosion so rapidly that "they will suffer irreparable loss of productive capacity" if protective measures are not taken within the next fifteen years. What has happened to American forests is a well-known story. The nation is growing. Its needs are growing. We cannot again afford the scarcity prices which a shortage of food and forest products inevitably brings. The Raushenbush proposal may or may not be the answer, but it is a serious effort to provide one, and it deserves a hearing.

The Bold New Program

Equally as important as these measures of domestic sanition is President Harry S. Truman's "bold new program" for aid to under-developed countries. This program may have a closer bearing on the problem of future resource adequacy, if not transcending importance for it, than can yet be realized.

The general and particularly the financial feasibility of the program may be subject to question, but the core of the idea is fundamentally sound. It constitutes a global approach to peace insurance. The West is engaged in a cold war with Russian communism, in which misery, hunger, hopelessness, and chaos are on the side of communism. The hope of the West lies in reducing these evils. Demographers have shown that the great future increases in world population will come from those parts of the earth which are industrially backward, especially Asia and Latin America.[10] The only possibility of forestalling the worst of the expected explosive increases is to help release the forces that in the West have brought on birth control: industrial progress which acts as a leaven of all progress. What these people need is robots to share the physical burden, and scientific know-how and managerial skills to render more efficient their efforts to cope with their environmental problems. The West constitutes a minority of mankind. It cannot possibly build industries for all the rest of the world. What it can do is to share with the rest of the world the fruits of its long head start, the imponderable resources of technology which "grow in a beneficial chain reaction by what they feed upon."[11] Our material resources are limited; many of them are exhaustible and nonrenewable. Our most precious key resource, knowledge, grows by being shared; it is not only not dissipated in use, it is enlarged thereby.

The world food problem is largely a problem of ignorance. Even in the United States, a country of miraculous performance, agricultural practice still lags far behind what existing knowledge makes feasible.[12] Commenting on this, M. K. Bennett has this to say:

The most impressive probability about the acres of the world now devoted to agricultural use is that a truly enormous gap exists between actual productivity and maximum productivity under optimum application of labor, capital, and management. This refers to maximum economic productivity, not maximum physical productivity, which no doubt is the greater. In all probability, a very large fraction of the managers of the world's agricultural land are inhibited from applying optimum doses of labor, capital, and management. Either they are not aware of the best in current technology, or they are helpless to make use of it, or they are unwilling even if able. The mere existence of cover crops and green manures, commercial fertilizers, effective sprays against weeds whether new or old, hybrid corn, rust-resistant wheats, inoculation against hog cholera, tests for animal tuberculosis, is literally unknown to thousands of land managers in the very areas of the world where population is alleged to be most obviously outrunning food supply. In those same areas and others are land managers who know of an improvement, but have no incentive to put it to use. Somewhere a large landholder, wealthy enough and socially important enough to satisfy all his ambitions, may remain content with farming methods reminiscent of the Middle Ages. Perhaps one could find instances in Spain or Chile. Elsewhere a lack of security of life and property—in essence, a lack of orderly government—may inhibit the application of improvements widely known. Bad though orderly government, exercising unwisely its power of taxation, may inhibit improvements in farming, simply because the fruit of effort is not permitted to accrue to the men who make it. The Soviet Union is a case in point. Above all, perhaps, a great many land managers of the world cannot apply what they both know and are willing to try for the reason that they lack capital to cover the initial cost. The purchase of a pound of improved seed, to say nothing of a good spade or plow, may unfortunately be quite beyond the capacity of a great many who cultivate the world's soil.[13]

Besides the points mentioned in this quotation, Bennett stresses the bearing of effective demand on agricultural performance. Rising living standards in underdeveloped countries not only will help to dispel ignorance of sound production methods, but will contribute toward effective demand which provides the vital

---

[10] In thus lumping these two parts of the earth together, the author is fully aware of the vital differences in their civilizations.

[11] New York *Times* editorial, January 21, 1949.

[12] Cf. S. E. Johnson, *Changes in Farming in War and Peace*, U.S. Department of Agriculture, Bureau of Agricultural Economics, June, 1946.

[13] M. K. Bennett, "Population and Food Supply: The Current Scare," *Scientific Monthly*, January, 1949, pp. 23-24.

stimulus to agricultural production, as to all production.

The Broader Issues

The pessimists of today base their predictions on two main arguments: Soils are being depleted because of erosion and overcropping, and people are multiplying too fast. Actually the issues involved are much broader. For one thing, the problem of the future supply of inanimate energy may embrace all other issues within itself. If, by the time the present sources of most of the inanimate energy used today, the fossil fuels, are exhausted, nuclear energy and other new forms of inanimate energy have not

---

[14] For a discussion of this question, see chap. 4, especially pp. 50 ff.

BIBLIOGRAPHY

Mather, K. F., *Enough and to Spare*, New York. Harper, 1944.

Osborn, F., *Our Plundered Planet*, Boston, Little Brown, 1948.

been developed[14] so that they can provide for the vastly enlarged needs of that future era, civilization as we now know it will come to an end anyway, regardless of the prevailing status of soil fertility, hydrologic cycle, and similar factors determining the food supply. In the world today, transportation is a prime necessity and in the absence of inanimate energy it will deteriorate to the point of virtual uselessness.

The problem of resource adequacy is also one of social institutions, of government policies, of international relations. If the preceding discussion has led to any vital conclusion, it is the altogetherness of things. In this inextricable mesh of forces and conditions man appears as the responsible agent. The problems of resource adequacy for the ages to come will involve human wisdom more than limits set by nature.

Patterson, E. M., *An Introduction to World Economics*, New York, Macmillan, 1947, chap. 12.

Vogt, W., *Road to Survival*, New York, William Sloane Associates, 1948.

Index